Standard Normal Distribution Table

0.3944

0 z = 1.25

Z	0	0.01	0.02	0.03	0.04	0.05	0.06	0.07	0.08	0.09
0.0	0.0000	0.0040	0.0080	0.0120	0.0160	0.0199	0.0239	0.0279	0.0319	0.0359
0.1	0.0398	0.0438	0.0478	0.0517	0.0557	0.0596	0.0636	0.0675	0.0714	0.0753
0.2	0.0793	0.0832	0.0871	0.0910	0.0948	0.0987	0.1026	0.1064	0.1103	0.1141
0.3	0.1179	0.1217	0.1255	0.1293	0.1331	0.1368	0.1406	0.1443	0.1480	0.1517
0.4	0.1554	0.1591	0.1628	0.1664	0.1700	0.1736	0.1772	0.1808	0.1844	0.1879
0.5	0.1915	0.1950	0.1985	0.2019	0.2054	0.2088	0.2123	0.2157	0.2190	0.2224
0.6	0.2257	0.2291	0.2324	0.2357	0.2389	0.2422	0.2454	0.2486	0.2517	0.2549
0.7	0.2580	0.2611	0.2642	0.2673	0.2704	0.2734	0.2764	0.2794	0.2823	0.2852
0.8	0.2881	0.2910	0.2939	0.2967	0.2995	0.3023	0.3051	0.3078	0.3106	0.3133
0.9	0.3159	0.3186	0.3212	0.3238	0.3264	0.3289	0.3315	0.3340	0.3365	0.3389
1.0	0.3413	0.3438	0.3461	0.3485	0.3508	0.3531	0.3554	0.3577	0.3599	0.3621
1.1	0.3643	0.3665	0.3686	0.3708	0.3729	0.3749	0.3770	0.3790	0.3810	0.3830
1.2	0.3849	0.3869	0.3888	0.3907	0.3925	0.3944	0.3962	0.3980	0.3997	0.4015
1.3	0.4032	0.4049	0.4066	0.4082	0.4099	0.4115	0.4131	0.4147	0.4162	0.4177
1.4	0.4192	0.4207	0.4222	0.4236	0.4251	0.4265	0.4279	0.4292	0.4306	0.4319
1.5	0.4332	0.4345	0.4357	0.4370	0.4382	0.4394	0.4406	0.4418	0.4429	0.4441
1.6	0.4452	0.4463	0.4474	0.4484	0.4495	0.4505	0.4515	0.4525	0.4535	0.4545
1.7	0.4554	0.4564	0.4573	0.4582	0.4591	0.4599	0.4608	0.4616	0.4625	0.4633
1.8	0.4641	0.4649	0.4656	0.4664	0.4671	0.4678	0.4686	0.4693	0.4699	0.4706
1.9	0.4713	0.4719	0.4726	0.4732	0.4738	0.4744	0.4750	0.4756	0.4761	0.4767
2.0	0.4772	0.4778	0.4783	0.4788	0.4793	0.4798	0.4803	0.4808	0.4812	0.4817
2.1	0.4821	0.4826	0.4830	0.4834	0.4838	0.4842	0.4846	0.4850	0.4854	0.4857
2.2	0.4861	0.4864	0.4868	0.4871	0.4875	0.4878	0.4881	0.4884	0.4887	0.4890
2.3	0.4893	0.4896	0.4898	0.4901	0.4904	0.4906	0.4909	0.4911	0.4913	0.4916
2.4	0.4918	0.4920	0.4922	0.4925	0.4927	0.4929	0.4931	0.4932	0.4934	0.4936
2.5	0.4938	0.4940	0.4941	0.4943	0.4945	0.4946	0.4948	0.4949	0.4951	0.4952
2.6	0.4953	0.4955	0.4956	0.4957	0.4959	0.4960	0.4961	0.4962	0.4963	0.4964
2.7	0.4965	0.4966	0.4967	0.4968	0.4969	0.4970	0.4971	0.4972	0.4973	0.4974
2.8	0.4974	0.4975	0.4976	0.4977	0.4977	0.4978	0.4979	0.4979	0.4980	0.4981
2.9	0.4981	0.4982	0.4982	0.4983	0.4984	0.4984	0.4985	0.4985	0.4986	0.4986
3.0	0.4987	0.4987	0.4987	0.4988	0.4988	0.4989	0.4989	0.4989	0.4990	0.4990

Business Statistics
A Decision-Making Approach

Custom Edition

Taken from:
Business Statistics: A Decision-Making Approach, Updated Sixth Edition
by David F. Groebner, Patrick W. Shannon, Phillip C. Fry, and Kent D. Smith

Cover Art: *Untitled #431,* by Barry Cronin

Taken from:

Business Statistics: A Decision-Making Approach, Updated Sixth Edition
by David F. Groebner, Patrick W. Shannon, Phillip C. Fry, and Kent D. Smith
Copyright © 2005, 2001 by Pearson Education, Inc.
Published by Prentice-Hall, Inc.
Upper Saddle River, New Jersey 07458

Printed in the United States of America

10 9 8 7 6 5 4 3 2 1

ISBN 0-536-95735-5

2005160291

KC

Please visit our web site at *www.pearsoncustom.com*

PEARSON CUSTOM PUBLISHING
75 Arlington Street, Suite 300, Boston, MA 02
A Pearson Education Company

To Jane and my family, who survived the process one more time.

David F. Groebner

To Kathy, my wife and best friend; to our children, Jackie and Jason; and to my parents, John and Ruth Shannon.

Patrick W. Shannon

To my wonderful family: Susan, Alex, Allie, Candace, and Courtney.

Phillip C. Fry

To Dottie, my loving wife, who dances much better than I write.

Kent D. Smith

ABOUT THE AUTHORS

David F. Groebner is a Professor of Production Management in the College of Business and Economics at Boise State University. He has bachelor's and master's degrees in Engineering and a Ph.D. in Business Administration. After working as an engineer, he has taught statistics and related subjects for 27 years. In addition to writing textbooks and academic papers, he has worked extensively with both small and large organizations, including Hewlett-Packard, Boise Cascade, Albertson's, and Ore-Ida. He has worked with numerous government agencies, including Boise City and the U.S. Air Force.

Patrick W. Shannon, Ph.D. is Professor of Production and Operations Management in the College of Business and Economics at Boise State University. He teaches graduate and undergraduate courses in business statistics, quality management, and production and operations management. In addition, Dr. Shannon has lectured and consulted in the statistical analysis and quality management areas for over 20 years. Listed among his consulting clients are Boise Cascade Corporation, Hewlett-Packard; PowerBar, Inc.; Potlatch Corporation; Woodgrain Millwork, Inc.; J.R. Simplot Company; Zilog Corporation; and numerous other public- and private-sector organizations. Professor Shannon has co-authored several university-level textbooks and has published numerous articles in such journals as *Business Horizons, Interfaces, Journal of Simulation, Journal of Production and Inventory Control, Quality Progress,* and *Journal of Marketing Research.* He obtained B.S. and M.S. degrees from the University of Montana and a Ph.D. in Statistics and Quantitative Methods from the University of Oregon.

Phillip C. Fry is a Professor in the College of Business and Economics at Boise State University, where he has taught since 1988. Phil received his B.A. and M.B.A degrees from the University of Arkansas, and his M.S. and Ph.D. degrees from Louisiana State University. His teaching and research interests are in the areas of business statistics, production management, and quantitative business modeling. In addition to his academic responsibilities, Phil has consulted with and provided training to small and large organizations, including Boise Cascade Corporation; Hewlett-Packard Corporation; The J.R. Simplot Company; United Water of Idaho; Woodgrain Millwork, Inc.; Boise City; and Micron Electronics.

Phil spends most of his free time with his wife Susan and his four children, Phillip Alexander, Alejandra Johanna, and twins, Courtney Rene and Candace Marie.

Kent D. Smith received a Ph.D. in Applied Statistics from the University of California, Riverside in 1981. He holds a Master of Science degree in Statistics from the University of California, Riverside and a Master of Science degree in Systems Analysis from the Air Force Institute of Technology. His Bachelor of Arts degree in Mathematics was obtained from the University of Utah. Dr. Smith has served as a University Statistical Consultant at the University of California, Riverside and at California Polytechnic State University, San Luis Obispo. While at the University of California, he served as a consultant for the Biometrical Services Unit of the Biometrical Project at the University of California, Riverside. His private consulting has ranged from serving as an expert witness in legal cases, survey sampling for corporations and private researchers, medical and orthodontic research, and assisting graduate students with analysis required for master and doctoral degrees in various disciplines.

Dr. Smith began teaching as a part-time lecturer at the California State University, San Bernardino. While completing his doctoral dissertation, he served as a lecturer at the University of California, Riverside. Currently, he is a Professor of Statistics at the California Polytechnic State University, San Luis Obispo, one of the minority of universities that offer an undergraduate degree in statistics. The subjects he teaches include upper-division courses in regression, analysis of variance, nonparametrics, linear models, and probability and mathematical statistics, as well as a full array of service courses.

CONTENTS

PREFACE

In today's workplace, graduating students can have an immediate competitive edge over existing employees by applying statistical analysis skills to real-world decision-making problems.

Our intent in writing the updated sixth edition of *Business Statistics* was to build on the strengths of past editions (captivating writing style; extensive use of real-world business applications; decision-making focus emphasizing the interpretation of data; and thorough computer integration of both Microsoft Excel and Minitab) and to take the text to a new level of excellence with *new* built-in study tools aimed at helping students develop the statistical skills necessary to meet the needs of business. Throughout the text the discussion of statistical techniques is reinforced with practical business applications to help students see the relevance of statistics to their daily lives.

All the authors share a passion for the subject as well as a devotion to teaching, and have significant consulting experience in applying the statistical tools in business and industry settings. Based on reviewer and student feedback, we have made substantive changes to this revision to further enhance an understanding of fundamental statistical concepts and techniques. Here are some of the highlights.

KEY CONTENT CHANGES

- Increased emphasis on using box plots for descriptive analyses and to check distribution assumptions
- Introduction to index numbers
- Employing the Durbin-Watson statistic for determining the presence of autocorrelation, now included in the forecasting material
- New section on the Wilcoxon Signed-Rank test
- Expanded emphasis on the assumptions behind the statistical tests
- Enhanced focus on the importance of using random sampling in the estimation and hypothesis testing sections
- New section on weighted means
- Special section on expected values and variances for the sum of two discrete random variables
- New discussion on covariance
- Introduction to the hypergeometric distribution
- New section on hypothesis testing for μ when σ is known
- Integration of Minitab 14 includes call out boxes that provide step-by-step Minitab commands
- Special review sections following the descriptive and inferential sections of the text, containing flow diagrams that help the students select appropriate statistical tools

NEW FEATURES

● NEW—SUMMARY BOXES

Throughout each chapter major techniques are summarized in easy-to-find boxes to clearly reinforce fundamental concepts and techniques. The methods for employing the statistical techniques are highlighted in an easy to follow step-by-step format.

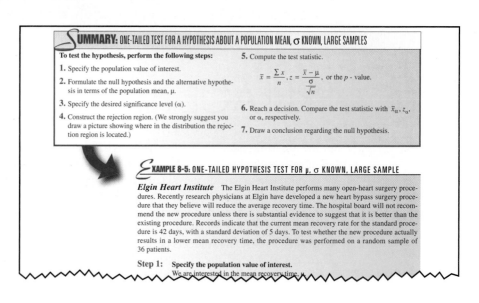

● NEW— STEP-BY-STEP EXAMPLES

New examples added throughout the text provide the step-by-step details to enable students to follow solution techniques easily and then to solve other problems. These specially marked examples are provided in addition to the vast array of business applications that were so widely praised in the fifth edition.

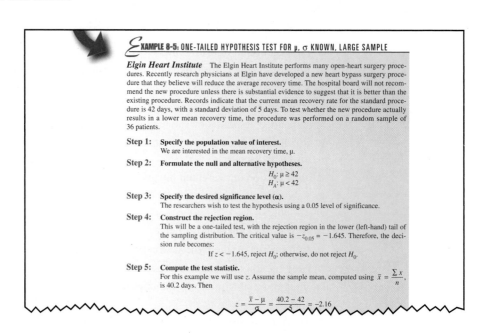

● NEW— EXERCISE SETS

The new edition includes a better balance of easy-to-advanced problems with more computational exercises and easier application exercises. The exercises at the end of each section and chapter involve realistic decision-making situations requiring the application of the statistical concepts introduced in the chapter. In addition to expanding the range of exercises, the exercises have been organized into the following three categories for ease of use and assignment purposes:

■ Skill Development   ■ Business Applications   ■ Advanced Business Applications

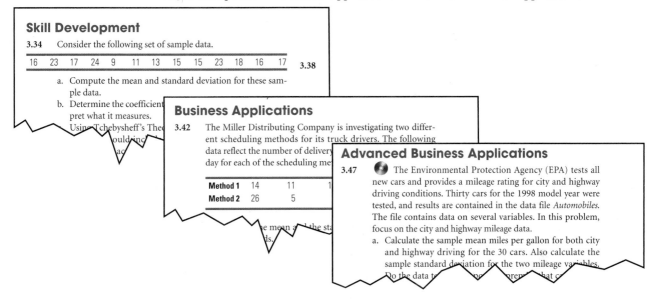

Skill Development

3.34 Consider the following set of sample data.

| 16 | 23 | 17 | 24 | 9 | 11 | 13 | 15 | 15 | 23 | 18 | 16 | 17 |

3.38

a. Compute the mean and standard deviation for these sample data.
b. Determine the coefficient...
pret what it measures.
Using Tchebysheff's Theo...

Business Applications

3.42 The Miller Distributing Company is investigating two different scheduling methods for its truck drivers. The following data reflect the number of delivery... day for each of the scheduling me...

Method 1	14	11
Method 2	26	5

...e mean a...d the sta...ds.

Advanced Business Applications

3.47 The Environmental Protection Agency (EPA) tests all new cars and provides a mileage rating for city and highway driving conditions. Thirty cars for the 1998 model year were tested, and results are contained in the data file *Automobiles*. The file contains data on several variables. In this problem, focus on the city and highway mileage data.

a. Calculate the sample mean miles per gallon for both city and highway driving for the 30 cars. Also calculate the sample standard deviation for the two mileage variables...

In addition to many exercises that can be worked manually, the text contains an extensive number of exercises that have computer data files and can be worked using Excel, Minitab, or other statistical software.

● NEW— SPECIAL REVIEW SECTIONS

Strategically placed at key points in the text, these Special Review Sections reinforce concepts learned in the immediately preceding chapters. Students are provided with flow diagrams and explanations that emphasize the principles, relationships, and properties of the techniques and procedures. These sections conclude with a set of comprehensive exercises that give students the opportunity to practice choosing the correct analytical technique for problem solving from diverse sections of the text.

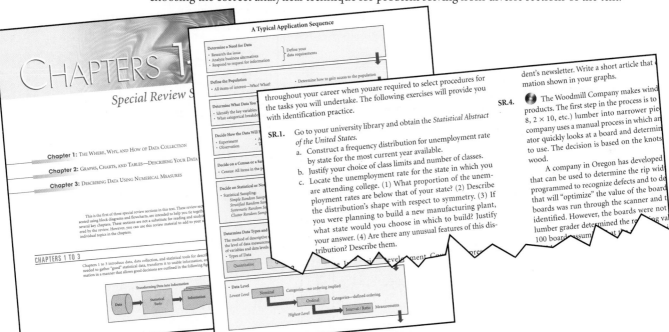

Special Review for Chapters 1-3: This section provides a summary and review of the key issues and statistical techniques associated with data, data collection and sampling, graphical descriptive analysis, and numerical descriptive analysis. These key topics are reviewed using block diagrams and flowcharts. Integrative questions and exercises are included that ask the student to demonstrate his or her comprehension of the topics covered in Chapters 1-3.

Special Review for Chapters 7-11: This section summarizes the key concepts associated with estimation and hypothesis testing. Through a series of color-coded flow diagrams, the students are provided with a template for determining which inferential technique to apply depending on the situation at hand. The summary covers one-, two-, and multiple-population situations. Integrative exercises and project assignments are included to provide the students with the opportunity to demonstrate their comprehension of estimation and hypothesis testing.

● NEW— ONLINE HOMEWORK AND ASSESSMENT SYSTEM

Prentice Hall is pleased to introduce PH Grade Assist. PH Grade Assist allows students to go online and work a nearly unlimited number of practice problems tied to the text. The problems are algorithmically generated so each student receives a slightly different problem with a different answer. Students either submit answers online for automatic grading and immediate feedback, or print out problems and submit complete solutions to their instructor. Students prefer the PH Grade Assist system because it provides immediate, individualized performance feedback and the opportunity to generate unlimited practice so they can "ace" the course.

For instructors, this online homework system allows professors to create, assign, and grade homework assignments quickly and easily. They can select problems from the text, create problems themselves, or use algorithmic variations of both. Plus, by registering and using the site, professors can post assignments, receive grades, and build detailed information on overall class performance on assignments. It's easy to use and helps manage the class. Contact your local Prentice Hall representative for more details.

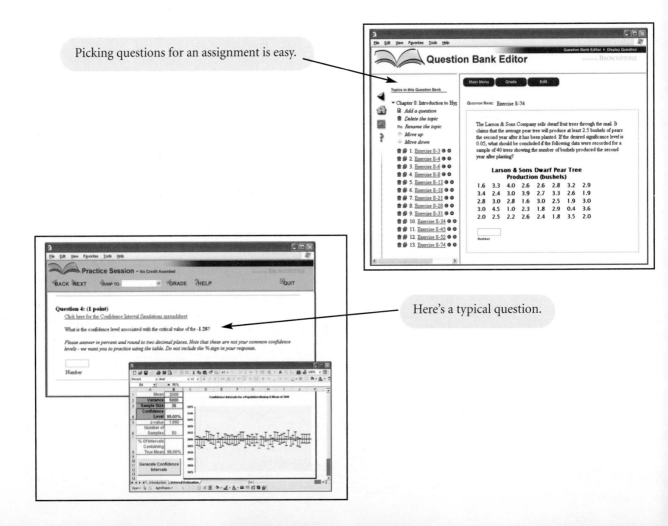

Picking questions for an assignment is easy.

Here's a typical question.

Setting rules and policies is quick and easy.

REAL-WORLD BUSINESS APPLICATIONS

Not only do the chapters focus on real companies, actual applications, and rich data sets, but increased effort has been placed on providing the student with an understanding of the role business statistics plays in decision making. Every effort has been made to communicate ideas using a nontechnical, nonthreatening, conversational writing style to stimulate student interest and involvement. This text is designed to help instructors create a climate in which students are motivated to learn statistical techniques in an applied context.

COMPUTER INTEGRATION

Unlike some business statistics texts that provide only end-of-chapter computer instructions, this text seamlessly integrates computer applications with the text examples, always focusing on interpreting the output. The goal is for the students to appreciate the role of spreadsheets and statistical software as business statistics tools.

Microsoft Excel and Minitab are extensively featured throughout the textbook. Chapter examples, exercises, and case studies are based on real industry data or data motivated by real-world examples. This approach helps students gain a greater understanding of what statistical tools to use, when and how to apply them, and how to interpret the results of their analyses to decision making. Special call-outs, positioned next to most of the text examples and output screen shots highlight key instructions and/or key points.

In addition, when students see a CD-ROM icon in the margin, labeled "Excel and Minitab Tutorials," these are available on the student CD-ROM. These animated PowerPoint tutorials provide a visual walk-through of the specific key-stroking steps necessary to create the output they see in the text.

CHAPTER CASES

Most chapters contain short cases that are designed to provide the students with an opportunity to apply the statistical tools to an unstructured situation. These cases challenge the student to define the problem, determine the appropriate statistical tools to use, apply those tools, and write a summary report.

STUDENT CD-ROM

This CD-ROM contains all the resources and tools your students need to succeed in the course:

❏ *Lecture PowerPoints*

Allow students to review and reinforce key points.

Excel and Minitab Tutorial

❏ *Excel and Minitab Tutorials*

Customized PowerPoint tutorials for both Minitab and Excel, illustrated above, which use data sets from text examples, are included on the CD-ROM. Students who need additional instruction in Excel or Minitab can access the menu-driven tutorial, which will show the exact steps needed to replicate all computer examples in the text.

❏ *Data Files*

An extensive number of data files for examples, cases, and exercises in the text are included on the CD-ROM in Excel, Minitab, SPSS, SAS, and ASCII formats. The text references these data files with a CD-ROM icon.

Optional CD-ROM Topic

❏ *CD-ROM Topics*

These CD-ROM Topics provide additional statistical concepts and data. Examples of topics include: Chapter 11, Experimental Design and Tukey's Method of Multiple Comparison; Chapter 14, Backward Elimination Regression; and Chapter 15, Regression-Based Forecasting Models.

❏ *Excel Simulations*

Excel Simulation

Several interactive simulations illustrate key statistical topics and allow students to do "what-if" scenarios.

❏ *PHStat2*

Included free with the Student CD-ROM is a specially developed Excel add-in package that contains a number of statistical features that are not included with Microsoft Excel. The added functions and procedures are useful in the study and application of business statistics. When installed, PHStat2 attaches itself to the Excel menu bar, providing users with a pull-down menu of topics that supplement the Data Analysis Add-in Tools in Microsoft Excel.

PHStat2 uses a set of simple and consistent dialog boxes that allow students to specify values and options for almost 50 tools included in the software. PHStat2 produces Excel worksheets organized into areas for the input data, intermediate calculations, and the results of the analysis. Unlike some competitors' add-ins, most of these worksheets contain live formulas that allow students to engage immediately in further "what-if" explorations of the data. (Where applicable, these worksheets contain special cell tints that distinguish the cells that contain user-modifiable input values from the cells containing the results, making "what-if" analysis even easier.) Completing the package is an excellent **online help system**.

ANCILLARIES

INSTRUCTOR'S SOLUTIONS MANUAL

The Instructor's Solutions Manual contains the worked-out solutions to all the problems and cases in the text. The manual can also be downloaded from Prentice Hall's Web site at *http://www.prenhall.com/groebner.*

TEST ITEM FILE

The Test Item File, created by Patrick W. Shannon, contains a variety of true/false, multiple choice, and short answer questions for each chapter. The Test Item File can also be downloaded from Prentice Hall's Web site at *http://www.prenhall.com/groebner.*

NEW TESTGEN SOFTWARE

The print Test Item File is designed for use with the TestGen test generating software. This computerized package allows instructors to custom design, save, and generate classroom tests. The test program permits instructors to edit, add, or delete questions from the test banks; edit existing graphics and create new graphics; analyze test results; and organize a database of tests and student results. This new software allows for greater flexibility and ease of use. It provides many options for organizing and displaying tests, along with a search and sort feature.

POWERPOINT PRESENTATION

An extensive set of PowerPoint Presentations, created by Dirk Yandell of the University of San Diego, is available for each chapter. These slides can also be downloaded from Prentice Hall's Web site at *http://www.prenhall.com/groebner.*

INSTRUCTOR'S RESOURCE CD-ROM

The Instructor's Resource CD-ROM provides the electronic files for the entire Instructor's Solutions Manual (in MS Word), PowerPoint presentations (in PowerPoint), Test Item File (in MS Word), and the computerized test bank (TestGen).

STUDENT SOLUTIONS MANUAL

The Student Solutions Manual contains worked-out solutions to all the odd-numbered problems in the text. More than just showing the answer, the Solutions Manual shows the detailed process that students should use to work each problem. The manual also provides interpretation of the answers and serves as a valuable learning tool for the student.

THE COMPANION WEB SITE

The Companion Web site features valuable resources for:

❏ *Online Study Guide*

Extensive quizzes provide a great review of text material with an assortment of multiple choice, true/false, and essay questions.

❏ *Interactive Excel Tutorials*

Dynamic video tutorials animate step-by-step demonstrations on how to use Excel for more than 20 statistical techniques.

❏ *In the News Articles*

Current events articles are added throughout the year. Each article is summarized by a team of experts and is fully supported by exercises, activities, and instructor material.

❏ *Internet Exercises*

Comprehensive exercises and activities expose students to the most current and relevant information on the Internet.

❏ *Instructor Resources*

Downloadable instructor supplements are available on the Web site.

ACKNOWLEDGMENTS

Publishing a textbook is a team effort and involves many people. At the risk of overlooking someone, we take this space to express our appreciation to many of the key contributors to this text. Throughout the more than two years that this revision has been in process, many faculty members from across the country have taken time from their busy schedules to provide valuable input and suggestions for improvement. We offer thanks to:

Suad Alwan
Chicago State University
Mary E. Camp
Indiana University
Cali M. Davis
University of Alabama
John Dutton
North Carolina State University
James Flynn
Cleveland State University
Kelly Haverstick
Brandeis University
John Janke
College of the Cariboo
Chun Jin
Central Connecticut State University
John Lawrence
California State University–Fullerton
Walt McCoy
University of Nebraska—Omaha
Thomas McCullough
University of California—Berkeley

Elaine McGivern
Duquesne University
Dick Morris
Winthrop University
John Nash
University of Ottawa
Pornpilai Ongardanunkul
Boston College
Ranjna Patel
Bethune Cookman College
Robert Patterson
Penn State—Erie
Robert Potter
University of Central Florida
Harold F. Rahmlow
St. Joseph's University
Farhad Raiszadeh
University of Tennessee—Chattanooga
Walter Rom
Cleveland State University
Mary Anne Rothermel
University of Akron

Farhad Saboori
Albright College
William Seaver
University of Tennessee–Knoxville
Gary Smith
Florida State University
David Stewart
Winston-Salem State University
Debra K. Stiver
University of Nevada–Reno
Joaquin Tadeo
University of Texas at El Paso

Mari Yetimyan
San Jose State University
W. F. Younkin
University of Miami
Oliver Yu
San Jose State University
Jiankang Zhang
Carleton University
George Zheng
Western Washington
Zhiwei Zhu
University of Louisiana at Lafayette

A special thanks goes to Frank Purcell at Twin Prime Editorial, who conscientiously read every page of this manuscript and provided valuable suggestions for improving this book in many ways. Thanks also to David Stephan for his expert work in developing the PHStat add-in for Excel.

We want to thank Dirk Yandell, at the University of San Diego, for preparing the best PowerPoint slides we have ever seen. They make teaching this course much easier and students will find them very helpful for their own review.

Accuracy checking a book of this scope is tremendously important, and we especially want to thank those who did a very careful job of reading the manuscript and supplements and carefully screening them for errors. Ruppert Rhodd and Paul Koku, both at Florida Atlantic University, did a terrific job of accuracy checking the final pages, the instructor's solutions manual, and student solutions manual. Geoff Willis, at the University of Central Oklahoma checked the test questions, which were written by the authors. Phillip D. Youngblood, at University of the Incarnate Word created the "In the News" articles and Internet exercises found on the Companion Website, and Jim Zimmer, of Chattanooga State Technical Community College wrote the Interactive Study Guide, also found on the Companion Website.

The team of professionals at Prentice Hall is the finest publishing group with whom we have had the pleasure of working. Anne Graydon and Carol Samet oversaw the production end of the publishing process and kept us on schedule; Blair Brown created the handsome book design; Nancy Welcher coordinated the CD-ROM materials; Erika Rusnak supervised the preparation of supplements; and Debbie Clare handled the very important marketing component with great creativity and enthusiasm. Finally, we wish to give a special thanks to Tom Tucker, Decision Sciences Executive Editor at Prentice Hall, for his belief in our text and for his professional assistance from beginning to end. Working with him has been both a pleasure and a terrific learning experience. He has provided the resources necessary to make this sixth edition a major advance from previous editions.

—DAVID F. GROEBNER
—PATRICK W. SHANNON
—PHILLIP C. FRY
—KENT D. SMITH

CHAPTER 1

The Where, Why, and How of Data Collection

CHAPTER OUTCOMES

After studying the material in Chapter 1, you should:

- Know the key data collection methods.
- Know the difference between a population and a sample.
- Understand how to categorize data by type and level of measurement.
- Understand the similarities and differences between different sampling methods.

WHY YOU NEED TO KNOW

This is a good time to be entering the business world. Never before have the opportunities been so numerous. Global markets have opened up literally a world of possibilities, and job functions in businesses are changing to meet the dynamic business environment. Organizations are scrambling to find people who have the knowledge, skills, and abilities to meet the ever increasing competitive challenges faced by businesses. Although businesses have always looked to colleges and universities to help provide them with the talent they need, the trend in this direction is stronger than ever. However, these businesses are not just seeking educated people. They are seeking individuals who have the ability to understand and apply key decision-making tools to the complexities of the business environment.

Many organizations have access to massive amounts of data, but decision makers have a difficult time using these data effectively. **Business statistics** offers students the necessary tools to effectively convert sets of data into usable information. This is why business statistics is a required course at any accredited business school.

Business statistics offers some very important tools for data conversion. You will have the opportunity to learn about these statistical tools from your professor and from this text. This text focuses on the practical application of statistics: We do not develop the statistical theory you could find in a mathematical statistics course. Will you need to use mathematics in this course? Yes, but it will be mainly basic concepts derived from college algebra.

Statistics does have its own terminology. You will need to learn various terms that have special statistical meaning. You will also learn certain do's and don'ts related to statistics. But most importantly, you will learn specific methods to effectively convert data into information. In all cases, the best way to learn is by doing. The text contains numerous problems and exercises that reinforce the concepts and methods in the chapters. Don't try to memorize the concepts; rather, go to the next level of learning, called *understanding*. Once you understand the underlying concepts, you will be able to *think statistically*.

We have taught business statistics for many years, and we are well aware that you may be approaching this course with a certain degree of apprehension. That's certainly understandable. Anything that is new is uncomfortable at first. However, we promise that once you are under way in this course, you will begin to see that business statistics is actually a logical subject that is applicable to all business areas. When you can think statistically, you will have truly set yourself apart from many others in the business world, and this will give you a competitive advantage for the rest of your life.

1-1 WHAT IS BUSINESS STATISTICS?

Every day, your local newspaper contains stories that report descriptors such as stock prices, crime rates, and government agency budgets. Such descriptors can be found in many places. However, these descriptors are just a small part of a discipline that shares the name of statistics. Statistics as a discipline provides a wide variety of methods to assist in data analysis and decision making. Business is one important area of application for these methods. Business statistics is defined as follows:

Business Statistics

A collection of tools and techniques that are used to convert data into meaningful information in a business environment.

DESCRIPTIVE STATISTICS

The tools and techniques that comprise business statistics include those specially designed to *describe data*, such as charts, graphs, and numerical measures. Also included are inferential tools that help decision makers *draw inferences* from a set of data. Inferential tools include estimation and hypothesis testing. A brief discussion of these tools and techniques follows. The examples illustrate data that have been entered into the Microsoft Excel and Minitab software packages.

Baker City Hospital—Because health care companies in the United States are facing increased competition, hospital administrators must become more efficient in managing operations. This demand means they must better understand their customers.

The financial vice president for Baker City Hospital recently collected data for 138 patients. The VP has entered these data into an Excel spreadsheet, as illustrated in Figure 1-1. Each column in the figure corresponds to a different factor for which data were collected. Each row corresponds

	Microsoft Excel - Baker.xls			
	File Edit View Insert Format Tools Data PHStat Window Help			
	Courier ▾ 10 ▾ B I			
E7	=			

	A	B	C	D	E
1	**Length of Stay**	**Age (Years)**	**Sex (M/F/U)**	**Total Charges**	
2	3	78	F	5,419	
3	3	74	F	4,575	
4	11	89	M	12,031	
5	3	81	M	3,618	
6	9	87	F	12,807	
7	3	65	M	5,296	
8	3	90	M	3,453	
9	3	61	M	1,760	
10	3	90	F	3,290	
11	5	78	M	6,254	
12	3	78	F	3,896	
13	2	71	M	1,795	
14	3	76	M	9,265	
15	3	76	F	3,283	

to a different patient. Many statistical tools might help the VP describe these patients' data, including *charts*, *graphs*, and *numerical measures*.

Charts and Graphs

Although we develop an extensive variety of methods to describe data using graphs and charts in Chapter 2, a few examples are offered here to give you an idea of what is possible. Figure 1-2 shows a graph called a *histogram*. This graph gives us some insight into how long patients stay at the Baker City Hospital by visually showing how many patients appear in each length-of-stay category. It describes the shape and spread of the patient length-of-stay distribution. The *bar chart* shown in Figure 1-3 breaks down the patient data showing the percentage of male and female patients. We can tell, looking at this chart, that the mix of patients has a higher number of females.

These are only a few of the graphical techniques that the Baker City Hospital VP might use to help describe her patient population. In Chapter 2 you will learn about these techniques.

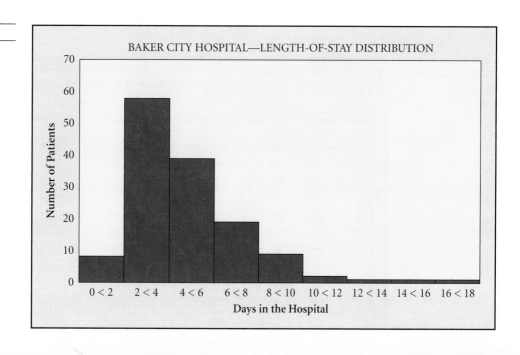

BAKER CITY HOSPITAL—LENGTH-OF-STAY DISTRIBUTION

FIGURE 1-3

Bar Chart of Baker City
Hospital

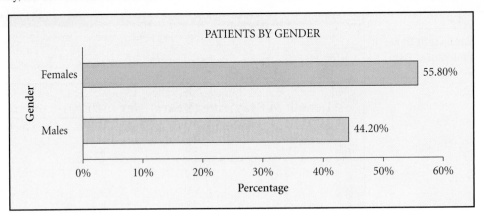

FIGURE 1-3

Bar Chart of Baker City
Hospital

Crown Investments—During the 1990s and early 2000s, many major changes occurred in the financial services industry. Numerous banks merged. Money flowed into the stock market at rates far surpassing anything the U.S. economy had previously witnessed. The international financial world fluctuated greatly. All these developments have spurred the need for more financial analysts who can critically evaluate financial data and explain them to customers.

At Crown Investments, a senior analyst is preparing to present data to upper management on the 100 fastest growing companies on the Hong Kong Stock Exchange. Figure 1-4 shows a Minitab worksheet containing a subset of the data. The columns correspond to the different items of interest (growth percentage, sales, and so on). The data for each company are in a single row.

In addition to preparing appropriate graphs, the analyst will compute important numerical measures. One of the most basic and most useful measures in business statistics is one with which you are already familiar: the **arithmetic mean** or **average**.

Average

The sum of all the values divided by the number of values. In equation form:

$$\text{Average} = \frac{\sum_{i=1}^{N} x_i}{N} = \frac{\text{sum of all data values}}{\text{number of data values}}$$

where:

N = Number of data values
x_i = ith data value

FIGURE 1-4

Crown Investment
Example—Minitab
Worksheet

MINITAB - FAST100.MPJ - [Fast100.MTW ***]

File Edit Data Calc Stat Graph Editor Tools Window Help

↓	C5	C6	C7	C8	C9	C10	C11	C12
	Growth %	Sales	EPS	Profits	Stk-Price	Last Yr Price	P/E ratio	Stk Market
1	256	185.3	-99	6.8	18.00	8.50	17	1
2	228	183.2	243	43.2	42.25	12.50	31	1
3	215	187.5	-99	26.5	21.25	11.13	17	1
4	209	229.8	129	35.4	27.38	26.25	16	1
5	209	249.9	97	8.9	23.38	15.00	53	2
6	203	399.7	18	4.2	2.31	1.13	17	1
7	200	731.4	95	77.7	11.63	10.00	24	2
8	180	93.0	116	8.6	6.63	-99.00	21	2
9	179	440.9	72	8.4	8.25	-99.00	9	1
10	167	131.8	-99	3.7	16.50	-99.00	66	1

FIGURE 1-5

The Role of Business
Statistics

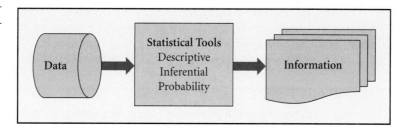

The analyst may be interested in the average profit (that is, the mean of the column labeled *Profits*) for the 100 companies. The total profit calculated for the 100 companies is $3,193.60, but profits are given in millions of dollars, so the total profit amount is actually $3,193,600,000. The average is found by dividing this total by the number of companies:

$$\text{Average} = \frac{\$3,193,600,000}{100} = \$31,936,000, \text{ or } \$31.936 \text{ million dollars}$$

As we will discuss in greater depth in Chapter 3, the average or mean is a measure of the center of the data. In this case, the analyst may use the average profit as an indicator—firms with above-average profits are rated higher than firms with below-average profits.

The graphical and numerical measures illustrated here are only some of the many descriptive tools that will be introduced in Chapters 2 and 3. The key to remember is that the purpose of the descriptive tools is to describe data. Your task will be to select the tool or tools that best accomplish this. As Figure 1-5 reminds you, the role of statistics is to convert data into meaningful information.

INFERENTIAL TOOLS

How do television networks determine which programs people prefer to watch? How does the network that carries the Super Bowl know how many people were watching the game? Advertisers pay for TV ads based on the audience level, so these numbers are important; millions of dollars are at stake. Clearly the networks don't check with everyone in the country. Instead, they use an area of statistics called **statistical inference** to come up with the information.

Statistical Inference Tools

Tools that allow a decision maker to reach a conclusion about a population of data based on a subset of data from the population.

There are two primary categories of statistical inference tools: *estimation* and *hypothesis testing*. These tools are closely related but serve very different purposes.

Estimation

In situations in which we would like to know about all the data in a large data set but it is impractical to work with all the data, decision makers can use techniques to estimate what the larger data set looks like. The estimates are formed by looking closely at a subset of the larger data set.

TV Ratings—The television networks cannot know for sure how many people watched last year's Super Bowl. They cannot possibly ask everyone what he or she saw that day on television. Instead, the networks rely on organizations that conduct surveys to supply program ratings. For example, the Nielsen Company asks people from only a small number of homes across the country what shows they watched, and then it uses that information to estimate the number of viewers per show for the entire population.

Consider this article, which appeared in newspapers across the country on May 16, 1998:

NEW YORK—Jerry and his three misfit friends ended "Seinfeld" arguing in a prison cell watched by an estimated 76 million people.

Ratings for the comedy's final episode were below the finals for "Cheers" and "M*A*S*H*" and a shade below NBC's predictions.

Advertisers and television networks enter into contracts in which each price per ad is based on a certain minimum viewership. If the Nielsen ratings estimate an audience smaller than this minimum, then a network must refund some money to its advertisers.

In Chapter 7, we will discuss the estimating techniques that companies such as Nielsen use.

Hypothesis Testing

Television advertising is full of product claims. For example, we might hear that "Goodyear tires will last at least 60,000 miles," or that "More doctors recommend Bayer Aspirin than any other brand." Other claims might include statements that "General Electric lightbulbs last longer than any other brand," or that "Customers prefer Burger King over McDonald's." Are these just idle boasts, or are they based on actual data? Probably some of both! However, consumer research organizations such as *Consumer Reports* regularly test these types of claims. For example, in the hamburger case, *Consumer Reports* might select a sample of customers who would be asked to blind taste test Burger King's and McDonald's hamburgers, under the hypothesis that there is no difference in customer preferences between the two restaurants. If the sample data showed a difference in preferences, then the hypothesis of no difference would be rejected. If only a slight difference in preferences were detected, then *Consumer Reports* writers could not reject the hypothesis. Chapters 8 and 9 introduce basic hypothesis-testing techniques that are used to test claims about products and services using information taken from samples.

1-1: EXERCISES

Skill Development

1.1 Describe the difference between a histogram and a bar chart.

1.2 Calculate the average of the total charges listed in Figure 1-1.

1.3 Calculate the averages of the total charges for men and for women in Figure 1-1. What conclusion might you draw concerning the difference in the average charges between the two genders?

1.4 Calculate the average of the ages of the patients listed in Figure 1-1.

1.5 For the data in Figure 1-1, calculate the average total charges for patients older than 75 and younger than 75. What conclusion might you draw about the difference in the average charges between the two age groups?

1.6 Using only the data given in Figure 1-4, construct a bar chart showing the average stock price for each stock market listed in column C12.

1.7 In your own terms, define what is meant by statistical estimation. Provide an example from your own experiences in which estimation is used.

1.8 Define what is meant by hypothesis testing. Provide an example in which you personally have tested a hypothesis (even if you didn't use formal statistical techniques to do so).

1.9 It is important to know when to employ estimation and when to employ hypothesis testing. Explain under what circumstances you would use hypothesis testing, as opposed to an estimation procedure.

Business Applications

1.10 Locate a business periodical, such as *Fortune* or *Forbes*, or a business newspaper, such as *The Wall Street Journal*. Find three examples of the use of a graph to display data. For each graph,
   a. Give the name, date, and page number of the periodical in which the graph appeared.
   b. Describe the main point made by the graph.
   c. Analyze the effectiveness of the graph.

1.11 A group of executives at a local company is considering introducing a new product into a market area. It is important to know the characteristics of the ages of the people in the market area.
   a. If the executives wish to calculate a number that would characterize the "center" of the age data, what statistical technique would you suggest? Explain your answer.
   b. The executives need to know the percentage of people in the market area who are senior citizens. Name the basic category of statistical inference tools they would use to provide this information.
   c. Describe a hypothesis upon which the executives might wish to conduct a test concerning the percentage of senior citizens in the market area.

1.12 An agribusiness company currently uses one brand of commercial fertilizer. However, a new fertilizer is available that the manufacturer says will produce higher-than-average crop yields.
   a. Name the basic category of statistical inference tools they would use to provide this information.
   b. Describe a hypothesis that a manufacturer might use to conduct a test concerning the relative effectiveness of the new fertilizer.

1.13 Locate an example from a business periodical or newspaper in which estimation has been used.
  a. What specifically was estimated?
  b. What conclusion was reached using the estimation?
  c. Describe how the data were extracted and how the data were used to produce the estimation.
  d. Keeping in mind the goal of the estimation, discuss whether you believe that the estimation was successful and why.
  e. Describe what inferences were drawn as a result of the estimation.

1-2 TOOLS FOR COLLECTING DATA

We have defined business statistics as a set of tools that are used to transform data into information. Before you learn how to use statistical tools, it is important that you become familiar with different types of data collection methods.

DATA COLLECTION METHODS

There are many methods and tools available for collecting data. The following are considered some of the most useful and frequently used data collection methods:

- experiments
- telephone surveys
- mail questionnaires
- direct observation and personal interviews

Experiments

Food Processing—A company often must conduct a specific experiment or set of experiments to get the data managers need to make informed decisions. For example, the J. R. Simplot Company in Idaho is a primary supplier of french fries to companies such as McDonald's. At its Caldwell factory, Simplot has a tech center that, among other things, houses a mini–french fry plant used to conduct experiments on its potato manufacturing process. McDonald's has strict standards on the quality of the french fries it buys. One important attribute is the color of the fries after cooking. They should be "golden brown"—uniformly not too light or too dark.

French fries are made from potatoes that are peeled, sliced into strips, blanched, partially cooked, and then freeze-dried—not a simple process. Because potatoes differ in many ways (such as sugar content and moisture), blanching time, cooking temperature, and other factors vary from batch to batch.

Simplot tech-center employees start their **experiments** by grouping the raw potatoes into batches with similar characteristics. They run some of the potatoes through the line with blanch time and temperature settings set at specific levels defined by an **experimental design**. After measuring one or more output variables for that run, they change the settings and run another batch, again measuring the output variables.

Experiment

Any process that generates data as its outcome.

Experimental Design

A plan for performing an experiment in which the variable of interest is defined. One or more factors are identified to be manipulated or changed so that the impact (or influence) on the variable of interest can be measured or observed.

Figure 1-6 shows a typical data collection form. The output variable (for example, percentage of fries without dark spots) for each combination of potato category, blanch time, and temperature is recorded in the appropriate cell in the table. Chapter 11 introduces the fundamental concepts related to experimental design and analysis.

FIGURE 1-6

Experiment Data Layout

Blanch Time	Blanch Temperature	Potato Category			
		1	2	3	4
10 minutes	100° 110° 120°				
15 minutes	100° 110° 120°				
20 minutes	100° 110° 120°				
25 minutes	100° 110° 120°				

Telephone Surveys

Public Issues—One common method of obtaining data about people and their opinions is the telephone survey. Chances are that you have been on the receiving end of one. "Hello. My name is Mary Jane and I represent the XYZ organization. I am conducting a survey on. . . ." Political groups use telephone surveys to poll people about candidates and issues.

Telephone surveys are a relatively inexpensive and efficient data collection tool. Of course, some people will refuse to respond to a survey, others are not home when the calls come, and a small percentage of people do not have phones or cannot be reached by phone for one reason or another.

Figure 1-7 shows the major steps in conducting a telephone survey. This example survey was run by a Seattle television station to determine public support for using tax dollars to build a new football stadium for the NFL Seattle Seahawks. The survey was aimed at property-tax payers only.

Because most people will not stay on the line very long, the phone survey must be short—usually 1 to 3 minutes. The questions are generally what are called **closed-end questions**.

Closed-End Questions

Questions that require the respondent to select from a short list of defined choices.

For example, a closed-end question might be, "To which political party do you belong? Republican? Democrat? Or other?" The survey instrument should have a short statement at the beginning explaining the purpose of the survey and reassuring the respondent that his or her responses will remain confidential. The initial section of the survey should contain questions relating to the central issue of the survey. The last part of the survey should contain **demographic questions** (such as gender, income level, and education level) that will allow you to break down the responses and look deeper into the survey results.

Demographic Questions

Questions relating to the respondents' own characteristics, backgrounds, and attributes.

A survey budget must be considered. For example, if you have $3,000 to spend on calls and each call costs $10 to make, you obviously are limited to making 300 calls. However, keep in mind that 300 calls may not result in 300 usable responses.

The phone survey should be conducted in a short time period. Typically, the prime calling time for a voter survey is between 7:00 P.M. and 9:00 P.M. However, some people are not home in the evening and will be excluded from the survey unless there is a plan for conducting callbacks.

FIGURE 1-7

**Major Steps for a
Telephone Survey**

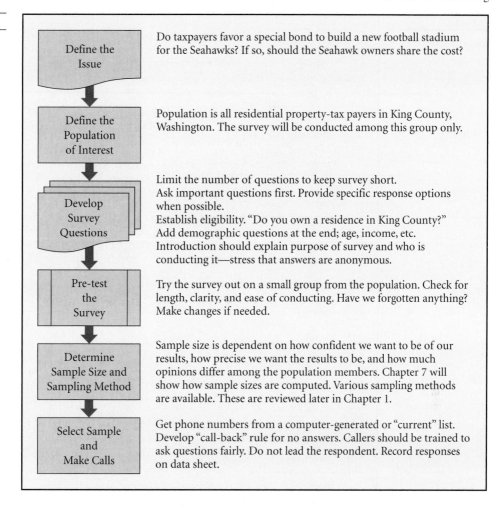

Do taxpayers favor a special bond to build a new football stadium for the Seahawks? If so, should the Seahawk owners share the cost?

Define the Issue

Define the Population of Interest

Population is all residential property-tax payers in King County, Washington. The survey will be conducted among this group only.

Develop Survey Questions

Limit the number of questions to keep survey short.
Ask important questions first. Provide specific response options when possible.
Establish eligibility. "Do you own a residence in King County?"
Add demographic questions at the end; age, income, etc.
Introduction should explain purpose of survey and who is conducting it—stress that answers are anonymous.

Pre-test the Survey

Try the survey out on a small group from the population. Check for length, clarity, and ease of conducting. Have we forgotten anything? Make changes if needed.

Determine Sample Size and Sampling Method

Sample size is dependent on how confident we want to be of our results, how precise we want the results to be, and how much opinions differ among the population members. Chapter 7 will show how sample sizes are computed. Various sampling methods are available. These are reviewed later in Chapter 1.

Select Sample and Make Calls

Get phone numbers from a computer-generated or "current" list. Develop "call-back" rule for no answers. Callers should be trained to ask questions fairly. Do not lead the respondent. Record responses on data sheet.

Mail Questionnaires and Other Written Surveys

The most frequently used method to collect opinions and factual data from people is a written survey. In some instances, the surveys are in the form of a mail questionnaire. At other times, the surveys are administered directly to the potential respondents. Written questionnaires are generally the least expensive means of collecting survey data. If the survey is mailed, the major costs include postage to and from the respondents, questionnaire development and printing costs, and data analysis.

Figure 1-8 shows the major steps in conducting a written survey. Note how written surveys are similar to telephone surveys; however, written surveys can be slightly more involved and, therefore, take more time to complete than those used for a telephone survey. However, you must be careful to construct a questionnaire that can be easily completed without requiring too much time.

A written survey can contain both closed-end and **open-end questions**.

Open-End Questions

Questions that allow respondents the freedom to respond with any value, words, or statements of their own choosing.

Open-end questions provide the respondent with greater flexibility in answering a question, however the responses can be difficult to analyze. Note, telephone surveys can use open-end questions, too. However, the caller may have to transcribe a potentially long response and may misinterpret what is being said.

Written surveys also should be formatted to make it easy for the respondent to provide accurate and reliable data. This means that proper space must be provided for the responses. The directions must be clear about how the survey is to be completed. A written survey needs to be pleasing to the eye. How it looks will affect the response rate, so it must look professional.

FIGURE 1-8

Written Survey Steps

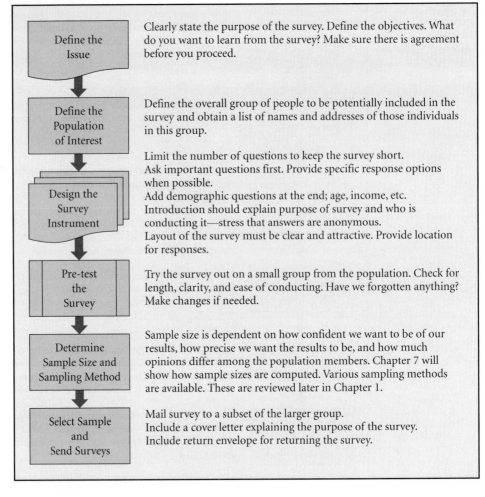

You also must decide whether to manually enter or scan the data gathered from your written survey. The survey design will be affected by the approach you take. If you are administering a large number of surveys, scanning is preferred. It cuts down on data entry errors and speeds up the data gathering process. However, you may be limited in the form of responses that are possible if you use scanning.

If the survey is administered directly to the desired respondents, you can expect a high response rate. For example, you probably have been on the receiving end of a written survey many times in your college career, when you were asked to fill out a course evaluation form at the end of the term. Most students will complete the form. On the other hand, if a survey is administered through the mail, you can expect a low response rate—typically 5% to 20%. Therefore, if you want 200 responses, you should mail out 1,000 to 4,000 questionnaires.

Overall, written surveys can be a low-cost, effective means of collecting data if you can overcome the problems of low response. Be careful to pretest the survey and spend extra time on the format and look of the survey instrument.

Direct Observation and Personal Interviews

Direct observation is another tool that is often used to collect data. As implied by the name, this technique requires that the process from which the data are being collected is physically observed and the data are recorded based on what takes place in the process.

Possibly the most basic way to gather data on human behavior is to watch people. If you are trying to decide whether a new method of displaying your product at the supermarket will be more pleasing to customers, change a few displays and watch customers' reactions.

If, as a member of a state's transportation department, you want to determine how well motorists are complying with the state's seat belt laws, place observers at key spots throughout the state to monitor people's seat belt habits. If, as a movie producer, you want information on whether your new movie will be a success, hold a preview showing and observe the reactions and comments of the movie patrons as they exit the screening. The major constraints when collecting observations are the time and money it takes to carry out the observations. For observations to be effective, trained observers must be used, which increases the cost. Personal observation is also time-consuming. Finally, personal perception is subjective. There is no guarantee that different observers will see a situation in the same way, much less report it the same way.

Personal interviews are often used to gather data from people. Interviews can be either **structured** or **unstructured**, depending on the objectives, and they can utilize either open-end or closed-end questions.

Structured Interview Interviews in which the questions are scripted.	***Unstructured Interview*** Interviews that begin with one or more broadly stated questions, with further questions being based on the responses.

Regardless of the tool used for data collection, care must be taken that the data collected are accurate and reliable and that they are the right data for the purpose at hand.

OTHER DATA COLLECTION METHODS

Data collection methods that take advantage of new technologies are becoming more prevalent all the time. For example, many people believe that Wal-Mart is the best company in the world at collecting and using data about the buying habits of its customers. Most of the data are collected automatically as checkout clerks scan the UPC bar codes on the products customers purchase. Not only are Wal-Mart's inventory records automatically updated, information about the buying habits of customers is recorded. The data help managers organize their stores to increase sales. For instance, Wal-Mart apparently decided to locate beer and disposable diapers close together when it discovered that many male customers also purchase beer when they are sent to the store for diapers.

Bar code scanning is used in many different data collection applications. In a DRAM wafer fabrication plant, lots of silicon wafers have bar codes. As the lots travel through the plant's work stations, their progress and quality are tracked through the data that are automatically obtained through scanning.

Every time you use your credit card, data are automatically collected by the retailer and the bank. Computer information systems are developed to store the data and to provide decision makers with tools to access the data.

DATA COLLECTION ISSUES

There are several data collection issues of which you need to be aware. When you need data to make a decision, we suggest that you first see if appropriate data have already been collected, because it is usually faster and less expensive to use existing data than to collect data yourself. However, before you rely on data that were collected by someone else for another purpose, you need to check out the source to make sure that the data were collected and recorded properly.

The *Value Lines* and *Fortune* magazines of the world have built their reputations on providing quality data. Although data errors are occasionally encountered, they are few and far between. You really need to be concerned with data that come from sources with which you are not familiar. This is an issue for many sources on the World Wide Web. Any organization, or any individual, can post data to the Web. Just because the data are there doesn't mean they are accurate. Be careful.

There are other general issues associated with data collection. One of these is the potential for *bias* in the data collection. There are many types of bias. For example, in a personal interview, the interviewer can interject bias (either accidentally or on purpose) by the way she asks the questions, by the tone of her voice, or by the way she looks at the subject being interviewed. We recently allowed ourselves to be interviewed at a trade show. The interviewer began by telling us that he would only get credit for the interview if we answered all of the questions. Next, he asked us to indicate our satisfaction with a particular display. He wasn't satisfied with our less-than-enthusiastic rating and kept asking us if we really meant what we said. He even asked us if we would consider upgrading our rating! How reliable do you think these data will be?

Another source of bias that can be interjected into a survey data collection process is called *nonresponse bias*. We stated earlier that mail surveys suffer from a high percentage of unreturned surveys. Phone calls don't always get through, or people refuse to answer. Subjects of personal interviews may refuse to be interviewed. There is a problem with nonresponse. Those who respond may provide data that are quite different from the data that would be supplied by those who chose not to respond. If you aren't careful, the responses may be heavily weighted by people who feel strongly one way or another on an issue.

Bias can be interjected through the way subjects are selected for data collection. This is referred to as *selection bias*. A study on the virtues of increasing the student athletic fee at your university might not be best served by collecting data from students attending a football game. Sometimes, the problem is more subtle. If we do a telephone survey during the evening hours, we will miss all of the people who work nights. Do they share the same views, income, education levels, and so on as people who work days? If not, the data are biased.

Written and phone surveys and personal interviews can also yield flawed data if the interviewees *lie* in response to questions. For example, people commonly give inaccurate data about such sensitive matters as income. Sometimes, the data errors are not due to lies. The respondents may not know or have accurate information to provide the correct answer.

Measurement error is another problem that can be encountered in data collection. A few years ago we were working with a window manufacturer. The company was having a quality problem with one of its saws. A study was developed to measure the width of boards that had been cut by the saw. Two people were trained to use digital calipers and record the data. This caliper is a U-shaped tool that measures distance (in inches) to three decimal places. The caliper was placed around the board and squeezed tightly against the sides. The width was indicated on the display. Each person measured 500 boards during an eight-hour day. When the data were analyzed, it looked like the widths were coming from two different saws; one set showed considerably wider widths than the other. Upon investigation, we learned that the person with the narrower width measurements was pressing down on the calipers much more firmly. The soft wood reacted to the pressure and gave narrower readings. Fortunately, we had kept the data from the two data collectors separate. Had they been merged, the measurement error might have gone undetected.

Data collection through personal observation is also subject to problems. People tend to view the same event or item differently. This is referred to as *observer bias*. One area in which this can easily occur is in safety check programs in companies. An important part of behavioral-based safety programs is the safety observation. Trained data collectors periodically conduct a safety observation on a worker to determine what, if any, unsafe acts might be taking place. We have seen situations in which two observers will conduct an observation on the same worker at the same time, yet record different safety data. This is especially true in areas in which judgment is required on the part of the observer, such as the distance a worker is from an exposed gear mechanism. People judge distance differently.

An extensive discussion of how to measure the magnitude of bias and how to reduce bias and other data collection problems is beyond the scope of this text. However, you should be aware that data may be biased or otherwise flawed. Always pose questions about the potential for bias and determine what steps have been taken to reduce its affect.

1-2: EXERCISES

Skill Development

1.14 Name one data collection method that is not subject to nonresponse bias. Explain and give an example.

1.15 In selecting between a telephone survey and a mail questionnaire, which is more adaptable to open-end questions? Explain.

1.16 *USA Today* (Dec. 15, 1998) reported that 8 out of 10 adults said that they would give to charities during the Christmas season. What data collection method do you think was used to collect this data? Explain your answer.

1.17 What type of data collection is used most frequently for political polls? Explain why.

1.18 If a bank wishes to determine the level of customer satisfaction with its services, would it likely be appropriate to conduct an experiment? Explain.

1.19 Which type of bias is most common when mail questionnaires are used as the data collection tool? Explain.

1.20 What type of bias is most likely to occur when a personal interview is conducted? Explain.

1.21 If an experiment is conducted in a factory to determine the time it takes to assemble a product using different sequences, what type of bias is most likely to occur? Explain.

Business Applications

1.22 The U.S. Department of Agriculture (USDA) estimates that Southern fire ants spread at a rate of 4 to 5 miles a year. What data collection method do you think was used to collect these data? Explain your answer.

1.23 The Blacker's Furniture Store general manager is interested in knowing how long customers spend shopping in his store. If the plan is to start a stopwatch when a customer enters the store and stop it when the customer leaves, what type of bias could occur in the data collection process?

1.24   Assume that you have been given the task of conducting a survey of basketball season ticket holders at your university to determine their satisfaction with the concessions. Describe the method of data collection you would recommend, and outline the steps you would take to conduct the survey.

1.25   What are the advantages and disadvantages of using a mail questionnaire to survey cable TV customers regarding their preferences for a new all-sports channel?

1.26   As production manager for a personal computer maker, you want to set up a data collection process to help deal with the warranty returns problem facing your company. It has been suggested that you use a written survey. Develop an appropriate survey form.

Advanced Business Applications

1.27   As manager of a department store in a local retail mall, you are interested in surveying your customers to determine whether they are pleased with the layout changes that have been made in the store. You wish to examine their attitudes concerning organization of the merchandise in the store, the ease of accessibility, locations of checkout stands, and the position of walkways.
a. State which of the four methods of collection given on page 7 you would use to collect your data.
b. Indicate the advantages and shortcomings of the method you chose.
c. Brainstorm a list of questions that you will ask.
d. Design the survey instrument, keeping in mind the method you plan to use for data collection.

1.28   Assume that you work as a checker in a grocery store. At a meeting you were advised that the store will be conducting a study of customer satisfaction. Your supervisor has suggested that you simply survey the customers as they come through the checkout line. Indicate any bias that might be introduced by this method. To reduce the potential for this type of bias, indicate what method you would suggest for performing the customer satisfaction survey.

1.29   The athletic department at your university is interested in determining why some people who hold season basketball tickets don't come to games. Suppose you were to use a mail questionnaire to contact ticket holders who did not attend.
a. List at least two open-end questions you would place on the survey.
b. Describe how you would transfer the answers to the open-end questions into computer-readable form.

1.30   The administrator of a major Detroit hospital has asked you to assist in a study of the hospital's medical staff. The study is trying to determine how satisfied these employees are and to learn what changes could be made to increase satisfaction. Suppose you choose to obtain your data using personal interviews.
a. Adapt the six steps in Figure 1-7 to develop your personal interviews and explain how this method would be implemented at the hospital.
b. Discuss the advantages and disadvantages of the method you have selected over other potential data collection methods.

1.31   In your position as assistant manager for the University Food Service Company, you have been asked to collect data regarding customer behavior in the food line at the university cafeteria. Specifically, you are interested in the beverage and dessert selections. The cafeteria offers (the same!) 10 dessert selections every day. Develop a form to collect the data on dessert selections made by food line customers. Use mock data to show what a completed form would look like.

1-3 POPULATIONS, SAMPLES, AND SAMPLING TECHNIQUES

POPULATIONS AND SAMPLES

Two of the most important terms in statistics are **population** and **sample**.

Population	*Sample*
The set of all objects or individuals of interest or the measurements obtained from all objects or individuals of interest.	A subset of the population.

The list of all objects or individuals of interest is referred to as the *frame*. The choice of the frame depends on what objects or individuals you wish to study and on the availability of the list of these objects or individuals. Once the frame is defined, it forms the list of sampling units. The next example illustrates what we mean.

CPA Firm—We can use a certified public accounting (CPA) firm to illustrate the difference between a population and a sample. When preparing to audit the financial records of a business, a CPA firm must determine the number of accounts to examine. Until recently, good accounting practice dictated that the auditors verify the balance of every account and each financial transaction. Though this is still done in some audits, the size and complexity of most businesses have forced accountants to select only some accounts and some transactions to audit.

Suppose one part of the financial audit is to verify the accounts receivable balances. By definition, a population includes measurements made on all the items of interest to the data gatherer. In our example, the accountant would define the population as *all accounts receivable balances* on record. The list of these accounts, possibly by account number, forms the frame. If she examines the entire population, she is taking a **census**. But suppose there are too many accounts receivable balances to work through. The CPA would then select a subset of the accounts, called a *sample*. The accountant uses the sample results to make inferences about the population. If the sample balances look good, she might conclude that the population balances also are acceptable. How inferences are drawn will be discussed at greater length in later chapters.

Census

An enumeration of the entire set of measurements taken from the whole population.

There are trade-offs between taking a census and taking a sample. Usually the main trade-off is whether the information gathered in a census is worth the extra cost. In organizations in which data are stored on computer files, the additional time and effort of taking a census may not be substantial. However, if there are many accounts that must be manually checked, a census may be impractical.

Another consideration is that the measurement error in census data may be greater than in sample data. A person obtaining data from fewer sources tends to be more complete and thorough in both gathering and tabulating the data. As a result, with a sample there are likely to be fewer human errors.

Parameters and Statistics

Descriptive numerical measures, such as an average or a percentage, that are computed from an entire population are called *parameters*. Corresponding measures for a sample are called *statistics*. In the previous example, if the CPA examined every accounts receivable balance, the percentage of correct balances would be a parameter, because it reflects the value for the population. However, if she selected a ample of balances from the population, the percentage of accurate balances in this sample is a statistic. These concepts are more fully discussed in Chapters 3 and 6.

SAMPLING TECHNIQUES

Once a manager decides to gather information by sampling, he can use a sampling technique that falls into one of two categories: **statistical** or **nonstatistical**.

Nonstatistical Sampling Techniques

Those methods of selecting samples using convenience, judgment, or other nonchance processes.

Statistical Sampling Techniques

Those sampling methods that use selection techniques based on chance selection.

Both nonstatistical and statistical sampling techniques are commonly used by decision makers. Regardless of which technique is used, the decision maker has the same objective—to obtain a sample that is a close representative of the population. There are some advantages to using a statistical sampling technique, as we will discuss at many places throughout this text. However, in many cases, nonstatistical sampling represents the only feasible way to sample, as illustrated in the following example.

Nonstatistical Sampling

Carpenter Orchards—Carpenter Orchards in central Washington State is a large fruit producer. Like other fruit producers in the region, Carpenter Orchards is part of a cooperative. When fruit is harvested, it is trucked to the packing plant. The growers are paid by weight, but higher quality fruit brings higher per pound prices. As the fruit is unloaded in 20-pound boxes, a sample of fruit in each box is collected by selecting one or two pieces from the top of the box. The sampled fruit is taken to a lab to be analyzed for quality characteristics. Based on these findings, the entire truckload is assigned a quality rating and priced accordingly. Because of the volume of fruit, the packing plant uses a nonstatistical sampling method called **convenience sampling**. In doing so, the quality analysts are assuming that the fruit is evenly distributed within each box and between the boxes on the truck.

Convenience Sampling

A sampling technique that selects the items from the population based on accessibility and ease of selection.

There are other nonstatistical sampling methods, such as *judgment sampling* and *ratio sampling*, which we will not discuss here. Instead, we now turn your attention to the most frequently used statistical sampling techniques.

Statistical Sampling

Statistical sampling methods (also called *probability sampling*) allow every item in the population to have a known or calculable chance of being included in the sample. The fundamental statistical sample is called a *simple random sample*. Other types of statistical sampling discussed in this text include *stratified random sampling*, *systematic sampling*, and *cluster sampling*.

Simple Random Sampling

Baird Life and Casualty—A salesperson at Baird Life and Casualty in Charleston, West Virginia, wishes to estimate the percentage of people in a local subdivision who already have life insurance policies. The result would indicate the potential market. The population of interest consists of all families living in the subdivision.

For this example, we simplify the situation by saying that there are only five families in the subdivision: James, Sanchez, Lui, White, and Fitzpatrick. We will let N be the population size and n be the sample size. From the five families ($N = 5$), we select three ($n = 3$) for the sample. There are 10 possible samples of size 3 that could be selected.

{James, Sanchez, Lui}	{James, Sanchez, White}	{James, Sanchez, Fitzpatrick}
{James, Lui, White}	{James, Lui, Fitzpatrick}	{James, White, Fitzpatrick}
{Sanchez, Lui, White}	{Sanchez, Lui, Fitzpatrick}	{Sanchez, White, Fitzpatrick}
{Lui, White, Fitzpatrick}		

Note that no family is selected more than once in a given sample. This method is called *sampling without replacement* and is the most commonly used random sampling method. If the families could be selected more than once, the method would be called *sampling with replacement*.

Simple random sampling is the method most people think of when they think of random sampling.

Simple Random Sampling

A method of selecting items from a population such that *every possible sample of a specified size has an equal chance of being selected.*

In a correctly performed simple random sample, each of these samples would have an equal chance of being selected. A simplified way of doing this would be to put each sample of three names on a piece of paper in a bowl and then blindly reach in and select one piece of paper. This method would be difficult to do if the number of possible samples were large. For example, if $N = 50$ and a sample of size $n = 10$ is to be selected, there are more than 10 billion possible samples. Try finding a bowl big enough to hold those!

Simple random samples can be obtained in a variety of ways. We will present several examples to illustrate how simple random samples are selected in practice.

Nordstrom's Payroll—Suppose the personnel manager at Nordstrom's Department Store in Seattle is considering changing the payday from once a month to once every two weeks. Before making any decisions, he wants to survey a sample of 10 employees from the store's 300 employees. He first assigns employees a number (001 to 300). He can then use the random number function in either Excel or Minitab to determine which employees to include in the sample. Figure 1-9, shows the results when Excel chooses 10 random numbers. The first employee sampled is number 115, followed by 31, and so forth. The important thing to remember is that assigning each employee a number and then randomly selecting a sample from those numbers gives each possible sample an equal chance of being selected.

If you don't have access to computer software such as Excel or Minitab, the items in the population to be sampled can be determined by using the *random numbers table* in Appendix A. Start by selecting a starting point in the random numbers table (row and column). Suppose we use row 5, column 8 as the starting point. Go down 5 rows and over 8 digits. Verify that the digit in this location is 1. Ignoring the blanks between columns that are there only to make the table more readable, the first three-digit number is 149. Employee number 149 is the first one selected in the sample. Each subsequent random number is obtained from the random numbers in the next row down. For instance, the second number is 127. The procedure continues selecting numbers from top to bottom in each subsequent column. Numbers exceeding 300 and duplicate numbers are eliminated. When enough numbers are found for the desired sample size, the process is completed. Employees whose numbers are chosen are then surveyed.

Stratified Random Sampling

Federal Reserve Bank—Sometimes, the sample size required to obtain a certain level of information from a simple random sampling may be greater than our budget permits. At other times it may take more time to collect than is available. **Stratified random sampling** is an alternative method that has the potential to provide the desired information with a smaller sample size. The following example illustrates how stratified sampling is performed.

Excel and Minitab Tutorial

Stratified Random Sampling

A statistical sampling method in which the population is divided into subgroups called *strata* so that each population item belongs to only one stratum. The objective is to form strata such that the population values of interest within each stratum are as much alike as possible. Sample items are selected from each stratum using the simple random sampling method.

Each year, the Federal Reserve Board asks its staff to estimate the total cash holdings of U.S. financial institutions as of July 1. The staff must base its estimate on a sample. Note that not all financial institutions (banks, credit unions, and the like) are the same size. A majority are small, some are medium-sized, and only a few are large. However, the few large institutions have a substantial percentage of the total cash on hand. To make sure that a simple random sample includes an appropriate number of small, medium, and large institutions, the sample size might have to be quite large.

FIGURE 1-9

Excel Output of Random Numbers for Nordstrom's Example

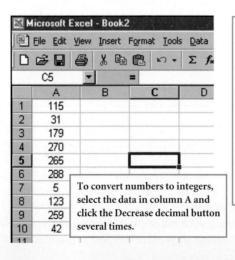

	A	B	C	D
1	115			
2	31			
3	179			
4	270			
5	265			
6	288			
7	5			
8	123			
9	259			
10	42			

To convert numbers to integers, select the data in column A and click the Decrease decimal button several times.

Excel Instructions:
1. Click on the **Tools** tab.
2. Select the **Data Analysis** option.
3. Select **Random Number Generation** option.
4. Select **Uniform** as the distribution.
5. Define range as between 1 and 300.
6. Indicate where the results are to go.
7. Click **OK**.

Minitab Instructions (for similar results):
1. Choose **Calc > Random Data > Integer.**
2. In **Generate _ rows of data** enter sample size.
3. In **Store in column(s),** enter destination column.
4. In **Minimum value** enter 1.
5. In **Maximum value** enter 300.
6. Click **OK.**

FIGURE 1-10

Stratified Sampling Example

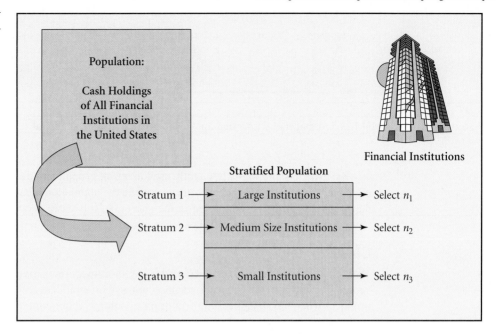

As an alternative to the simple random sample, the Federal Reserve staff could divide the institutions into three groups called *strata*: small, medium, and large. Staff members could then select a simple random sample of institutions from each stratum and estimate the total cash on hand for all institutions from this combined sample. Figure 1-10 shows the stratified random sampling concept. Note that the combined sample size ($n_1 + n_2 + n_3$) is the sum of the simple random samples taken from each stratum.

The key behind stratified sampling is to develop strata that, for the characteristic of interest (such as cash on hand), have items that are quite *homogeneous*. In this example, the size of the financial institution may be a good factor to use in stratifying. Here the combined sample size ($n_1 + n_2 + n_3$) will be less than the sample size that would have been required if no stratification had occurred. Because sample size is directly related to cost (in both time and money), a stratified sample can be more cost-effective than a simple random sample.

Multiple layers of stratification can further reduce the overall sample size. For example, the Federal Reserve might break the three strata in Figure 1-10 into *substrata* based on type of institution: state bank, interstate bank, credit union, and so on.

Most large-scale market research studies use stratified random sampling. The well-known political polls, such as the Gallup and Harris polls, use this technique also. For instance, the Gallup poll typically samples between 1,800 and 2,500 people nationwide to estimate how more than 60 million people will vote in a presidential election.

Systematic Random Sampling

National Association of Accountants—A few years ago, the National Association of Accountants (NAA) considered establishing a code of ethics. To determine the opinion of its 20,000 members, a questionnaire was sent to a sample of 500 members. Although simple random sampling could have been used, an alternative method called **systematic random sampling** was chosen.

Systematic Random Sampling

A statistical sampling technique that involves selecting every kth item in the population after a randomly selected starting point between 1 and k. The value of k is determined as the ratio of the population size over the desired sample size.

The NAA's systematic random sampling plan called for it to send the questionnaire to every fortieth member (20,000/500 = 40) from the list of members. The list was in alphabetical order. They could have begun by using Excel or Minitab to generate a single random number in the range 1 to 40. Suppose this value was 25. The twenty-fifth person in their alphabetic list would be selected. After that, every fortieth member would be selected (25, 65, 105, 145, . . .) until they had 500 NAA members.

Algeria	Illinois	Scotland	California	Alaska	New York	Florida	Idaho	Mexico	Australia
25	47	22	105	20	36	52	152	76	37

FIGURE 1-11   Mid-Level Managers by Location for Washington Group International

Systematic sampling is frequently used in business applications. Use it as an alternative to simple random sampling only when you can assume the population is randomly ordered with respect to the measurement being addressed in the survey. In this case, peoples' views on ethics are likely unrelated to the spelling of their last name.

Cluster Sampling

Washington Group International—With a telephone survey or a mail questionnaire, the geographical location of the respondents is not a significant data collection issue. However, in some instances when physical measurement or observation is required to collect the data, location can be an important issue.

Suppose Washington Group International, a large worldwide construction company, wants to develop a new corporate bidding strategy. Upper management wants input on possible new strategies from its middle-level managers. Assume that Figure 1-11 illustrates the current distribution of middle-level managers throughout the world. For example, there are 25 middle-level managers in Algeria, 47 in Illinois, and so forth. Upper management decides to hold face-to-face personal interviews with a sample of these mid-level managers.

One sampling technique is to select a simple random sample of size *n* from the population of middle managers. Unfortunately, this technique would likely require the interviewer(s) go to each state or country in which Washington Group International has middle-level managers. This would prove to be an expensive and time-consuming process. A systematic or stratified sampling procedure also would probably require visiting each location. The geographical spread in this case causes problems.

A sampling technique that overcomes the traveling (time and money) problem is **cluster sampling**.

Cluster Sampling

A method by which the population is divided into groups, or clusters, that are each intended to be mini-populations. A simple random sample of *m* clusters is selected. The items selected from a cluster can be selected using any probability sampling technique.

Ideally, the clusters would each have the same characteristics as the population as a whole. In the Washington Group International example, the states or countries where the company has managers would be the clusters.

After the clusters have been defined, a sample of *m* clusters is selected at random from the list of possible clusters. The number of clusters to select depends on various factors, including our survey budget. Suppose WGI selects *m* = 3 clusters randomly as follows:

Scotland   Florida   Illinois

These are the *primary clusters*. Next, the company can either survey all the managers in each cluster or select a simple random sample of managers from each cluster, depending on time and budget considerations.

1-3: EXERCISES

Skill Development

1.32   The U.S. Department of Transportation reported the average number of mishandled bags per 1,000 passengers for October was 4.39. State whether this number is a statistic or a population parameter. Explain your answer.

1.33   What conditions must hold in order for a sampling technique to be considered a statistical sample?

1.34 Explain the difference between stratified random sampling and cluster sampling.

1.35 Why is it that systematic random sampling can be considered a statistical sampling technique?

1.36 If a manager surveys a sample of 100 customers to determine how many miles they live from the store, is the mean travel distance for this sample considered a parameter or a statistic? Explain.

1.37 Using row 20, column 18 in the random numbers table in Appendix A, what are the first 3 five-digit numbers that would be used to select a random sample from a population with 52,000 items.

1.38 Explain why a census does not necessarily have to involve a population of people. Use an example to illustrate.

1.39 Use Excel or Minitab to generate five random numbers between 1 and 900.

Business Applications

1.40 An Ernst & Young survey of 1,363 consumers and more than 120 retailers and consumer-goods manufacturers indicated that in 2001, 12% of retailers sold online to consumers. Is this percentage a statistic? Explain.

1.41 On October 31, Reuters news service announced that housing starts in November are estimated to be 1.68 million. They were 1.695 million for October. Indicate which number is a population parameter and give your reasons for your selection.

1.42 The Standard & Poor's 500 index on May 11, 2000, stood at 1,383.05. Give the general statistical term that is used to describe the set of measurements that was used to obtain this index.

1.43 Give the name of the kind of sampling that was most likely used in each of the following cases:
a. A *Washington Post*/ABC News Poll of 2,000 people to determine the President's approval rating.
b. A poll taken of each of the General Motor dealerships in Ohio in December 1999 to determine an estimate of the average number of 1999-model Chevrolets not yet sold by GM dealerships in the United States.
c. A quality assurance procedure within a B. F. Goodrich manufacturing plant that takes every thousandth tire produced to test for cord strength of the tire.
d. A sampling technique in which a random sample from each of the tax brackets is obtained by the Internal Revenue Service to audit tax returns.

1.44 A student has suggested that one could use a systematic sampling technique to sample from the primary clusters of a cluster sampling scheme. Explain why this is either a good or a bad idea.

1.45 What are the potential advantages of stratified random sampling over simple random sampling? Explain with an example of your own how this advantage might be realized.

Advanced Business Applications

1.46 The U.S. Forest Service plans to survey backcountry hikers to determine the quality of their outdoor experience. They will ask randomly selected hikers to rate the quality on a scale from 1 to 5. One indicates total dissatisfaction; 5 indicates total satisfaction.
a. Define the population of interest. Be sure to specify the measurement of interest as part of your definition. Assume a sample of 200 is to be obtained.
b. Describe an approach you would suggest to take a statistical sample from the population. State which sampling technique you would use.
c. Assuming the population of hikers is 1,500, use either Excel or Minitab to generate the list of hikers to be selected in the sample.

1.47 The Ritz-Carlton hotel chain wishes to select a random sample of guests who stayed at their Atlanta hotel on February 11. They have a list of 742 guests and their mailing addresses. Each guest is given an identification number from 001 to 742. Use Excel or Minitab to generate a list of 30 guest identification numbers so the guests with those numbers can be surveyed.

1.48 Suppose the Ritz-Carlton wishes to personally interview guests who will stay at their hotels throughout the United States next March 20.
a. Describe an approach for using cluster sampling to select the sample.
b. What are the potential advantages of using cluster sampling in this case instead of simple random sampling?
c. Would it be possible to conduct a census in this situation? Why or why not?

1.49 The Fairview Title Company has more than 4,000 customer files listed alphabetically in its computer system. The office manager wants to survey a statistical sample of these customers to determine how satisfied they were with service provided by the title company. She plans to use a telephone survey of 100 customers.
a. Describe how you would attach identification numbers to the customer files (e.g., how many digits (and which digits) would you use to indicate the first customer file)?
b. Describe how the first random number would be obtained to begin a simple random sample method.
c. How many random digits would you need for each random number you selected?
d. Use Excel or Minitab to generate the list of customers to be surveyed.

1.50 The Craigthorp Company is a statewide food distributor to restaurants, universities, and other establishments that prepare and sell food. The company has a very large warehouse where food is stored until it is pulled from the shelves to be delivered to customers. The warehouse has 64 storage racks numbered 1 to 64. Each rack has three shelves, labeled A, B, and C. The shelves are divided into 80 sections, numbered 1 to 80.

Products are located by rack number, shelf letter, and section number. For example, breakfast cereal is located at 43-A-52 (rack 43, shelf A, section 52).

Each week, employees perform an inventory for a sample of products. Certain products are selected and counted. The *actual count* is compared to the *book count* (the quantity in the records that should be in stock). To simplify things, assume that the company has selected breakfast cereals to inventory. Also, suppose that cereals occupy racks 1 through 5, only.

a. Assume that you plan to use simple random sampling to select the sample. Use Excel or Minitab to determine the sections on each of the five racks to be sampled.

b. Assume that you wish to use cluster random sampling to select the sample. Discuss the steps you would take to carry out the sampling.

c. In this case, why might cluster sampling be preferred over simple random sampling? Discuss.

1.51 A major retail store plans to select a sample of people entering the store on a given Saturday morning. The purpose of the sample is to determine which mode of advertising drew the customer to the store. Assume that the store manager does not care whether the survey is done using statistical or nonstatistical methods.

a. Give reasons why you might choose a nonstatistical method for this survey.

b. Assume 100 customers are to be sampled. Give details of how you would select the customers needed for the survey.

c. Discuss any bias issues you considered in constructing your survey method.

1-4 DATA TYPES AND DATA MEASUREMENT LEVELS

Chapters 2 and 3 will introduce a variety of techniques for describing data and transforming the data into information. As you will see in those chapters, the statistical techniques deal with different forms of data. The level of measurement may vary greatly from application to application. In general, there are four types of data: *quantitative, qualitative, time series, and cross-sectional*. A discussion of each follows.

QUANTITATIVE AND QUALITATIVE DATA

In some cases, data values are best expressed in purely numerical, or **quantitative** terms, such as in dollars, pounds, inches, or percentages.

Quantitative Data

Measurements whose values are inherently numerical.

As an example, a study of college students at your campus might obtain data on the number of hours each week that students work at a paying job and the income level of the students' parents.

In other cases, the observation may signify only the category to which an item belongs. Categorical data are referred to as **qualitative** data.

Qualitative Data

Data whose measurement scale is inherently categorical.

For example, a study might be interested in the class standings—*freshman, sophomore, junior, senior,* or *graduate*—of college students. The same study also might ask the students to judge the quality of their education as *very good, good, fair, poor,* or *very poor*. Note, even if the students are asked to record a number (1 to 5) to indicate the quality level at which the numbers correspond to a category, the data would still be considered qualitative because the numbers are just codes for the categories.

TIME-SERIES DATA AND CROSS-SECTIONAL DATA

Data may also be classified as being either **time-series** or **cross-sectional**.

Time-Series Data

A set of ordered data values observed at successive points in time.

Cross-Sectional Data

A set of data values observed at a fixed point in time.

The data collected from the study of college students about their quality ratings would be cross-sectional because the data from each student relates to a fixed point in time. In another case, if we sampled 100 stocks from the stock market and determined the closing stock price on March 15, the data would be considered cross-sectional because all measurements corresponded to one point in time.

On the other hand, Ford Motor Company tracks the sales of its Taurus automobiles on a monthly basis. Data values observed at intervals over time are referred to as time-series data. If we determined the closing stock price for a particular stock on a daily basis for a year, the stock prices would be time-series data.

DATA MEASUREMENT LEVELS

Data can also be identified by their *level of measurement*. This is important because the higher the data level, the more sophisticated the analysis that can be performed. This will be clear when you study the material in the remaining chapters of this text.

We shall discuss and give examples of four levels of data measurements: *nominal, ordinal, interval, and ratio*. Figure 1-12 illustrates the hierarchy among these data levels, with nominal data being the lowest level.

Nominal Data

Nominal data are the lowest form of data, yet you will encounter this type of data many times. Assigning codes to categories generates nominal data. For example, a survey question that asks for marital status provides the following responses:

1. Married   2. Single   3. Divorced   4. Other

For each person, a code of 1, 2, 3, or 4 would be recorded. These codes are nominal data. Note that the values of the code numbers have no specific meaning, because the order of the categories is arbitrary. We might have shown it this way:

1. Single   2. Divorced   3. Married   4. Other

With nominal data we also have complete control over what codes are used. For example, we could have used:

88. Single   11. Divorced   33. Married   55. Other

All that matters is that you know which code stands for which category. Recognize also that the codes need not be numeric. We might use:

S = Single   D = Divorced   M = Married   O = Other

Ordinal Data

Ordinal, or **rank, data** are one notch above nominal data on the measurement hierarchy. At this level, the data elements can be rank-ordered on the basis of some relationship among them, with the assigned values indicating this order. For example, a typical market-research technique is to offer

FIGURE 1-12

Data Level Hierarchy

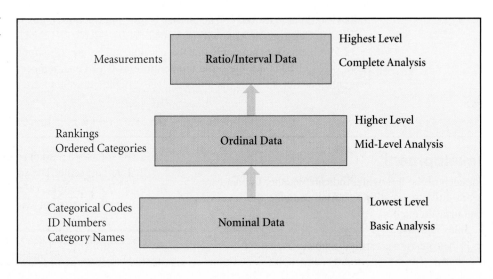

potential customers the chance to use two unidentified brands of a product. The customers are then asked to indicate which brand they prefer. The brand eventually offered to the general public depends on how often it was the preferred test brand. The fact that an ordering of items took place makes this an ordinal measure.

Bank loan applicants are asked to indicate the category corresponding to their household incomes:

_____Under $20,000	_____$20,000 to $40,000	_____over $40,000
(1)	(2)	(3)

The codes 1, 2, and 3 refer to the particular income categories, with higher codes assigned to higher incomes.

Ordinal measurement allows decision makers to equate two or more observations, or to rank-order the observations. In contrast, nominal data can be compared only for equality. You cannot order nominal measurements. Thus, a primary difference between ordinal and nominal data is that ordinal data contain both an equality (=) and a greater than (>) relationship, whereas nominal data contain only an equality (=) relationship.

Interval Data

If the distance between two data items can be measured on some scale and the data have ordinal properties (>, <, or =), the data are said to be **interval data**. The best example of interval data is the temperature scale. Both the Fahrenheit and Celsius temperature scales have ordinal properties of ">" and "=." In addition, the distances between equally spaced points are preserved. For example, $32°F > 30°F$, and $80°C > 78°C$. The difference between $32°F$ and $30°F$ is the same as the difference between $80°F$ and $78°F$, two degrees in each case. Thus, interval data allow us to precisely measure the difference between any two values. With ordinal data this is not possible, because all we can say is that one value is larger than another.

Ratio Data

Data that have all the characteristics of interval data but also have a true zero point (at which zero means "none") are called **ratio data**. Ratio measurement is the highest level of measurement.

Packagers of frozen foods encounter ratio measures when they pack their products by weight. Weight, whether measured in pounds or grams, is a ratio measurement because it has a unique zero point—zero meaning no weight. Many other types of data encountered in business environments involve ratio measurements, for example, distance, money, and time.

The difference between interval and ratio measurements can be confusing because it involves the definition of a true zero. If you have $5 and your brother has $10, he has twice as much money as you. If you convert your dollars to pounds, lire, yen, or marks, your brother will still have twice as much. If your money is lost or stolen, you have no dollars. Money has a true zero. Likewise, if you travel 100 miles today and 200 miles tomorrow, the ratio of distance traveled will be 2/1, even if you convert the distance to kilometers. If on the third day you rest, you have traveled no miles. Distance has a true zero. Conversely, if today's temperature is $35°F$ ($1.67°C$) and tomorrow's is $70°F$ ($21.11°C$), is tomorrow twice as warm as today? The answer is no. One way to see this is to convert the Fahrenheit temperature to Celsius: The ratio will no longer be 2/1 (12.64/1). Likewise, if the temperature reads $0°F$ ($-17.59°C$), this does not imply that there is no temperature. It's simply colder than $10°F$ ($-12.22°C$). Also, $0°C$ ($32°F$) is not the same temperature as $0°F$. Thus, temperature, measured with either the Fahrenheit or Celsius scale (an interval-level variable), does not have a true zero.

1-4: EXERCISES

Skill Development

1.52 For each of the following, indicate whether the data are quantitative or qualitative. Also indicate the level of data measurement.
   a. Sales regions.
   b. Price-to-earnings ratio of a stock.
   c. Quarterly profit reported by Microsoft Corporation.
   d. Response to market research survey measured on the Likehart scale. The scale is in integer steps from 1 to 5. For example, rate the level of satisfaction you have had with our service department as

(1) exceptional, (2) very good, (3) good, (4) satisfactory, or (5) unsatisfactory

e. Market share captured by Intel Corporation's Pentium II processor.

f. Quarterly dividend paid by Paine Webber Group, Inc.

1.53 Indicate whether each of the following is cross-sectional or time-series data.

a. your income last year

b. weekly defect rate for one assembly line over past 52 weeks

c. yearly size of the population of your city since 1970

d. customer bank balances on December 1

e. students' grade point averages for the 1999 fall term

f. annual student enrollment from 1970 to 2000

1.54 For each of the following variables, indicate what the level of data measurement is.

a. number of years of education

b. hair color

c. type of business

d. salaries of the CEOs of the Fortune 500 companies

e. temperature of furnaces in steel smelteries

f. job classification

Business Applications

1.55 The company for which you work wishes to determine the percentage of Internet sales made by the companies with which it competes. You are assigned this task. You are deciding between two survey questions to use: (1) List the percentage of your sales obtained through the Internet; or (2) The percentage of your sales obtained through the Internet is (1) 0 to 10, (2) 10 to 20, . . . , (10) 90 to 100.

a. State the level of measurement the responses would be to each of these survey questions.

b. State whether each of the survey question responses would be qualitative or quantitative.

c. Which of these two survey questions would allow you to calculate the average percentage of sales obtained through the Internet?

1.56 In a study of Internet sales, the following question appears on a survey instrument: The percentage of your sales obtained through the Internet is (1) 0 to 10, (2) 10 to 20, . . . , (10) 90 to 100. Your supervisor tells you to assign the number in parentheses corresponding to each customer's response. He then instructs you to calculate the average of these assigned numbers and then transform the number obtained back to the appropriate category to find the average percentage of sales through the Internet.

a. Respond to your supervisor's idea by classifying the assigned numbers as qualitative or quantitative data.

b. Does an assigned number of 4 indicate twice as large a percentage of sales through the Internet than a 2? Explain.

c. What is the level of measurement for these assigned numbers?

d. Would such data be classified as time-series or cross-sectional data?

1.57 As part of a marketing survey, you ask customers to list the number of children they have by placing a check by the appropriate category: ____0, ____1, ____2, ____3, ____>3.

a. Specify the level of measurement that such responses exhibit.

b. Would it be possible to calculate the average number of children for the respondents to this survey? Indicate how you would modify the survey so you could calculate such a statistic.

1.58 The manufacturer of a top-selling brand of laser printers has a support center where customers can call to get information about their printers. The manager in charge of this support center has recently conducted a study in which she surveyed 2,300 customers. The customers who called the support center were transferred to a third party, who asked the customers a series of questions.

a. Indicate whether the data that will be generated from this study will be considered cross-sectional or time series. Explain why.

b. One of the questions asked the customers to indicate approximately how many minutes they had been on hold waiting to get through to a support person. What level of data measurement is obtained from this question? Explain.

c. Another question asked the customers to rate the service on a scale of 1 to 7, with 1 being the worst possible service and 7 being the best possible service. What level of data measurement is achieved from this question? Will the data be quantitative or qualitative? Explain.

Summary and Conclusions

Business statistics is about converting data into useful information. There are three main components in this process: *descriptive statistics*, *probability*, and *inferential statistics*. The tools for descriptive statistics include graphs, charts, tables, and various numerical measures. Chapters 2 and 3 will introduce the important descriptive tools.

Probability is the way decision makers express their uncertainty about whether some event will take place. We use probability distributions as a means of defining the chances of any outcome occurring based on a set of business conditions. Chapters 4 and 5 introduce the key rules and concepts you will need to work effectively with probability.

Drawing inferences about a population based on sample data takes up a good portion of the remainder of the text. We will introduce you to a variety of inferential tools to help you learn to think statistically. Figure 1-13 summarizes the differences between populations and samples and the different types of sampling techniques you may have reason to use.

FIGURE 1-13

Sampling Techniques

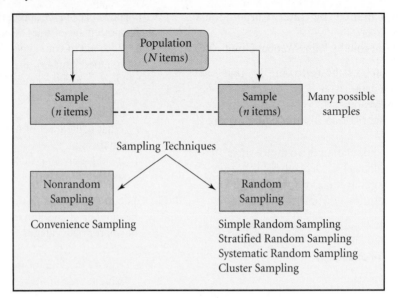

FIGURE 1-14

Data Collection Techniques

Data Collection Method	Advantages	Disadvantages
Experiments	Provide controls Preplanned objectives	Costly Time consuming Requires planning
Telephone Surveys	Timely Relatively inexpensive	Poor reputation Limited scope and length
Mail Questionnaires Written Surveys	Inexpensive Can expand length Can use open-ended questions	Low response rate Requires exceptional clarity
Direct Observation Personal Interview	No respondent bias Expands analysis opportunities	Potential observer bias

FIGURE 1-15

Data Classification

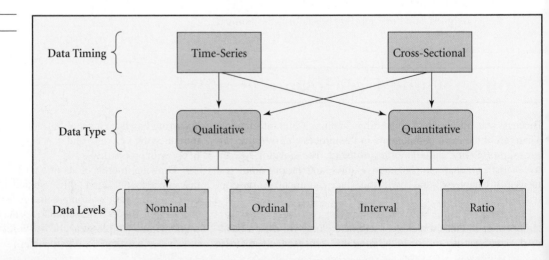

Businesses have access to more data than ever. Much of this data they generate internally through normal operations. In other cases the data they need is found outside the organization. We have discussed the fact that there are numerous ways to gather data. *Surveys* (phone or written) are effective when gathering data from people. Observation and direct measurement are appropriate when collecting data from a process. Figure 1-14 summarizes the most frequently used data collection techniques and the advantages and disadvantages of each.

The type of data that is collected varies, too. The data may be *quantitative* or *qualitative*, it may be *time series* or *cross-sectional*, and it may be *nominal*, *ordinal*, *interval*, or *ratio* level. The type and level of data that we have is important in determining the type of analysis we can perform. Please refer to Figure 1-15 for a quick summary of the ways in which we classify data.

Many of the things you will be doing in this course can be better done using computer software. The software selected for this text is Microsoft Excel and Minitab. Although not a special-purpose statistics software package, Excel contains a great many tools and techniques for performing descriptive and inferential statistical analysis. Minitab is a fully functional statistics package with a spreadsheet look and feel. You will find that whichever software package is used during this course it will be a valuable tool that will free you from tedious computations, allowing you more time to analyze and interpret the output to make better business decisions.

Key Terms

Arithmetic Mean, or average, 4
Business statistics, 2
Census, 14
Closed-end questions, 8
Cluster sampling, 18
Convenience sampling, 15
Cross-sectional data, 20
Demographic questions, 8
Experiment, 7

Experimental design, 7
Nonstatistical sampling, 14
Open-end questions, 9
Population, 13
Qualitative data, 20
Quantitative data, 20
Ratio data, 22
Sample, 13

Simple random sampling, 15
Statistical inference tools, 5
Statistical sampling techniques, 14
Stratified random sampling, 16
Structured interview, 11
Systematic random sampling, 17
Time-series data, 20
Unstructured interview, 11

CHAPTER EXERCISES

Business Applications

1.59 The Ford Motor Company has been advertising a series of comparisons between its cars and competitors' cars. What level of data measurement would each of the following be?
   a. the sound level measured in decibels inside the car
   b. drivers' ratings of the handling characteristics of the car
   c. the mileage ratings in miles per gallon for the cars
   d. the indication of whether a stereo radio is standard equipment on a car

1.60 A local television station has asked its viewers to call in and respond to the question, "Do you believe police officers are using too much force in routine traffic stops?"
   a. Would the results of this phone-in survey be considered a random sample?
   b. What type of bias might be associated with a data collection system such as this? Discuss what options might be used to reduce this bias potential.

1.61 At the start of 1997, 41% of the nearly 900 independent beer distributors affiliated with Anheuser-Busch carried only its brand. The data set that resulted in this summary parameter consists of the distributors' names and the brands of beer they carry. Indicate the data level for each of the two variables in the data set.

1.62 A company financial manager recently made a presentation that showed that during the previous 16 quarters (three months per quarter) the company recorded a profit 12 times and a loss 4 times.
   a. Give the level of data for the data used in this presentation.
   b. Are these data considered time series or cross-sectional? Explain.

Advanced Business Applications

1.63 The maker of Creamy Good Ice Cream is concerned about the quality of ice cream produced by its Illinois plant. The particular trait of concern is the texture of the ice cream in each carton.
   a. Discuss a plan by which Creamy Good managers might determine the percentage of cartons of ice cream believed to have an unacceptable texture by potential purchasers of a particular brand of their ice cream. Define (1) the sampling procedure to be used, (2) the randomization method to be used to select the sample, and (3) the measurement to be obtained.
   b. Explain why it would or wouldn't be feasible (or, perhaps, possible) to take a census to address this issue.

1.64 The makers of a particular brand of skiing equipment selected a random sample of skiers at the Aspen Ski Resort. Their method for selecting the sample required that individuals waiting in one of the lift lines be asked questions about various brands of skiing equipment.
   a. Reconsider the data collection issues in Section 1 of this chapter. Comment on the sampling met' employed in this problem.

b. Suggest a better sampling method and explain why it is a better method.

c. Indicate the level of data measurement you will be obtaining.

d. Specify whether the data is qualitative or quantitative.

1.65 A beer manufacturer is considering abandoning can containers and going exclusively to bottles because the sales manager believes beer drinkers prefer drinking beer from bottles. However, the vice president in charge of marketing is not convinced the sales manager is correct.

a. Indicate the data collection method you would use.

b. Indicate what procedures you would follow to apply this technique in this setting.

c. State which level of data measurement applies to the data you would collect. Justify your answer.

d. Is the data qualitative or quantitative? Explain.

General References

1. Berenson, Mark L., and David M. Levine, *Basic Business Statistics: Concepts and Applications*, 7th ed. (Upper Saddle River, NJ: Prentice Hall, 1999).

2. Cryer, Jonathan D., and Robert B. Miller, *Statistics for Business: Data Analysis and Modeling*, 2nd ed. (Belmont, CA: Duxbury Press, 1994).

3. Dodge, Mark, and Craig Stinson, *Running Microsoft Excel 2000* (Redmond, WA: Microsoft Press, 1999).

4. Groves, R. M., *Survey Errors and Survey Costs* (New York: John Wiley & Sons, 1989).

5. Hildebrand, David, and R. Lyman Ott, *Statistical Thinking for Managers*, 4th ed. (Belmont, CA: Duxbury Press, 1998).

6. Kenkel, James L., *Introductory Statistics for Management and Economics*, 4th ed. (Belmont, CA: Duxbury Press, 1996).

7. *Microsoft Excel 2000* (Redmond, WA: Microsoft Corp., 1999)

8. *Minitab for Windows Version 13* (State College, PA: Minitab, 1999).

9. Pelosi, Marilyn K., and Theresa M. Sandifer, *Doing Statistics for Business with Excel*. (New York: John Wiley & Sons, 2000).

10. Scheaffer, Richard L., William Mendenhall, and Lyman Ott, *Elementary Survey Sampling*, 5th ed. (Belmont, CA: Duxbury Press, 1996).

11. Siegel, Andrew F., *Practical Business Statistics*, 4th ed. (Burr Ridge, IL: Irwin, 2000).

CHAPTER 2

Graphs, Charts, and Tables— Describing Your Data

CHAPTER OUTCOMES

After studying the material in Chapter 2, you should:

- Be able to construct frequency distributions both manually and with your computer.
- Be able to construct and interpret a frequency histogram.
- Know how to construct and interpret various types of bar charts.
- Be able to build a stem and leaf diagram.
- Be able to create a line chart and interpret the trend in the data.
- Be able to construct a scatter plot and interpret it.
- Be able to develop and interpret joint frequency tables.

WHY YOU NEED TO KNOW

Several years ago, a vice president for General Motors spoke at the University of Montana's spring alumni and scholarship banquet. After his speech, a student asked him what factor he considered to be the most important in his rise to the vice presidency of one of the world's largest companies. He responded that a short time after joining GM he took part in a presentation to a group of upper-level managers. He previously had been taught the skills to *effectively organize and present* complex data. His ability to translate the data into meaningful information caught the attention of the company's senior managers. A short time later, he was asked to coordinate another presentation. He stated that he was certain that upper management remembered his presentations for their effective display of business data. When they needed someone to lead a special project, he was selected. The success of that project led to a significant promotion, and the rest was history.

Although you may not end up working at a company as large as General Motors, we are absolutely convinced that you will have numerous opportunities to organize, summarize, analyze, and present data. In fact, of all the tools and techniques introduced in this text, you very likely will use those discussed in this chapter and Chapter 3 more than any others.

Not only will you be called on to actually do the data analysis necessary to make sense out of data, you will find yourself on the receiving end of many statistical reports. Therefore, not only should you be able to perform appropriate data analysis, but you also need to be able to question the accuracy and validity of the charts, graphs, and analysis you receive from others.

Business periodicals, such as *Fortune* and *Business Week*, use graphs and charts extensively in conjunction with their articles to help readers better understand key concepts. Many advertisements will even use graphs and charts to effectively convey their message. What better proof of the potential value of descriptive statistics than to observe ads costing $50,000 or more per page using the concepts we will be discussing in this text?

This chapter introduces some of the most frequently used tools and techniques for describing data with graphs, charts, and tables. Although this analysis can be done manually, we will provide output from Excel and Minitab showing that these software packages can be used as tools for doing the analysis easily, quickly, and with a finished quality that once required a graphic artist.

2-1 FREQUENCY DISTRIBUTIONS AND HISTOGRAMS

Next time you are in your statistics class, look around at your classmates. How many hours a week do they spend studying? How are the students' ages distributed? How is income distributed among the students? How many credits have they completed? A simple survey of the students would provide data to answer each of these questions. However, the data alone would not be enough. You would need to perform a descriptive analysis of the data.

FREQUENCY DISTRIBUTION

One of the first steps would be to construct a **frequency distribution** for each of the variables.

Frequency Distribution

A summary of a set of data that displays the number of observations in each of the distribution's distinct categories or classes.

Books and Music—Consider a national book and music retailer that is considering locating into one of two cities (say, City 1 and City 2). To obtain data to aid in the decision process, the retailer has conducted a marketing study in the two cities. Among the questions asked of individuals is how many years of college they have completed. Experience in other markets indicates that cities with higher-educated populations are more-profitable locations. The variable, years of college, is **discrete** because the possible responses (1, 2, 3, 4, etc.) can be counted.

Discrete Data

Data whose possible values are countable.

TABLE 2-1	
Frequency Distribution of Years of College	
CITY 1	
YEARS OF COLLEGE	**FREQUENCY**
0	35
1	21
2	24
3	22
4	31
5	13
6	6
7	5
8	3
Total	**160**

TABLE 2-2	
Frequency Distribution of Years of College	
CITY 2	
YEARS OF COLLEGE	**FREQUENCY**
0	187
1	62
2	34
3	19
4	14
5	7
6	3
7	4
Total	**330**

To construct the frequency distribution for City 1, we need only count the number of times individuals in that city indicate each of these possible responses (years of education). The results are shown in Table 2-1. This frequency distribution shows that, of the 160 people in the survey, few (35 out of 160) have spent less than one year in college.

Suppose now we wished to compare the college years variable for City 1 with the same variable for City 2. The data for City 2 can be organized into the frequency distribution shown in Table 2-2. How do the two market areas compare? Do you see any difficulties in making this comparison? Because the surveys contained a different number of people, it is difficult to compare the frequencies of each category directly. When the number of total observations differs, comparisons are aided if **relative frequencies** are computed. Equation 2-1 is used to compute the relative frequencies.

Relative Frequency

The proportion of total observations that are in a given category. Relative frequency is computed by dividing the frequency in a category by the total number of observations. The relative frequencies can be converted to percentages by multiplying by 100.

$$\text{Relative frequency} = \frac{f_i}{n} \qquad \textbf{2-1}$$

where:

f_i = Frequency of the ith value of the discrete variable

$$n = \sum_{i=1}^{k} f_i$$

k = The number of different values for the discrete variable

Table 2-3 shows the relative frequencies for each market area. This makes a comparison of the two market areas much easier. We see that City 2 has relatively more people without any college (56.7%) or one year of college (18.8%) than City 1 (21.9% and 13.1%). At all other levels of education, City 1 has relatively more people than City 2.

TABLE 2-3		**CITY 1**		**CITY 2**	
Relative Frequency Distribution for the Book and Music Example	**Years of College**	**Frequency**	**Relative Frequency**	**Frequency**	**Relative Frequency**
	0	35	35/160 = 0.219	187	187/330 = 0.567
	1	21	21/60 = 0.131	62	62/330 = 0.188
	2	24	24/160 = 0.150	34	34/330 = 0.103
	3	22	22/160 = 0.138	19	19/330 = 0.058
	4	31	31/160 = 0.194	14	14/330 = 0.042
	5	13	13/160 = 0.081	7	7/330 = 0.021
	6	6	6/160 = 0.038	3	3/330 = 0.009
	7	5	5/160 = 0.031	4	4/330 = 0.012
	8	3	3/160 = 0.019	0	0/330 = 0.00
	Total	160		330	

$\mathcal{S}$UMMARY: DEVELOPING FREQUENCY AND RELATIVE FREQUENCY DISTRIBUTIONS FOR DISCRETE DATA

To develop a discrete data frequency distribution, perform the following steps:

1. List all possible values of the variable. If the variable is quantitative, order the possible values from low to high.

2. Count the number of occurrences at each value of the variable and place this value in a column labeled "frequency."

To develop a relative frequency distribution, do the following:

3. Use Equation 2-1 and divide each frequency count by the total number of data values and place in a column headed "relative frequency."

$\mathcal{E}$XAMPLE 2-1: FREQUENCY AND RELATIVE FREQUENCY DISTRIBUTIONS

International Airline Travel   Following the tragic events of September 11, 2001, there was a sharp reduction in international travel by U.S. citizens. A travel magazine recently surveyed 16 business executives to determine how many international trips they made in 2002. The following data were observed:

3	0	0	1
1	2	2	0
0	2	1	0
2	1	4	2

The editors wish to construct a frequency distribution and a relative frequency distribution for the number of international trips taken by these executives.

Step 1:   List the possible values.
The possible values listed in order for the discrete variable are 0, 1, 2, 3, 4.

Step 2:   Count the number of occurrences at each value.
The frequency distribution follows:

International Trips	Frequency	Relative Frequency
0	5	5/16 = .3125
1	4	4/16 = .2500
2	5	5/16 = .3125
3	1	1/16 = .0625
4	1	1/16 = .0625
	Total = 16	1.0000

Step 3:   Determine the relative frequencies.
The relative frequencies are determined by dividing each frequency by 16, as shown. Thus, just over 31% of those responding took no trips during 2002.

$\mathcal{E}$XAMPLE 2-2: FREQUENCY DISTRIBUTION FOR QUALITATIVE DATA

Lawn Care Companies   A subdivision in northern California has 20 homes. Recently a survey was conducted to determine which lawn service the homeowners used last summer. Fifteen homeowners responded to the survey with the following results:

Emerald	Green Thumb	Green Thumb	Self	Self
Master Care	Emerald	Self	Master Care	Green Thumb
Emerald	Self	Master Care	Emerald	Self

The frequency distribution for this qualitative variable is found as follows:

Step 1:   List the possible values.
The possible values for the variable are Emerald, Green Thumb, Master Care, and Self.

Step 2:   Count the number of occurrences at each value.
The frequency distribution is:

Lawn Company	Frequency
Emerald	4
Green Thumb	3
Master Care	3
Self	5
	Total = 15

Excel and Minitab Tutorial

Athletic Shoe Survey—In recent years, a status symbol for many students has been the brand and style of athletic shoes they wear. Companies such as Nike, Adidas, and Reebok compete for the top position in the sport shoe market. A survey was recently conducted in which 100 college students at a southern state school were asked a number of questions, including how many pairs of Nike shoes they currently own. The data are in a file called *SportsShoes* on the CD-ROM that comes with this text.

The variable *Number of Nike* is a discrete quantitative variable. Figures 2-1 and 2-2 show frequency distributions (Excel and Minitab versions) for the number of Nike shoes owned by those surveyed. These frequency distributions show that, although a few people own more than six pairs of Nike shoes, the bulk of those surveyed own two or fewer pairs.

GROUPING DATA BY CLASSES

Cox Enterprises—In the previous examples, the variable of interest was a discrete variable and the number of possible values for the variable was limited to only a few. However, there are many instances in which the variable of interest will be either **continuous** (weight, time, length) or discrete and have many possible outcomes (age, income, stock prices), yet we want to describe the variable using a frequency distribution.

Continuous Data

Data whose possible values are uncountable and which may assume any value in an interval.

FIGURE 2-2

Minitab Output—Nike Shoes Frequency Distribution

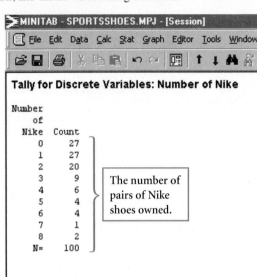

Cox Enterprises owns and operates a large cattle feedlot operation in the plains of west Texas. The company purchases young steer calves at auctions and from cattle ranchers. The company keeps the calves on feedlots for approximately six months before selling them to packing plants.

The more weight the cattle gain on the feedlots, the greater Cox's profit. Cox managers constantly study calves' growth patterns to determine which species offer the best profit potential. Table 2-4 shows the weight gains in pounds, to the nearest tenth of a pound, for a sample of 100 polled Hereford steers. The range for this continuous quantitative variable is 131.3 to 205.6 pounds.

The data have been sorted in order of weight from low to high, forming a **data array**.

Data Array

Data that have been sorted in ascending or descending order.

Even sorted, the weight-gain data provide little information about these cattle. However, a good first step in understanding the data would be to construct a frequency distribution.

The variable, weight gain, can assume many different weights in these data. If we counted the number of values at each weight, we would have many frequencies of 1 and 2. This would provide little new information. Instead, we need to group the data into *classes* and then count the number of cattle that had weight gains in each class.

The first step in this procedure is to form data groups (or classes). Care needs to be taken when constructing these classes to ensure each data point is put into one, and only one, possible class. Therefore, the classes should meet four criteria. First, they must be **mutually exclusive**.

Mutually Exclusive Classes

Classes that do not overlap so that a data value can be placed in only one class.

TABLE 2-4

Cox Enterprises Cattle Weight Gain

131.3	148.3	155.9	160.2	164.5	168.7	173.2	179.3	183.0	191.7
137.2	149.4	156.2	160.5	164.6	169.5	173.7	179.6	183.1	191.7
138.2	150.8	156.3	161.5	165.1	169.6	174.8	180.1	183.5	194.9
142.3	150.8	157.3	162.1	165.2	170.0	176.7	180.4	186.4	196.0
143.4	152.0	157.4	162.3	165.3	170.4	176.8	180.7	186.7	198.3
143.9	153.3	157.7	163.2	165.5	171.1	177.0	181.4	188.0	198.8
144.6	153.7	158.4	163.6	166.4	171.7	177.3	181.4	188.6	199.6
145.8	154.2	159.0	163.9	166.5	172.0	178.1	182.4	189.1	202.9
146.6	154.6	159.6	164.3	167.2	172.0	178.4	182.4	189.6	203.1
147.2	155.3	160.2	164.4	168.7	172.1	178.9	182.9	190.1	205.6

Second, they must be **all inclusive**.

All-Inclusive Classes

A set of classes that contains all the possible data values.

Third, if at all possible, they should be of **equal-width**.

Equal-Width Classes

The distance between the lowest possible value and the highest possible value in each class is equal for all classes.

Equal-width classes make analyzing and interpreting the frequency distribution easier. However, there are some instances in which the presence of extreme high or low values makes it necessary to have an open-ended class. For example, annual family incomes in the United States are mostly between $15,000 and $200,000. However, there are some families with much higher family incomes. In order to best accommodate these high incomes, you might consider having the highest income class be "over $200,000" or "$200,000 and over" as a catchall for the high-income families.

Fourth, avoid **empty classes** if possible. Empty classes are those for which there are no data values. If this occurs, it may be because you have set up classes that are too narrow.

Steps for Grouping Data into Classes

There are four steps for grouping data, such as that found in Table 2-4, into classes.

Step 1: Determine the number of groups or classes to use. Although there is no absolute right or wrong number of classes, the rule of thumb is to have *between 5 and 20 classes*. A formula known as **Sturges's Rule** is often used to provide a guideline for determining the number of classes for a given number of data values, *n*, as shown in Equation 2-2:

Sturges's Rule

$$\text{Classes} = 1 + 3.322 \, [\log_{10}(n)]$$

2-2

where:

$$n = \text{Number of data values}$$

In the Cox Enterprises example, for $n = 100$ values, using Sturges's rule we get:

$$1 + 3.322 \times \log_{10}(100)$$

This formula returns the value 7.644, or 8 classes.

Remember, this is only a guideline for the number of classes. There is no specific right or wrong number. In general, use fewer classes for smaller data sets; more classes for larger data sets. However, using too few classes tends to condense data too much, and information is lost. Using too many classes spreads out the data so much that little advantage is gained over the original raw data.

Step 2: Establish the class width.

Class Width

The distance between the lowest possible value and the highest possible value for a frequency class.

The minimum **class width** is determined by Equation 2-3.

Class Width

$$W = \frac{\text{Largest Value} - \text{Smallest Value}}{\text{Number of Classes}}$$

2

For the Cox Enterprises data using eight classes, we get:

$$W = \frac{205.6 - 131.3}{8} = \frac{74.3}{8} = 9.288$$

This means we could construct eight classes that are each 9.288 pounds wide to provide mutually exclusive and all-inclusive classes. However, because our purpose is to make the data more understandable, we suggest that you *round up to a more convenient class width*, such as 10 pounds or even 15 pounds. A major concern in determining class widths is to select ones that are readily understandable. Be aware, people tend to do better with multiples of 2 and 5 than they do with multiples of 3 or 4, so 10 is a better choice than 12.

Step 3: Determine the class boundaries for each class.

Class Boundaries

The upper and lower values of each class.

The **class boundaries** determine the lowest possible value and the highest possible value for each class. In the Cox Enterprises example, if we start the first class at 130 pounds, we get the class boundaries shown in the first column of Table 2-5.

Notice the classes have been formed to be *mutually exclusive* and *all inclusive*. The weight data were recorded in pounds to one decimal place. For instance, a weight value of 149.9 pounds will fall in the second class. A value of 150 pounds will fall in the third class.

Step 4: Count the number of values in each class. From the raw data in Table 2-4, we count the number of steers with weight gains in each class. The results are shown in the Frequency column in Table 2-5. This shows that more steers (24) gained from 160.1 to 170 pounds than any other single category. The vast majority of steers (77 out of 100) in the sample gained from 150.1 pounds to 190 pounds. If the company had multiple feedlots, we might need to compute relative frequencies, as shown in the Relative Frequency column in Table 2-5.

The relative frequencies can be transformed into percentages, which would mean, for example, that 19% of the steers in the sample gained from 170.1 to 180 pounds.

Another step we can take to help analyze the steer weight-gain data is to construct a **cumulative frequency distribution** and a **cumulative relative frequency distribution**.

Cumulative Frequency Distribution

A summary of a set of data that displays the number of observations with values less than or equal to the upper limit of each of its classes.

Cumulative Relative Frequency Distribution

A summary of a set of data that displays the proportion of observations with values less than or equal to the upper limit of each of its classes.

The cumulative frequency distribution is shown in the Cumulative Frequency column of Table 2-5. We can then form the cumulative relative frequency distribution as shown in the Cumulative

TABLE 2-5

Cattle Weight Gain Data for Cox Enterprises

CLASSES	FREQUENCY	RELATIVE FREQUENCY	CUMULATIVE FREQUENCY	CUMULATIVE RELATIVE FREQUENCY
130.1 to 140.0 lbs.	3	3/100 = 0.03	3	0.03
140.1 to 150.0 lbs.	9	9/100 = 0.09	12	0.12
150.1 to 160.0 lbs.	17	17/100 = 0.17	29	0.29
160.1 to 170.0 lbs.	24	24/100 = 0.24	53	0.53
170.1 to 180.0 lbs.	19	19/100 = 0.19	72	0.72
180.1 to 190.0 lbs.	17	17/100 = 0.17	89	0.89
190.1 to 200.0 lbs.	8	8/100 = 0.08	97	0.97
200.1 to 210.0 lbs.	3	3/100 = 0.03	100	1.00
	$\Sigma = 100$	$\Sigma = 1.00$		

Relative Frequency column of Table 2-5. The cumulative relative frequency distribution indicates, as an example, that 72% of the sample steers had weight gains of 180 pounds or less.

$\mathcal{S}$UMMARY: DEVELOPING FREQUENCY DISTRIBUTIONS FOR CONTINUOUS VARIABLES

To develop a continuous data frequency distribution, perform the following steps:

1. Determine the desired number of classes or groups. The rule of thumb is to use 5 to 20 classes. Sturges's rule can be used.

2. Determine the minimum class width using:

$$W = \frac{\text{Largest Value} - \text{Smallest Value}}{\text{Number of Classes}}$$

Round the class width up to a more convenient value.

3. Define the class boundaries, making sure that the classes that are formed are *mutually exclusive* and *all inclusive*. Ideally, the classes should have equal widths and should all contain at least one observation.

4. Count the number of values in each class.

$\mathcal{E}$XAMPLE 2-3: FREQUENCY DISTRIBUTION FOR CONTINUOUS VARIABLES

Airport Security Screening   Example 2-1 referred to the international travel difficulties after the September 11, 2001, attack on the World Trade Center in New York City. As a result, airports throughout the world have stepped up their security, and passengers have had to spend more time waiting to pass through security screening. At the Miami, Florida, airport, officials each week select a random sample of passengers. For each person selected, the time spent in the security screening line is recorded. The waiting times (already sorted from high to low), in seconds, for one such sample of 72 passengers are as follows:

35	339	650	864	1,025	1,261
38	340	655	883	1,028	1,280
48	395	669	883	1,036	1,290
53	457	703	890	1,044	1,312
70	478	730	934	1,087	1,341
99	501	763	951	1,091	1,355
138	521	788	969	1,126	1,357
164	556	789	985	1,176	1,360
220	583	789	993	1,199	1,414
265	595	802	997	1,199	1,436
272	596	822	999	1,237	1,479
312	604	851	1,018	1,242	1,492

The airport security manger wishes to construct a frequency distribution for the time passengers wait for security screening. The frequency distribution is determined as follows:

Step 1:   **Group the data into classes.**

The number of classes is arbitrary but typically will be between 5 and 20, depending on the volume of data. Sturges's rule can be used as a guideline. In this example, we have $n = 72$ data items.

$$\text{Classes} = 1 + 3.322 \times \log_{10}(72) = 7.170$$

We might round this down to 7 classes.

Step 2:   **Determine the class width.**

$$W = \frac{\text{Largest Value} - \text{Smallest Value}}{\text{Number of Classes}} = \frac{1,492 - 35}{7} = 208.1429 \Rightarrow 225$$

Note, we have rounded the class width up from the minimum required value of 208.1429 to the more convenient value of 225.

Step 3:   **Define the class boundaries.**

0	and under	225
225	and under	450
450	and under	675
675	and under	900
900	and under	1,125
1,125	and under	1,350
1,350	and under	1,575

These classes are mutually exclusive, all inclusive, and have equal width.

Step 4:   **Count the number of values in each class.**

Waiting Time	Frequency
0 and under 225	9
225 and under 450	6
450and under 675	12
675and under 900	13
900and under 1,125	14
1,125and under 1,350	11
1,350and under 1,575	7

This frequency distribution shows that for this sample of passengers, most people wait between 450 and 1,350 seconds.

HISTOGRAMS

Although frequency distributions are useful in analyzing large sets of data, they are in table format and may not be as visually informative as a graph. A graph called a **frequency histogram** can be used to transform a frequency distribution into a visually appealing format.

Frequency Histogram

A graph of a frequency distribution with the horizontal axis showing the classes, the vertical axis showing the frequency count, and (for equal class widths) the rectangles having a height equal to the frequency in each class.

A histogram shows three general types of information:

1. It provides a visual indication of where the approximate center of the data is. Look for the center point along the horizontal axes in the histograms in Figure 2-3. Even though the shapes of the histograms are the same, there is a clear difference in where the data are centered.
2. We can gain an understanding of the degree of spread (or variation) in the data. The more the data cluster around the center, the smaller the variation in the data. If the data are spread out from the center, the data exhibit greater variation. The examples in Figure 2-4 all have the same center but are different in terms of spread.
3. We can observe the shape of the distribution. Is it reasonably flat, is it weighted to one side or the other, is it balanced around the center, or is it bell-shaped?

Capital Credit Union—Even for applications with small amounts of data, such as the Cox Enterprises cattle weight-gain example, constructing grouped data frequency distributions and histograms is a time-consuming process. Decision-makers may hesitate to try different numbers of classes and different class limits because of the effort involved and the "best" presentation of the data may be missed.

Excel and Minitab Tutorial

We showed earlier that Excel and Minitab both provide the capability of constructing frequency distributions. Both software packages are also quite capable of generating grouped data frequency distributions and histograms.

Consider Capital Credit Union (CCU) in Mobile, Alabama, which recently began issuing a new credit card. Managers at CCU have been wondering how customers have been using the card, so a

FIGURE 2-3

Histograms Showing Different Centers

sample of 300 customers was selected. Data on the current credit card balance (rounded to the nearest dollar) and the genders of the cardholders appear in the file *Capital*, which is stored on your CD-ROM.

As with the manual process, the first step in Excel or Minitab is to determine the number of classes. Recall that the rule of thumb is to use between 5 and 20 classes, depending on the amount of data. Suppose we decide to use 10 classes.

Next, we determine the class width using Equation 2-3. The highest account balance in the sample is $1,493.00. The minimum is $99.00. Thus, the class width is

$$W = \frac{1,493.00 - 99.00}{10} = 139.40$$

which we round up to $150.00.

Our classes will be

$90   <$240 (includes all balances between $90.00 and $239.99)

$240 < $390

$390 < $540

etc.

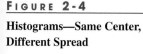

FIGURE 2-4

Histograms—Same Center, Different Spread

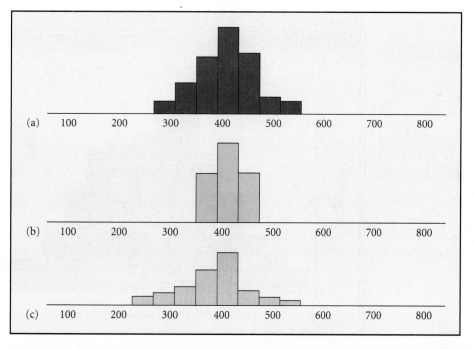

FIGURE 2-5

Excel Output of Credit Card Balance Histogram

Excel Instructions:
1. Open file: Capital.xls
2. Click on the **Tools** tab.
3. Select the **Data Analysis** option.
4. Select **Histogram**.
5. **Input Range** specifies the cells containing the actual data values. Define Bin range (upper limit of each class 239.99, 389.99, etc.).
6. Use **Format Data Series**, **Options**, to set gap width to zero.
7. Convert the bins to actual class labels by typing labels in column A. Note, the bin 239.99 is labeled 90 < 240, etc.

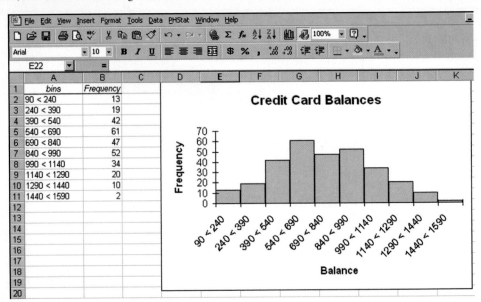

The resulting histogram in Figure 2-5 shows that the data are centered between $690 and $840. The customers vary considerably in their credit card balances, but the distribution is quite symmetrical and bell-shaped. Capital Credit Union managers must decide whether the usage rate for the credit card is sufficient to warrant the cost of maintaining the credit card accounts.

ISSUES WITH EXCEL

If you use Excel to construct a histogram as indicated in the instructions in Figure 2-5, the initial graph will come up with gaps between the bars. Because histograms illustrate the distribution of data across the range of all possible values for the variable, *histograms do not have gaps*. Therefore, to get the proper histogram format, you need to close these gaps by setting the gap width to zero, as indicated in the Excel instructions shown in Figure 2-5. Minitab provides no gaps with its default output, as shown in Figure 2-6.

FIGURE 2-6

Minitab Output of Credit Card Balance Histogram

Minitab Instructions:
1. Open file: Capital.MTW.
2. Choose **Graph > Histogram**.
3. Click **Simple**.
4. Click **OK**.
5. In **Graph variables**, enter data column.
6. Click **OK**.

SUMMARY: CONSTRUCTING FREQUENCY HISTOGRAMS

To construct a frequency histogram, perform the following steps:

1. Follow the steps for constructing a frequency distribution (see Examples 2-1 or 2-3).

2. Use the horizontal axis to represent the variable of interest. Use the vertical axis to represent the frequency in each class.

3. Draw vertical bars for each class or data value so that the heights of the bars correspond to the frequencies. Make sure there are no gaps between the bars. (Note, if the classes do not have equal widths, the bar height should be adjusted to make the area of the bar proportional to the frequency.)

4. Label the histogram appropriately.

EXAMPLE 2-4: FREQUENCY HISTOGRAMS

Emergency Response Times   The director of emergency responses in Montreal, Canada, is interested in analyzing the time needed for response teams to reach their destinations in emergency situations after leaving their stations. She has acquired the response times for 1,220 calls last month. To develop the frequency histogram, perform the following steps:

Step 1: **Construct a frequency distribution.**
Because response time is a continuous variable measured in seconds, the data should be broken down into classes and the steps given in Example 2-3 should be used. The following frequency distribution with 10 classes was developed:

Response Time	Frequency	Response Time	Frequency
0 < 30	36	180 < 210	145
30 < 60	68	210 < 240	80
60 < 90	195	240 < 270	43
90 < 120	180	270 < 300	31
120 < 150	260		1,220
150 < 180	182		

Step 2: **Construct the axes for the histogram.**
The horizontal axis will be response time and the vertical axis will be frequency

Step 3: **Construct bars with heights corresponding to the frequency of each class and label appropriately.**
This is shown as follows:

This histogram indicates that the response times vary considerably. The center is somewhere in the range of 120 to 180 seconds.

RELATIVE FREQUENCY HISTOGRAMS AND OGIVES

Histograms can also be used to display relative frequency distributions and cumulative relative frequency distributions. A relative frequency histogram is formed in the same manner as a frequency histogram, but relative frequencies are used rather than frequencies. The cumulative relative frequency is presented using a graph called an **ogive**. Example 2-5 illustrates each of these graphical tools.

EXAMPLE 2-5: RELATIVE FREQUENCY HISTOGRAMS AND OGIVES

Emergency Response Times (continued)   Example 2-4 introduced the situation facing the emergency response manager in Montreal. In that example, she formed a frequency distribution for a sample of 1,220 response times. She is now interested in graphing the relative frequencies and the cumulative relative frequencies. To do so, use the following steps:

Step 1:   **Convert the frequency distribution into relative frequencies and cumulative relative frequencies.**

Response Time	Frequency	Relative Frequency	Cumulative Relative Frequency
0 < 30	36	36/1220 = 0.0295	0.0295
30 < 60	68	68/1220 = 0.0557	0.0852
60 < 90	195	195/1220 = 0.1598	0.2451
90 < 120	180	180/1220 = 0.1475	0.3926
120 < 150	260	260/1220 = 0.2131	0.6057
150 < 180	182	182/1220 = 0.1492	0.7549
180 < 210	145	145/1220 = 0.1189	0.8738
210 < 240	80	80/1220 = 0.0656	0.9393
240 < 270	43	43/1220 = 0.0352	0.9746
270 < 300	31	31/1220 = 0.0254	1.0000
	1,220	1.0000	

Step 2:   **Construct the relative frequency histogram.**
Place the quantitative variable on the horizontal axis and the relative frequencies on the vertical axis. The vertical bars are drawn to heights corresponding to the relative frequencies of the classes.

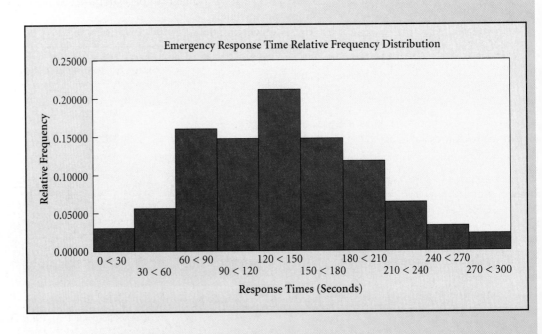

Note the relative frequency histogram has exactly the same shape as the frequency histogram. However, the vertical axis has a different scale.

Step 3:   **Construct the ogive.**

Draw a line connecting the points plotted above the *upper limit* of each class at a height corresponding to the cumulative relative frequency.

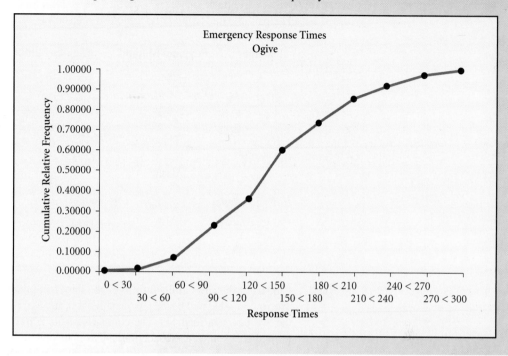

JOINT FREQUENCY DISTRIBUTIONS

Frequency distributions are effective tools for describing data. Thus far we have discussed how to develop grouped and ungrouped frequency distributions for one variable at a time. For instance, in the Capital Credit Union example, we were interested in customer credit card balances for all customers. We constructed a frequency distribution and histogram for that variable. However, often we need to examine the data more closely. This may involve constructing a *joint frequency distribution* for two variables.

Joint frequency distributions can be constructed for qualitative or quantitative variables.

SUMMARY: CONSTRUCTING JOINT FREQUENCY DISTRIBUTIONS

A joint frequency distribution is constructed using the following steps:

1. Obtain a set of data consisting of paired responses for two variables. The responses can be qualitative or quantitative. If the responses are quantitative, they can be discrete or continuous.

2. Construct a table with *r* rows and *c* columns, in which the number of rows represents the number of categories (or numeric classes) of one variable and the number of columns corresponds to the number of categories (or numeric classes) of the second variable.

3. Count the number of joint occurrences at each row level and each column level for all combinations of row and column values and place these frequencies in the appropriate cells.

4. Compute the row and column totals, which are called the marginal frequencies.

5. If a joint relative frequency distribution is desired, divide each cell frequency by the total number of paired observations.

EXAMPLE 2-6: JOINT FREQUENCY DISTRIBUTION

VideoLand   VideoLand is a national chain that rents VHS and DVD movies for home use. Recently, the sales manager at a Minnesota store collected data dealing with customer purchases. Among the data collected were two variables: payment method (cash or charge) and number of movies rented. The manager wishes to develop a joint frequency distribution to better understand the buying habits of his customers. To do this, he can use the following steps:

Step 1:   **Obtain the data.**
The paired data for the two variables for a sample of 12 customers are obtained.

Customer	Payment Method	Movies Rented
1	Charge	2
2	Charge	1
3	Cash	2
4	Charge	2
5	Charge	1
6	Cash	1
7	Cash	3
8	Charge	1
9	Charge	3
10	Cash	2
11	Cash	1
12	Charge	1

Step 2:   **Construct the rows and columns of the joint frequency table.**
The row variable will be the payment method, and two rows will be used, corresponding to the two payment methods. The column variable is movies rented, and it will have three levels, because the data for this variable contain only the values 1, 2, and 3. (Note, if a variable is continuous, classes should be formed using the methods discussed in Example 2-3.)

		Movies Rented		
		1	2	3
Payment	Charge			
	Cash			

Step 3:   **Count the number of joint occurrences at each row level and each column level for all combinations of row and column values and place these frequencies in the appropriate cells.**

		Movies Rented			Total
		1	2	3	
Payment	Charge	4	2	1	7
	Cash	2	2	1	5
	Total	6	4	2	12

Step 4:   **Calculate the row and column totals (see Step 3).**
The manager can now see that for this sample, most people charged their purchase (seven people) and most people rented only one movie (six people). Likewise, four people both rented one movie and charged their purchase.

Capital Credit Union (continued)—Recall that the Capital Credit Union discussed earlier was interested in evaluating the success of its new credit card. Figures 2-5 and 2-6 showed the frequency distribution and histogram for a sample of customer credit card balances. Although this information is useful, the managers would like to know more. Specifically, what does the credit card balance distribution look like for male versus female cardholders?

One way to approach this is to sort the data by the gender variable and develop frequency distributions and histograms for males and females separately. You could then make a visual compari-

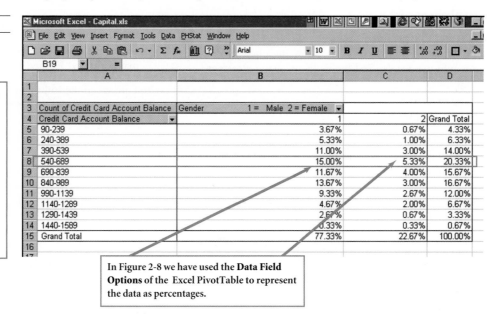

FIGURE 2-7

Excel Output of the Capital Credit Union Joint Frequency Distribution

Excel Instructions:
1. Place Cursor anywhere in the table.
2. Right click - select **Wizard**.
3. Select **Layout**.
4. Double click on **Data** field item.
5. Click **OK**.

Minitab Instructions (for similar results):
1. Open file: Capital.MTW.
2. Click on **Data > Code > Numeric to Text**.
3. Under **Code data from columns**, select data column.
4. Under **Into columns**, specify destination column: *Classes*.
5. In **Original values**, define each data class range.
6. In **New**, specify code for each class.
7. Click **OK**.
8. Click on **Stat > Tables > Cross Tabulation and Chi-square**.
9. Under **Categorical variables For rows** enter *Classes* column and **For columns** enter *Gender* column.
10. Under **Display** check **Column Frequency**.
11. Click **OK**.

son of the two to determine what, if any, difference exists between males and females. However, an alternative approach is to jointly analyze the two variables: gender and credit card balance.

Although the process is different for Excel and Minitab, both software packages provide methods for analyzing two variables jointly. In Figure 2-5, we constructed the frequency distribution for the 300 credit card balances using 10 classes. The class width was set at $150. Figure 2-7 shows a table that is called a *joint frequency distribution*. This type of table is also called a *cross-tabulation* table.[1]

The Capital Credit Union managers can use a joint frequency table to analyze the credit card balances for males versus females. For instance, for the 61 customers with balances of $540 to $689, Figure 2-7 shows that 45 were males and 16 were females. Previously, we discussed the concept of relative frequency (proportions, which Excel converts to percentages) as a useful tool for making comparisons between two data sets. In this example, comparisons between males and females would be easier if the frequencies were converted to proportions (or percentages). The result is the *joint relative frequency table* shown in Figure 2-8. Notice that the percentages in each cell are percentages of the total 300 people in the survey. For example, the $540-to-$689 class had 20.33% (61) of the 300 customers.

FIGURE 2-8

Excel Output of the Joint Relative Frequencies

Excel Instructions (for similar results):
1. Place Cursor anywhere in the table.
2. Right click and select **Wizard**.
3. Select **Layout**.
4. Double click on **Data** field item.
5. For "**Show Data As _** select % of Column.
6. Click **OK**.

In Figure 2-8 we have used the **Data Field Options** of the Excel PivotTable to represent the data as percentages.

[1]In Excel, the joint frequency distribution is developed using a tool called Pivot tables. In Minitab, the joint frequency distributions are constructed using the Cross Tabulation option.

FIGURE 2-9

Minitab Relative Frequency Distribution—Males and Females

Minitab Instructions:
1. Open file: Capital.MTW
2. Steps 2-7 as in Figure 2-7.
3. Click on **Stat > Tables > Cross Tabulation and Chi-square**.
4. Under **Categorical variables For rows** enter *Classes* column and **For columns** enter *Gender* column.
5. Under **Display**, check **Total Percents**.
6. Click **OK**.

```
MINITAB - CAPITAL.MPJ - [Session]
File  Edit  Data  Calc  Stat  Graph  Editor  Tools

Tabulated statistics: Classes, Gender

Rows: Classes    Columns: Gender

                  1       2      All

90-239          3.667   0.667    4.333
240-389         5.333   1.000    6.333
390-539        11.000   3.000   14.000
540-689        15.000   5.333   20.333
690-839        11.667   4.000   15.667
840-989        13.667   3.000   16.667
990-1139        9.333   2.667   12.000
1140-1289       4.667   2.000    6.667
1290-1439       2.000   0.667    2.667
1290-1429       0.667   0.000    0.667
1440-1589       0.333   0.333    0.667
All            77.333  22.667  100.000

Cell Contents:      % of Total
```

The male customers with balances in the $540-to-$689 range constituted 15% (45) of the 300 customers, whereas females with that balance level made up 5.33% (16) of all 300 customers. On the surface, this result seems to indicate a big difference between males and females at this credit balance level.

Suppose we really wanted to focus on the male-versus-female issue and control for the fact that there are far more male customers than female. We could compute the percentages differently. Rather than using a base of 300 (the entire sample size), we might instead be interested in the percentages of the males who have balances at each level, and the same data for females.[2] Figure 2-9 shows the relative frequencies converted to percentages of the column total. In general, there seems to be little difference in the male and female distributions with respect to credit card balances.

There are many options for transferring data into useful information. Thus far, we have introduced frequency distributions, joint frequency tables, and histograms. In the next section, we discuss one of the most useful graphical tools: the bar chart.

2-1: EXERCISES

Skill Development

2.1 A data set has a maximum value of 700 and a minimum value of 300. Using 10 classes, show the class limits you would use for the first three classes using a format similar to:
   a. "130 to <145 lbs."
   b. "130 to 144.99 lbs."

2.2 A data set has 200 observations. The maximum value in the data set is $16,300, and the minimum value is $11,500.
   a. Use Sturges's rule to determine the number of classes that you will use.
   b. Based on the number of classes determined in part a, indicate the class width for each class.
   c. Show the class limits for the first five classes, using a format similar to "130 to <145 lbs."

2.3 A data set has 160 observations. The maximum value is 3.25 and the minimum value is −2.80.
   a. Use Sturges's rule to determine the number of classes that you will use.

   b. Based on the number of classes determined in part a, indicate the class width for each class.
   c. Show the class limits for the first three classes. Use a format similar to "225 and under 450 seconds" on page 36.

2.4 You are given the following data.

6	10	6	4	9	5
5	5	5	7	6	2
5	5	5	4	5	7
6	7	8	6	8	4
7	5	5	5	5	7
8	7	6	7	5	4
6	4	4	7	4	6
6	7	8	6	7	6
7	8	5	6	5	7
3	6	4	7	4	4

   a. Construct a frequency distribution for these data.
   b. Based on the frequency distribution, develop a histogram.

[2]Such distributions are known as *marginal distributions*.

c. Construct a relative frequency distribution.
d. Develop a relative frequency histogram.
e. Compare the two histograms. Why do they look alike?

2.5 Use the data from problem 2.4.
   a. Construct a relative frequency distribution of the data. Use Sturges's rule to determine the number of classes.
   b. Construct a cumulative frequency distribution of the data.
   c. Construct a relative frequency histogram.
   d. Construct an ogive.

2.6 Consider these two sets of data.

Value	2	3	4	5	6	7	8	9	10
Frequency	5	3	10	10	10	10	5	1	6

Value	2	3	4	5	6	7	8	9	10
Frequency	1	1	10	15	13	13	5	1	1

   a. Construct a frequency distribution for these two sets of data using the same classes.
   b. Which distribution appears to have the largest "center" value?
   c. Which distribution appears to have the greatest variation?

2.7 You have been given the following joint frequency distribution. Convert the frequencies to relative frequencies.

		Years of College			
Income	None	1–2 Years	3–4 Years	5–6 Years	>6 Years
<$20,000	16	33	30	6	4
$20,000 to <$40,000	22	28	40	26	5
$40,000 to <$60,000	9	12	21	46	9
≥$60,000	3	5	15	13	6

   a. Determine the proportion of those having at least five years of college who earn at least $40,000. Compare this proportion to a similar proportion for those having fewer than five years of college.
   b. Determine the proportion of those who make at least $60,000 who have more than four years of college.
   c. Determine the proportion of the entire sample who make less than $20,000. Compare this to the proportion of those who have not gone to college who make less than $20,000.
   d. Calculate the proportion of those who have not gone to college who make at least $60,000. Calculate a similar proportion for each of the years-of-college categories.

Business Applications

2.8 One strategy that some investors take is to invest in local companies. Each day, the city newspaper carries the daily closing stock prices for some of the local com-

panies. On a recent day the closing prices for 37 companies were listed as follows:

61.00	50.06	6.50	45.56	22.13	13.88	18.13	38.75	26.94	91.44
28.38	64.56	7.13	59.94	72.94	37.88	27.75	73.19	25.88	25.38
60.06	14.63	28.88	27.31	52.75	1.69	30.25	52.38	31.81	72.98
118.00	19.88	45.31	31.00	72.63	120.00	25.88			

   a. Create a data array for these data.
   b. Develop a frequency distribution with five classes for these data. Use zero as the lower limit of the first class.
   c. Develop a histogram based on the frequency distribution.
   d. Determine the proportion of stock highs that are greater than $50.
   e. Write a short statement that describes the stock price data.

2.9 Each month the American Automobile Association (AAA) generates a report on gasoline prices that they distribute to the newspapers throughout the state. On February 17th, AAA called a random sample of 51 stations to determine the price of unleaded gasoline that day. The resulting data are shown as follows:

1.07	1.31	1.18	1.01	1.23	1.09	1.29	1.10	1.16	1.08
0.96	1.66	1.21	1.09	1.02	1.04	1.01	1.03	1.09	1.11
1.11	1.17	1.04	1.09	1.05	0.96	1.32	1.09	1.26	1.11
1.03	1.20	1.21	1.05	1.10	1.04	0.97	1.21	1.07	1.17
0.98	1.10	1.04	1.03	1.12	1.10	1.03	1.18	1.11	1.09
1.06									

   a. Create a data array with the gasoline price data.
   b. Construct two histograms for this data set, using 5 classes for the first and 15 classes for the second. Use $0.95 as the lower limit of the first class.
   c. A local radio station has reported that 30% of the gas stations are charging $1.15 a gallon or more for gasoline. (1) Use one of the histograms you have produced to respond to this report. (2) Which histogram did you use? Why?

2.10 The American Automobile Association study discussed in problem 2.9 produced the following data on unleaded gasoline prices:

1.07	1.31	1.18	1.01	1.23	1.09	1.29	1.10	1.16	1.08
0.96	1.66	1.21	1.09	1.02	1.04	1.01	1.03	1.09	1.11
1.11	1.17	1.04	1.09	1.05	0.96	1.32	1.09	1.26	1.11
1.03	1.20	1.21	1.05	1.10	1.04	0.97	1.21	1.07	1.17
0.98	1.10	1.04	1.03	1.12	1.10	1.03	1.18	1.11	1.09
1.06									

Using $0.90 as the lower limit of the first class, construct the following distributions using seven classes.
   a. a frequency distribution.
   b. a relative frequency distribution.
   c. a cumulative frequency distribution and a cumulative relative frequency distribution.

2.11   The loan officer at Money First National Bank wants to obtain information about the loans she has made over the past five years. She is preparing a report for the bank's regional spring conference. As part of the report, she has decided to develop a distribution showing the loan frequency by size of loan. The data indicates that the smallest loan she made was for $1,000 and the largest loan was $25,000.

    a. If she wants to have 10 classes in her distribution, define the 10 classes in terms of lower and upper limits.

    b. She knows that other loan officers will also be making similar presentations. If she wishes to compare the information in her distribution with that of the others, what kind of distribution do you recommend? Give your reasons.

2.12   🔘 The data file *Wallingford* contains a sample of 60 accounts receivable balances selected from accounts at the Wallingford Department Store. Each week, the sales manager asks to summarize the current status of the accounts receivable.

    a. Using 10 classes and 5.00 as the lower limit of the first class, develop a frequency distribution and histogram for the accounts receivable.

    b. Write a one-paragraph statement describing the accounts receivable balances as reflected by the sample. Specifically, (1) state the range of the account balances, (2) identify any account balances that may warrant more scrutiny by the collections department, and (3) determine the proportion of accounts larger than $100. Describe any other significant features of the data of which the manager should be made aware. (Remember that in business, report writing is an important way of conveying information.)

2.13   In a survey conducted by NFO Interactive, investors were asked to rate how knowledgeable they felt they were as investors. Both online and traditional investors were included in the survey. The survey resulted in the following data:

    a. Of the online investors, 8%, 55%, and 37% responded they were "savvy," "experienced," and "novice," respectively.

    b. Of the traditional investors, the percentages were 4%, 29%, and 67%, respectively.

Six hundred investors were surveyed, of which 200 were traditional investors.

    a. Use this information to construct a joint frequency distribution.

    b. Use the information to construct a joint relative frequency distribution.

    c. Determine the proportion of investors who were both online investors and rated themselves experienced.

    d. Calculate the proportion of investors who were online investors.

2.14   The makers of the PowerChew Energy Bar recently weighed 10 bars from each of their two production lines. The following data were observed:

Line	1	1	1	1	1	1	1	1	1	1
Weight	2.78	2.95	3.03	2.89	3.04	2.97	3.04	2.99	2.95	3.10

Line	2	2	2	2	2	2	2	2	2	2
Weight	3.02	3.11	2.98	2.90	3.02	3.05	3.01	2.97	2.98	3.00

    a. Develop a joint frequency distribution showing manufacturing line and the weights broken into two categories: under 3.00 and 3.00 and over.

    b. Referring to part a, convert the joint frequency distribution to a joint relative frequency distribution.

    c. Write a short paragraph using the information in parts a and b to describe the output for the PowerChew company.

Advanced Business Applications

2.15   🔘 Lotteries have become very popular across the nation. Information regarding lottery sales between July 1, 1996, and June 30, 1997, are provided in the file *Lottery*. This data set was provided by the North American Association of State and Provincial Lotteries, as reported in the March 15, 1998, issue of the *Idaho Statesman*.

    a. Develop a frequency distribution for the lottery sales using five classes and zero as lower limit of first class.

    b. Develop a frequency distribution for the state profit. Determine an appropriate number of classes, determine the frequency of each class, and calculate the relative frequency of each class.

    c. Develop a frequency distribution for the per capita spending. Determine an appropriate number of classes, determine the frequency of each class, and calculate the relative frequency and the cumulative relative frequency of each class.

    d. Develop histograms for parts a, b, and c.

2.16   💿 The Franklin Tire Company is interested in demonstrating the durability of their steel-belted radial tires. To do this, the managers have decided to put 4 tires on 100 different sport utility vehicles and drive them throughout Alaska. The data collected indicate the number of miles (rounded to the nearest 1,000 miles) that each of the SUVs traveled before one of the tires on the vehicle did not meet minimum federal standards for tread thickness. The data file is called *Franklin*.

    a. Construct a frequency distribution and histogram using eight classes. Use 51 as the lower limit of the first class.

    b. The marketing department wishes to know the tread life of at least 50% of the tires, the 10% with the longest tread life, and the longest tread life of these tires. Provide this information to the marketing department. Also provide any other significant items that point out the desirability of this line of steel-belted tires.

    c. Construct a frequency distribution and a histogram using 12 classes, with 51 as the lower limit of the first class. Compare your results with those in parts a and b. Which distribution gives the best information about the desirability of this line of steel-belted tires?

2.17 A research project conducted by the State Transportation Department has as its objective determining whether a truck scale that will weigh a truck while it is moving down the highway (WIM scale) could be used to augment the traditional Port-of-Entry scale (POE scale) for enforcement and data-collection purposes. A portion of the data collected in this study is contained in the file called *Trucks*. Two of the variables collected in the study are POE length and WIM length.

a. Develop a frequency distribution for POE length using eight classes.

b. Develop a relative frequency distribution for POE length.

c. Construct both a frequency histogram and an ogive for POE length.

d. Develop a frequency distribution and a histogram for WIM length of trucks. Use the same classes as those used for the POE length-of-trucks distribution so you can compare them. How do the two distributions compare? Discuss.

e. Construct a joint frequency distribution using POE length as the row variable and WIM length as the column variable. Based on this distribution, would you recommend that the WIM truck lengths be used in place of the POE truck lengths? Are there any systematic differences between the two distributions? Write a short report that discusses the similarities and differences between these two length variables.

2.18 The High Desert Banking Company is a small bank that specializes in making consumer loans, small commercial loans, and real estate loans (both home improvement and new-home construction). The data file *High-Desert-Banking* contains the loans made by the bank last year. The loan-type codes are 1 = Consumer, 2 = Commercial, and 3 = Real Estate.

In your position as an intern at the bank, you have been given the task of developing a presentation to the bank's loan officers. You are planning to include the following in your presentation:

a. A frequency distribution of loans by type of loan.

b. A relative frequency distribution.

c. A frequency distribution of loan amounts using class intervals of width equal to $15,000.

d. A histogram of loan amounts using the frequency distribution in part c.

e. A joint frequency distribution of loan amount and type of loan using class intervals of $15,000 for loan amount.

f. Develop a written report that fully discloses the loan data. This report should be developed using word processing. The various frequency distributions and histograms should be pasted into the document and clearly labeled. Make sure your report points out differences and similarities among the various distributions of loan data in the regions of the country. For instance, examine which regions have the largest loans, which regions have similar distributions, and how the regions' distributions are different.

2.19 The research and development department at Hydronics, Inc., has developed two weight-loss systems that they are considering introducing on the market. One month ago, the managers conducted a study in which they put a sample of people into three separate programs: 1, 2, and a placebo. They then recorded the number of pounds each person gained or lost during the month. These data are recorded in the file called *Hydronics*.

You have been asked to analyze the weight-loss data using the following statistical tools:

a. Develop a frequency distribution for each program and the placebo. Use 5-pound class widths.

b. Based on the results in part a, develop histograms for each program and the placebo.

c. Produce relative frequency distributions for each program and for the placebo.

d. Prepare a report that summarizes the information generated in parts a, b, and c. You must include in your report a recommendation concerning which weight-loss system they should introduce and the reasons for the recommendation.

2-2 BAR CHARTS, PIE CHARTS, AND STEM AND LEAF DIAGRAMS

BAR CHARTS

Section 2-1 introduced some of the basic tools for describing numerical variables, both discrete and continuous, when the data were in their raw form. However, in many instances, you will be working with categorical data or data that have already been summarized to some extent. In this case, an effective presentation tool is often a **bar chart**.

Bar Chart

A graphical representation of a categorical data set in which a rectangle or bar is drawn over each category or class. The length of each bar represents the frequency or percentage of observations, or some other measure associated with the category. The bars may be vertical or horizontal. The bars may all be the same color or they may be different colors depicting different categories. Additionally, multiple variables can be graphed on the same bar chart.

TABLE 2-6

1997 U.S. Income from Emerging-Market Countries

Brazil	$4.55	Malaysia	$1.21
Mexico	$3.97	Venezuela	$0.87
Indonesia	$1.74	Argentina	$0.85
Panama	$1.30	China	$0.81
Chile	$1.22	Nigeria	$0.78

Note: Data are in billions of dollars, U.S. currency.

International Banking—In today's business climate, the U.S. economy is closely linked to the international marketplace. Recently an executive for the Wall Street brokerage house Hoenig & Co. gave a speech at an international economic summit in New York City. The talk centered on Brazil, the world's ninth-largest economy, and one that by many accounts is in great peril.[3]

In preparing the speech, the Hoenig executive assembled the data in Table 2-6, which shows the 1997 income, in billions of dollars, derived by U.S. businesses from emerging-market countries.

Although the table format contains the data and is informative, a graphical presentation is often desirable. A bar chart would work well in this instance. Recall that the bars can be vertical or horizontal. Figure 2-10 shows an example. Note, because Brazil is the focus, that bar is highlighted with a different shading than the other countries. The bar chart shows very clearly how important Brazil is to the United States as a source of income. Do you agree that the chart makes the point more effectively than the table?

People sometimes confuse histograms and bar charts. Although there are some similarities, they are two very different graphical tools. Histograms are used to represent a frequency distribution associated with a quantitative (ratio or interval-level) variable. Refer to the histogram illustrations in Section 2-1. In every case, the variable on the horizontal axis was numerical, with values moving from low to high. There are no gaps between the histogram bars. On the other hand, bar charts are used when the variable of interest is categorical, as in this case in which the category is country.

FIGURE 2-10

Bar Chart of U.S. Income from Emerging Countries

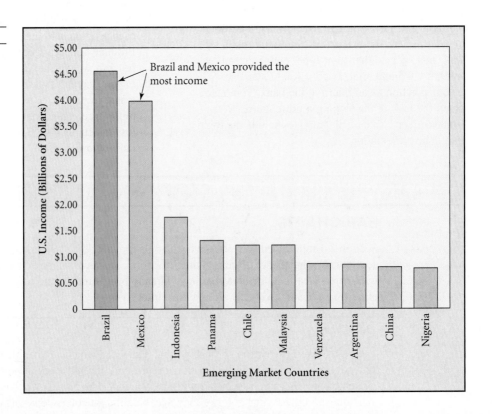

[3]Fox, Justin, "A Prayer for Brazil," *Fortune*, November 9, 1998, pp. 30–31.

SUMMARY: CONSTRUCTING BAR CHARTS

A bar chart is constructed using the following steps:

1. Define the categories for the variable of interest.

2. For each category, determine the appropriate measure or value.

3. For a vertical bar chart, locate the categories on the horizontal axis. The vertical axis is set to a scale correspond-

ing to the values in the categories. For a horizontal bar chart, place the categories on the vertical axis and set the scale of the horizontal axis in accordance with the values in the categories. Then construct bars, either vertical or horizontal, for each category such that the height corresponds to the value for the category.

EXAMPLE 2-7: BAR CHARTS

Attending Higher Education in Idaho   The fact that you are taking this course means that you are pursuing a higher education, either in the United States or internationally. However, not everyone does. A study conducted in Idaho in January 2002 addressed the issue of percentage of high school graduates who continue their education. The objective is to display the data effectively. A bar chart can be conducted using the following steps:

Step 1:   **Define the categories.**

Data are available for four years and for three factors, as shown in the following table.

	% Higher Ed	% in Idaho	% Out of State
1992	48	36	12
1994	47	35	12
1996	47	34	13
1998	49	36	13

The main category is the year. For each year, there are three values of interest: percentage of Idaho high school graduates who enroll in higher education; the percentage who enroll in Idaho higher education institutions; and the percentage who go out of state.

Step 2:   **Determine the appropriate measure.**

The measure for each category is the percentage of high school graduates.

Step 3:   **Develop the bar chart.**

The vertical bar chart that is developed is shown as follows. Note, each percentage value is assigned a different color, and the data are displayed over the four different years.

This bar chart illustrates that the percentage of Idaho's high school graduates who go on to higher education has been fairly stable at just under 50 percent. It also shows that most Idaho students who do enroll tend to stay in state for their higher education.

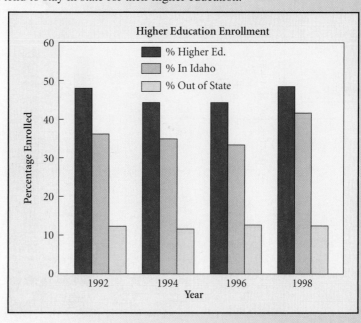

YEAR	MALES: AVERAGE STARTING SALARIES	FEMALES: AVERAGE STARTING SALARIES
1992	$44,456	$41,789
1993	$47,286	$46,478
1994	$56,234	$53,854
1995	$57,890	$58,600
1996	$63,467	$59,070
1997	$61,090	$55,321
1998	$67,543	$64,506

Excel and Minitab Tutorial

Bach, Lombard, & Wilson—One of the most useful features of bar charts is that they can display multiple issues. Consider Bach, Lombard, & Wilson, the New England law firm. Recently, the firm handled a case in which a woman was suing her employer, a major electronics firm, claiming the company gave higher starting salaries to men than to women. Consequently, she stated, even though the company tended to give equal percentage raises to women and men, the gap between the two groups widened.

Attorneys at Bach, Lombard, & Wilson had their staff assemble massive amounts of data. Table 2-7 provides an example of the type of data they collected.

A bar chart is a more effective way to convey this information, as Figure 2-11 shows. From this graph we can quickly see that in all years except 1995 the starting salaries for males did exceed females. The bar chart also illustrates that the general trend in starting salaries for both groups has been increasing, though with a slight downturn in 1997. Do you think the information in Figure 2-11 alone is sufficient to rule in favor of the claimant in this lawsuit?

Suppose other data are available showing the percentage of new hires having MBA degrees by gender, as illustrated in Table 2-8. The bar charts in Figure 2-12a and Figure 2-12b present these data clearly. These charts show that every year the percentage of new hires with MBA degrees was substantially higher for male hires than for female hires. What might this imply about the reason for the difference in starting salaries?

FIGURE 2-11

Excel Output—Bar Chart of Starting Salaries

Excel Instructions:
1. Open file: **Bach.xls**
2. Click on **Chart Wizard**.
3. Select **Column** type.
4. Define **Data Range**.
5. Label chart as desired.

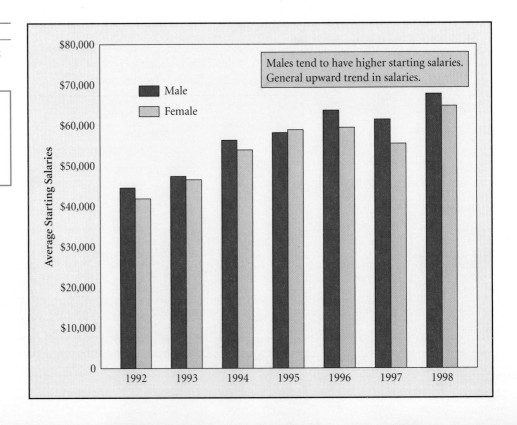

TABLE 2-8

Salary Data for the Bach, Lombard, & Wilson Example

YEAR	MALES: AVERAGE STARTING SALARIES	MALES: PERCENTAGE WITH MBA	FEMALES: AVERAGE STARTING SALARIES	FEMALES: PERCENTAGE WITH MBA
1992	$44,456	35	$41,789	18
1993	$47,286	39	$46,478	20
1994	$56,234	49	$53,854	22
1995	$57,890	40	$58,600	30
1996	$63,467	46	$59,070	25
1997	$61,090	32	$55,321	24
1998	$67,543	48	$64,506	26

FIGURE 2-12A

Excel Output—Bar Chart of MBA Hire Data

Excel Instructions:
1. Open file: Bach.xls
2. Click on **Chart Wizard**.
3. Select **Bar type**.
4. Define **Data Range**.
5. Label chart as desired.

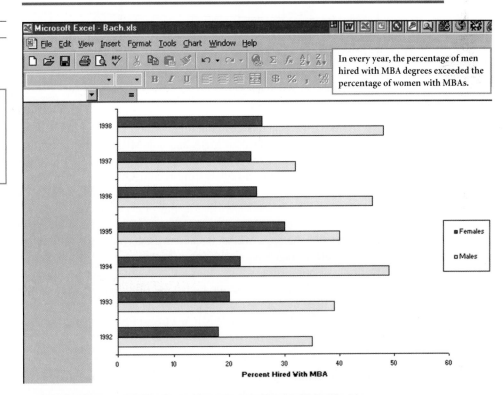

FIGURE 2-12B

Minitab Output—Bar Chart of MBA Hire Data

Minitab Instructions:
(Create stacked columns for *Percent Hired, Years,* and *Gender. See Tutorial.*)
1. Open file: Bach.MTW
2. Click on **Graph > Bar Chart**.
3. Under **Bars represent,** select *Values from a table*.
4. Under **One column of values,** select *Cluster,* click **OK**.
5. In **Graph variables,** enter *PercentHired* column.
6. In **Categorical variables for grouping (1-4 outermost first)**, enter *Year* and *Gender* columns.
7. Click **OK**.

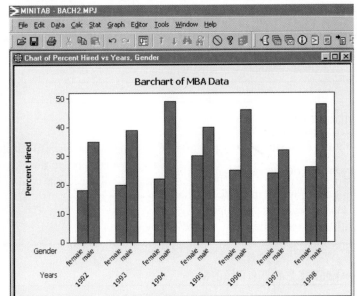

FIGURE 2-13

Excel Output—Bar Chart
of Average Salaries by
Degree Type

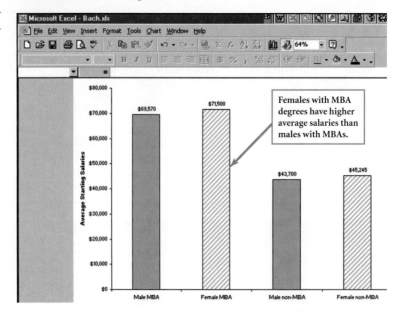

After viewing the bar charts in Figures 2-12a and 2-12b, the lead attorney had her staff look at the average starting salary for MBA and non-MBA graduates for the combined seven-year period, broken down by male and female employees. Figure 2-13 shows the bar chart for those data.

Figure 2-13 shows an interesting result. Over the seven-year period, females actually had higher starting salaries than males for those with and without MBA degrees. Then how can Figure 2-11 be correct, when it shows that in almost every year the male average starting salary exceeded the female average starting salary? The answer lies in Figure 2-12, which shows that far more of the newly hired males have MBAs. Because MBAs tend to get substantially higher starting salaries, the overall male average salary was higher. In this case, the initial data looked like the electronics firm had been discriminating against females by paying lower starting salaries. After digging deeper, we see that females actually get the higher starting average salaries with and without MBA degrees. However, does this prove that the company is not discriminating in its hiring practices? Perhaps it purposefully hires fewer female MBAs or fewer females in general. More research is needed.

PIE CHARTS

Another graphical tool that can be used to transform data into information is the **pie chart**.

Pie Chart

A graph in the shape of a circle. The circle is divided into "slices" corresponding to the categories or classes to be displayed. The size of each slice is proportional to the magnitude of the displayed variable associated with each category or class.

SUMMARY: CONSTRUCTING PIE CHARTS

A pie chart is constructed using the following steps:

1. Define the categories for the variable of interest.

2. For each category, determine the appropriate measure or value. The value assigned to each category is the proportion the category is to the total for all categories.

3. Construct the pie chart by displaying one slice for each category that is proportional in size to the proportion the category value is to the total of all categories.

EXAMPLE 2-8: PIE CHARTS

Gold Equipment   A survey was recently conducted of 300 golfers that asked questions about the impact of new technology on the game. One question asked the golfers to indicate which area of golf equipment is most responsible for improving an amateur golfer's game. The following data were obtained:

Equipment	Frequency
Golf Ball	81
Club Head Material	66
Shaft Material	63
Club Head Size	63
Shaft Length	3
Don't Know	24

To display these data in pie-chart form, use the following steps:

Step 1:   **Define the categories.**
The categories are the six equipment-response categories.

Step 2:   **Determine the appropriate measure.**
The appropriate measure is the proportion of the golfers surveyed. The proportion for each category is determined by dividing the number of golfers in a category by the total sample size. For example, for the category golf ball, the percentage is $81/300 = 0.27$.

Step 3:   **Construct the pie chart.**
The pie chart is constructed by dividing a circle into six slices (one for each category) such that each slice is proportional to the percentage of golfers in the category.

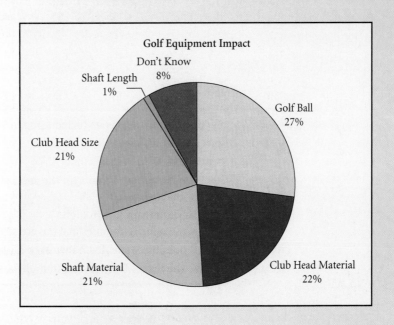

STEM AND LEAF DIAGRAMS

Another graphical technique that is useful for doing a preliminary analysis of quantitative data is called the *stem and leaf diagram*. The stem and leaf diagram is similar to the histogram introduced in Section 2-1 in that it displays the distribution for the quantitative variable. However, unlike the histogram, in which the individual values of the data are lost if the variable of interest is broken into classes, the stem and leaf diagram shows the individual data values.

Minitab has a procedure for constructing stem and leaf diagrams. Although Excel does not have a stem and leaf procedure, the PHStat add-ins to Excel that are included on the CD-ROM do have a stem and leaf procedure.

SUMMARY: CONSTRUCTING STEM AND LEAF DIAGRAMS

To construct the stem and leaf diagram for a quantitative variable, use the following steps:

1. Analyze the data for the variable of interest to determine how you wish to split the values into a stem and a leaf.

2. Sort the data from low to high.

3. List all possible stems in a single column between the lowest and highest values in the data.

4. For each stem, list all leaves associated with the stem.

EXAMPLE 2-9: STEM AND LEAF DIAGRAMS

Regis Auto Rental   The operations manager for Regis Auto Rental is interested in performing an analysis of the miles driven for the cars the company rents on weekends. A quick method for analyzing the data for a sample of 200 rentals is the stem and leaf diagram. The following data represent the miles driven in the cars.

113	112	63	127	110	129	142	115	192	94
165	121	105	140	85	93	105	140	93	126
183	118	67	104	162	110	76	109	91	132
88	96	132	80	144	112	57	139	123	124
172	149	198	114	88	111	133	117	138	134
53	147	108	109	153	89	159	99	130	93
161	118	115	117	128	98	125	184	134	132
117	127	166	72	122	109	124	92	82	69
110	128	151	67	142	177	135	121	143	89
160	115	138	79	104	76	89	110	44	140
117	103	59	109	145	117	162	108	141	139
148	175	107	117	87	87	150	152	80	168
88	127	131	85	143	101	137	111	128	147
110	81	111	149	154	90	150	117	101	116
153	176	112	147	87	177	190	66	62	154
143	122	176	153	97	106	86	62	146	98
134	135	127	118	109	143	146	152	140	95
102	137	158	69	122	135	136	129	91	136
135	86	131	154	132	59	136	85	142	137
155	190	120	154	102	109	97	157	144	149

The stem and leaf diagram is constructed using the following steps:

Step 1:   **Split the values into a stem and leaf.**

Stem = tens place   leaf = units place

For example, for the value 113, the stem is 11 and the leaf is 3. We are keeping one digit for the leaf.

Step 2:   **Sort the data from low to high.**

The lowest value is 44 miles and the highest value is 198 miles.

Step 3:   **List all possible stems from lowest to highest.**

Step 4:   **Itemize the leaves from lowest to highest and place next to the appropriate stems.**

4	4
5	3 7 9 9
6	2 2 3 6 7 7 9 9
7	2 6 6 9
8	0 0 1 2 5 5 5 6 6 7 7 7 8 8 8 9 9 9
9	0 1 1 2 3 3 3 4 5 6 7 7 8 8 9
10	1 1 2 2 3 4 4 5 5 6 7 8 8 9 9 9 9 9 9
11	0 0 0 0 0 1 1 1 2 2 2 3 4 5 5 5 6 7 7 7 7 7 7 7 8 8 8
12	0 1 1 2 2 2 3 4 4 5 6 7 7 7 7 8 8 8 9 9
13	0 1 1 2 2 2 2 3 4 4 4 5 5 5 5 6 6 6 7 7 7 8 8 9 9
14	0 0 0 0 1 2 2 2 3 3 3 3 3 4 4 5 6 6 7 7 7 8 9 9 9
15	0 0 1 2 2 3 3 3 4 4 4 4 5 7 8 9
16	0 1 2 2 5 6 8
17	2 5 6 6 7 7
18	3 4
19	0 0 2 8

The stem and leaf diagram shows that most people drive the rental car between 80 and 160 miles, with the most frequent value in the 110- to 120-mile range.

2-2: EXERCISES

Skill Development

2.20 You are given the following data reflecting the number of people in a study having each of the particular investments.

Investments	No. of People
Mutual Fund	357
Savings Account	506
Certificate of Deposit	158
Individual Stocks	347
Bonds	86
Real Estate	169
Other	41

You wish to demonstrate which investments are the most popular. Based on these data, construct a bar chart to effectively display the data.

2.21 Given the following data on gasoline prices, construct a bar chart that displays the data effectively.

Year	Average Unleaded Price	Average Premium Price
1999	$1.22	$1.34
2000	$1.29	$1.39
2001	$1.37	$1.48
2002	$1.21	$1.31

2.22 A mutual fund recently sent a letter to its customers outlining the planned capital-gains distributions for the current year. The following values reflect the per share capital-gains allocation for each type of fund managed by the company:

Fund	Capital Gains Distributions
Balanced	$0.13
Equity Income	$0.75
Growth	$0.19
Select	$0.91
Utilities	$0.63

Construct a chart that will effectively display these data.

2.23 You are given the following data reflecting the number of people in a study having each of the particular investments.

Investments	No. of People
Mutual Fund	357
Savings Account	506
Certificate of Deposit	158
Individual Stocks	347
Bonds	86
Real Estate	169
Other	41

Construct a pie chart showing the percentage of people having each type of investment.

2.24 Given the following data, construct a stem and leaf diagram.

79	104	76	89	110
109	145	117	162	108
117	87	87	150	152
85	143	101	137	111
149	154	90	150	117
147	87	177	190	66
153	97	106	86	62

2.25 Given the following data, construct a stem and leaf diagram.

0.7	1.7
0.8	1.8
1.0	2.0
1.1	2.1
1.4	2.4
2.0	3.0
2.8	3.8
3.3	4.3
4.4	5.4
5.3	6.3
5.4	6.4

2.26 A university has the following number of students at each grade level.

Freshman	3,450	Senior	1,980
Sophomore	3,190	Graduate	750
Junior	2,780		

a. Construct a bar chart that effectively displays these data.
b. Construct a pie chart to display these data.
c. Referring to the graphs constructed in parts a and b, which would you favor as the most effective way of presenting these data? Discuss.

Business Applications

2.27 Ed Christianson has been asked by the director of marketing to make a presentation at next week's annual meeting of the Brown Manufacturing Company. The presentation concerns the company's advertising budget for the past year and the projected budget for the next year. In preparing for the meeting, Ed has obtained the following data:

Medium	This Year's Expense	Next Year's Budget
Newspaper	$35,000	$40,000
Television	$60,000	$80,000
Trade Publications	$25,000	$25,000
Miscellaneous	$10,000	$10,000

a. Use these data to develop a bar chart that effectively shows both this year's expenses for advertising and next year's proposed budget.

b. Develop two pie charts that show the dollar allocation to each media for the two years.

c. Referring to parts a and b, indicate whether bar charts or pie charts are more effective in displaying the media spending data. Discuss.

2.28　Growing companies must make regular capital expenditures to update and improve their production facilities. The following information, taken from the 1997 annual report of Flowers Industries, Inc., shows the capital expenditures made to renovate, automate, and modernize the firm's bakeries.

Year	Capital Expenditures (millions of dollars)
1992	34
1993	52
1994	64
1995	73
1996	76
1997	78
1998 estimated	40

Prepare a bar chart using this information. Comment on the pattern of capital expenditures since 1992.

2.29　Real estate investment trusts (REITs) were created by Congress in 1960 so small investors could invest in real estate as shareholders rather than as landlords. Using information taken from Paine Webber and SEC filings, the *Orlando Sentinel* on April 5, 1998, reported the following proportions of REIT money invested in different categories:

Category	Percentage
Shopping Centers	20
Multifamily	18
Office	17
Health Care	8
Hotels	8
Industrials	7
Mixed Industrial/Office	5
Mortgage Backed	5
Diversified	5
Self-Storage	4
Specialty	3

a. Present this information graphically using a pie chart and, alternatively, a bar chart.

b. Which do you feel is most effective? Why?

2.30　Real estate investment trusts provided investors with a convenient way to invest in real estate. Of the more than 300 U.S. REITs, 210 are publicly traded on the following exchanges:

Where Traded	Number
NYSE	158
AMEX	37
NASDAQ	15

Source: Paine Webber, SEC Filings, *Orlando Sentinel* (April 5, 1998).

Summarize this information using a bar chart and a pie chart. Discuss.

2.31　The Pennsylvania State Retirement Fund is overseen by an advisory board. At a recent meeting, the funds director suggested investing a sizable amount of money in a well-known mutual fund. As part of her presentation, she collected weekly closing prices for the fund over the past 52 weeks. These data are shown as follows:

41.0	27.4	31.9	29.4	30.0	39.9	27.9	37.4	32.3	33.4
37.0	36.0	32.2	29.1	30.1	36.2	27.1	28.8	16.7	32.0
27.7	30.6	24.8	33.4	28.7	42.5	38.5	35.7	34.7	36.9
33.3	26.7	27.9	29.7	33.0	28.8	31.2	37.3	39.6	26.3
36.6	29.8	32.4	26.0	31.8	34.1	34.9	33.4	33.2	35.8
33.7	30.5								

Construct a stem and leaf diagram for these data and write a short report indicating what this diagram shows.

Advanced Business Applications

2.32　　The Celltone Company is a provider of cellular phone service. They have two plans, a basic plan and a business plan. Recently, the local Celltone store manager examined the accounts for 200 customers. The manager was interested in the total number of minutes of cell calls used by customers on each plan. He needed the information presented in an effective way for a sales meeting the next week. Use the file *Celltone* located on your CD-ROM.

a. Develop a bar chart to display the data, and write a short statement that describes the graph.

b. Develop two stem and leaf diagrams, one for the basic plan users and one for the business plan users, which show the distribution of cell phone minutes used. Discuss.

2.33　　The real estate loan manager for Citizens Bank uses three appraisal companies to appraise residential property when a customer wants a home mortgage or wants to refinance an existing mortgage. Recently he conducted a test by having three companies appraise the same five properties. The results (in thousands of dollars) are in the file called *Citizens*.

After completing the test, the manager would like your help in displaying the data in an effective way. (Hint, you might consider using total appraisal values.) Provide a graphical display to oblige the manager.

2.34 The Future Vision Company is thinking of opening a TV-dish franchise in a new market area. However, prior to securing a location and taking other necessary steps to make the move, they conducted a survey of 548 residents in the market area. The data from this survey is in the file called *Future-Vision*. As site selection manager, you have been asked to develop a presentation for next week's staff meeting.

a. First, develop a chart that effectively displays the total number of residents in the following two categories: cable subscriber and not a cable subscriber. Be sure to do a good job of labeling the graph.

b. Develop a bar chart that shows number of households that subscribe to cable and do not subscribe broken down by family size. Use the following family size categories: 1 to 3, 4 to 6, and 7 to 10.

2.35 The file *Home-Prices* contains data on median home prices (the point below which 50% of the house prices fall) for 100 different U.S. cities. In your job with Farm-Life Insurance, you have been asked to break the cities into regions (North, South, East, and West). Prepare a graphical presentation that compares the median prices by region. Write a short summary report on your findings. Which region tends to have the highest home prices?

2.36 In your capacity as assistant to the administrator at Freedom Hospital, you have been asked to develop a graphical presentation that focuses on the insurance carried by the geriatric patients at the hospital. The data file *Patients* contains data for a sample of geriatric patients. In developing your presentation, please do the following:

a. Construct a pie chart that shows the percentage of patients with each health insurance payer.

b. Develop a bar chart that shows total charges for patients by insurance payer.

c. Develop a stem and leaf diagram for the length-of-stay variable.

d. Develop a bar chart that shows the number of males and females by insurance carrier.

2-3 LINE CHARTS AND SCATTER DIAGRAMS

LINE CHARTS

Most of the examples that have been presented thus far have involved *cross-sectional data*, or data gathered from many observations, all taken at the same time. However, if you have data that are measured over time (e.g., monthly, quarterly, or annually), an effective tool for presenting such data is a **line chart**.

Line Chart

A two-dimensional chart showing time on the horizontal axis and the variable of interest on the vertical axis.

Excel and Minitab Tutorial

McGregor Vineyards—McGregor Vineyards owns and operates a winery in the Sonoma Valley in northern California. At a recent company meeting, the financial manager expressed concern about the company's profit trend over the past 20 weeks. He presented weekly profit and sales data to McGregor management personnel. The data are on the CD-ROM that accompanies this text in the file *McGregor*.

Initially, the financial manager developed two separate line charts for this data: one for sales, the other for profits. These are displayed in Figures 2-14a and 2-14b. These line charts provide an indication that, although sales have been increasing, the profit trend is downward. But to fit both graphs on one page, he had to compress the size of the graphs. This "flattened" the lines somewhat, masking the magnitude of the problem.

What the financial manager needed is one graph with both profits and sales. Figure 2-15 shows his first attempt. This is better, but there still is a problem: The sales and profit variables are of different magnitudes. This results in the profit line being flattened out to almost a straight line. The profit trend is hidden.

To overcome this problem, the financial manager needed to construct his graph using two scales, one for each variable. Figure 2-16 shows the improved graph. We can now clearly see that although sales are moving steadily higher, profits are headed downhill. For some reason, costs are rising faster than revenues, and this graph should motivate McGregor Vineyards to look into the problem.

FIGURE 2-14A

Excel Output Showing
McGregor Line Charts

Excel Instructions:
1. Open file: McGregor.xls
2. Select the Data to be
   Graphed.
3. Click on the **Chart
   Wizard**.
4. Select **Line Graph**
   (option with data points
   shown).
5. Select **Series** Tab.
6. Define the X Axis
   Labels.
7. Remove unneeded vari-
   ables.
8. Click **Next**.
9. Define **Titles**.
10. Click **Finish**.

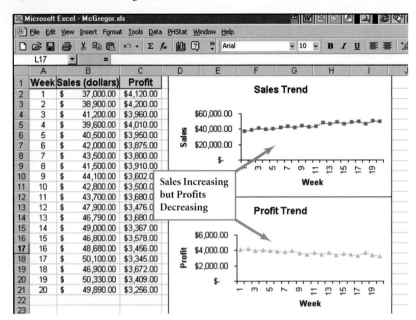

FIGURE 2-14B

Minitab Output Showing
McGregor Line Charts

Minitab Instructions:
1. Open file:
   McGregor.MTW.
2. Choose **Graph > Times
   Series Plot**.
3. Select **Simple**.
4. Click **OK**.
5. In **Series** enter *Sales* and
   Profit columns.
6. Select **Multiple Graphs**.
7. Under **Show Graph
   Variables**, select **In
   separate panels of the
   same graph**.
8. Click **OK. OK**.

FIGURE 2-15

Excel Line Charts of McGregor Profit and Sales

Excel Instructions:
1. Open File McGregor.xls
2. Select the two variables to be graphed.
3. Go to the **Chart Wizard**.
4. Select the **Line Chart** Option.
5. Add **Titles** and **Labels**.

Minitab Instructions (for similar results):
1. Open File: McGregor.MTW.
2. Choose **Graph > Times Series Plot**.
3. Select **Simple**.
4. Click **OK**.
5. In **Series**, enter *Sales* and *Profit* columns.
6. Select **Multiple Graphs**.
7. Under **Show Graph Variables**, select **Overlaid on the same graph**.
8. Click **OK. OK.**

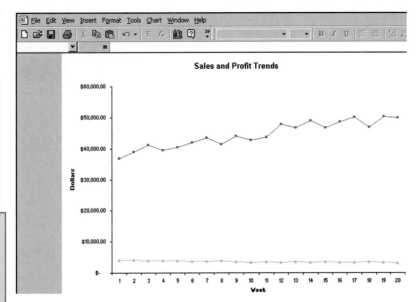

FIGURE 2-16

Excel Sales and Profits Line Chart

Excel Instructions:
1. Select the two variables to be graphed.
2. Go to the **Chart Wizard**.
3. Click on the **Custom Types** Tab.
4. Select **Lines on 2 Axes**.
5. Finish **Line Chart**.

Minitab Instructions (for similar results):
1. Open File: McGregor.MTW.
2. Choose **Graph > Times Series Plot**.
3. Select **Multiple**.
4. Click **OK**.
5. In **Series**, enter *Sales* and *Profit* columns.
6. Select **Multiple Graphs**.
7. Click **OK**.

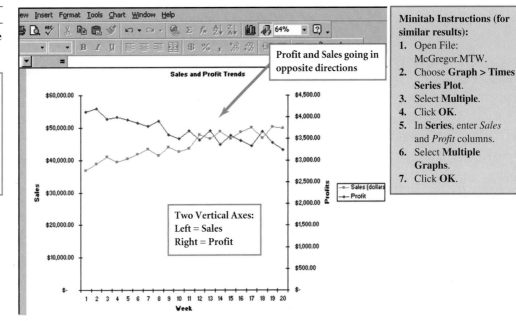

SUMMARY: CONSTRUCTING LINE CHARTS

A line chart, also commonly called a *trend chart*, is developed using the following steps:

1. Identify the time-series variable of interest and determine the maximum value and the range of time periods covered in the data.

2. Construct the horizontal axis for the time periods using equal spacing between each time period. Construct the ver-

tical axis with a scale appropriate for the range of values of the time-series variable.

3. Plot the points on the graph and connect the points with straight lines.

EXAMPLE 2-10: LINE CHARTS

Grogan Builders   Grogan Builders produces mobile homes in Alberta, Canada. The owners are planning to expand the manufacturing facilities. To do so requires additional financing. In preparation for the meeting with the bankers, the owners have assembled data on total annual sales for the past 10 years. These data are shown as follows:

1993	1994	1995	1996	1997	1998	1999	2000	2001	2002
1,426	1,678	2,591	2,105	2,744	3,068	2,755	3,689	4.003	3,997

The owners wish to present these data in a line chart to effectively show the company's sales growth over the 10-year period. To construct the line chart, the following steps are used:

Step 1:   **Identify the time-series variable.**

The time-series variable is measured over 10 years, with a maximum value of 4,003.

Step 2:   **Lay out the horizontal and vertical axes.**

The horizontal axis will have the 10 time periods equally spaced. The vertical axis will start at zero and go to a value exceeding 4,003. We will use 4,500. The vertical axis will also be divided into 500-unit increments.

Step 3:   **Plot the data values on the graph and connect the points with straight lines.**

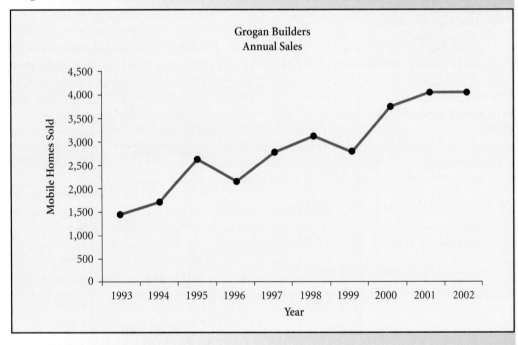

SCATTER DIAGRAMS

In Section 2-1 we introduced a set of statistical tools known as joint frequency distributions that allow the decision maker to examine two variables at the same time. Another tool used to study two variables simultaneously is the **scatter diagram**, or the **scatter plot**.

Scatter Diagram

A two-dimensional graph of plotted points in which the vertical axis represents values of one variable and the horizontal axis represents values of the other. Each plotted point has coordinates whose values are obtained from the respective variables.

There are many situations in which we are interested in understanding the *bivariate* relationship between two *quantitative* variables. For example, a company would like to know the relationship between sales and advertising. A bank might be interested in the relationship between savings-

FIGURE 2-17

Scatter Diagrams Showing Relationships Between *X* and *Y*

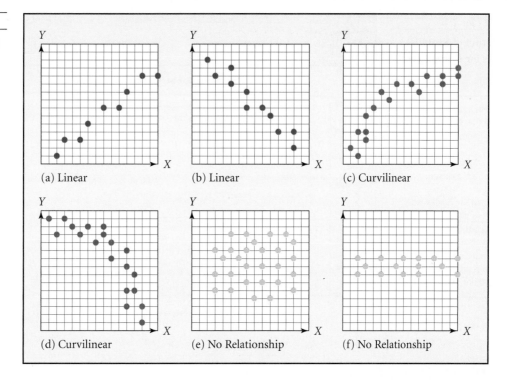

(a) Linear   (b) Linear   (c) Curvilinear

(d) Curvilinear   (e) No Relationship   (f) No Relationship

account balances and credit-card balances for its customers. A real estate agent might wish to know the relationship between the selling price of houses and the number of days that the houses have been on the market. The list of possibilities is almost limitless.

Regardless of the variables involved, there are several key relationships we are looking for when we develop a scatter diagram. Figure 2-17 shows scatter diagrams representing some key bivariate relationships that might exist between two quantitative variables.

Chapters 13 and 14 make extensive use of scatter diagrams. They introduce a statistical tool called *regression analysis* that focuses on the relationship between two variables. These variables are known as **dependent** and **independent variables**.

Dependent Variable

A variable whose values are thought to be a function of, or dependent on, the values of another variable called the *independent variable*. On a scatter plot, the dependent variable is placed on the y axis and is often called the response variable.

Independent Variable

A variable whose values are thought to impact the values of the *dependent variable*. The independent variable, or explanatory variable, is often within the direct control of the decision maker. On a scatter plot, the independent variable, or explanatory variable, is graphed on the X axis.

Excel and Minitab Tutorial

Personal Computers—Can you think of any product that has increased in quality and capability as rapidly as personal computers? Not that long ago an 8-MB RAM system with a 486 processor and a 640 K hard drive sold for the mid-$2500 range. Now the same money would buy a 2.4GHz or faster machine with a 40+ GB hard drive and 512-MB RAM or more!

In December 1998, a PC industry analyst for one of the major business publications wrote an article on computer capability and price. She looked at the relationship between PC cost and such factors as RAM and processor speed. A data file called *Computers* contains price and other information for 36 of the best-known PCs on the market.[4] The dependent variable is the price. One potential independent variable of interest is processor speed. Figure 2-18 illustrates the Excel scatter diagram for price and processor speed. The relationship is positive (that is, as the processor speed increases, so does the price) and somewhat linear.

[4]*Fortune*, December 7, 1998, special computer-hardware supplement.

FIGURE 2-18

Excel Output of Scatter
Diagrams for Computers
Data

Excel Instructions:
1. Open file: Computers.xls
2. Put cursor in any data cell.
3. Go to the **Chart Wizard**.
4. Select **XY Scatter Plot**—default type.
5. Click on the **Series** tab.
6. Remove all but one variable from series list.
7. Define X and variable data ranges.
8. Go to **Next**.
9. Add Titles, etc.

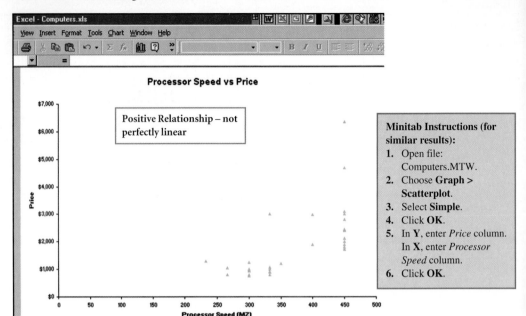

Minitab Instructions (for similar results):
1. Open file: Computers.MTW.
2. Choose **Graph > Scatterplot**.
3. Select **Simple**.
4. Click **OK**.
5. In **Y**, enter *Price* column. In **X**, enter *Processor Speed* column.
6. Click **OK**.

SUMMARY: CONSTRUCTING SCATTER DIAGRAMS

A scatter diagram is a two-dimensional graph showing the joint values for two quantitative variables. It is constructed using the following steps:

1. Identify the two quantitative variables and collect paired responses for the two variables.

2. Determine which variable will be placed on the vertical axis and which variable will be placed on the horizontal axis. Often the vertical axis can be considered the dependent variable (y) and the horizontal axis can be considered the independent variable (x).

3. Define the range of values for each variable and define the appropriate scale for the x and y axes.

4. Plot the joint values for the two variables by placing a point in the x,y space. Do not connect the points.

EXAMPLE 2-11: SCATTER DIAGRAMS

Fortune's Best Eight Companies   Each year, *Fortune* Magazine surveys employees regarding job satisfaction to try to determine which companies are the "best" companies to work for in the United States. *Fortune* also collects a variety of data associated with these companies. For example, the table here shows data for the top eight companies on three variables: number of U.S. employees; number of training hours per year per employee; and total revenue in millions of dollars.

Company	U.S. Employees	Training Hrs/Yr.	Revenues
Southwest Airlines	24,757	15	$3,400
Kingston Technology	552	100	$1,300
SAS Institute	3,154	32	$653
Fel-Pro	2,577	60	$450
TD Industries	976	40	$127
MBNA	18,050	48	$3,300
W.L. Gore	4,118	27	$1,200
Microsoft	14,936	8	$8,700

To better understand these companies, we might be interested in the relationship between number of U.S. employees and revenue, and between training hours per year and revenue. To construct these scatter diagrams, we can use the following steps:

Step 1:   **Identify the two variables of interest.**
In the first case, one variable is U.S. employees and the second is revenue. In the second case, one variable is training hours and the other is revenue.

Step 2:   **Identify the dependent variable.**
In each case, think of revenue as the dependent (y) variable. Thus,

Case 1: y = revenue (vertical axis)   x = U.S. employees (horizontal axis)

Case 2: y = revenue (vertical axis)   x = training hours (horizontal axis)

Step 3:   **Establish the scales for the vertical and horizontal axes.**
The maximum value for each variable is

revenue = \$8,700   U.S. employees = 24,757   training hours = 100

Step 4:   **Plot the joint values for the two variables by placing a point in the x, y space.**

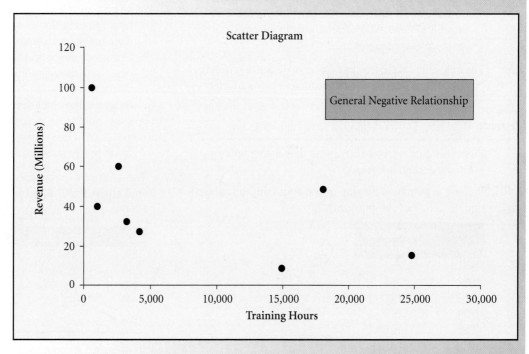

2-3: EXERCISES

Skill Development

2.37 The following data represent expenditures on advertising from 1989 to 1999 by the Swanson Lumber Company.

Year	Advertising	Year	Advertising
1989	$12,500	1995	18,790
1990	14,600	1996	23,500
1991	16,250	1997	24,000
1992	19,800	1998	25,600
1993	23,700	1999	27,800
1994	22,700		

Construct a line graph of the advertising variable and write a short statement indicating what this graph shows.

2.38 The following data represent the number of hours individual employees spent assembling component parts and the number of parts produced.

Hours	Parts Made	Hours	Parts Made
5	192	3	122
3	135	2	97
2	100	4	161
4	148	6	225
6	213	2	94
4	154	8	280
3	123	6	224
2	102	3	130
2	98	3	135
1	63		

a. Assuming that the production manager wishes to estimate the number of parts that could be made in, say, 10 hours, which variable would be classified as the dependent variable and which would be the independent variable?

b. Construct and interpret a scatter plot for these two variables. What type of relationship (if any) exists for these two variables?

2.39 The following data reflect the number of defective products produced each week at a local manufacturing company.

Week:	1	2	3	4	5	6	7	8	9	10	11
Defects:	80	76	79	72	68	70	64	60	64	58	52

From this data set, construct the appropriate graph to display the trend in defects.

2.40 Prepare a graphical display of the following information on U.S. bicycle shipments.

Year	Shipments (in Millions)
1991	15.1
1992	15.4
1993	17.0
1994	16.7
1995	16.0
1996	15.5

2.41 Given the following data, construct a scatter diagram and indicate what, if any, relationship exists between the two variables.

y:	40	33	27	50	18	40	56	70	27	19	30	18	42	11
x:	8	9	3	12	9	18	7	12	6	10	8	10	20	7

Business Applications

2.42 A company's human resources department recently selected a sample of 15 people. They compared the employees' performance ratings (based on a 100-point scale) and the number of overtime hours the employees had worked in the past six months. The following data were recorded:

Employee	Rating	Overtime Hours
1	87	50
2	67	30
3	90	100
4	88	95
5	80	70
6	60	20
7	40	25
8	95	72
9	80	65
10	75	50
11	82	68
12	70	48
13	50	33
14	89	80
15	96	85

a. The human resources department wishes to estimate an employee's rating using the number of overtime hours the employee compiled. Identify the dependent and independent variables.

b. Construct the appropriate chart that can be used to determine the relationship between rating and hours worked.

c. Based on the chart developed in part b, what conclusion might be reached about how ratings are assigned in this company. What cautions need to be made before such a conclusion is reached?

2.43 The Morrison Center for the Performing Arts has operated since 1990. The center's annual ticket sales for 1990 through 1999 are as follows:

Year	Ticket Sales	Year	Ticket Sales
1990	$204,000	1995	368,000
1991	275,000	1996	401,000
1992	280,000	1997	344,000
1993	299,000	1998	359,000
1994	345,000	1999	405,000

a. Prepare a line graph for the sales data.

b. The director of the Morrison Center initially only had data from 1990 to 1996, before the downturn in 1997. He had set a goal to reach ticket sales of $500,000. If the trend in the data from 1990 to 1996 had continued, in what year could the director have expected to meet his goal?

c. Consider the magnitude of the 1997 downturn. Also note that the upturn from 1997 on seems to have approximately the same slope as that from 1990 to 1996. Using this information, estimate the year in which the director will reach his goal.

2.44 Increasing dividends over time is an important factor for many investors when considering whether to purchase a company's stock. Shown here are net income and dividends paid per share of common stock for Flowers Industries, Inc., for 1987 to 1997.

Year	Net Income	Dividends
1987	$0.350	$0.163
1988	0.530	0.191
1989	0.380	0.227
1990	0.370	0.262
1991	0.310	0.291
1992	0.410	0.309
1993	0.470	0.327
1994	0.350	0.345
1995	0.500	0.362
1996	0.360	0.383
1997	0.720	0.413

Source: Flowers Industries, Inc., 1997 annual report.

a. Use this information to prepare a line graph to illustrate the pattern of dividends paid per share of common stock for 1987 to 1997.

b. Prepare a scatter plot that shows whether a relationship exists between net income per share of common stock and dividends per share of common stock. Does there appear to be a relationship between these two variables? If so, briefly describe the relationship.

c. Construct a line chart showing both net income and dividends on the same graph. Does there appear to be a relationship between these two variables?

Would you prefer a line chart or a scatter plot to determine such a relationship? Give reasons for your choice.

Advanced Business Applications

2.45 As part of a study on the banking industry, the data in the file *Banks* has been collected. As part of your study, construct the appropriate graph to determine the relationship between bank revenues and bank profits based on these data. Discuss your results. Discuss whether there are any decreasing economies of scale in the relationship between revenues and profits. That is, does the increase in profit get smaller as bank revenues get larger?

2.46 Chapman Bakery sells a variety of bakery products at its San Jose location. The data file *Bakery* contains information for a sample of daily sales. Of particular interest to the managers is determining the relationship between the number of wheat loaves and the number of white loaves. Construct an appropriate graph to identify the relationship.

2.47 The Ajax Taxi Company has collected data on the number of miles their cabs travel each week. Suppose four cabs are singled out and over a period of 40 weeks the miles that each is driven is recorded. The data are in the file *Ajax*.

a. Combine all four taxis together by summing the miles. Construct a line graph for the total miles. Do the total miles traveled by the cabs seem to be increasing or decreasing over time?

b. Construct a line graph that shows the pattern for each individual taxi over the 40 weeks.

2.48 The State Department of Commerce is in the process of generating a plan to attract new businesses to the state. You have been assigned to this team. At last week's meeting, you were given a data file called *BestCompanies*. The team leader has asked you to prepare a descriptive summary of the data. Specifically, she wants you to examine the relationship between new jobs added and the companies' revenues. In addition, prepare any other graphs or tables that you think would be helpful to better understand the data.

Summary and Conclusions

This chapter has introduced some of the most commonly used statistical techniques for organizing data and presenting them in a meaningful way to aid in the decision-making process. Organizing raw data into a frequency distribution is a major step in transforming data into information. We have outlined the steps for developing frequency distributions and for producing histograms.

The chapter also has introduced other graphical techniques for displaying data to make them more usable to a decision maker. The choices for effective graphical data displays are numerous. Bar charts, pie charts, stem and leaf diagrams, scatter diagrams, and line graphs are among the more commonly used techniques. Figure 2-19 summarizes the conditions under which each descriptive technique is appropriate.

Software packages, such as Excel and Minitab, have made graphical representation of data much easier. You are now able to analyze large volumes of data quickly and easily. The output from these packages can be pasted directly into word-processing documents to create professional-looking business reports.

FIGURE 2-19

**Summary: Descriptive
Statistical Techniques**

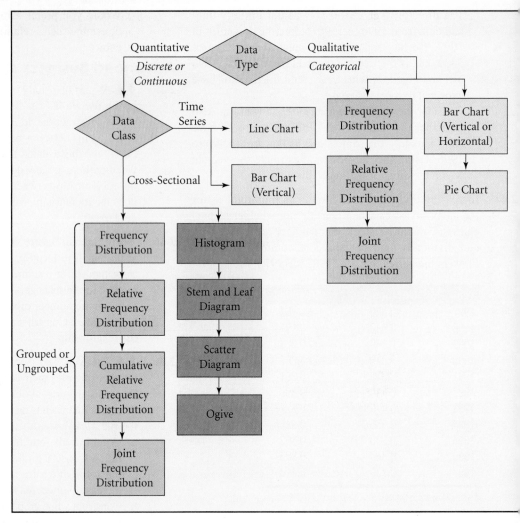

EQUATIONS

Relative Frequency

$$RF = \frac{f_i}{n} \qquad \textbf{2-1}$$

Sturges's Rule

$$\text{Classes} = 1 + 3.322\,[\log_{10}(n)] \qquad \textbf{2-2}$$

Class Width

$$W = \frac{\text{Largest Value} - \text{Smallest Value}}{\text{Number of Classes}} \qquad \textbf{2-3}$$

Key Terms

All-Inclusive Classes, 33
Bar Chart, 47
Class Boundaries, 34
Class Width, 33
Continuous Data, 31
Cumulative Frequency Distribution, 34
**Cumulative Relative Frequency
   Distribution,** 34

Data Array, 32
Dependent Variable, 61
Discrete Data, 28
Equal-Width Classes, 33
Frequency Distribution, 28
Frequency Histogram, 36
Independent Variable, 61
Line Chart, 57

Mutually Exclusive Classes, 32
Pie Chart, 52
Relative Frequency, 29
Scatter Diagram, 60

CHAPTER EXERCISES

Business Applications

2.49 The Green Glow Lawn Company spreads liquid fertilizer on lawns. It charges by square footage of the lawn, so it has records of the lawn sizes of its customers. The

company is now in the process of planning for next year and assumes the yard-size distribution will probably be much like it was this year. Raw data on yard sizes has been converted to the following frequency distribution:

Class	Frequency
Lawn Size (sq. ft.)	f_i
0 to less than 400	8
400 to less than 800	12
800 to less than 1,200	20
1,200 to less than 1,600	50
1,600 to less than 2,000	125
2,000 to less than 2,400	103
2,400 to less than 2,800	24

a. Develop a histogram from the frequency distribution.
b. Determine the relative frequency distribution for the lawn sizes. Explain why it is often useful to convert a frequency distribution to a relative frequency distribution.
c. Develop a cumulative relative frequency distribution and construct an ogive.

2.50 The Minnesota State Fishing Bureau has contracted with a university biologist to study the length of walleyes (fish) caught in Minnesota lakes. The biologist has collected data on a sample of 1,000 fish caught and has developed the following relative frequency distribution.

Class	Relative Frequency
Length (inches)	f_i
8 to less than 10	0.22
10 to less than 12	0.15
12 to less than 14	0.25
14 to less than 16	0.24
16 to less than 18	0.06
18 to less than 20	0.05
20 to less than 22	0.03

a. Construct a frequency distribution from this relative frequency distribution and then produce a histogram based on the frequency distribution.
b. Construct a pie chart from the relative frequency distribution. Discuss which of the two graphs, the pie chart or histogram, you think is more effective in presenting the fish length data.

2.51 Kronos (NASDAQ: KRON) is a leader in providing employee time and attendance systems to industry. Its 1997 annual report reported the following figures for primary net income per common share for 1993 to 1997.

1993	1994	1995	1996	1997
$0.50	$0.62	$1.03	$1.37	$1.34

Source: 1997 Kronos annual report.

a. Draw a bar chart to present these earnings-per-share values.
b. Develop a line chart for these data.
c. Which do you prefer in this case, a bar chart or a line chart? Discuss why.

2.52 Wendy Harrington is a staff accountant at a regional accounting firm in Miami, Florida. One of her clients has had a problem with balancing the cash register at the end of the day. Wendy has made a study of the ending shortage (indicated with parentheses) or overage for the past 30 days when the cash register did not balance, and she has recorded the following data.

30-Day Study of Cash Shortage or Overage

12.00	(2.55)	13.05	(55.20)	10.00	(18.00)	(11.00)	6.35	(19.02)	(33.00)
11.00	14.00	(10.00)	9.50	23.00	16.00	8.30	2.00	(24.00)	2.38
20.01	(43.50)	17.20	(41.04)	11.00	(19.33)	23.01	(0.34)	1.01	(23.04)

a. Develop a frequency distribution and a histogram for these data.
b. Develop a stem and leaf diagram for these data. Explain the differences between a histogram and a steam and leaf diagram.

2.53 The following data represent the commuting distances for employees of the Pay-and-Carry department store.

Commuting Distance (Miles)

3.5	2.0	4.0	2.5	0.3	1.0	12.0	17.5	3.0	3.5	6.5	9.0	3.0	
4.0	9.0	16.0	3.5	0.5	2.5	1.0	0.7	1.5	1.4	12.0	9.2	8.3	
1.0	3.0	7.5	3.2	2.0	1.0	3.5	3.6	1.9	2.0	3.0	1.5	0.4	
6.4	11.0	2.5	2.4	2.7	4.0	2.0	2.0	3.0					

a. The personnel manager for Pay-and-Carry would like you to develop a frequency distribution and a histogram for these data.
b. Develop a stem and leaf diagram for these data.
c. Break the data into three groups: under 3.0 miles; 3.0 and under 6 miles; and 6 miles and over. Construct a pie chart to illustrate the proportion of employees in each category.
d. Referring to part c, construct a bar chart to depict the proportion of employees in each category.

2.54 A local branch of the Government Employees' Credit Union has been keeping track of the types of errors its tellers have been making. You are responsible for providing training to reduce these errors. The following data show the categories of errors and the frequency of each for the past month.

Category of Errors	Frequency
Errors posting debits/credits	182
Errors posting other entries	158
Entries not posted	77
Cash letter errors	31
Claims	24
Adjustment tickets	16
Multiple postings	9
Incorrect totals	7

Use these data to select and justify the areas in which you will start your training effort. Construct a Pareto chart to display the data effectively.

2.55 A computer software company has been looking at the amount of time customers spend on hold after their calls are answered by the central switchboard. The company would like to have only 2% of the callers have to wait more than 2 minutes. The company's calling service has provided the following data showing how long each of last month's callers spent on hold.

Class	Number
Less than 15 seconds	456
15 to less than 30 seconds	718
30 to less than 45 seconds	891
45 to less than 60 seconds	823
60 to less than 75 seconds	610
75 to less than 90 seconds	449
90 to less than 105 seconds	385
105 to less than 120 seconds	221
120 to less than 150 seconds	158
150 to less than 180 seconds	124
180 to less than 240 seconds	87
More than 240 seconds	153

a. Develop a relative frequency distribution and an ogive for these data.

b. The company estimates it loses an average of $30 in business from callers who must wait more than 2 minutes before receiving assistance. The company thinks that last month's distribution of waiting times is typical. Estimate how much money the company is losing in business per month because people have to wait too long before receiving assistance.

2.56 The marketing director of a company manufacturing small disk drives for notebook computers has directed her sales force to accept orders based on a projected production rate of 3,000 disk drives per day. The production manager objected strongly when hearing this and presented the following frequency distribution to support his claim that this goal was impossible, given the present production process.

Production Rate	Frequency
2,000 to 2,499	3
2,500 to 2,749	7
2,750 to 2,999	10
3,000 to 3,249	15
3,250 to 3,499	22
3,500 to 3,999	11
4,000 or more	2

a. Construct a histogram to display these data. Discuss the three factors that can be addressed by examining a histogram.

b. Discuss whether it is possible to construct a stem and leaf diagram from the data in the form supplied here.

2.57 The regional sales manager for American Toys, Inc., recently collected data on weekly sales (in dollars) for the 15 stores in his region. He also collected data on the number of sales-clerk work hours during the week for each of the stores. The data are as follows:

Store	Sales	Hours	Store	Sales	Hours
1	23,300	120	9	27,886	140
2	25,600	135	10	54,156	300
3	19,200	96	11	34,080	254
4	10,211	102	12	25,900	180
5	19,330	240	13	36,400	270
6	35,789	190	14	25,760	175
7	12,540	108	15	31,500	256
8	43,150	234			

a. Develop a scatter plot of these data. Determine which variable should be the dependent variable and which should be the independent variable.

b. Based on the scatter plot, what, if any, conclusions might the sales manager reach with respect to the relationship between sales and number of clerk hours worked? Do any stores stand out as being different? Discuss.

Advanced Business Applications

2.58 *The Wall Street Journal* reported retail sales for February 1997 and February 1998 for many top retailers. The file *Retailers* contains sales figures for 26 different retailers divided into four categories. In your capacity as marketing manager for a major department store, you plan to develop a report and a presentation on the retail industry using these data. To make your report complete, you plan to do the following:

a. Develop grouped frequency distributions for each year and then develop a histogram from each frequency distribution.

b. Create bar charts comparing the two years' February sales for the stores in each category. This means that you will have four different bar charts.

c. Create a pie chart for the Department Store category for February 1997.

d. Create a bar chart for the Apparel category for February 1998.

e. Using the information generated in parts a through d, create a report on the retail industry.

2.59 The data file *McCormick* contains selected information from the annual report for McCormick & Company, Inc., the leader in the manufacture, marketing, and distribution of spices, seasonings, and flavors for the food industry. Use the data to perform the following:

a. For 1988 through 1997, construct a line chart of net sales. Determine the relationship between year and net sales.

b. For 1988 through 1997, construct a scatter plot of net sales and capital expenditures. Briefly describe the relationship between net sales and capital expenditures for these years.

c. Develop a line chart that displays both net sales and long-term debt. Do you prefer this display to that produced in part b? Discuss which of them gives a better presentation of the relationship between the two variables.

2.60 The following information, taken from the 1997 annual report of McCormick & Company, Inc., reports the company's consumer sales (in millions) by region.

Region	Consumer Sales
Americas	$596.4
Europe	$221.2
Asia/Pacific	$43.2

a. Construct a bar chart of this data.

b. Construct a pie chart of this data.

c. Which graphical summary, the bar chart or the pie chart, better describes the relative proportion of total sales by geographic region? Explain the reasons that support your opinion.

2.61 💿 The file *Home-Prices* contains information about single-family housing prices in 100 metropolitan areas in the United States.

a. Construct a frequency distribution and a histogram of 1997 median single-family home prices. Use Sturges's Rule to determine the appropriate number of classes.

b. Construct a cumulative relative frequency distribution and an ogive for 1997 median single-family home prices.

c. Repeat parts a and b but this time use five class intervals. What was the impact of using more class intervals?

2.62 Stock investors often look to beat the performance of the S&P 500 Index, which generally serves as a proxy for the market as a whole. The following table shows a comparison of five-year cumulative total shareholder returns for Idaho Power Company common stock (NYSE symbol: IDA), the S&P 500 Index, and the Edison Electric Institute (EEI) 100 Electric Utilities Index. The data assume that $100 was invested on December 31, 1992, with returns compounded monthly.

Year	Idaho Power	S&P 500	EEI 100 Electric Utilities
1992	$100.00	$100.00	$100.00
1993	117.38	110.08	111.15
1994	97.62	111.53	98.29
1995	134.11	153.45	128.78
1996	147.92	188.69	130.32
1997	189.73	251.63	166.00

Source: Idaho Power Company, *1997 Notice of Annual Meeting of Shareholders*, p. 34.

a. Construct a graph that illustrates the performance of the three investment options for 1992 through 1997.

b. How well has Idaho Power Company performed during this period compared with the S&P 500?

c. How well has it performed relative to its industry?

2.63 💿 Elliel's Department Store tracks its inventory on a monthly basis. Monthly data for 1996 through 2000 are in the file *Elliels*.

a. Construct a line chart showing the monthly inventory over the five years. Discuss what this graph implies about inventory.

b. Sum the monthly inventory figures for each year. Present the sums in bar-chart form. Discuss whether you think this is an appropriate graph to describe the inventory situation at Elliel's.

2.64 💿 The commercial banking industry is undergoing rapid changes due to advances in technology and competitive pressures in the financial services sector. The data file *Banks* contains selected information tabulated by *Fortune* magazine concerning the revenues, profitability, and number of employees for the 51 largest U.S. commercial banks in terms of revenues. Use the information in this file to do the following:

a. Construct a chart to determine whether there is a relationship between revenues and number of employees. Briefly comment on your findings.

b. Develop a frequency distribution and a histogram for profits per employee. (Hint: Construct a new variable from the existing variables.) What does the histogram imply?

CASE 2-A:

AJ's Fitness Center 💿

When A. J. Reeser signed papers to take ownership of the fitness center previously known as The Park Center Club, he realized that he had just taken the biggest financial step in his life. Every asset he could pull together had been pledged against the mortgage. If the new AJ's Fitness Center didn't succeed, he would be in really bad shape financially. But A. J. didn't plan on failing. After all, he had never failed at anything.

As a high school football All-American, A. J. had been heavily recruited by major colleges around the country. Although he loved football, he and his family had always put academics ahead of sports. Thus, he surprised almost everyone other than those who knew him

best when he chose to attend an Ivy League university not particularly noted for its football success. Although he excelled at football and was a member of two winning teams, he also succeeded in the classroom and graduated in four years. He spent six years working for McKinsey & Company, a major consulting firm, in which he gained significant experience in a broad range of business situations.

He was hired away from McKinsey & Company by the Dryden Group, a management services company that specializes in running health and fitness operations and recreational resorts throughout the world. After eight years of leading the Fitness Center section at Dryden, A. J. found that earning a high salary and the perks associated with corporate life were not satisfying him.

Besides, the travel was getting old now that he had married and had two young children. When the opportunity to purchase The Park Center Club came, he decided that the time was right to control his own destiny.

A key aspect of the deal was that AJ's Fitness Club would keep its existing clientele, consisting of 1,833 memberships. One of the things that A. J. was very concerned about was whether these members would stay with the club after the sale or move on to other fitness clubs in the area. He knew that keeping existing customers is a lot less expensive than attracting new customers.

Within days of assuming ownership, A. J. developed a survey that was mailed to all 1,833 members. The letter that accompanied the survey discussed A. J.'s philosophy and asked several key questions regarding the current level of satisfaction. Survey respondents were eligible to win a free lifetime membership in a drawing—an inducement that was no doubt responsible for the 1,214 usable responses.

To get help with the analysis of the survey data, A. J. approached the College of Business at a local university with the idea of having a senior student serve as an intern at AJ's Fitness Center. In addition to an hourly wage, the intern would get free use of the fitness facilities for the rest of the academic year.

The intern's first task was to key the data from the survey into a file that could be analyzed using a spreadsheet or a statistical software package. The survey contained eight questions that were keyed into eight columns as follows:

Column 1: Satisfaction with the club's weight- and exercise-equipment facilities

Column 2: Satisfaction with the club's staff
Column 3: Satisfaction with the club's exercise programs (aerobics, etc.)
Column 4: Satisfaction with the club's overall service

Note, Columns 1 through 4 were coded on an ordinal scale as follows:

1	2	3	4	5
Very Unsatisfied	Unsatisfied	Neutral	Satisfied	Very Satisfied

Column 5: Number of years that the respondent had been a member at this club
Column 6: Gender (1 = Male, 2 = Female)
Column 7: Typical number of visits to the club per week
Column 8: Age

The data, saved in the file *AJFitness*, were clearly too much for anyone to comprehend in raw form. At yesterday's meeting, A. J. asked the intern to "make some sense of the data." When the intern asked for some direction, A. J.'s response was, "That's what I'm paying you the big bucks for. I just want you to develop a descriptive analysis of these data. For now, let's limit it to whatever charts, graphs, and tables that will help us understand our customers. After we see what that shows, maybe we will do some other analysis. For right now, give me a report that discusses the data. Why don't we set a time to get together next week to review your report?"

CASE 2-B:

Westbrook Graphic Arts

Lisa Westbrook founded Westbrook Graphic Arts in 1997, right after her graduation. Throughout college Lisa had worked part time for a local graphics arts company and had gained significant experience in the business. She had a job offer to stay with the same company and several other offers from graphics companies in the area, but her independent spirit pushed her to go out on her own. Business has been slow to develop. However, she has been able to pay her bills and sock a few dollars away for a trip to Europe she promised herself as a graduation present.

As Lisa looked at her e-mail messages in her small office on 13th Street, the phone rang. It was Charles Eddy, who works for the State Department of Commerce in the International Division. Charles had called Lisa yesterday about a possible project and had promised to call back when he had more information about what his boss wanted. Charles explained that C. J. Riley, the director of the Department of Commerce, was going to give an address at a

national conference. The director wanted to contrast the United States with a number of other developed countries around the world. Charles added that he had collected quite a bit of data on various issues for each country. He, however, had not had time to create the presentation for his boss. He wanted Westbrook Graphics to prepare the presentation and the speaker notes.

As Charles hung up, Lisa knew that this was a tremendous opportunity. If she could do a good job on this project, there very likely would be other work coming to her from the Department of Commerce. Charles had agreed to e-mail the data. Charles gave her total leeway in designing the presentation, but he did say that C. J. was big on graphs and charts. The data are in a file called *Westbrook*. Charles had indeed collected some interesting data for each country.

Lisa sent a reply to Charles telling him that she had received the data (which she stored in the file *Countries*) and would have the presentation by next Tuesday. As she leaned back in her chair, she wondered where she should begin.

General References

1. Albright, Christian S., Wayne L. Winston, and Christopher Zappe, *Data Analysis and Decision Making with Microsoft Excel* (Pacific Grove, CA: Duxbury, 1999).
2. Berenson, Mark L., and David M. Levine, *Basic Business Statistics: Concepts and Applications*, 7th ed. (Upper Saddle River, NJ: Prentice Hall, 1999).
3. Cleveland, William, S., "Graphs in Scientific Publications," *The American Statistician* 38 (November 1984), pp. 261–269.
4. Cleveland, William S., and R. McGill, "Graphical Perception: Theory, Experimentation, and Application to the Development of Graphical Methods," *Journal of the American Statistical Association* 79 (September 1984), pp. 531–554.

5. Cryer, Jonathan D., and Robert B. Miller, *Statistics for Business: Data Analysis and Modeling*, 2nd ed. (Belmont, CA: Duxbury Press, 1994).

6. Dodge, Mark, and Craig Stinson, *Running Microsoft Excel 2000* (Redmond, WA: Microsoft Press, 1999).

7. *Microsoft Excel 2000* (Redmond, WA: Microsoft Corp., 1999).

8. *Minitab for Windows Version 13* (State College, PA: Minitab, 2000).

9. Siegel, Andrew F., *Practical Business Statistics,* 4th ed. (Burr Ridge, IL: Irwin, 2000).

10. Tufte, Edward R., *Envisioning Information* (Cheshire, CT: Graphics Press, 1990).

11. Tufte, Edward R., *The Visual Display of Quantitative Information*, reprint ed. (Cheshire, CT: Graphics Press, 1992).

12. Tukey, John W., *Exploratory Data Analysis* (Reading, MA: Addison-Wesley, 1977).

CHAPTER 3

Describing Data
Using Numerical Measures

3-1 MEASURES OF CENTER AND LOCATION

3-2 MEASURES OF VARIATION

3-3 USING THE MEAN AND STANDARD DEVIATION TOGETHER

CHAPTER OUTCOMES

After studying the material in Chapter 3, you should be able to:

- Compute the mean, weighted average, median, and mode for a set of data and understand what these values represent.
- Compute the range, variance, and standard deviation and know what these values mean.
- Know how to construct a box and whisker graph and be able to interpret it.
- Compute the coefficient of variation and z scores and understand how they are applied in decision-making situations.
- Use numerical measures along with graphs, charts, and tables to effectively describe data.

WHY YOU NEED TO KNOW

Graphs and charts provide effective tools for transforming data into information; however, they are only a starting point. Graphs and charts do not reveal all the information contained in a set of data. To make your descriptive tool-kit complete, you need to become familiar with the key descriptive measures that quantify the center of the data and its spread.

Suppose you are an advertising manager for a major tire company and you want to develop an ad campaign touting how much longer your company's tires last than the competition's. You must be careful that your claims are valid. First, the Federal Trade Commission (FTC) is charged with regulating advertising and requires that advertising be truthful. Second, customers who could show that they were misled by an incorrect claim about your tires could sue you and your company. You have no choice. You must use statistical procedures to determine the validity of any claim you might want to make about your tires.

You might start by sampling tires from your company and from the competition. You could measure the number of miles each tire lasts before a specified portion of the tread is depleted. You might graph the data for each company as a histogram, but a clear comparison with this graph might be difficult. Instead, you could compute the mileage numbers for the various tires and show these values side-by-side, perhaps in a bar chart. Thus, to effectively describe data, you will need to combine the graphical tools discussed in Chapter 2 with the numerical measures introduced in this chapter.

3-1 MEASURES OF CENTER AND LOCATION

You learned in Chapter 2 that frequency histograms are an effective way of converting quantitative data into useful information. The histogram provides a visual indication of where data are centered and how much spread there is in the data around the center. However, to fully describe a quantitative variable, we can compute measures of its center and spread. These measures can then be coupled with the histogram to give a clear picture of the variable's distribution. This section focuses on measures of the center of data. Section 3-2 introduces measures of the spread of data.

PARAMETERS AND STATISTICS

Depending on whether we are working with a population or a sample, a numerical measure is either a **parameter** or a **statistic**.

Parameter	*Statistic*
A measure computed from the entire population. As long as the population does not change, the value of the parameter will not change.	A measure computed from a sample that has been selected from a population. The value of the statistic will depend on which sample is selected.

POPULATION MEAN

There are three important measures of the center of a set of data. The first of these is the **mean**, or average of the data. To find the mean, we sum the values and divide the sum by the number of data values, as shown in Equation 3-1.

Mean
A numerical measure of the center of a set of quantitative measures computed by dividing the sum of the values by the number of values in the data.

The **population mean** is represented by the Greek symbol μ, pronounced "mu." The formal notation in the numerator for the sum of the x values reads:

$$\sum_{i=1}^{N} x_i \rightarrow \text{sum each } x_i \text{ value where } i \text{ goes from 1 to } N$$

Population Mean

$$\mu = \frac{\displaystyle\sum_{i=1}^{N} x_i}{N}$$

3-1

where:

μ = Population mean (mu)
N = Population size
x_i = ith individual value of variable x

In other words, we are summing all N values in the population.

Because you almost always sum all the data values, to simplify notation in this text, we generally will drop the subscripts after the first time we introduce a formula. Thus the formula for the population mean will be written as

$$\mu = \frac{\sum x}{N}$$

Foster City Hotel—The manager of a small hotel in Foster City, California, was asked by the corporate vice president to analyze the Sunday night registration information for the past eight weeks. Data on three variables were collected:

x_1 = Total number of rooms rented
x_2 = Total dollar revenue from the room rentals
x_3 = Number of customer complaints that came from guests each Sunday

These data are shown in Table 3-1. They are a population because they include all data that interest the vice president.

Figure 3-1 shows the frequency histogram for the number of rooms rented. If the manager wants to describe the data further, she can locate the center of the data by finding the balance point for the histogram. Think of the horizontal axis as a plank and the histogram bars as weights proportional to their area. The center of the data would be the point at which the plank would balance. As shown in Figure 3-1, the balance point seems to be about 15 rooms.

Eyeing the histogram might yield a reasonable approximation of the center. However, computing a numerical measure of the center directly from the data is preferable. The most frequently used measure of the center is the mean.

The population mean for number of rooms rented is computed using Equation 3-1 as follows.

$$\mu = \frac{\sum x}{N} = \frac{22 + 13 + 10 + 16 + 23 + 13 + 11 + 13}{8}$$
$$= \frac{121}{8}$$
$$\mu = 15.125$$

TABLE 3-1 **Foster City Hotel Data**	**WEEK**	**ROOMS RENTED**	**REVENUE**	**COMPLAINTS**
	1	22	$1,870	0
	2	13	$1,590	2
	3	10	$1,760	1
	4	16	$2,345	0
	5	23	$4,563	2
	6	13	$1,630	1
	7	11	$2,156	0
	8	13	$1,756	0

FIGURE 3-1

**Balance Point, Rooms
Rented at Foster City Hotel**

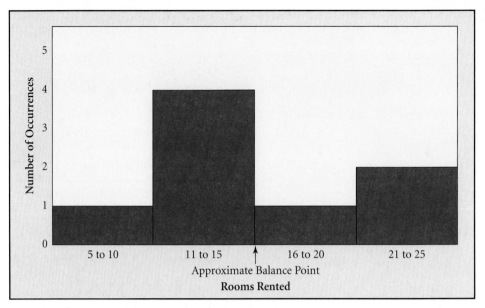

Thus, the average number of rooms rented each Sunday for the past eight weeks is 15.125. This is the true balance point for the data. Turn to Table 3-2, where we find what is called a *deviation* $(x - \mu)$ by subtracting the mean from each value.

Note that the sum of the deviations of the data from the mean is zero. This is not a coincidence. *For any set of data, the sum of the deviations around the mean will be zero.*

SUMMARY: COMPUTING THE POPULATION MEAN

When the available data constitute the population of interest, the population mean is computed using the following steps:

1. Collect the data for the variable of interest for all items in the population. The data must be quantitative and can be discrete or continuous.

2. Sum all values in the population (Σx).

3. Divide the sum (Σx) by the number of values (N) in the population to get the population mean. The formula for the population mean is

$$\mu = \frac{\Sigma x}{N}$$

EXAMPLE 3-1: COMPUTING THE POPULATION MEAN

Viking Distributors   Viking Distributors sells equipment and supplies to companies in the airline maintenance business. During the past year, Viking has made 10 sales to a customer in Spain. The sales manager is interested in knowing the mean dollar value of sales to this customer. These 10 sales constitute the population of interest. The population mean is computed using the following steps:

Step 1:   **Collect the data for the quantitative variable of interest.**
In this case, the variable is dollar value of the sale for each of the 10 sales made. These are recorded as follows:

$$x = \$42,000 \quad \$23,900 \quad \$115,600 \quad \$13,800 \quad \$7,900$$
$$\$41,000 \quad \$52,900 \quad \$76,100 \quad \$5,800 \quad \$33,200$$

Step 2:   **Add the data values.**
$$\Sigma x = \$42,000 + \$23,900 + \$115,600 + \$13,800 + \$7,900 + \$41,000$$
$$+ \$52,900 + \$76,100 + \$5,800 + \$33,200 = \$412,200$$

Step 3:   **Divide the sum by the number of values in the population.**
$$\mu = \frac{\Sigma x}{N} = \frac{\$412,200}{10} = \$41,220$$

Thus, the mean sales amount to this company in Spain is $41,220.

TABLE 3-2

Centering Concept of the Mean Using Hotel Data

x	x − μ
22	22 − 15.125 = 6.875
13	13 − 15.125 = −2.125
10	10 − 15.125 = −5.125
16	16 − 15.125 = 0.875
23	23 − 15.125 = 7.875
13	13 − 15.125 = −2.125
11	11 − 15.125 = −4.125
13	13 − 15.125 = −2.125
	Σ = 0.000

Excel and Minitab Tutorial

Foster City Hotel (continued)—In addition to collecting data on the number of rooms rented on Sunday nights, the Foster City Hotel manager also collected data on the room-rental revenue generated, and the number of complaints, on Sunday nights. Both Excel and Minitab have procedures for computing numerical measures such as the mean. Because these data are the population of all nights of interest to the hotel manager, she can compute the population mean, μ, revenue per night. The population mean is μ = $2,208.75 (rounded to $2,209 in Minitab), as shown in the Excel and Minitab outputs in Figure 3-2a and 3-2b. Likewise, the mean number of complaints is μ = 0.75 per night. (Note, there are other measures shown in the figures. We will discuss several of these later in the chapter.)

Now, for these eight Sunday nights, the manager can report to the corporate vice president that the mean number of rooms rented is 15.125. This level of business generated an average nightly revenue of $2,208.75. The number of complaints averaged 0.75 (less than one) per night. These values are the true means for the population and are, therefore, called parameters.

SAMPLE MEAN

The data for the Foster City Hotel constituted the population of interest. Thus, μ = 15.125 nights is the parameter measure. However, if we have a sample rather than a population, the mean for the sample is computed using Equation 3-2. Notice, Equation 3-2 is the same as Equation 3-1 *except* that we sum the sample values, not the population values, and divide by the sample size, not the population size.

FIGURE 3-2A

Excel Output Showing Mean Revenue for the Foster City Hotel

Excel Instructions:
1. Open file: Foster.xls
2. Select **Tools.**
3. Select **Data Analysis.**
4. Click on **Descriptive Statistics.**
5. Define data range for the variables.
6. Check **Summary Statistics.**
7. Name output sheet.

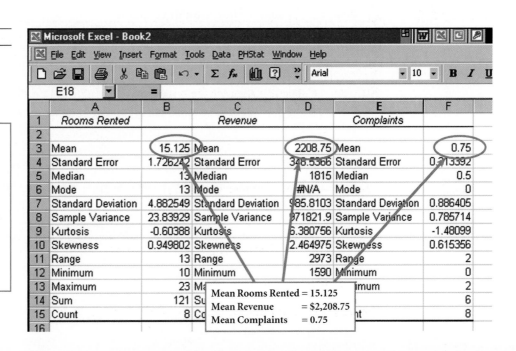

FIGURE 3-2B

Minitab Output Showing Mean Revenue for the Foster City Hotel

Minitab Instructions:
1. Open file: Foster.MTW.
2. Choose **Stat > Basic Statistics > Display Descriptive Statistics**.
3. In **Variables**, enter columns *Rooms Rented, Revenue*, and *Complaints*.
4. Click **Statistics**.
5. Check required statistics.
6. Click **OK**.

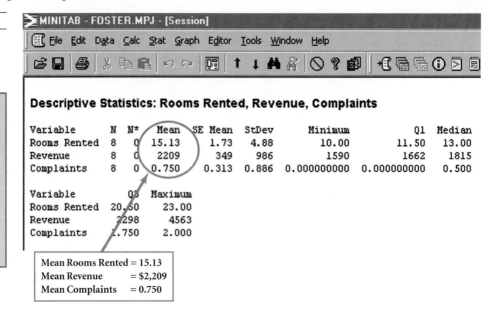

MINITAB - FOSTER.MPJ - [Session]

File Edit Data Calc Stat Graph Editor Tools Window Help

Descriptive Statistics: Rooms Rented, Revenue, Complaints

Variable	N	N*	Mean	SE Mean	StDev	Minimum	Q1	Median
Rooms Rented	8	0	15.13	1.73	4.88	10.00	11.50	13.00
Revenue	8	0	2209	349	986	1590	1662	1815
Complaints	8	0	0.750	0.313	0.886	0.000000000	0.000000000	0.500

Variable	Q3	Maximum
Rooms Rented	20.50	23.00
Revenue	3298	4563
Complaints	1.750	2.000

Mean Rooms Rented = 15.13
Mean Revenue   = $2,209
Mean Complaints   = 0.750

Sample Mean

$$\bar{x} = \frac{\sum\limits_{i=1}^{n} x_i}{n}$$

3-2

where:

$\bar{x}$ = Sample mean (pronounced "x-bar")
n = Sample size

The notation for the sample mean is $\bar{x}$. Sample descriptors (statistics) are usually assigned a Roman character. (Recall that population values usually are assigned a Greek character.)

EXAMPLE 3-2: COMPUTING A SAMPLE MEAN

Housing Prices   Consider a sample of seven house prices in Modesto, California. The real estate agency is interested in computing the mean price for this sample of homes. The following steps can be used:

Step 1:   **Collect the sample data.**

$\{x_i\}$ = {house prices} = {$144,000; $98,000; $204,000; $177,000; $155,000; $316,000; $100,000}

Step 2:   **Add the values in the sample.**

$\sum x$ = $144,000 + 98,000 + 204,000 + 177,000 + 155,000 + 316,000 + 100,000
        = $1,194,000

Step 3:   **Divide the sum by the sample size (Equation 3-2).**

$$\bar{x} = \frac{\sum x}{n} = \frac{\$1,194,000}{7} = \$170,571.43$$

Therefore, the mean price for the sample of seven houses in Modesto is $170,571.43.

THE IMPACT OF EXTREME VALUES ON THE MEAN

The mean (population or sample) is the balance point for data, so using the mean as a measure of the center generally makes sense. However, the mean does have one potential disadvantage: *The mean can be highly affected by extreme values.* There are many instances in business when this may occur. For example, in a population or sample of income data, there likely will be extremes on the high end that will pull the mean upward from the center. Example 3-3 illustrates how an extreme value can affect the mean. In these situations, a second measure called the *median* may be more appropriate.

EXAMPLE 3-3: IMPACT OF EXTREME VALUES

Housing Prices   Suppose the sample of house prices in Modesto (see Example 3-2) had been slightly different. If the house recorded as $316,000 had actually been $1,000,000, how would the mean be affected? We can see the impact as follows:

Step 1:   Collect the sample data.

$$\{x_i\} = \{\text{house prices}\} = \{\$144,000; \$98,000; \$204,000; \$177,000;$$
$$\$155,000; \$1,000,000; \$100,000\}$$

extreme value

Step 2:   Add the values.

$$\Sigma x = \$144,000 + 98,000 + 204,000 + 177,000 + 155,000 + 1,000,000 + 100,000$$
$$= \$1,878,000$$

Step 3:   Divide the sum by the number of values in the sample.

$$\bar{x} = \frac{\Sigma x}{n} = \frac{\$1,878,000}{7} = \$268,285.71$$

Recall, in Example 3-2, the sample mean was $170,571.43.

With only one value in the sample changed, the mean is now substantially higher than before. Because the mean is affected by extreme values, it may be a misleading measure of the data's center.

MEDIAN

Another measure of the center is called the **median**.

Median

The median is a center value that divides a data array into two halves. We use $\tilde{\mu}$ to denote the population median and M_d to denote the sample median.

The median is found by first arranging data in numerical order from smallest to largest. Data that are sorted in order are referred to as a **data array**.

Data Array

Data that have been arranged in numerical order.

After the data have been sorted, we locate the value that is halfway from either end. This middle value is the median. If the number of data points in the array is odd, then the median is the middle value in the ordered list. However, if the number of data points is even, then the median is the average of the two middle values.[1]

---
[1]A more-precise definition of the median exists. In that definition the median is defined as a data value (or possibly set of data values) for which at least half of the data are at least as large as the data value and at least half of the data are small or smaller than that data value. The definition we present in this text does, however, identify one median and w' fice as an introductory definition.

$\mathcal{E}$XAMPLE 3-4: COMPUTING THE MEDIAN

Housing Prices   Consider again the original Modesto, California, house-price data shown in Example 3-2. The median for these data is computed using the following steps:

Step 1:   **Collect the sample data.**

$$\{x_i\} = \{\text{house prices}\} = \{\$144,000; \$98,000; \$204,000; \$177,000; \$155,000;$$
$$\$316,000; \$100,000\}$$

Step 2:   **Sort the data from smallest to largest, forming a data array.**

$$\{x_i\} = \{\$98,000; \$100,000; \$144,000; \$155,000; \$177,000; \$204,000; \$316,000\}$$

Step 3:   **Locate the middle value in the data.**
Because we have seven houses in the sample, the median is the fourth value from either end of the data array.

$$\{x_i\} = \{\$98,000; \$100,000; \$144,000; \$155,000; \$177,000; \$204,000; \$316,000\}$$

$$\uparrow$$
$$\text{fourth value} = M_d$$

The median price house is $155,000. The notation for the sample median is M_d.

Note, if the number of data values in a sample or population is an even number, the median is the average of the two middle values. (See Example 3-6.)

SKEWED AND SYMMETRIC DISTRIBUTIONS

Data in a population or sample can be either **symmetric** or **skewed**, depending on how the data are distributed around the center.

Symmetric Data	***Skewed Data***
Data sets whose values are evenly spread around the center. For symmetric data, the mean and median are equal.	Data sets that are not symmetric. For skewed data, the mean will be larger or smaller than the median.

In the original Modesto house-price example (Examples 3-2), the mean for the sample of seven homes was $170,571.43. In Example 3-4, the median home price was $155,000. Thus, for these data the mean and the median are not equal. This sample data set is **right skewed**, because $\bar{x} = \$170,571.43 > M_d = \$155,000$.

Right-Skewed Data	***Left-Skewed Data***
A data distribution is right skewed if the mean for the data is larger than the median.	A data distribution is left skewed if the mean for the data is smaller than the median.

Figure 3-3 illustrates examples of right-skewed, left-skewed, and symmetric distributions. The greater the difference between the mean and the median, the more skewed the distribution. *Example 3-5 shows that an advantage of the median over the mean is that the median is not affected by extreme values.* Thus, the median is particularly useful as a measure of the center when the data are highly skewed.[2]

---

[2]Excel's Descriptive Statistics tool outputs a skewness statistic. The sign on the skewness statistic implies the direction of skewness. The higher the absolute value, the more the data are skewed.

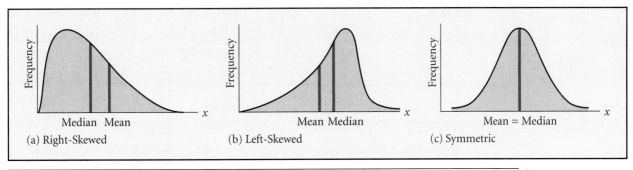

FIGURE 3-3   **Skewed and Symmetric Distributions**

EXAMPLE 3-5: IMPACT OF EXTREME VALUES ON THE MEDIAN

Housing Prices (Continued)   In Example 3-3, when we substituted a $1,000,000 price for the house priced at $316,000, the sample mean increased from $170,571.43 to $268,285.71. What will happen to the median? The median is determined using the following steps:

Step 1:   **Collect the sample data.** The sample house-price data (including the extremely high-priced house) are

$$\{x_i\} = \{\text{house prices}\} = \{\$144,000; \$98,000; \$204,000; \$177,000;$$
$$\$155,000; \$1,000,000; \$100,000\}$$

Step 2:   **Sort the data from smallest to largest, forming a data array.**

$$\{x_i\} = \{\$98,000; \$100,000; \$144,000; \$155,000; \$177,000; \$204,000; \$1,000,000\}$$

Step 3:   **Locate the middle value in the data.**
Because we have seven houses in the sample, the median is the fourth value from either end of the data array.

$$\{x_i\} = \{\$98,000; \$100,000; \$144,000; \$155,000; \$177,000; \$204,000; \$1,000,000\}$$

$$\text{fourth value} = M_d$$

The median-price house is $155,000, the same value as in Example 3-4, when the high house price was not included in the data.

When the sample or population has an even number of data values, the median can be approximated by the average of the two middle values. Example 3-6 illustrates this.

EXAMPLE 3-6: COMPUTING THE MEDIAN FOR AN EVEN NUMBER OF VALUES

Clonninger's Texaco   Clonninger's Texaco in Canton, Ohio, offers a free car wash when a customer fills his or her car with gas. The manager is interested in knowing the median number of gallons of gasoline that are purchased when a car wash is given out. A sample of 10 customers has been randomly selected. The median is approximated as follows:

Step 1:   **Collect the sample data.**
$$\{x_i\} = \{\text{gallons}\} = \{13.5, 17.9, 11.5, 22.1, 15.0, 16.9, 29.6, 9.6, 17.7, 20.5\}$$

Step 2:   **Sort the data from smallest to largest, forming a data array.**
$$\{x_i\} = \{\text{gallons}\} = \{9.6, 11.5, 13.5, 15.0, 16.9, 17.7, 17.9, 20.5, 22.1, 29.6\}$$

Step 3:   **Locate the middle value in the data.**
Because we have an even number of values, the median is approximated by finding the average of the middle two data values. Thus, we would average the fifth and sixth data values from either end.

$$\{x_i\} = \{\text{gallons}\} = \{9.6, 11.5, 13.5, 15.0, 16.9, 17.7, 17.9, 20.5, 22.1, 29.6\}$$

$$M_d = \frac{16.9 + 17.7}{2} = 17.3 \text{ gallons}$$

MODE

The mean is the most commonly used measure of central location, followed closely by the median. However, the **mode** is another measure that is occasionally used as a measure of location.

Mode

The mode is the value in a data set that occurs most frequently.

A data set may have more than one mode if two or more values tie for the most frequently occurring value. Example 3-7 illustrates this concept and shows how the mode is determined.

*E*XAMPLE 3-7: DETERMINING THE MODE

Smoky Mountain Pizza   The owners of Smoky Mountain Pizza are planning to expand their restaurant to include an open-air patio. Before finalizing the design, the managers want to know what the most frequently occurring group size is so that they can organize the seating arrangements to best meet demand. They wish to know the mode, which can be calculated using the following steps:

Step 1:   Collect the sample data.
A sample of 20 groups was selected at random. These data are

$$\{x_i\} = \{people\} = \{2, 4, 1, 2, 3, 2, 4, 2, 3, 6, 8, 4, 2, 1, 7, 4, 2, 4, 4, 3\}$$

Step 2:   Organize the data into a frequency distribution.

x_i	Frequency
1	2
2	6
3	3
4	6
5	0
6	1
7	1
8	1
	Total = 20

Step 3:   Determine the value that occurs most frequently.
In this case, there are two modes, because the values 2 and 4 each occurred six times. Thus the modes are 2 and 4.

A common mistake is to state the mode as being the frequency of the most frequently occurring value. In Example 3-6, you might be tempted to say that the mode = 6 because that was the highest frequency. Instead there were two modes, 2 and 4, both of which occurred six times.

If no value occurs more frequently than any other, the data set is said to not have a mode. The mode might be particularly useful in describing the central location value for clothes sizes. For example, shoes come in full and half sizes. Consider the following sample data that have been sorted from low to high:

$$\{x\} = \{7.5, 8.0, 8.5, 9.0, 9.0, 10.0, 10.0, 10.0, 10.5, 10.5, 11.0, 11.5\}$$

The mean for these sample data is

$$\bar{x} = \frac{\sum x}{n} = \frac{7.5 + 8.0 + \cdots + 11.5}{12} = \frac{115.50}{12} = 9.625$$

Although 9.625 is the numerical average, the mode is 10, because more people wore that size shoe than any other. In making purchasing decisions, a shoe store manager would order more shoes at the modal size than at any other size. The mean isn't of any particular value in her purchasing decision.

Excel and Minitab Tutorial

APPLYING THE MEASURES OF CENTRAL TENDENCY

Weigh in Motion—The state transportation department is experimenting with a system called weigh in motion (WIM) that can weigh trucks as they drive down a highway. It may prove to be a substitute for traditional static scales at ports of entry (POE), which require trucks to stop to be weighed. In the experiment, trucks have been weighed on two scales: WIM and POE. The sample data are on your CD-ROM in the file, *Trucks*. Weights were recorded to the nearest pound.

The issue of interest in this study is whether the WIM scale produces measurements that are close to POE measurements. The POE weight is assumed to be accurate. For the purposes of this discussion, we focus on two variables: WIM gross weight and POE gross weight.

Figures 3-4 and 3-5 show the frequency histograms generated for these two variables using Excel. We have used the same class intervals for both variables. The histograms are a good place to start our analysis of whether the WIM scale weighs trucks accurately. What is your initial conclusion based on the histograms in Figures 3-4 and 3-5? Do the truck-weight distributions from the two scales look alike? Are the distributions symmetric or skewed?

We can extend our analysis by computing the appropriate statistical measures. Specifically, we want to look at measures of central location. Figure 3-6 illustrates the Excel output, with the descriptive measures for both WIM and POE gross weight.[3]

We first focus on the primary measures of central location: the mean and the median.

Measures	WIM Weight	POE Weight
Mean	64,171.15 lbs	61,057.25 lbs
Median	71,380.00 lbs.	67,655.00 lbs.

FIGURE 3-4

Excel Frequency Histogram—WIM Gross Weight

Excel Instructions:
1. Open file: Trucks.xls
2. Identify data and bins range.
3. Define bins (upper limit of each class).
4. Click on **Tools.**
5. Select **Data Analysis.**
6. Select **Histogram.**
7. Identify Output Sheet name.
8. Check "Chart Output."
9. Close Gaps (Format Data Series, Options, Gap Width).
10. Modify Class Labels.

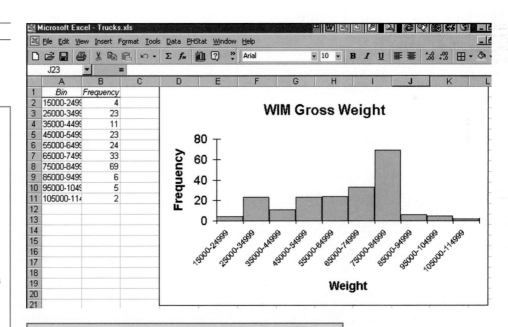

Minitab Instructions (for similar results):
1. Open file: Trucks.MTW.
2. Choose **Graph > Histogram.**
3. Click **Simple.**
4. Click **OK.**
5. In **Graph variables**, enter data column *WIM Gross Wgt.*
6. Click **OK.**

---

[3]*Note:* The Descriptive Statistics tool in Excel and Minitab provides additional statistical measures beyond the mean, the median and the mode. Several of these will be discussed later in this chapter.

FIGURE 3-5

Excel Frequency
Histogram—POE Gross
Weight

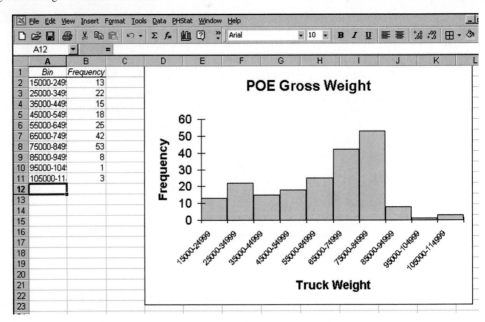

FIGURE 3-5

Excel Frequency
Histogram—POE Gross
Weight

These statistics indicate that, for the sample data, the WIM scale weights are, on average, heavier than the POE scale. Likewise, the median WIM weight exceeds the median POE weight. In both cases, the means are less than the medians. Thus, the sample data from both scales are left skewed.

Issues with Excel

In many instances, data files will have "missing values." That is, the values for one or more variables may not be available for some of the observations. The data have been lost, or they were not measured when the data were collected. Many times when you receive data like this, the missing values will be coded in a special way. For example, the code "N/A" might be used or a "−99" might be entered to signify that the data for that observation is missing.

FIGURE 3-6

Excel Descriptive Statistics Output

Excel Instructions:
1. Open file: Trucks.xls
2. Click on the **Tools** button.
3. Select **Data Analysis** option.
4. Choose **Descriptive Statistics** and select the appropriate data ranges.
5. Click on "Summary Statistics."

Microsoft Excel - Trucks.xls

	A	B	C	D	E	F
1	WIM Gross Weight		POE Gross Weight			
2						
3	Mean	64171.15	Mean	61057.25		
4	Standard Error	1393.64	Standard Error	1489.836		
5	Median	71380	Median	67655		
6	Mode	78720	Mode	105470		
7	Standard Deviation	19709.04	Standard Deviation	21069.46		
8	Sample Variance	3.88E+08	Sample Variance	4.44E+08		
9	Kurtosis	-0.48604	Kurtosis	-0.66973		
10	Skewness	-0.50291	Skewness	-0.49413		
11	Range	92860	Range	91620		
12	Minimum	15180	Minimum	13850		
13	Maximum	108040	Maximum	105470		
14	Sum	12834230	Sum	12211450		
15	Count	200	Count	200		
16						

Mean, median, and mode for each variable

Note: The Skewness statistic is negative, implying a left skew in the data. The higher the absolute value of this measure, the greater the skewness.

Minitab Instructions (for similar results):
1. Open file: Trucks.MTW.
2. Choose **Stat > Basic Statistics > Display Descriptive Statistics**.
3. In **Variables**, enter columns *WIM Gross Weight* and *POE Gross Weight*.
4. Click **Statistics**.
5. Check required statistics.
6. Click **OK. OK.**

Statistical software packages typically have flexible procedures for dealing with missing data. Minitab provides you with missing data options and properly adjusts the results to account for the missing data. *However, Excel does not contain a missing-value option.* If you attempt to use certain data-analysis options in Excel, such as Descriptive Statistics, in the presence of nonnumeric ("N/A") data, you will get an error message. When that happens you must clear the missing values, generally by deleting all rows with missing values. In some instances, you can save the good data in the row by using **Edit-Clear-All** for the cell in question. However, a bigger problem exists when the missing value has been coded as an arbitrary numeric value (-99). In this case, unless you go into the data and clear these values, Excel will use the -99 values in the computations as if they are real values. The result will be incorrect calculations.

Also, if a data set contains more than one mode, Excel will only show the first mode in the list of modes and will not warn you that multiple modes exist. (Minitab does not have a mode output option in its Descriptive Statistics tool.)

OTHER MEASURES OF LOCATION

Weighted Mean

The arithmetic mean is the most frequently used measure of central location. Equations 3-1 and 3-2 are used when you have either a population or a sample. For instance, the sample mean is computed using

$$\bar{x} = \frac{\sum x}{n} = \frac{x_1 + x_2 + x_3 + \cdots + x_n}{n}$$

In this case, each x value is given an equal weight in the computation of the mean. However, in some applications there is reason to weight the data values differently. In that case, we need to compute a **weighted mean**.

Weighted Mean

The mean value of data values that have been weighted according to their relative importance.

Equations 3-3 and 3-4 are used to find the weighted mean (or weighted average) for a population and for a sample, respectively.

Weighted Mean for a Population	**Weighted Mean for a Sample**
$$\mu_W = \frac{\sum w_i x_i}{\sum w_i} \qquad \text{3-3}$$	$$\bar{x}_w = \frac{\sum w_i x_i}{\sum w_i} \qquad \text{3-4}$$
	where:
	w_i = The weight of the ith data value
	x_i = The ith data value

$\mathcal{E}$XAMPLE 3-8: CALCULATING A WEIGHTED POPULATION MEAN

Fallon & Associates   Recently, the law firm of Fallon & Associates was involved in a discrimination suit concerning ski instructors at a ski resort in Colorado. One ski instructor from Germany had sued the operator of the ski resort, claiming that he had not received equitable pay compared with the other ski instructors from Norway and the United States. In preparing a defense, the Fallon attorneys planned to compute the mean annual salary for all seven Norwegian ski instructors at the resort. However, because these instructors worked different numbers of days during the ski season, a weighted mean needed to be computed. This was done using the following steps:

Step 1: **Collect the desired data and determine the weight to be assigned to each data value.**
In this case, the variable of interest was the salary of the ski instructors. The population consisted of seven Norwegian instructors. The weights were the number of days that the instructors worked. The following data and weights were determined:

$x_i = $ *Salary:*						
$7,600	$3,900	$5,300	$4,000	$7,200	$2,300	$5,100
$w_i = $ *Days:*						
50	30	40	25	60	15	50

Step 2: **Multiply each weight by the data value and sum these.**
$$\Sigma w_i x_i = (50)(\$7,600) + (30)(\$3,900) + \cdots + (50)(\$5,100) = \$1,530,500$$

Step 3: **Sum the weights for all values** (the weights are the days).
$$\Sigma w_i = 50 + 30 + 40 + 25 + 60 + 15 + 50 = 270$$

Step 4: **Compute the weighted mean.**
Divide the weighted sum by the sum of the weights. Because we are working with the population, the result will be the population weighted mean.

$$\mu_W = \frac{\Sigma w_i x_i}{\Sigma w_i} = \frac{\$1,530,500}{270} = \$5,668.519$$

Thus, taking into account the number of days worked, the Norwegian ski instructors had a mean salary of $5,668.52.

One weighted-mean example that you are probably very familiar with is your college grade point average (GPA). At most schools, A = 4 points, B = 3 points, and so forth. Each class has a certain number of credits (usually 1 to 5). The credits are the weights. Your GPA is computed by summing the product of points earned in a class times the credits for the class, and then dividing this sum by the total number of credits earned.

Percentiles

In some applications, we might wish to describe the location of the data in terms other than the center of the data. For example, prior to enrolling at your university you took the SAT or ACT test and received a **percentile** score in math and verbal skills.

If you received word that your standardized exam score was at the 90th percentile, it means that you scored as high or higher than 90% of the other students who took the exam. The score at the 50th percentile would indicate that you were at the median, where at least 50% scored at or below and at least 50% scored at or above your score.[4]

Percentiles

The pth percentile in a data array is a value that divides the data set into two parts. The lower segment contains at least $p\%$, and the upper segment contains at least $(100 - p)\%$, of the data. The 50th percentile is the median.

To illustrate how to manually approximate a percentile value, consider a situation in which you have 309 customers enter a bank during the course of a day. The time (rounded to the nearest minute) that each customer spends in the bank is recorded. If we wish to approximate the 10th percentile, we would begin by first sorting the data into order from low to high. Assign each data value a location indicator from 1 to 309. Next determine the location indicator that corresponds to the 10th percentile using Equation 3-5.

---

[4]More rigorously, the percentile is that value (or set of values) such that at least $p\%$ of the data is as small or smaller than that value and at least $(100 - p)\%$ of the data is at least as large as that value. For introductory courses, a convention has been adopted to average the largest and smallest values that qualify as a certain percentile. This is why the median was defined as it was earlier for data sets with an even number of data values.

Percentile Location Value

$$i = \frac{p}{100}(n+1)$$ **3-5**

where:

p = Desired percentile
n = Number of values in the data set

If i is an integer, then the pth percentile is the value in location i. If i is not an integer, then use interpolation.

Thus, the location of the 10th percentile is

$$i = \frac{p}{100}(n+1) = \frac{10}{100}(309+1) = 31$$

Because i is an integer, the 10th percentile is approximated by the value in the 31st position from the low end of the sorted data.

The location for the 26th percentile is

$$i = \frac{p}{100}(n+1) = \frac{26}{100}(309+1) = 80.60$$

Because 80.60 is not an integer, we interpolate 60% of the way between the 80th and 81st value in the data. For instance suppose the 80th data value is 5 minutes and the 81st value is 7 minutes, the 26th percentile would be $5 + 0.60(7 - 5) = 6.2$ minutes.

SUMMARY: CALCULATING PERCENTILES

To calculate a specific percentile for a set of quantitative data, you can use the following steps:

1. Sort the data into order from the lowest to highest value.

2. Determine the percentile location value, i, using Equation 3-5.

$$i = \frac{p}{100}(n+1)$$

where
p = desired percentile
n = number of values in the data set

3. If i is not an integer, then interpolate between the integer portion of i and the next value.

EXAMPLE 3-9: CALCULATING PERCENTILES

Henson Trucking   The Henson Trucking Company is a small company that is in the business of moving people from one home to another within the Dallas, Texas, area. Historically, the owners have charged the customers on an hourly basis, regardless of the distance of the move within the Dallas city limits. However, they are now considering adding a surcharge for moves over a certain distance. They have decided to base this charge on the 80th percentile. They have a sample of travel-distance data for 30 moves. These data are as follows:

13.5	8.6	16.2	21.4	21.0	23.7	4.1	13.8	20.5	9.6
11.5	6.5	5.8	10.1	11.1	4.4	12.2	13.0	15.7	13.2
13.4	13.1	21.7	14.6	14.1	12.4	24.9	19.3	26.9	11.7

The 80th percentile can be computed using these steps.

Step 1:   Sort the data from lowest to highest.

4.1	4.4	5.8	6.5	8.6	9.6	10.1	11.1	11.5	11.7
12.2	12.4	13.0	13.1	13.2	13.4	13.5	13.8	14.1	14.6
15.7	16.2	19.3	20.5	21.0	21.4	21.7	23.7	24.9	26.9

Step 2: **Determine percentile location value, i, using Equation 3-5.**
The 80th percentile location value is:

$$i = \frac{p}{100}(n+1) = \frac{80}{100}(30+1) = 24.80$$

Step 3: **Interpolate if necessary.**
Because $i = 24.80$ is not an integer value, the 80th percentile is found by interpolation. First locate the 24th value, which is 20.5. The next higher value is 21.0. The 80th percentile is

$$20.5 + .80(21.0 - 20.5) = 20.90$$

Therefore, any customer with a move distance exceeding 20.90 miles will receive a surcharge.

Quartiles

Quartiles are another location measure that can be used to describe data.

Quartiles

Quartiles in a data array are those values that divide the data set into four equal-sized groups. The median corresponds to the second quartile.

The first quartile corresponds to the 25th percentile. That is, it is the value at or below which there is at least 25% (one quarter) of the data and at or above which there is at least 75% of the data. The third quartile is also the 75th percentile. It is the value at or below which there is at least 75% of the data and at or above which there is at least 25% of the data. The second quartile is the 50th percentile and is also the median.

A quartile value can be approximated manually using the same method as for percentiles with Equation 3-5. For the 309 bank customer-service times mentioned earlier, the location of the first-quartile (25th percentile) value is found, after sorting the data, as

$$i = \frac{p}{100}(n+1) = \frac{25}{100}(309+1) = 77.5$$

Because 77.5 is not an integer value, the first quartile is approximated by interpolating between the values in the 77th and the 78th locations from the lower end of the sorted data.

Issues with Excel

The procedure that Excel uses to compute quartiles *is not standard*. Therefore, the quartile and percentile values from Excel will be slightly different from those we found using Equation 3-5 and from what other statistical software packages, including Minitab, will provide. For example, referring to Example 3-9, when Excel is used to compute the 80th percentile for the moving distances, the value returned is 20.58 miles. This is slightly different than the 20.90 we found in Example 3-9. Equation 3-5, the method used by Minitab, is generally accepted by statisticians to be correct. Therefore, if you need precise values for quartiles, use software such as Minitab. However, Excel will give reasonably close percentile and quartile values.

BOX AND WHISKER PLOTS

A descriptive tool that many decision makers like to use is called a **box and whisker plot** (or a box plot). The box and whisker plot incorporates the median and the quartiles to graphically display quantitative data. It is also used to identify *outliers* that are extremely small or large data values that lie mostly by themselves.

Box and Whisker Plot

A graph that is composed of two parts: a box and the whiskers. The box has a width that ranges from the first quartile (Q_1) to the third quartile (Q_3). A vertical line through the box is placed at the median. Limits are located at a value that is 1.5 times the difference between Q_1 and Q_3 below Q_1 and above Q_3. The whiskers extend to the left to the lowest value within the limits and to the right to the highest value within the limits.

SUMMARY: CONSTRUCTING A BOX AND WHISKER PLOT

A box and whisker plot is graphical summary of a quantitative variable. It is constructed using the following steps:

1. Sort the data values from low to high.

2. Use Equation 3-5 to find the 25th percentile ($Q1$ = first quartile), the 50th percentile ($Q2$ = median), and the 75th percentile ($Q3$ = third quartile).

3. Draw a box so that the ends of the box are at $Q1$ and $Q3$. This box will contain the middle 50% of the data values in the population or sample.

4. Draw a vertical line through the box at the median. Half the data values in the box will be on either side of the median.

5. Calculate the *interquartile range* ($IQR = Q3 - Q1$). (The interquartile range will be discussed more fully in Section 3-2.) Compute the lower limit for the box and whisker plot as $Q1 - 1.5(Q3 - Q1)$. The upper limit is $Q3 + 1.5(Q3 - Q1)$. Any data values outside these limits are referred to as outliers.

6. Extend dashed lines (called the whiskers) from each end of the box to the lowest and highest value within the limits.

7. Any value outside the limits (outlier) found in 5 is marked with an asterisk (*).

EXAMPLE 3-10: CONSTRUCTING A BOX AND WHISKER PLOT

Rolling Hills Golf Course   Rolling Hills is a semiprivate golf club in rural North Carolina. Like most golf courses, Rolling Hills constantly battles the slow-play issue. Recently, the course manager collected a random sample of times for 18-hole rounds at the course. He plans to make a presentation to the board of directors and wishes to construct a box and whisker plot as part of the presentation. The sorted sample data (time measured in minutes) for 45 rounds are shown as follows:

231	236	241	242	242	243	243	243	248
248	249	250	251	251	252	252	254	255
255	256	256	257	259	260	260	260	260
262	262	264	265	265	265	266	268	268
270	276	277	277	280	286	300	324	345

The box and whisker plot is computed using the following steps:

Step 1:   **Sort the data from low to high.**

Step 2:   **Calculate the 25th percentile ($Q1$), the 50th percentile (median), and the 75th percentile ($Q3$).**
The location for $Q1$ is

$$i = \frac{p}{100}(n + 1) = \frac{25}{100}(45 + 1) = 11.50$$

Thus, $Q1$ will be halfway between the 11th and 12th values, which is $249 + 0.50(250 - 249) = 249.50$.
The median location is

$$i = \frac{p}{100}(n + 1) = \frac{50}{100}(45 + 1) = 23$$

In the sorted data, the median is the 23rd value, which has a value of 259 minutes. The third-quartile location is

$$i = \frac{p}{100}(n + 1) = \frac{75}{100}(45 + 1) = 34.50$$

Thus, $Q3$ is halfway between the 34th and 35th data values. This is $266 + 0.50(268 - 266) = 267$.

Step 3:   **Draw the box so the ends correspond to Q1 and Q3.**

Step 4:   **Draw a vertical line through the box at the median.**

Step 5:   **Compute the upper and lower limits.**
The lower limit is computed as $Q1 - 1.5(Q3 - Q1)$. This is

$$\text{Lower Limit} = 249.50 - 1.5(267 - 249.5) = 223.25$$

The upper limit is $Q3 + 1.5(Q3 - Q1)$. This is

$$\text{Upper Limit} = 267 + 1.5(267 - 249.5) = 293.25$$

Any value outside these limits is identified as an outlier.

Step 6:   **Draw the whiskers.**
The whiskers are drawn to the smallest and largest values inside the limits.

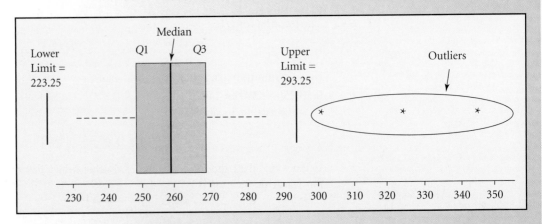

Step 7:   **Plot the outliers.**
The outliers are plotted as values outside the limits.

DATA-LEVEL ISSUES

You need to be very aware of the level of data you are working with before computing the numerical measures introduced in this chapter. A common mistake is to compute means on nominal-level data. For example, a major electronics manufacturer recently surveyed a sample of customers to determine whether they preferred black, white, or colored stereo cases. The data were coded as follows.

$$1 = \text{black}$$
$$2 = \text{white}$$
$$3 = \text{colored}$$

A few of the responses are

$$\text{Color code} = \{1, 1, 3, 2, 1, 2, 2, 2, 3, 1, 1, 1, 3, 2, 2, 1, 2\}$$

Using these codes, the sample mean is

$$\bar{x} = \frac{\sum x}{n}$$
$$= \frac{30}{17} = 1.765$$

As you can see, reporting that customers prefer a color somewhere between black and white but closer to white would be meaningless. The mean should not be used with nominal data. This type of mistake tends to happen when people use computer software to perform their calculations. It is easy to ask Excel, Minitab, or other statistical software to compute mean, median, and so on for all the variables in the data set. Then a table is created and, before long, the meaningless measures creep into your report.

There is also some disagreement about whether means should be computed on ordinal data. For example, in market research a 5- or 7-point scale is often used to measure customers' attitudes about products or TV commercials. For example, we might set up the following scale:

$$1 = \text{Strongly Agree}$$
$$2 = \text{Agree}$$
$$3 = \text{Neutral}$$
$$4 = \text{Disagree}$$
$$5 = \text{Strongly Disagree}$$

Customer responses to a particular question are obtained on this scale from 1 to 5. For a sample of $n = 10$ people, we might get the following responses to a question.

$$\text{Response} = \{2, 2, 1, 3, 3, 1, 5, 2, 1, 3)$$

The mean rating is 2.3. We could then compute the mean for a second issue and compare the means. However, what exactly do we have? First, when we compute a mean for a scaled variable, we are making two basic assumptions:

1. We are assuming the distance between a rating of 1 and 2 is the same as the distance between 2 and 3. We are also saying these distances are exactly the same for the second issue's variable to which you wish to compare it. Although from a numerical standpoint this is true, in terms of what the scale is measuring, is the difference between strongly agree and agree the same as the difference between agree and neutral? If not, is the mean really a meaningful measure?
2. We are also assuming people who respond to the survey have the same definition of what "strongly agree" means or what "disagree" means. When you mark a 4 (disagree) on your survey, are you applying the same criteria as someone else who also marks a 4 on the same issue? If not, then the mean might be misleading.

Although these difficulties exist with ordinal data, we see many examples in which means are computed and used for decision purposes. In fact, we once had a dean who focused on one particular question on the course evaluation survey that was administered in every class each semester. This question was "Considering all factors of importance to you, how would you rate this instructor?"

$$1 = \text{Excellent} \quad 2 = \text{Good} \quad 3 = \text{Average} \quad 4 = \text{Poor} \quad 5 = \text{Very Poor}$$

The dean then had his staff compute means for each class and for each professor. He then listed classes and faculty in order based on the mean values, and he based a significant part of the performance

FIGURE 3-7

Descriptive Measures of the Center

Descriptive Measure	Computation Method	Data Level	Advantages/ Disadvantages
Mean	Sum of values divided by the number of values	Ratio Interval	• Numerical center of the data • Sum of deviations from the mean is zero • Sensitive to extreme values
Median	Middle value for data that have been sorted	Ratio Interval Ordinal	• Not sensitive to extreme values • Computed only from the center values • Does not use information from all the data
Mode	Value(s) that occur most frequently in the data	Ratio Interval Ordinal Nominal	• May not reflect the center • May not exist • Might have multiple modes

evaluation on where a faculty member stood with respect to mean score on this one question. By the way, he carried the calculations for the mean out to three decimal places!

In general, the median is the preferred measure of central location for ordinal data instead of the mean.

Figure 3-7 summarizes the three measures of the center that have been discussed in this section.

3-1: EXERCISES

Skill Development

3.1   The number of cars that have gone through a car wash during the noon hour over each of the past eight days are shown as follows:

6	3	9	6	6	5	4	1

Compute the mean, median, and mode for these sample data.

3.2   The following data are the average per-hour wages in dollars, after deductions, for the workers in an orthodontist's office:

17.87	19.95	22.95	18.74	9.95
11.22	21.98	14.52	16.65	14.98

Determine the mean, median, and mode for the data.

3.3   Another orthodontist's office employees receive the following hourly wages, in dollars.

15.67	23.45	18.95	20.79	25.49	
25.49	20.79	25.49	18.95	23.45	15.67

a. Using measures of central tendency, determine the shape of this data.
b. Determine the first and third quartiles for this data.

3.4   During one weekend, 11 houses were sold in Half Moon Bay, California. The prices paid for these houses are given here (in thousands of dollars).

264	305	287	325	298	271
112	317	293	325	289	

a. Compute the mean, median, and mode for this population. Which measure of central tendency would you use to describe the "center" of these data?
b. Calculate the quartiles for this data.

3.5   The number of hot dogs sold by 12 randomly selected hot dog vendors in a large city park on July 4 are as follows:

142	97	105	76	90	83
123	115	92	94	73	104

Compute the mean, median, first quartile, and third quartile for these sample data.

3.6   Five wheat farms have been selected at random from those in a particular county. The following crop yields (total bushels of wheat) are given for each of the five, along with the number of acres on each farm.

Yield	15,030	43,400	10,260	13,200	89,200
Acres	80	60	75	55	140

a. Compute the mean yield for this sample of five farms.
b. Taking into account the number of acres on each farm, compute a weighted mean for this sample.

3.7   The following frequency distribution is given for the ages of students at a small private university.

Age	Frequency
18 to 20	345
21 to 22	560
23 to 25	200
26 to 28	80

a. Compute the mean age at this university. (Hint: use the midpoint of each age class to represent all values in the class. Find a weighted mean.)

b. What is the median age at this university?

3.8 The following data constitute a sample of hours of Internet usage per week by students.

5	4	3	10	8	5	2
6	9	6	9	7	6	12
9	11	10	9	7	7	6
9	9	3	7	11	5	11
7	6	4	10	7	3	5

a. Comptue the mean, median, and mode for these data.

b. Develop a box and whisker plot for these data.

3.9 The following data reflect the number of books sold at a used book store in Brooklyn, New York, each day for a random sample of 45 days

17	18	19	20	16	15	17	22	16
16	19	21	15	14	17	21	19	15
19	15	15	19	18	22	13	14	17
18	21	15	13	10	13	20	12	15
21	15	16	16	14	19	15	16	13

a. Develop a box and whisker plot. Are there any outliers in this sample?

b. What number of books constitutes the 60th percentile for this sample?

3.10 The following set of data is the number of employees at 1/30th of the franchises of a prominent fast-food restaurant:

16	23	17	24	9	11	13	15
18	21	16	23	17	16	10	14

a. Determine the mean, median, and mode for the data.

b. Indicate whether the data are skewed or symmetric.

3.11 A question appears on a job application for sales persons at a national insurance company. It asks the applicants to rate their gregariousness on a scale from 1 to 10. The answers obtained from 18 such applications appear here:

8	6	9	9	7	10	7	8	9
8	7	7	10	9	8	5	6	10

a. Consider the type of data carefully and calculate the most appropriate measure of central tendency for this data. Explain your answer.

b. Calculate the interquartile range for this data.

3.12 Examine the following data:

23	65	45	19	35	28	39	100	50	26	25	27
24	17	12	106	23	19	39	70	20	18	44	31

a. Compute the quartiles.

b. Calculate the 90th percentile.

c. Develop a box and whisker plot.

d. Calculate the 20th and 30th percentiles.

Business Applications

3.13 Gayle Pooley, the marketing director for South East Insurance, has been worried about the increasing age of the company's policyholder base. She wants to determine whether the new advertising campaign has had the desired effect of attracting a larger number of younger customers. As a first step in this analysis, she has selected two samples of customers. The first sample is from the customer base before the new advertising campaign. The data are the ages of the customers at the time the policies went into effect. The second sample was taken from the customers who were added after the advertising campaign.

Pre-Advertising		Post-Advertising	
33	30	23	34
44	40	31	40
52	29	40	28
34	55	28	25
25	36	26	29

a. Determine the mean, median, and mode for each sample.

b. Discuss whether either of the two data sets is skewed and show why or why not.

c. Is there any indication from these two samples that the new policyholders may tend to be younger? Write a short report that uses the findings in parts a and b to justify your answer.

3.14 The Soccer Shoppe was recently opened in Sonoma, California, to provide soccer equipment and supplies to players and teams in the area. During the first month that it was open, the managers kept track of the number of customers who entered the store each day. The following data were collected.

21	19	21	19	19	20	18	12	20	19	17	14
21	22	25	21	22	23	10	19	25	14	17	18

a. Compute the mean, median, and mode for these data.

b. Indicate whether the data are skewed or symmetrical.

c. Construct a box and whisker plot for these data. Referring to your answer in part a, does the box plot support your conclusion about skewness? Discuss.

3.15 One of the leading business periodicals recently conducted a study of its subscribers to determine the total credit card debt for each customer. A sample of 50 subscribers responded to the survey, with the following results, in dollars.

$1,366	$0	$1,692	$2,973	$2,426	$2,090	$2,429	$3,306	$3,050	$2,085
3,269	2,261	3,011	3,617	2,273	2,960	3,203	347	0	2,441
2,516	3,727	2,085	2,010	700	2,301	2,096	2,008	2,653	3,088
2,257	8,345	2,523	1,948	2,685	3,393	2,591	1,209	3,621	300
3,612	2,380	0	2,681	2,506	3,076	4,065	2,218	3,287	3,712

a. Develop a box and whisker plot for these sample data.

b. Based on the box and whisker plot, does it appear that the distribution of credit card debt is skewed? If so, in which direction is it skewed? Discuss.

3.16 The Ollander Corporation operates five food processing plants in western Europe. Recently, the company was considering modifying its financial reward system for the plant managers. In doing the analysis, the director of human resources collected information on the profits (in thousands of U.S. dollars) generated from each plant last year. She also collected data on the number of employees at the plants. These data are shown as follows:

Profits	$7,400	$14,400	$12,300	$6,200	$3,100
Employees	123	402	256	109	67

a. Compute the weighted mean profit for these five plants using the number of employees as the weights.

b. Explain why the human resources director would want a weighted average to be computed in this situation rather than a simple numeric average.

Advanced Business Applications

3.17 The Golden Calendar Company produces a variety of specialized calendars that it sells to commercial customers, who then resell the calendars. The sales manager at Golden has selected a sample of 16 major customers and recorded the total number of calendars purchased by each customer last year. The data here list the number of calendars purchased. The data are in a file called *Golden* on your CD-ROM.

a. Compute the mean and median for these sales data.

b. Develop a box and whisker plot for these sales data.

c. Write a short statement that describes these sales data using the information generated in parts a and b. Make special note of any unusually low or high number of calendar purchases, because these accounts often require more attention. The company wishes to increase sales to the low accounts and keep clients who purchase large amounts.

3.18 The Cozine Corporation operates a garbage hauling business. Up to this point, the company has been charged a flat fee for each of its garbage trucks that enters the county landfill. The flat fee is based on an assumed truck weight of 45,000 pounds. In two weeks, the company is required to appear before the county commissioners to discuss a rate adjustment. In preparation for this meeting, Cozine has hired an independent company to weigh a sample of Cozine's garbage trucks just before they enter the landfill. The data file *Cozine* shows the data the company has collected.

a. Based on the sample data, what percentile does the 45,000-pound weight fall closest to?

b. Compute appropriate measures of central location for the data.

c. Construct a frequency histogram based on the sample data. Use Sturges' rule (see Chapter 2) to determine the number of classes. Also, construct a box and whisker plot for these data. Discuss the relative advantages of histograms and box and whisker plots for presenting these data.

d. Use the information determined in parts a, b, and c to develop a presentation to the county commissioners. Make sure the presentation attempts to answer the question of whether Cozine deserves a rate reduction.

3.19 The High Desert Bank loan manager recently selected a random sample of loan files from the bank's loan portfolio. Her objective in selecting the sample is to gain a better understanding of the relationship between commercial and real estate loans. In particular, she wishes to analyze the loan amounts by type of loan. The data file *High-Desert* contains the data on a sample of 350 loans. Determine appropriate measures of central location for the overall sample.

a. Compute the measures of central location for each category of loan.

b. Develop a box and whisker plot for loan amount for each type of loan. Compare these.

3-2 MEASURES OF VARIATION

TABLE 3-3

Manufacturing Output for Bryce Lumber

PLANT A	PLANT B
15 units	23 units
25 units	26 units
35 units	25 units
20 units	24 units
30 units	27 units

Bryce Lumber Company—Consider the situation involving two manufacturing facilities for the Bryce Lumber Company. The division vice president asked the two plant managers to record their production output for five days. The resulting sample data are shown in Table 3-3.

Instead of reporting these raw data, the managers reported only the mean and median for their data. The following are the computed statistics for the two plants:

Plant A	Plant B
$\bar{x}$ = 25 units	$\bar{x}$ = 25 units
M_d = 25 units	M_d = 25 units

The division vice president looked at these statistics and concluded:

1. Average production is the same at both plants.

2. At both plants, the output is at or more than 25 units half the time and at or fewer than 25 units half the time.

3. Because the mean and median are equal, the distribution of production output at the two plants is symmetrical.

4. Based on these statistics, there is no reason to believe that the two plants are any different in terms of their production output.

However, if he had taken a closer look at the raw data, he would have seen there is a very big difference between the two plants. The difference is the production **variation** from day to day. Plant B is very stable, producing almost the same amount every day. Plant A varies considerably, with some high-output days and some low-output days. Thus, looking at only measures of the data's central location can be misleading.

To fully describe a set of data, we need a measure of variation or spread.

Variation

A set of data exhibits variation if all the data are not the same value.

There is variation in everything that is made by humans or that occurs in nature. The variation may be small, but it is there. Given a fine enough measuring instrument, we can detect the variation. Variation is either a natural part of a process (or inherent to a product) or can be attributed to a special cause that is not considered random.

There are several different measures that are used in business decision-making. In this section, we introduce four of these measures: range, interquartile range, variance, and standard deviation.

RANGE

The simplest measure of variation is the **range**. It is both easy to compute and easy to understand.

Range

The range is a measure of variation that is computed by finding the difference between the maximum and minimum values in a data set.

The range is computed using Equation 3-6.

Range

$$R = \text{Maximum Value} - \text{Minimum Value}$$ **3-6**

Bryce Lumber (continued)—Table 3-3 showed the production-volume data for the two Bryce Lumber Company plants. The range for each plant is determined using Equation 3-6 as follows:

Plant A	Plant B
$R = \text{Maximum} - \text{Minimum}$	$R = \text{Maximum} - \text{Minimum}$
$R = 35 - 15$	$R = 27 - 23$
$R = 20$	$R = 4$

We see plant A has a range that is five times as great as plant B.

Although the range is quick and easy to compute, it does have some limitations. First, because we use only the high and low values to compute the range, it is very sensitive to extreme values in the data. Second, regardless of how many values are in the sample or population, the range is computed from only two of these values. For these reasons, it is considered a weak measure of variation.

INTERQUARTILE RANGE

A measure of variation that tends to overcome the range's susceptibility to extreme values is called the **interquartile range**.

Interquartile Range

The interquartile range is a measure of variation that is determined by computing the difference between the third and first quartiles.

Equation 3-7 is used to compute the interquartile range.

Interquartile Range	
Interquartile Range = Third Quartile − First Quartile	**3-7**

EXAMPLE 3-11: COMPUTING THE INTERQUARTILE RANGE

D.C. Hilton Investment Company   The D.C. Hilton Investment Company, headquartered in New Orleans, has a number of individual clients who have recently opened a Roth IRA. Each client must decide on how much they will contribute on a monthly basis. The manager in charge of Roth investments at D.C. Hilton has collected a random sample of 100 clients who make monthly contributions to a Roth IRA. He has recorded the net dollars, after brokerage fees, that each client deposits into his or her account. He wishes to analyze the variation in these data by computing the range and the interquartile range. He could use the following steps to do so:

Step 1:   **Sort the data into a data array from lowest to highest.**
The 100 sorted deposit values, in dollars, are shown as follows:

$33	$164	$173	$184	$190	$197	$207	$216	$224	$237
53	164	175	186	191	197	207	217	225	240
150	164	175	186	191	198	208	217	225	240
152	166	175	186	192	200	208	217	229	240
157	166	178	187	193	200	208	219	231	250
160	168	178	188	193	201	210	222	231	251
161	169	179	188	194	202	211	223	234	259
162	171	180	188	194	204	212	223	234	270
162	171	182	190	196	205	213	223	235	379
163	172	183	190	196	205	216	224	236	479

Step 2:   **Compute the range using Equation 3-6.**

$$R = \text{Maximum Value} - \text{Minimum Value}$$
$$R = \$479 - \$33 = \$446$$

Note, the range is sensitive to extreme values. The small value of $33 and the high value of $479 cause the range value to be very large.

Step 3:   **Compute the first and third quartiles.**
Equation 3-5 can be used to find the location of the third quartile (75th percentile) and the first quartile (25th percentile).

For $Q3$, the location is $\dfrac{75}{100}(100 + 1) = 75.75$

Thus, $Q3$ is .75 of the way between the 75th and 76th data values, which is found as follows:

$$Q3 = 219 + 0.75(222 - 219) = \$221.25$$

For $Q1$, the location is $\dfrac{25}{100}(100 + 1) = 25.25$

Then $Q1$ is a quarter of the way between the 25th and 26th data values, which is found as follows:

$$Q1 = 178 + 0.25(178 - 178) = \$178$$

Step 4: **Compute the interquartile range.**

The interquartile range overcomes the range's sensitivity problem. It is computed using Equation 3-7:

$$\text{Interquartile Range} = Q3 - Q1$$
$$= \$221.25 - \$178 = \$43.2$$

Note, the interquartile range would be unchanged even if the values on the high or low end of the distribution were even more extreme than those shown in these sample data.

POPULATION VARIANCE AND STANDARD DEVIATION

Although the range is easy to compute and understand and the interquartile range is designed to overcome the range's sensitivity to extreme values, neither measure uses all the available data in its computation. Thus, both measures ignore potentially valuable information in data.

Two measures of variation that incorporate all the values in a data set are the **variance** and the **standard deviation**.

Variance	*Standard Deviation*
The population variance is the average of the squared distances of the data values from the mean.	The standard deviation is the positive square root of the variance.

These two measures are closely related. The standard deviation is the square root of the variance. The standard deviation is in the original units (dollars, pounds, etc.), whereas the units of measure in the variance are squared. Because dealing with original units is easier than dealing with the square of the units, we usually use the standard deviation to measure variation in a population or sample.

Bryce Lumber (continued)—Recall the Bryce Lumber example, in which we compared the production output for two of the company's plants. Table 3-3 showed the data, which are considered a population for our purposes here.

Previously we examined the variability in the output from these two plants by computing the ranges. Although those results gave us some sense of how much more variable Plant A is than Plant B, we also pointed out some of the deficiencies of the range. The variance and standard deviation offer alternatives to the range for measuring variation in data.

Equation 3-8 is the formula for the population variance. Like the population mean, the population variance and standard deviation are assigned a Greek symbol.

Population Variance

$$\sigma^2 = \frac{\sum_{i=1}^{N}(x_i - \mu)^2}{N}$$

3-8

where:

μ = Population mean
N = Population size
σ^2 = Population variance (sigma squared)

We begin by computing the variance for the output data from Plant A. The first step in manually calculating the variance is to find the mean using Equation 3-1.

$$\mu = \frac{\sum x}{N} = \frac{15 + 25 + 35 + 20 + 30}{5} = \frac{125}{5} = 25$$

Next, subtract the mean from each value, as shown in Table 3-4. Notice the sum of the deviations from the mean is 0. Recall from Section 3-1 that this will be true for any set of data. The

TABLE 3-4		
Computing the Population Variance: Squaring the Deviations		

x	$(x - \mu)$	$(x - \mu)^2$
15	$15 - 25 = -10$	100
25	$25 - 25 = 0$	0
35	$35 - 25 = 10$	100
20	$20 - 25 = -5$	25
30	$30 - 25 = 5$	25
	$\Sigma = 0$	$\Sigma = 250$

positive differences are cancelled out by the negative differences. To overcome this fact when computing the variance, we square each of the differences and then sum the squared differences. These calculations are also shown in Table 3-4.

The final step in computing the population variance is to divide the sum of the squared differences by the population size, $N = 5$.

$$\sigma^2 = \frac{\Sigma(x - \mu)^2}{N} = \frac{250}{5} = 50$$

The population variance is 50 *products-squared*.

Manual calculations for the population variance may be easier if you use an alternative formula for σ^2 that is the algebraic equivalent. This is shown as Equation 3-9.

Population Variance Shortcut

$$\sigma^2 = \frac{\Sigma(x - \mu)^2}{N} = \frac{\Sigma x^2 - \dfrac{(\Sigma x)^2}{N}}{N} \qquad \textbf{3-9}$$

Example 3-12 will illustrate the application of Equation 3-9 for the population variance.

Because we squared the deviations to keep the plus values and minus values from canceling, the units of measure were also squared, but the term *products-squared* doesn't have a meaning. To get back to the original units of measure, take the square root of the variance. The result is the standard deviation. Equation 3-10 shows the formula for the population standard deviation.

Population Standard Deviation

$$\sigma = \sqrt{\sigma^2} = \sqrt{\frac{\sum\limits_{i=1}^{N}(x_i - \mu)^2}{N}} \qquad \textbf{3-10}$$

Therefore, the population standard deviation of Plant A's production output is

$$\sigma = \sqrt{50}$$
$$\sigma = 7.07 \text{ products}$$

The population standard deviation is a parameter and will not change unless the population values change.

We could repeat this process using the data for Plant B, which also had a mean output of 25 products. You should verify that the population variance is

$$\sigma^2 = \frac{\Sigma(x - \mu)^2}{N} = \frac{10}{5} = 2$$

The standard deviation is found by taking the square root of the variance.

$$\sigma = \sqrt{2}$$
$$\sigma = 1.414 \text{ products}$$

Thus, Plant A has an output standard deviation that is five times larger than Plant B. The fact that Plant A's range was also five times larger than the range for Plant B is merely a coincidence.

$\mathcal{S}$UMMARY: COMPUTING THE POPULATION VARIANCE AND STANDARD DEVIATION

The population variance and standard deviation are computed using the following steps:

1. Collect quantitative data for the variable of interest for the entire population.

2. Use either Equation 3-8 or Equation 3-9 to compute the variance. If Equation 3-9 is used:

3. Find the sum of the x values ($\sum x$) and then square this sum ($\sum x)^2$

4. Square each x value and sum these squared values ($\sum x^2$)

5. Compute the variance using

$$\sigma^2 = \frac{\sum x^2 - \frac{(\sum x)^2}{N}}{N}$$

6. Compute the standard deviation by taking the square root of the variance:

$$\sigma = \sqrt{\sigma^2}$$

$\mathcal{E}$XAMPLE 3-12: COMPUTING A POPULATION VARIANCE AND A STANDARD DEVIATION

Boydson Shipping Company   Boydson Shipping Company owns and operates a fleet of tanker ships that carry commodities between the countries of the world. In the past six months, the company has had seven contracts that called for shipments between Vancouver, Canada, and London, England. For many reasons, the travel time varies between these two locations. The scheduling manager is interested in knowing the variance and standard deviation in shipping times for these seven shipments. To find these values, he can follow these steps:

Step 1:   **Collect the data for the population.**
These shipping times are shown as follows:

$$x = \text{shipping weeks}$$
$$= \{5, 7, 5, 9, 7, 4, 6\}$$

Step 2:   **Select Equation 3-9 to find the population variance.**

$$\sigma^2 = \frac{\sum x^2 - \frac{(\sum x)^2}{N}}{N}$$

Step 3:   **Add the x values and square the sum.**
$$\sum x = 5 + 7 + 5 + 9 + 7 + 4 + 6 = 43$$
$$(\sum x)^2 = (43)^2 = 1{,}849$$

Step 4:   **Square each of the x values and sum these squares.**
$$\sum x^2 = 5^2 + 7^2 + 5^2 + 9^2 + 7^2 + 4^2 + 6^2 = 281$$

Step 5:   **Compute the population variance.**

$$\sigma^2 = \frac{\sum x^2 - \frac{(\sum x)^2}{N}}{N} = \frac{281 - \frac{1{,}849}{7}}{7} = 2.4082$$

The variance is in units squared, so in this example the population variance is 2.4082 weeks squared.

Step 6:   **Calculate the standard deviation as the square root of the variance.**

$$\sigma = \sqrt{\sigma^2} = \sqrt{2.4082} = 1.5518 \text{ weeks}$$

Thus, the standard deviation for the number of shipping days between Vancouver and London for the seven shipments is 1.5518 weeks.

SAMPLE VARIANCE AND STANDARD DEVIATION

Equations 3-8, 3-9, and 3-10 are the equations for the population variance and standard deviation. Any time you are working with a population, these are the equations that are used. However, in most instances, you will be describing sample data that have been selected from the population. In addition to using different notation for the sample variance and standard deviation, the equations are also slightly different. Equations 3-11 and 3-12 can be used to find the sample variance. Note that Equation 3-12 is considered the shortcut formula for manual computations.

Sample Variance

$$s^2 = \frac{\sum_{i=1}^{n}(x_i - \bar{x})^2}{n - 1}$$ **3-11**

Sample Variance Shortcut

$$s^2 = \frac{\sum x^2 - \frac{(\sum x)^2}{n}}{n - 1}$$ **3-12**

where:

n = Sample size
$\bar{x}$ = Sample mean
s^2 = Sample variance

The sample standard deviation is found by taking the square root of the sample variance, as shown in Equation 3-13.

Sample Standard Deviation

$$s = \sqrt{s^2} = \sqrt{\frac{\sum_{i=1}^{n}(x_i - \bar{x})^2}{n - 1}}$$ **3-13**

Take note in Equations 3-11, 3-12, and 3-13 that the denominator is $n - 1$ (sample size minus 1). This may seem strange, given that the denominator for the population variance and the standard deviation is simply N, the population size. The mathematical justification for the $n - 1$ divisor is outside the scope of this text. However, the general reason for this is that we want the average sample variance to equal the population variance. If we were to select all possible samples of size n from a given population and for each sample we computed the sample variance using Equation 3-11 or Equation 3-12, the average of all the sample variances would equal σ^2 (the population variance), provided we used $n - 1$ as the divisor. Using n instead of $n - 1$ in the denominator would produce an average sample variance that would be smaller than σ^2, the population variance. Because we do not want an estimator on average to underestimate the population variance, we use $n - 1$ in the denominator of s^2.

*E*XAMPLE 3-13: COMPUTING A SAMPLE VARIANCE AND STANDARD DEVIATION

Red Line Taxi   The managers at Red Line Taxi selected a random sample of 10 taxicabs and recorded the number of round-trips made to the local international airport on November 15. The manager can find the sample variance and the sample standard deviation using the following steps:

Step 1:   **Select the sample and record the data for the variable of interest.**

Cab	Round-Trips = x
1	4
2	7
3	1
4	0
5	5
6	0
7	3
8	2
9	6
10	2

Step 2:   **Select either Equation 3-11 or Equation 3-12 to compute the sample variance.**
If we use Equation 3-11,

$$s^2 = \frac{\sum(x - \bar{x})^2}{n - 1}$$

Step 3:   **Compute $\bar{x}$.**
The sample mean number of trips is

$$\bar{x} = \frac{\sum x}{n} = \frac{30}{10} = 3.0$$

Step 4:   **Determine the sum of the squared deviations of each x value from $\bar{x}$.**

Cab	Round Trips = x	(x − x̄)	(x − x̄)²
1	4	1	1
2	7	4	16
3	1	−2	4
4	0	−3	9
5	5	2	4
6	0	−3	9
7	3	0	0
8	2	−1	1
9	6	3	9
10	2	−1	1
		Σ = 0	Σ = 54

Step 5:   **Compute the sample variance using Equation 3-11.**

$$s^2 = \frac{\sum(x - \bar{x})^2}{n - 1} = \frac{54}{9} = 6$$

The sample variance is measured in squared units. Thus, the variance in this example is 6 trips squared.

Step 6:   **Compute the sample standard deviation by taking the square root of the variance (see Equation 3-13):**

$$s = \sqrt{\frac{\sum(x - \bar{x})^2}{n - 1}} = \sqrt{\frac{54}{9}} = \sqrt{6}$$

$$s = 2.4495 \text{ trips}$$

This sample standard deviation measures the variation in the sample data for daily round-trips to the airport for Red Line Taxi.

Weigh in Motion (continued)—The state transportation department has conducted a study to determine whether the Weigh-in-Motion scale can substitute for the static scale located at a port of entry. (See page 83.) The state collected data on a sample of $n = 200$ trucks over several months. Each truck was weighed on both scales.

Previously, we computed measures of central tendency and constructed histograms to better understand the sample data. We focused on the WIM gross vehicle weight and the POE gross vehicle weight. We saw that there were only "small" differences in the mean and median values for the two variables.

We now turn our attention to measures of variability. The question is whether the two scales provide weight distributions of similar variability. The range (maximum − minimum) is one measure of variability, and Excel and Minitab can compute the range. Figures 3-8a and 3-8b show the Excel and Minitab descriptive statistics results for POE and WIM gross weights.

FIGURE 3-8A

Excel Descriptive Statistics Output—Truck Weight Data

Excel Instructions:
1. Open file: Trucks.xls
2. Click on the **Tools** button.
3. Select the **Data Analysis** option.
4. Choose **Descriptive Statistics** and select the appropriate data ranges.
5. Click on "Summary Statistics."

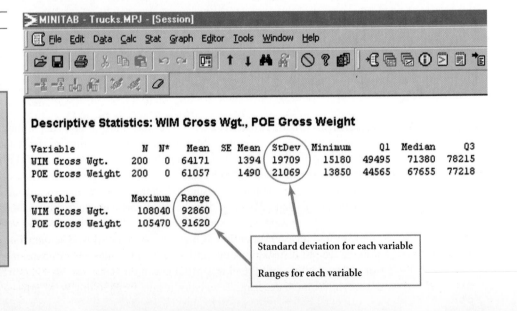

	A	B	C	D	
1	WIM Gross Weight		POE Gross Weight		
2					
3	Mean	64171.15	Mean	61057.25	
4	Standard Error	1393.64	Standard Error	1489.836	
5	Median	71380	Median	67655	
6	Mode	78720	Mode	105470	
7	Standard Deviation	19709.04	Standard Deviation	21069.46	Standard deviation and variance for each variable
8	Sample Variance	3.88E+08	Sample Variance	4.44E+08	
9	Kurtosis	-0.48604	Kurtosis	-0.66973	
10	Skewness	-0.50291	Skewness	-0.49413	
11	Range	92860	Range	91620	Ranges for each variable
12	Minimum	15180	Minimum	13850	
13	Maximum	108040	Maximum	105470	
14	Sum	12834230	Sum	12211450	
15	Count	200	Count	200	
16					

Excel and Minitab Tutorial

The values based on the sample data are

WIM scale gross weight: $R = 92,860$ pounds
POE scale gross weight: $R = 91,620$ pounds

The ranges are reasonably close in value, which seems to indicate that the variability in weights for the two scales is similar.

The standard deviation is a more-powerful measure of variation because it measures the deviation of all the values around the center. Again, Excel and Minitab have options for computing the standard deviation. The standard deviations for the two scales are

WIM scale gross weight: $s = 19,709.04$ pounds
POE scale gross weight: $s = 21,069.46$ pounds

These statistics show there is variation between truck weights. (Recall that the mean weights for trucks over both scales were less than 65,000 pounds.) These data also indicate that the WIM scale provided slightly less variation than the POE scale.

Up to this point, considering the graphical analyses we did in Chapter 2 and this numerical descriptive analysis, what are your conclusions about the effectiveness of the weigh-in-motion process? Are the measures given by the two scales close enough to use? The answer probably depends on how close the weights must be to be useful to the engineers at the transportation department. Table 3-5 summarizes the descriptive statistics.

FIGURE 3-8B

Minitab Descriptive Statistics Output—Truck Weight Data

Minitab Instructions:
1. Open file: Trucks.MTW.
2. Choose **Stat > Basic Statistics > Display Descriptive Statistics.**
3. In **Variables**, enter columns *WIM Gross Weight* and *POE Gross Weight*.
4. Click **Statistics.**
5. Check required statistics.
6. Click **OK. OK.**

MINITAB - Trucks.MPJ - [Session]

File Edit Data Calc Stat Graph Editor Tools Window Help

Descriptive Statistics: WIM Gross Wgt., POE Gross Weight

Variable	N	N*	Mean	SE Mean	StDev	Minimum	Q1	Median	Q3
WIM Gross Wgt.	200	0	64171	1394	19709	15180	49495	71380	78215
POE Gross Weight	200	0	61057	1490	21069	13850	44565	67655	77218

Variable	Maximum	Range
WIM Gross Wgt.	108040	92860
POE Gross Weight	105470	91620

Standard deviation for each variable

Ranges for each variable

STATISTICAL MEASURE	WIM SCALE	POE SCALE
Mean	64,171 lbs.	61,057 lbs.
Median	71,380	67,655
Mode	78,720	105,470
1st Quartile	49,885	45,255
3rd Quartile	78,125	77,112
Range	92,860	91,620
Standard Deviation	19,709	21,069

TABLE 3-5
Summary Statistics—
WIM versus POE
Weights

3-2: EXERCISES

Skill Development

3.20 Assume the following data set represents the population:

16	23	17	24	9	11	13	15
18	21	16	23	17	16	10	14

Determine the range, variance, and standard deviation for the data set.

3.21 The following data are a sample from a larger population.

33	42	39	17	27	32	40	37
30	35	37	19	34	37	41	35

Calculate the mean, median, range, interquartile range, variance, and standard deviation.

3.22 You are given the following data for the number of times a population of six families dined out during the previous month:

4	6	9	4	5	7

a. Compute the range for these data.
b. Compute the variance and the standard deviation.
c. Assume that these data represented a sample rather than a population. Compute the variance and the standard deviation. Discuss the difference between the values computed here and in part b.

3.23 For the following set of sample sales data, in dollars, compute the range, interquartile range, variance, and standard deviation.

$17.87	19.95	22.95	18.74	9.95
11.22	21.98	14.52	16.65	14.98

3.24 Assume the following sample represents vehicle speeds.

51	43	58	67	67	69	40	52
66	44	47	41	41	45	47	41

a. Determine the proportion of this data set that is within one standard deviation of the mean.
b. Determine the proportion of this data set that is within two standard deviations of the mean.
c. Determine the proportion of this data set that is within three standard deviations of the mean.

Business Applications

3.25 The Price Corporation has built six homes during the past year. The number of square feet in each home (treated as the population of interest) is listed as follows:

square feet = {1,560; 2,340; 1,990; 1,750; 4,000; 2,200}

a. Compute the range.
b. Compute the variance.
c. Compute the standard deviation.
d. Write a short paragraph that describes these data. Please feel free to also compute measures of the center and include these values in your discussion.

3.26 The Stop N' Go convenience chain recently selected a random sample of 10 customers. The store monitored the number of times each customer made a purchase at the store over a two-month period. The following data were collected.

10	19	17	19	12	20	20	15	16	13

Store executives are considering a promotion in which they reward frequent purchases with a small gift. They have decided that they will only give gifts to those shoppers whose number of visits in the previous two-month period is above the mean plus one standard deviation. Find the minimum number of visits required to receive a prize.

3.27 The marketing director for South East Insurance (see Problem 3.13) continues to worry about the increasing age of the company's policyholders. She wants to determine whether the new advertising campaign has helped retain younger customers. She has taken a sample of ten renewed policies and has found the following ages:

32	22	24	27	27
33	28	23	24	21

a. Compute the range, the interquartile range, and the standard deviation for these data.
b. Before the new advertising campaign, the average age of the customers was 37.8. Based on your calculations in part a, has the advertising campaign been effective in reducing the average age of the customers?

3.28 Grover's Pay n' Pak sells hardware supplies to "do-it-your-selfers." One of the things the company prides itself on is fast service. It uses a number system and takes customers in the order in which they arrive at the store. Recently, the assistant manager tracked the time customers spent in the store from the time they took a number until they left. A sample of 16 customers was selected, and the following data (measured in minutes) were recorded.

15	14	16	14	14	14	13	8
12	9	7	17	10	15	16	16

a. Compute the mean, median, mode, range, interquartile range, and standard deviation.
b. Develop a box and whisker plot for these data.

3.29 Welton Corporation makes dynamic random access memory chips (DRAMS) for use in personal computers. DRAMS are made on silicon wafers. The company's goal is to yield as many good chips from each wafer as possible in order to make more profit from its production operations. The following data represent the number of usable DRAM chips (yield) from each of the wafers:

488	449	510	551	548	569	413	491
544	457	472	432	426	461	469	415
477	484	505	485	487	485	554	497
493	479	579	535	595	474	566	436

a. Compute the following numerical measures for these yield data: (a) mean, (b) median, (c) mode, (d) range, (e) quartiles, (f) interquartile range, (g) variance, and (h) standard deviation.
b. Develop a box and whisker plot for these data.
c. Write a short report that describes the yield data.

Advanced Business Applications

3.30 A complaint was recently filed in Nevada by a California resident who claimed that drivers with California license plates on their cars were being unfairly singled out by Nevada law enforcement officers and given speeding tickets. The court ordered a study done in which the speeds on a particular section of Nevada highway were monitored with speed-measurement equipment. Speeds for only Nevada and California cars were recorded. The data for this test is in the file called *Speed-Test*.
a. For each state, construct a box and whisker plot.
b. Calculate the mean and median speed for vehicles from each state.

c. Compute the sample standard deviation, the range, and the interquartile range for vehicles from each state.
d. Write a report using the information generated in parts a, b, and c to inform the court about the speeds of vehicles from California and Nevada.

3.31 The B.T. Longmont Department Store has recently conducted a study related to the losses it has incurred due to shoplifting. The file called *Longmont* contains data that show the dollar losses over the past 17 months. Consider these data to be the population of interest.
a. Compute the mean, median, mode, range, variance, and standard deviation for these data.
b. Construct a box and whisker plot for the data.
c. Constuct a line chart for the 17 months.
d. Write a short report to the management of B.T. Longmont describing the shoplifting data.

3.32 The Amalgamated Sugar Company is in the process of revamping their maintenance program. As part of that effort, employees at the plant have collected equipment-downtime data for a sample of days from last year's records. Downtime is measured in seconds for each of the three shifts. The data are in the file called *Amalgamated*.
a. Compute the mean, median, mode, range, variance, and standard deviation for the downtime data for each shift individually.
b. Compute a box and whisker plot for each shift.
c. Write a short report that describes the data for the three shifts. Indicate whether the data seem to imply a difference between the three shifts in terms of equipment downtime.

3.33 The managers at the Capital Credit Union have to issue a report to the State Bank Commission regarding credit card balances for their customers. In response to this request, the managers have selected a random sample of their customers and have determined current credit card balances and genders of the cardholders. The resulting data are contained in the file called *Capital*.
a. Compute the mean, median, range, interquartile range, variance, and standard deviation of credit card balances for all customers in the sample.
b. Compute the mean, median, range, interquartile range, variance, and standard deviation of credit card balances for males and for females separately.
c. Draft a report to the State Bank Commission that describes the credit card balances. Specifically address any notable or systematic differences in the distribution of credit card balances between males and females.

3-3 USING THE MEAN AND THE STANDARD DEVIATION TOGETHER

In the previous sections, we introduced several important descriptive measures that are useful for transforming data into meaningful information. Two of the most important of these measures are the mean and the standard deviation. In this section, we discuss several statistical tools that combine these two.

COEFFICIENT OF VARIATION

The standard deviation measures the variation in a set of data. For decision makers, the standard deviation indicates how spread out a distribution is. For distributions having the same mean, the distribution with the largest standard deviation has the greatest relative spread. When two or more distributions have different means, the relative spread cannot be determined by merely comparing standard deviations.

The **coefficient of variation**, (*CV*), is used to measure the relative variation for distributions with different means.

Coefficient of Variation

The ratio of the standard deviation to the mean expressed as a percentage. The coefficient of variation is used to measure the relative variation in data.

The coefficient of variation for a population is computed using Equation 3-14, whereas Equation 3-15 is used for sample data.

Population Coefficient of Variation

$$CV = \frac{\sigma}{\mu}\,(100)$$

3-14

Sample Coefficient of Variation

$$CV = \frac{s}{\bar{x}}\,(100)$$

3-15

When the coefficients of variation for two or more distributions are compared, the distribution with the largest CV is said to have the greatest relative spread.

In finance, the CV measures the relative risk of a stock portfolio. Assume portfolio A has a collection of stocks that average a 12% return with a standard deviation of 3% and portfolio B has an average return of 6% with a standard deviation of 2%. We can compute the CV values for each as follows:

$$CV(A) = \frac{3}{12}\,(100) = 25\%$$

and

$$CV(B) = \frac{2}{6}\,(100) = 33\%$$

Even though portfolio B has a lower standard deviation, it would be considered more risky than portfolio A because B's CV is 33% and A's CV is 25%.

$\mathcal{E}$XAMPLE 3-14: COMPUTING THE COEFFICIENT OF VARIATION

Agra-Tech Industries Agra-Tech Industries has recently introduced feed supplements for both cattle and hogs that will increase the rate at which the animals gain weight. Three years of feedlot tests indicate that steers fed the supplement will weigh an average of 125 pounds more than those not fed the supplement. However, not every steer on the supplement has the same weight gain; results vary. The standard deviation in weight gain advantage for the steers in the three-year study has been 10 pounds.

Similar tests with hogs indicate those fed the supplement average 40 additional pounds compared with hogs not given the supplement. The standard deviation for the hogs was also 10 pounds. Even though the standard deviation is the same for both cattle and hogs, the mean added weight differs. Therefore the coefficient of variation is needed to compare relative variability. The coefficient of variation for each is computed using the following steps:

Step 1: **Collect the sample (or population) of data for the variable of interest.**
In this case, we have two sets of data: weight gain for cattle and weight gain for hogs.

Step 2:   Compute the mean and the standard deviation.
For the two data sets in this example, we get

$$\text{Cattle: } \bar{x} = 125 \text{ lbs. and } s = 10 \text{ lb}$$

$$\text{Hogs: } \bar{x} = 40 \text{ lbs. and } s = 10 \text{ lb}$$

Step 3:   Compute the coefficient of variation using Equation 3-14 (for populations) or Equation 3-15 (for samples).
Because the data in this example is from a sample, the *CV* is computed using

$$CV = \frac{s}{\bar{x}}(100)$$

For each data set, we get

$$CV(\text{cattle}) = \frac{10}{125}(100) = 8\%$$

$$CV(\text{hogs}) = \frac{10}{40}(100) = 25\%$$

These results indicate that hogs exhibit much greater relative variability in weight gain compared with cattle.

Excel and Minitab Tutorial

THE EMPIRICAL RULE

A tool that is helpful in describing data in certain circumstances is called the **Empirical Rule**. In order for the Empirical Rule to be used, the frequency distribution must be bell-shaped, such as the one shown in Figure 3-9.

Empirical Rule

If the data distribution is bell-shaped, then the interval:
$\mu \pm 1\sigma$ contains approximately 68% of the values
$\mu \pm 2\sigma$ contains approximately 95% of the values
$\mu \pm 3\sigma$ contains virtually all of the data values

Burger n' Brew—The standard deviation can be thought of as a measure of distance from the mean. Consider the Phoenix Burger n' Brew restaurant chain, which records the number of each hamburger option it sells each day at each location. The number of chili burgers sold each day for

FIGURE 3-9

Illustrating the Empirical Rule for the Bell-Shaped Distribution

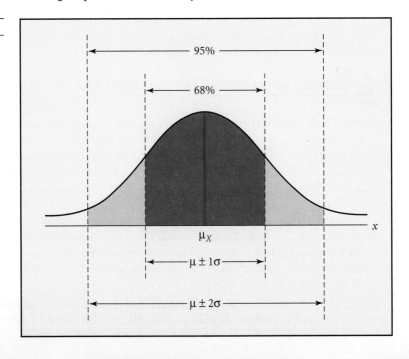

the past 365 days are in the file called *BurgerNBrew*. Figure 3-10 shows the frequency histogram for those data. The distribution is nearly *symmetrical* and approximately *bell-shaped*. The mean number of chili burgers sold was 15.1, with a standard deviation of 3.1.

The Empirical Rule is a very useful statistical concept for helping us understand the data in a bell-shaped distribution. In the Burger n' Brew example, with $\bar{x} = 15.1$ and $s = 3.1$, if we move one standard deviation in each direction from the mean, *approximately* 68% of the data should lie within the range:

$$15.1 \pm 1(3.1)$$

$$12.0 - - - - - - - - - - - - -18.2$$

The actual number of days Burger n' Brew sold between 12 and 18 chili burgers is 262. Thus, out of 365 days, 72% of the days Burger n' Brew sold between 12 and 18 chili burgers. (The reason that we didn't get exactly 68% is that the distribution in Figure 3-12 is not perfectly bell-shaped.)

If we look at the interval two standard deviations from either side of the mean, we would expect approximately 95% of the data. The interval is

$$15.1 \pm 2(3.1)$$
$$15.1 \pm 6.2$$

$$8.9 - - - - - - - - - - - - -21.30$$

Counting the values between these limits, we find 353 of the 365 values, or 97%. Again this is close to what the Empirical Rule predicted. Finally, according to the Empirical Rule, we would expect almost all of the data to fall within three standard deviations. The interval is

$$15.1 \pm 3(3.1)$$
$$15.1 \pm 9.3$$

$$5.80 - - - - - - - - - - - - -24.40$$

Looking at the data in Figure 3-10, we find that in fact all the data do fall within this interval.

FIGURE 3-10

Excel Histogram for Burger n' Brew Data

Excel Instructions:
1. Open file: BurgerNBrew.xls
2. Set up Bins (upper limit of each class)
3. Click on **Tools—Data Analysis—Histogram**.
4. Supply data range and bin range.
5. Check **Chart Output**.

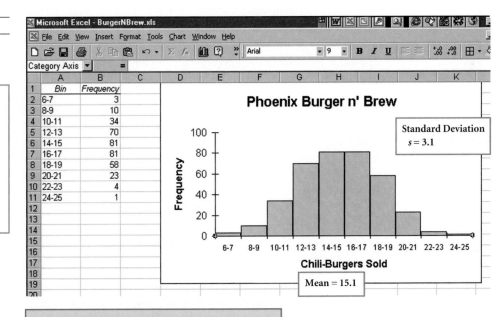

Bin	Frequency
6-7	3
8-9	10
10-11	34
12-13	70
14-15	81
16-17	81
18-19	58
20-21	23
22-23	4
24-25	1

Phoenix Burger n' Brew

Standard Deviation $s = 3.1$

Mean = 15.1

Minitab Instructions (for similar results):
1. Open file: BurgerNBrew.MTW.
2. Choose **Graph > Histogram**.
3. Click **Simple**.
4. Click **OK**.
5. In **Graph variables**, enter data column *Chili-Burgers Sold*.
6. Click **OK**.

Therefore, if we know only the mean and the standard deviation for a set of data, the Empirical Rule gives us a tool for describing how the data are distributed, if the distribution is bell-shaped.

TCHEBYSHEFF'S THEOREM

The Empirical Rule applies when a distribution is bell-shaped. But what about the many situations when a distribution is skewed and not bell-shaped? In these cases, we can use **Tchebysheff's theorem**.

Tchebysheff's Theorem

Regardless of how data are distributed, *at least* $(1 - 1/k^2)$ of the values will fall within k standard deviations of the mean. For example:

At least $(1 - \frac{1}{1}^2) = 0 = 0\%$ of the values will fall within $k = 1$ standard deviation of the mean.

At least $(1 - \frac{1}{2}^2) = \frac{3}{4} = 75\%$ of the values will lie within $k = 2$ standard deviations of the mean.

At least $(1 - \frac{1}{3}^2) = \frac{8}{9} = 89\%$ of the values will lie within $k = 3$ standard deviations of the mean.

Tchebysheff's theorem is conservative. It tells us nothing about the data within one standard deviation of the mean. Tchebysheff indicates that *at least* 75% of the data will fall within two standard deviations—it could be more. If we applied Tchebysheff's theorem to bell-shaped distributions, the percentage estimates are very low. The thing to remember is that Tchebysheff's theorem applies to *any distribution*. This gives it great flexibility.

STANDARDIZED DATA VALUES

When you are dealing with quantitative data, you will sometimes want to convert the measures to a form called **standardized data values**. This is especially useful when we wish to compare data from two or more distributions when the data scales for the two distributions are substantially different.

Standardized Data Values

The number of standard deviations a value is from the mean. Standardized data values are sometimes referred to as z-scores.

Human Resources—Consider a company that uses placement exams as part of its hiring process. The company currently will accept scores from either of two tests: AIMS Hiring and BHS-Screen. The problem is that the AIMS Hiring test has an average score of 2,000 and a standard deviation of 200, whereas the BHS-Screen test has an average score of 80 with a standard deviation of 12. (These means and standard deviations were developed from a large number of people who have taken the two tests.) How can the company compare applicants when the average scores and measures of spread are so different for the two tests? One approach is to *standardize* the test scores.

Suppose the company is considering two applicants, John and Mary. John took the AIMS Hiring test and scored 2,344, whereas Mary took the BHS-Screen and scored 95. Their scores can be standardized using Equation 3-16.

Standardized Population Data

$$z = \frac{x - \mu}{\sigma}$$ **3-16**

where:

x = Original data value
μ = Population mean
σ = Population standard deviation
z = Standard score (number of standard deviations x is from μ)

If you are working with sample data rather than a population, Equation 3-17 can be used to standardize the values.

Standardized Sample Data

$$z = \frac{x - \bar{x}}{s}$$

3-17

where:

z = The standard score
$\bar{x}$ = Sample mean
s = Sample standard deviation
x = Original data value

We can standardize the test scores for John and Mary using

$$z = \frac{x - \mu}{\sigma}$$

For AIMS Hiring test, the mean, μ, is 2,000, and the standard deviation, σ, equals 200. John's score of 2,344 converts to

$$z = \frac{2,344 - 2,000}{200}$$
$$z = 1.72$$

The BHS Screen has $\mu = 80$ and $\sigma = 12$. Mary's score of 95 converts to

$$z = \frac{95 - 80}{12}$$
$$z = 1.25$$

Compared to the average score on the AIMS Hiring test, John's score is 1.72 standard deviations higher. Mary's score is only 1.25 standard deviations higher than the average score on the BHS-Screen test. Therefore, even though the two tests used different scales, standardizing the data allows us to conclude John scored relatively better on his test than Mary did on her test.

SUMMARY: CONVERTING DATA TO STANDARDIZED VALUES

For a set of quantitative data, each data value can be converted to a corresponding standardized value by determining how many standard deviations the value is from the mean. Here are the steps to do this.

1. Collect the population or sample values for the quantitative variable of interest.

2. Compute the population mean and standard deviation or the sample mean and standard deviation.

3. Convert the values to standardized z values using Equation 3-16 or Equation 3-17. For populations,

$$z = \frac{x - \mu}{\sigma}$$

For samples,

$$z = \frac{x - \bar{x}}{s}$$

EXAMPLE 3-15: CONVERTING DATA TO STANDARDIZED VALUES

SAT and ACT Exams   Many colleges and universities require students to submit either SAT or ACT scores or both. One eastern university requires both exam scores. However, in assessing whether to admit a student, the university uses whichever exam score favors the student among all the applicants. Suppose the school receives 4,000 applications for admission. To determine which exam will be used for each student, the school will standardize the exam scores from both tests. To do this, it can use the following steps:

Step 1:   Collect data.
The university will collect the data for the 4,000 SAT scores and the 4,000 ACT scores for those students who applied for admission.

Step 2:   Compute the mean and standard deviation.
Assuming that these data reflect the population of interest for the university, the population mean is computed using

$$\text{SAT:} \quad \mu = \frac{\Sigma x}{N} = 1{,}255 \qquad\qquad \text{ACT:} \quad \mu = \frac{\Sigma x}{N} = 28.3$$

The standard deviation is computed using

$$\text{SAT:} \quad \sigma = \sqrt{\frac{\Sigma(x-\mu)^2}{N}} = 72 \qquad \text{ACT:} \quad \sigma = \sqrt{\frac{\Sigma(x-\mu)^2}{N}} = 2.4$$

Step 3: **Standardize the data.**
Convert the x values to z values using

$$z = \frac{x - \mu}{\sigma}$$

Suppose a particular applicant has an SAT score of 1,228 and an ACT score of 27. These test scores can be converted to standardized scores.

$$\text{SAT:} \quad z = \frac{x-\mu}{\sigma} = \frac{1{,}228 - 1{,}255}{72} = -0.375$$

$$\text{ACT:} \quad z = \frac{x-\mu}{\sigma} = \frac{27 - 28.3}{2.4} = -0.5417$$

The negative z values indicate that this student is below the mean on both the SAT and ACT exams. Because the university wishes to use the score that most favors the student, it will use the SAT score. The student is only 0.375 standard deviations below the SAT mean, compared with 0.5417 standard deviations below the ACT mean.

3-3: EXERCISES

Skill Development

3.34 Consider the following set of sample data.

16	23	17	24	9	11	13	15	15	23	18	16	17

  a. Compute the mean and standard deviation for these sample data.
  b. Determine the coefficient of variation for the set and interpret what it measures.
  c. Using Tchebysheff's Theorem, determine the range of values that should include at least 75% of the data. Count how many actually fell into this interval and discuss whether your interval range was, in fact, conservative.
  d. Assume that the distribution of values is bell-shaped and determine the range of values that should contain approximately 68% of the data values.

3.35 Two distributions of data are being analyzed. Distribution A has a mean of 500 and a standard deviation equal to 100. Distribution B has a mean of 10 and a standard deviation equal to 4.0. Based on this information, use the coefficient of variation to determine which distribution has a greater relative variation.

3.36 If a sample mean is known to be 500 and the sample standard deviation is 75, what is the standardized value for a value of $x = 615$?

3.37 Two distributions have the following characteristics:

Distribution A	Distribution B
$\mu = 45{,}600$	$\mu = 33.40$
$\sigma = 6{,}333$	$\sigma = 4.05$

If a value from distribution A is 50,000 and a value from distribution B is 40, convert each value to a standardized z value and indicate which one is relatively closer to its respective mean.

3.38 A population of unknown shape has a mean of 3,000 and a standard deviation of 200.
  a. Find the minimum proportion of observations in the population that are in the range 2,600 to 3,400.
  b. Determine the maximum proportion of the observations that are greater than 3,600.
  c. What statement could you make concerning the proportion of observations that are smaller than 2,400?

3.39 Consider the following data representing samples from two populations.

A	B
191	1,135
162	996
207	1,219
238	935
236	952
252	974
134	930
193	968

  a. Compute the standard deviation for each sample. Which has the largest dispersion (or spread) according to the standard deviation?
  b. Now compute the coefficient of variation for each variable and indicate which one has the greatest *relative* variation.

3.40 A sample contains 1,000 values. The histogram for this sample is bell-shaped. Approximately 950 values in the sample are known to be within $100 of the mean. Suppose the mean is $5,000. Use the Empirical Rule to perform the following:
  a. Calculate a value for the standard deviation.
  b. Determine the data value that is the 97.5th percentile.
  c. Calculate the z-score for the 16th percentile.

3.41 A population has a mean of 400 and a standard deviation of 30.
  a. Calculate the standardized z-score for the number 455 from this population.
  b. Determine the z-score for the mean value of 400.
  c. Find the proportion of data that have z–scores between -2 and 2 when the population is bell-shaped. Next, find the proportion of data that have z-scores between -2 and 2 when the population is highly skewed. Does this make a difference in your answer?

Business Applications

3.42 The Miller Distributing Company is investigating two different scheduling methods for its truck drivers. The following data reflect the number of delivery miles each driver drove per day for each of the scheduling methods.

Method 1	14	11	19	6	10
Method 2	26	5	9	6	14

  a. Compute the mean and the standard deviation for each of these methods. Assume the data are sample data.
  b. Compute the coefficient of variation for each method and discuss which scheduling method seems to provide the least relative variability in the distances traveled.
  c. Referring to part b, in this case would it be acceptable to compare standard deviations directly to compare relative variability? Explain your answer.

3.43 Sportway Manufacturing has been experimenting with new materials to use for golf ball covers. Two recently developed compounds have been shown to be equally resistant to cutting, and the development lab is now looking at the distance the balls will travel during a simulated drive. However, both distance and consistency are important for a golf ball. A sample of 10 balls with each type of cover was selected, and the following distances were measured (in yards) using a mechanical driver that struck each ball with the same force.

Type A	298	291	290	310	296	299	300	305	289	285
Type B	297	315	291	292	301	286	287	290	302	323

  a. A new technician records the next ball hit as traveling only 274. He says the ball was a Type B ball. Do you believe the technician? Use Tchebysheff's Theorem to provide calculations and reasoning to support your answer.
  b. The technician also recorded a ball hit 312 yards. However, he does not remember which type of ball it was. Help the technician decide which type of ball he

used for this experiment. Give reasons and calculations to support your answer. Use Tchebysheff's Theorem.
  c. Do you believe it is likely that one of these types of balls can be hit 325 yards? Explain your answer.

3.44 The Rippon Investment Company offers two different mutual funds. The stocks in the Growth Fund have generated an average return of 8%, with a standard deviation of 2%. The stocks in the Specialized Fund have generated an average return of 18%, with a standard deviation of 6%.
  a. Based on the data provided, which of these funds has exhibited greater relative variability? Use the proper statistical measure to make your determination.
  b. Suppose and investor who is very risk averse is interested in one of these two funds. Based strictly on relative variability, which fund would you recommend? Discuss.
  c. Suppose the distributions for the two stock funds had a bell-shaped distribution with the means and standard deviations previously indicated. Which fund would appear to be the best investment, assuming future returns will mimic past returns? Explain.

3.45 The division manager for Northern Pipe and Steel Company decided to implement a new incentive system for the managers of Northern's three plants. The plan called for a bonus to be paid the next month to the manager whose plant had the greatest relative improvement over the average monthly production volume. The following data reflected the historical production volumes at the three plants.

Plant 1	**Plant 2**	**Plant 3**
$\mu = 700$	$\mu = 2,300$	$\mu = 1,200$
$\sigma = 200$	$\sigma = 350$	$\sigma = 30$

At the close of the next month, the monthly output for the three plants was

Plant 1 = 810	Plant 2 = 2,600	Plant 3 = 1,320

Suppose the division manager awarded the bonus to the manager of Plant 2 because her plant increased its production by 300 units over the mean. This was a bigger increase than that of any of the other managers. Do you agree with who received the bonus this month? Explain, using the appropriate statistical measures to support your position.

3.46 Each week for the past 40 weeks the Ajax Taxi Company has collected data on the miles driven by four taxis. These data are in the file called *Ajax*. Combine the data from the four taxis into one variable with $n = 160$ observations.
  a. Develop a frequency distribution for this new variable.
  b. Standardize the data (z-values) and develop a frequency distribution for the standardized data values. Compare this distribution to the one computed for the raw scores in part a.
  c. Produce a box plot and determine if any of the taxis are being driven unusually small or large amounts. (Hint: Identify the mild and extreme outliers.)

Advanced Business Applications

3.47 🔘 The Environmental Protection Agency (EPA) tests all new cars and provides a mileage rating for city and highway driving conditions. Thirty cars for the 1998 model year were tested, and results are contained in the data file *Automobiles*. The file contains data on several variables. In this problem, focus on the city and highway mileage data.
  a. Calculate the sample mean miles per gallon for both city and highway driving for the 30 cars. Also calculate the sample standard deviation for the two mileage variables. Do the data tend to support the premise that cars will get better mileage on the highway than around town? Discuss.
  b. Referring to part a, what can the EPA conclude about the relative variability between car models for highway versus city driving? (Hint: Compute the appropriate measure to compare relative variability.)
  c. Assume that mileage ratings are approximately bell-shaped. Approximately what proportion of cars get at least as good a mileage in city driving conditions as the mean mileage for highway driving for all cars?

3.48 💿 Zepolle's Bakery makes a variety of bread types that it sells to supermarket chains in the area. One of Zepolle's problems is the number of loaves of each type of bread sold each day by the chain stores varies considerably, making it difficult to know how many loaves to make. A sample of daily demand data is contained in the file called *Bakery*.
  a. Which bread type has the highest average daily demand?
  b. Develop a frequency distribution for each bread type.
  c. Which bread type has the highest standard deviation in demand?
  d. Which bread type has the greatest relative variability? Which type has the lowest relative variability?
  e. Assuming that these sample data are representative of demand during the year, determine how many loaves of each type of bread should be made so demand would be met on at least 75% of the days during the year.
  f. Create a new variable called Total Loaves Sold. On which day of the week is the average for total loaves sold the highest?

Summary and Conclusions

Transforming data into useful information is an important activity for business decision makers. Chapter 3 has introduced a variety of numerical measures that can be used either by themselves or in conjunction with the graphical techniques introduced in Chapter 2.

These measures can be computed for the population as a whole or from a sample taken from the population.

Two main categories of measures were introduced. These were measures of the center and measures of spread or variation.

FIGURE 3-11

Summary of Numerical Statistical Measures

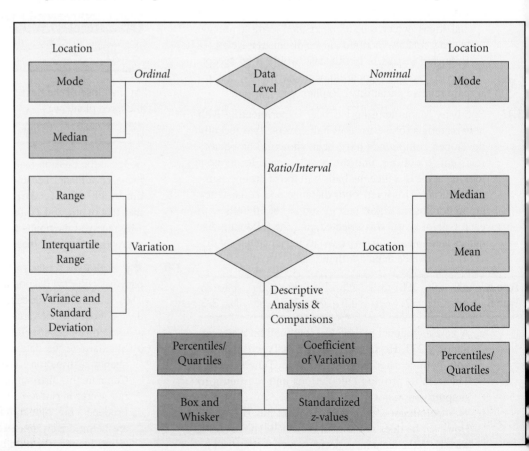

The two most frequently used measures of central location are the mean and the median. Generally, the mean is preferred. However, when the data are highly skewed or when the data level is ordinal, the median is preferred. Other measures of location, including the mode, percentiles, and quartiles, were introduced.

The most frequently used measure of variation is the standard deviation. This measure uses all the data and measures the spread of the individual observations around the mean. Other measures include the range and the interquartile range. Figure 3-11 summarizes the measures of location and spread that were discussed in this chapter.

When the numerical measures introduced in this chapter are effectively combined with the graphical techniques from Chapter 2, you will have the capability of transforming data into information. These concepts and skills will be utilized throughout the remainder of this text and will be highly valuable to you in other classes and in your careers after graduation.

EQUATIONS

Population Mean

$$\mu = \frac{\sum_{i=1}^{N} x_i}{N} \qquad \text{3-1}$$

Sample Mean

$$\bar{x} = \frac{\sum_{i=1}^{n} x_i}{n} \qquad \text{3-2}$$

Weighted Mean for a Population

$$\mu_W = \frac{\sum w_i x_i}{\sum w_i} \qquad \text{3-3}$$

Weighted Mean for a Sample

$$\bar{x}_w = \frac{\sum w_i x_i}{\sum w_i} \qquad \text{3-4}$$

Percentile Location Value

$$i = \frac{p}{100}(n+1) \qquad \text{3-5}$$

Range

$$R = \text{Maximum Value} - \text{Minimum Value} \qquad \text{3-6}$$

Interquartile Range

Interquartile Range = Third Quartile − First Quartile   **3-7**

Population Variance

$$\sigma^2 = \frac{\sum_{i=1}^{N}(x_i - \mu)^2}{N} \qquad \text{3-8}$$

Population Variance Shortcut

$$\sigma^2 = \frac{\sum(x - \mu)^2}{N} = \frac{\sum x^2 - \frac{(\sum x)^2}{N}}{N} \qquad \text{3-9}$$

Population Standard Deviation

$$\sigma = \sqrt{\sigma^2} = \sqrt{\frac{\sum_{i=1}^{N}(x_i - \mu)^2}{N}} \qquad \text{3-10}$$

Sample Variance

$$s^2 = \frac{\sum_{i=1}^{n}(x_i - \bar{x})^2}{n-1} \qquad \text{3-11}$$

Sample Variance Shortcut

$$s^2 = \frac{\sum x^2 - \frac{(\sum x)^2}{n}}{n-1} \qquad \text{3-12}$$

Sample Standard Deviation

$$s = \sqrt{s^2} = \sqrt{\frac{\sum_{i=1}^{n}(x_i - \bar{x})^2}{n-1}} \qquad \text{3-13}$$

Population Coefficient of Variation

$$CV = \frac{\sigma}{\mu}(100) \qquad \text{3-14}$$

Sample Coefficient of Variation

$$CV = \frac{s}{\bar{x}}(100) \qquad \text{3-15}$$

Standardized Population Data

$$z = \frac{x - \mu}{\sigma} \qquad \text{3-16}$$

Standardized Sample Data

$$z = \frac{x - \bar{x}}{s} \qquad \text{3-17}$$

Key Terms

Box and Whisker Plots, 88
Coefficient of Variation, 105
Data Array, 79
Empirical Rule, 106

Interquartile Range, 96
Left-Skewed Data, 80
Mean, 74
Median, 79

Mode, 82
Parameter, 74
Percentiles, 86
Quartiles, 88

Range, 95	**Standardized Data Values,** 108	**Variance,** 97
Right-Skewed Data, 80	**Statistic,** 74	**Variation,** 95
Skewed Data, 80	**Symmetric Data,** 80	**Weighted Mean,** 85
Standard Deviation, 98	**Tchebysheff's Theorem,** 108	

CHAPTER EXERCISES

Conceptual Questions

3.49 Discuss the circumstances under which you would prefer the median to the mean as a measure of location.

3.50 Considering the relative positions of the mean, median, and mode,
a. Draw a symmetrical distribution and label the three measures of location.
b. Draw a left-skewed distribution and label the three measures of location.
c. Draw a right-skewed distribution and label the three measures of location.

3.51 The marketing manager for Sweetright Cola has just received the results of two separate marketing studies performed in the Ohio Valley market region. One study was based on a random sample of 300 people, and it indicated that the mean income is $2,450 per month. The second study was based on a random sample of 400 people, and it indicated that the mean income in the region is $2,375 per month. The manager is confused. Should he have expected the two samples to yield exactly the same mean? Why or why not? Also, is it reasonable to believe that a sample mean should exactly equal the mean of the population? Discuss.

3.52 Discuss the advantages and disadvantages of using a range as a measure of spread in a set of data.

3.53 At almost every university in the United States, the university computes student grade point averages. The following scale is typically used by universities:

A = 4 points	B = 3 points	C = 2 points	D = 1 point	F = 0 points

Discuss what, if any, problems might exist when GPAs for two students are compared? What about comparing GPAs for students from two different universities?

3.54 Why is it inappropriate to compare the standard deviations of two or more distributions with different means? What measure is more appropriate? Discuss this measure and indicate what large versus small values of the measure imply.

3.55 Explain in your own terms, and through an example that you develop, why the standard deviation is considered a measure of dispersion.

Business Applications

3.56 Ivan Horton is a building contractor whose company builds many homes every year. In planning for each job, Ivan needs some idea about the direct labor hours required to build a home. He has collected sample information on the labor hours for 10 jobs during the past year.

645	802	791	651	653	542	418	695	552	575

a. Calculate the mean for this sample and explain what it means.
b. Calculate the median for this sample.
c. Calculate the variance and the standard deviation.
d. If Ivan had to select the mean or the median as the measure of location for direct labor hours, what factors about each should he consider before making the decision? Which measure would you suggest he use?

3.57 The Hillside Bowling Alley manager selected a random sample of his league customers. He asked them to record the number of lines they bowl during December, including league and open bowling. The reason for his interest in this data is that he is planning to offer a special discount to customers who bowl more than a specified number of games each month. The sample of eight people produced the following data:

13	32	12	9	16	17	16	12

a. Compute the mean for these sample data.
b. Compute the median for these sample data.
c. Compute the mode for these sample data.
d. Calculate the variance and the standard deviation for these sample data.
e. Note that one person bowled 32 lines. What effect, if any, does this large value have on each of the three measures of location? Discuss.
f. For these sample data, which measure of location provides the best measure of the center of the data? Discuss.
g. Given the sample data, suppose the manager wishes to give discounts to bowlers in the top quartile. What should the minimum number of games bowled be in order to receive a discount?

3.58 After performing the analysis on the Hillside Bowling Alley, the manager in the previous exercise collected data for a second bowling alley owned by his company. These data showed an average lines bowled of 10, with a standard deviation of 2. Do the bowlers at this second alley exhibit relatively more variation in the number of games bowled in December than those at the Hillside alley? Use the appropriate measures to make your point.

3.59 The Wilnet Development Company proposed building a new housing development in Warwick, Rhode Island. The city's planning department required that the developer conduct a traffic study as part of project planning. One part of that traffic study involved analyzing the trips from home made by residents in the "impact area" located near the proposed project location. The Wilnet Company selected 15 families at random from those in the impact area and asked them to keep track of their trips from home during the next week. The data returned to the Wilnet Company are shown.

38	44	11	26	19	13	45	27	11	19	19	26	20	19	34

a. Compute the mean for these data and describe what it measures.

b. Compute the median for these data and compare it with the mean found in part a.

c. Compute the mode for these data.

d. Compute the sample standard deviation and discuss what it measures.

e. Compute the interquartile range for these data and discuss why it is often preferred as a measure of variation over the range.

f. Use the values computed in previous parts of this problem to develop a box and whisker plot. Write a short statement explaining what the plot shows.

3.60 The Indiana Transportation Department recently set up a speed-check station on one of the interstate highways and collected speed data on 12 vehicles selected at random during a four-hour period. The data collected (in miles per hour) are

62	75	81	64	81	66	70	70	69	73	72	75

a. Compute the average speed for the sample.

b. Compute the median speed for the sample data.

c. Compute the mode speed for these sample data.

d. Compute the variance and the standard deviation of these sample data.

3.61 The Norton Oil Company has 20 oil wells operating in the Gulf of Mexico. The output of these wells has been recorded in terms of barrels per day pumped, as follows.

800	100	230	700	1,900	300	400	700	250	500
340	670	340	250	450	700	500	200	75	1,200

a. Compute the mean daily production for these 20 wells. Assume the data represent the population of interest.

b. Determine the median oil production per day for this population.

c. Norton Oil will cease oil production in those oil wells that are below the 33rd percentile. Determine which oil wells will be closed.

3.62 A simple random sample of six oil wells was selected from the population of 20 Norton Oil Company wells shown in Exercise 3-61. This sample was

700	700	670	700	1,200	450

a. Describe the method that is used to determine such a sample.

b. Compute the median for the sample.

c. Compute the mean for the sample.

d. Does it trouble you that there are three "700s" contained in the sample? Before answering this question, make sure that you review the definition of a random sample. Explain why you are either troubled or not troubled.

3.63 Since deregulation has taken place, the airline industry has undergone substantial changes with respect to ticket prices. Many discount fares are available if a customer knows how to obtain the discounts. Many travelers complain that they get a different price every time they call. The American Consumer Institute recently priced tickets between Spokane, Washington, and St. Louis, Missouri. The passenger was to fly coach class, round-trip, and stay seven days. Calls were made directly to airlines and to travel agents with the following results. Note that the data reflect round-trip airfare.

$229	$345	$599	$229	$429	$605
$339	$339	$229	$279	$344	$407

a. Compute the mean quoted airfare.

b. Compute the variance and the standard deviation in airfares quoted. Treat the data as a sample.

3.64 The C. A. Whitman Investment Company recently offered two mutual funds to its customers. A mutual fund is a group of stocks and bonds that is managed by an investment company. Individuals purchase shares of the mutual fund, and the investment company uses the money to buy stocks. Many investors feel comfortable with a mutual fund because their money is not tied up in one or two stocks but is spread over many stocks, thereby, they hope, reducing the risk.

Each of the two mutual funds offered by C. A. Whitman currently has 60 stocks. During the past six months, the average increase in stock prices in fund A has been $3.30, with a standard deviation of $1.25. The stocks in fund B have shown an average increase of $8.00, with a standard deviation of $3.50.

a. Based on this information, which of the two funds has stocks that have shown the greater relative variability?

b. Compute the appropriate measures and explain why we cannot simply compare standard deviations in this case.

3.65 A survey of local airline passengers shows that the mean height of male passengers is 69.5 inches, with a standard deviation of 2.5 inches. The mean weight is 177 pounds, with a standard deviation of 12 pounds. Which of the two distributions has the greater relative variability?

3.66 The data in the file named *Fast100* was collected by D. L. Green & Associates, a regional investment management company that specializes in working with clients who wish to invest in smaller companies with high growth potential. To aid the investment firm in locating appropriate investments for its clients, Sandra Williams, an assistant client manager, put together the database on 100 fast-growing companies. The data were compiled in the late summer of 2001. The database consists of data on eight variables for each of the 100 companies. Note that in some cases data are not available. A code of -99 has been used to signify missing data. These data must be omitted from any calculations.

a. Select the variable Sales. Develop a frequency distribution and histogram for Sales.

b. Compute the mean, median, and standard deviation for the Sales variable.

c. Determine the interquartile range for the Sales variable.

d. Construct a box and whisker plot for the Sales variable. Identify any outliers. Discard the outliers and recalculate the measures in b.

e. Each year a goal is set for sales. Next year's goal will be to have an average sales level that is at this year's 65th percentile. Identify next year's sales goal.

3.67 The file *McCormick* contains selected information from the 1997 annual report for McCormick & Company, Inc., the leader in the manufacture, marketing, and distribution of spices, seasonings, and flavors for the food industry. Use the table data to answer the following questions. (All values are in millions of dollars.)

a. For 1988 to 1997, compute the mean, median, and standard deviation for each variable, assuming that the 10 years represent a sample.

b. Convert each value to a z-value. Then analyze the z-values for each year. Treating all variables as being on an equal footing, which year seems to stand out as most unique from the others?

3.68   The file *Industrial Rents* contains the average annual cost per square foot for Class A warehouses in 51 selected cities for the fourth quarter for 1996 and 1997. Use this information to:

a. Construct a histogram of square-footage costs for each time period.

b. Compute the mean, median, and standard deviation for cost per square foot.

c. Devlop a box and whisker plot for cost per square foot.

d. Use the information generated in parts a, b, and c to prepare a report on the square-footage costs for Class A warehouses in the 51 cities in the sample.

Advanced Business Applications

3.69   The manager of the Clark Fork Station Restaurant recently selected a random sample of 18 customers and kept track of how long the customers were required to wait from the time they arrived at the restaurant until they were actually served dinner. This study resulted from several complaints the manager had received from customers saying that their wait time was unduly long and that it appeared that the objective was to keep people waiting in the lounge for as long as possible to increase the lounge business. The following data were recorded, with time measured in minutes.

34	24	43	56	74	20	19	33	55
43	54	34	27	34	36	24	54	39

a. Compute the mean waiting time for this sample of customers.

b. Compute the median waiting time for this sample of customers.

c. Compute the variance and standard deviation of waiting time for this sample of customers.

d. Develop a frequency distribution using six classes each with a class width of 10. Make the lower limit of the first class 15.

e. Develop a frequency histogram for the frequency distribution.

f. Constuct a box and whisker plot of this data.

g. The manager is considering giving a complimentary drink to customers whose waiting time is longer than the third quartile. Determine the minimum number of minutes a customer would have to wait in order to receive a complimentary drink.

3.70   Stock investors often look to beat the performance of the S&P 500 Index, which generally serves as a yardstick for the market as a whole. The following table shows a comparison of five-year cumulative total shareholder returns for Idaho Power Company common stock (NYSE Symbol: IDA), the S&P 500 Index, and the Edison Electric Institute (EEI) 100 Electric Utilities Index. The data assumes that $100 was invested on December 31, 1992, with returns compounded monthly. Construct appropriate statistical measures that illustrate the performance of the three investment options for

1992 through 1997. How well has Idaho Power Company performed during this period compared with the S&P 500? How well has it performed relative to its industry?

Year	Idaho Power	S&P 500	EEI 100 Electric Utilities
1992	$100.00	$100.00	$100.00
1993	117.38	110.08	111.15
1994	97.62	111.53	98.29
1995	134.11	153.45	128.78
1996	147.92	188.69	130.32
1997	189.73	251.63	166.00

3.71   The Smithfield Agricultural Company operates in the Midwest. The company owns and leases a total of 34,000 acres of prime farmland. Most of the crops are grain. Because of its size, the company can afford to do a great amount of testing to determine what seed types produce greatest yields. Recently, the company tested three types of corn seed on test plots. The following values were observed after the first year.

	Seed Type A	Seed Type B	Seed Type C
Mean bushels/acre	88	56	100
Standard deviation	25	15	16

a. Based on the results of this testing, which seed seems to produce the greatest average yield per acre? Comment on the type of testing controls that should have been used to make this study valid.

b. Suppose the company is interested in consistency. Which seed type shows the least relative variability?

c. Using the Empirical Rule, describe the production distribution for each of the three seed types.

d. Suppose you were a farmer and had to obtain at least 135 bushels per acre to escape bankruptcy. Which seed type would you plant? Explain your choice.

e. Rework your answer to part d assuming the farmer needed 115 bushels per acre instead.

3.72   The B. L. Williams Company makes tennis balls. The company has two manufacturing plants. The plant in Portland, Maine, is a unionized plant with an average daily production of 34,000 tennis balls. The output varies, with a standard deviation of 4,500 tennis balls per day. The San Antonio, Texas, plant is nonunion and is quite a bit smaller than the Portland plant. The San Antonio plant averages 12,000 tennis balls per day, with a standard deviation of 3,000.

Recently, the production manager was giving a speech to the Association of Sporting Goods Manufacturers. In that speech he stated that the B. L. Williams Company has been having real problems with its union plant maintaining consistency in production output and that the problem is not as large at the nonunion plant.

Based on the production data, was the manager justified in drawing the conclusions he made in the speech? Discuss and support your discussion with any appropriate calculations.

3.73   The Internal Revenue Service has come under a great deal of criticism in recent years for various actions it is purported to have taken against U.S. citizens related to collect ing federal income taxes. The IRS is also criticized for the complexity of the tax code, although the tax laws are actually written by congressional staff and passed by Congress. For the past few years, one of the country's biggest tax-preparation companies has sponsored an event in which 50 certified public accountants from all sizes of CPA firms are asked to determine the tax owed for a fictitious citizen. The IRS is also asked to determine the "correct" tax owed. Last year, the "correct" figure stated by the IRS was $11,560. The file *Taxes* contains the data for the 50 accountants.

a. Compute a new variable that is the difference between the IRS number and the number determined by each accountant.
b. For the new variable computed in part a, develop a frequency distribution.
c. For the new variable computed in part a, determine the mean, median, and standard deviation.
d. Determine the percentile that would be attached to the "correct" tax figure if the IRS figure were one of the CPA's estimated tax figures. Describe what this implies about the agreement between the IRS and tax consultants around the country.

3.74 The Soft-Sole Shoe Company is considering opening a new shoe outlet in a U.S. city. As part of the company's analysis, the managers have gained access to data on a target group of cities. To avoid bias, the names of the cities have been omitted from the data file *Cities*. The first step in the analysis is to analyze the populations of these potential franchise locations.

a. Compute the appropriate descriptive statistical measures for this variable.
b. Construct a frequency histogram.
c. The company is only interested in locating outlets in cities with populations above the 84th percentile. Determine this value for the data.
d. If the populations were bell-shaped, determine the 84th percentile. Discuss what this says about whether this data could be assumed to be bell-shaped.

3.75 The Soft-Sole Shoe Company referred to in the previous problem knows that income levels in a city will be important to the success of the new store. Using the data file *Cities*, locate the income variables for manufacturing workers and white-collar workers.

a. Develop a frequency histogram for both variables.
b. Compute the mean, median, and mode for each variable.
c. Convert each income to a *z*-score within its own group.
d. If the Soft-Sole Shoe Company will consider only companies with white-collar and manufacturing incomes over two standard deviations above the mean for the entire group, which cities (by number) are still in the running?

3.76 Continuing to work with the data file *Cities* and the Soft-Sole Shoe Company's location decision, locate the income variables for manufacturing workers and for white-collar workers.

a. Compute a new variable that is the paired difference between manufacturing and white-collar incomes.
b. Construct a frequency distribution for the paired difference variable.
c. Compute the descriptive measures for this new variable and write a short report that summarizes your findings. Discuss primarily what your measures indicate about whether manufacturing jobs are more lucrative than white-collar incomes, any outliers, and the proportion of cities in which manufacturing incomes are larger than white-collar incomes.

3.77 Sandra Williams of D. L. Green & Associates has been asked to prepare an analysis on the earnings per share for the companies located in the *Fast 100* database.

a. Select the variable EPS. Develop a frequency distribution and histogram for EPS.
b. Compute the mean, median, and standard deviation for EPS.
c. Determine the interquartile range for EPS.
d. Constuct a box and whisker plot for EPS.
e. Sandra Williams is certain that the number of negative earnings per share will stand out in the data. She, therefore, wishes to determine the largest negative value and its percentile. Provide these measures to her for her report.

3.78 The file *Home-Prices* contains information about single-family housing prices in 100 metropolitan areas in the United States. The price variable represents the median price of homes in each area. In preparation for a speech to a national real estate association, you plan to use these data to illustrate real estate patterns. Discuss why it might be appropriate to have recorded the median price home in each area rather than the mean.

a. Compute the mean of the median home prices. Is this a reasonable measure to compute? Why or why not?
b. Construct a frequency histogram for the annualized price-change variable for 1993 to 1998.
c. Referring to part b, compute the mean, median, and standard deviation for the annualized price change of homes in the sampled areas.
d. As an investment, you have purchased a house that just happened to sell for the median price in your metropolitan area of $109,333. You were hoping that you could obtain a quick profit and sell your house for $120,000. Considering the analysis you have performed previously, do you think this is realistic? Support your answer with reasons and calculations.

CASE 3-A:

Wilson Corporation

The certified letter was delivered about 4:00 P.M. to Andrew Wilson, CEO and principle owner of the Wilson Corporation. It was from the state Department of Environmental Services, and it sent shivers down Andrew's spine. In bold-faced type at the top of the letter was the message:

"Notice of Water Quality Violation—Wilson Corporation"

The letter went on to outline the situation. The state had performed tests at the outflow location from Wilson's main processing plant and had found problems with nitrates and pH levels. A hearing was scheduled in two weeks to outline the issues and to assess damages to be paid by the Wilson Corp. In the

FIGURE 3-12

Excel Worksheet for Water Samples Data

	A	B	C	D	E	F
1	Temp	pH	Nitrates	Phosphates	Oxygen	CO2
2	16.5	7.82	8.2	0.15	7.00	13
3	16.1	7.9	6.7	0.52	10.00	37
4	16.6	7.9	7.3	0.54	10.00	10
5	17	7.82	6.8	0.42	10.00	10
6	16.5	7.8	7.1	0.66	9.00	15
7	16.2	7.5	7.4	0.47	10.00	15
8	16.4	7.6	6.4	0.35	10.00	10
9	16	7.5	7.2	0.79	9.00	10
10	17	7.6	2.5	0.32	8.00	10

(Microsoft Excel - Wilson Water.xls)

meantime, all effluent from the plant was to be immediately halted.

Accompanying the letter was a computer disk file containing data from 95 water samples selected at the Wilson plant over a three-week period. The file is labeled *Wilson Water*. Figure 3-12 illustrates the type of data that was included in the file.

Andrew reached for his phone to make two calls. The first was to Randy Glover, his production scheduler. He explained the prob-lem and told Randy to immediately stop production and schedule an employee meeting at 8:00 the next morning.

The second call went to Jennifer Scranton, the company's environmental liaison. Andrew explained the essence of the letter and the action he was taking. He wanted Jennifer to halt all other work and immediately perform an analysis on the sample data sup-plied by the state. Andrew wanted a comprehensive descriptive analysis as soon as possible so he could prepare for the hearing.

CASE 3-B:

Holcome Financial Planners

Marsha Holcome founded Holcome Financial Planners almost three years ago, after working for Merrill Lynch for more than 14 years. Although she was able to bring several clients with her, she found that getting the business started was pretty much a "chicken and egg" problem. Potential customers would ask her how much money she had under management. When she responded with a rel-atively small number, the customers would tell her to call back when she had a bigger portfolio and a better track record. However, without customers she couldn't have much money under manage-ment, so it was a circular problem.

Marsha countered this problem by attempting to provide superior service to major brokerage firms. One talent on which she prided herself was her ability to analyze an industry.

Recently she had met with a potential client who was interested in the computer industry. At the close of the meeting, Marsha agreed to prepare an industry analysis to show the client what she could do.

Marsha's assistant collected appropriate data using Standard and Poor's industry publications and generated a data file called *Computer Industry*. Figure 3-13 illustrates the types of data col-lected. Now Marsha had to get to work. She wanted to prepare a first-rate descriptive analysis of the data using graphs, charts, and appropriate numerical measures. It would be important to break out the analysis by type of computer company, too. She decided to develop a clear written narrative to go along with the descriptive information. A key to success was the way the finished product looked. It had to have "eye appeal," as well as be informative.

FIGURE 3-13

Excel Worksheet for Computer Industry Financial Data

	A	B	C	D	E	F	G	H	I	J	K
1	Company	Type of Company	Risk	Rev (millions) 97	Rev (millions) 96	% change	Oper Inc. 97	Oper Inc 96	% change	Recent Price	Current Ratio
2	Compaq Computer	1	2	24584	18109	1.36	3532	2162	1.634	33.50	2.3
3	Dell Computer	1	2	12327	7759	1.59	1383	761	1.817	66.00	1.5
4	IBM	1	2	78508	75947	1.03	13116	12272	1.069	133.50	1.2
5	Micron Electronics	1	3	1956	1765	1.11	172	127	1.354	16.75	1.6
6	Apple Computer	1	2	7081	9833	0.72	-284	-1047	0.271	17.13	1.9
7	Gateway 2000, Inc.	1	3	6294	5035	1.25	377	418	0.902	54.88	1.5
8	Hewlett-Packard	1	2	42895	38420	1.12	5895	5023	1.174	54.88	1.9
9	Intergraph Corp.	1	2	1124	1095	1.03	6.5	17.6	0.369	6.75	1.7

(Microsoft Excel - Computer Industry.xls)

CASE 3-C:

AJ's Fitness Center

A. J. Reeser was mildly surprised at the quality of the report that the intern from the local university had prepared for him. (Refer to Case 2-A in Chapter 2. The data file is *AJFitness*.) The report contained a wide variety of informative charts and graphs that effectively displayed the data. When A. J. had given the assignment, he had asked the intern to limit the descriptive analysis to charts and graphs. He wasn't sure what to expect. Now that he could see how good "this kid" was, he wanted more analysis.

When the knock on the door came, A. J. realized how quickly time had passed as he was reading the survey report. As the intern settled into the chair to the right of A. J.'s desk, the phone rang but A. J. ignored it. He stretched out his hand to the young intern and congratulated him on such a fine job.

"Now that I know how good you are, I need you to take this project a step further," A. J. said with a big grin. "What I need you to do now is combine the graphical analysis you have already done with a complete numerical analysis of the data. I want you to fully analyze this survey using whatever statistics will help, and then put your work in a full report."

After discussing the graphs and charts for a few minutes, A. J. said he would like the revised report next week. He suggested that they meet for dinner next Thursday to take a look at it.

General References

1. Albright, Christian S., Wayne L. Winston, and Christopher Zappe, *Data Analysis and Decision Making With Microsoft Excel* (Pacific Grove, CA: Duxbury, 1999).
2. Berenson, Mark L., and David M. Levine, *Basic Business Statistics: Concepts and Applications*, 7th ed. (Upper Saddle River, NJ: Prentice Hall, 1999).
3. Dodge, Mark, and Craig Stinson, *Running Microsoft Excel 2000* (Redmond, WA: Microsoft Press, 1999).
4. *Microsoft Excel 2000* (Redmond, WA: Microsoft Corp., 1999).
5. *Minitab for Windows Version 13* (State College, PA: Minitab, 2000).
6. Siegel, Andrew F., *Practical Business Statistics*, 4th ed. (Burr Ridge, IL: Irwin, 2000).
7. Tukey, John W., *Exploratory Data Analysis* (Reading, MA: Addison-Wesley, 1977).

CHAPTERS 1-3

Special Review Section

This is the first of two special review sections in this text. These sections, which are presented using block diagrams and flowcharts, are intended to help you tie together the material from several key chapters. These sections are not a substitute for reading and studying the chapters covered by the review. However, you can use this review material to add to your understanding of the individual topics in the chapters.

CHAPTERS 1–3

Chapters 1 to 3 introduce data, data collection, and statistical tools for describing data. The steps needed to gather "good" statistical data, transform it to usable information, and present the information in a manner that allows good decisions are outlined in the following figures.

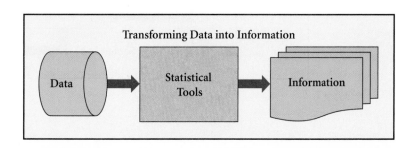

A Typical Application Sequence

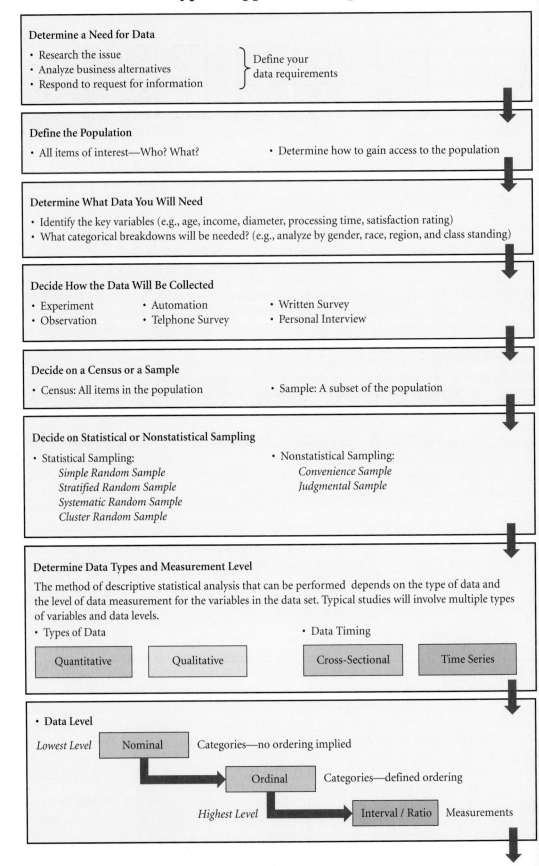

Determine a Need for Data

- Research the issue
- Analyze business alternatives
- Respond to request for information

} Define your data requirements

Define the Population

- All items of interest—Who? What?
- Determine how to gain access to the population

Determine What Data You Will Need

- Identify the key variables (e.g., age, income, diameter, processing time, satisfaction rating)
- What categorical breakdowns will be needed? (e.g., analyze by gender, race, region, and class standing)

Decide How the Data Will Be Collected

- Experiment
- Observation
- Automation
- Telephone Survey
- Written Survey
- Personal Interview

Decide on a Census or a Sample

- Census: All items in the population
- Sample: A subset of the population

Decide on Statistical or Nonstatistical Sampling

- Statistical Sampling:
  Simple Random Sample
  Stratified Random Sample
  Systematic Random Sample
  Cluster Random Sample
- Nonstatistical Sampling:
  Convenience Sample
  Judgmental Sample

Determine Data Types and Measurement Level

The method of descriptive statistical analysis that can be performed depends on the type of data and the level of data measurement for the variables in the data set. Typical studies will involve multiple types of variables and data levels.

- Types of Data

  | Quantitative | Qualitative |

- Data Timing

  | Cross-Sectional | Time Series |

- Data Level

  Lowest Level | Nominal | Categories—no ordering implied

  | Ordinal | Categories—defined ordering

  Highest Level | Interval / Ratio | Measurements

Select Graphical Presentation Tools

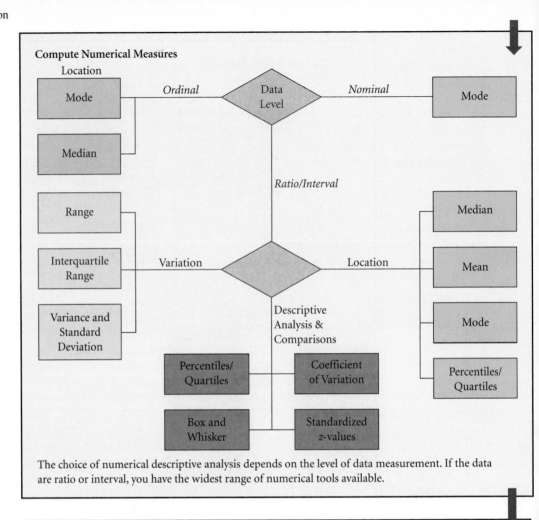

Compute Numerical Measures

The choice of numerical descriptive analysis depends on the level of data measurement. If the data are ratio or interval, you have the widest range of numerical tools available.

Write the Statistical Report

There is no one set format for writing a statistical report. However, there are a few suggestions you may find useful.

- *Lay the foundation:*
  Provide background and motivation for the analysis.

- *Describe the data collection methodology:*
  Explain how the data were gathered and the sampling techniques were used.

- *Use a logical sequence:*
  Follow a systematic plan for presenting your findings and analysis.

- *Label figures and tables by number:*
  Employ a consistent numbering and labeling format.

EXERCISES

Integrative Application Exercises

Chapters 1 to 3 have introduced you to the basics of descriptive statistics. Many of the business application problems, advanced business application problems, and cases in these chapters will give you practice at performing descriptive statistical analysis. However, too often you are told which procedure you should use, or you can surmise which to use by the location of the exercise. It is important that you learn to identify the appropri-

ate procedure on your own in order to solve problems for test purposes. But more important, this ability is essential throughout your career when you are required to select procedures for the tasks you will undertake. The following exercises will provide you with identification practice.

SR.1 Go to your university library and obtain the *Statistical Abstract of the United States*.

a. Construct a frequency distribution for unemployment rate by state for the most current year available.

b. Justify your choice of class limits and number of classes.

c. Locate the unemployment rate for the state in which you are attending college. (1) What proportion of the unemployment rates are below that of your state? (2) Describe the distribution's shape with respect to symmetry. (3) If you were planning to build a new manufacturing plant, what state would you choose in which to build? Justify your answer. (4) Are there any unusual features of this distribution? Describe them.

SR.2 The State Industrial Development Council is presently working on a financial services brochure to send to out-of-state companies. It is hoped that the brochure will be helpful in attracting companies to relocate to your state. You are given the following frequency distribution on banks in your state:

Deposit Size (in Millions)	Number of Banks	Total Deposits (in Millions)
Less than 5	2	7.2
5 to less than 10	7	52.1
10 to less than 25	6	111.5
25 to less than 50	3	95.4
50 to less than 100	2	166.6
100 to less than 500	2	529.8
Over 500	2	1663.0

a. Does this frequency distribution violate any of the rules of construction for frequency distributions? If so, re-construct the frequency distribution to remedy this violation.

b. The Council wishes to target companies that would require financial support from banks that have at least $25 million in deposits. Reconstruct the frequency distribution to attract such companies to relocate to your state. Do this by considering different classes that would accomplish such a goal.

c. Reconstruct the frequency distribution to attract companies that require financial support from banks that have between $5 million and $25 million in deposits.

d. Present an eye-catching, two-paragraph summary of what the data would mean to a company that is considering moving to the state. Your boss has said you need to include relative frequencies in this presentation.

SR.3 As an intern for the Intel company, suppose you have been asked to help the vice president prepare a newsletter to the shareholders. You have been given access to the data in a file called *Intel* that contains Intel Corporation financial data for the years 1987–1996. Go to the Internet or to Intel's annual report and update the file to include the same variables for the years 1997 to present. Then, use graphs to effectively present the data in a format that would be usable for the vice president's newsletter. Write a short article that discusses the information shown in your graphs.

SR.4 The Woodmill Company makes windows and door trim products. The first step in the process is to rip dimension (2 × 8, 2 × 10, etc.) lumber into narrower

pieces. Currently, the company uses a manual process in which an experienced operator quickly looks at a board and determines what rip widths to use. The decision is based on the knots and defects in the wood.

A company in Oregon has developed an optical scanner that can be used to determine the rip widths. The scanner is programmed to recognize defects and to determine rip widths that will "optimize" the value of the board. A test run of 100 boards was run through the scanner and the rip widths were identified. However, the boards were not actually ripped. A lumber grader determined the resulting values for each of the 100 boards assuming that the rips determined by the scanner had been made. Next, the same 100 boards were manually ripped using the normal process. The grader then determined the value for each board after the manual rip process was completed. The resulting data in the file, *Woodmill*, consist of manual rip values and scanner rip values for each of the 100 boards.

a. Develop a frequency distribution for the board values for the scanner and the manual process.

b. Compute appropriate descriptive statistics for both manual and scanner values. Use these data along with the frequency distribution developed in part (a) to prepare a written report that describes the results of the test. Be sure to include in your report a conclusion regarding whether the scanner outperforms the manual process.

c. Which process, scanner, or manual generated the most values that were more than two standard deviations from the mean?

d. Which of the 2 processes has the least relative variability?

SR.5 The commercial banking industry is undergoing rapid changes due to advances in technology and competitive pressures in the financial services sector. The data file *Banks* contains selected information tabulated by *Fortune* magazine concerning the revenues, profitability, and number of employees for the 51 largest U.S. commercial banks in terms of revenues. Use the information in this file to complete the following:

a. Compute the mean, median, and standard deviation for the three variables, Revenues, Profits, and Number of Employees.

b. Convert the data for each variable to a *z*-value. Consider Mellon Bank Corporation headquartered in Pittsburgh. How does it compare to the average bank in the study on the three variables? Discuss.

c. As you can see by examining the data and by looking at the statistics computed in part (a), not all banks had the same revenue, same profit, or the same number of employees. Which variable had the greatest relative variation among the banks in the study?

d. Calculate a new variable: profits per employee. Develop a frequency distribution and a histogram for this new variable. Also compute the mean, median, and standard deviation for the new variable. Write a short report that describes the profits per employee for the banks.

e. Referring to part d, how many Banks had a profit per employee ratio which exceeded 2 standard deviations from the mean?

Here is an integrative case study designed to give you additional experience. In addition, we have included several term project assignments that require you to collect and analyze data.

REVIEW CASE 1:

State Department of Insurance

This case study describes the efforts undertaken by the director of the Department of Insurance Division to assess the magnitude of the uninsured motorist problem in a western state. The objective of the case study is to introduce you to a data collection application and show how one organization developed a database. The database on your data diskette called *Liabins* is a subset of the data actually collected by the state department.

The impetus for the case came from the Legislative Transportation Committee, which heard much testimony during the recent legislative session about the problems that occur when an uninsured motorist is involved in a traffic accident where damages to individuals and property occur. The state's law enforcement officers also testified that a large number of vehicles are not covered by liability insurance.

Because of both political pressure and a sense of duty to do what is right, the legislative committee spent many hours wrestling with what to do about drivers who do not carry the mandatory liability insurance. Because the actual magnitude of the problem was unknown, the committee finally arrived at a compromise plan, which required the State Insurance Division to perform random audits of vehicles to determine whether the vehicle was covered by liability insurance. The audits are to be performed on approximately 1% of the state's 1 million registered vehicles each month. If a vehicle is found not to have liability insurance, the vehicle license and the owner's driver's license will be revoked for 3 months and a $250 fine will be imposed.

However, before actually implementing the audit process, which is projected to cost $1.5 million per year, Herb Kriner, director of the Insurance Department, was told to conduct a preliminary study of the uninsured motorists problem in the state and to report back to the legislative committee in 6 months.

The Study

A random sample of twelve counties in the state was selected in a manner that gave the counties with higher numbers of registered vehicles proportionally higher chances of being selected. Two locations were selected in each county and the State Police set up roadblocks on a randomly selected day. Vehicles with in-state license plates were stopped at random until approximately 100 vehicles had been stopped at each location. The target total was about 2,400 vehicles statewide.

The issue of primary interest was whether the vehicle was insured. This was determined by observing whether the vehicle was carrying the required certificate of insurance. If so, the officer took down the insurance company name and address and the policy number. If the certificate was not in the car, but the owner stated that insurance was carried, the owner was given a postcard to return within 5 days supplying the required information. A vehicle was determined to be uninsured if no postcard was returned or if, subsequently, the insurance company reported that the policy was not valid on the day of the survey.

In addition to the issue of insurance coverage, Herb Kriner wanted to collect other information about the vehicle and the owner. This was done using a personal interview during which the police officer asked a series of questions and observed certain things such as seat belt usage and driver's and vehicle license expiration status. Also, the owners' driving records were obtained through the Transportation Department's computer division and added to the information gathered by the State Police.

The Data

The data are contained in the file *Liabins*. The sheet, titled Description, contains an explanation of the data set and the variables.

Issues to Address

Herb Kriner has two weeks before making a presentation to the Legislative subcommittee that has been dealing with the liability insurance issue. As Herb's chief analyst, your job is to perform a comprehensive analysis of the data and to prepare the report that Herb will deliver to the Legislature. Remember, this report will go a long way in determining whether the state should spend the $1.5 million to implement a full liability insurance audit system.

Term Project Assignments

For the project selected, you are to devise a sampling plan, collect appropriate data, and carry out a full descriptive analysis aimed at shedding light on the key issues for the project. The finished project will include a written report of a length and format specified by your professor.

Project A:

Issue: Your College of Business and Economics seeks input from business majors regarding class scheduling. Some potential issues are:

- Day or evening
- Morning or afternoon
- 1-day, 2-day, or 3-day schedules
- Weekend
- Location (on or off campus)

Project B:

Issue: Intercollegiate athletics is a part of any major university. Revenue from attendance at major sporting events is one key to financing the athletic program. Investigate the drivers of attendance at your university's men's basketball and football games. Some potential issues:

- Game times
- Game days (basketball)
- Ticket prices
- Athletic booster club memberships
- Competition for entertainment dollars

Project C:

Issue: The department of your major is interested in surveying department alumni. Some potential issues are

- Satisfaction with degree
- Employment Status
- Job satisfaction
- Suggestions for improving course content

CHAPTER 4

Using Probability and Probability Distributions

CHAPTER OUTCOMES

After studying the material in Chapter 4, you should:

- Understand the three approaches to assessing probabilities.
- Be able to apply the common rules of probability.
- Know how to use Bayes' Theorem for applications involving conditional probabilities.
- Be able to distinguish the difference between discrete and continuous probability distributions.
- Be able to compute the expected value and standard deviation for a discrete probability distribution.

WHY YOU NEED TO KNOW

Business managers frequently must choose a course of action from among several alternatives to move their companies closer to their goals and objectives. For example, suppose the quality control manager at the American Plywood plant examines three pieces of plywood to determine whether the thickness of the boards meets specifications. The manager records her findings by labeling a good piece of plywood "G" and a defective piece of plywood "D." For three pieces of plywood she has just sampled, she obtains the following results: G, D, G. How can this sample help her decide between the two alternatives of closing the plant to make adjustments to the production equipment or keeping the plant operating as it is?

Consider a second example in which an accountant randomly examines 15 accounts and finds that 14 of them are accurate. What does this tell him about whether the firm has major problems in its accounting information system?

In both of these cases someone had to make a decision—about equipment operation in one case and an accounting information system in the other. Decision making means selecting among two or more alternatives. To make good decisions, managers must establish general criteria for deciding among alternatives. Certainly the criteria must somehow be related to the objective of the decision-making situation. This objective may involve revising a plant operation, updating an accounting system, analyzing a profit or sales level, or even creating an orderly situation from near chaos. In addition, good decisions must be based on correctly using available information. This chapter explores how to use information.

Chapter 1 described how managers must often operate with sample information collected from the population of interest. They are uncertain about the population, but they know a great deal about the sample. This is the case in our previous examples, in which we know the number of good sheets of plywood and the number of accurate accounts in the samples. Probability theory allows managers to use this sample information to make inferences about a population and to have confidence in these inferences.

In Chapter 2, we saw how a frequency distribution transforms raw data into a useful form that provides meaningful insight into the data. Frequency distributions are one way in which decision makers deal with uncertainty in their decision environments. Because all managers operate in an uncertain environment, they must be able to make the connection between descriptive statistics and probability. Moving from frequency distributions to *probability distributions* makes this connection.

Constructing and analyzing a frequency distribution for every decision-making situation would be time-consuming. Just deciding on the correct data-gathering procedures, the appropriate class intervals, and the right methods of presenting the data are not trivial issues. Fortunately, many physical and organizational events that appear to be unrelated have the same underlying characteristics and can be described by the same probability distribution. If decision makers are dealing with an application described by a predetermined *theoretical* probability distribution, they can use a great deal of developmental statistical work already known and can save considerable personal effort in analyzing their situation. Therefore, decision makers need to become comfortable with probability distributions if they are to apply them effectively. Fortunately for both the quality control manager and the accountant, their situations can be described by a well-known probability distribution.

4-1 THE BASICS OF PROBABILITY

Before we can apply *probability* to the decision-making process, we must understand what it means. The mathematical study of probability originated more than 300 years ago. The Chevalier de Méré, a French nobleman (who today would probably own a gaming house in Monte Carlo), began asking questions about games of chance. He was mostly interested in the probability of observing various outcomes (a pair of ones in 24 tosses of a pair of dice or a one in four tosses of a die) when dice were repeatedly rolled. The French mathematician Blaise Pascal (you may remember studying Pascal's triangle in a mathematics class) with the help of his friend Pierre de Fermat was able to answer de Méré's questions. Of course, Pascal began asking more and more complicated questions of himself and his colleagues, and the formal study of probability began.

IMPORTANT PROBABILITY TERMS

Several explanations of what probability is have come out of this mathematical study. However, the definition of probability is quite basic.

> *Probability*
>
> The chance that a particular event will occur.
>
> The probability of an event will be a value in the range 0 to 1. A value of 0 means the event will not occur. A probability of 1 means the event will occur. Anything between 0 and 1 reflects the uncertainty of the event occurring. The definition given is for a countable number of events.

Events and Sample Space

As discussed in Chapter 1, data come in many forms and are gathered in many ways. In a business environment, when a sample is selected or a decision is made, there are generally many possible outcomes. In probability language, the process that produces the outcomes is an **experiment**. In business situations, the experiment can range from an investment decision to a personnel decision to a choice of warehouse location.

Experiment

A process that produces a single outcome whose result cannot be predicted with certainty.

The individual outcomes from an experiment are called **elementary events**.

Elementary Events

The most rudimentary outcomes resulting from a simple experiment.

The collection of the most elementary events is called the **sample space**.

Sample Space

The collection of all elementary outcomes that can result from a selection, decision, or experiment.

The sample space for an experiment consists of all the elementary events that the experiment can produce.

EXAMPLE 4-1: DEFINING THE SAMPLE SPACE

Able Accounting   A partner for Able Accounting, a large regional accounting firm, is analyzing the performance of her many audit teams. She is particularly interested in whether the audits are finished by the projected completion date. She is interested in determining the sample space (possible outcomes) under different circumstances. To do this, she can use the following steps:

Step 1:   Define the experiment.
The experiment is the audit. Of interest is the status of an audit completion.

Step 2:   Define the elementary events for one trial of the experiment.
The partner can define the elementary events to be
$$e_1 = \text{Audit done early}$$
$$e_2 = \text{Audit done on time}$$
$$e_3 = \text{Audit done late}$$
The sample space (SS) for an experiment involving a single audit is
$$SS = \{e_1, e_2, e_3\}$$
If the experiment is expanded to include two audits, the sample space is
$$SS = \{e_1, e_2, e_3, e_4, e_5, e_6, e_7, e_8, e_9\}$$
where the events include what happens on both audits and are defined as:

Elementary Event	Audit 1	Audit 2
e_1	early	early
e_2	early	on time
e_3	early	late
e_4	on time	early
e_5	on time	on time
e_6	on time	late
e_7	late	early
e_8	late	on time
e_9	late	late

EXAMPLE 4-2: DEFINING THE SAMPLE SPACE

Lincoln Marketing Research   Recently, Lincoln Marketing Research in Lincoln, Nebraska, was retained to interview television viewers to determine whether they objected to having ads for hard liquor on TV. The analyst assigned to the project is interested in listing the sample space (possible outcomes). To do this, he can use the following steps:

Step 1:   **Define the experiment.**
The experiment involves selecting a television viewer and posing the question: "Would you object to hard-liquor advertisements on television?"

Step 2:   **Determine the elementary events for a single trial of the simple experiment.**
The possible outcomes when one person is interviewed are

$$e_1 = \text{no}$$
$$e_2 = \text{yes}$$

Step 3:   **Define the sample space.**
If three people (3 trials) are interviewed, the sample space (possible outcomes) is

Viewer 1	Viewer 2	Viewer 3
no	no	no
no	no	yes
no	yes	no
no	yes	yes
yes	no	no
yes	no	yes
yes	yes	no
yes	yes	yes

Using Tree Diagrams

A tree diagram is often a useful way to define the sample space for an experiment that helps ensure that no elementary events are omitted. Example 4-3 illustrates how a tree diagram is used.

EXAMPLE 4-3: USING A TREE DIAGRAM TO DEFINE THE SAMPLE SPACE

Lincoln Marketing Research   In Example 4-2, Lincoln Marketing Research was involved in a project in which television viewers were asked whether they objected to hard-liquor advertisements being shown on television. The analyst is interested in listing the sample space, using a tree diagram as an aid, when three viewers are interviewed. The following steps can be used:

Step 1:   **Define the experiment.**
Three people are interviewed and asked, "Would you object to hard-liquor advertisements on television?" Thus, the experiment consists of three trials.

Step 2:   **Define the elementary events for a single trial of the experiment.**
The possible outcomes when one person is interviewed are:

$$e_1 = \text{no}$$
$$e_2 = \text{yes}$$

Step 3:   **Define the sample space for three trials using a tree diagram.**
Begin by determining the elementary events for a single trial. Illustrate these with tree branches beginning on the left side of the page:

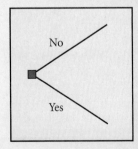

For each of these branches, add branches depicting the outcomes for a second trial. Continue until the tree has the number of sets of branches corresponding to the number of trials:

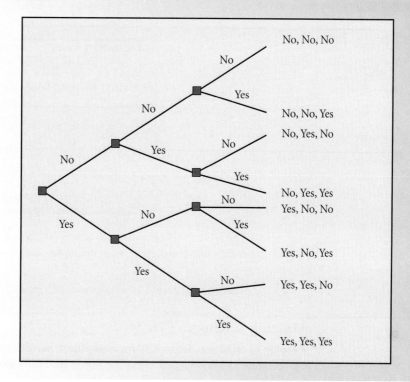

A collection of elementary events is called an **event**. An example will help clarify these terms.

Event

A collection of elementary events.

$\mathscr{E}$XAMPLE 4-4: DEFINING AN EVENT OF INTEREST

Able Accounting   The Able Accounting firm in Example 4-1 is interested in the sample space for an audit experiment in which the outcome of interest is the audit's completion status. The sample space is the list of all possible elementary events from the experiment. The accounting firm is also interested in specifying the elementary events that make up an event of interest. This can be done using the following steps:

Step 1:   **Define the experiment.**
            The experiment is the audit.

Step 2:   **List the elementary events associated with one trial of the experiment.**
            For a single audit the following completion-status possibilities exist:

$$e_1 = \text{Audit done early}$$
$$e_2 = \text{Audit done on time}$$
$$e_3 = \text{Audit done late}$$

The sample space (*SS*) for an experiment involving a single audit is

$$SS = \{e_1, e_2, e_3\}$$

Step 3: **Define the event of interest.**

For two audits (two trials), the event of interest is at least one audit is completed late. Here, each elementary event consists of the combined outcomes of audit 1 and audit 2. We define the sample space for two trials:

Elementary Event	Audit 1	Audit 2
e_1	early	early
e_2	early	on time
e_3	early	late
e_4	on time	early
e_5	on time	on time
e_6	on time	late
e_7	late	early
e_8	late	on time
e_9	late	late

Then, the event (at least one audit is completed late) is composed of all the elementary events in which one or more audits are late. This event (E) is

$$E = \{e_3, e_6, e_7, e_8, e_9\}$$

There are five ways in which one or more audits are completed late.

Mutually Exclusive Events

Keeping in mind the definitions for *experiment, sample space, elementary events*, and *events*, we introduce two additional concepts. The first is **mutually exclusive events**.

Mutually Exclusive Events

Two events are mutually exclusive if the occurrence of one event precludes the occurrence of the other event.

Able Accounting (continued)—Consider again the Able Accounting firm example. The possible elementary events for different audits done by two teams are

Elementary Event	Audit 1	Audit 2
e_1	early	early
e_2	early	on time
e_3	early	late
e_4	on time	early
e_5	on time	on time
e_6	on time	late
e_7	late	early
e_8	late	on time
e_9	late	late

Suppose we define one event as consisting of the elementary events in which at least one of the two audits is late.

$$E_1 = \{e_3, e_6, e_7, e_8, e_9\}$$

Further, suppose we define two more events as follows:

$$E_2 = \text{neither audit is late} = \{e_1, e_2, e_4, e_5\}.$$
$$E_3 = \text{both audits are finished at the same time} = \{e_1, e_5, e_9\}$$

Events E_1 and E_2 are mutually exclusive: If E_1 occurs, E_2 cannot occur; if E_2 occurs, E_1 cannot occur. That is, if at least one audit is late, then it is not possible for neither audit to be late. We can verify this fact by observing that no elementary events in E_1 appear in E_2. This observation provides another way of defining mutually exclusive events: Two events are mutually exclusive if they have no common elementary events.

Independent and Dependent Events

The second additional probability concept is that of **independent** versus **dependent** events.

Independent Events

Two events are independent if the occurrence of one event in no way influences the probability of the occurrence of the other event.

Dependent Events

Two events are dependent if the occurrence of one event impacts the probability of the other event occurring.

Mobile Exploration—Mobile Exploration is a subsidiary of the Mobile Corporation and is responsible for oil and natural gas exploration worldwide. During the exploration phase, seismic surveys are conducted that provide information about the earth's underground formations. Based on past history, the company knows that if the seismic readings are favorable, oil or gas more likely will be discovered than if the seismic readings are not favorable. However, the readings are not perfect indicators. Suppose the company currently is exploring in the eastern part of Australia. The elementary events for the seismic survey are defined as:

$$e_1 = \text{favorable}$$
$$e_2 = \text{unfavorable}$$

If the company decides to drill, the elementary events are defined as:

$$e_3 = \text{strike oil or gas}$$
$$e_4 = \text{dry hole}$$

If we let the Event A be that the seismic survey is favorable and Event B be that the hole is dry, we can say that the events A and B are not mutually exclusive, because if one event occurs, it does not preclude the other event from occurring. We can also say that the two events are dependent because the chance of a dry hole depends on whether the seismic survey is favorable or unfavorable.

$\mathcal{E}$XAMPLE 4-5: INDEPENDENT, DEPENDENT, AND MUTUALLY EXCLUSIVE EVENTS

Barcelona Assembly   Barcelona Assembly, located in Barcelona, Spain, does contract assembly work for Hewlett-Packard. Each item produced on the assembly line can be thought of as an experimental trial. The managers at this facility can analyze their process to determine whether the events of interest are mutually exclusive and are independent or dependent using the following steps:

Step 1:   **Define the experiment.**
The experiment is producing a part on an assembly line.

Step 2:   **Define the elementary events for a single trial.**
On each trial the outcome is either a *good* or a *defective* item. Thus, the sample space for a single trial is
$$SS = \{\text{good, defective}\}$$

Step 3:   **Determine whether the events are mutually exclusive.**
If two products are produced (two trials), the following sample space is defined:

good	good
good	defective
defective	good
defective	defective

Let Event A be defined as both products produced are good (good, good), and let Event B be defined as at least one product is defective.

good	defective
defective	good
defective	defective

Then Events *A* and *B* are determined to be mutually exclusive because the two events have no elementary events in common. Having two good items and at the same time having at least one defective item is not possible.

Step 4:   **An analysis of whether events are independent or dependent is made based on whether the occurrence of one event affects the probability of the second event occurring.**

As long as the machine is properly adjusted, it may produce some good outcomes and some defective outcomes with no apparent pattern, or dependency, between trials. That is, the production of one item, good or bad, has no influence on the probability of the outcome of subsequent trials. In that case, the events (defective item and good item) would be independent. However, if the machine goes out of adjustment, one item made defective because of maladjustment may cause still further adjustment problems and increase the chances that subsequent items will be defective. In this case, the trials are dependent, because the probability of the outcome of one trial is in some way influenced by the outcome of a previous trial.

METHODS OF ASSIGNING PROBABILITY

Part of the confusion surrounding probability may be due to the fact that probability means different things to different people. There are three common ways to assign probability to events: *classical probability assessment*, *relative frequency of occurrence*, and *subjective probability assessment*. The following notation is used when we refer to the probability of an event:

$$P(E_i) = \text{probability of event } E_i \text{ occurring}$$

Classical Probability Assessment

The first method of probability measurement is **classical probability**, or *a priori* probability.

Classical Probability Assessment

The method of determining probability based on the ratio of the number of ways the event of interest can occur to the number of ways *any* event can occur when the individual elementary events are equally likely.

You are probably already familiar with classical probability. It had its beginning with games of chance and is still most often discussed in those terms.

In those situations in which all possible elementary events are *equally likely*, the classical probability measurement is defined in Equation 4-1.

Classical Probability Measurement

$$P(E_i) = \frac{\text{Number of ways } E_i \text{ can occur}}{\text{Total number of elementary events}} \qquad \textbf{4-1}$$

$\mathcal{E}$XAMPLE 4-6: CLASSICAL PROBABILITY ASSESSMENT

Galaxy Furniture   The managers at Galaxy Furniture plan to hold a special promotion over Labor Day Weekend. Each customer making a purchase exceeding $100 will qualify to select an envelope from a large drum. Inside the envelope are coupons for percentage discounts off the purchase total. At the beginning of the weekend, there were 500 coupons. Four hundred of these were for 10% discount, 50 were for 20% discount, 45 were for 30%, and 5 were for 50% discount. Customers were interested in determining the probability of getting a particular discount amount. The probabilities can be determined using classical assessment with the following steps:

Step 1:   **Determine whether the elementary events are equally likely.**
In this case, the envelopes with the different discount amounts are unmarked from the outside and are thoroughly mixed in the drum. Thus, any one coupon has the same probability of being selected as any other coupon.

Step 2: **Determine the total number of elementary events.**
There are 500 envelopes in the drum.

Step 3: **Define the event of interest.**
We might be interested in assessing the probability that a customer will get a 20% discount.

Step 4: **Determine the number of elementary events associated with the event of interest.**
There are 50 coupons with a discount of 20% marked on them.

Step 5: **Compute the classical probability using Equation 4-1:**

$$P(E_i) = \frac{\text{Number of ways } E_i \text{ can occur}}{\text{Total number of elementary events}}$$

$$P(20\% \text{ Discount}) = \frac{\text{Number of ways 20\% can occur}}{\text{Total number of elementary events}} = \frac{50}{500} = 0.10$$

Note: After each customer selects an envelope from the drum, the probability that the next customer will get a particular discount will change, because the values in both the numerator and the denominator will change.

As you can see, the classical approach to probability measurement is fairly straightforward. Many games of chance are based on classical probability assessment. However, classical probability assessment is difficult to apply to most business situations. Rarely are the elementary events equally likely. For instance, you might be thinking of starting a business. The sample space listing the elementary events is

$$SS = \{\text{Succeed, Fail}\}$$

Would it be reasonable to use classical assessment to determine the probability that your business will succeed? We would make the following assessment:

$$P(\text{Succeed}) = \frac{1}{2}$$

If this were true, then the chance of any business succeeding would be 0.50. Of course, this is not true. Too many factors go into determining the success or failure of a business. The elementary events (Succeed, Failure) are not equally likely. Instead, we need another method of assessment in these situations.

Relative Frequency of Occurrence

The **relative frequency of occurrence** approach is based on actual observations.

Relative Frequency of Occurrence

The method that defines probability as the number of times an event occurs divided by the total number of times an experiment is performed in a large number of trials.

Equation 4-2 shows how the relative frequency of occurrence can assess these probabilities.

Relative Frequency of Occurrence

$$\text{Relative frequency of } E_i = \frac{\text{Number of times } E_i \text{ occurs}}{N}$$

4-2

where:

$$E_i = \text{The event of interest}$$
$$N = \text{Number of trials}$$

Hathaway Heating & Air Conditioning—The sales manager at Hathaway Heating & Air Conditioning has recently developed the customer profile shown in Table 4-1. The profile is based on a random sample of 500 customers. As a promotion for the company, the sales manager plans to randomly select a customer once a month and do a free service to the customer's system. What is the

TABLE 4-1	**CUSTOMER CATEGORY**		
Hathaway Heating & Air Conditioning Co.	Commercial	Residential	Total
Heating Systems	55	145	200
Air Conditioning Systems	45	255	300
Total	100	400	500

probability that the customer selected is a residential customer? What is the probability that the customer has a heating system?

To determine the probability that the customer selected is residential, we determine from Table 4-1 the number of residential customers and divide by the total number of customers, both residential and commercial.

$$P(\text{Residential}) = RF(\text{Residential}) = \frac{400}{500} = 0.80$$

Thus, there is an 80% chance the customer selected will be a residential customer.

The probability the customer selected has a heating system is determined by the ratio of the number of customers with heating systems to the number of total customers.

$$P(\text{Heating}) = RF(\text{Heating}) = \frac{200}{500} = 0.40$$

There is a 40% chance the randomly selected customer will have a heating system.

The sales manager hopes the customer selected is a residential customer with a heating system. Because there are 145 customers in this category, the relative frequency of occurrence method assesses the probability of this event occurring as follows:

$$P(\text{Residential with Heating}) = \frac{145}{500} = 0.29$$

There is a 29% chance the customer selected will be a residential customer with a heating system.

EXAMPLE 4-7: RELATIVE FREQUENCY OF OCCURRENCE PROBABILITY ASSESSMENT

Thomas' Dairy Bar   Thomas' Dairy Bar is located in a busy mall in Pittsburgh, Pennsylvania. Thomas' sells ice cream and frozen yogurt products. One of the difficulties in this business is knowing how much of a given product to prepare for the day. The manager is interested in determining the probability that a customer will select yogurt over ice cream. She has maintained records of customer purchases for the past three weeks. The probability can be assessed using relative frequency of occurrence with the following steps:

Step 1:   **Define the events of interest.**
The manager is interested in two events: customer selects yogurt and customer selects ice cream.

Step 2:   **Determine the total number of occurrences.**
In this case, she has observed 2,250 sales of ice cream and yogurt in the past three weeks.

Step 3:   **For the event of interest, determine the number of occurrences.**
In the past three weeks, 1,570 sales were for yogurt and 680 were ice cream.

Step 4:   The probability that a customer will purchase yogurt is found using Equation 4-2.

$$\text{Relative frequency of } E_i = \frac{\text{Number of times } E_i \text{ occurs}}{N} = \frac{1,570}{2,250} = 0.6978$$

Thus, based on past history, the chance that a customer will purchase yogurt is just under 0.70.

Subjective Probability Assessment

Unfortunately, even though managers may have some past experience to guide their decision making, there always will be new factors affecting each decision that make that experience only an approximate guide to the future. In other cases, managers may have little or no past experience and, therefore, may not be able to use a relative frequency of occurrence as even a starting point in assessing the desired probability. When past experience is not available, decision makers must make a **subjective probability assessment**. A subjective probability is a measure of a personal conviction that an outcome will occur. Therefore, in this instance, probability represents a person's belief that an event will occur.

Subjective Probability Assessment

The method that defines probability of an event as reflecting a decision maker's state of mind regarding the chances that the particular event will occur.

Harrison Construction—The Harrison Construction Company is preparing a bid for a road construction project. The company's engineers are very good at defining all the elements of the projects (labor, materials, and so on) and know the costs of these with a great deal of certainty. In finalizing the bid amount, the managers add a profit markup to the projected costs. The problem is how much markup to add. If they add too much, they won't be the low bidder and may lose the contract. If they don't mark it up enough, they may get the project and make less profit than they might have made had they used a higher markup. The managers are considering four possible markup values, stated as percentages of base costs:

10%	12%	15%	20%

To make their decision, the managers need to figure the probability of winning the contract at each of these markup levels. Because they have never done another project exactly like this one, they can't rely on relative frequency of occurrence. Instead, they must subjectively assess the probability based on whatever information they currently have available, such as who the other bidders are, the rapport Harrison has with the potential client, and so forth.

After considering these values, the Harrison managers make the following assessments:

$$P(\text{Win at } 10\%) = 0.30$$
$$P(\text{Win at } 12\%) = 0.25$$
$$P(\text{Win at } 15\%) = 0.15$$
$$P(\text{Win at } 20\%) = 0.05$$

These assessments indicate the managers' state of mind regarding the chances of winning the contract. If new information (for example, a competitor drops out of the bidding) becomes available before the bid is submitted, these assessments could change.

Each of the three methods by which probabilities are assigned to events has specific advantages and specific applications. Regardless of how decision makers arrive at a probability assessment, the rules by which people use these probabilities in decision making are the same.

4-1: EXERCISES

Skill Development

4.1 The following table reflects data that have been collected on a store's customers.

Age	Male	Female
under 20	168	208
20 to 40	340	290
over 40	170	160

a. Using the relative frequency of occurrence approach, what is the probability that a customer is a male?

b. What is the probability that a customer is 20 to 40 years old?

c. What is the joint probability of a customer being 20 to 40 years old and a male?

d. Calculate the probability that a customer selected from the male customers would be under 20 years old. Calculate the same for the female customers. Does it appear that gender is independent of age. Support your answer with calculations and reasons.

4.2 The following data refer to products produced by a company.

Model	Color		
	Blue	Brown	White
XB-50	302	105	200
YZ-99	40	205	130

a. Based on the relative frequency of occurrence method, what is the probability that an item manufactured is brown?

b. What is the probability that the product manufactured is a YZ-99?

c. What is the joint probability that a product manufactured is a YZ-99 and brown?

d. Suppose a product is chosen at random. Consider two events: the event that model YZ-99 was chosen and the event that a white product was chosen. Are these two events mutually exclusive? Explain.

4.3 A room contains four empty chairs. One chair is red. Assuming that the next person who enters the room will select a chair at random, what is the chance that the red chair will be the one selected?

4.4 If a paper carrier has delivered his route for 50 days and during that time has been shorted papers by the publisher five times, what is the probability that he will be shorted tomorrow?

4.5 A study of weather data in a particular area reveals that measurable precipitation has occurred on 25 of the 200 days studied. Based upon this information, what is the probability that it will not rain tomorrow?

4.6 If two customers are asked their opinions on a new product and if their opinion is confined to "Like It" or "Don't Like It," list the sample space of possible responses from the customers. How many of these events indicate a customer likes the product?

4.7 Two thousand people were recently interviewed by a marketing consulting company. Six hundred indicated that they currently smoke. If a follow-up study is to be conducted, what is the probability that a person selected at random from the 2,000 will be a smoker?

Business Applications

4.8 A study of the classified advertisements in a local newspaper shows that 204 are help-wanted ads, 520 are real estate ads, and 306 are for other ads.

a. If the newspaper plans to select an ad at random each week to be published free, what is the probability that the ad for a specific week will be a help-wanted ad?

b. What method of probability assessment is used to determine the probability in part a?

c. Are the events that a help-wanted ad is chosen and that an ad for other types of products or services is chosen for this promotion on a specific week mutually exclusive? Explain?

4.9 A major airline has tracked its on-time status during the past year for flights originating in San Francisco and Los Angeles. The following data reflect the data for 400 flights.

Origination	On-Time Status		
	Early	On Time	Late
San Francisco	25	50	100
Los Angeles	50	100	75

a. Based on these data, what is the probability that a flight from one of the two cities will arrive early?

b. What is the probability that a flight will have originated in Los Angeles?

c. Given that the flight originated in Los Angeles, determine the probability that it will arrive early. What would this probability have to be if the event arriving early were independent from the event in Los Angeles?

d. If three flights are selected at random, list the sample space indicating the possible "on-time" status for all three.

4.10 The manager at Filger's Furniture Store is in the process of negotiating a contract with a new supplier for dining tables. He has assessed the probability that the supplier will take the price he is willing to offer to be 0.70.

a. Explain what type of probability assessment method the manager would use to assess this probability.

b. Would it make sense to use the classical probability assessment approach in this case? Explain.

4.11 The Skateworld Company operates ice rinks in several major cities throughout the United States. During each session of open skating, one customer is selected at random to receive a free pass for a future open skating session. At a recent session there were 150 males and 130 females skating.

a. What is the probability that the person selected for the free pass will be a female?

b. Referring to part a, what method of probability assessment is used to determine the probability?

c. Suppose the company decides to give free passes to two customers. Are the events that a female received the first pass and a male received the second pass independent? Why or why not?

Advanced Business Applications

4.12 A shipping company can send a package through one of three cities (A, B, or C) before it gets to its final destination. Two packages are sent by the company. An elementary event will designate which city each package goes through [e.g., (A, B) will indicate the first package goes through city A and the second through city B]. Assume the package is equally likely to go through any of the cities. List the sample space for the possible cities through which the two packages might go.

a. Using classical probability assessment, determine the probability the first package did go and the second package did not go through city A.

b. Using classical probability assessment, determine the probability that neither of the packages went through city A.

4.13 A gasoline filling station recently began a promotion on its full-service island. If the dollar value shown on the pump stops at $9.99 when the pump clicks off, the customer will get the gasoline free.

a. If we define three events, one for each digit, can we conclude that the three events are independent? Why or why not?

b. Are the three events referred to in part a considered to be mutually exclusive? Why or why not?

c. What is the relationship between mutually exclusive events and independent events? (Hint: Consider two events that are mutually exclusive. If one occurs what is the probability that the other will occur?)

4.14 A Courtyard Hotel by Marriott conducted a survey of its guests. Sixty-two surveys were completed. The data can be found in the file named *CourtyardSurvey*. Based on the survey data, determine the following probabilities using the relative frequency of occurrence method:

a. What is the probability a customer either *probably will* or *definitely will* stay at a Courtyard again?

b. What is the probability the customer is on a business trip?

c. What is the probability that the customer previously has stayed at a Courtyard?

d. What is the joint probability of a customer being on a business trip and rating the hotel *better* than other hotels in the area?

4.15 The ECCO company makes backup alarms for machinery such as forklifts and commercial trucks. When a customer returns one of the alarms under warranty, the quality manager logs data on the product. Using the available data in the file named *ECCO*, use relative frequency of occurrence to find the following probabilities:

a. What is the probability the product was made at the Atlanta plant?

b. What is the probability that the customer returned the product due to a wiring problem?

c. What is the joint probability the returned item was from the Atlanta plant and had a wiring-related problem?

d. What is the probability that a returned item was made on the day shift at the Atlanta plant and had a cracked lens problem?

e. If an item was returned, what is the most likely profile for the item, including plant location, shift, and cause of problem?

4-2 THE RULES OF PROBABILITY

MEASURING PROBABILITIES

The probability attached to an event represents the likelihood the event will occur on a specified trial of an experiment. This probability also measures the perceived uncertainty about whether the event will occur.

Possible Values and Sum

The probability of any event will be between 0 and 1 inclusively. If we are certain about the outcome of an event, we will assign the event a probability of 0 or 1, where $P(E_i) = 0$ indicates the event E_i will not occur, and $P(E_i) = 1$ means that E_i will definitely occur. If we are uncertain about the result of an experiment, we measure this uncertainty by assigning a probability between 0 and 1. Probability Rule 1 shows that the probability of an event occurring is always between 0 and 1.

Probability Rule 1

For any event E_i,

$$0 \le P(E_i) \le 1 \quad \text{for all } i \qquad \textbf{4-3}$$

All possible elementary events associated with an experiment form the sample space. Therefore, the sum of the probabilities of all possible elementary events is 1, as shown by Probability Rule 2.

Probability Rule 2

$$\sum_{i=1}^{k} P(e_i) = 1 \qquad \textbf{4-4}$$

where:

k = Number of elementary events in the sample

e_i = ith elementary event

Addition Rule for Elementary Events

If a single event is composed of two or more elementary events, then the probability of the event is found by summing the probabilities of the elementary events. This is illustrated by Probability Rule 3.

Probability Rule 3: Addition Rule for Elementary Events

The probability of an event E_i is equal to the *sum* of the probabilities of the elementary events forming E_i. For example, if

$$E_i = \{e_1, e_2, e_3\}$$

then

$$P(E_i) = P(e_1) + P(e_2) + P(e_3)$$ **4-5**

Veronica's Cineplex—Veronica's Cineplex is considering opening a 20-screen complex in Lansing, Michigan, and has recently performed a resident survey as part of its decision-making process. One question of particular interest is how often a respondent goes to a movie. Table 4-2 shows the results of the survey for this question.

The sample space for the experiment for each respondent is

$$SS = \{e_1, e_2, e_3, e_4\}$$

where:

$$e_1 = \geq 10 \text{ movies}$$
$$e_2 = 3 \text{ to } 9 \text{ movies}$$
$$e_3 = 1 \text{ to } 2 \text{ movies}$$
$$e_4 = 0 \text{ movies}$$

Using the relative frequency of occurrence approach, we assign the following probabilities.

$$
\begin{aligned}
P(e_1) &= 400/5{,}000 = 0.08 \\
P(e_2) &= 1{,}900/5{,}000 = 0.38 \\
P(e_3) &= 1{,}500/5{,}000 = 0.30 \\
P(e_4) &= 1{,}200/5{,}000 = \underline{0.24} \\
&\qquad\qquad\qquad \Sigma = 1.00
\end{aligned}
$$

Assume we are interested in the event "respondent attends 1 to 9 movies per month."

$$E = \text{Respondent attends 1 to 9 movies}$$

The elementary events that make up E are

$$E = (e_2, e_3)$$

We can find the probability $P(E)$ by using Probability Rule 3, as follows:

$$
\begin{aligned}
P(E) &= P(e_2) + P(e_3) \\
&= 0.38 + 0.30 \\
&= 0.68
\end{aligned}
$$

TABLE 4-2

Veronica's Cineplex Survey Results

Movies Per Month	Frequency	Relative Frequency
≥10	400	0.08
3 to 9	1,900	0.38
1 to 2	1,500	0.30
0	1,200	0.24
Total	5,000	1.00

EXAMPLE 4-8: THE ADDITION RULE FOR ELEMENTARY EVENTS

Cranston Forest Products   The inventory manager at the Cranston Forest Products Company has reported the following data on boards in inventory:

	Dimension		
Length	2″ × 4″	2″ × 6″	2″ × 8″
8 feet	1,400	1,500	1,100
10 feet	2,000	3,500	2,500
12 feet	1,600	2,000	2,400

The manager plans to select one board at random from the inventory to show visiting customers. He is interested in the probability that he will get a 2″ × 4″ board that is 10 or more feet long. To do this he can employ the following steps.

Step 1:   **Define the elementary events of interest.**
The elementary events of interest deal with the 2″ × 4″ board length. The following elementary events are defined: e_1 = 8-foot 2″ × 4″, e_2 = 10-foot 2″ × 4″, and e_3 = 12-foot 2″ × 4″.

Step 2:   **Determine the probability of each elementary event.**
The probabilities can be assessed using classical probability assessment. There are 18,000 boards in inventory. Of these, 1,400 are 2″ × 4″ 8 feet long, 2,000 are 2″ × 4″ 10 feet long, and 1,600 are 2″ × 4″ 12 feet long. The probabilities of the three events are

$$P(e_1) = \frac{1,400}{18,000} = 0.0778$$

$$P(e_2) = \frac{2,000}{18,000} = 0.1111$$

$$P(e_3) = \frac{1,600}{18,000} = 0.0889$$

Step 3:   **Define the event for which the probability is desired.**
In this case, the manager is interested in the 2″ × 4″ boards that are 10 feet or 12 feet long. The elementary events making up this event are

$$2″ × 4″ \text{ boards 10 or more feet} = E = \{e_2, e_3\}$$

Step 4:   **Use Probability Rule 3 to find the desired probability.**
$$P(E) = P(e_2) + P(e_3)$$
$$= 0.1111 + 0.0889$$
$$= 0.2000$$

Complement Rule

Closely connected with Probability Rules 1 and 2 is the **complement** of an event. The complement of an event E is the collection of all possible elementary events not contained in event E. The complement of event E is represented by $\overline{E}$. Thus, the Complement Rule is a corollary to Probability Rules 1 and 2.

Complement Rule

$$P(\overline{E}) = 1 - P(E)$$

4-6

That is, the probability of the complement of event E is 1 minus the probability of event E.

EXAMPLE 4-9: THE COMPLEMENT RULE

Haupert Machinery   The sales manager for Haupert Machinery in Medford, Oregon, is preparing to call on a new customer, a building contractor. The sales manager wants to sell the contractor some equipment. Before making the presentation, the manager lists four possible outcomes and his subjectively assessed probabilities related to the sales prospect.

Events (Sales)	P(Sales)
$ 0	0.70
$ 2,000	0.20
$15,000	0.07
$50,000	0.03
	1.00

Note that each probability is between 0 and 1 and that the sum of the probabilities is 1, as required by Rules 1 and 2.

The owner is interested in knowing the probability of sales >$0. This can be found using the complement rule with the following steps:

Step 1:   Determine the probabilities for the events.

$$P(\$0) = 0.70$$
$$P(\$2,000) = 0.20$$
$$P(\$15,000) = 0.07$$
$$P(\$50,000) = 0.03$$

Step 2:   Find the desired probability.

Let E be the event sales = $0. The probability of not selling anything to the building contractor is

$$P(E) = 0.70$$

The complement, $\overline{E}$, is all sales >$0. Using the Complement Rule, the probability of sales >$0 is

$$P(\text{Sales} >\$0) = 1 - P(\text{sales} = \$0)$$
$$P(\text{Sales} >\$0) = 1 - 0.70$$
$$P(\text{Sales} >\$0) = 0.30$$

Based on his subjective assessment, there is a 30% chance the sales manager will sell something to the building contractor.

Addition Rule for Two Events

Veronica's Cineplex (continued)—Suppose the people who conducted the survey for Veronica's Cineplex also asked questions about the respondents' ages. The company's managers consider age important in deciding on location because its theaters do better in areas with a younger population base. Table 4-3 shows the breakdown of the sample by age group and by the number of times a respondent goes to a movie per month.

TABLE 4-3

Veronica's Cineplex

MOVIES PER MONTH	E_5 Less than 30	E_6 30 to 50	E_7 Over 50	TOTAL
E_1 ≥10 Movies	e_1 200	e_2 100	e_3 100	**400**
E_2 3 to 9 Movies	e_4 600	e_5 900	e_6 400	**1,900**
E_3 1 to 2 Movies	e_7 400	e_8 600	e_9 500	**1,500**
E_4 0 Movies	e_{10} 700	e_{11} 500	e_{12} 0	**1,200**
TOTAL	1,900	2,100	1,000	5,000

AGE GROUP

TABLE 4-4

Veronica's Cineplex—
Joint Probability Table

MOVIES PER MONTH	AGE GROUP			TOTAL
	E_5 Less than 30	E_6 30 to 50	E_7 Over 50	
E_1 ≥10 Movies	e_1 200/5,000 = 0.04	e_2 100/5,000 = 0.02	e_3 100/5,000 = 0.02	400/5,000 = 0.08
E_2 3 to 9 Movies	e_4 600/5,000 = 0.12	e_5 900/5,000 = 0.18	e_6 400/5,000 = 0.08	1,900/5,000 = 0.38
E_3 1 to 2 Movies	e_7 400/5,000 = 0.08	e_8 600/5,000 = 0.12	e_9 500/5,000 = 0.10	1,500/5,000 = 0.30
E_4 0 Movies	e_{10} 700/5,000 = 0.14	e_{11} 500/5,000 = 0.10	e_{12} 0/5,000 = 0	1,200/5,000 = 0.24
TOTAL	1,900/5,000 = 0.38	2,100/5,000 = 0.42	1,000/5,000 = 0.20	5,000/5,000 = 1

Table 4-3 illustrates two important concepts in data analysis: *joint frequencies* and *marginal frequencies*. Joint frequencies, which were discussed in Chapter 2, are the values inside the table. They provide information on age group and movie viewing jointly. Marginal frequencies are the row and column totals. These values give information on only the age group or only movie attendance.

For example, 2,100 people in the survey are in the 30 to 50 year age group. This column total is a marginal frequency for the age group 30 to 50 years, which is represented by E_6. Now notice that 600 respondents are younger than 30 years old and attend a movie three to nine times a month. The 600 is a joint frequency whose elementary event is represented by e_4. The joint frequencies are the number of times their associated elementary events occur.

Table 4-4 shows the relative frequencies for the data in Table 4-3. These values are the probabilities of the events and elementary events.

Suppose we wish to find the probability of E_4 (0 movies) **or** E_6 (being in the 30-to-50 age group). That is,

$$P(E_4 \text{ or } E_6) = ?$$

To find this probability, we must use Probability Rule 4.

Probability Rule 4: Addition Rule for Any Two Events, E_1 and E_2

$$P(E_1 \text{ or } E_2) = P(E_1) + P(E_2) - P(E_1 \text{ and } E_2) \qquad \textbf{4-7}$$

The key word in knowing when to use Rule 4 is *or*. The word *or* indicates addition. (You may have covered this concept as a *union* in a math class. $P(E_1 \text{ or } E_2) = P(E_1 \cup E_2)$.). Figure 4-1 is a Venn diagram that illustrates the application of the Addition Rule for Two Events. Notice that the overlap between the two events, E_1 and E_2, is double counted when E_1 is added to E_2. Thus, the overlap, which is E_1 and E_2, needs to be subtracted to avoid the double counting.

FIGURE 4-1

Venn Diagram—Addition
Rule for Two Events

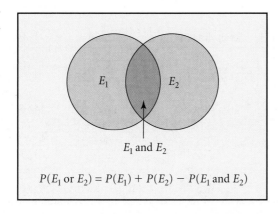

TABLE 4-5

Veronica's Cineplex—
Addition Rule Example

MOVIES PER MONTH	AGE GROUP E_5 Less than 30	E_6 30 to 50	E_7 Over 50	TOTAL
E_1 ≥10 Movies	e_1 200/5,000 = 0.04	e_2 100/5,000 = 0.02	e_3 100/5,000 = 0.02	400/5,000 = 0.08
E_2 3 to 9 Movies	e_4 600/5,000 = 0.12	e_5 900/5,000 = 0.18	e_6 400/5,000 = 0.08	1,900/5,000 = 0.38
E_3 1 to 2 Movies	e_7 400/5,000 = 0.08	e_8 600/5,000 = 0.12	e_9 500/5,000 = 0.10	1,500/5,000 = 0.30
E_4 0 Movies	e_{10} 700/5,000 = 0.14	e_{11} 500/5,000 = 0.10	e_{12} 0/5,000 = 0	1,200/5,000 = 0.24
TOTAL	1,900/5,000 = 0.38	2,100/5,000 = 0.42	1,000/5,000 = 0.20	5,000/5,000 = 1

Referring to the Veronica Cineplex situation, suppose we wish to find the probability of E_4 (0 movies) *or* E_6 (being in the 30-to-50 age group). That is,

$$P(E_4 \text{ or } E_6) = ?$$

Table 4-5 shows the relative frequencies with the events of interest shaded. The overlap corresponds to the *joint occurrence* (intersection) of attending 0 movies *and* being in the 30-to-50 age group. The probability of the overlap is represented by $P(E_4 \text{ and } E_6)$ and must be subtracted. This is done to avoid double counting the probabilities of the elementary events that are in both E_4 and E_6 when calculating the $P(E_4 \text{ or } E_6)$. Thus

$$P(E_4 \text{ or } E_6) = P(E_4) + P(E_6) - P(E_4 \text{ and } E_6)$$
$$= 0.24 + 0.42 - 0.10$$
$$= 0.56$$

Therefore, the probability that a respondent will either be in the 30-to-50 age group or attend a movie less than once a month is 0.56.

What is the probability a respondent will go to 0 movies *or* be in the over-50 age group? Again, we can use Rule 4:

$$P(E_4 \text{ or } E_7) = P(E_4) + P(E_7) - P(E_4 \text{ and } E_7)$$

Table 4-6 shows the relative frequencies for these events. We have

$$P(E_4 \text{ or } E_7) = 0.24 + 0.20 - 0 = 0.44$$

In this case, there were no joint occurrences, so $P(E_4 \text{ and } E_7)$ was assessed as 0, using the relative frequency approach.

TABLE 4-6

Veronica's Cineplex—
Addition Rule Example

MOVIES PER MONTH	AGE GROUP E_5 Less than 30	E_6 30 to 50	E_7 Over 50	TOTAL
E_1 ≤10 Movies	e_1 200/5,000 = 0.04	e_2 100/5,000 = 0.02	e_3 100/5,000 = 0.02	400/5,000 = 0.08
E_2 3 to 9 Movies	e_4 600/5,000 = 0.12	e_5 900/5,000 = 0.18	e_6 400/5,000 = 0.08	1,900/5,000 = 0.38
E_3 1 to 2 Movies	e_7 400/5,000 = 0.08	e_8 600/5,000 = 0.12	e_9 500/5,000 = 0.10	1,500/5,000 = 0.30
E_4 0 Movies	e_{10} 700/5,000 = 0.14	e_{11} 500/5,000 = 0.10	e_{12} 0/5,000 = 0	1,200/5,000 = 0.24
TOTAL	1,900/5,000 = 0.38	2,100/5,000 = 0.42	1,000/5,000 = 0.20	5,000/5,000 = 1

$\mathcal{E}$XAMPLE 4-10: ADDITION RULE FOR TWO EVENTS

Cranston Forest Products   In Example 4-8, the inventory manager at the Cranston Forest Products Company reported the following data on boards in inventory:

	Dimension		
Length	**2″ × 4″**	**2″ × 6″**	**2″ × 8″**
8 feet	1,400	1,500	1,100
10 feet	2,000	3,500	2,500
12 feet	1,600	2,000	2,400

He will be selecting one board at random from the inventory to show a visiting customer. He is interested in the probability that the board selected will be 8 feet long or a $2″ \times 6″$. To find this probability, he can use the following steps:

Step 1:   **Define the events of interest.**
The manager is interested in boards that are 8 feet long.

$$E_1 = \text{8-foot boards}$$

He is also interested in the $2″ \times 6″$ dimension, so

$$E_2 = 2″ \times 6″ \text{ boards}$$

Step 2:   **Determine the probability for each event.**
There are 18,000 boards in inventory, and 4,000 of these are 8 feet long, so

$$P(E_1) = \frac{4,000}{18,000} = 0.2222$$

Of the 18,000 boards, 7,000 are $2″ \times 6″$, so the probability is

$$P(E_2) = \frac{7,000}{18,000} = 0.3889$$

Step 3:   **Determine whether the two events overlap and if so, compute the joint probability.**
Of the 18,000 total boards, 1,500 are 8 feet long and $2″ \times 6″$. Thus the joint probability is

$$P(E_1 \text{ and } E_2) = \frac{1,500}{18,000} = 0.0833$$

Step 4:   **Compute the desired probability using Probability Rule 4.**

$$P(E_1 \text{ or } E_2) = P(E_1) + P(E_2) - P(E_1 \text{ and } E_2)$$
$$P(E_1 \text{ or } E_2) = 0.2222 + 0.3889 - 0.0833$$
$$= 0.5278$$

The chance of selecting an 8-foot board or a $2″ \times 6″$ is just under 0.53.

Addition Rule for Mutually Exclusive Events

We indicated previously that when two events are mutually exclusive, both events cannot occur at the same time. Thus for mutually exclusive events,

$$P(E_1 \text{ and } E_2) = 0$$

Therefore when you are dealing with mutually exclusive events, the addition rule assumes a special form, shown as Rule 5.

Probability Rule 5: Addition Rule for Mutually Exclusive Events
For two mutually exclusive events E_1 and E_2:
$$P(E_1 \text{ or } E_2) = P(E_1) + P(E_2)$$
4-8

Figure 4-2 is a Venn diagram illustrating the application of the Addition Rule for Mutually Exclusive Events.

FIGURE 4-2

Venn Diagram—Addition Rule for Two Mutually Exclusive Events

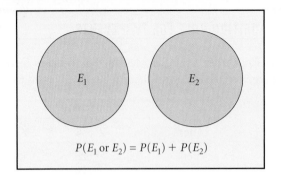

$$P(E_1 \text{ or } E_2) = P(E_1) + P(E_2)$$

CONDITIONAL PROBABILITY

In dealing with probabilities, you will often need to determine the chances of two or more events occurring either at the same time or in succession. For example, a quality control manager for a manufacturing company may be interested in the probability of selecting two successive defective products from an assembly line. If the probability of this event is low, the quality control manager will be surprised when it occurs and might readjust the production process. In other instances, the decision-maker might know that an event has occurred and may want to know the probability of a second event occurring. For instance, suppose that an oil company geologist who believes oil will be found at a certain drilling site makes a favorable report. Because oil is not always found at locations with a favorable report, the oil company's exploration vice president might well be interested in the probability of finding oil, given the favorable report.

Situations such as this refer to a probability concept known as **conditional probability**.

Conditional Probability

The probability that an event will occur *given* that some other event has already happened.

Probability Rule 6 offers a general rule for conditional probability. The notation, $P(E_1|E_2)$, reads probability of event E_1 *given* event E_2 has occurred. Thus, the probability of one event is conditional upon a second event having occurred.

Probability Rule 6: Conditional Probability for Any Two Events

For any two events E_1, E_2:

$$P(E_1|E_2) = \frac{P(E_1 \text{ and } E_2)}{P(E_2)}$$ **4-9**

where:

$$P(E_2) > 0$$

Rule 6 uses a *joint probability*, $P(E_1 \text{ and } E_2)$, and a *marginal probability*, $P(E_2)$, to calculate the conditional probability $P(E_1|E_2)$. Note that to find a conditional probability, we find the ratio of how frequently E_1 occurs to the total number of observations, given that we restrict our observations to only those cases in which E_2 has occurred.

West.net—West.net, an Internet service provider, is in an increasingly competitive industry. The company has studied its customers' Internet habits. Among the information collected are the data shown in Table 4-7.

TABLE 4-7

West.net Example

	GENDER		
HOURS PER MONTH	E_4 Female	E_5 Male	TOTAL
E_1 <20	e_1 450	e_2 500	950
E_2 20 to 40	e_3 300	e_4 800	1,100
E_3 >40	e_5 100	e_6 350	450
TOTAL	850	1,650	2,500

TABLE 4-8

West.net Example

HOURS PER MONTH	GENDER E_4 Female	E_5 Male	TOTAL
E_1 <20	e_1 450/2,500 = 0.18	e_2 500/2,500 = 0.2	950/2,500 = 0.38
E_2 20 to 40	e_3 300/2,500 = 0.12	e_4 800/2,500 = 0.32	1,100/2,500 = 0.44
E_3 >40	e_5 100/2,500 = 0.04	e_6 350/2,500 = 0.14	450/2,500 = 0.18
TOTAL	850/2,500 = 0.34	1,650/2,500 = 0.66	2,500/2,500 = 1.00

The company is focusing on high-volume users, and one of the factors that will influence West.net's marketing strategy is whether time spent using the Internet is related to a customer's gender. For example, suppose the company knows a user is female and wants to know the chances this woman will spend between 20 and 40 hours a month on the Internet. Let:

$$E_2 = \{e_3, e_4\} = \text{Event: Person uses services 20 to 40 hours per month}$$
$$E_4 = \{e_1, e_3, e_5\} = \text{Event: User is female}$$

A marketing analyst needs to know the probability of E_2 *given* E_4.

Table 4-8 shows the frequencies and relative frequencies of interest. One way to find the desired probability is as follows.

1. We know E_4 has occurred (customer is female). There are 850 females in the survey.
2. Of the 850 females, 300 use Internet services 20 to 40 hours per month.
3. Then,

$$P(E_2 | E_4) = \frac{300}{850}$$
$$= 0.35$$

However, we can also apply Rule 6, as follows:

$$P(E_2 | E_4) = \frac{P(E_2 \text{ and } E_4)}{P(E_4)}$$

From Table 4-8, we get the joint probability $P(E_2 \text{ and } E_4) = 0.12$ and

$$P(E_4) = 0.34$$

Then,

$$P(E_2 | E_4) = \frac{0.12}{0.34} = 0.35$$

EXAMPLE 4-11: COMPUTING CONDITIONAL PROBABILITIES

Retirement Planning   After the Enron Corporation collapse in late fall, 2001, in which thousands of Enron employees lost most or all of their retirement savings, many people began to take a closer look at how their own retirement money is invested. A recent survey conducted by a major financial publication yielded the following table.

AGE OF INVESTOR	PERCENTAGE OF RETIREMENT INVESTMENTS IN THE STOCK MARKET <5%	5 < 10%	10 < 30%	30 < 50%	50% or More	TOTAL
<30 years	70	240	270	80	55	715
30 < 50 years	90	300	630	1,120	1,420	3,560
50 < 65 years	110	305	780	530	480	2,205
65+ years	200	170	370	260	65	1,065
TOTAL	470	1,015	2,050	1,990	2,020	7,545

The publication's editors are interested in knowing the probability that someone 65 or older will have 50% or more of their retirement funds invested in the stock market. Assuming the data collected in this study reflect the population of investors, the editors can find this conditional probability using the following steps:

Step 1:   **Define the events of interest.**

In this case, we are interested in two events:

$$E_1 = 65 \text{ years or older}$$
$$E_2 = 50\% \text{ or more in stocks}$$

Step 2:   **Define the probability statement of interest.**

The editors are interested in:

$$P(E_2|E_1) = \text{probability of 50\% stocks } given \text{ 65 and older}$$

Step 3:   **Convert the data to probabilities using the relative frequency of occurrence method of assessment.**

We begin with the event that is given to have occurred (E_1). A total of 1,065 people in the study were 65+ years of age. Of the 1,065 people, 65 had 50% or more of their retirement funds in the stock market.

$$P(E_2|E_1) = \frac{65}{1,065} = 0.061$$

Thus, the conditional probability that someone 65 or older will have 50% or more of their retirement assets in the stock market is 0.061. This value can be found using Step 4 as well.

Step 4:   **Use Probability Rule 6 to find the conditional probability.**

$$P(E_2|E_1) = \frac{P(E_1 \text{ and } E_2)}{P(E_1)}$$

The necessary probabilities are found using the relative frequency of occurrence method

$$P(E_1) = \frac{1,065}{7,545} = 0.1412$$

and the joint probability is

$$P(E_1 \text{ and } E_2) = \frac{65}{7,545} = 0.0086$$

Then using Probability Rule 6 we get:

$$P(E_2|E_1) = \frac{P(E_1 \text{ and } E_2)}{P(E_1)} = \frac{0.0086}{0.1412} = 0.061$$

Tree Diagrams

Another way of organizing the events of an experiment that aids in the calculation of probabilities is the *tree diagram*.

West.net (cont.)—Figure 4-3 illustrates the tree diagram for West.net. Note that the branches at each node in the tree diagram represent mutually exclusive events. Moving from left to right, the first two branches indicate the two customer types (male and female—mutually exclusive events). Three branches grow from each of these original branches, representing the three possible categories for Internet use. The probabilities for the events male and female are shown on the first two branches. The probabilities shown on the right of the tree are the joint probability for each combination of gender and hours of use. These figures are found using Table 4-8, which was shown earlier. The probabilities on the branches following the male and female branches showing hours of

FIGURE 4-3

Tree Diagram for West.net

use are conditional probabilities. For example, we can find the probability that a male customer (E_5) will spend more than 40 hours on the Internet (E_3) by

$$P(E_3|E_5) = \frac{P(E_3 \text{ and } E_5)}{P(E_5)} = \frac{0.14}{0.66} = 0.2121$$

Conditional Probability for Independent Events

We earlier discussed that two events are independent if the occurrence of one event has no bearing on the probability that the second event occurs. Therefore, when two events are independent, the rule for conditional probability takes a special form, as indicated in Probability Rule 7.

Probability Rule 7: Conditional Probability for Independent Events

For independent events E_1, E_2:

$$P(E_1|E_2) = P(E_1); \quad P(E_2) > 0 \qquad \textbf{4-10}$$

and

$$P(E_2|E_1) = P(E_2); \quad P(E_1) > 0$$

As Rule 7 shows, the conditional probability of one event occurring, given a second independent event has already occurred, is simply the probability of the first occurring.

EXAMPLE 4-12: CHECKING FOR INDEPENDENCE

Cranston Forest Products   In Examples 4-8 and 4-10, the inventory manager at the Cranston Forest Products Company reported the following data on boards in inventory:

	Dimension		
Length	2″ × 4″	2″ × 6″	2″ × 8″
8 feet	1,400	1,500	1,100
10 feet	2,000	3,500	2,500
12 feet	1,600	2,000	2,400

He will be selecting one board at random from the inventory to show a visiting customer. Of interest is whether the length of the board is independent of the dimension. This can be determined using the following steps:

Step 1: **Define one event for length and one event for dimension.**
Let E_1 = event that the board is 10 feet long and E_2 = event that the board is a 2″ × 6″ dimension.

Step 2: **Determine the probability for each event.**

$$P(E_1) = \frac{8,000}{18,000} = 0.4444 \quad \text{and} \quad P(E_2) = \frac{7,000}{18,000} = 0.3889$$

Step 3: **Assess the joint probability of the two events occurring.**

$$P(E_1 \text{ and } E_2) = \frac{3,500}{18,000} = 0.1944$$

Step 4: **Compute the conditional probability of one event given the other using Probability Rule 6.**

$$P(E_1|E_2) = \frac{P(E_1 \text{ and } E_2)}{P(E_2)} = \frac{0.1944}{0.3889} = 0.4999$$

Step 5: **Check for independence using Probability Rule 7.**
Because $P(E_1|E_2) = 0.4999 \neq P(E_1) = 0.4444$, the two events are not independent and, therefore, board length and board dimension are not independent.

MULTIPLICATION RULES

We needed the joint probability of two events in the discussion on addition of two events and in the discussion on conditional probability. We were able to find $P(E_1 \text{ and } E_4)$ simply by examining the joint relative frequency tables. However, we often need to find $P(E_1 \text{ and } E_2)$ when we do not know the joint relative frequencies. When this is the case, we can use the multiplication rule for two events.

Multiplication Rule for Two Events

Probability Rule 8: Multiplication Rule for Any Two Events

For two events, E_1 and E_2:

$$P(E_1 \text{ and } E_2) = P(E_1)P(E_2|E_1) \qquad \qquad \textbf{4-11}$$

Real Computer Co.—To illustrate how to find a joint probability, consider an example involving classical probability. Real Computer Co., a manufacturer of personal computers, uses two suppliers for CD-ROM drives. These parts are intermingled in the manufacturing-floor inventory rack. When a computer is assembled, the CD-ROM unit is pulled randomly from inventory without regard to which company made it. Recently a customer ordered two personal computers. At the time of assembly, the CD-ROM inventory contained 30 MATX units and 50 Quinex units. What is the probability that both computers ordered by this customer will have MATX units?

To answer this question, we must recognize that two events are required to form the desired outcome. Therefore, let

E_1 = Event: MATX CD-ROM on first computer
E_2 = Event: MATX CD-ROM on second computer

The probability that both computers contain MATX units is written as $P(E_1 \text{ and } E_2)$. The key word here is *and*, as contrasted with the addition rule, in which the key word is *or*. The *and* signifies that we are interested in the joint probability of two events, as noted by $P(E_1 \text{ and } E_2)$. To find this probability, we employ Probability Rule 8.

$$P(E_1 \text{ and } E_2) = P(E_1)P(E_2|E_1)$$

We start by assuming that each CD-ROM in the inventory has the same chance of being selected for assembly. For the first computer,

$$P(E_1) = \frac{\text{Number of MATX units}}{\text{Number of CD-ROMs in inventory}}$$

$$= \frac{30}{80} = 0.375$$

Then, because we are not replacing the first CD-ROM, we find $P(E_2|E_1)$ by

$$P(E_2|E_1) = \frac{\text{Number of remaining MATX units}}{\text{Number of remaining CD-ROM units}}$$
$$= \frac{29}{79} = 0.3671$$

Now, by Rule 8,

$$P(E_1 \text{ and } E_2) = P(E_1)P(E_2|E_1) = (0.375)(0.3671)$$
$$= 0.1377$$

Therefore, there is a 13.77% chance the two personal computers will get MATX CD-ROM drives.

Using a Tree Diagram

Real Computer (continued)—A tree diagram can be used to display the situation facing the computer manufacturer. The two branches on the left side of the tree in Figure 4-4 show the possible CD-ROM options for the first computer. The two branches coming from each of the first branches show the possible CD-ROM options for the second computer. The probabilities at the far right are the joint probabilities for the CD-ROM options for the two computers. As we determined previously, the probability that both computers will get a MATX unit is 0.1377, as shown on the top right on the tree diagram.

We can use the multiplication rule and the addition rule in one application when we determine the probability that two systems will have different CD-ROMs. Looking at Figure 4-4, we see there are two ways this can happen.

$$P[(\text{MATX } and \text{ Quinex}) \text{ } or \text{ (Quinex } and \text{ MATX})] = ?$$

If the first CD-ROM is a MATX and the second one is a Quinex, then the first cannot be a Quinex and the second a MATX. These two events are mutually exclusive and, therefore, Rule 6 can be used to calculate the required probability. The joint probabilities (generated from the multiplication rule) are shown on the right side of the tree. To find the desired probability, using Rule 6 we can add the two joint probabilities:

$$P[(\text{MATX } and \text{ Quinex}) \text{ } or \text{ (Quinex } and \text{ MATX})] =$$
$$0.2373 \quad + \quad 0.2373 \quad = 0.4746$$

The chance that a customer buying two computers will get two different CD-ROMs is 47.46%.

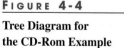

FIGURE 4-4

Tree Diagram for the CD-Rom Example

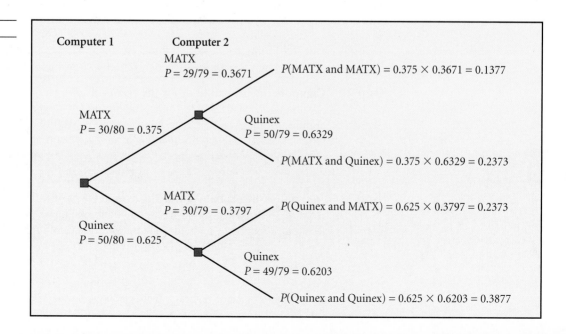

Multiplication Rule for Independent Events

When we determined the probability that two computers would have an MATX CD-ROM unit, we used the general multiplication rule (Rule 8). The general multiplication rule requires that conditional probability be used because the result for the second computer depends on the CD-ROM selected for the first computer. The chance of obtaining a MATX was lowered from 30/80 to 29/79, given the first CD-ROM was a MATX.

However, if the two events of interest are *independent*, the imposed condition does not alter the probability, and the multiplication rule takes the form shown in Probability Rule 9.

Probability Rule 9: Multiplication Rule for Independent Events

For independent events E_1, E_2:

$$P(E_1 \text{ and } E_2) = P(E_1)P(E_2)$$

4-12

The joint probability of two independent events is simply the product of the marginal probabilities of the two events. Rule 9 is the primary way that you can determine whether any two events are independent. If the product of the probabilities of the two events equals the joint probability, then the events are independent.

$\mathcal{E}$XAMPLE 4-13: USING THE MULTIPLICATION RULE AND THE ADDITION RULE

Medlin Accounting   Medlin Accounting prepares tax returns for individuals and companies. Over the years, the firm has tracked its clients and has discovered that 12% of the individual returns have been selected for audit by the Internal Revenue Service. On one particular day, the firm signed two new individual tax clients. The firm is interested in the probability that at least one of these clients will be audited. This probability can be found using the following steps:

Step 1:   **Define the overall event of interest.**
The event that Medlin Accounting is interested in is
$$E = \text{at least one client is audited}$$

Step 2:   **Define the elementary events.**
For a single client, the following elementary events are defined:
$$A = \text{audit}$$
$$N = \text{no audit}$$

For each of the clients, we define the elementary events as:

Client 1: A_1 and N_1

Client 2: A_2 and N_2

Step 3:   **List the sample space for the events of interest.**
The possible outcomes for which at least one client will be audited are as follows:

E_1:	A_1	A_2	both are audited
E_2:	A_1	N_2	} one client is audited
E_3:	N_1	A_2	

Step 4:   **Compute the probabilities for the events of interest.**
Assuming the chances of the clients being audited are independent of each other, probabilities for the events are determined using Probability Rule 9 for independent events:
$$P(E_1) = P(A_1 \text{ and } A_2) = 0.12 \times 0.12 = 0.0144$$
$$P(E_2) = P(A_1 \text{ and } N_2) = 0.12 \times 0.88 = 0.1056$$
$$P(E_3) = P(N_1 \text{ and } A_2) = 0.88 \times 0.12 = 0.1056$$

Step 5:   **Determine the probability for the overall event of interest.**
Because events E_1, E_2, and E_3 are mutually exclusive, compute the probability of at least one client being audited using the addition rule for mutually exclusive events:
$$P(E_1 \text{ or } E_2 \text{ or } E_3) = P(E_1) + P(E_2) + P(E_3)$$
$$= 0.0144 + 0.1056 + 0.1056$$
$$= 0.2256$$

The chance of one or both of the clients being audited is 0.2256.

BAYES' THEOREM

As decision makers, you will often encounter situations that require you to assess probabilities for events of interest. Your assessment may be based on relative frequency of occurrence or subjectivity. However, you may then come across new information that causes you to revise the probability assessment. For example, a human resource manager who has interviewed a person for a sales job might assess a low probability that the person will succeed in sales. However, after seeing the person's very high score on the company's sales aptitude test, the manager might revise her assessment upward. A medical doctor might assign an 80% chance that a patient has a particular disease. However, after seeing positive results from a lab test, he might increase his assessment to 95%.

In these situations, you will need a way to formally incorporate the new information. One very useful tool for doing this is called *Bayes' Theorem*, which is named for the Reverend Thomas Bayes, who developed the special application of conditional probability in the 1700s. Letting event B be an event that is given to have occurred, the conditional probability of event E_i occurring can be computed using Equation 4-9:

$$P(E_i|B) = \frac{P(E_i \text{ and } B)}{P(B)}$$

The numerator can be reformulated using the multiplication rule (Equation 4-11) as:

$$P(E_i \text{ and } B) = P(E_i)P(B|E_i)$$

The conditional probability is then:

$$P(E_i|B) = \frac{P(E_i)P(B|E_i)}{P(B)}$$

The denominator, $P(B)$, can be found by adding the probability of the k ways that event B can occur. This is

$$P(B) = P(E_1)P(B|E_1) + P(E_2)P(B|E_2) + \cdots + P(E_k)P(B|E_k)$$

Then Bayes' Theorem is formulated as Equation 4-13.

Bayes' Theorem

$$P(E_i|B) = \frac{P(E_i)P(B|E_i)}{P(E_1)P(B|E_1) + P(E_2)P(B|E_2) + \cdots + P(E_k)P(B|E_k)}$$

4-13

where:

$$E_i = i\text{th event of interest of the } k \text{ possible events}$$
$$B = \text{Event that has occurred that might impact } P(E_i)$$

Events E_1 to E_k are mutually exclusive and collectively exhaustive.

Varden Soap Co.—The Varden Soap Company has two production facilities, one in Ohio and one in Virginia. The company makes the same type of soap at both facilities. The Ohio plant makes 60% of the company's total soap output, and the Virginia plant 40%. All soap from the two facilities is sent to a central warehouse, where it is intermingled. After extensive sampling, the quality assurance manager has determined that 5% of the soap produced in Ohio and 10% of the soap produced in Virginia is unusable due to quality problems. When the company sells a defective product, it incurs not only the cost of replacing the item but also the loss of goodwill. The vice president for production would like to allocate these costs fairly between the two plants. To do so, he knows he must first determine the probability that a defective item was produced by a particular production line. Specifically, he needs to answer these questions:

1. What is the probability that the soap was produced at the Ohio plant, given that the soap is defective?
2. What is the probability that the soap was produced at the Virginia plant, given that the soap is defective?

In notation form, with D representing the occurrence of a defective item, what the manager wants to know is

$$P(\text{Ohio plant}|D) = ?$$
$$P(\text{Virginia plant}|D) = ?$$

We can use Bayes' Theorem to determine these probabilities, as follows.

$$P(Ohio|D) = \frac{P(Ohio)P(D|Ohio)}{P(D)}$$

We know that D(defective soap) can happen if it is made in either Ohio or Virginia. Thus,

$$P(D) = P(Ohio)P(D|Ohio) + P(Virginia)P(D|Virginia)$$

We already know that 60% of the soap comes from Ohio and 40% from Virginia. So, P(Ohio) = 0.60 and P(Virginia) = 0.40. These are called the *prior* probabilities. Without Bayes' Theorem, we would likely allocate the total cost of defects in a 60/40 split between Ohio and Virginia, based on total production. However, the new information about the quality from each line is

$$P(D|Ohio) = 0.05 \quad \text{and} \quad P(D|Virginia) = 0.10$$

which can be used to properly allocate the cost of defects. This is done using Bayes' Theorem.

$$P(Ohio|D) = \frac{P(Ohio)P(D|Ohio)}{P(Ohio)P(D|Ohio) + P(Virginia)P(D|Virginia)}$$

then,

$$P(Ohio|D) = \frac{(0.60)(0.05)}{(0.60)(0.05) + (0.40)(0.10)} = 0.4286$$

and

$$P(Virginia|D) = \frac{P(Virginia)P(D|Virginia)}{P(Virginia)P(D|Virginia) + P(Ohio)P(D|Ohio)}$$

$$P(Virginia|D) = \frac{(0.40)(0.10)}{(0.40)(0.10) + (0.60)(0.05)} = 0.5714$$

These probabilities are called the *revised* probabilities. The prior probabilities have been revised given the new quality information. We now see that 42.86% of the cost of defects should be allocated to the Ohio plant, and 57.14% should be allocated to the Virginia plant.

Note, the denominator $P(D)$ is the overall probability of defective soap. This probability is

$$P(D) = P(Ohio)P(D|Ohio) + P(Virginia)P(D|Virginia)$$
$$= (0.60)(0.05) + (0.40)(0.10)$$
$$= 0.03 + 0.04$$
$$= 0.07$$

Thus, 7% of all the soap made by Varden is defective.

You might prefer to use a tabular approach like that shown in Table 4-9 when you apply Bayes' Theorem. Another alternative is to use a tree diagram, as illustrated in the following example.

Bayes' Theorem Using a Tree Diagram

IRS Audit—This year experts project that 20% of all taxpayers will file an incorrect tax return. The Internal Revenue Service (IRS) itself is not perfect. IRS audits indicate there is an error when no problem exists about 10% of the time. The audits also indicate no error with a tax return when in fact there really is a problem about 30% of the time.

The IRS has just notified a taxpayer there is an error in his return. What is the probability that the return actually has an error? We use the following notation:

$$E = \text{the return actually contains an error}$$
$$NE = \text{the return contains no error}$$
$$AE = \text{audit says an error exists}$$
$$ANE = \text{audit says no error}$$

		Prior Probabilities	Conditional Probabilities	Joint Probability	Revised Probability
TABLE 4-9 **Bayes' Theorem Calculations for Varden Soap**	**Events**				
	Ohio	0.60	0.05	(0.60)(0.05) = 0.03	0.03/0.07 = 0.4286
	Virginia	0.40	0.10	(0.40)(0.10) = 0.04	0.04/0.07 = 0.5714
				0.07	1.0000

FIGURE 4-5

Tree Diagram for the IRS Audit Example

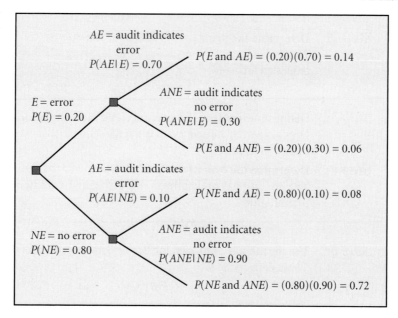

Then, we are interested in determining the following:

$$P(E \mid AE) = ?$$

We know the following:

$$P(E) = 0.20 \qquad P(ANE \mid E) = 0.30 \qquad P(AE \mid NE) = 0.10$$
$$P(ANE \mid NE) = 0.90 \qquad P(AE \mid E) = 0.70$$

We need to use Bayes' Theorem to determine the probability of interest. A tree diagram can be used to do this. Figure 4-5 shows the tree diagram and probabilities. Now,

$$P(E \mid AE) = \frac{P(E \text{ and } AE)}{P(AE)} = ?$$

From Figure 4-5 we see that $P(E \text{ and } AE) = 0.14$. To find $P(AE)$, we add the probabilities of the ways in which AE occurs (audit says an error occurred), because those two ways are mutually exclusive.

$$P(AE) = P(E \text{ and } AE) + P(NE \text{ and } AE) = 0.14 + 0.08 = 0.22$$

Then,

$$P(E \mid AE) = \frac{P(E \text{ and } AE)}{P(AE)} = \frac{0.14}{0.22} = 0.6364$$

The probability that the return contains an error, given that the IRS audit indicates an error exists, is 63.64%.

EXAMPLE 4-14: BAYES' THEOREM

Techtronics Equipment Corporation   The Techtronics Equipment Corporation has developed a new electronic device that it would like to sell to the U.S. military for use in fighter aircraft. The sales manager believes there is a 0.60 chance that the military will place an order. However, after making an initial sales presentation, military officials will often ask for a second presentation to other military decision makers. Historically, 70% of successful companies are asked to make a second presentation, whereas 50% of unsuccessful companies are asked back a second time. Suppose Techtronics Equipment has just been asked to make a second presentation, what is the revised probability that the company will make the sale? This probability can be determined using the following steps:

Step 1:   **Define the events.**

In this case, there are two events:

$$S = \text{sale} \qquad N = \text{no sale}$$

Step 2: **Determine the prior probabilities for the events.**
The probability of the events prior to knowing whether a second presentation will be requested are

$$P(S) = 0.60 \qquad P(N) = 0.40$$

Step 3: **Define an event that if it occurs, could alter the prior probabilities.**
In this case, the altering event is the invitation to make a second presentation. We label this event as SP.

Step 4: **Determine the conditional probabilities.**
The conditional probabilities are associated with being invited to make a second presentation:

$$P(SP \mid S) = 0.70 \qquad P(SP \mid N) = 0.50$$

Step 5: **Use the tabular approach for Bayes' Theorem to determine the *revised probabilities*.**
These correspond to

$$P(S \mid SP) \qquad \text{and} \qquad P(N \mid SP)$$

Event	Prior Probability	Conditional Probability	Joint Probability	Revised Probability
S = sale	0.60	$P(SP\mid S) = 0.70$	$P(S)P(SP\mid S) = (0.60)(0.70) = 0.42$	$0.42/0.62 = 0.6774$
N = no sale	0.40	$P(SP\mid N) = 0.50$	$P(S)P(SP\mid S) = (0.40)(0.50) = \underline{0.20}$	$0.20/0.62 = \underline{0.3226}$
			0.62	1.0000

Thus, using Bayes' Theorem, if Techtronics Equipment gets a second presentation opportunity, the probability of making the sale is revised upward from 0.60 to 0.6774.

4-2: EXERCISES

Skill Development

4.16 You are given the following table:

	A	B	C
D	100	150	50
E	600	150	150
F	300	300	300

a. What is the probability of event A?
b. What is the probability of event A and B?
c. What is the probability of event B and F?
d. What is the probability of event E given that event A has occurred?
e. What is the probability of event A or event F?

4.17 Historically, on Christmas the weather in a certain Midwest city has occurred according to the following distribution:

Event	Relative Frequency
Clear and dry	0.20
Cloudy and dry	0.30
Rain	0.40
Snow	0.10

a. Based on these data, what is the probability that next Christmas will be dry?
b. Based on the data, what is the probability that next Christmas will be rainy or cloudy and dry?
c. Suppose next Christmas is dry, determine the probability that it will also be cloudy.

4.18 The television schedule lists three different sitcoms in each of three consecutive 30-minute time slots on channels 2, 6, and 7.
a. What is the probability that a person will randomly select programs using all three stations over the course of the 1.5 hours?
b. Suppose you know that the person who will randomly select programs will watch at least two of the sitcoms on the same channel. Determine the probability that the person will watch all three sitcoms on the same channel.

4.19 Your neighbor has just returned from a trip to Atlantic City and claims to have a foolproof method to make money on the roulette wheel. She knows the odds are slightly with the house on any single spin. However, she claims that all you need to do is to watch the wheel and any time three successive rolls have the same color bet the next roll on the opposite color. Comment on her technique.

4.20 A store carries sweaters in three colors (brown, gray, and red). Assume the store has an unlimited number of sweaters and that customers select color at random.
a. What is the probability that three customers will select the same color?
b. Determine the probability that the three customers will not all select the same color.

4.21 A paint store carries three brands of paint. A customer arrives and wants to buy another gallon of paint to match paint that she purchased at the store previously. She can't recall the brand name and does not wish to return home to find the old can of paint. She selects two of the three brands of paint at random and buys them.
a. What is the probability that she matched the paint?
b. Her husband also goes to the paint store and fails to remember what brand to buy. He also purchases two of the three brands of paint at random. Determine the probability that both the woman and her husband fail to get the correct brand of paint. (Hint: Are the two events independent?)

4.22 A fast-food restaurant has determined that the chance that a customer will order a soft drink is 0.90. The chance that a customer will order a hamburger is 0.60. The chance that a customer will order French fries is 0.50.
a. If a customer places an order, what is the probability that the order will include a soft drink and no fries if these two events are independent?
b. The restaurant has also determined that if a customer orders a hamburger the chance the customer will also order fries is 0.80. Determine the probability that the order will include a hamburger and fries.

4.23 If 15 of the Fortune 500 companies have their headquarters in Michigan and 6 have their headquarters in Maryland, what is the probability that of 2 firms selected at random from the 500, one would have Michigan headquarters and one would have Maryland headquarters?

Business Applications

4.24 The Fortune 500 ranks the 500 largest U.S. corporations. The 1998 list revealed that 30 firms have their headquarters in Ohio. What is the probability that a firm selected at random from the list would have its headquarters in Ohio?

4.25 A local ski area offers private ski lessons with professionally qualified ski instructors. There are three ski instructors available. One is Austrian, one is German, and the third is from the United States. According to company policy, the instructors are assigned randomly. Thus, when a customer calls, a random selection is made and the selected instructor is scheduled with that customer.
a. On a given day, five customers call for lessons. Of these, four are assigned to the German instructor and one to the American. What is the probability of this happening if the assignments are random?
b. On a different day, three customers call for lessons and all three are assigned to the German instructor. What is the probability of this happening?
c. Referring to parts a and b, compute the probability that both the outcomes for day one and day two happen. Based on this probability, is there any cause for concern that the ski-lesson assignment may not be random? Explain.

4.26 A local photocopy shop has three black-and-white copy machines and two color copiers. Based on historical data, the chance that each black-and-white copier will be down for repairs is 0.10. The color copiers are more of a problem and are down 20% of the time each.
a. Based on this information, what is the probability that, if a customer needs a color copy, both color machines will be down for repairs?
b. If a customer wants both a color copy and a black-and-white copy, what is the probability that the necessary machines will be available? (Assume that the color copier can also be used to make a black-and-white copy if needed.)
c. If the manager wants to have at least a 99% chance of being able to furnish a black-and-white copy upon demand, is the present configuration sufficient? (Assume that the color copier can also be used to make a black-and-white copy if needed.) Back up your answer with appropriate probability computations.
d. What is the probability that all five copies will be up and running at the same time? Suppose the manager added a fourth black-and-white copier, how would the probability of all copiers being ready at any one time be affected?

4.27 Refer to Exercise 4.26. The owners of the photocopy shop are going to open a new photocopy store. They wish to meet the increasing demand for color photocopies and have more reliable service. As a goal, they would like to have at least a 99.9% chance of being able to furnish a black-and-white copy or a color copy upon demand. They also wish to purchase only four copiers. They have asked for your advice regarding the mix of black-and-white and color copiers. Supply them with your advice. Provide calculations and reasons to support your advice.

4.28 The Skiwell Manufacturing Company gets materials for its cross-country skis from two suppliers. Supplier A's materials make up 30% of what is used, with supplier B providing the rest. Past records indicate that 15% of supplier A's materials are defective, and 10% of B's are defective. Because it is impossible to tell which supplier the materials came from once they are in inventory, the manager wants to know which supplier most likely supplied the defective materials the foreman has brought to his attention. Provide the manager this information.

4.29 Alpine Cannery is currently processing vegetables from the summer harvest. The manager has found a case of cans that has not been properly sealed. There are three lines that processed cans of this type, and the manager wants to know which line is most likely to be responsible for this mistake. Provide the manager this information.

Line	Contribution to Total	Proportion Defective
1	0.40	0.05
2	0.35	0.10
3	0.25	0.07

4.30 Cascade paint mixes paint in three separate plants and then ships the unmarked cans to a central warehouse. Plant A supplies 50% of the paint, and past records indicate that the paint is incorrectly mixed 10% of the time. Plant B contributes 30%, with a defective rate of 5%. Plant C supplies 20%, with paint mixed incorrectly 20% of the time. If Cascade guarantees its product and spent $10,000 replacing improperly mixed paint last year, how should the cost be distributed among the three plants?

4.31 The Chocolate House specializes in hand-dipped chocolates for special occasions. Recently, several long-time customers have complained about the quality of the chocolates. It seems there are several partially covered chocolates in each box. The defective chocolates should have been caught when the boxes were packed. The manager is wondering which of the three packers is not doing the job properly. Clerk 1 packs 40% of the boxes and usually has a 2% defective rate. Clerk 2 packs 30% with a 2.5% defective rate. Clerk 3 boxes 30% of the chocolates, and her defective rate is 1.5%. Which clerk is most likely responsible for the boxes that raised the complaints?

4.32 As the owner of the Union Nursery, Kelly is concerned about the quality of some of the plants purchased from a local wholesaler but is not certain why the problem has suddenly cropped up. The company has been buying plants from this particular wholesaler for years, and the quality has always been excellent. A new employee of Kelly's who worked for the wholesaler explains that just before he left his previous position, the wholesaler started purchasing plants from a new grower in order to meet demand. The old grower has a good reputation and only 2% of his plants are unusable. The new grower's plants are of poor quality 30% of the time. The old grower currently supplies 80% of the wholesaler's plants. If Kelly buys a plant that is poor quality, which grower most likely supplied the plants?

4.33 The Carlisle Medical Clinic has five doctors on staff. The doctors have agreed to keep the office open on Saturdays but with only three doctors. The office manager has decided to make up Saturday schedules in such a way that no set of three doctors will be in the office together more than once. How many weeks can be covered by this schedule? (Hint: Use a tree diagram to list the sample space.)

4.34 In the late 1960s, the U.S. government instituted a lottery system for determining how young men 18 to 26 years old would be drafted into military service. Balls, each marked with a different day of the year (365 of them), were placed in a large drum and mixed. Balls were selected from the drum randomly.
a. What is the probability that the first two balls selected were for birthdays in March?
b. What is the probability that the first ball selected was a December birthday or a birthday on the first of any month?
c. If the first ball selected was a March birthday, what is the probability that the second ball selected was a June birthday?
d. What is the probability that the first three balls selected were for birthdays in the same month?

4.35 The Ace Construction Company has submitted a bid on a state government project in Delaware. The price of the bid was predetermined in the bid specifications. The contract is to be awarded on the basis of a blind drawing from those who have bid. Five other companies have also submitted bids.
a. What is the probability of Ace Construction winning the bid?
b. Suppose that there are two contracts to be awarded by a blind draw. What is the probability of Ace winning both contracts?
c. Referring to part b, what is the probability of Ace not winning either contract?
d. Referring to part b, what is the probability of Ace winning exactly one contract?
e. Referring to part b, what is the probability of Ace winning at least one contract?

Advanced Business Applications

4.36 A manager of a gasoline filling station is thinking about a promotion that she hopes will bring in more business to the full-service island. She is considering the option that when a customer requests a fill-up, if the pump stops with the dollar amount at $9.99, the customer will get the gasoline free. Previous studies show that 70% of customers pay $10.00 or more when they fill up their gas tanks, so they would not be eligible for the free gas. What is the probability that a customer will get free gas at this station if the promotion is implemented?

4.37 Referring to Exercise 4.36, suppose the manager is concerned about alienating customers who buy $10.00 or more, because they would not be eligible to win free gas under the original concept. To overcome this, she is thinking about changing the contest. A customer will get free gas if any of the following happens:

$9.99	$11.11	$12.22	$13.33	$14.44	$15.55
$16.66	$17.77	$18.88	$19.99		

Past data show that only 5% of all customers spend $20.00 or more. If one of these big-volume customers arrives, he or she will get a blind draw of a ball from a box containing 100 balls (99 red, 1 white). If the white ball is picked, the customer will get a free tank of gas. Considering this new promotion, what is the probability that a customer will get free gas?

4.38 A Courtyard Hotel by Marriott conducted a survey of its guests. Sixty-two surveys were completed. Based upon the data from the survey, found in the file named *CourtyardSurvey*, determine the following probabilities using the relative frequency of occurrence method.

a. Two customers are selected. What is the probability that both will be on a business trip?

b. What is the probability that a customer will be on a business trip or will experience a hotel problem during a stay at the Courtyard?

c. What is the probability that a customer on business will have an in-state-area-code phone number?

d. Based on the data, can the Courtyard manager conclude that a customer's rating regarding staff attentiveness is independent of whether he or she is traveling on business, pleasure, or both? Use the rules of probability to make this determination.

4.39 The ECCO company makes backup alarms for machinery, such as forklifts and commercial trucks. When a customer returns one of the alarms under warranty, the quality manager logs data on the product. Using the available data in the *ECCO* file, use relative frequency of occurrence to find the following probabilities.

a. If a part was made in the Atlanta plant, what is the probability the cause of the returned part was due to wiring?

b. If the company incurs a $30 cost for each returned alarm, what percentage of the cost should be assigned to each plant?

4-3 INTRODUCTION TO PROBABILITY DISTRIBUTIONS

RANDOM VARIABLES

As discussed earlier in this chapter, when a random experiment or trial is performed, some outcome, or event, must occur. When the trial or experiment has a quantitative characteristic, we can associate a number with each outcome. For example, an inspector who examines three sheets of plywood can judge each sheet as "acceptable" or "unacceptable." The outcome of the experiment defines a **random variable** in which the specific number of acceptable sheets of plywood is

$$x = \{0, 1, 2, 3\}$$

Although the inspector knows these are the possible values for the variable before she samples, she does not know which will occur in any given trial. Further, the value of the random variable may vary each time three plywood sheets are inspected.

Random Variable

A variable that assigns a numerical value to each outcome of a random experiment or trial.

Two classes of random variables exist: **discrete random variables** and **continuous random variables**. For instance, if a bank auditor randomly examines 15 accounts to verify the accuracy of the balances, the number of inaccurate account balances can be represented by a discrete random variable with the following values:

$$x = \{0, 1, \ldots 15\}$$

Discrete Random Variable

A random variable that can only assume a countable number of values.

In another situation, 10 employees were recently hired by a major electronics company. The number of females in that group can be described as a discrete random variable with possible values equal to:

$$x = \{0, 1, 2, 3, \ldots 10\}$$

Notice that the value for a discrete random variable is often determined by counting. In the bank auditing example, the variable, x, is determined by counting the number of accounts with errors. In the hiring example, the value for the variable, x, is determined by counting the number of females hired.

In other situations, the random variable is said to be continuous.

Continuous Random Variables

Random variables that can assume any value in an interval.

For example the exact time it takes a trainee to perform a job task may be any value between two points, say 1 minute and 10 minutes. If x is the time required, then x is continuous because, if measured precisely enough, the possible values, x, can be any value in the interval 1 to 10 minutes.[1] Other examples of continuous variables include measures of distance and measures of weight when measured precisely. A continuous random variable is generally defined by measuring, which is contrasted with a discrete random variable, whose value is typically determined by counting.

Comparing Discrete and Continuous Probability Distributions Graphically

The probability distribution for a discrete random variable is composed of the values the variable can assume and the probabilities associated with the variable assuming those values. For example if three parts are tested to determine if they are defective, the probability distribution for number of defectives might be

x = Number of Defectives	$P(x)$
0	0.10
1	0.30
2	0.40
3	0.20
	1.00

Graphically, the discrete probability distribution associated with these defectives can be represented by the areas of rectangles in which the base is one unit wide and the height corresponds to the probability. The areas of the rectangles sum to 1.

The probability distribution of a continuous random variable is represented by a probability density function that defines a curve. The area under the curve corresponds to the probabilities for the random variable. Figure 4-6 illustrates the relationship of discrete probability distributions and a typical probability density function. Figure 4-6(a) shows a discrete random variable with only three possible outcomes. Figure 4-6(b) shows the probability distribution for a discrete variable that has 21 possible outcomes. Note, as the number of possible outcomes increases, the distribution becomes smoother. In Figure 4-6(c), the graph of the continuous variable is a smooth curve. This smooth curve represents the probability density function for a continuous variable.

The total area (probability) under the density function curve is equal to 1. In addition, the probability that the variable will have a value between any two points $P(a < x < b)$, on the continuous scale equals the area under the curve between these two points. However, for any chosen x value $P(x) = 0$. This indicates the probability that a continuous random variable will assume a specific value is zero. Thus, when dealing with continuous random variables, we will determine probabilities for ranges of values and not for specific values. For instance, we might ask, "What is the probability of a student in this class weighing 160 pounds?" If we mean exactly 160.0000 pounds, the probability is zero. But we could find the probability of a weight between 159.5 and 160.5 pounds by finding the area under the probability density function between these two values. If we want the probability of a student weighing less than 160 pounds, we would need to find the area under the probability density function to the left of 160 pounds.

Both discrete and continuous probability distributions have extensive applications in business decision-making situations. In the remainder of this section we discuss several important issues that are of particular importance to discrete probability distributions. We will follow this in Chapter with further discussion of discrete and continuous distributions.

---

[1]If the time were observed to the nearest minute, then there would only be 10 possible values (a countable number) for the random variable. It would then be considered a discrete random variable.

FIGURE 4-6

Probability Density Functions Versus Discrete Probability Distributions

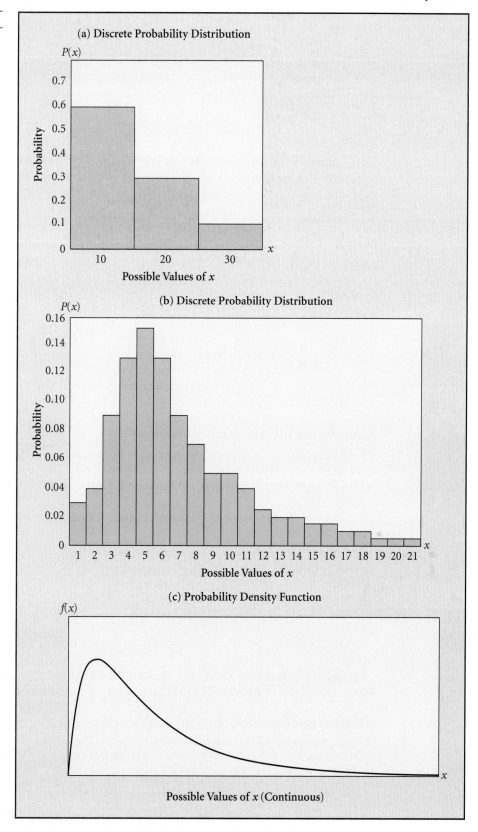

MEAN AND STANDARD DEVIATION OF DISCRETE DISTRIBUTIONS

A probability distribution, like a frequency distribution, can be only partially described by a graph. Often decision makers will need to calculate the distribution's *mean* and *standard deviation*. These values measure the central location and spread, respectively, of the probability distribution.

Calculating the Mean

The mean of a discrete probability distribution is also called the **expected value** of the discrete random variable.

Expected Value

The mean of a discrete probability distribution. The average value when the experiment that generates values for the random variable is repeated over the long run.

The expected value is actually a *weighted average* of the random variable values, in which the weights are the probabilities assigned to the values. The expected value is given in Equation 4-14.

Expected Value of a Discrete Distribution

$$E(x) = \sum x P(x) \qquad\qquad \textbf{4-14}$$

where:

$E(x)$ = Expected value of x
x = Values of the random variable
$P(x)$ = Probability of the random variable taking on the value x

---

Calculating the Standard Deviation

The standard deviation measures the spread, or dispersion, in a set of data. The standard deviation also measures the spread in the values of a random variable. To calculate the standard deviation for a discrete probability distribution, use Equation 4-15.

Standard Deviation of a Discrete Probability Distribution

$$\sigma_x = \sqrt{\sum [x - E(x)]^2 P(x)} \qquad\qquad \textbf{4-15}$$

where:

x = Values of the random variable
$E(x)$ = Expected value of x
$P(x)$ = Probability of the random variable taking on the value x

---

$\mathcal{E}$XAMPLE 4-15: COMPUTING THE MEAN AND STANDARD DEVIATION OF A DISCRETE RANDOM VARIABLE

Wagner Investments   Wagner Investment is located in Fairfax, West Virginia. The company manages assets for clients throughout the Southeast. Recently the managing partner conducted a study of the firm's clients with respect to the number of their stock transactions during the past week. The random variable, x, is the number of transactions per client, ranging from 0 to 3. The following frequency distribution was developed.

x	Frequency
0	120
1	72
2	30
3	78
	$\sum = 300$

Assuming that these data reflect the typical week, the manager wishes to develop a discrete probability distribution and compute the mean and standard deviation for the distribution. This can be done using the following steps:

Step 1: **Convert the frequency distribution into a probability distribution using the relative frequency of occurrence method.**

x	Frequency
0	120/300 = 0.40
1	72/300 = 0.24
2	30/300 = 0.10
3	78/300 = 0.26
	$\Sigma = 1.00$

Step 2: **Compute the expected value using Equation 4-14.**

$$E(x) = \Sigma\, xP(x)$$
$$E(x) = 0(0.40) + 1(0.24) + 2(0.10) + 3(0.26)$$
$$= 1.22$$

The expected number of stock trades per week is 1.22 per client.

Step 3: **Compute the standard deviation using Equation 4-15 or the shortcut algebraic equivalent.**

$$\sigma_x = \sqrt{\Sigma[x - E(x)]^2 P(x)} \;=\; \sqrt{\Sigma\, x^2 P(x) - [E(x)]^2}$$
$$= \sqrt{0^2(0.40) + 1^2(0.24) + 2^2(0.10) + 3^2(0.26) - [1.22]^2}$$
$$= 1.2213$$

The expected value and the standard deviation are virtually the same for this probability distribution.

WORKING WITH TWO DISCRETE RANDOM VARIABLES

So far we have discussed the basics of discrete random variables, including how to find the expected value and standard deviation. Each example and application has focused on a single random variable. However, there are many instances in which business decision making will involve working with two or more random variables simultaneously. Decision makers need tools for working with two discrete random variables.

Expected Value of the Sum of Two Discrete Random Variables

The expected value of a random variable was defined previously as the mean outcome for the random variable, and it is computed using Equation 4-14.

$$E(x) = \Sigma\, xP(x)$$

If we have two random variables, x and y, and we wish to know the expected value of the sum of the two variables, Equation 4-16 is used.

Expected Value of the Sum of Two Random Variables
$$E(x + y) = E(x) + E(y) \qquad\qquad \textbf{4-16}$$

The expected value of the sum of two random variables is the sum of the two expected values.

EXAMPLE 4-16: FINDING THE EXPECTED VALUE OF THE SUM OF TWO RANDOM VARIABLES

White, Barney & Associates At White, Barney & Associates, investment clients are offered opportunities to invest in both stock and bond mutual funds. Suppose an individual has $10,000 to invest and is considering splitting the investment equally between a stock fund and a bond fund.

The returns that will be earned on each of these investments are thought to be related to what will happen to interest rates during the coming year. After discussions with her broker, the investor has subjectively assessed the following probability distribution for interest rates and the associated return for each investment that will occur during the coming year:

Interest Rate	Probability	x Stock Return	y Bond Return
Increase	0.20	−$1,000	$300
No Change	0.30	$ 400	$500
Decrease	0.50	$ 900	−$200

The investor is interested in knowing the expected total return if she invests in both the stock fund and the bond fund. To determine this, she can use the following steps:

Step 1:   **Compute the expected value of each random variable using Equation 4-14.**
For variable x, the stock-fund return, we use $E(x) = \sum xP(x)$, and for variable y, the bond fund, we use $E(y) = \sum yP(y)$. These expected values are

x	P(x)	xP(x)		y	P(y)	yP(y)
−$1,000	0.20	−$200		$300	0.20	$ 60
$ 400	0.30	$120		$500	0.30	$150
$ 900	0.50	$450		−$200	0.50	−$100
		$\sum = \$370$				$\sum = \$110$

Thus, $E(x) = \$370$ and $E(y) = \$110$.

Step 2:   **Add the expected values.**
Using Equation 4-16, we get:

$$E(x + y) = E(x) + E(y)$$
$$= \$370 + \$110$$
$$= \$480$$

The investor can expect to earn $480 from the two investments.

Covariance of Two Discrete Random Variables

You may also be interested in determining the extent to which two discrete random variables are jointly related. That is, to what extent do the values of the two variables move together? A measure of this joint relationship is called the **covariance**. Equation 4-17 can be used to compute the covariance.

Covariance

$$\sigma_{xy} = \sum [x_i - E(x)][y_j - E(y)]P(x_i y_j)$$

4-17

where:

x_i = Possible values of the x discrete random variable
y_j = Possible values of the y discrete random variable
$P(x_i y_j)$ = Joint probability of values of x_i and y_j occurring

The covariance can be positive or negative depending on whether the two variables move together in the same or opposite directions. If the covariance is zero or close to zero, this implies that the two variables do not move closely together.

EXAMPLE 4-17: COMPUTING THE COVARIANCE

White, Barney & Associates Example 4-16 introduced an investor at White, Barney & Associates who was planning to invest in both a stock fund and a bond fund. She assessed the following probability distributions for the returns that would be earned on the investments over the coming year:

Interest Rate	$P(xy)$ Probability	x Stock Return	y Bond Return
Increase	0.20	−$1,000	$300
No Change	0.30	$ 400	$500
Decrease	0.50	$ 900	−$200

She determined that her total expected return for the two investments was $480. Now she is interested in determining the extent to which the returns on these two investments move together. This is measured by the covariance and can be computed using the following steps.

Step 1: **Compute the expected values of each random variable.**
Refer to Example 4-16, in which we found:

$$E(x) = \$370 \qquad \text{and} \qquad E(y) = \$110$$

Step 2: **Find the joint probabilities for all possible pairs of outcomes for the two discrete random variables.**
In this example, because returns were tied to interest rate movements, the joint probabilities are given. For example, the joint probability of $x = -\$1,000$ and $y = \$300$ (associated with an increase in interest rates) is assessed as 0.20. Thus, in the above table, $P(xy)$ are the joint probabilities for each combination of x and y.

Step 3: **Use Equation 4-17 to compute the covariance.**

$$\sigma_{xy} = \Sigma[x_i - E(x)][y_j - E(y)]P(x_iy_j)$$

x	y	$P(xy)$	$x - E(x)$	$y - E(y)$	$[x - E(x)][y - E(y)]$	$[x - E(x)][y - E(y)]P(xy)$
−1,000	300	0.20	−1,370	190	−260,300	−52,060
400	500	0.30	30	390	11,700	3,510
900	−200	0.50	530	−310	−164,300	−82,150
						$\sigma_{xy} = -130,700$

The covariance for these two investments is −130,700. The negative sign indicates the two variables tend to move in opposite directions as interest rates change. Note, the covariance is not in the original units (dollars) because it was computed using the product of two dollar amounts.

Correlation Between Two Discrete Random Variables

As Example 4-17 showed, the covariance between two random variables provides information about whether the two variables move in the same or opposite directions. However, the covariance alone does not measure the strength of the relationship between the two variables. Instead, a measure called the **correlation coefficient** is used to measure the strength of the linear relationship between two variables.

Correlation Coefficient

A quantitative measure of the strength of the linear relationship between two variables. The correlation ranges from −1.0 to +1.0. A correlation of ±1.0 indicates a perfect linear relationship, whereas a correlation of 0.0 indicates no linear relationship.

If two variables have a strong linear relationship, the correlation will be close to ±1.0, depending on whether they move in the same or opposite directions. The correlation coefficient is computed using Equation 4-18. Note, the numerator in the correlation coefficient equation is the covariance between the two variables. Therefore, if the covariance is positive, the correlation will be positive and vice versa.

Correlation Coefficient

$$\rho = \frac{\sigma_{xy}}{\sigma_x \sigma_y}$$

4-18

where:

ρ = Correlation coefficient (rho)

σ_{xy} = Covariance between variables x and y

σ_x = Standard deviation of variable x

σ_y = Standard deviation of variable y

ℰXAMPLE 4-18: COMPUTING THE CORRELATION COEFFICIENT

White, Barney & Associates Examples 4-16 and 4-17 introduced an investor who was going to invest in a stock fund and a bond fund. She assessed the following probability distributions for the return on each investment at different interest rates. These distributions are shown as follows:

Interest Rate	P(xy) Probability	x Stock Return	y Bond Return
Increase	0.20	−$1,000	$300
No Change	0.30	$ 400	$500
Decrease	0.50	$ 900	−$200

The investor is interested in measuring the strength of the linear relationship between these two investment options. To do this, she can compute the correlation coefficient using the following steps:

Step 1: **Compute the covariance between the two variables using Equation 4-17.**
Refer to Example 4-17, in which the covariance was computed using

$$\sigma_{xy} = \Sigma[x_i - E(x)][y_j - E(y)]P(x_i y_j)$$

The value for the covariance was −130,700, which indicated that the relationship between the two variables is negative.

Step 2: **Compute the standard deviation for each discrete random variable using Equation 4-15.**
Recall from Example 4-16 that the expected values of variables x and y were

$$E(x) = 370 \qquad \text{and} \qquad E(y) = 110$$

Then the standard deviations are

$$\sigma_x = \sqrt{\Sigma[x_i - E(x)]^2 P(x_i)} = \sqrt{(-1,000 - 370)^2(.20) + (400 - 370)^2(.30) + (900 - 370)^2(.50)}$$
$$= \sqrt{516,100} = 718.401$$

$$\sigma_y = \sqrt{\Sigma[y_j - E(y)]^2 P(y_j)} = \sqrt{(300 - 110)^2(.20) + (500 - 110)^2(.30) + (-200 - 110)^2(.50)}$$
$$= \sqrt{100,900} = 317.648$$

Step 3: **Compute the correlation coefficient using Equation 4-18.**

$$\rho = \frac{\sigma_{xy}}{\sigma_x \sigma_y} = \frac{-130,700}{(718.401)(317.648)} = -0.573$$

The correlation between the stock and bond investments is −0.573, indicating a negative linear relationship.

4-3: EXERCISES

Skill Development

4.40 Examine this discrete probability distribution.

x	P(x)
10	0.05
15	0.20
25	0.40
40	0.35

a. Find the expected value, variance, and standard deviation.
b. Develop a graphical picture of the discrete probability distribution.

4.41 Given this discrete probability distribution:

x	P(x)
100	0.30
150	0.40
160	0.30

a. Find the expected value of x.
b. Find the variance of x.
c. Find the standard deviation of x.

4.42 Four possible prizes are being awarded by a real estate developer to people who will look at new property. The prizes are being awarded based on a blind drawing with the following probability distribution:

x	P(x)
$ 10	0.80
$ 20	0.10
$ 100	0.08
$1,000	0.02

a. What is the expected prize award?
b. What is the standard deviation for the prize award?
c. If one person is allowed to have two chances at the drawing and keep the highest prize, what is the probability that she will leave with at least $100?

4.43 At one Las Vegas casino, if you bet $5 that a 12 will come up as the total points on two dice, and you win, you will get back $50. If any total other than 12 comes up, you get back $0. Based on the assumption that the dice are fair, what is the expected payoff for placing this bet?

4.44 An investment opportunity has the following possible net returns and associated probabilities:

x = return	P(x)
$ 500	0.25
$ 1,000	0.40
$ 5,000	0.30
$10,000	0.05

a. If you have the opportunity to participate in this investment opportunity, what is your expected net return?

b. Suppose you have the opportunity to participate in this investment situation twice. What is the probability that you will have a total net return of more than $10,000?

4.45 The following probability distributions are given for two discrete random variables, x and y.

x	y	P(x)	P(y)
100	500	0.25	0.25
200	300	0.40	0.40
300	400	0.20	0.20
400	600	0.15	0.15

Find the expected value for the sum of the two random variables.

4.46 The following probability distributions are given for two discrete random variables, x and y.

x	y	P(x)	P(y)	P(xy)
100	500	0.25	0.25	0.10
200	300	0.40	0.40	0.50
300	400	0.20	0.20	0.30
400	600	0.15	0.15	0.10

Determine the covariance for the two random variables. Is the relationship positive or negative?

4.47 The following probability distributions are given for two discrete random variables, x and y.

x	y	P(x)	P(y)	P(xy)
100	500	0.25	0.25	0.10
200	300	0.40	0.40	0.50
300	400	0.20	0.20	0.30
400	600	0.15	0.15	0.10

Compute the correlation coefficient and indicate what it means with respect to these two variables.

Business Applications

4.48 For the past four years, Armonco Manufacturing has been offering a three-year limited warranty on all appliances it manufactures. Although all appliances are given a unique serial number when manufactured, until this year Armonco had no capability of determining how often any appliance was brought to an authorized service facility. At the beginning of the year, the long-promised computer database linking all service facilities with a central system was finally operational. A preliminary report shows the following results for one of the appliances Armonco manufactures.

Times Brought for Repair	Probability
0	0.55
1	0.25
2	0.14
3	0.04
4	0.02

a. Find the expected number of repairs for this appliance.
b. Find the standard deviation of this repair distribution.
c. If the average cost of a service call is $40, provide an estimate for the average cost of a warranty for Armonco per year for this appliance.

4.49 The Seremonte Emergency Medical Department has recorded the number of emergency calls received each day for the past 200 days. These data are shown in this frequency distribution.

Calls	Number of Days
0	22
1	20
2	40
3	55
4	28
5	20
6	5
7	10
	200

a. Determine the probability distribution based on the frequency distribution.
b. What is the mean of the probability distribution?
c. What is the standard deviation of the probability distribution?
d. Compute the coefficient of variation.
e. Each emergency call requires a team of three individuals to respond. How many employees must Seremonte have so they can respond to at least 75% of the emergency calls?

4.50 The Nu-Look Car Wash recently opened at a new location. The manager at this location is concerned about staffing levels, so he has taken a sample of 100 days from the company's other location and has found the following frequency distribution.

Cars	Frequency
0 and under 10	10
10 and under 20	17
20 and under 30	35
30 and under 40	22
40 and under 50	16
	100

a. Use the midpoints of each class to develop a probability distribution for the number of cars arriving at the car wash.
b. Determine the expected number of cars.
c. Determine the variance and standard deviation.
d. Two employees wash each car. It takes approximately 20 minutes to wash each car. Determine the number of employees the manager must have on hand each day to meet demand at least 85% of the days.

4.51 Refer to Exercise 4.50. The manager of Nu-Look Car Wash has had complaints from his employees. He pays them each $2 a car. However, on some days there just aren't very many cars to wash and on others there are lots of cars. The employees' wages vary substantially. The manager, therefore, has offered a salary of $6 an hour to any employee who wishes to accept. Suppose you are advising the employees. What would you advise them to do? (Hint: You may wish to calculate the probability distribution, average dollars earned, and standard deviation under the two systems of pay.)

4.52 Adams Car Sales owns two used-car dealerships in suburban Detroit. The following table is a joint frequency distribution for the number of cars sold each day at the two dealerships. Note, the sample consists of 1,100 days.

		Location A				
		0	1	2	3	4	Total
	0	10	40	50	50	50	200
	1	30	60	90	50	20	250
Location B	**2**	20	60	50	70	100	300
	3	10	30	40	20	50	150
	4	30	10	70	10	80	200
	Total	100	200	300	200	300	1,100

a. Using the relative frequency of occurrence approach for assessing probabilities, convert the joint frequency distri-bution table to a joint probability distribution.
b. Compute the expected number of cars sold per day at each of the two locations.
c. Compute the expected value for the sum of cars sold at the two dealerships.
d. Compute the covariance.
e. Compute the correlation coefficient and discuss what it means.

Summary and Conclusions

Probability provides decision makers a quantitative measure of the chance a particular outcome will occur. Probability allows decision makers to quantify uncertainty. The objectives of this chapter have been to discuss the various types of probability and to provide the basic rules that govern probability operations. In addition, we have introduced the basic concepts associated with discrete probability distributions, including how to compute the expected value and standard deviation for discrete distributions.

By understanding the basic rules of probability, you will be able to effectively measure the chances of events of interest occurring. If you need to combine probabilities, the addition rule and the multiplication rule are useful in specific instances. Bayes Theorem helps when dealing with conditional probabilities in special circumstances and in revising prior probabilities based on new information. Table 4-10 presents a summary classification of several of the basic rules of probability.

TABLE 4-10

Probability Rules Summary

Event Type	KEYWORD "OR" Addition Rule	KEYWORD "AND" Multiplication Rule	KEYWORD "GIVEN" Conditional Rule
Mutually Exclusive	$P(A \text{ or } B) = P(A) + P(B)$	$P(A \text{ and } B) = 0$	$P(A \mid B) = 0$
Independent	$P(A \text{ or } B) = P(A) + P(B) - P(A \text{ and } B)$	$P(A \text{ and } B) = P(A) \times P(B)$	$P(A \mid B) = P(A)$
Dependent	$P(A \text{ or } B) = P(A) + P(B) - P(A \text{ and } B)$	$P(A \text{ and } B) = P(A)P(B \mid A)$	$P(A \mid B) = \dfrac{P(A \text{ and } B)}{P(B)}$

Chapter 5 expands on the discussion of probability and introduces several very useful discrete and continuous probability distributions, including the binomial, Poisson, hypergeometric and normal distributions, which will be used throughout the remainder of the text.

EQUATIONS

Classical Probability Measurement

$$P(E_i) = \frac{\text{Number of ways } E_i \text{ can occur}}{\text{Total number of elementary events}} \qquad \textbf{4-1}$$

Relative Frequency of Occurrence

$$RF(E_i) = \frac{\text{Number of times } E_i \text{ occurs}}{N} \qquad \textbf{4-2}$$

Probability Rule 1

For any event E_i

$$0 \le P(E_i) \le 1 \quad \text{for all } i \qquad \textbf{4-3}$$

Probability Rule 2

$$\sum_{i=1}^{k} P(e_i) = 1 \qquad \textbf{4-4}$$

Probability Rule 3

Addition rule for elementary events:

The probability of an event E_i is equal to the *sum* of the probabilities of the elementary events forming E_i. For example, if

$$E_i = \{e_1, e_2, e_3\}$$

then

$$P(E_i) = P(e_1) + P(e_2) + P(e_3) \qquad \textbf{4-5}$$

Complement Rule

$$P(\overline{E}) = 1 - P(E) \qquad \textbf{4-6}$$

Probability Rule 4

Addition rule for any two events E_1 and E_2:

$$P(E_1 \text{ or } E_2) = P(E_1) + P(E_2) - P(E_1 \text{ and } E_2) \qquad \textbf{4-7}$$

Probability Rule 5

Addition rule for mutually exclusive events E_1, E_2:

$$P(E_1 \text{ or } E_2) = P(E_1) + P(E_2) \qquad \textbf{4-8}$$

Probability Rule 6

Conditional probability for any two events E_1, E_2:

$$P(E_1 \mid E_2) = \frac{P(E_1 \text{ and } E_2)}{P(E_2)} \qquad \textbf{4-9}$$

Probability Rule 7

Conditional probability for independent events E_1, E_2:

$$P(E_1 \mid E_2) = P(E_1); \qquad P(E_2) > 0 \qquad \textbf{4-10}$$

and

$$P(E_2 \mid E_1) = P(E_2); \qquad P(E_1) > 0$$

Probability Rule 8

Multiplication rule for two events, E_1 and E_2:

$$P(E_1 \text{ and } E_2) = P(E_1)P(E_2 \mid E_1) \qquad \textbf{4-11}$$

Probability Rule 9

Multiplication rule for independent events E_1, E_2:

$$P(E_1 \text{ and } E_2) = P(E_1)P(E_2) \qquad \textbf{4-12}$$

Bayes' Theorem

$$P(E_i \mid B) = \frac{P(E_i)P(B \mid E_i)}{P(E_1)P(B \mid E_1) + P(E_2)P(B \mid E_2) + \ldots + P(E_k)P(B \mid E_k)}$$

$$\textbf{4-13}$$

Expected Value of a Discrete Distribution

$$E(x) = \sum xP(x) \qquad \textbf{4-14}$$

Standard Deviation of a Discrete Probability Distribution

$$\sigma_x = \sqrt{\sum [x - E(x)]^2 P(x)} \qquad \textbf{4-15}$$

Expected Value of the Sum of Two Random Variables

$$E(x + y) = E(x) + E(y) \qquad \textbf{4-16}$$

Covariance

$$\sigma_{xy} = \sum [x_i - E(x)][y_j - E(y)]P(x_i y_j) \qquad \textbf{4-17}$$

Correlation Coefficient

$$\rho = \frac{\sigma_{xy}}{\sigma_x \sigma_y} \qquad \textbf{4-18}$$

Key Terms

CHAPTER EXERCISES

Conceptual Questions

4.53 Discuss what is meant by the relative frequency of occurrence approach to probability assessment. Provide a business-related example, other than those given in the text, in which this method of probability assessment might be used.

4.54 Discuss what is meant by *subjective probability*. Provide a business-related example in which subjective probability assessment would likely be used. Also provide an example of when you have personally used subjective probability assessment.

4.55 Discuss what is meant by *classical probability assessment* and indicate why classical assessment is not often used in business applications.

4.56 Based on your experience thus far in this class, what is the probability that you will receive an "A" grade? Discuss the factors you have used in arriving at this probability assessment. Do you believe that all students in your class will arrive at the same probability assessment as you? Why or why not?

4.57 Define and list five business examples of each of the following:
a. Mutually exclusive events
b. Independent events

4.58 How old is your statistics instructor? Rather than trying to pick an exact age, assess a probability to each of the following categories. Make sure that the sum of the probabilities you assess equals 1.0.

Under 30
30 to 40
41 to 50
51 to 60
Over 60

Business Applications

4.59 There are four defective power supplies in a package of 10. If two power supplies are randomly selected one after another, what is the probability of
a. One defective and one good power supply being selected?
b. Two good power supplies being selected?

4.60 A small town has two ambulances. Records indicate that the first ambulance is in service 60% of the time and the second one is in service 40% of the time.
a. What is the probability that when an ambulance is needed, one will not be available?
b. What is the probability that at least one ambulance will be available?

4.61 The Goldberg Construction Company recently bid on three contracts, each of which the company could be either awarded or not awarded.

a. Define the elementary events for a given bid.
b. List the sample space for a bid on one contract.
c. List the sample space for all three contracts.

4.62 The Harrison Corporation manufactures electronic components for the U.S. government. One particular component can be made without defect, with a minor defect, or with a major defect. If the company makes only one of these components, list the sample space.

4.63 Assume that the outcomes of a lottery are equally likely.
a. What is the probability that an individual will win if he or she holds one ticket out of 500 sold?
b. What is the probability of winning if he or she holds three tickets out of 500 sold?
c. What method of probability assessment did you use to answer parts a and b?

4.64 Gossage's Beverages recently sent a special advertisement to a large number of people in its marketing area. It offered a special price on root beer for purchases of one to four packages of six bottles or cans. In planning for the special promotion, Jane Gossage assessed the probability distribution of the number of packages of six that each customer would buy during the promotion as follows:

Number of Packages	
x	$P(x)$
0	0.30
1	0.10
2	0.10
3	0.05
4	0.45

Based on the probability assessments, what is the expected number of packages to be sold per customer? Comment on whether any particular customer is likely to purchase exactly this amount.

4.65 Amstar Airlines has just supplied data to the U.S. government indicating that out of 10,000 flights, 4,900 arrived on time (within 5 minutes of schedule), 4,000 arrived late, and the remaining flights arrived early.
a. Using the relative frequency of occurrence method, provide an assessment of the chances that an Amstar Airlines flight will arrive on time.
b. Assess the probability that a flight will be late.
c. Assess the chances that a flight will be early.
d. Comment on some of the potential problems associated with using relative frequency of occurrence probability assessment in this kind of case.

4.66 The Harris Newspaper Company sometimes makes printing errors in its advertising and is forced to provide corrected advertising in the next issue of the paper. The managing editor has done a study of this problem and has found the following data:

No. of Errors x	Relative Frequency
0	0.56
1	0.21
2	0.13
3	0.07
4	0.03

a. Using the relative frequencies as probabilities, what is the expected number of errors? Interpret what this value means to the managing editor.
b. Compute the variance and standard deviation for the number of errors and explain what these values measure.

4.67 Suppose you are given a three-question multiple-choice quiz in which each question has four optional answers.
a. What is the probability of getting a perfect score if you are forced to guess at each question?
b. Suppose it takes at least two correct answers out of three to pass the test. What is the probability of passing if you are forced to guess at each question? What does this indicate about studying for such an exam?
c. Suppose through some late-night studying you are able to correctly eliminate two answers on each question. Now answer parts a and b.

4.68 The Aims Photo Company sends photographers around to various department stores in the South to take pictures of children. The company charges only $0.99 for a sitting, which consists of six poses. The company then makes up three packages that are offered to the parents, who have a choice of buying zero, one, two, or all three of the packages. Based on his experience in the business, Samuel Aims has assessed the following probabilities of the number of packages that might be purchased by a parent.

Number of Packages x	P(x)
0	0.30
1	0.40
2	0.20
3	0.10

a. What is the expected number of packages to be purchased by each parent?
b. What is the standard deviation for the random variable, x?
c. Suppose all of the picture packages are to be priced at the same level. How much should they be priced if the Aims Company wants to break even? Assume that the production costs are $3.00 per package. Remember that the sitting charge is $0.99.

4.69 The Iverson Investment Company recently gave a public seminar in which its representative discussed a number of issues, including investment risk analysis. In that seminar the company reminded people that the coefficient of variation often can be used as a measure of an investment's risk. To demonstrate its point, it used two hypothetical stocks as examples. It let x equal the change in assets for a $1,000 investment in stock 1 and y reflect the change in assets for a $1,000 investment in stock 2. It showed the seminar participants the following probability distributions:

x	P(x)	y	P(y)
−$1,000	0.10	−$1,000	0.20
0	0.10	0	0.40
500	0.30	500	0.30
1,000	0.30	1,000	0.05
2,000	0.20	2,000	0.05

a. Compute the expected values for random variables x and y.
b. Compute the standard deviations for x and y.
c. Recalling that the coefficient of variation is determined by the ratio of the standard deviation over the mean, compute the coefficient of variation for each random variable.
d. Referring to part c, suppose the seminar director said that the first stock was more risky, because its standard deviation was greater than the standard deviation of the second stock. How would you respond? (Hint: What do the coefficients of variation imply?)

4.70 The Bentfield Electronics Company purchases parts from a variety of vendors. In each case the company is particularly concerned with the quality of the products it purchases. Part number 34-78D is used in the company's new laser printer. The parts are sensitive to dust and can easily be damaged in shipment, even if they are acceptable when they leave the vendor's plant. In a shipment of four parts, the purchasing agent has assessed the following probability distribution for the number of defective products.

x	P(x)
0	0.20
1	0.20
2	0.20
3	0.20
4	0.20

a. What is the expected number of defectives in a shipment of four parts? Discuss what this value really means to Bentfield.
b. Compute and interpret the standard deviation of the number of defective parts in a shipment of four.
c. Examine the probabilities as assessed and indicate what this probability distribution is called. Provide some reasons why the probabilities might all be equal, as they are in this case.

4.71 If the probability of a particular stock increasing in value is assessed at 0.60 and the probability of a second stock increasing is 0.70, are the two stocks independent if the probability of both stocks increasing is 0.15? Discuss.

4.72 Approximately 90% of executives indicate that Microsoft Windows is standard software at their companies (Source: 1997 Olsten Forum and **www.usatoday.com/snapshot/money/msnap039.htm**). What is the probability that a sample of 3 executives would reveal:
a. At least two using Microsoft Windows?
b. None using Microsoft Windows?
c. Exactly one uses Microsoft Windows?

4.73 In the sales business, repeat calls to finalize a sale are common. Suppose a particular salesperson has a 0.70 probability of selling on the first call and that the probability of selling drops by 0.10 on each successive call. If the salesperson is willing to make up to four calls on any client, what is the probability of a sale?

Advanced Business Applications

4.74 Recreational developers are considering opening a skiing area near a western U.S. town. They are trying to decide whether to open an area catering to family skiers or to some other group. To help make their decision, they gather the following information. If

A_1 = Family will ski
A_2 = Family will not ski
B_1 = Family has children but none in the 8-to-16 age group
B_2 = Family has children in the 8-to-16 age group
B_3 = Family has no children

Then, for this location,

$$P(A_1) = 0.40$$
$$P(B_2) = 0.35$$
$$P(B_1) = 0.25$$
$$P(A_1 | B_2) = 0.70$$
$$P(A_1 | B_1) = 0.30$$

a. Use the probabilities given to construct a joint probability distribution table.
b. What is the probability a family will ski *and* have children who are not in the 8-to-16 age group? How do you write this probability?
c. What is the probability a family with children in the 8-to-16 age group will not ski?
d. Are the categories *skiing* and *family composition* independent?

4.75 A company is considering changing its starting hour from 8:00 A.M. to 7:30 A.M. A census of the company's 1,200 office and production workers shows 370 of its 750 production workers favor the change and a total of 715 workers favor the change. To further assess worker opinion, the region manager decides to talk with randomly selected workers.
a. What is the probability a randomly selected worker will be in favor of the change?
b. What is the probability a randomly selected worker will be against the change *and* be an office worker?

c. Is the relationship between job type and opinion independent? Explain.

4.76 Bill Jones and Herman Smith are long-time business associates. They know that regular exercise improves their productivity and have made a practice of playing either tennis or golf every Saturday for the past 10 years. Jones enjoys tennis, but Smith prefers golf. Each Saturday they flip a coin to decide which sport to play. Jones beats Smith at tennis 80% of the time, whereas he beats Smith at golf only 30% of the time.
a. Suppose Jones walks into the Monday morning staff meeting and announces he beat Smith on Saturday. What sport do you think they played and why?
b. Assume open tennis courts are hard to find on Saturday, so instead of flipping a coin, Smith and Jones always first look for a tennis court. If they find one open, they play tennis; if not, they play golf. Further, suppose the chance of finding an open court is 30%. Given this, what sport do you think they played on Saturday, given that Jones won?

4.77 A marketing research team is considering using a mailing list for an advertising campaign. They know that 40% of the people on the list have only a MasterCard and that 10% have only an American Express card. Another 20% hold both MasterCard and American Express. Finally, 30% of those on the list have neither card. Suppose a person on the list is known to have a MasterCard. What is the probability that person also has an American Express card?

4.78 American International Drilling Company explores for oil worldwide. Recently, the company was considering drilling for oil in Fiji. Based on the best analysis of the company's engineers, the company believes that there is a 30% chance of striking oil. Before drilling, there is an expensive, but imperfect, test that can be conducted. The final reading of the test will indicate "positive" or "negative," depending on the data recorded during the test. This test will show a positive result 70% of the time when it turns out that there actually is oil. The test also will show a negative result 80% of the time when it turns out that there is no oil. Suppose American International Drilling has just run the test on the Fiji site and the result is negative. What is the revised probability of oil at the site?

4.79 The American Society for Quality is preparing to host their 40th annual Spring Quality Conference. Leaders of the conference feel that there is a 0.90 chance that the registration revenues will exceed the conference costs and the group will make money. In the past, when the conference has been a financial success, the governor has appeared on the program 80% of the time. When the conference has not been a financial success, the governor has been on the program 60% of the time. Suppose the conference chairman has just received a call from the governor's office indicating that the governor will be unable to attend this year. What will be the revised thinking on the probability that this year's conference will be a financial success?

CASE 4-A:

Great Air Commuter Service

The Great Air Commuter Service Company started in 1984 to provide efficient and inexpensive commuter travel between Boston and New York City. People in the airline industry know Peter Wilson, the principal owner and operating manager of the company, as "a real promoter." Before founding Great Air, Peter operated a small regional airline in the Rocky Mountains with varying success. When Cascade Airlines offered to buy his company, Peter decided to sell and return to the East.

Peter arrived at his office near Fenway Park in Boston a little later than usual this morning. He had stopped to have a business breakfast with Aaron Little, his long-time friend and sometime partner in various business deals. Peter needed some advice and through the years has learned to rely on Aaron as a ready source, no matter what the subject.

Peter explained to Aaron that his commuter service needed a promotional gimmick to improve its visibility among the business communities in Boston and New York. Peter was thinking of running a contest on each flight and awarding the winner a prize. The idea would be that travelers who commute between Boston and New York might just as well have fun on the way and have a chance to win a nice prize.

As Aaron listened to Peter outlining his contest plans, his mind raced through contest ideas. Aaron thought that a large variety of contests would be needed, because many of the passengers would likely be repeat customers and might tire of the same old thing. In addition, some of the contests should be chance-type contests, whereas others should be skill-based.

"Well, what do you think?" asked Peter. Aaron finished his scrambled eggs before responding. When he did, it was completely in character. "I think it will fly," Aaron said, and proceeded to offer a variety of suggestions.

Peter felt good about the enthusiastic response Aaron had given to the idea and thought that the ideas discussed at breakfast presented a good basis for the promotional effort. Now back at the office, Peter does have some concerns with one part of the plan. Aaron thought that in addition to the regular in-flight contests for prizes (such as free flights, dictation equipment, and business-periodical subscriptions), each month on a randomly selected day a major prize should be offered on all Great Air flights. This would encourage regular business fliers to fly Great Air all the time. Aaron proposed that the prize could be a trip to the Virgin Islands or somewhere similar, or the cash equivalent.

Great Air has three flights daily to New York and three flights returning to Boston, for a total of six flights. Peter is concerned that the cost of funding six prizes of this size each month plus six daily smaller prizes might be excessive. He also believes that it might be better to increase the size of the large prize to something such as a new car, but use a contest that will not guarantee a winner.

But what kind of a contest can be used? Just as he is about to dial Aaron's number, Margaret Runyon, Great Air's marketing manager, enters Peter's office. He has been waiting for her to return from a meeting so he can run the contest idea past her and get her input.

Margaret's response is not as upbeat as Aaron's, but she does think the idea is worth exploring. She offers an idea for the large-prize contest that she thinks might be workable. She outlines the contest as follows:

On the first of each month she and Peter will randomly select a day for that month on which the major contest will be run. That date will not be disclosed to the public. Then on each flight that day, the flight attendant will have passengers write down their birthdays (month and day). If any two people on the plane have the same birthday, they will place their names in a hat and one name will be selected to receive the grand prize.

Margaret explains that because the capacity of each flight is 40 passengers plus the crew, there is a very low chance of a birthday match and, therefore, the chance of giving away a grand prize on any one flight is small. Peter likes the idea, but when he asks Margaret what the probability is that a match will occur, her response does not sound quite right. She believes the probability for a match will be 40/365 for a full plane and less than that when there are fewer than 40 passengers aboard.

After Margaret leaves, Peter decides that it would be useful to know the probability of one or more birthday matches on flights with 20, 30, and 40 passengers. Further, he wants to know what the chances are that he will end up awarding two or more major prizes during a given month, assuming that the six flights carry the same number of passengers (20, 30, or 40). He realizes that he will need some help from someone with a knowledge of statistics.

CASE 4-B:

Let's Make a Deal

Quite a few years ago, a popular show called *Let's Make a Deal* appeared on network television. Contestants were selected from the audience. Each contestant would bring some silly item that they would trade for a cash prize or a prize behind one of three doors.

Suppose that you have been selected as a contestant on the show. You are given a choice of three doors. Behind one door is a new sports car. Behind the other doors are a pig and chicken—booby prizes to be sure! Let's suppose that you pick door number one. Before opening that door, the host, who knows what is behind each door, opens door two to show you the chicken. He then asks you, "Would you be willing to trade door one for door three?" What should you do?

General References

1. Albright, Christian S., Wayne L. Winston, and Christopher Zappe, *Data Analysis and Decision Making with Microsoft Excel* (Pacific Grove, CA: Duxbury, 1999).

2. Blyth, C. R., "Subjective vs. Objective Methods in Statistics." *American Statistician*, 26 (June 1972), pp. 20–22.

3. Brightman, Harvey, and Howard Schneider, *Statistics for Business Problem Solving*, 2nd ed. (Cincinnati, Ohio: South-Western, 1992).

4. Dodge, Mark, and Craig Stinson, *Running Microsoft Excel 2000* (Redmond, WA: Microsoft Press, 1999).

5. Hogg, R. V., and Elliot A. Tanis, *Probability and Statistical Inference*, 5th ed. (Upper Saddle River, NJ: Prentice Hall, 1997).

6. Marx, Morris L., and Richard J. Larsen, *Mathematical Statistics and Its Applications*, 3rd ed. (Upper Saddle River, NJ: Prentice Hall, 2000).

7. *Microsoft Excel 2000* (Redmond, WA: Microsoft Corp., 1999).

8. *Minitab for Windows Version 13* (State College, PA: Minitab, 2000).

9. Raiffa, H., *Decision Analysis: Introductory Lectures on Choices Under Uncertainty* (Reading, MA: Addison-Wesley, 1968).

10. Siegel, Andrew F., *Practical Business Statistics*, 4th ed. (Burr Ridge, IL: Irwin, 2000).

CHAPTER 5

Discrete and Continuous Probability Distributions

CHAPTER OUTCOMES

After studying the material in this chapter, you should:

- Be able to apply the binomial distribution to business decision-making situations.
- Be able to compute probabilities for the Poisson and hypergeometric distributions.
- Be able to discuss the important properties of the normal probability distribution.
- Recognize when the normal distribution might apply in a decision-making process.
- Be able to calculate probabilities using the normal distribution table and be able to apply the normal distribution in appropriate business situations.
- Recognize situations in which the uniform and exponential distributions apply.

WHY YOU NEED TO KNOW

Consider a major wood-products company that has perfected a new strain of disease-resistant Douglas fir tree. Even though the tree seeds are clones of each other, company biologists find the trees exhibit different growth rates. Also consider a tire manufacturer that has developed a new tread design for sport utility vehicles. The testing team, measuring tread life by the number of miles driven, has found that the tires don't all wear at the same rate, even when they are tested on the same vehicle.

In addition to the discrete random variable examples introduced in Chapter 4, there are many situations in which a variable of interest is not restricted to discrete, integer values. For example, the growth rates of trees can take on any value between zero and some large number, and tire tread life, measured in miles driven, could also take on values between zero and some large number. Variables that are measured in units of length, time, weight, volume, or distance are often assumed to be *continuous* variables.

Technically, a continuous variable is one that can take on an infinitely uncountable number of values (measured to as many decimal places as necessary). Because of measuring limitations, some argue that there is no such thing as a truly continuous variable. They consider all variables discrete even though they can take on values containing several decimal values. However, if a variable of interest is measured such that it takes on a very large number of possible values in a specified interval, we might make the assumption that it is continuous. It depends on the situation. For instance, if the time required to complete a small project that will last less than a day is tracked in hours, the time variable is not assumed to be continuous. However, if the time is measured in seconds, we would be justified in treating the variable as continuous.

Because many business applications involve discrete and continuous or quasi-continuous variables, decision makers need to become acquainted with both discrete and continuous probability distributions and learn how to use them in decision making.

5-1 THE BINOMIAL PROBABILITY DISTRIBUTION

In Chapter 4 you learned that variables can be classified as either **discrete** or **continuous**, depending on the number of values that the variable can assume.

Discrete Random Variable	*Continuous Random Variable*
A random variable that can assume only a countable number of possible values.	Random variables that can assume any value in an interval.

In most instances, the value of a discrete random variable is determined by counting. For instance, the number of customers who arrive at a store is a discrete variable. Its value is determined by counting the customers.

In many other instances, decision makers will be faced with variables that can take on a seemingly unlimited number of values. The values for these continuous random variables are typically determined by measurement instead of counting. Examples include:

Time required to perform a job   Interest rates

Financial ratios   Income levels

Product weights   Distances between two points

Volume of soft drink in a can

In general, *measurement* is required to determine the value for a continuous random variable, whereas the value for a discrete random variable comes from *counting*.

Several theoretical discrete distributions have extensive application in business decision making. A probability distribution is called *theoretical* when the mathematical properties of its random variable are used to produce its probabilities. Such distributions are different than the distributions that are obtained subjectively or from observation.

Sections 5-1 and 5-2 focus on theoretical discrete probability distributions, whereas Sections 5-3 and 5-4 introduce important theoretical continuous probability distributions.

THE BINOMIAL DISTRIBUTION

The simplest theoretical probability distribution we will consider is one that describes processes whose trials have only two possible outcomes. The physical events described by this type of process are widespread. For instance, a quality control system in a manufacturing plant labels each tested item as either defective or acceptable. A firm bidding for a contract either will or will not get the contract. A marketing research firm may receive responses to a questionnaire in the form of "Yes, I will buy" or "No, I will not buy." The personnel manager in an organization is faced with a two-stage process each time he offers a job—either the applicant accepts the offer or rejects it.

CHARACTERISTICS OF THE BINOMIAL DISTRIBUTION

These examples are all situations that can be described by a discrete probability distribution called the **binomial distribution.**

Binomial Probability Distribution Characteristics

A distribution that gives the probability of x successes in n trials in a process that meets the following conditions.
1. A trial has only two possible outcomes: a success or a failure.
2. There is a fixed number, n, of identical trials.
3. The trials of the experiment are independent of each other. This means that if one outcome is a success, this does not influence the chance of another outcome being a success.
4. The process must be consistent in generating successes and failures. That is, the probability, p, associated with a success remains constant from trial to trial.
5. If p represents the probability of a success, then $(1 - p) = q$ is the probability of a failure.

The binomial distribution requires that the experiment trials be independent. This can be assured in a finite population if the sampling is performed with replacement. This means that an item is sampled from a population and returned to the population, after its characteristic(s) have been recorded, before the next item is sampled. However, sampling with replacement is the exception rather than the rule in business applications. Most often the sampling is performed without replacement. Strictly speaking, when sampling is performed without replacement, the conditions for the binomial distribution cannot be satisfied. However, the conditions are approximately satisfied if the sample selected is quite small relative to the size of the population from which the sample is selected.

A commonly used rule of thumb is that the binomial distribution can be applied if the sample size is at most 5% of the population size.

Household Security—Household Security produces and installs 300 custom-made home security units every week. The units are priced to include one-day installation service by two technicians. A unit with either a design or production problem must be modified on site and will require more than one day to install.

Household Security has completed an extensive study of its design and manufacturing systems. The information shows that if the company is operating at standard quality, 10% of the security systems will have problems and will require more than one day to install.

The binomial distribution applies to this situation because the following conditions exist.

1. There are only two possible outcomes when a unit is sold: it is good or it is defective (will take more than one day to install). Finding a defective system in this application will be considered a success. A success occurs when we observe the outcome of interest.
2. Each unit is designed and made in the same way.
3. The outcome of a security system (good or defective) is independent of whether the preceding system was good or defective.
4. The probability of a defective system, $p = 0.10$, remains constant from unit to unit.
5. The probability of a good system, $q = 1 - p = 0.90$, remains constant from unit to unit.

To determine the likely cause of defects—design or manufacturing—the quality assurance group at Household Security has developed a plan for dismantling a random sample of four security systems each week. Because the sample size is small ($4/300 = 1.33\%$) relative to the size of the population (300 units per week), the conditions of independence and constant probability will be approximately satisfied because the sample is less than 5% of the population.

We let the number of defective units be the random variable of interest. The number of defectives is limited to discrete values, $x = 0, 1, 2, 3,$ or 4. We can determine the probability that the random variable will have any of the discrete values. One way is to list the sample space, as shown in

TABLE 5-1	RESULTS	NO. OF DEFECTIVES	NO. OF WAYS
Sample Space	G,G,G,G	0	1
	G,G,G,D	1	
	G,G,D,G		
	G,G,D,G		4
	G,D,G,G,		
	D,G,G,G		
	G,G,D,D	2	
	G,D,G,D		
	D,G,G,D		
	G,D,D,G		6
	D,G,D,G		
	D,D,G,G		
	D,D,D,G	3	
	D,D,G,D		
	D,G,D,D		4
	G,D,D,D		
	D,D,D,D	4	1

Table 5-1. We can find the probability of zero defectives, for instance, by employing the multiplication rule for independent events.

$$P(x = 0 \text{ defectives}) = P(G \text{ and } G \text{ and } G \text{ and } G)$$

where:

$$G = \text{Unit is good (not defective)}$$

Here

$$P(G) = 0.90$$

and we have assumed the units are independent. Using the multiplication rule for independent events introduced in Chapter 4 (Rule 4-12):

$$P(G \text{ and } G \text{ and } G \text{ and } G) = P(G)P(G)P(G)P(G) = (0.90)(0.90)(0.90)(0.90)$$
$$= 0.90^4$$
$$= 0.6561.$$

We can also find the probability of exactly one defective in a sample of four. This is accomplished using both the multiplication rule for independent events and the addition rule for mutually exclusive events, which was also introduced in Chapter 4 (Rule 4-8):

$$P(1 \text{ defective}) = P(G \text{ and } G \text{ and } G \text{ and } D) + P(G \text{ and } G \text{ and } D \text{ and } G) + P(G \text{ and } D \text{ and } G \text{ and } G) + P(D \text{ and } G \text{ and } G \text{ and } G)$$

where:

$$P(G \text{ and } G \text{ and } G \text{ and } D) = P(G)P(G)P(G)P(D) = (0.90)(0.90)(0.90)(0.10)$$
$$= (0.90^3)(0.10)$$

Likewise:

$$P(G \text{ and } G \text{ and } D \text{ and } G) = (0.90^3)(0.10)$$
$$P(G \text{ and } D \text{ and } G \text{ and } G) = (0.90^3)(0.10)$$
$$P(D \text{ and } G \text{ and } G \text{ and } G) = (0.90^3)(0.10)$$

Then:

$$P(1 \text{ defective}) = (0.90^3)(0.10) + (0.90^3)(0.10) + (0.90^3)(0.10) + (0.90^3)(0.10)$$
$$= (4)(0.90^3)(0.10)$$
$$= 0.2916$$

Note that each of the four possible ways of finding one defective unit has the same probability $[(.90^3)(.10)]$. We determine the probability of one of the ways to obtain one defective unit and multiply this value by the number of ways (four) of obtaining one defective unit. This produces the overall probability of one defective unit.

Combinations

In this relatively simply application, we can fairly easily list the sample space and from that count the number of ways that each possible number of defectives can occur. However, for larger examples, this approach is inefficient. A more effective method exists for counting the number of ways binomial events can occur. This method is called the **counting rule for combinations**. This rule is used to count the number of outcomes from an experiment in which x objects are to be selected from a group of n objects. Equation 5-1 is used to find the combinations.

Counting Rule for Combinations

$$C_x^n = \frac{n!}{x!(n-x)!}$$

5-1

where:

C_x^n = Number of combinations of x objects selected from n objects
$n! = n(n-1)(n-2)\dots(2)(1)$
$0! = 1$ by definition

Using Equation 5-1, we find the number of ways that $x = 2$ defectives can occur in a sample of $n = 4$ as:

$$C_x^n = \frac{n!}{x!(n-x)!} = \frac{4!}{2!(4-2)!} = \frac{(4)(3)(2)(1)}{(2)(1)(2)(1)} = \frac{24}{4} = 6 \text{ ways}$$

Refer to Table 5-1 to see that this is the same value obtained by listing the sample space.

Now we can find the probabilities of two defectives.

$$P(2 \text{ defectives}) = (6)(0.90^2)(0.10^2)$$
$$= 0.0486$$

Use this method to verify the following:

$$P(3 \text{ defectives}) = (4)(0.90)(0.10^3)$$
$$= 0.0036$$
$$P(4 \text{ defectives}) = (1)(0.10^4)$$
$$= 0.0001$$

The key to developing the probability distribution for a binomial process is first to determine the probability of any one way the event of interest can occur and then to multiply this probability by the number of ways that event can occur. Table 5-2 shows the binomial probability distribution for the number of defective security units in a sample size of 4 when the probability of any individual unit being defective is 0.10. The probability distribution is graphed in Figure 5-1. Most samples would contain zero or one defective units when the production system is functioning as designed.

Binomial Formula

The steps that we have taken to develop this binomial probability distribution can be summarized through a formula called the **binomial formula**, shown as Equation 5-2. Note, this formula is composed of two parts: the combinations of x items selected from n items and the probability of one of the ways that x items can occur.

TABLE 5-2

Binomial Distribution for Household Security:
$n = 4$,
$p = 0.10$

x = # OF DEFECTS	P(x)
0	0.6561
1	0.2916
2	0.0486
3	0.0036
4	0.0001
$\Sigma P(x) =$	1.0000

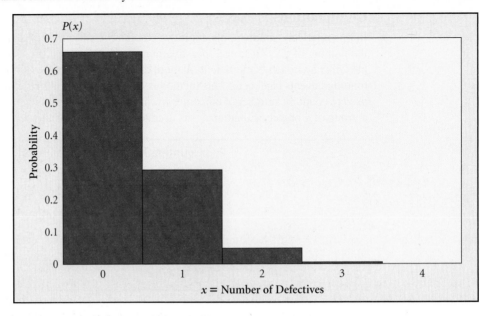

FIGURE 5-1

Binomial Distribution for Household Security

Binomial Formula

$$P(x) = \frac{n!}{x!(n-x)!} p^x q^{n-x}$$

5-2

where:

n = Random sample size
x = Number of successes (when a success is what we are looking for)
$n - x$ = Number of failures
p = Probability of a success
$q = 1 - p$ = Probability of a failure
$n! = n(n - 1)(n - 2)(n - 3) \cdots 1$
$0! = 1$ by definition

Applying Equation 5-2 to the security system example for $n = 4$, $p = 0.10$, and $x = 2$ defects, we get:

$$P(x) = \frac{n!}{x!(n-x)!} p^x q^{n-x}$$

$$P(x = 2) = \frac{4!}{2!\,2!}(0.10^2)(0.90^2) = 6(0.10^2)(0.90^2) = 0.0486$$

This is the same value we obtained earlier when we listed out the sample space.

EXAMPLE 5-1: USING THE BINOMIAL FORMULA

Hanson's Car Wash   Hanson's Car Wash offers a full refund to anyone who is not satisfied with the way their car looks after it is washed. The owners believe the wash results from car to car are independent and that the probability that a customer will ask for a refund is 0.20. Suppose a random sample of six cars is observed. In four instances, the owner has asked for a refund. The owner might be interested in the probability of four refunds in six cars. If the binomial distribution applies, the probability can be found using the following steps:

Step 1:   Define the characteristics of the binomial distribution.
In this case, the characteristics are

$$n = 6, p = 0.20, q = 1 - p = 0.80$$

Step 2:   Determine the probability of x successes in n trials using the binomial formula, Equation 5-2.

In this case, $n = 6$, $p = 0.20$, $q = 0.80$, and we are interested in the probability of $x = 4$ successes.

$$P(x) = \frac{n!}{x!(n-x)!} p^x q^{n-x}$$

$$P(4) = \frac{6!}{4!(6-4)!}(0.20^4)(0.80^{6-4})$$

$$P(4) = 15(0.20^4)(0.80^2)$$

$$P(4) = 0.0154$$

There is only a 0.0154 chance that exactly four customers will want a refund in a sample of six if the chance that any one of the customers will want a refund is 0.20.

Using the Binomial Distribution Table

Using Equation 5-2 to develop the binomial distribution is not difficult, but it can be time-consuming. To make binomial probabilities easier to find, you can use the binomial table in Appendix B. This table is constructed to give individual probabilities for different sample sizes and probabilities of success. Each column is headed by a probability, p, which is the probability associated with a success. The column headings correspond to probabilities of success ranging from 0.01 to 0.50. Down the left side of the table are integer values that correspond to the number of successes, x, for the specified sample size, n. If we are dealing with probabilities ranging from 0.51 to 1.0, we use the values of p located at the bottom of the columns. The corresponding values of x are on the right side of the table, running from bottom to top.

U.S. Bio—U.S. Bio, a pharmaceutical company, has developed a drug to restore hair growth in men. Like most drugs, this product has potential side effects. One of these is increased blood pressure. The company is willing to market the drug if there are blood-pressure increases in 2% or fewer of the men using the drug.

The company plans to conduct a clinical test with 10 randomly selected men. The number of men with increased blood pressure will be $x = 0, 1, 2, \ldots 10$. We can use the binomial table in Appendix B to develop the probability distribution. Table 5-3 shows the portion of the binomial table we need for $p = 0.02$ and $n = 10$. Go to the column for $p = 0.02$. The values of x are listed down the left side of the table. For example, the probability of 3 occurrences is 0.0008. This means that it is extremely unlikely that 3 men, in a sample of 10, would exhibit increased blood pressure if the overall fraction having this side effect is 0.02. Note, in Table 5-3, the probabilities for all values of $x > 3$ is 0.0000. So, to four decimal places, the probability of four men experiencing increased blood pressure is zero. The true probability is not zero but is very small. Then:

$$P(x \geq 3) = 0.0008 + 0.0000 + 0.0000 + \ldots + 0.0000 = 0.0008$$

There are about 8 chances in 10,000 that we would find three or more men with increased blood pressure if the probability of it happening for any one person is $p = 0.02$. If the test did show that

TABLE 5-3

Binomial Table ($n = 10$)

x	p = 0.01	p = 0.02	p = 0.03	p = 0.04	p = 0.05	p = 0.06	p = 0.07	p = 0.08	p = 0.09	p = 0.10	
0	0.9044	0.8171	0.7374	0.6648	0.5987	0.5386	0.4840	0.4344	0.3894	0.3487	10
1	0.0914	0.1667	0.2281	0.2770	0.3151	0.3438	0.3643	0.3777	0.3851	0.3874	9
2	0.0042	0.0153	0.0317	0.0519	0.0746	0.0988	0.1234	0.1478	0.1714	0.1937	8
3	0.0001	0.0008	0.0026	0.0058	0.0105	0.0168	0.0248	0.0343	0.0452	0.0574	7
4	0.0000	0.0000	0.0001	0.0004	0.0010	0.0019	0.0033	0.0052	0.0078	0.0112	6
5	0.0000	0.0000	0.0000	0.0000	0.0001	0.0001	0.0003	0.0005	0.0009	0.0015	5
6	0.0000	0.0000	0.0000	0.0000	0.0000	0.0000	0.0000	0.0000	0.0001	0.0001	4
7	0.0000	0.0000	0.0000	0.0000	0.0000	0.0000	0.0000	0.0000	0.0000	0.0000	3
8	0.0000	0.0000	0.0000	0.0000	0.0000	0.0000	0.0000	0.0000	0.0000	0.0000	2
9	0.0000	0.0000	0.0000	0.0000	0.0000	0.0000	0.0000	0.0000	0.0000	0.0000	1
10	0.0000	0.0000	0.0000	0.0000	0.0000	0.0000	0.0000	0.0000	0.0000	0.0000	0
	p = 0.99	p = 0.98	p = 0.97	p = 0.96	p = 0.95	p = 0.94	p = 0.93	p = 0.92	p = 0.91	p = 0.90	**x**

n = 10

three men had elevated blood pressure after taking the new drug, the true rate of high blood pressure likely exceeds 2%, and the company should have serious doubts about marketing the drug.

EXAMPLE 5-2: USING THE BINOMIAL TABLE

Nielsen TV Ratings   The Nielsen Company is the best-known television ratings company. On Tuesday after the 2002 Masters Golf Tournament in Augusta, Georgia, which Tiger Woods won, the company announced that slightly more than 9% of all televisions were tuned to the final round on Sunday. Assuming that the 9% rating is correct, what is the probability that in a random sample of 20 television sets, two or fewer would have been tuned to the Masters? This question can be answered, assuming that the binomial distribution applies, using the following steps:

Step 1:   Define the characteristics of the binomial distribution.
In this case, the characteristics are
$$n = 20, p = 0.09, q = 1 - p = 0.91$$

Step 2:   Go to the binomial table in Appendix B. Locate the appropriate column for p and the appropriate section in the table for the sample size, n.
In this case, we locate the section of the table corresponding to sample size equal to $n = 20$ and go to the column headed $p = 0.09$. The probabilities from the binomial table are

x	P(x)
0	0.1516
1	0.3000
2	0.2818
3	0.1672
4	0.0703
5	0.0222
6	0.0055
7	0.0011
8	0.0002

Step 3:   Define the event of interest and obtain the probabilities from the binomial table.
We are interested in the probability of two or fewer sets tuned to the Masters. This is
$$P(x \leq 2) = P(x = 0) + P(x = 1) + P(x = 2)$$
From the binomial table we get:
$$P(x \leq 2) = 0.1516 + 0.3000 + 0.2818$$
$$= 0.7334$$
Thus, there is a 0.7334 chance that two or fewer sets in a random sample of 20 were tuned to the Masters.

EXAMPLE 5-3: USING THE BINOMIAL DISTRIBUTION

Naumann Research   Naumann Research is a full-service marketing research consulting firm. Recently it was retained to do a project for a major U.S. airline. The airline was considering changing from an assigned-seating reservation system to one in which fliers would be able to take any seat they wished on a first-come-first-served basis. The airline believes that 80% of its fliers would like this change if it was accompanied with a reduction in ticket prices. Naumann Research will survey a large number of customers on this issue, but prior to conducting the full research, it has selected a random sample of 20 customers and determined that 12 like the proposed change. What is the probability of finding 12 or fewer who like the change if the probability is 0.80 that a customer will like the change?

If we assume the binomial distribution applies, we can use the following steps to answer this question.

Step 1:   Define the characteristics of the binomial distribution.
In this case, the characteristics are
$$n = 20, p = 0.80, q = 1 - p = 0.20$$

Step 2: **Go to the binomial table in Appendix B. Locate the appropriate column for p and the appropriate section in the table for the sample size, *n*.**
First, locate the section of the table corresponding to sample size equal to $n = 20$. Then, because $p > 0.50$, we find the desired column by looking to the p values at the bottom of each column. Locate the column for $p = 0.80$.

Step 3: **Define the event of interest.**
We are interested in knowing:
$$P(x \le 12) = P(x = 12) + P(x = 11) + \cdots + P(x = 0)$$

Step 4: **Locate the desired probabilities in the binomial table and sum them.**
Since $p > 0.50$, the values of x are in the far right column of the binomial table. Go to the row corresponding to $x = 12$ and the column for $p = 0.80$ in the section of the table for $n = 20$ to get:
$$P(x = 12) = 0.0222$$
Repeat this for the values of x from 12 down to 0:
$$P(x \le 12) = 0.0222 + 0.0074 + 0.0020 + 0.0005 + 0.0001 + 0.0000 + \cdots + 0.0000$$
$$= 0.0322$$

Thus, it is quite unlikely that if 80% of customers like the new seating plan that 12 or fewer in a sample of 20 would like it. The airline may want to rethink its plan.

MEAN AND STANDARD DEVIATION OF THE BINOMIAL DISTRIBUTION

In Chapter 4 we stated the mean of a discrete probability distribution is also referred to as the *expected value*. The expected value of a discrete random variable, x, is found using Equation 5-3.

Expected Value of a Discrete Random Variable

$$\mu_x = E(x) = \sum xP(x)$$ **5-3**

where:

x = Values of the random variable
$P(x)$ = Probability of the random variable taking on the value of x

---

Mean of a Binomial Distribution

Equation 5-3 can be used with any discrete probability distribution, including the binomial. However, if we are working with a binomial distribution, the mean can be found more easily by using Equation 5-4.

Expected Value of a Binomial Distribution

$$\mu_x = E(x) = np$$ **5-4**

where:

n = Sample size
p = Probability of a success

Excel and Minitab Tutorial

Catalog Sales—Catalog sales have been a part of the U.S. economy for many years, and in the 1990s companies such as Lands' End, L.L. Bean, and Eddie Bauer enjoyed increased business. One feature that has made mail-order buying so popular is the ease with which customers can return merchandise. Nevertheless, one mail-order catalog has the goal of having no more than 11% of all purchased items returned.

FIGURE 5-2A

Output for Mail-Order Sales Returns

Excel Instructions:
1. Click on f_x on tool bar.
2. Select **Statistical** and then **BINOMDIST** options.
3. Fill in requested information.
4. "True" indicates Cumulative Probabilities.

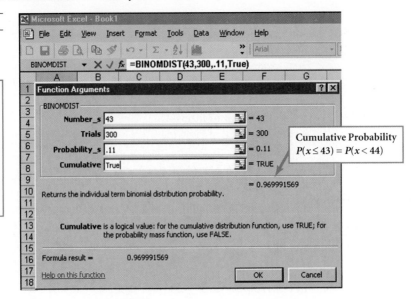

The binomial distribution can describe the number of items returned. For instance, in a given hour the company shipped 300 items. If the probability of an item being returned is $p = 0.11$, the expected number of items (mean) to be returned is

$$\mu_x = E(x) = np$$
$$\mu_x = E(x) = (300)(0.11) = 33.0$$

Thus, the average number of returned items for each 300 items shipped is 33.

Suppose the company sales manager wants to know if the return rate is stable at 11%. To test this, she monitors a random sample of 300 items and finds that 44 have been returned. This return rate exceeds the mean of 33 units, which concerns her. However, before reaching a conclusion, she will be interested in the probability of observing 44 or more returns in a sample of 300.

$$P(x \geq 44) = 1 - P(x < 44)$$

The binomial table in Appendix B does not contain sample sizes of 300. Instead, we can use Excel's **BINOMDIST** function or the binomial tool in Minitab's **CALC—Probability Distribution** menu to find the probability. The Excel and Minitab output in Figures 5-2a and Figure 5-2b show the cumulative probability of 43 or fewer is equal to

$$P(x \leq 43) = P(x < 44) = 0.9700$$

Then the probability of 44 or more returns is

$$P(x \geq 44) = 1 - 0.9700 = 0.0300$$

There is only a 3% chance of 44 or more items being returned if the 11% return rate is still in effect. This low probability suggests that the return rate may have increased above 11%.

FIGURE 5-2B

Minitab Output for Mail-Order Sales Return

Minitab Instructions:
1. Choose **Calc > Probability Distribution > Binomial**.
2. Choose **Cumulative probability**.
3. In **Number of trials** enter sample size.
4. In **Probability of success** enter p.
5. In **Input constant** enter the number of successes: x.
6. Click **OK**.

ℰXAMPLE 5-4: FINDING THE MEAN OF THE BINOMIAL DISTRIBUTION

Naumann Research   In Example 5-3, Naumann Research had been hired to do a study for a major airline that is planning to change from a designated-seat assignment plan to an open-seating system. The company believes that 80% of its customers approve of the idea. Naumann Research interviewed a sample of $n = 20$ and found 12 who like the proposed change. If the airline is correct in its assessment of the probability, what is the expected number of people in a sample of $n = 20$ who will like the change? We can find this using the following steps:

Step 1:   **Define the characteristics of the binomial distribution.**
In this case, the characteristics are
$$n = 20, p = 0.80, q = 1 - p = 0.20$$

Step 2:   **Use Equation 5-4 to find the expected value.**
$$\mu_x = E(x) = np$$
$$E(x) = 20(0.80) = 16$$

The average number who would say they like the proposed change is 16 in a sample of 20.

Standard Deviation of a Binomial Distribution

In Chapter 4, we introduced the standard deviation for a discrete probability distribution and showed how it is calculated. Equation 5-5 can be used to compute the standard deviation for any discrete probability distribution.

Standard Deviation of a Discrete Random Variable

$$\sigma_x = \sqrt{\sum[x - E(x)]^2 P(x)} \qquad \text{5-5}$$

where:

$x = $ Value for the random variable
$E(x) = $ Expected value of the random variable
$P(x) = $ Probability of the random variable taking on the value of x

---

If a discrete probability distribution meets the binomial distribution conditions, the standard deviation is defined by Equation 5-6.

Standard Deviation of the Binomial Distribution

$$\sigma = \sqrt{npq} \qquad \text{5-6}$$

where:

$n = $ Sample size
$p = $ Probability of a success
$q = 1 - p = $ Probability of a failure

ℰXAMPLE 5-5: FINDING THE STANDARD DEVIATION OF A BINOMIAL DISTRIBUTION

Naumann Research   Refer to Examples 5-3 and 5-4, in which Naumann Research surveyed a sample of $n = 20$ airline customers about changing the way seats are assigned on flights. The airline believes that 80% of its customers approve of the proposed change. Example 5-4 showed that if the airline is correct in its assessment, the expected number in a sample of 20 who would like the change is 16. However, there are other possible outcomes if 20 customers are surveyed. What is the standard deviation of the random variable, x, in this case? We can find the standard deviation for the binomial distribution using the following steps.

Step 1: **Define the characteristics of the binomial distribution.**
In this case, the characteristics are
$$n = 20, p = 0.80, q = 1 - p = 0.20$$

Step 2: **Use Equation 5-6 to calculate the standard deviation.**
$$\sigma = \sqrt{npq} = \sqrt{20(0.80)(0.20)} = 1.7889$$

ADDITIONAL INFORMATION ABOUT THE BINOMIAL DISTRIBUTION

At this point, several comments about the binomial distribution are worth making. If p, the probability of a success, is 0.50, the binomial distribution is *symmetrical* and bell-shaped, regardless of the sample size. This is illustrated in Figure 5-3, which shows frequency histograms for samples of $n = 5$, $n = 10$, and $n = 50$. Notice that all three distributions are centered at the expected value, $E(x) = \mu_x$.

When the value of p differs from 0.50 in either direction, the binomial distribution is skewed. The skewness will be most pronounced when n is small and p approaches 0 or 1. However, the binomial distribution becomes more bell-shaped as n increases. The frequency histograms shown in Figure 5-4 bear this out.

FIGURE 5-3 **The Binomial Distribution with Varying Sample Sizes ($p = 0.50$)**

FIGURE 5-4 **The Binomial Distribution with Varying Sample Sizes ($p = 0.05$)**

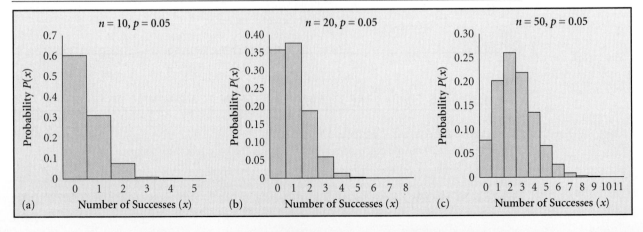

5-1: EXERCISES

Skill Development

5.1 Use the binomial formula to develop the probability distribution for an experiment in which $n = 4$ and $p = 0.2$.

5.2 Use the binomial formula to calculate the following probabilities for an experiment in which $n = 5$ and $p = 0.4$.
a. the probability that x is at most one
b. the probability that x is at least four
c. the probability that x is less than one

5.3 Use the binomial distribution table to calculate the following probabilities for a binomial random variable where $n = 20$ and $p = 0.40$.
a. $P(x = 10)$
b. $P(7 < x < 12)$
c. $P(x \geq 12)$

5.4 For a binomial distribution with $n = 10$ and $p = 0.70$, determine:
a. $P(x > 7)$
b. $P(x < E(x))$

5.5 Use the counting rule for combinations to determine:
a. the number of ways 4 items can be selected from 8 items
b. the number of ways 6 items can be selected from 10 items
c. the number of ways 3 items can be selected from 10 items
d. the number of ways 7 items can be selected from 10 items

5.6 For a sample of $n = 10$, assuming that the binomial probability distribution applies, find the following.
a. the probability of 3 successes if the probability of a success is 0.20
b. the probability of 3 successes if the probability of a success is 0.80

5.7 Assuming that the binomial distribution applies, if a sample size of $n = 5$ is selected and the probability of a success is 0.40,
a. What is the probability of 4 successes?
b. What is the probability of 4 or more successes?
c. What is the expected value and standard deviation for the number of successes?

5.8 Assuming that the binomial distribution applies, given a sample size of $n = 20$, find the following.
a. the probability of 5 successes if the probability of a success is 0.75
b. the probability of 4 or fewer failures if the probability of a success is 0.20
c. the probability of 11 successes if the probability of a failure is 0.33

5.9 If a binomial distribution applies with a sample size of $n = 20$, find
a. the probability of 5 successes if the probability of a success is 0.40

b. the probability of at least 7 successes if the probability of a success is 0.25
c. the expected value, n = 20, p = .20
d. the standard deviation, n = 20, p = .20

5.10 A binomial random variable, x, has parameters $n = 250$ and $p = 0.70$. Find the mean, variance, standard deviation, and coefficient of variation of the random variable, x.

5.11 The following probability distribution is provided for a binomial random variable with $n = 4$ and $p = 0.20$:

x	P(x)
0	0.4096
1	0.4096
2	0.1536
3	0.0256
4	0.0016

a. Use Equation 5-3 to compute the expected value of this probability distribution.
b. Use Equation 5-4 to find the expected value.

5.12 Indicate the conditions under which a binomial distribution will be symmetric. Under what conditions will a binomial distribution be skewed? Discuss the role that sample size plays in determining whether a binomial distribution is skewed or symmetric.

Business Applications

5.13 A credit card company knows that 70% of its customers are males. The company is considering randomly selecting five people each month to receive a free vacation.
a. What is the probability in a given month that all five people selected will be males?
b. Suppose that in a given month, all five people selected are females. What is the probability of this happening?

5.14 An auto parts store in Chicago believes that it has parts in inventory to meet the needs of 90% of its customers. If a random sample of 10 customers is selected, what is the probability that the store will have parts for all of them? Discuss the conditions in this situation that are required to assume that the binomial distribution applies.

5.15 The Lexington School Board has agreed to help the A. P. Stevens School Furniture Company test a new type of elementary school chair. Using the present school furniture, school administrators have found that 15% of the chairs must be replaced each year. A. P. Stevens claims its chair will average a 10% replacement rate. Assume that characteristics for a binomial distribution apply.
a. Calculate the probability that 2 or more of the A. P. Stevens' chairs will have to be replaced each year. Assume its claim of a 10% replacement rate is correct and that there are 10 chairs.

b. Calculate the probability that 2 or more currently used chairs will have to be replaced each year. Assume the school administrators' claim of a 15% replacement rate is correct and that there are 10 chairs sampled.

c. Assume 10 Stevens chairs are tested for one year and 2 need to be replaced. Comment on Stevens' claim that this proves its chair is superior to the present brand. Support your comments with probabilities and reasons.

5.16 The 1997 Tenth Planet Teachers and Technology Survey reported that 21% of elementary teachers use the Web. If five teachers are selected at random, what is the probability that
a. exactly three of the teachers use the Web
b. fewer than four teachers use the Web
c. more than one teacher uses the Web

5.17 A survey by KRC Research for *U.S. News* reported that 37% of people plan to spend more on eating out after they retire. If eight people are randomly selected, determine the following probabilities.
a. Exactly five people plan to spend more on eating out after they retire.
b. Fewer than four people plan to spend more on eating out after they retire.
c. More than two plan to spend more on eating out after they retire.

5.18 Gateway 2000, Inc., receives large shipments of microprocessors from Intel Corp. It must try to ensure that the proportion of microprocessors that are defective is small. Suppose Gateway decides to test five microprocessors out of a shipment of thousands of them. Suppose that if at least one of the microprocessors is defective, the shipment is returned.
a. If Intel Corp.'s shipment contains 10% defective microprocessors, calculate the probability the entire shipment will be returned.
b. If Intel and Gateway agree that Intel will not provide more than 5% defective chips, calculate the probability that the entire shipment will be returned even though only 5% are defective.
c. Calculate the probability that the entire shipment will be kept by Gateway even though the shipment has 10% defective microprocessors.

5.19 A CBS News survey reported that 67% of adults said the U.S. Treasury should continue making pennies. If six adults are selected at random, determine the expected number of adults who will say the U.S. Treasury should continue making pennies.

5.20 A CBS News survey reported that 67% of adults said the U.S. Treasury should continue making pennies. What is the probability that for six adults selected at random
a. Exactly five adults would want the Treasury to continue making pennies?
b. Three or fewer adults would want the Treasury to continue making pennies?
c. More than two adults would want the Treasury to continue making pennies?

5.21 The 1997 Tenth Planet Teachers and Technology Survey reported that 21% of elementary teachers use the Web. If five teachers are selected at random, determine the
a. expected number of these teachers who use the Web
b. standard deviation of these teachers who use the Web

5.22 A survey by KRC Research for *U.S. News* reported that 37% of people plan to spend more on eating out after they retire. If eight people are randomly selected, then determine
a. the expected number of people who plan to spend more eating out after they retire
b. the standard deviation of the individuals who plan to spend more eating out after they retire
c. the probability that two or fewer in the sample indicate that they actually plan to spend more on eating out after retirement.

Advanced Business Applications

5.23 The Ziteck Corporation buys parts from international suppliers. One part is currently being purchased from a Malaysian supplier under a contract that calls for at most 5% of the 10,000 parts to be defective. When a shipment arrives, Ziteck randomly samples 10 parts. If they find 2 or fewer defectives in the sample, they keep the shipment; otherwise they return the entire shipment to the supplier.
a. Assuming that the conditions for the binomial distribution are satisfied, what is the probability that the sample will lead Ziteck to keep the shipment if the defect rate is actually 0.05?
b. Suppose the supplier is actually sending Ziteck 10% defects, what is the probability that the sample will lead Ziteck to accept the shipment anyway?
c. Comment on this sampling plan (sample size and accept/reject point.) Do you think it favors either Ziteck or the supplier? Discuss.

5.24 A food-packaging business in California has a process that fills tomato juice into 24-ounce containers. When the process is in control, half the cans actually contain more than 24 ounces and half contain less. Suppose a quality inspector has just randomly sampled nine cans and has found that all nine had more than 24 ounces. Calculate the probability that this would occur if the filling process was in control. Based on this probability, what conclusion might be reached? Discuss.

5.25 In addition to microprocessors, Intel also supplies Gateway with memory modules (RAM). An important issue for Gateway is the proportion of defective modules it receives. Gateway must be very careful to negotiate a contract with Intel that will ensure the quality of its own product. Suppose that Gateway can tolerate 2.5% of its computers being returned because of failures in the memory modules. Assume each computer has three memory modules installed. If any one of the modules malfunctions, the computer will be returned for repair. Define x to be the random variable, whose value equals the number of defective memory modules in a randomly chosen Gateway computer.

a. Does the random variable (*x*) have a binomial distribution? If so, list the parameters that define this specific binomial distribution.

b. If Gateway negotiates a contract that allows Intel to send shipments in which 5% of the modules are defective, calculate the probability that a randomly chosen Gateway computer with these memory modules installed will be returned for repair. Is this probability larger than the 0.025 (2.5%) required by Gateway?

c. If the contract negotiated in part b doesn't meet with Gateway's approval, suggest a defect rate that Intel can deliver so that no more than 2.5% of Gateway's computers are returned for repairs.

5.26 Suppose a training program for electronics repair technicians has a goal that 70% of those who complete the program will be able to carry out a standard set of repairs on a personal computer. Five individuals who are believed to have completed the training are assigned the task of making the PC repairs. Of the five, one is successful.

a. What is the expected number of technicians who should be successful?

b. Assuming that these individuals did complete the training and that the 70% goal was met, what is the probability that one or fewer would be able to make the repairs? What might this result imply? Discuss some of the optional scenarios.

5-2 OTHER DISCRETE PROBABILITY DISTRIBUTIONS

The binomial distribution is very useful in many business situations, as indicated by the examples and applications presented in the previous section. However, as we pointed out, there are several requirements that must hold before we can use the binomial distribution to determine probabilities. If those conditions are not satisfied, there may be other theoretical probability distributions that could be employed. In this section we introduce two other very useful discrete probability distributions: the Poisson distribution and the hypergeometric distribution.

THE POISSON DISTRIBUTION

To use the binomial distribution, we must be able to count the number of successes and the number of failures. Although in many situations you may be able to count the number of successes, you often cannot count the number of failures. For example, suppose a company builds freeways in Vermont. The company could count the number of chuckholes that develop per mile (here a chuckhole is a success because it is what we are looking for), but how could it count the number of non-chuckholes? Or what about a hospital supplying emergency medical services in Los Angeles? It could easily count the number of emergencies its units respond to in one hour, but how could it determine how many calls it did not receive? Obviously, in these cases the number of possible outcomes (successes + failures) is difficult, if not impossible, to determine. If the total number of possible outcomes cannot be determined, the binomial distribution cannot be applied. In these cases you may be able to use the Poisson distribution.

Characteristics of the Poisson Distribution

The Poisson distribution[1] describes a process that extends over time or space. The outcomes of interest, such as emergency calls or chuckholes, occur at random, and we count the number of outcomes that occur in a given segment of time or space. We might count the number of emergency calls in a 15-minute period or the number of chuckholes in a two-mile stretch of freeway. As we did with the binomial distribution, we will call these outcomes *successes* even though (like chuckholes) they might be undesirable.

The possible counts are the integers 0, 1, 2, . . . and we would like to know the probability of each of these values. For example, what is the chance of getting exactly 4 emergency calls in a particular quarter hour? What is the chance that a chosen two-mile stretch of freeway will contain 0 chuckholes?

We can use the Poisson probability distribution to answer these questions if we make the following assumptions.

1. We know λ, the average number of successes in a segment of *unit* size. For example, we know that there is an average of 8 emergency calls per hour ($\lambda = 8$), or an average of 15 chuckholes per mile of freeway ($\lambda = 15$).

2. The probability of *x* successes in a segment is the same for all segments of the same size. For example, the probability distribution of emergency calls is the same for any 15-minute period of time at the hospital.

3. What happens in one segment has no influence on any nonoverlapping segment. For example, the number of calls arriving between 9:30 P.M. and 9:45 P.M. has no influence on the number of calls between 10:00 P.M. and 10:15 P.M.

[1]The Poisson distribution can be derived as the limiting distribution of the binomial distribution as the number of trials, *n*, tends to infinity. It serves as a good approximation to the binomial when *n* is large.

4. We imagine dividing time or space into tiny subsegments. Then the chance of *more* than one success in a subsegment is negligible and the chance of exactly one success in a tiny subsegment of length t is λt. For example, the chance of two emergency calls in the same second is essentially 0, and if $\lambda = 8$ calls per hour, the chance of a call in any given second is $(8)(1/3600) \approx 0.0022$.

Once λ has been determined, we can calculate the average occurrence rate for a segment of any size t. This is λt. Note that λ and t must be in compatible units. If we have $\lambda = 20$ arrivals per hour, the segments must be in hours or fractional parts of an hour.

That is, if we have $\lambda = 20$ per hour and we wish to work with half-hour time periods, the segment would be

$$t = \tfrac{1}{2} \text{ hour};$$

not $t = 30$ minutes.

Although the Poisson distribution is often used to describe situations such as the number of customers who arrive at a hospital emergency room per hour or the number of calls the Hewlett-Packard LaserJet printer service center receives in a 30-minute period, the segments need not be time intervals. Poisson distributions are also used to describe such random variables as the number of knots in a sheet of plywood or the number of contaminants in a certain volume of lake water. The segments would be the sheet of plywood and the volume of water.

Another important point is that λt, the average number in a segment of size t, is not necessarily the number we will see if we observe the process for one segment. We might expect an average of 20 people to arrive at a checkout stand in any given hour, but we do not expect to find exactly that number arriving every hour. The actual arrivals will form a distribution with an expected value, or mean, equal to λt. So, for the Poisson distribution,

$$\mu_x = \lambda t$$

Once λ and t have been specified, the probability for any discrete value in the Poisson distribution can be found using Equation 5-7.

Poisson Probability Distribution

$$P(x) = \frac{(\lambda t)^x \, e^{-\lambda t}}{x!}$$

5-7

where:

t = Size of the segment of interest
x = Number of successes in the segment of interest
λ = Expected number of successes in a segment of unit size
e = Base of the natural logarithm system (2.71828...)

First City Bank—A study conducted at First City Bank shows that the average number of arrivals to the teller section of the bank per hour is 15. Further, the distribution for the number of arrivals is considered to be Poisson distributed. Figure 5-5 shows the shape of the Poisson distribution for $\lambda = 15$. The probability of each possible number of customers arriving can be computed using Equation 5-7. For example, we can find the probability of $x = 12$ customers in one hour ($t = 1$) as follows.

$$P(x = 12) = \frac{(\lambda t)^x e^{-\lambda t}}{x!} = \frac{15^{12} e^{-15}}{12!} = 0.0829$$

Poisson Probability Distribution Table

As was the case with the binomial distribution, a table of probabilities exists for the Poisson distribution. (The full Poisson table appears in Appendix C.) The Poisson table shows the probabilities for different λt values. We can use the following business example to illustrate how to use the Poisson table.

Acme Taxi Service—The Acme Taxi Service has studied the demand for taxis at the local airport and has found that, on average, six taxis are demanded per hour. Thus, $\lambda = 6/\text{hour}$. If the company is considering locating six taxis at the airport during each hour, what is the probability that demand will exceed six and people will have to wait for taxi service?

To answer this question, we recognize that the segment of interest, t, equals one hour, so $\lambda t = 6$. We are interested in

$$P(x > 6) = 1 - P(x \le 6)$$

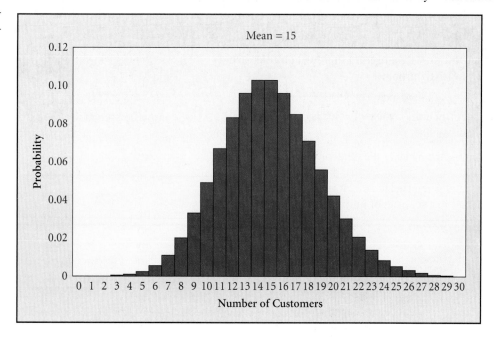

FIGURE 5-5

Poisson Distribution for Bank Customer Arrivals with $\lambda = 15$

To use the Poisson probability tables, turn to Appendix C and locate the column with $\lambda t = 6$. Table 5-4 shows the portion of the Poisson table that we will need. Locate the values of x down the left-hand side of the table. We first wish to determine the sum of the probabilities for $x = 0$ to $x = 6$. This sum is found by adding the probabilities under the column for $\lambda t = 6$ from $x = 0$ through $x = 6$. Doing this, we get:

$$P(x \leq 6) = 0.0025 + 0.0149 + 0.0446 + 0.0892 + 0.1339 + 0.1606 + 0.1606$$
$$= 0.6063$$

Therefore, the desired probability is

$$P(x > 6) = 1 - P(x \leq 6)$$
$$= 1 - 0.6063$$
$$= 0.3937$$

Thus, there is a 0.3937 probability that demand for taxis at the airport will exceed supply if the company puts only six taxis at the airport. This means that in almost 4 of every 10 hours, at least one more cab will be demanded than Acme will have available.

TABLE 5-4

Poisson Distribution Table

					λt					
x	5.10	5.20	5.30	5.40	5.50	5.60	5.70	5.80	5.90	6.00
0	.0061	.0055	.0050	.0045	.0041	.0037	.0033	.0030	.0027	.0025
1	.0311	.0287	.0265	.0244	.0225	.0207	.0191	.0176	.0162	.0149
2	.0793	.0746	.0701	.0659	.0618	.0580	.0544	.0509	.0477	.0446
3	.1348	.1293	.1239	.1185	.1133	.1082	.1033	.0985	.0938	.0892
4	.1719	.1681	.1641	.1600	.1558	.1515	.1472	.1428	.1383	.1339
5	.1753	.1748	.1740	.1728	.1714	.1697	.1678	.1656	.1632	.1606
6	.1490	.1515	.1537	.1555	.1571	.1584	.1594	.1601	.1605	.1606
7	.1086	.1125	.1163	.1200	.1234	.1267	.1298	.1326	.1353	.1377
8	.0692	.0731	.0771	.0810	.0849	.0887	.0925	.0962	.0998	.1033
9	.0392	.0423	.0454	.0486	.0519	.0552	.0586	.0620	.0654	.0688
10	.0200	.0220	.0241	.0262	.0285	.0309	.0334	.0359	.0386	.0413
11	.0093	.0104	.0116	.0129	.0143	.0157	.0173	.0190	.0207	.0225
12	.0039	.0045	.0051	.0058	.0064	.0073	.0082	.0092	.0102	.0113
13	.0015	.0018	.0021	.0024	.0028	.0032	.0036	.0041	.0046	.0052
14	.0006	.0007	.0008	.0009	.0011	.0013	.0015	.0017	.0019	.0022
15	.0002	.0002	.0003	.0003	.0004	.0005	.0006	.0007	.0008	.0009
16	.0001	.0001	.0001	.0001	.0001	.0002	.0002	.0002	.0003	.0003
17	.0000	.0000	.0000	.0000	.0000	.0001	.0001	.0001	.0001	.0001

$\mathcal{S}$UMMARY: USING THE POISSON DISTRIBUTION

The following steps are used to find probabilities using the Poisson Distribution:

1. Define the segment units.
The segment units are usually blocks of time, areas of space, or volume.

2. Determine the mean of the random variable.
The mean is the parameter that defines the Poisson distribution and is referred to as λ. It is the average number of successes in a segment of unit size.

3. Determine t, the size of the segments to be considered, and λt.

4. Define the event of interest and use the Poisson formula or the Poisson tables to find the probability.

$\mathcal{E}$XAMPLE 5-6: USING THE POISSON DISTRIBUTION

Grogan Fabrics   Grogan Fabrics, headquartered in Auckland, New Zealand, makes wool fabrics for export to many other countries around the world. Before shipping, fabric-quality tests are performed. The industry standards call for the average number of defects per fabric bolt to not exceed 5. During a recent test, the inspector selected a 30-yard bolt at random and carefully examined the first 3 yards finding 3 defects. To determine the probability of this event occurring if the fabric meets the industry standards, assuming that the Poisson distribution applies, the company can perform the following steps:

Step 1: **Define the segment unit.**
Because the mean was stated as 5 defects per fabric bolt, the segment unit in this case is one 30-yard fabric bolt.

Step 2: **Determine the mean of the random variable.**
In this case if the company meets the industry standards, the mean will be:
$$\lambda = 5$$

Step 3: **Determine the segment size t.**
The company quality inspectors analyzed 3 yards from a 30-yard bolt, which is equal to .1 units. So $t = .1$. Then
$$\lambda t = 5(.1) = .5$$
When looking at 3 yards, the company would expect to find .5 defects if the industry standards are being met.

Step 4: **Define the event of interest and use the Poisson formula or the Poisson tables to find the probability.**
In this case, 3 defects were observed. Because 3 exceeds the expected number ($\lambda t = .5$) the company would want to find:
$$P(x \geq 3) = P(x = 3) + P(x = 4) + \cdots$$
The Poisson table in Appendix C is used to determine these probabilities. Locate the desired probability under the column headed $\lambda t = .5$. Then find the values of x down the left-hand column.

$$\begin{aligned} P(x \geq 3) &= 0.0126 + 0.0016 + 0.0002 \\ &= 0.0144 \end{aligned}$$

This low probability may cause the company some concern about whether it is actually meeting the quality standards.

The Mean and Standard Deviation of the Poisson Distribution

The mean of the Poisson distribution is λt. This is the value we use to specify which Poisson distribution we are using. We must know the mean before we can find probabilities for a Poisson distribution.

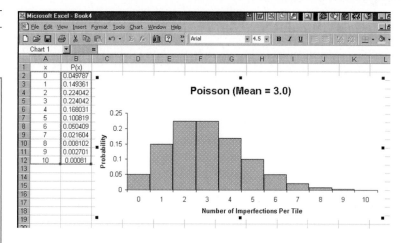

FIGURE 5-6A

Excel Output for Heritage Tile Example

Excel Instructions:
1. Enter values for *x* ranging from 0 to 10.
2. Click on f_n on the toolbar.
3. Select the **Statistical** and **POISSON** options.
4. Supply mean and enter "FALSE" for cumulative option.
5. Graph using the Column chart option in the Chart Wizard.

Figure 5-5 illustrated that the outcome of a Poisson distribution variable is subject to variation. Like any other discrete probability distribution, the standard deviation for the Poisson can be computed using Equation 5-5:

$$\sigma_x = \sqrt{\sum [x - E(x)]^2 P(x)}$$

However, for a Poisson distribution, the standard deviation also can be found using Equation 5-8.

Standard Deviation of the Poisson Distribution

$$\sigma = \sqrt{\lambda t}$$ 5-8

The standard deviation of the Poisson distribution is simply the square root of the mean. Therefore, if you are working with a Poisson process, reducing the mean can reduce the variability also.

Excel and Minitab Tutorial

Heritage Tile—To illustrate the importance of the relationship between the mean and standard deviation of the Poisson distribution, consider Heritage Tile in New York City. The company makes ceramic tile for kitchens and bathrooms. The quality standards call for the number of imperfections in tile to average 3 or fewer. The distribution of imperfections is thought to be Poisson. Both Minitab and Excel generate Poisson probabilities in much the same way as for the binomial distribution, which was discussed in Section 5-1. If we assume that the company is meeting the standard, Figure 5-6a and Figure 5-6b show the Poisson probability

FIGURE 5-6B

Minitab Output for Heritage Tile Example

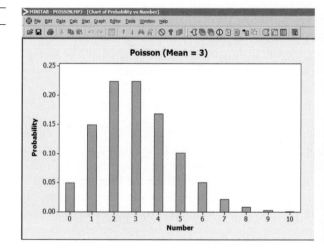

Minitab Instructions:
1. Create column *Number* with integers from 0 to 10.
2. Choose **Calc > Probability Distributions > Poisson**.
3. Select **Probability**.
4. In **Mean**, enter 3.
5. Select **Input column**.
6. In **Input column**, enter the column of integers.
7. In **Optional storage**, enter column *Probability*.
8. Click **OK**.
9. Choose **Graph > Bar Chart**.
10. In **Bars represent**, select **Values from a Table**, select **Simple**.
11. Click **OK**.
12. In **Graph variables**, insert *Probability*.
13. In **Categorical variable**, insert *Number*.
14. Click **OK**.

distribution generated using Excel and Minitab when $\lambda t = 3.0$. Even though the average number of defects is 3, the manager is concerned about the large number of instances in which the number of imperfections is 4, 5, 6, or more on a tile. The variability is too great. Using Equation 5-8, the standard deviation for this distribution is

$$\sigma = \sqrt{3.0} = 1.732$$

This large standard deviation means that although some tiles will have few if any imperfections, others will have several, causing problems for installers and unhappy customers.

A quality improvement effort directed at reducing the average number of imperfections to 2.0 would also reduce the standard deviation to

$$\sigma = \sqrt{2.0} = 1.414$$

Further reductions in the average would also reduce variation in the number of imperfections between tiles. This would mean more consistency for installers and higher customer satisfaction.

THE HYPERGEOMETRIC DISTRIBUTION

Although the binomial and Poisson distributions are very useful in many business decision-making situations, they both require that the trials be independent. For instance, in binomial applications the probability of a success on one trial must be the same as the probability of a success on any other trial. Although there are certainly times when this assumption can be satisfied, or at least approximated, in instances in which the population is fairly small and we are sampling without replacement, the condition of independence will not hold. In these cases, a discrete probability distribution referred to as the *hypergeometric distribution* can be useful.

Lindell Corporation—The Lindell Corporation manufactures high-speed line printers for computer systems. Lindell printers are compatible with most of the major computer vendors' hardware. Because of the intense competition in the marketplace for printers and other peripherals, Lindell has made every attempt to make a high-quality printer. However, a recent production run of 20 printers contained two printers that tested out as defective. The problem was traced to a shipment of defective cables that Lindell received shortly before the production run started.

The production manager ordered that the entire batch of 20 printers be isolated from other production output until further testing could be completed. Unfortunately, a new shipping clerk packaged 10 of these isolated printers and shipped them to the California State Purchasing Department to fill an order that was already overdue. By the time the production manager noticed what had happened, the printers were already in transit.

The immediate concern was whether one or more of the defectives had been included in the shipment. The new shipping clerk thought there was a good chance that no defectives were included. Short of reinspecting the remaining printers, how might the Lindell Corporation determine the chances that no defectives were actually shipped?

At first glance, it might seem that the question could be answered by employing the binomial distribution with $n = 10$, $p = 2/20 = 0.10$, and $x = 0$. Using the binomial distribution table in Appendix B we get:

$$P(x = 0) = 0.3487$$

There is a 0.3487 chance that no defectives were shipped, assuming the selection process satisfied the requirements of a binomial distribution. However, for the binomial distribution to be applicable, the trials must be independent, and the probability of a success, p, must remain constant from trial to trial. In order for this to occur when the sampling is from a "small," *finite* population, the sampling must be performed with *replacement*. This means that after each item is selected, it is returned to the population and, therefore, may be selected again later in the sampling.

In the Lindell example the sampling was performed without replacement because each printer could only be shipped one time. Also, the population of printers is finite with size $N = 20$, which is a "small" population. Thus, p, the probability of a defective printer, does not remain equal to 0.10 on each trial. The value of p on any particular trial depends on what has already been selected on previous trials.

The event of interest is

$$G\,G\,G\,G\,G\,G\,G\,G\,G\,G$$

The probability that the first printer selected for shipment would be good would be 18/20, because there were 18 good printers in the batch of 20. Now, assuming the first printer selected was good, the probability the second printer was good is 17/19, because we then had only 19 printers to select from and 17 of those would be good. The probability that all 10 printers selected were good is

$$\frac{18}{20} \times \frac{17}{19} \times \frac{16}{18} \times \frac{15}{17} \times \frac{14}{16} \times \frac{13}{15} \times \frac{12}{14} \times \frac{11}{13} \times \frac{10}{12} \times \frac{9}{11} = 0.2368$$

This value is not the same as the 0.3847 probability we got when the binomial distribution was used. This demonstrates that when sampling is performed without replacement from finite populations, the binomial distribution *cannot* be used to compute exact probabilities unless the sample is small relative to the size of the population. Under that circumstance, the value of p will not change very much as the sample is selected, and the binomial distribution will be a reasonable approximation to the actual probability distribution.

In those cases in which the sample is large relative to the size of the population, a discrete probability distribution, called the hypergeometric distribution is the correct distribution for computing probabilities for the random variable of interest.

The hypergeometric distribution is formed by the ratio of the number of ways an event of interest can occur over the total number of ways any event can occur. The number of ways these events can occur can be determined by listing the sample space or, more simply, by using Equation 5-1 for combinations.

$$C_x^n = \frac{n!}{x!(n - x)!}$$

We then use the formula for counting combinations to form the equation for computing probabilities for the hypergeometric distribution when each trial has two possible outcomes (success and failure), as defined in Equation 5-9.

Hypergeometric Distribution (Two Possible Outcomes per Trial)

$$P(x) = \frac{C_{n-x}^{N-X} \cdot C_x^X}{C_n^N} \qquad \textbf{5-9}$$

where:

N = Population size
X = Number of successes in the population
n = Sample size
x = Number of successes in the sample
$n - x$ = Number of failures in the sample

Notice that the numerator of Equation 5-9 is the product of the number of ways you can select x successes in a random sample out of the X successes in the population and the number of ways you can select $n - x$ failures in a sample from the $N - X$ failures in the population. The denominator in the equation is the number of ways the sample can be selected from the population.

In the Lindell example, the probability of zero defectives being shipped ($x = 0$) is

$$P(x = 0) = \frac{C_{10-0}^{20-2} \cdot C_0^2}{C_{10}^{20}}$$

$$P(x = 0) = \frac{C_{10}^{18} \cdot C_0^2}{C_{10}^{20}}$$

Carrying out the arithmetic, we get

$$P(x) = \frac{(43,758)(1)}{184,756} = 0.2368$$

As we found before, the probability that zero defectives were included in the shipment is 0.2368, or approximately 24%.

The probabilities of $x = 1$ and $x = 2$ defectives can also be found by using Equation 5-9, as follows:

$$P(x = 1) = \frac{C_{10-1}^{20-2} \cdot C_1^2}{C_{10}^{20}} = 0.5264$$

and

$$P(x = 2) = \frac{C_{10-2}^{20-2} \cdot C_2^2}{C_{10}^{20}} = 0.2368$$

Thus, the hypergeometric probability distribution for the number of defective printers in a random selection of 10 is

x	P(x)
0	0.2368
1	0.5264
2	0.2368
	$\Sigma = 1.0000$

EXAMPLE 5-7: THE HYPERGEOMETRIC DISTRIBUTION (TWO OUTCOMES PER TRIAL)

Gender Equity   One of the biggest changes in U.S. business practice in the past few decades has been the inclusion of women into the management ranks of companies. Tom Peters, management consultant and author of such books as *In Search of Excellence*, recently stated that one of the reasons the Middle Eastern countries have suffered economically compared with countries such as the United States is that they have not included women in their economic system. However, there are still issues in U.S. business. Consider a situation in which a Maryland company needed to downsize one department having 30 people—12 women and 18 men. Ten people were laid off, and upper management said the layoffs were done randomly. Of the 10 laid off, 8 were women. By chance, 40% (12/30) of the layoffs would be women. A labor attorney is interested in the probability of 8 or more women being laid off by chance alone. This can be done using the following steps:

Step 1:   **Determine the population size and the combined sample size.**
The population size and sample size are
$$N = 30 \quad \text{and} \quad n = 10$$

Step 2:   **Define the event of interest.**
The attorney is interested in the event:
$$P(x \geq 8) = ?$$
What are the chances that 8 or more women would be selected?

Step 3:   **Determine the number of successes in the population and the number of successes in the sample.**
In this situation, a success is the event that a woman is selected. There are $X = 12$ women in the population and $x \geq 8$ in the sample. We will break this down as $x = 8, x = 9, x = 10$.

Step 4:   **Compute the desired probabilities using Equation 5-9.**
$$P(x) = \frac{C_{n-x}^{N-X} \cdot C_x^X}{C_n^N}$$

We want:[2]

$$P(x \geq 8) = P(x = 8) + P(x = 9) + P(x = 10)$$
$$P(x = 8) = \frac{C_{10-8}^{30-12} \cdot C_8^{12}}{C_{10}^{30}} = \frac{C_2^{18} \cdot C_8^{12}}{C_{10}^{30}} = 0.0025$$
$$P(x = 9) = \frac{C_1^{18} \cdot C_9^{12}}{C_{10}^{30}} = 0.0001$$
$$P(x = 10) = \frac{C_0^{18} \cdot C_{10}^{12}}{C_{10}^{30}} \approx 0.0000$$

Therefore, $P(x \geq 8) = 0.0025 + 0.0001 + 0.0000 = 0.0026$
The chances that 8 or more women would have been selected among the 10 people chosen for layoff strictly due to chance is 0.0026. The attorney will likely wish to challenge the layoffs based on this extremely low probability.

[2]Note, you can use Excel's HYPGEOMDIST function to compute these probabilities.

THE HYPERGEOMETRIC DISTRIBUTION WITH MORE THAN TWO POSSIBLE OUTCOMES PER TRIAL

Equation 5-9 assumes that on any given sample selection or trial only one of two possible outcomes will occur. However, the hypergeometric distribution can easily be extended to consider any number of possible categories of outcomes on a given trial by employing Equation 5-10.

Hypergeometric Distribution (k Possible Outcomes per Trial)

$$P(x_1, x_2, x_3, \ldots, x_k) = \frac{C_{x_1}^{X_1} \cdot C_{x_2}^{X_2} \cdot C_{x_3}^{X_3} \cdot \cdots \cdot C_{x_k}^{X_k}}{C_n^N}$$

5-10

where:

$$\sum_{i=1}^{k} X_i = N$$

$$\sum_{i=1}^{k} x_i = n$$

N = Population size
n = Total sample size
X_i = Number of items in the population with outcome i
x_i = Number of items in the sample with outcome i

$\mathcal{E}$XAMPLE 5-8: THE HYPERGEOMETRIC DISTRIBUTION FOR MULTIPLE OUTCOMES

Brand Preference Study   Consider a marketing study that involves placing toothpaste made by four different companies in a basket at the exit to a drugstore. A sign on the basket invites customers to take one tube free of charge. At the beginning of the study, the basket contains the following:

5 brand A tubes
4 brand B tubes
6 brand C tubes
4 brand D tubes

The researchers were interested in the brand selection patterns for customers who could select without regard to price. Suppose six customers were observed and three selected brand B, two selected brand D, and one selected brand C. No one selected brand A. The probability of this selection mix, assuming the customers were selecting entirely at random without replacement from a finite population, can be found using the following steps:

Step 1:   **Determine the population size and the combined sample size.**
The population size and sample size are

$$N = 19 \quad \text{and} \quad n = 6$$

Step 2:   **Define the event of interest.**
The event of interest is

$$P(x_1 = 0; x_2 = 3; x_3 = 1; x_4 = 2) = ?$$

Step 3:   **Determine the number in each category in the population and the number in each category in the sample.**

$X_1 = 5$	(brand A)	$x_1 = 0$
$X_2 = 4$	(brand B)	$x_2 = 3$
$X_3 = 6$	(brand C)	$x_3 = 1$
$X_4 = 4$	(brand D)	$x_4 = 2$
$N = 19$		$n = 6$

Step 4: **Compute the desired probability using Equation 5-10.**

$$P(x_1, x_2, x_3, \ldots, x_k) = \frac{C_{x_1}^{X_1} \cdot C_{x_2}^{X_2} \cdot C_{x_3}^{X_3} \cdot \cdots \cdot C_{x_k}^{X_k}}{C_n^N}$$

$$P(0, 3, 1, 2) = \frac{C_0^5 \cdot C_3^4 \cdot C_1^6 \cdot C_2^4}{C_6^{19}}$$

$$= \frac{(1)(4)(6)(6)}{27{,}132} = \frac{144}{27{,}132}$$

$$= 0.0053$$

There are slightly more than five chances in 1,000 of this exact selection occurring by random chance.

5-2: EXERCISES

Skill Development

5.27 If the mean value of a Poisson-distributed variable is 5.0, find the following:
a. $P(x = 5) =$
b. $P(x \leq 5) =$
c. $P(x \geq 3) =$

5.28 If $\lambda t = 3.5$ for a Poisson-distributed variable, find the following:
a. $P(2 \leq x \leq 5) =$
b. $P(x = 3) =$
c. $P(x \geq 1) =$

5.29 If $\lambda = 5$ and $t = 2$ for a Poisson distribution,
a. Determine the mean and standard deviation of this Poisson distribution.
b. What is the probability of three or fewer successes?

5.30 If $\lambda = 18$ and $t = \frac{1}{3}$ for a Poisson distribution,
a. Find the expected value, variance, and standard deviation of this Poisson distribution.
b. Determine the probability of exactly zero successes.

5.31 A sample of 4 is taken from a population of 20 containing 4 defective items. Determine the probability distribution that defines the defectives that can be found in the sample.

5.32 A sample of 3 is taken from a population of 12 engines, 5 of which are built to metric standards and 7 of which are built to English standards. Determine the probability distribution that defines the number of English standard engines that could be found in the sample.

5.33 A population consists of 40 items. Ten of these are red, 15 are green, and 15 are yellow. If a sample of size 10 is randomly selected from the population, what is the probability that sample will contain two red, two green, and six yellow?

5.34 A gathering contained 15 people, six of whom were Republicans, five were Democrats, and the rest were Independents. If three of these people were selected at random to give a speech to the group, what is the probability that the three would consist of one Democrat, one Republican, and one Independent?

Business Applications

5.35 East-West Translations publishes textbooks of ancient Oriental teachings for English-speaking universities. The company currently is testing a computer-based translation service. Because Oriental symbols are difficult to translate, East-West assumes the computer program will make some errors, but then so do human translators. The computer service claims its error rate will average 3 per 400 words of translation. East-West randomly selects a 1,200-word passage. Assuming the computer company's claim is accurate and the Poisson distribution applies,
a. Determine the probability no errors will be found.
b. Calculate the probability more than 14 errors will be found.
c. Find the probability that fewer than 9 errors will be found.
d. If 15 errors are found in the 1,200-word passage, what would you conclude about the computer company's claim? Why?

5.36 Your company president has told you that your company experiences product returns at the rate of two per month, distributed as a Poisson random variable. Determine the probability that next month there will be
a. No returns.
b. One return.
c. Two returns.
d. More than two returns.
e. In the past three months your company has only had one month in which the number of returns was at most two. Calculate the probability of this event occurring. What will you tell the president of your company concerning the return rate for your company? Make sure you support your statement with something other than opinion.

5.37 The Defense Department has recently advertised for bids for producing a new night-vision binocular. Vista Optical decided to submit a bid for the contract. The first step was to supply a sample of binoculars for the army to test at its Kentucky development grounds. Vista makes a superior night-vision binocular. However, the four sent for testing were taken from a development-lab project of 20 units that contained four defectives. The army has indicated it will reject any manufacturer that submits one or more defective binoculars. What is the probability that this mistake has cost Vista any chance for the contract?

5.38 An inventory of kitchen ranges contains 11 white, 9 almond, and 6 salmon pink. Five new homes are being built in a subdivision by five different builders, and the kitchen ranges will be taken randomly from this inventory.
   a. What is the probability that three of the homes will have a white range and the other two almond?
   b. What is the probability that all five ranges will be the same color?

c. What is the probability that three ranges will be white and the other two will be of the same color but not white?

5.39 The Farmhill Nursery sells trees and other yard and garden items. Currently, the nursery has 10 fruit trees, 8 pine trees, and 14 maple trees. It plans to give 4 trees away at next Saturday's lawn and garden show in the city park. The four winners can select which type of tree they want. Assume they select randomly.
   a. What is the probability that all four winners will select the same type of tree?
   b. What is the probability that three winners will select pine trees and the other tree will be a maple?
   c. What is the probability that no fruit trees and two of each of the others will be selected?

5-3 THE NORMAL PROBABILITY DISTRIBUTION

THE NORMAL DISTRIBUTION

You will encounter many business situations in which the random variable of interest will be treated as a continuous variable. There are several continuous distributions that are frequently used to describe physical situations. The most useful continuous probability distribution is the **normal distribution**.[3] The reason is that the output from a great many processes (both man-made and natural) are normally distributed.

Normal Distribution

The normal distribution is a bell-shaped distribution with the following properties:
1. It is *unimodal*; that is, the normal distribution peaks at a single value.
2. It is *symmetrical*; this means that the two areas under the curve between the mean and any two points equidistant on either side of the mean are identical. One side of the distribution is the mirror image of the other side.
3. The mean, median, and mode are equal.
4. The normal approaches the horizontal axis on either side of the mean toward plus and minus infinity (∞). In more formal terms, the normal distribution is *asymptotic* to the x-axis.
5. The amount of variation in the random variable determines the width of the normal distribution.

Figure 5-7 illustrates a typical normal distribution and highlights the normal distribution's characteristics. All normal distributions have the same general shape as the one shown in Figure 5-7.

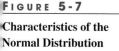

FIGURE 5-7

Characteristics of the Normal Distribution

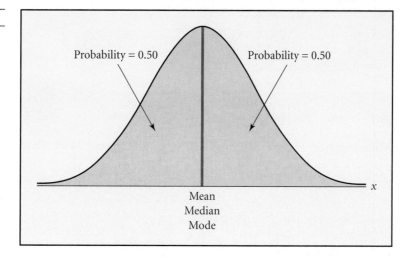

Probability = 0.50   Probability = 0.50

Mean
Median
Mode

x

---

[3]It is common to refer to the very large family of normal distributions as "*the* normal distribution." Keep in mind, however, that "the normal distribution" really is a very large family of distributions.

However, they can differ in their mean value and their variation, depending on the situation being considered. The process being represented determines the scale of the horizontal axis. It may be pounds, inches, dollars, or any other physical attribute with a continuous measurement. Figure 5-8 shows several normal distributions with different centers and different spreads. Note that the total area (probability) under each normal curve equals 1.

The normal distribution is described by the rather-complicated-looking probability density function, shown in Equation 5-11.

Normal Distribution Density Function

$$f(x) = \frac{1}{\sigma\sqrt{2\pi}} e^{-(x-\mu)^2/2\sigma^2}$$

5-11

where:

x = Any value of the continuous random variable
σ = Population standard deviation
e = Base of the natural log $\approx 2.71828\ldots$
μ = Population mean

To graph the normal distribution, we need to know the mean, μ, and the standard deviation, σ. Placing μ, σ, and a value of the variable, x, into the probability density function, we can calculate a height, $f(x)$, of the density function. If we try enough x values, we will get a curve like those shown in Figures 5-7 and 5-8.

The area under the normal curve corresponds to probability. The probability, $P(x)$, is equal to 0 for any particular x. However, we can find the probability for a range of values between x_1 and x_2 by finding the area under the curve between these two values. Integral calculus is used to find areas under a curve. Alternatively, a special normal distribution called the *standard normal distribution* is also used to find areas (probabilities) for a normal distribution.

THE STANDARD NORMAL DISTRIBUTION

The trick to finding probabilities for a normal distribution is to convert the normal distribution to a **standard normal distribution**.

FIGURE 5-8

Difference Between Normal Distributions

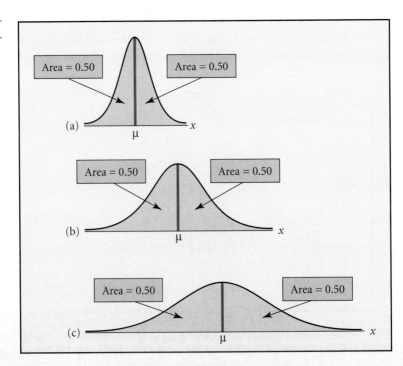

Standard Normal Distribution

A normal distribution that has a mean = 0.0 and a standard deviation = 1.0. The horizontal axis is scaled in z-values that measure the number of standard deviations a point is from the mean. Values above the mean have positive z-values. Values below the mean have negative z-values.

To convert a normal distribution to a standard normal distribution, the values (x) of the random variable are standardized as outlined previously in Chapter 3. The conversion formula is shown as Equation 5-12.

Standardized Normal z-Value

$$z = \frac{x - \mu}{\sigma} \qquad\qquad \textbf{5-12}$$

where:

z = Scaled value (the number of standard deviations a point x is from the mean)
x = Any point on the horizontal axis
μ = Mean of the normal distribution
σ = Standard deviation of the normal distribution

Equation 5-12 *rescales* any normal distribution axis from its true units (time, weight, dollars, barrels, and so forth) to the standard measure referred to as a *z-value*. Thus, any value of the normally distributed continuous random variable can be represented by a unique z-value.

Westex Oil Company—Westex Oil, headquartered in Midland, Texas, budgets most of its cash flow from wells it owns on maturing oil fields. Most oil fields in the lower 48 states are maturing and facing declining production, but substantial oil often remains, though it is not recoverable by conventional means. Some companies inject water into a well to force out this additional oil. Westex management is considering adding a newly developed enzyme to the injected water to increase the amount of oil extracted, but they will do so only if the increased production covers the additional costs. Suppose the new enzyme will increase oil output by an average of 50 barrels a day, but because of differences in rock structures, this output varies with a standard deviation of 10 barrels a day.

Assume data suggest that the number of barrels of oil is described by the normal distribution with $\mu = 50$ and a standard deviation of $\sigma = 10$. Equation 5-11 will determine the height of the normal distribution curve for each possible value of the random variable. Figure 5-9 shows the resulting distribution.

Suppose in the Westex situation we select a level of
$$x = 50$$
barrels per day. (Note that 50 is also μ, the mean increase.) We can find the z-value for this point using Equation 5-12:

$$z = \frac{x - \mu}{\sigma} = \frac{50 - 50}{10} = 0$$

The z-value corresponding to the population mean, μ, is zero. This indicates that the mean is 0 standard deviations from itself.

FIGURE 5-9

Distribution of Oil Barrels Produced per Day for Westex Oil

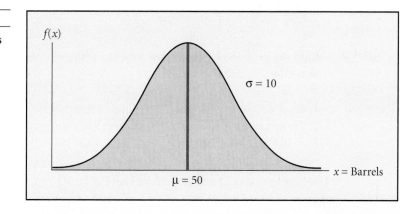

Next, we select

$$x = 60$$

barrels per day. The z-value for this point is

$$z = \frac{x - \mu}{\sigma} = \frac{60 - 50}{10} = \frac{10}{10} = 1$$

Thus, for this distribution, the value, 60 barrels is 1 standard deviation above the mean of 50. A value,

$$x = 35$$

has a standardized z-value $= -1.50$, as follows:

$$z = \frac{x - \mu}{\sigma} = \frac{35 - 50}{10} = \frac{-15}{10} = -1.50$$

This indicates that the value, 35 barrels is 1.50 standard deviations below the mean of 50 barrels. Verify for yourself that $x = 40$ barrels per day corresponds to a z-value of -1. Note that a negative z-value indicates that the specified value of x is less than the mean.

The z-value represents the number of standard deviations a point, x, is away from the population mean. In this Westex Oil example, the standard deviation is 10 barrels per day. Therefore, an output increase to 60 barrels per day is 1 standard deviation above the mean of 50 barrels per day. Likewise, an output increase to 70 barrels per day is 2 standard deviations above the mean. Figure 5-10 shows the standard normal distribution for the Westex Company example.

Using the Standard Normal Table

The *standard normal table* in Appendix D provides probabilities (or areas under the normal curve) for many different z-values. The standard normal table is constructed so that the probabilities provided represent the chance of a value falling between the z-value and the population mean.

The standard normal table is also reproduced in Table 5-5. This table provides probabilities for z-values between $z = 0.00$ and $z = 3.09$.

*E*XAMPLE 5-9: USING THE STANDARD NORMAL TABLE

Employee Commute Time   After completing a study, a company in Kansas City concluded the time its employees spend commuting to work each day is normally distributed with a mean equal to 15 minutes and a standard deviation equal to 3.5 minutes. One employee has indicated that she commutes 22 minutes per day. To find the probability that an employee would commute 22 or more minutes per day, you can use the following steps:

Step 1:   Determine the mean and standard deviation for the random variable.
The parameters of the probability distribution are
$$\mu = 15 \quad \text{and} \quad \sigma = 3.5$$

Step 2:   Define the event of interest.
The employee has a commute time of 22 minutes. We wish to find:
$$P(x \geq 22) = ?$$

Step 3:   Convert the random variable to a standardized value using Equation 5-12.
$$z = \frac{x - \mu}{\sigma} = \frac{22 - 15}{3.5} = 2.00$$

Step 4:   Find the probability associated with the z-value in the standard normal distribution table (Appendix D).
To find the probability for $z = 2.00$, [i.e., $P(0 \leq z \leq 2.00)$], do the following:

1. Go down the left-hand column of the table to $z = 2.0$.
2. Go across the top row of the table to 0.00 for the second decimal place in $z = 2.00$.
3. Find the value where the row and column intersect.

The value, 0.4772, is the probability that a value in a normal distribution will lie between the mean and 2.00 standard deviations above the mean.

FIGURE 5-10

Standard Normal Distribution

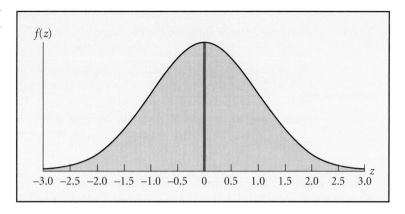

TABLE 5-5

Standard Normal Distribution Table

To illustrate: 19.85% of the area under a normal curve lies between the mean, μ, and a point 0.52 standard deviation units away.

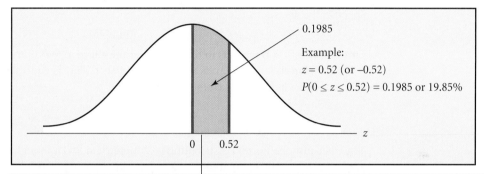

0.1985

Example:
$z = 0.52$ (or -0.52)
$P(0 \le z \le 0.52) = 0.1985$ or 19.85%

z	.00	.01	.02	.03	.04	.05	.06	.07	.08	.09
0.0	.0000	.0040	.0080	.0120	.0160	.0199	.0239	.0279	.0319	.0359
0.1	.0398	.0438	.0478	.0517	.0557	.0596	.0636	.0675	.0714	.0753
0.2	.0793	.0832	.0871	.0910	.0948	.0987	.1026	.1064	.1103	.1141
0.3	.1179	.1217	.1255	.1293	.1331	.1368	.1406	.1443	.1480	.1517
0.4	.1554	.1591	.1628	.1664	.1700	.1736	.1772	.1808	.1844	.1879
0.5	.1915	.1950	.1985	.2019	.2054	.2088	.2123	.2157	.2190	.2224
0.6	.2257	.2291	.2324	.2357	.2389	.2422	.2454	.2486	.2517	.2549
0.7	.2580	.2611	.2642	.2673	.2704	.2734	.2764	.2794	.2823	.2852
0.8	.2881	.2910	.2939	.2967	.2995	.3023	.3051	.3078	.3106	.3133
0.9	.3159	.3186	.3212	.3238	.3264	.3289	.3315	.3340	.3365	.3389
1.0	.3413	.3438	.3461	.3485	.3508	.3531	.3554	.3577	.3599	.3621
1.1	.3643	.3665	.3686	.3708	.3729	.3749	.3770	.3790	.3810	.3830
1.2	.3849	.3869	.3888	.3907	.3925	.3944	.3962	.3980	.3997	.4015
1.3	.4032	.4049	.4066	.4082	.4099	.4115	.4131	.4147	.4162	.4177
1.4	.4192	.4207	.4222	.4236	.4251	.4265	.4279	.4292	.4306	.4319
1.5	.4332	.4345	.4357	.4370	.4382	.4394	.4406	.4418	.4429	.4441
1.6	.4452	.4463	.4474	.4484	.4495	.4505	.4515	.4525	.4535	.4545
1.7	.4554	.4564	.4573	.4582	.4591	.4599	.4608	.4616	.4625	.4633
1.8	.4641	.4649	.4656	.4664	.4671	.4678	.4686	.4693	.4699	.4706
1.9	.4713	.4719	.4726	.4732	.4738	.4744	.4750	.4756	.4761	.4767
2.0	.4772	.4778	.4783	.4788	.4793	.4798	.4803	.4808	.4812	.4817
2.1	.4821	.4826	.4830	.4834	.4838	.4842	.4846.	.4850	.4854	.4857
2.2	.4861	.4864	.4868	.4871	.4875	.4878	.4881	.4884	.4887	.4890
2.3	.4893	.4896	.4898	.4901	.4904	.4906	.4909	.4911	.4913	.4916
2.4	.4918	.4920	.4922	.4925	.4927	.4929	.4931	.4932	.4934	.4936
2.5	.4938	.4940	.4941	.4943	.4945	.4946	.4948	.4949	.4951	.4952
2.6	.4953	.4955	.4956	.4957	.4959	.4960	.4961	.4962	.4963	.4964
2.7	.4965	.4966	.4967	.4968	.4969	.4970	.4971	.4972	.4973	.4974
2.8	.4974	.4975	.4976	.4977	.4977	.4978	.4979	.4979	.4980	.4981
2.9	.4981	.4982	.4982	.4983	.4984	.4984	.4985	.4985	.4986	.4986
3.0	.4987	.4987	.4987	.4988	.4988	.4989	.4989	.4989.	.4990	.4990

Step 5:   Determine the probability for the event of interest.

$$P(x \geq 22) = ?$$

We know that the area on each side of the mean under the normal distribution is equal to 0.50. In Step 4 we computed the probability for $z = 2.00$ to be 0.4772, which is the probability of a value falling between the mean and 2.00 standard deviations above the mean. Then, the probability we are looking for is

$$P(x \geq 22) = P(z \geq 2.00) = 0.5000 - 0.4772 = 0.0228$$

Westex Oil Company (continued)—In the Westex Oil example, recall the mean increase in oil output was 50 barrels per day and the standard deviation was 10 barrels per day. Company cost accountants have estimated that the output level must be increased by at least 45 barrels per day to pay for the additional cost of the enzyme injection. Therefore, if the enzyme is tried on one well, we are interested in the probability that production will be increased by 45 or more barrels per day. Specifically, we want

$$P(x \geq 45).$$

This probability corresponds to the area under the curve to the right of $x = 45$ barrels per day.

First, convert $x = 45$ barrels per day to a z-value. This is equivalent to determining the number of standard deviations 45 is from the mean.

$$z = \frac{x - \mu}{\sigma} = \frac{45 - 50}{10} = -0.50$$

Note, because the normal distribution is symmetrical, even though the z-value is a negative 0.50, we find the probability by looking for a z-value of positive 0.50. From the standard normal table, the

$$P(-0.50 \leq z \leq 0) = 0.1915.$$

This is shown as the area between $x = 45$ and $\mu = 50$ in Figure 5-11. The normal curve is symmetrical, and half the total area lies on each side of the mean. By adding 0.1915 to 0.5000, we can find

$$P(x \geq 45 \text{ barrels per day}) = 0.1915 + 0.5000 = 0.6915$$

FIGURE 5-11

**Probabilities from the
Normal Curve for Westex**

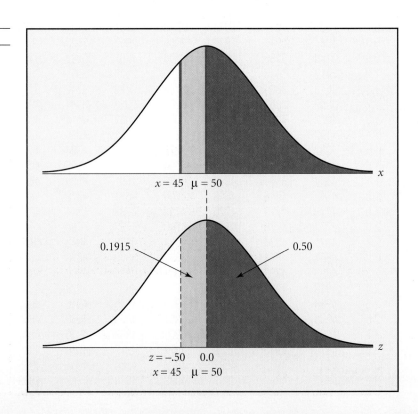

So

$$P(x \geq 45) = P(z \geq -0.50)$$

Therefore, based on the mean and standard deviation values, the probability that the well will increase production by 45 or more gallons per day is 0.6915. Conversely,

$$P(x < 45 \text{ barrels per day}) = 1 - 0.6915 = 0.3085$$

is the probability that increased production will be less than 45 barrels, thus unprofitable for Westex Oil.

Longlife Battery Company—Several states, predominately California, have passed legislation requiring automakers to sell a certain percentage of zero-emissions cars within their borders. One current alternative is battery-powered cars. The major problem with battery-operated cars is the limited time they can be driven before the batteries must be recharged. Longlife Battery, a start-up company, has developed a battery pack it claims will power a car at a sustained speed of 45 miles per hour for an average of 8 hours. But of course there will be variations: Some battery packs will last longer and some shorter than 8 hours. Current data indicate that the standard deviation of battery operation time before a charge is needed is 0.4 hours. Data show a normal distribution of uptime on these battery packs. Automakers are concerned that batteries may run short. For example, drivers might find an "8-hour" battery that lasts 7.5 hours or less unacceptable. What are the chances of this happening with the Longlife battery pack?

To calculate the probability the batteries will last 7.5 hours or less, find the appropriate area under the normal curve shown in Figure 5-12. There is approximately 1 chance in 10 that a battery will last 7.5 hours or less when the vehicle is driven at 45 miles per hour.

Suppose this level of reliability is unacceptable to the automakers. Instead of a 10% chance of an "8-hour" battery lasting 7.5 hours or less, the automakers will accept no more than a 2% chance. Longlife Battery asks the question, what would the mean uptime have to be to meet the 2% requirement?

Assuming that uptime is normally distributed, we can answer this question by using the standard normal distribution. However, instead of using the standard normal table to find a probability, we use it in reverse to find the z-value that corresponds to a known probability. Figure 5-13 shows the uptime distribution for the battery packs. Note, the 2% probability is shown in the left tail of the distribution. This is the allowable chance of a battery lasting 7.5 hours or less. We must solve for μ, the mean uptime that will meet this requirement.

1. Go to the body of the standard normal table, where the probabilities are located, and find the probability as close to 0.48 as possible. This is 0.4798.

FIGURE 5-12

Longlife Battery Company

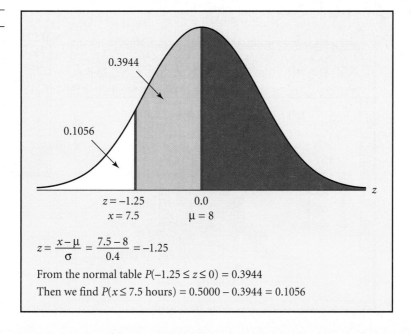

From the normal table $P(-1.25 \leq z \leq 0) = 0.3944$

Then we find $P(x \leq 7.5 \text{ hours}) = 0.5000 - 0.3944 = 0.1056$

FIGURE 5-13

Longlife Battery Company, Solving for the Mean

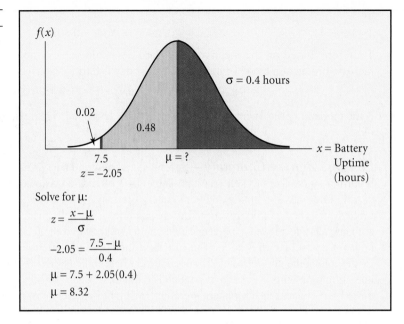

2. Determine the z-value associated with 0.4798. This is $z = 2.05$. Because we are below the mean, the z is negative. Thus, $z = -2.05$.
3. The formula for z is

$$z = \frac{x - \mu}{\sigma}$$

4. Substituting the known values, we get

$$-2.05 = \frac{7.5 - \mu}{0.4}$$

5. Solve for μ:

$$\mu = 7.5 + 2.05(0.4) = 8.32 \text{ hours}$$

Longlife Battery will need to increase the mean life of the battery pack to 8.32 hours to meet the automakers' requirement that no more than 2% of the batteries fail in 7.5 hours or less.

FIGURE 5-14

Excel Output for State Bank and Trust Service Times

Excel Instructions:
1. Open file: **State Bank.xls**
2. Define Bins upper limit of each class.
3. Select **Tools > Data Analysis**.
4. Click on **Histogram**.
5. Identify Data range and bin range.
6. Check **Chart Output**.
7. Define output location.
8. Click **OK**.

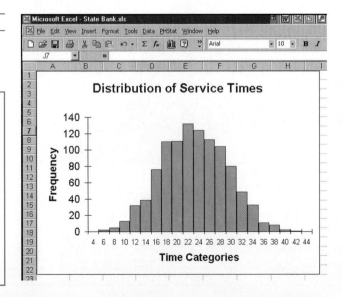

Minitab Instructions (for similar results):
1. Open file: State Bank. MTW.
2. Choose **Graph > Histogram**.
3. Click **Simple**.
4. Click **OK**.
5. In **Graph variables**, enter data column **Service Time**.
6. Click **OK**.

FIGURE 5-15

Normal Distribution for the State Bank Example

Excel and Minitab Tutorial

State Bank and Trust—The director of operations for the State Bank and Trust recently performed a study of the time bank customers spent from the time they arrived in the parking lot until they exited the parking lot after completing their banking. The data file, *State Bank*, contains the data for a sample of 1,045 customers randomly observed over a four-week period. The customers in the survey were limited to those who were there for "basic bank business," such as making a deposit or a withdrawal, or cashing a check. The histogram in Figure 5-14 shows that the times appear to be distributed quite closely to a normal distribution.[4]

The mean service for the 1,045 customers was 22.14 minutes, with a standard deviation equal to 6.09 minutes.

On the basis of these data, the manager assumes that the service times are normally distributed with $\mu = 22.14$ and $\sigma = 6.09$. Given these assumptions, the manager is considering providing a gift certificate to a local restaurant to any customer who is required to spend more than 30 minutes in the service process for basic bank business. Before doing this, she is interested in the probability of having to pay off on this offer.

Figure 5-15 shows the theoretical distribution, with the area of interest identified.

The manager is interested in finding

$$P(x > 30 \text{ minutes})$$

This can be done manually or with Excel or Minitab. Figure 5-16a and Figure 5-16b show the output. The cumulative probability is

$$P(x \le 30) = 0.9016$$

Then to find the probability of interest, we subtract this value from 1.0, giving

$$P(x > 30 \text{ minutes}) = 1.0 - 0.9016 = 0.0984$$

Thus, there are just under 10 chances in 100 that the bank would have to give out a gift certificate. Suppose the manager believes this policy is too liberal. She wants to set the time limit so that the chance

[4]A statistical technique known as the chi-square goodness-of-fit test is introduced in Chapter 12 that can be used to determine statistically whether the data follow a normal distribution.

FIGURE 5-16A

Excel Output for State Bank and Trust

Excel Instructions:
1. Select the Function Wizard.
2. Click on **Statistical**.
3. Select **NORMDIST**.
4. Enter the mean, standard deviation, and *x* value.
5. Set Cumulative equal to True.
6. Click **OK**.

FIGURE 5-16B

Minitab Output for State Bank and Trust

Minitab Instructions:
1. Choose **Calc > Probability Distribution > Normal**.
2. Choose **Cumulative probability**.
3. In **Mean**, enter μ.
4. In **Standard deviation**, enter σ.
5. In **Input constant**, x.
6. Click **OK**.

of giving out the gift is only 5%. You can use the standard normal table, the **Probability Distribution** command in Minitab, or the **NORMSINV** function in Excel to find the new limit.[5] To use the table, we first consider that the manager wants a 5% area in the upper tail of the normal distribution. This will leave

$$0.50 - 0.05 = 0.45$$

between the new time limit and the mean. Now go to the body of the standard normal table, where the probabilities are, and locate the value as close to 0.45 as possible (0.4495 or 0.4505). Next, determine the z-value that corresponds to this probability. Because 0.45 lies midway between 0.4495 and 0.4505, we interpolate halfway between $z = 1.64$ and $z = 1.65$ to get

$$z = 1.645$$

Now, we know

$$z = \frac{x - \mu}{\sigma}$$

We then substitute the known values and solve for x:

$$1.645 = \frac{x - 22.14}{6.09}$$
$$x = 22.14 + 1.645(6.09)$$
$$x = 32.158 \text{ minutes}$$

Therefore, any customer required to wait more than 32.158 (or 32) minutes will receive the gift. This should result in about 5% of the customers getting the restaurant certificate. Obviously, the bank will work to reduce the average service time or standard deviation so even fewer customers will have to be in the bank for more than 32 minutes.

[5]The function is =NORMSINV(.95) in Excel. This will return the z-value corresponding to the area to left of the upper tail equaling .05.

SUMMARY: USING THE NORMAL DISTRIBUTION

If a continuous random variable is distributed as a normal distribution, the distribution is symmetrically distributed around the mean, or expected value, and is described by the mean and standard deviation. To find probabilities associated with a normally distributed random variable, use the following steps:

1. Determine the mean, μ, and the standard deviation, σ.

2. Define the event of interest, such as $P(x \geq x_1)$.

3. Convert the normal distribution to the standard normal distribution using Equation 5-12:

$$z = \frac{x - \mu}{\sigma}$$

4. Use the standard normal distribution tables to find the probability associated with the calculated z-value. The table gives the probability of value between the z-value and the mean.

5. Determine the desired probability using the knowledge that the probability of a value being on either side of the mean is 0.50 and the total probability under the normal distribution is 1.0.

EXAMPLE 5-10: USING THE NORMAL DISTRIBUTION

McMillin Assembly   McMillin Assembly has a contract to assemble components for radar systems to be used by the U.S. military. The time required to complete one part of the assembly is thought to be normally distributed, with a mean equal to 30 hours and a standard deviation equal to 4.7 hours. In order to keep the assembly flow moving on schedule, this assembly step needs to be completed in 26 to 35 hours. To determine the probability of this happening, use the following steps:

Step 1:   **Determine the mean, μ, and the standard deviation, σ.**

The mean assembly time for this step in the process is thought to be 30 hours, and the standard deviation is thought to be 4.7 hours.

Step 2:   **Define the event of interest.**

We are interested in determining the following:

$$P(26 \leq x \leq 35) = ?$$

Step 3:   **Convert the normal distribution to the standard normal distribution using Equation 5-12:**

$$z = \frac{x - \mu}{\sigma}$$

We need to find the z-value corresponding to $x = 26$ and to $x = 35$.

$$z = \frac{x - \mu}{\sigma} = \frac{26 - 30}{4.7} = -0.85 \quad \text{and} \quad z = \frac{35 - 30}{4.7} = 1.06$$

Step 4:   **Use the standard normal table to find the probabilities associated with each z-value.**

For $z = -0.85$, the probability is 0.3023.
For $z = 1.06$, the probability is 0.3554.

Step 5:   **Determine the desired probability for the event of interest.**

$$P(26 \leq x \leq 35) = 0.3023 + 0.3554 = 0.6577$$

Thus, there is a 0.6577 chance that this step in the assembly process will stay on schedule.

Approximate Areas Under the Normal Curve

In Figure 3-9 we introduced the empirical rule for probabilities with bell-shaped distributions. For the normal distribution we can make this rule more precise. Knowing the area under the normal curve between $\pm 1\sigma$, $\pm 2\sigma$, and $\pm 3\sigma$ provides a useful benchmark for estimating probabilities and checking reasonableness of results. Figure 5-17 shows these benchmark areas for any normal distribution.

FIGURE 5-17

Approximate Areas Under the Normal Curve

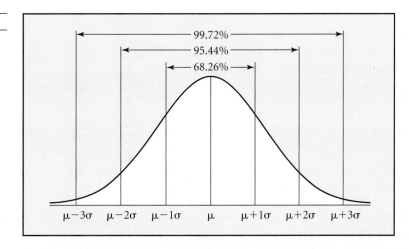

5-3: EXERCISES

Skill Development

5.40   Assuming that we have a normal distribution, find the following probabilities if the mean is 60 and the standard deviation is 10.
   a. $P(x > 60)$
   b. $P(x \geq 70)$
   c. $P(50 \leq x \leq 70)$
   d. $P(x \leq 40)$

5.41   Assume a normal distribution, with a mean of 15 and a standard deviation of 2.5.
   a. Determine the probability of a value exceeding 18.7.
   b. Calculate the distribution's 90th percentile.
   c. Determine the probability of a value being within two standard deviations of the mean.

5.42   A variable is distributed as a normal distribution, with a standard deviation equal to 2.5.
   a. If the probability of a value being larger than 16.3 is to be set at 0.10, what must the mean value be? (Assume the standard deviation remains at 2.5.)
   b. Suppose the mean of the distribution is 13. Determine the value of the standard deviation so that the probability that a value is larger than 16.3 is 0.10.

5.43   For a standardized normal distribution, calculate the following probabilities:
   a. $P(0.00 < z \leq 2.33)$
   b. $P(-1.00 < z \leq 1.00)$
   c. $P(1.78 < z < 2.34)$

5.44   For a standardized normal distribution, determine a value, say z_0, so that
   a. $P(0 < z < z_0) = 0.4772$
   b. $P(-z_0 \leq z < 0) = 0.45$
   c. $P(-z_0 \leq z \leq z_0) = 0.95$
   d. $P(z > z_0) = 0.025$
   e. $P(z \leq z_0) = 0.01$

5.45   For a normal distribution with a mean of 7.5 and a variance of 9, find the following probabilities:
   a. $P(x \geq 8.5)$
   b. $P(x \geq 6.5)$
   c. $P(x \geq 9.5)$
   d. $P(3 \leq x \leq 5.5)$

5.46   Find the following probabilities assuming a normal distribution, with a mean of 7,450 and a standard deviation of 300:
   a. $P(x \leq 7,000)$
   b. $P(x \geq 8,000)$
   c. $P(x \geq 8,250)$
   d. $P(7,400 \leq x \leq 7,700)$

5.47   For a normal distribution, with a mean of 10.5 and a variance of 16.7, determine a value, x_0, so that
   a. $P(10.5 < x < x_0) = 0.4987$
   b. $P(-x_0 \leq x < 10.25) = 0.4750$

5.48   A distribution has a normal distribution, with a mean of 109 and a standard deviation of 23.5.
   a. Calculate the probability of a value being less than 101.3.
   b. Determine the probability of a value being more than two standard deviations above the mean.
   c. Suppose three values are randomly sampled from this distribution. Calculate the probability that at least two out of the three values are more than two standard deviations above the mean.

5.49   A variable is normally distributed with $\sigma = 9.3$.
   a. If the probability of a value being less than 23 is to be set at 0.13, what must the mean value be?
   b. If the mean of this variable is 12.5, determine the probability that at least four out of five randomly chosen values are more than one standard deviation below the mean.

5.50   A variable is normally distributed with a mean equal to 100 and a standard deviation equal to 15. One value, x_A, is on the high side of the mean. Another value, x_B, is the same distance from the mean as x_A, but on the low side of the mean. If the probability of a value falling between x_A and x_B is 0.70, what are the values for x_A and x_B?

5.51   Assume a normal distribution with a mean of 22. If the probability of a value being greater than 17 is 0.75, calculate the standard deviation.

Business Applications

5.52   The average number of acres burned by forest and range fires in a large New Mexico county is 4,300 acres per year, with a standard deviation of 750 acres. The distribution of the number of acres burned is normal.
   a. Compute the probability in any year that more than 5,000 acres will be burned.
   b. Determine the probability in any year that fewer than 4,000 acres will be burned.
   c. What is the probability that between 2,500 and 4,200 acres will be burned?
   d. In those years when more than 5,500 acres are burned, help is needed from eastern-region fire teams. Determine the probability help will be needed in any year.

5.53   The Bureau of Land Management and the U.S. Forest Service are responsible for estimating the amount of damage (in dollars) that occurs as a result of such fires (see Problem 5.52). Suppose the damage is estimated to be

Acres (A)	Cost ($M)	# Firefighters (F)
$0 \leq A < 2,050$	0.05	25
$2,050 \leq A < 2,800$	0.15	50
$2,800 \leq A < 3,550$	0.25	100
$3,550 \leq A < 4,300$	0.35	130
$4,300 \leq A < 5,050$	0.40	150
$5,050 \leq A < 5,600$	0.75	160
$5,600 \leq A < 6,550$	1.00	175
$A \geq 6,550$	1.50	200

a. Calculate the average monetary damage occurring as a result of a forest fire.

b. Calculate the average number of fire fighters needed as a result of a forest fire.

c. If it is desired to have enough firefighters on hand for 75% of the fires, how many firefighters are required?

d. If only 160 firefighters are available, calculate the percentage of fires that can be fought successively.

5.54 Micron Electronics makes both desktop and laptop personal computers that they sell directly to customers by phone or over the Internet. In addition to making the computers, Micron provides customer support via a 1-800 number. Recently, the manager of the service department conducted a study of the time customers spent on hold waiting for a Micron representative to become available. The data showed that the distribution of time spent on hold is approximately normally distributed, with a mean of 18 minutes and a standard deviation of 4 minutes.

a. Based on this information, what is the probability that a customer will have to wait more than 11.3 minutes?

b. Considering the data collected in this study, what is the probability that a customer will wait less than 2 minutes?

c. Suppose a customer has complained to the customer service manager that she was on hold for 22 minutes. Based on the data collected in the study, how would you respond to this customer? Do you think that the customer is accurate with her claim?

d. The service manager wants to make sure (for all practical purposes) that no one waits longer than 18 minutes. Determine the standard deviation that would be required to meet this goal.

5.55 A commuter airline has studied the passenger counts on a flight between Boston and Atlanta and has found that the number of passengers who purchase tickets for this flight is approximately normally distributed, with a mean of 72 and a standard deviation of 4. The data were determined for all days, regardless of the number of tickets sold on the flight. Keep in mind, some people do not show up for their flight.

a. If the capacity on the plane is 85, what percentage of the time should the flight be full?

b. The catering manager who is responsible for snack and beverage provisions on the flight plans to stock 90 snack packs. What is the probability that there will be 8 or fewer left over, assuming that each passenger gets one snack pack?

c. Comment on the potential problems in assuming that the number of fliers on a flight is normally distributed? What type of variable is the number of fliers? Discuss.

5.56 J & G Painting has been gathering data on its painting speed in an effort to be more accurate in submitting bids. Based on data gathered after considering washing, taping, painting, and cleanup, one person can paint an average of 100 square feet of indoor wall space per hour (because of extra taping time, doors and windows are counted as plain wall space), with a standard deviation of 12 square feet. The distribution of square feet painted is considered to be normally distributed.

A painter has just started an 8-foot-wide-by-10-foot-long room at 2:00 P.M. (assume an 8-foot-high ceiling). The painter will be paid overtime if she is not finished by 5:00 P.M. The ceiling is not to be painted.

a. Determine the probability overtime will not be paid.

b. Calculate the earliest she can expect to be finished with the room.

5.57 The Nelson Company makes the machines that automatically dispense soft drinks into cups. Many national fast food chains such as McDonald's and Burger King use these machines. A study by the company shows that the actual volume of soft drink that goes into a 16-ounce cup per fill is normally distributed, with a mean of 16 ounces and a standard deviation 0.35 ounces. A new 16-ounce cup that is being considered actually holds 16.7 ounces of drink.

a. Calculate the proportion of cups that will be "overfilled" by the filling machine.

b. They wish to adjust the machine so that the overfill percentage is no greater than 0.5%. Determine the mean required to fulfill this wish.

c. If the mean is set at 16 ounces, calculate the standard deviation that would be required to meet the stipulation in part b.

d. Which of the two procedures described in parts b and c do you prefer? Explain your answer.

5.58 Referring to the Nelson Company example in Exercise 5.57, suppose the managers wish to have no more than 1 cup in 1,000 overfill. What should the mean fill setting on the machine be to assure that this takes place? (Assume the standard deviation stays at 0.35 ounces.)

5.59 Once a machine has been set at the value determined in Exercise 5.58, the machine is put into use. After a period of time, the mean amount of soft drink dispensed changes. It is important to know when this occurs so that the machine can be serviced and the mean level of soft drink dispensed can be adjusted. One of the decision rules developed for quality control would have the machine shut down if two out of three observations are outside (and on the same side of the mean) two standard deviations from the mean.

a. Calculate the value that is two standard deviations above the mean.

b. Calculate the probability that the amount of liquid dispensed in one cup is above the value found in part a.

c. Now calculate the probability that at least two out of three observations are above the value found in a. (Hint: You are counting something that assumes one of two things per trial.) For this calculation assume that the mean has not changed (i.e., the mean is still 16 oz.).

5.60   A new filter system for swimming pools is designed to filter out certain harmful particles that can get into the water. A study shows that the number of particles per gallon of water is normally distributed, with a mean of 20,000 and a standard deviation of 3,000. The filter is designed to catch 25,000 particles per gallon.

a. Determine the probability that the filter will allow some particles to escape back into the pool.

b. The manufacturer of the filter claims that the filter removes 90% of the particles from the water. Is this statement correct? Support your answer with probability calculations and reasons.

c. If the filter fulfilled the claim made by the manufacturer, how many particles per gallon of water would the filter remove?

5.61   The Edward's Theater chain has studied its movie customers to determine how much they spend on concessions. The study based on a large number of customers shows that the spending distribution is approximately normally distributed, with a mean of $4.11 and a standard deviation of $1.37.

a. Compute the probability that a customer will spend more than $7.50 on concessions.

b. Suppose the manager would like the chances that a customer will spend less than $3.50 on concessions to be at most 5%. If the standard deviation remains at $1.37, what would the mean spending value need to be?

5.62   The length of french fries made by the J. R. Simplot Company for one of its biggest customers is normally distributed, with a mean of 4.2 inches and a standard deviation of 0.5 inch. The customer purchases the fries by the pound but sells to its customers by volume. Thus, it prefers the longer fries and wants no more than a 5% chance that a fry will be shorter than 3.5 inches. Based on the current data, does the Simplot Company meet the customer's requirements? Show why or why not.

5.63   The Simplot Company, which produces french fries, is considering changing its purchasing standards for raw potatoes in an effort to change the average length of fries. If the standard deviation for fries is to remain at 0.50 inches, what will the average fry length have to be to meet Simplot's customer's requirement that no more than 5% of the fries be shorter than 3.5 inches?

Advanced Business Applications

5.64   ◉ The Hydronics Company is in the business of developing health supplements. Recently, the company's R&D department came up with two weight-loss plans that included products produced by Hydronics. To determine whether these products are effective, the company has conducted a test. A total of 300 people who each were 30 pounds or more overweight were recruited to participate in the study. Of these, 100 people were given a placebo supplement, 100 people were given plan 1, and 100 people were given plan 2. As might be expected, some people dropped out before the four-week study period was completed. The weight loss (or gain) for each individual is listed in the data file called *Hydronics*. Note, positive values indicate that the individual actually gained weight during the study period.

a. Develop a frequency histogram for the weight loss (or gain) for those people on plan 1. Does it appear from this graph that weight loss is approximately normally distributed?

b. Referring to part a, assuming that a normal distribution does apply, compute the mean and standard deviation weight loss for the plan 1 subjects.

c. Referring to parts a and b, assuming that the weight-change distribution for plan 1 users is normally distributed and that the sample mean and standard deviation are used to directly represent the population mean and standard deviation. Then, what is the probability that a plan 1 user will lose more than 12 pounds in a four-week period?

d. Referring to your answer in part c, would it be appropriate for the company to claim that plan 1 users can expect to lose as much as 12 pounds in four weeks? Discuss.

5.65   ◉ Refer to the Hydronics Company in Exercise 5.64. Using the data set in the file *Hydronics*:

a. Develop a frequency histogram for the weight loss (or gain) for those people on plan 2. Does it appear from this graph that weight loss is approximately normally distributed?

b. Referring to part a, assuming that a normal distribution does apply, compute the mean and standard deviation weight loss for the plan 2 subjects.

c. Referring to parts a and b, assume that the weight-change distribution for plan 2 users is normally distributed and that the sample mean and standard deviation are used to directly represent the population mean and standard deviation. Then, what is the probability that a plan 2 user will lose more than 12 pounds in a four-week period?

d. Referring to your answer in part c, would it be appropriate for the company to claim that plan 2 users can expect to lose as much as 12 pounds in four weeks? Discuss.

5.66   ◉ Refer to Exercise 5.65.

a. Twin sisters were part of this study. One was put on plan 1 and the other on plan 2. Determine the probability that at least one of the sisters will lose 12 pounds.

b. Provide the number of pounds lost such that 10% will lose at least that many pounds on plan 2.

5.67   ◉ The Future-Vision Cable TV Company recently surveyed its customers. A total of 548 responses were received. Among other things, the respondents were asked to indicate their household income. The data from the survey are found in the file *Future-Vision*.

a. Develop a frequency histogram for the income variable. Does it appear from the graph that income is approximately normally distributed? Discuss.
b. Compute the mean and standard deviation for the income variable.
c. Referring to parts a and b and assuming that income is normally distributed and the sample mean and standard deviation are good substitutes for the population values, what is the probability that a Future-Vision customer will have an income exceeding $40,000?
d. Suppose that Future-Vision managers are thinking about offering a monthly discount to customers who

have a household income below a certain level. If the management wants to grant discounts to no more than 7% of the customers, what income level should be used for the cutoff?

5.68   Refer to the Future-Vision managers of Exercise 5.67. The company targets the $40,000 through $60,000 income group with special advertising. As part of the program, it offers a discount coupon of $10 off of next month's cable bill. Of those in the $40,000 to $60,000 category, 75% return the coupons. Determine the percentage of Future-Visions' customers who both receive the promotion and send in the coupon.

5-4 OTHER CONTINUOUS PROBABILITY DISTRIBUTIONS

The normal distribution is the most frequently used continuous probability distribution in statistics. However, there are other continuous distributions that apply to business decision-making. This section introduces two of these: the uniform distribution and the exponential distribution.

UNIFORM PROBABILITY DISTRIBUTION

The **uniform distribution** is sometimes referred to as the *distribution of little information*, because the probability over any interval of the continuous random variable is the same as for any other interval of the same width.

Equation 5-13 defines the *continuous uniform distribution*.

Continuous Uniform Distribution

$$f(x) = \begin{cases} \dfrac{1}{b-a} & \text{if } a \le x \le b \\ 0 & \text{otherwise} \end{cases} \qquad \textbf{5-13}$$

where:

$$f(x) = \text{Value of the density function at any } x \text{ value}$$
$$a = \text{Lower limit of the interval from } a \text{ to } b$$
$$b = \text{Upper limit of the interval from } a \text{ to } b$$

Figure 5-18 illustrates two examples of uniform probability distributions with different a to b intervals. Note the height of the probability distribution is the same for all values of x between a and b for a given distribution. The graph of the uniform distribution is a rectangle.

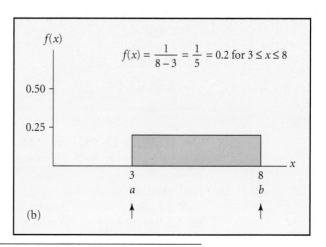

FIGURE 5-18   Uniform Distributions

EXAMPLE 5-11: USING THE UNIFORM DISTRIBUTION

Stern Manufacturing Company   The Stern Manufacturing Company makes seat-belt buck-les for all types of vehicles. The inventory level for the spring mechanism used in producing the buckles is only enough to continue production for two more hours. The purchasing clerk estimates that the springs will be delivered one to four hours from the time they are ordered. Because the dispatcher offers no other information about the pending delivery schedule, the time it will take to replenish the inventory is said to be *uniformly distributed* over the interval of one-to-four hours. We are interested in the probability that the company will run out of parts due to the shipment taking more than two hours. The probability can be determined using the following steps:

Step 1:   **Define the probability distribution.**
The height of the probability rectangle, $f(x)$, for the delivery time interval one-to-four hours is determined using Equation 5-13, as follows:

$$f(x) = \frac{1}{b-a}$$

$$f(x) = \frac{1}{4-1} = \frac{1}{3} = 0.33$$

Step 2:   **Define the event of interest.**
The production scheduler is specifically concerned that shipment will take longer than two hours to arrive. We determine the probability as follows:

$$\begin{aligned} P(x > 2.0) &= 1 - P(x \le 2.0) \\ &= 1 - f(x)(2.0 - 1.0) \\ &= 1 - 0.33(1.0) \\ &= 1 - 0.33 \\ &= 0.67 \end{aligned}$$

Thus, there is a 67% chance that production will be delayed because the shipment is more than two hours late.

Like the normal distribution, the uniform distribution can be further described by specifying the mean and the standard deviation. These values are computed using Equations 5-14 and 5-15.

Mean and Standard Deviation of a Uniform Distribution

Mean (Expected Value):

$$E(x) = \mu = \frac{a+b}{2} \qquad\qquad \textbf{5-14}$$

Standard Deviation:

$$\sigma = \sqrt{\frac{(b-a)^2}{12}} \qquad\qquad \textbf{5-15}$$

where:

a = Lower limit of the interval from a to b
b = Upper limit of the interval from a to b

EXAMPLE 5-12: THE MEAN AND STANDARD DEVIATION OF A UNIFORM DISTRIBUTION

Austrian Airlines   The service manager for Austrian Airlines is uncertain about the time needed for the ground crew to turn an airplane around from the time it lands until it is ready to take off. He has been given information from the operations supervisor indicating that the times seem to range between 15 and 45 minutes. Without any further information, the service manager will apply a uniform distribution to the turnaround. Based on this, he can determine the mean and standard deviation for the airplane turnaround times using the following steps:

Step 1:   **Define the probability distribution.**

Equation 5-13 can be used to define the distribution:

$$f(x) = \frac{1}{b - a} = \frac{1}{45 - 15} = \frac{1}{30} = 0.0333$$

Step 2:   **Compute the mean of the probability distribution using Equation 5-14.**

$$\mu = \frac{a + b}{2} = \frac{15 + 45}{2} = 30$$

Thus, the mean turnaround time is 30 minutes.

Step 3:   **Compute the standard deviation using Equation 5-15.**

$$\sigma = \sqrt{\frac{(b - a)^2}{12}} = \sqrt{\frac{(45 - 15)^2}{12}} = \sqrt{75} = 8.66$$

The standard deviation is 8.66 minutes.

THE EXPONENTIAL PROBABILITY DISTRIBUTION

Another continuous probability distribution that is frequently used in business situations is called the **exponential distribution**. The exponential distribution is used to measure the time that elapses between two occurrences of an event, such as the time between "hits" on an Internet homepage. The exponential distribution might also be used to describe the time between arrivals of customers at a bank drive-in teller window or the time between failures of an electronic component.

Equation 5-16 shows the probability density function for the exponential distribution.

Exponential Distribution

A continuous random variable that is exponentially distributed has the probability density function given by

$$f(x) = \lambda e^{-\lambda x}, x \geq 0 \qquad\qquad \textbf{5-16}$$

where:

$$e = 2.71828\ldots$$
$$1/\lambda = \text{the mean time between events } (\lambda > 0)$$

Note, the parameter that defines the exponential distribution is λ (lambda). You should recall from Section 5-2 that λ is the mean value for the Poisson distribution. If the number of occurrences per time period is known to be Poisson distributed with a mean of λ, then the time between occurrences will be exponentially distributed with a mean time of $1/\lambda$.

If we select a value for λ, we can graph the exponential distribution by substituting λ and different values for x into Equation 5-16. For instance, Figure 5-19 shows exponential distributions for $\lambda = 0.5$, $\lambda = 1.0$, $\lambda = 2.0$, and $\lambda = 3.0$. Note in Figure 5-19 that for any exponential distribution, with density function $f(x)$, $f(0) = \lambda$, and as x increases, $f(x)$ approaches zero. It can also be shown that *the standard deviation of any exponential distribution is equal to the mean, $1/\lambda$.*

As with any continuous probability distribution, the probability that a value will fall within an interval is the area under the graph between the two points defining the interval.[6] Equation 5-17 is used to find the probability that a value will be equal to or less than a particular value for an exponential distribution.

Exponential Probability

$$P(0 \leq x \leq a) = 1 - e^{-\lambda a} \qquad\qquad \textbf{5-17}$$

---

[6]Integral calculus is used to find the area.

FIGURE 5-19   Exponential Distributions

FIGURE 5-19   Exponential Distributions

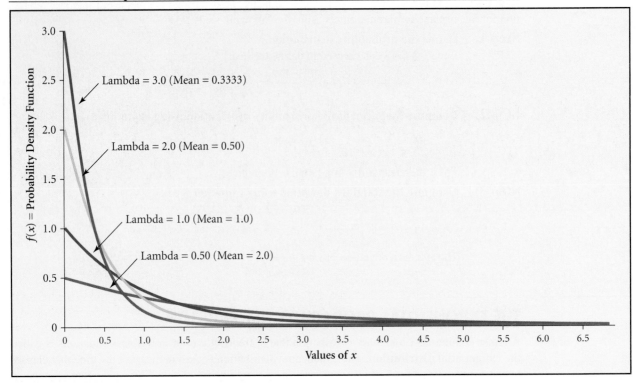

Appendix E contains a table of $e^{-\lambda a}$ values for different values of λa. You can use this table and Equation 5-17 to find the probabilities when the λa of interest is contained in the table. You can also use Minitab or Excel to find exponential probabilities, as the following application illustrates.

Excel and Minitab Tutorial

Haines Internet Services—The Haines Internet Services Company has determined that the number of customers who attempt to connect to the Internet per hour is Poisson distributed with $\lambda = 30$ per hour. The time between connect requests is exponentially distributed with a mean time between calls of 2.0 minutes, computed as follows:

$$\lambda = 30 \text{ per } 60 \text{ minutes} = 0.50 \text{ per minute}$$

The mean time between calls, then, is

$$1/\lambda = 1/0.50 = 2.0 \text{ minutes.}$$

Because of the system that Haines uses, if customer requests are too close together—45 seconds (0.75 minutes) or less—some customers fail to connect. The managers at Haines are analyzing whether they should purchase new equipment that will eliminate this problem. They need to know the probability that a customer will fail to connect. Thus they want:

$$P(x \leq 0.75 \text{ minutes}) = ?$$

FIGURE 5-20A

Excel Exponential Probability Output for Haines Internet Services

Excel Instructions:
1. Click on Function Wizard.
2. Select **Statistics**.
3. Select **EXPONDIST** function.
4. Supply x and lamda.
5. Set **Cumulative = TRUE** for cumulative probability.

FIGURE 5-20B

Minitab Exponential Probability Output for Haines Internet Services

To find this probability using a calculator, we need to first determine λa. In this example, $\lambda = 0.50$ and $a = 0.75$. Then

$$\lambda a = (0.50)(0.75) = 0.3750.$$

We find the desired probability is:

$$1 - e^{-\lambda a} = 1 - e^{-0.3750}$$
$$= 0.3127$$

The managers can also use the **EXPONDIST** function in Excel or the **Probability Distributions** command in Minitab to compute the precise value for the desired probability.[7] Figure 5-20a and Figure 5-20b show that the chance of failing to connect is 0.3127. This means that nearly one-third of the customers will experience a problem with the current system.

5-4: EXERCISES

Skill Development

5.69 A continuous random variable is uniformly distributed between 20 and 60.
  a. What is the probability a randomly selected value will be above 50?
  b. Calculate the probability a randomly selected value will be exactly 45.
  c. Determine the probability that a randomly selected value will be between 25 and 35.
  d. Find the probability that a randomly selected value will be less than 34.

5.70 A random variable is known to be exponentially distributed, with a mean time between occurrences equal to 2.0 minutes.
  a. What is the probability that the time between the next two occurrences is more than 2.0 minutes?
  b. Determine the probability that the time between the next two occurrences is between 1.0 and 2.0 minutes. [Hint, find $P(x \le 1.0)$ and subtract from $P(x \le 2.0)$].
  c. Calculate the probability that the time between the next two occurrences is greater than 2.5 minutes.

5.71 A continuous random variable is uniformly distributed between 100 and 400.
  a. Determine the probability a randomly selected value will be above 200.
  b. Calculate the probability a randomly selected value will be between 150 and 300.
  c. What is the probability that a randomly selected value will fall between 260 and 180?

5.72 A variable is uniformly distributed between the values 300 and 1,000.
  a. Draw a graph that describes the probability distribution.
  b. Find the probability of a value exceeding 700.
  c. Find the probability that a randomly selected value is less than 650.
  d. What is the probability that a randomly selected value exceeds 500?

5.73 A variable is uniformly distributed between the values -0.40 and 1.7.
  a. Draw a graph that describes the probability distribution.
  b. Find the probability of a value exceeding 0.0.

5.74 The Poisson distribution is known to describe the number of occurrences for a random variable with $\lambda = 60$ arrivals per hour.
  a. What is the probability that the time between arrivals will exceed 1.0 minute?
  b. Determine the probability that the time between arrivals will be between 45 and 75 seconds.

5.75 The time between occurrences for a random variable is known to be exponentially distributed with $\lambda = 4$ seconds.
  a. Find the probability that the time between occurrences is between 0.20 and 0.60 seconds.
  b. Calculate the probability that the time between occurrences will exceed the mean.
  c. Determine the probability that the time between occurrences will be greater than 0.30 seconds.

[7]The Excel EXPONDIST function requires that λ be inputted rather than $1/\lambda$.

Business Applications

5.76 When only the value-added time is considered, the time it takes to build a laser printer is thought to be uniformly distributed between 8 and 15 hours.
   a. What are the chances that it will take more than 10 value-added hours to build a printer?
   b. How likely is it that a printer will require fewer than 9 value-added hours?
   c. Suppose a single customer orders two printers. Determine the probability that the first and second printer each will require fewer than 9 value-added hours to complete.

5.77 In western Oregon, the growth distribution for a pine tree is thought to be uniformly distributed between 5 and 8.5 inches per year. A forest-products company is building a computer simulation model that they will use to help determine how many trees should be harvested each year.
   a. The modelers are thinking of using a constant growth rate of 7.0 inches per year. Based on the growth distribution, what is the probability that a tree will grow fewer than 7.0 inches in a year? Comment on the potential impact of using this growth level in the model. Would the model tend to understate or overstate the actual pine tree growth? Discuss.
   b. Suppose the modelers are also considering using a growth rate of 6.0 inches per year. What is the probability that a tree will grow more than 6.0 inches per year? If they use this as their model input, what might be the general impact on tree-growth projections by the model? Discuss?

5.78 The Sea Pines Golf Course is preparing for a major LPGA golf tournament. Because parking near the course is extremely limited (room for only 500 cars), the course officials have contracted with the local community to provide parking and a bus shuttle service. Sunday, the final day of the tournament, will draw the largest crowd, and the officials estimate they will have between 8,000 and 12,000 cars needing parking spaces. However, they think no value is more likely than another. The tournament committee is discussing how many parking spots to contract from the city. If they want to limit the chance of not having enough parking to 10%, how many spaces do they need from the city on Sunday?

5.79 The manager for Select-a-Seat, a company that sells tickets to athletic games, concerts, and other events, has determined that the number of people arriving at the Broadway location on a typical day is Poisson distributed with a mean of 12 per hour. It takes approximately 4 minutes to process a ticket request. Thus, if customers arrive in intervals that are shorter than 4 minutes, they will have to wait. Assuming that a customer has just arrived and the ticket agent is starting to serve that customer, what is the probability that the next customer who arrives will have to wait in line?

5.80 The Barineer Hospital in Sarasota, Florida, has determined that the time between patient arrivals to the emergency room is exponentially distributed with a mean time between arrivals of 11 minutes. Processing a patient into the hospital requires 5 minutes. A person has just begun to be processed and there are no other patients waiting.
   a. What is the probability that the next arriving patient will have to wait to be processed? What does this imply about the hospital's need to add another check-in station in the emergency room? Discuss.
   b. The emergency room often has several patients arriving at once as a result of a traffic accident or fire. Suppose the emergency room has five patients from a traffic accident arrive at the same time. How many other patients will arrive at the emergency room while the original five are being processed? (Hint: Recall the relationship between the Poisson distribution and the exponential distribution.) Can you visualize why at times it takes a long time to see a doctor in a hospital's emergency room?

5.81 The time to failure for a power supply unit used in a particular brand of personal computer is thought to be exponentially distributed with a mean of 4,000 hours, as per the contract between the vendor and the PC maker. The PC manufacturer has just had a warranty return from a customer who had the power supply fail after 2,100 hours of use.
   a. What is the probability that the power supply would fail at 2,100 hours or fewer? Based on this probability, do you feel the PC maker has a right to require that the power supply maker refund the money on this unit?
   b. Assuming that the PC maker has sold 100,000 computers with this power supply, approximately how many should be returned due to failure at 2,100 hours or fewer?

Summary and Conclusions

This chapter introduced several discrete and continuous probability distributions, including the binomial, Poisson, hypergeometric, normal, uniform, and exponential distributions. All of these distributions are used by decision makers. The choice of which distribution to use depends on whether the random variable of interest is discrete or continuous. Figure 5-21 summarizes the different distributions introduced in this chapter.

The binomial distribution is useful when the value of a discrete random variable is based on independent trials when on a given trial there are two possible outcomes and we can count the number of successes and failures. The Poisson distribution, also a discrete distribution, deals with situations in which the trials are independent but we are able to count only the successes. The final discrete distribution introduced in this chapter is the hypergeomet-

FIGURE 5-21

FIGURE 5-21

Probability Distribution Summary

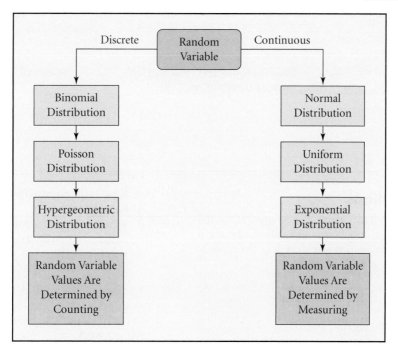

ric distribution. This distribution applies when the trials are dependent and the sample size is large relative to the size of the finite population.

In Section 5-3, we showed that the normal distribution, with its special properties, is used extensively in statistical decision making. The chapter discussed in some detail the standard normal distribution. It showed how the standard normal can be used to produce probability characteristics of any normal distribution. We also illustrated the use of Excel and Minitab to find probabilities for the normal and exponential distributions. The exponential and uniform distributions are also continuous distributions that have specific application in business situations.

Subsequent chapters will introduce other continuous probability distributions. Among these will be the *t distribution*, the *chi-square distribution*, and the *F distribution*. These additional distributions play important roles in statistical decision making. The basic concept that the area under a continuous curve is equivalent to the probability is true for all continuous distributions.

EQUATIONS

Counting Rule for Combinations

$$C_x^n = \frac{n!}{x!(n-x)!}$$ 5-1

Binomial Formula

$$P(x) = \frac{n!}{x!(n-x)!} p^x q^{n-x}$$ 5-2

Expected Value of a Discrete Random Variable

$$E(x) = \sum xP(x)$$ 5-3

Expected Value of a Binomial Distribution

$$\mu_x = E(x) = np$$ 5-4

Standard Deviation of a Discrete Random Variable

$$\sigma_x = \sqrt{\sum [x - E(x)]^2 P(x)}$$ 5-5

Standard Deviation of the Binomial Distribution

$$\sigma = \sqrt{npq}$$ 5-6

Poisson Probability Distribution

$$P(x) = \frac{(\lambda t)^x e^{-\lambda t}}{x!}$$ 5-7

Standard Deviation of the Poisson Distribution

$$\sigma = \sqrt{\lambda t}$$ 5-8

Hypergeometric Distribution (Two Possible Outcomes per Trial)

$$P(x) = \frac{C_{n-x}^{N-X} \cdot C_x^X}{C_n^N}$$ 5-9

Hypergeometric Distribution (k Possible Outcomes per Trial)

$$P(x_1, x_2, x_3, \ldots, x_k) = \frac{C_{x_1}^{X_1} \cdot C_{x_2}^{X_2} \cdot C_{x_3}^{X_3} \cdots \cdot C_{x_k}^{X_k}}{C_n^N}$$ 5-10

Normal Distribution Density Function

$$f(x) = \frac{1}{\sigma\sqrt{2\pi}} e^{-(x-\mu)^2/2\sigma^2}$$ 5-11

Standardized Normal z-Value

$$z = \frac{x - \mu}{\sigma}$$ 5-12

Continuous Uniform Distribution

$$f(x) = \begin{cases} \dfrac{1}{b-a} & \text{if } a \leq x \leq b \\ 0 & \text{otherwise} \end{cases}$$ 5-13

Mean of the Uniform Distribution

$$E(x) = \mu = \frac{a+b}{2}$$ 5-14

Standard Deviation of the Uniform Distribution

$$\sigma = \sqrt{\frac{(b-a)^2}{12}}$$ 5-15

Exponential Distribution

$$f(x) = \lambda e^{-\lambda x}, x \geq 0$$ 5-16

Exponential Probability

$$P(0 \leq x \leq a) = 1 - e^{-\lambda a}$$ 5-17

Key Terms

Binomial Distribution, 177
Continuous Random Variable, 176

Discrete Random Variable, 176
Normal Distribution, 199

Standard Normal Distribution, 201

CHAPTER EXERCISES

Conceptual Questions

5.82 Discuss the characteristics that must be present for the binomial probability distribution to apply. Relate these to a particular business application and show how the application meets the binomial requirements.

5.83 Discuss why, in the strictest sense, if the sampling is performed without replacement, the binomial distribution does not apply. Also, indicate under what conditions it is considered acceptable to use the binomial distribution even when the sampling is without replacement. Identify a business application that supports your answer.

5.84 How is the shape of a binomial distribution changed for a given sample size as p approaches 0.50 from either side? Discuss.

5.85 How is the shape of the binomial distribution changed for a given value of p as the sample size is increased? Discuss.

5.86 Discuss the basic differences and similarities between the binomial distribution and the Poisson distribution.

5.87 Through an example, discuss why, if the mean of the Poisson distribution can be reduced, the spread of the distribution can also be reduced.

5.88 The probability that a value for a normally distributed random variable will exceed the mean is 0.50. The same is true for the uniform distribution. Why is this not necessarily true for the exponential distribution? Discuss and show examples to illustrate your point.

5.89 One of your fellow students tells you that when working with a continuous distribution, it does not make sense to try to compute the probability of any specific value because it will be zero. She then says that this can't be true because when the experiment is performed some value must occur, so the probability can't be zero. Your task is to respond to her statement and in doing so explain why it is appropriate to find the probability for specific ranges of values for a continuous distribution.

5.90 Discuss the difference between discrete and continuous probability distributions. Discuss two situations in which a variable of interest may be considered either continuous or discrete.

Business Applications

5.91 The American Testing Service has determined that examination scores on the Indiana real estate exam are uniformly distributed between scores of 40% and 80% correct.
   a. Develop a graph of the probability distribution.
   b. Determine the probability of a score under 65% correct on the exam.
   c. What is the probability of scoring 70% correct or better on the exam?
   d. What is the probability of scoring between 60% and 75% correct on the exam?
   e. Determine the score you would need to achieve the 90th percentile on this test.

5.92 The manager of a local convenience-food and gasoline store has observed that the number of customers failing to pay for their gasoline is Poisson distributed, with a mean of five per week.
   a. What is the probability that during a given week, no customers fail to pay?
   b. Suppose that during the initial week of a new employee's hire, more than nine people failed to pay for their gasoline. Based on the probability of this happening, what should the store manager conclude about the distribution of the people who fail to pay?

5.93 Assuming that the customer arrivals at the Fidelity Credit Union drive-through window are Poisson distributed, with a mean of five per hour, find
   a. the probability that in a given hour more than eight customers will arrive at the drive-through window
   b. the probability that between three and six customers, inclusive, will arrive at the drive-through window in a given hour.
   c. the probability that fewer than three customers will arrive at the window in a given 30-minute period.

5.94 The manager for the Inland Food Market chain has determined that the occurrence of spoiled fruit is Poisson distributed, with a mean of 4 pieces per case.
   a. What is the probability that in two cases more than 10 pieces of spoiled fruit will be discovered?
   b. Suppose a new employee has been assigned the task of unpacking two cases of fruit and he reports that none of the pieces were spoiled. What are some conclusions you might reach and why?

5.95 The Hilgren Map Company produces topographical maps covering all parts of Utah, Arizona, and New Mexico. Past studies have indicated that the number of errors per map is Poisson distributed, with an average of 0.5 error per map.
   a. What is the probability that a map will contain no errors?
   b. What is the probability that a map will contain fewer than three errors?
   c. What is the probability that a series of three maps will contain no errors?
   d. What is the probability that a map will have five or more errors? What would you conclude if this did occur? Discuss.

5.96 A new battery designed especially for children's toys has been found to have a lifetime between 2.5 hours and 7 hours, with probabilities uniformly distributed between these two points.

a. Develop a graph showing the probability distribution.

b. Determine the probability that a battery will last more than 6 hours.

c. What is the probability that a battery will last between 3.5 and 5.5 hours?

d. You have been given the task of deciding whether to purchase these batteries for the toy manufacturer. Your firm will purchase the batteries if you can verify the lifetime distribution claimed. A sample of 10 batteries is tested. Only 1 battery lasted longer than 6 hours. Discuss what you will report to your superiors concerning your decision to purchase these batteries. Include probability calculations in your discussion.

5.97 Suppose a study performed at St. Jude's Hospital shows that 30% of all patients arriving at the emergency room are subsequently admitted to the hospital for at least one night. Assuming that in a sample of seven who arrived at the emergency room the number of people needing to be admitted to the hospital meets the requirements for the binomial distribution:

a. What is the probability that five or more in the sample of seven will require admittance to the hospital?

b. What is the expected number of patients in the sample who will require admittance to the hospital?

5.98 It has been determined that vehicles arriving at a drive-through pharmacy window arrive according to a Poisson distribution at the rate of 12 per hour.

a. In a half-hour time period, what is the probability that three or fewer cars will arrive at the window?

b. In a 15-minute period, what is the probability that three or fewer cars will arrive at the window?

c. If the pharmacist can serve 4 cars per half-hour, what is the probability that during the first half-hour of business a customer will not be served and will still be waiting in line when the half-hour ends?

5.99 The Telephone Company of America recently made the claim that only 10% of the people who have telephones in their residences make enough local calls during a month to justify paying their monthly bills if the calls would be billed at a rate of $0.25 per call. A consumer agency decided to follow up this claim by selecting a random sample of 15 people who have telephones.

a. Assuming the binomial distribution applies, what is the probability that the survey will show fewer than 7 people actually making the necessary number of calls to justify their phone bills if in fact the true percentage in the population is 10%, as claimed by the Telephone Company of America?

b. If the binomial distribution applies, what is the probability that no customer in the sample will be found to be making enough calls to justify their bill at the rate of $0.25 per call?

5.100 A typist in Austin Company's typing pool makes errors periodically. In fact, a study has shown that errors made are random and independent of each other at an average rate of three per page ($\lambda = 3$).

a. Develop the appropriate probability distribution for the number of errors made by the typist on a particular page.

b. Based on the distribution developed in part a, determine the average number of errors the typist will make per page.

c. Compute the variance and standard deviation for the probability distribution in part a.

5.101 The manager of consumer loans at Farwest National Bank has indicated that the distribution of account balances is a normal distribution.

a. He has determined that the average credit card account balance is $700, with a median balance of $600. Comment on this conclusion.

b. Having seen your comments in a, he recounts and says, "I was mistaken. It is the standard deviation that is $600." Comment on this conclusion.

5.102 Suppose personal daily water usage in California is normally distributed, with a mean of 18 gallons and a standard deviation of 6 gallons.

a. What percentage of the population uses more than 18 gallons.

b. What percentage of the population uses between 10 and 20 gallons?

c. What is the probability of finding a person who uses fewer than 10 gallons?

d. La Niña (the little sister weather pattern of her more famous brother, el Niño) has been cited as the cause of drought conditions in the southern portion of the United States. The city manager of Morro Bay, California (population: 14,500), has been trying to gain support for Morro Bay's participation in a state water project to bring water from northern to southern California. He contends that the city's population has grown to the point that the city's water needs cannot be met. Recently, he noted that the city's current water sources could provide only 350,000 gallons of water a day. Do you see a need for additional water for Morro Bay? Provide statistical evidence to support your views.

5.103 Referring to Exercise 5.102, the daily water usage in California was thought to be normally distributed, with a mean of 18 gallons and a standard deviation of 6 gallons. Because of a perpetual water shortage in California, the governor wants to give a tax rebate to the 20% of the population who use the least amount of water.

a. What should the governor use as the maximum water limit for a person to qualify for a tax rebate?

b. Referring to your answer in part a, suppose the governor's proposed tax rebate causes a shift in the average water usage from 18 gallons to 14 gallons per person per day, but it causes no change in the standard deviation. What percentage of the water users will now get a rebate? Assume the tax rebates will be given to those using less water than you specified in part a.

5.104 Cattle are often fattened in a feedlot before being shipped to a slaughterhouse. Suppose the weight gain per steer at a feedlot averages 1.5 pounds per day, with a standard deviation of 0.25 pound. Assume a normal distribution.

a. What is the probability a steer will gain more than 2 pounds on a given day?

b. Determine the probability a steer will gain between 1 and 2 pounds in any given day.

c. Provide the probability of selecting two steers that both gain fewer than 1.5 pounds on a given day, assuming the two are independent.

d. Compute the probabilities found in parts a, b, and c, assuming a standard deviation of 0.2 pound. Why are these probabilities different?

5.105 The dollar amount of dairy products consumed per week by adults is thought to be normally distributed, with a mean of $4.50 and a standard deviation of $1.10.

a. What is the probability that an individual adult from the population will consume more than $4.90 in dairy products in a week?

b. Determine the probability that an individual selected at random from the population will consume less than $6.25 in dairy products in a week.

c. Compute the probability that a person will consume between $3.25 and $5.75 in dairy products in a week.

5.106 The Town-Pump service station has performed an analysis of its customers and has found that 80% pay on credit and the rest pay cash. If five customers are sampled, what is the probability that three or fewer of them will pay on credit?

5.107 The makers of Time-Tell digital watches claim that their watches are of very high quality. Specifically, they have claimed that no more than 10% of their watches will fail within the first six months of use. Suppose the distribution of watch failures in a sample of 10 watches has a binomial distribution.

a. What is the mean of the probability distribution? Interpret this value.

b. What is the standard deviation of the random variable? Interpret this value.

5.108 Jamieson Airlines has a central office that takes reservations for all flights flown by the airline. The calls received during any week are approximately normally distributed, with a mean of 12,000 and a standard deviation of 2,500.

a. During what percentage of weeks does the airline receive more than 11,000 calls?

b. During what percentage of weeks does it receive fewer than 12,300 calls?

c. During what percentage of weeks does it receive between 10,800 an 13,400 calls?

d. During the past year, the manager of the central office has kept track of the number of calls received each week. She has determined that the smallest number of calls was 10,800 and the largest number of calls was 13,400. If the calls received are normally distributed, determine the mean and standard deviations this data suggests.

Advanced Business Applications

5.109 The Ziegler Lumber Company sets the cut length on its 2 x 12 lumber a little longer than the specified length because its trim saw is fairly old. The mill foreman discovered that the saw would cut any set length short by an average of 3 inches, with a standard deviation of 1.5 inches. Fortunately, the errors seem to be normally distributed.

a. If the foreman is setting up the trim saw to cut 2 x 12 boards 10 feet long, what should the trim-saw length setting be if he wants no more than a 5% chance of a board being shorter than 10 feet?

b. Suppose the machine can be fixed so that the standard deviation in cut error can be controlled to a specified level. What would the standard deviation have to be so that trim length could be set 1 inch shorter than the answer to part a?

5.110 Exercise 5.109 refers to the Ziegler Lumber Company, which discovered its old trim saw would cut any length short by an average of 3 inches, with a standard deviation of 1.5 inches. The errors seen are normally distributed. Suppose an adjustment is made to the machine that reduces the average error to 2 inches but increases the standard deviation to 2 inches.

a. Determine the trim-saw length setting if the foreman wants no more than a 5% chance of a board being cut shorter than 10 feet.

b. The foreman has kept track of the complaints concerning the length of the 10-foot boards. He is convinced that about 10% of the boards are more than 4.56 inches shorter than they were intended to be. About 5% of the boards are cut longer than they were intended to be. Do these figures convince you that the supposed adjustment really was made? Provide statistical evidence with your opinion?

5.111 The personnel manager for a large company is interested in the distribution of sick-leave hours for employees of her company. A recent study revealed the distribution to be approximately normal, with a mean of 58 hours per year and a standard deviation of 14 hours.

An office manager in one division has reason to believe that during the past year, two of his employees have taken excessive sick leave relative to everyone else. The first employee used 74 hours of sick leave, and the second used 90 hours. What would you conclude about the office manager's claim and why?

5.112 Exercise 5.111 considers a company's allocation of sick-leave hours for its employees. The personnel manager has found the distribution of time lost per year due to illness to be approximately normal, with a mean of 58 hours per year and a standard deviation of 14 hours. Suppose the company grants 40 hours of paid sick leave per year. Given the distribution of time lost due to illness, what would you conclude about the adequacy of the company's sick-leave policy? Why?

5.113 The Bryce Brothers Lumber Company is considering buying a machine that planes lumber to the correct thickness. The machine is advertised to produce "6-inch lumber" having a thickness that is normally distributed, with a mean of 6 inches and a standard deviation of 0.10 inch.

a. If building standards in the industry require a 99% chance of a board being between 5.85 and 6.15 inches, should Bryce Brothers purchase this machine? Why or why not?

b. To what level would the company that manufactures the machine have to reduce the standard deviation for the machine to conform to industry standards?

5.114 After a recent freeze in Florida, the Sweetbrand Citrus Company was concerned about the quality of its grapefruit. Estimates by the U.S. Department of Agriculture (USDA) indicated that 25% of the grapefruit were damaged by the freeze. The problem is that there seems to be no pattern to indicate which grapefruit suffered freeze damage. For instance, given two grapefruit growing side by side on a tree, one could be perfect and the other damaged. Suppose the Sweetbrand Company selected a random sample of 50 grapefruit.

a. What conditions must be satisfied so that the number of damaged grapefruit has a probability distribution described by the binomial distribution?

b. Assuming that the binomial distribution does apply, what is the probability of finding fewer than 5 damaged grapefruit, given that the 25% estimate is correct?

c. Assuming that the binomial distribution applies, what is the probability of finding more than 20 damaged grapefruit if the 25% estimate is correct?

d. Referring to your answer in part c, suppose that the company actually did observe more than 20 damaged grapefruit in a sample of 50. What might be concluded about the USDA's 25% estimate? Discuss.

5.115 The Bayhill City Council claims that 40% of the parking spaces downtown are used by employees of the downtown businesses. A sample of 5 parking spaces was selected from the 4,000 parking spaces.

a. Suppose the sample results showed 4 or more of the spaces were filled by employees. What would you conclude about the council's claim? Discuss.

b. What is the expected number of employees' cars in a sample of 5 parking spaces?

5.116 The Milky-Way Dairy buys milk bottles in lots of 5,000. According to the supplier, 80% of the bottles will be acceptable for use without any additional cleaning by the company's "scrubber." Assuming that the binomial distribution applies:

a. In a sample of 200 bottles, what is the expected number of bottles that will need to be cleaned by the scrubber?

b. In a sample of 100 bottles, what is the expected number of bottles that will not require additional cleaning by the Milky-Way Dairy?

c. Suppose it costs the Milky-Way Dairy $0.03 per bottle to use the scrubber. What is the expected cost of scrubbing for a sample of 300 bottles?

d. Compute the standard deviation of the probability distribution for a sample of 100 bottles, when x_1 is defined as the number of bottles that require scrubbing. Assume that the estimate of 80%-acceptable clean bottles applies.

5.117 The manager at the Town Square Movie Theater has determined that in the 15 minutes prior to the start of a movie, the number of customers who go to the concession stand to make a purchase averages 45 and the distribution for the number of arrivals is Poisson distributed. Based upon this information, determine each of the following:

a. Find the probability that the time between arrivals for any two customers is less than 20 seconds.

b. Determine the probability that the time between two customers arriving is more than 30 seconds.

c. What is the probability that the time between arrivals for two customers is between 30 seconds and 1 minute?

5.118 One of the production steps for a company that makes equipment for the semiconductor industry involves polishing. The polishing machine requires a polishing disk. The amount of time this disk lasts varies from disk to disk. Once a disk wears to a certain point, it must be replaced with a new one. Experience indicates that the time to failure is exponentially distributed, with a mean of 4.5 hours. The operators are required to log the amount of time each disk lasts. One operator reported the following times for her machine on her 12-hour shift: 2.4 hours, 1.5 hours, 2.8 hours, and 3.1 hours. (Note, the fifth disk was still okay when she went off shift after 12 hours.)

a. What is the probability that an operator would find four successive disks with time to failure under 3.1 hours?

b. Based on your answers to part a, comment on whether you think there is evidence to suggest that the disks currently being used are not meeting the 4.5-hour mean life.

5.119 Referring to semiconductor equipment company of Exercise 5.118, suppose the shift supervisor is concerned that this operator is changing polishing disks too quickly. Explain how the probabilities computed in Exercise 5.118 could be used to help analyze the situation and reach a conclusion about the operator. How might the supervisor determine whether the problem was with the disks or with the operator? Discuss.

5.120 The Askot Publishing Company publishes paperback romance novels. At the page-proof stage, it has been determined that spelling errors appear randomly and are independent of each other at an average rate of 1.3 errors per page ($\lambda = 1.3$). Suppose a proofreader has been hired to read a new book.

a. If the proofreader does a perfect job, what is the average number of errors he will find for each two pages read?

b. What is the variance of the number of errors per two pages? What is the standard deviation?

c. Suppose a proofreader has just finished four pages and has found no errors. What are some of the possible conclusions you might reach and why?

5.121 The Dade County Emergency Services dispatcher is trained to determine from the call received whether an emergency exists or whether the problem can be handled on a nonemergency basis. Past evidence indicates that 50% of calls are true emergencies.

a. If the binomial distribution applies, develop the probability distribution for a sample of 10, and graph the distribution in histogram form. Does the distribution appear to be symmetric? Discuss.

b. Referring to part a, suppose that the probability of a call being a true emergency is actually 70%. Develop the probability distribution, and graph the distribution in histogram form. Compare the distribution in part a with this one in terms of symmetry. Discuss.

5.122 A small private ambulance service in Oklahoma has determined that the time between emergency calls is exponentially distributed, with a mean of 41 minutes. When a unit goes on call, it is out of service for 60 minutes. If a unit is busy when an emergency call is received, the call is immediately routed to another service. The company is considering buying a second ambulance. However, before doing so, the owners are interested in determining the probability that a call will come in before the ambulance is back in service. Without knowing the costs involved in this situation, does this probability tend to support the need for a second ambulance? Discuss.

5.123 The Stevens Company in Seattle, Washington, recently conducted a study regarding customer satisfaction with its winter boots, which are marketed throughout the United States. A basic premise that the company has been operating under for the past several years is that 90% of its customers have been satisfied with the boots they purchased. However, H. B. Stevens, the company president, felt that a survey should be taken to see if this was, in fact, the case.

a. Assuming that the characteristics of the binomial distribution are satisfied, what is the probability of finding fewer than 90 satisfied customers in a sample of 100 if the company's assumption about consumer satisfaction is correct?

b. Assuming that the binomial distribution is applicable, what is the probability of finding more than 10 dissatisfied customers in a sample of 100 if the probability of any 1 customer being satisfied is 90%?

c. Suppose the sample reveals 78 satisfied customers. What is the probability of exactly 78 satisfied customers if the probability of a customer being satisfied is 90%?

5.124 The Cozine Corporation runs the land fill operation outside Little Rock, Arkansas. Each day, each of the company's trucks makes several trips from the city to the land fill. On each entry the truck is weighed. The data file *Cozine* contains a sample of 200 truck weights. Determine the mean and standard deviation for the garbage truck weights. Assuming that these sample values are representative of the population of all Cozine garbage trucks, and assuming that the distribution is normally distributed,

a. Determine the probability that a truck will arrive at the landfill weighing in excess of 46,000 pounds.

b. Compare the probability in part a to the proportion of trucks in the sample that weighed over 46,000 pounds. What does this imply to you?

c. Suppose the managers are concerned that trucks are returning to the landfill before they are fully loaded. If they have set a minimum weight of 38,000 pounds before a truck returns to the landfill, what is the probability that a truck will fail to meet the minimum standard?

5.125 The St. Maries plywood plant is part of the Potlatch Corporation's Northwest Division. The plywood superintendent organized a study of the diameters of trees that are being shipped to the mill. After collecting a large amount of data on diameters, he concluded that the distribution is approximately normally distributed, with a mean of 14.25 inches and a standard deviation of 2.92 inches. Because of the way plywood is made, there is a certain amount of waste on each log because the peeling process leaves a core that is approximately 3 inches thick. For this reason, he feels that any log that is less than 10 inches in diameter is not profitable for making plywood.

a. Based on the data he has collected, what is the probability that a log will be unprofitable?

b. An alternative is to peel the log and then sell the core as "peeler logs." These peeler logs are sold as fence posts and for various landscape projects. There is not as much profit in these peeler logs, however. The superintendent has determined that he can make a profit if a peeler log's diameter is not more than 32% of the diameter of the log. Using this additional information, calculate the proportion of logs that will be unprofitable.

5.126 Referring to the plywood plant discussed in the previous problem, suppose the manager of the plywood mill wants no more than a 3% chance that any log will be unprofitable (fewer than 10 inches in diameter). One way to get to this value is to have the tree cutters do a better job sorting the logs, to reduce the standard deviation. Assume that the mean diameter does not change.

a. What standard deviation would have to be achieved to meet the manager's requirements?

b. Answer part a, if the peeler logs defined in Exercise 5.125 are included.

CASE 5-A:

East Mercy Medical Center

Dorothy Jacobs recently was hired as assistant administrator of the East Mercy Medical Center. She is a new graduate of a well-regarded master's degree program in hospital administration and is expected to incorporate some advanced thinking into the apparently lax practices at East Mercy.

Hospitals have recently been under increasing pressure from both government and local sources because of escalating costs. Although members of the board of directors of East Mercy feel that cost considerations are secondary to quality care, its members also are sensitive to the increasing public pressure.

East Mercy is located in a rapidly growing area and is experiencing capacity limitations. In particular, according to staff personnel, the obstetrics, adult medical/surgical, and pediatric wards are "bursting at the seams." East Mercy is considering an extensive expansion program, including expansion of the obstetric, adult medical/surgical, and pediatric wards. The board has allocated a total of $400,000 for new beds in these three wards. Dorothy is currently trying to determine how many beds current demand levels justify for each ward and how many beds to add, given the $400,000 cost constraint.

Dorothy and her staff have computed statistics based on the current year's patient census data in each of the three wards. These figures are as follows:

WARD	AVERAGE NO. BEDS USED PER DAY	STANDARD DEVIATION
Obstetrics	24	6.1
Surgery	13	4.3
Pediatrics	19	4.7

Histogram plots of bed usage show a close approximation to a normal distribution for each department.

The present capacity of each ward is

Obstetrics:	30
Surgery:	20
Pediatrics:	24

The hospital's architects have given the following estimates for the cost of adding one bed and all necessary supporting equipment to each of the wards:

Obstetrics:	$20,000
Surgery:	$26,000
Pediatrics:	$15,500

It is possible for a ward to exceed its capacity, but according to state guidelines, this should not occur more than 5% of the time.

Dorothy is in the process of preparing a report to the administrator showing how many beds are to be added to each of the three wards.

CASE 5-B:

Rutledge Collections

Bob and Lisa Rutledge have operated a small collection company in New Hampshire for 14 years. Throughout this time, they have worked as agents for various companies in the area doing debt collection work. For example, they currently are under contract with Dalton Chevrolet to collect past due accounts for Dalton's service department. As with most of their contracts, Rutledge gets a percentage of all money collected. This has worked well over the years, and the Rutledges have earned a decent income.

However, Bob and Lisa are now facing a major decision that involves significant risk and significant reward, as well. The Bell Home Furnishings Company in Vermont recently declared bankruptcy. At the time, Bell had more than 8,000 receivable accounts that had balances that were more than 90 days late. This delay in collecting payments from so many customers put a cash flow strain on the company, causing their lenders to call due Bell's short-term loans.

The bankruptcy judge handling the case has ordered the delinquent accounts to be sold. Bob and Lisa have the opportunity to purchase these accounts at a fraction of their face value. If they do, then any money they collect will be theirs. Bob has figured that if they can collect on 30% or more of the accounts, they will make a sizable profit. However, if the collection rate is 20% or less, they will be in big trouble themselves. The judge has agreed to allow the Rutledges the opportunity to test their collection process on a random sample of 50 of Bell's accounts. Bob and Lisa agree that if they are able to collect 15 or more, they will take the deal. If they are successful on 14 or fewer, they will walk away from the opportunity.

However, they are both uneasy about this plan. If they would actually be successful in collecting on 30% or more of the accounts, they don't want to miss out. On the other hand, if the collection rate is really as low as 20%, they don't want the deal. Bob wonders how effective the proposed sampling plan might be. He decides to make a call to the local university to see if he can get some advice.

CASE 5-C:

American Oil Company

Chad Williams, field geologist for the American Oil Company, settled into his first-class seat on the Sun-Air flight between Los Angeles and Oakland, California. Earlier that afternoon, he had attended a meeting with the design engineering group at the Los Angeles New Product Division. He was now on his way to the home office in Oakland. He was looking forward to the one-hour flight because it would give him a chance to reflect on a problem that surfaced during the meeting. It would also give him a chance to think about the exciting opportunities that lay ahead in Australia.

Chad works with a small group of highly trained people at American Oil who literally walk the earth looking for new sources of oil. They make use of the latest in electronic equipment to take a wide range of measurements from many thousands of feet below the earth's surface. It is one of these electronic machines that is the source of Chad's current problem. Engineers in Los Angeles have designed a sophisticated enhancement that will greatly improve the equipment's ability to detect oil. The enhancement requires 800

capacitors, which must operate within ± 0.50 microns from the specified standard of 12 microns.

The problem is that the supplier can provide capacitors that operate according to a normal distribution, with a mean of 12 microns and a standard deviation of 1 micron. Thus, Chad knows that not all capacitors will meet the specifications required by the new piece of exploration equipment. This will mean that in order to have at least 800 usable capacitors, American Oil will have to order more than 800 from the supplier. However, these items are very expensive, so he wants to order as few as possible to meet their needs. At the meeting, the group agreed that they wanted a 98% chance that any order of capacitors would contain the sufficient number of usable items. If the project is to remain on schedule, Chad must place the order by tomorrow. He wants the new equipment ready to go by the time he leaves for an exploration trip in Australia. As he reclined in his seat, sipping a cool lemonade, he wondered whether a basic statistical technique could be used to help determine how many capacitors to order.

CASE 5-D:

Boise Cascade Corporation

At the Boise Cascade Corporation, lumber mill logs arrive by truck and are scaled (measured to determine the number of board feet) before they are dumped into a log pond. Figure 5-22 illustrates the basic flow. The mill manager must determine how many scale stations to have open during various times of the day. If he has too many stations open, the scalers will have excessive idle time and the cost of scaling will be unnecessarily high. On the other hand, if too few scale stations are open, some log trucks will have to wait.

The manager has studied the truck arrival patterns and has determined that during the first open hour (7:00–8:00 A.M.), the trucks randomly arrive at 12 per hour on average. Each scale sta-

tion can scale 6 trucks per hour (10 minutes each). If the manager knew how many trucks would arrive during the hour, he would know how many scale stations to have open.

0 to 6 trucks:	open 1 scale station
7 to 12 trucks:	open 2 scale stations
etc.	

However, the number of trucks is a random variable and is uncertain. Your task is to provide guidance to the decision.

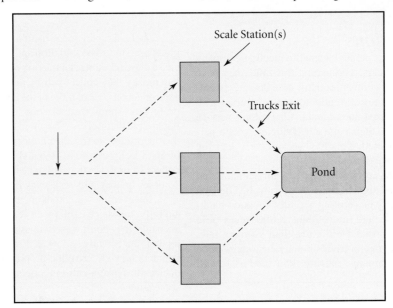

FIGURE 5-22

Truck Flow for Boise Cascade Mill Example

General References

1. Albright, Christian S., Wayne L. Winston, and Christopher Zappe, *Data Analysis and Decision Making with Microsoft Excel* (Pacific Grove, CA: Duxbury, 1999).
2. Dodge, Mark, and Craig Stinson, *Running Microsoft Excel 2000* (Redmond, WA: Microsoft Press, 1999).
3. Hogg, R. V., and Elliot A. Tanis, *Probability and Statistical Inference*, 5th ed. (Upper Saddle River, NJ: Prentice Hall, 1997).
4. Marx, Moriss L., and Richard J. Larsen, *Mathematical Statistics and Its Applications*, 3rd ed. (Upper Saddle River, NJ: Prentice Hall, 2000).
5. *Microsoft Excel 2000* (Redmond, WA: Microsoft Corp., 1999).
6. *Minitab for Windows Version 13* (State College, PA: Minitab, 2000).
7. Siegel, Andrew F., *Practical Business Statistics*, 4th ed. (Burr Ridge, IL: Irwin, 2000).

CHAPTER 6

Introduction to Sampling Distributions

CHAPTER OUTCOMES

After studying the material in Chapter 6, you should be able to:

- Understand the concept of sampling error.
- Determine the mean and standard deviation for the sampling distribution of $\bar{x}$.
- Determine the mean and standard deviation for the sampling distribution of the sample proportion, $\bar{p}$.
- Understand the importance of the Central Limit Theorem.
- Apply sampling distributions for both $\bar{x}$ and $\bar{p}$.

WHY YOU NEED TO KNOW

A marketing research executive receives a summary report from her analyst that indicates the mean dollars spent by adults on winter-sports recreation activities per year is $302.45. As she reads further, she learns that the mean value is based on a statistical sample of 540 adults in Vermont. The $302.45 is a *statistic*, not a *parameter*, because it is based on a sample rather than an entire population. If you were this marketing executive, you might have several questions:

- Is the actual population mean equal to $302.45?
- If the population mean is not $302.45, how close is $302.45 to the true population mean?
- Is a sample of 540 taken from a population of several million sufficient to provide a "good" estimate of the population mean?

A major manufacturer of personal computers selects a random sample of computers boxed and ready for shipment to customers. These computers are unboxed and inspected to see whether what is in the box matches exactly what the customer order specifies. This past week, 233 systems were sampled and 18 had one or more discrepancies. This is a 7.7% defect rate. Should the quality engineer conclude that exactly 7.7% of the 13,300 computers made this week reached the customer with one or more order discrepancies? Is the actual percentage higher or lower than 7.7%, and by how much? Should the quality engineer request that more computers be sampled?

The questions facing the marketing executive and the quality engineer are common to those faced by people in business everywhere. If you haven't already, you will almost assuredly find yourself in a similar situation many times in the future. To help answer these questions, you need to have an understanding of *sampling distributions*. Whenever decisions are based on samples rather than an entire population, questions about the sample results exist. Anytime we sample from a population, there are many, many possible samples that could have been selected. Each sample will contain different items. Because of this, the sample means for each possible sample can be different, or the sample percentages can be different. The sampling distribution describes the distribution of possible sample outcomes. If you know what this distribution looks like, it will help you understand the specific result you have obtained from the one sample you have selected.

This chapter introduces you to sampling error and sampling distributions and discusses how you can use this knowledge to help answer the questions facing the marketing executive and the quality engineer. The information presented here provides an essential building block to understanding statistical estimation and hypothesis testing, which will be covered in upcoming chapters.

6-1   SAMPLING ERROR: WHAT IT IS AND WHY IT HAPPENS

As discussed in previous chapters, you will encounter many situations in business in which a sample will be taken from a population and you will be required to analyze the sample data. Chapter 1 introduced several different statistical sampling techniques. Chapters 2 and 3 introduced a variety of descriptive tools that are useful in analyzing sample data. The objective of sampling is to gather data that mirror a population. Then when analysis is performed on the sample data, the results will be as though we had worked with all the population data. However, we very rarely know if our objective has been achieved. To be able to determine if a sample mirrors the population, we must know the entire population, and if that is the case, we do not need to sample. We can just census the population. Because we do not know the population, we require that our sample be random so that bias is not introduced into an already difficult task.

CALCULATING SAMPLING ERROR

Regardless of how careful we are in using proper sampling methods, the sample may not be a perfect reflection of the population. For example a *statistic* such as $\bar{p}$ might be computed for sample data. Unless the sample is a mirror image of the population, the statistic will likely not equal the *parameter*, μ. In this case, the difference between the sample mean and the population mean is called **sampling error**. In the case in which we are interested in the mean value, the sampling error is computed using Equation 6-1.

Sampling Error

The difference between a value computed from a sample (a statistic) and the corresponding value computed from the population (a parameter).

Sampling Error of the Sample Mean

$$\text{Sampling Error} = \bar{x} - \mu \qquad \textbf{6-1}$$

where:

$\bar{x}$ = sample mean
μ = population mean

Kornfield, Harrington & Sandmeyer—The architectural firm of Kornfield, Harrington & Sandmeyer (KH&S) has designed 12 shopping centers. Table 6-1 shows a list of the 12 projects and the total square footage of each project.

Because these 12 projects are all the shopping centers the company has worked on, the square-feet area for all 12 projects, shown in Table 6-1, is a population. Equation 6-2 is used to compute the mean square feet in the population of projects.

Population Mean

$$\mu = \frac{\sum x}{N} \qquad \textbf{6-2}$$

where:

μ = Population mean
x = Values in the population
N = Population size

The mean square feet for the 12 shopping centers is

$$\mu = \frac{114{,}560 + 202{,}300 + \cdots + 125{,}200 + 156{,}900}{12}$$

$$\mu = 158{,}972 \text{ square feet}$$

The average-size shopping center designed by the firm is 158,972 square feet. This value is a **parameter**. No matter how many times we compute the value, assuming no arithmetic mistakes, we will get the same value for the population mean.

Parameter

A measure computed from the entire population.

KH&S is a finalist to be the architect for a new shopping center in Orlando, Florida. The developers who will hire the architect plan to select a **simple random sample** of $n = 5$ projects from

TABLE 6-1

Square Feet for Shopping Center Projects

PROJECT	SQUARE FEET
1	114,560
2	202,300
3	78,600
4	156,700
5	134,600
6	88,200
7	177,300
8	155,300
9	214,200
10	303,800
11	125,200
12	156,900

those that the finalists have completed. The developers will travel to these shopping centers and examine the designs and interview owners and shoppers. (You may want to refer to Chapter 1 to review the material on simple random samples.)

Simple Random Sample

A sample selected in such a manner that each possible sample of a given size has an equal chance of being selected.

Refer to the shopping center data in Table 6-1, and suppose the developers randomly select the following five KH&S projects from the population:

Project	Square Feet
5	134,600
4	156,700
1	114,560
8	155,300
9	214,200

Key in the selection process is the finalists' past performance on large projects, so the developers might be interested in the mean size of the shopping centers that the finalists have designed. Equation 6-3 is used to compute the sample mean.

Sample Mean

$$\bar{x} = \frac{\sum x}{n}$$

6-3

where:

$\bar{x}$ = Sample mean
x = Sample value selected from the population
n = Sample size

The sample mean is:

$$\bar{x} = \frac{134,600 + 156,700 + 114,560 + 155,300 + 214,200}{5} = \frac{775,360}{5} = 155,072$$

The average number of square feet in the sample of five shopping centers selected by the developers is 155,072. This value is a *statistic* based on the sample.

Recall the mean for the population:

$$\mu = 158,972 \text{ square feet}$$

The sample mean is

$$\bar{x} = 155,072 \text{ square feet}$$

As you can see, the sample mean does not equal the population mean. This difference is called *sampling error*. Using Equation 6-1, we compute the sampling error as follows.

$$\text{Sampling error} = \bar{x} - \mu$$
$$= 155,072 - 158,972 = -3,900 \text{ square feet}$$

The sample mean for the sample of $n = 5$ shopping centers is 3,900 square feet less than the population mean. Regardless of how carefully you construct your sampling plan, you can expect to see sampling error. A sample will almost never be a perfect mirror image of its population. The sample value and the population value will most likely be different.

Suppose the developer who selected the random sample throws these five projects back into the stack and selects a second sample of five as follows:

Project	Square Feet
9	214,200
6	88,200
5	134,600
12	156,900
10	303,800

The mean for this sample is

$$\bar{x} = \frac{214,200 + 88,200 + 134,600 + 156,900 + 303,800}{5} = \frac{897,700}{5} = 179,540 \text{ square feet}$$

This time, the sample mean is higher than the population mean. This time the sampling error is

$$\bar{x} - \mu = 179,540 - 158,972 = 20,568 \text{ square feet}$$

This illustrates some useful fundamental concepts.

- The size of the sampling error depends on which sample is selected.
- The sampling error may be positive or negative.
- There is potentially a different $\bar{x}$ for each possible sample.

If the developers wanted to use the sample mean to estimate the population mean, in one case they would be 3,900 square feet too low and in the other, they would be 20,568 square feet too high.

EXAMPLE 6-1: COMPUTING THE SAMPLING ERROR

Jim's Appliances Jim's Appliances is a discount appliance dealer that specializes in kitchen appliances. On Saturday morning, among the store's inventory were 10 electric ranges. The retail prices, in dollars, on these 10 ranges were:

$479	$569	$599	$649	$649	$699	$699	$749	$799	$799

Suppose the manager wished to do a quick analysis of the electric range inventory and randomly sampled $n = 4$ ranges. The ranges selected had retail prices of:

$569	$649	$799	$799

Assuming that the manager was hoping that the sampled ranges would be representative of the population, the sampling error can be computed using the following steps:

Step 1: Determine the population mean using Equation 6-2:

$$\mu = \frac{\Sigma x}{N} = \frac{479 + 569 + 599 + \cdots + 799 + 799}{10} = \frac{6,690}{10} = \$669$$

Step 2: Compute the sample mean using Equation 6-3:

$$\bar{x} = \frac{\Sigma x}{n} = \frac{569 + 649 + 799 + 799}{4} = \frac{2,816}{4} = \$704$$

Step 3: Compute the sampling error using Equation 6-1:

$$\bar{x} - \mu = 704 - 669 = \$35$$

This sample of four has a sampling error of $35. The sample of electric ranges has a slightly larger mean than the population as a whole.

THE ROLE OF SAMPLE SIZE IN SAMPLING ERROR

Kornfield, Harrington & Sandmeyer (continued)—Previously, we selected potential samples of size 5 and computed the resulting sampling error. There are actually 792 possible samples of size 5 taken from 12 projects. This value is found using the counting rule for combinations, which was discussed in Chapter 5.[1]

[1]The number of combinations of x items from a sample of n is $\frac{n!}{(x)!\,(n-x)!}$.

In actual situations, only one sample is selected, and the decision maker uses the sample value to estimate the population value. A "small" sampling error may be acceptable. However, if the sampling error is "too large," conclusions about the population value could be misleading.

We can look at the extremes on either end to evaluate the potential for extreme sampling error. The population of square feet for the 12 projects is:

Project	Square Feet
1	114,560
2	202,300
3	78,600
4	156,700
5	134,600
6	88,200
7	177,300
8	155,300
9	214,200
10	303,800
11	125,200
12	156,900

Suppose, by chance, the developers ended up with the five smallest shopping centers in their sample. These would be

Project	Square Feet
3	78,600
6	88,200
1	114,560
11	125,200
5	134,600

The mean of this sample is

$$\bar{x} = 108,232 \text{ square feet}$$

Of all the possible samples, this one provides the smallest sample mean. The sampling error is

$$\bar{x} - \mu = 108,232 - 158,972 = -50,740 \text{ square feet}$$

Thus, if this sample had been selected, the sampling error would be $-50,740$ square feet.

On the other extreme, suppose the sample contained the five largest shopping centers, as follows.

Project	Square Feet
10	303,800
9	214,200
2	202,300
7	177,300
12	156,900

The mean for this sample is $\bar{x} = 210,900$.

This is the largest possible sample mean from all the possible samples. The sampling error in this case would be

$$\bar{x} - \mu = 210,900 - 158,972 = 51,928 \text{ square feet}$$

The potential for extreme sampling error ranges from

$$-50,740 \text{ to } +51,928 \text{ square feet}$$

TABLE 6-2	SMALLEST SHOPPING CENTERS		LARGEST SHOPPING CENTERS	
Shopping Center Example for $n = 3$ **(Extreme Samples)**	Project	Square Feet	Project	Square Feet
	3	78,600	10	303,800
	6	88,200	9	214,200
	1	114,560	2	202,300

$\bar{x} = 93,786.67$ sq. feet
Sampling Error:
$93,786.67 - 158,972 = -65,185.33$ square feet

$\bar{x} = 240,100$ sq. feet
Sampling Error:
$240,100 - 158,972 = 81,128$ square feet

The remaining possible samples will provide sampling error between these limits.

What happens if the sample size is larger or smaller? Suppose the developers scale back their sample size to $n = 3$ shopping centers. Table 6-2 shows the extremes. By reducing the sample size from 5 to 3, the range of potential sampling error has increased from

$$(-50,740 \cdots +51,928 \text{ square feet})$$

to

$$(-65,185.33 \cdots +81,128 \text{ square feet})$$

This illustrates that the potential for extreme sampling error is greater when smaller-sized samples are used.

Although larger sample sizes reduce the potential for extreme sampling error, there is no guarantee that the larger sample size will always give the smallest sampling error. For example, Table 6-3 shows two further applications of the shopping center data. As illustrated, the sample of 3 had a sampling error of $-2,672$ square feet, whereas the sample of 5 had a sampling error of 16,540 square feet. In this case, the smaller sample was "better" than the larger sample. However, in Section 6-2, you will learn that, on average, the sampling error produced by large samples will be less than the sampling error from small samples.

TABLE 6-3	$n = 5$		$n = 3$	
Shopping Center Example with Different Sample Sizes	Project	Square Feet	Project	Square Feet
	4	156,700	12	156,900
	1	114,560	8	155,300
	7	177,300	4	156,700
	11	125,200		
	10	303,800		

$\bar{x} = 175,512$ sq. feet
Sampling Error:
$175,512 - 158,972 = 16,540$ square feet

$\bar{x} = 156,300$ sq.feet
Sampling Error:
$156,300 - 158,972 = -2,672$ square feet

6-1: EXERCISES

Skill Development

6.1 Consider the following data to be a population of $N = 20$ values.

| 5 | 3 | 2 | 6 | 6 | 7 | 3 | 3 | 6 | 7 |
| 7 | 9 | 7 | 5 | 3 | 12 | 6 | 10 | 7 | 2 |

a. Compute the population mean.
b. A random sample of $n = 6$ produced the following numbers: 6, 12, 10, 3, 2, 2. Find the sample mean and determine the sampling error for this sample.

c. Find the range of extreme sampling error for a sample of 6. (Hint: Find the lowest possible sample mean and highest possible sample mean.)

6.2 Consider the following values to represent a population

| 29 | 33 | 10 | 20 | 50 | 10 | 10 | 30 | 19 | 40 | 20 |
| 11 | 40 | 60 | 20 | 20 | 13 | 20 | 20 | 19 | 30 | 20 |

a. If a random sample of $n = 8$ items includes the following, compute the sampling error.

| 33 | 20 | 20 | 11 | 19 | 10 | 20 | 29 |

b. Determine the range for the possible sampling error when a sample of size $n = 8$ is used. (Hint: find the sampling error for the eight smallest values and the sampling error for the eight largest values.)

c. Refer to part b and determine the range of potential sampling error if the sample size is reduced to 5. Discuss the impact of sample size on the potential for extreme sampling error.

6.3   Consider the following values to represent a population:

129	330	100	200	150	105	100	130	190	400	120

a. If a random sample of $n = 3$ items includes the following, compute the sampling error.

150	100	400

b. Determine the range for the possible sampling error when a sample of size $n = 3$ is used. (Hint: find the sampling error for the three smallest values and the sampling error for the three largest values.)

c. Refer to part b and determine the range of potential sampling error if the sample size is increased to 5. Discuss the impact of sample size on the potential for extreme sampling error.

6.4   A population is known to have a mean value of 112,000. If a random sample of 6 items had the following values, what is the sampling error for this sample?

105,000	112,900	104,600	120,700	115,000	106,000

Business Applications

6.5   The Patterson Real Estate Company has 20 listings for homes in Fresno, California. The number of days that each house has been on the market without selling is shown as follows:

26	45	16	77	33	50	19	23	55	107
88	15	7	19	30	60	80	66	31	17

a. Considering these 20 values to be the population of interest, what is the mean of the population?

b. The company is making a sales brochure and wishes to feature five homes selected at random from the list. The number of days the five sampled homes have been on the market is:

77	60	15	31	23

If these five houses were used to estimate the mean for all 20, what would the sampling error be?

c. What is the range of possible sampling error if five homes are selected at random from the population?

6.6   Holland Management Services manages apartment complexes in Tucson, Arizona. They currently have 30 units available for rent. The monthly rental prices, in dollars, for this population of 30 units are

455	690	450	495	550	780	800	395	500	405
675	550	490	495	700	995	650	550	400	750
600	780	650	905	415	600	600	780	575	750

a. What is the range of possible sampling error if a random sample of size $n = 6$ is selected from the population?

b. What is the range of possible sampling error if a random sample of size $n = 10$ is selected? Compare your answers to parts a and b and explain why the difference exists.

6.7   The owner of Miller's Union 76 in Rochester, New York, has tracked gasoline sales for several years and is confident that the true mean sale is 16.9 gallons. Assuming that this is the population mean, if a random sample of 10 fill-ups is collected, what is the sampling error if the gallons per fill are

13.3	19.8	22.6	15.0	19.3	9.7	17.5	22.4	18.0	13.0

6.8   A major airline has stated that the mean ticket price for a round-trip flight between Dallas, Texas, and Atlanta, Georgia, is $337. Suppose a travel agency has recently selected a random sample of seven round-trip tickets for this trip with the following prices recorded in dollars.

176	459	379	588	467	802	198

Given this sample, how much sampling error exists? Discuss whether you would expect more or less sampling error if the sample size were increased to 20 tickets.

Advanced Business Applications

6.9   The State Transportation Department has conducted a study of drivers to determine whether they were carrying proof of liability insurance in their cars. The data are located in the CD-ROM file called *Liabins*. Treat the data in this file as a population. The State Insurance Department is interested in the ages of the participants in the study.

A simple random sample of 10 drivers was selected from the population. It produced the following ages: 18, 18, 68, 58, 42, 22, 55, 61, 31, 36.

Compute the sample mean. Discuss how this value compares with the population mean.

6.10   The Golden Calendar Company has a population of 16 customers. These customers are brokers who sell the calendars to stores and catalogs. The following data reflect the number of calendars sold to each of the 16 customers last year. These data are also contained in the CD-ROM file called *Golden*.

41,591	48,600	48,348	60,977
26,226	51,269	21,519	20,124
36,526	51,836	40,444	43,572
47,091	31,444	39,580	67,452

a. Compute the population mean and standard deviation.

b. Suppose that Golden managers selected four customers to take part in a special promotional test. The test is designed to increase the number of calendars that each customer will purchase next year. The simple random sample of four was obtained from this population. The data were

40,444	21,519	67,452	47,091

1. Calculate the sample mean number of calendars sold.
2. How much sampling error is present in this sample?

c. A second simple random sample of 4 was obtained from the population of 16 customers. The data obtained were

36,526	51,836	20,124	43,572

1. Determine the sampling error for this sample.
2. Explain why sampling error occurs and why the sampling error in part c is different than the sampling error in part b.
3. Discuss the ramifications of sampling error. What problems might it cause in this case, in

which the promotion is intended to increase calendar sales next year?

d. Take a sample of size $n = 8$ from the original population.
1. Compute the sampling error.
2. Compare the sampling error for this sample with those for the two samples of size $n = 4$.
3. Without regard to the results you obtained here, explain why it is possible for a smaller sample to have a smaller sampling error than a larger sample from the same population.

(Hint: In Excel, use the Sampling feature under Tools—Data Analysis. In Minitab, use the Calc—Random Data—Sample from Columns options.)

6-2 SAMPLING DISTRIBUTION OF THE MEAN

Section 6-1 introduced the fundamental concepts of sampling error. A sample selected from a population will not perfectly match the population. This means that the sample value (statistic) likely will not equal the population value (parameter). If this difference arises because the sample is not a perfect representation of the population, it is called sampling error.

In business applications, decision makers select a single sample from a population. They compute the sample value and use it to make decisions about the entire population. For example, the Nielsen Company takes a single sample of television viewers to determine the percentage who are watching a particular program during a particular week. Of course, the sample selected is only one of many possible samples that could have been selected from the same population. The sampling error will differ depending on which sample is selected. If, in theory, you were to select all possible random samples of a given size and compute the sample means for each one, these means would vary above and below the true population mean. If we graphed these values as a frequency distribution, the graph would be the **sampling distribution**.

Sampling Distribution

A distribution of the possible values of a statistic for a given-size random sample selected from a population.

In this section, we introduce the basic concepts of sampling distributions. We will use an Excel tool to select repeated samples from the same population for demonstration purposes only. The same thing can be done using Minitab.

SIMULATING THE SAMPLING DISTRIBUTION FOR $\bar{x}$

Excel and Minitab Tutorial

Aims Investment Company—Aims Investment Company handles employee retirement funds, primarily for small companies. The CD-ROM file called *AIMS* contains data on the number of mutual funds in each client's portfolio. The file contains data for all 200 Aims customers, so it is a population. Figure 6-1 shows a graph of the population distribution and important numerical measures for the population.

The mean number of mutual funds in a portfolio is 2.505 funds. The standard deviation is 1.507 funds. The graph in Figure 6-1 indicates that the population is spread between 0 and 6 funds, with more customers owning 2 funds than any other number.

Suppose the controller at Aims plans to select a random sample of 10 accounts. In Excel, we can use the **Sampling** tool to generate the random sample.[2] Figure 6-2 shows the resulting sample of the

[2]The same thing can be achieved in Minitab by using the **Sample from Columns** option under **Calc–Random Data** options.

FIGURE 6-1

**Distribution of Mutual
Funds for the Aims
Investment Company**

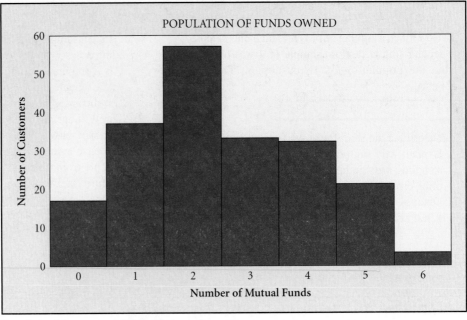

Population Mean = μ = 2.505 funds owned
Population Standard Deviation = σ = 1.507 funds owned

number of mutual funds owned for a random sample of 10 clients. The sample mean of 1.8 is also shown. To illustrate the sampling distribution, we repeat this process 500 times, generating 500 different samples of size 10. After each sample, we compute the sample mean. Figure 6-3 shows the frequency histogram for these sample means. Note that the horizontal axis represents the $\bar{x}$ values. The graph in Figure 6-3 is not a complete sampling distribution because it is based on only 500 samples out of the many possible samples that could be selected. However, this simulation gives us an idea of what the sampling distribution looks like.

Look again at the population distribution in Figure 6-1 and compare it with the shape of the frequency distribution in Figure 6-3. Although the population distribution is somewhat skewed, the sampling distribution is taking the shape of a bell curve, or normal distribution.

Note also that the population mean for the 200 individual customers in the population is 2.505 mutual funds. If we average the 500 sample means in Figure 6-3, we get 2.41. This value is the *mean of the sample means*. It is reasonably close to the population mean. Although beyond the scope of this text, it can be shown that the average of all possible sample means will equal the population mean. When the average of all possible values of the sample statistic equals a parameter, we call that statistic an *unbiased estimator* of the parameter.

FIGURE 6-2

**Excel Output for the Aims
Investment Company
First Sample Size *n* = 10**

	Cutomer Number	Number of Mutual Fund Accounts		Sample n = 10
1				
2	19100	4		2
3	5034	4		1
4	29824	1		3
5	44955	0		1
6	44230	5		0
7	47923	5		4
8	725	2		2
9	20371	3		1
10	43162	4		1
11	6929	1		3
12	12252	4		
13	2274	2	Mean =	1.8
14	1619	0		

Excel Instructions:
1. Open file: AIMS.xls
2. Click on the Tools tab.
3. Select the Data Analysis option.
4. Select Sampling.
5. Indicate the population data range and sample size.

Minitab Instructions (for similar results):
1. Open file: AIMS.MTW.
2. Choose **Calc > Random Data > Sample From Columns**.
3. In **Sample**, enter the sample size.
4. In box following **row from column(s)**, enter data column: *Number of Mutual Fund Accounts*.
5. In **Store Samples in**, enter sample's storage column.
6. Click **OK**.
7. Choose **Calc > Calculator**.
8. In **Store Result in Variable** enter column to store mean.
9. Choose **Mean** from **Functions**. Expression: Mean (Sample Column).
10. Repeat steps 3–10 multiple times to form sampling distribution.

FIGURE 6-3

Aims Investment Company,
Histogram of Sample
Means

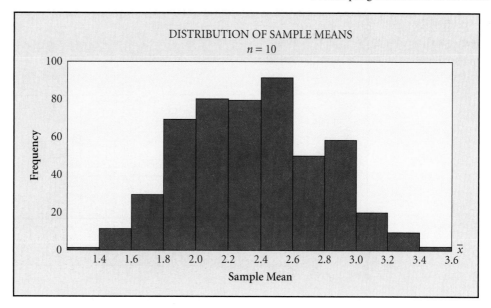

FIGURE 6-3

Aims Investment Company, Histogram of Sample Means

Unbiased Estimator

A characteristic of certain statistics in which the average of all possible values of the sample statistic equals a parameter.

Also, the population standard deviation is 1.507 mutual funds. This measures the variation in the number of mutual funds between individual customers. When we compute the standard deviation of the 500 sample means, we get 0.421, which is considerably smaller than the population standard deviation. As we will show shortly, this will always be the case.

Now suppose we increased the sample size from $n = 10$ to $n = 20$ and selected 500 different samples. Figure 6-4 shows the distribution of the 500 different sample means.

The distribution in Figure 6-4 is even more bell-shaped than what we observed in Figure 6-3. As sample size increases, the distribution of sample means will become shaped more like a normal distribution. The average sample mean for these 500 samples is 2.53, and the standard deviation of the different sample means is 0.376.

Keep in mind the distributions shown in Figures 6-3 and 6-4 are not true sampling distributions because they are developed from only 500 sample means. A true sampling distribution would be developed from the sample means of all possible random samples of a given size that could be selected from the population.

FIGURE 6-4

Aims Investment Company, Histogram of Sample Means

FIGURE 6-5

Simulated Normal Population Distribution

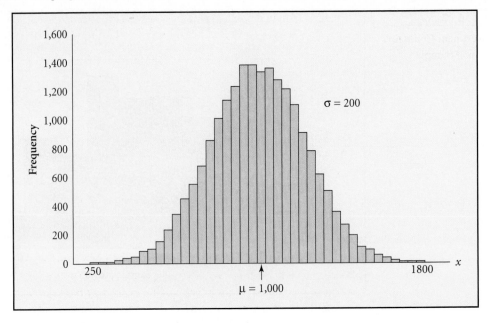

Sampling from Normal Populations

We can again use Excel or Minitab to illustrate some additional sampling distribution concepts by first generating a normally distributed population.[3] Recall from Chapter 5 that many populations appear to closely approximate a normal distribution, so you may find yourself sampling from such a distribution.

Figure 6-5 shows a simulated population that is normally distributed with a mean equal to 1,000 and a standard deviation equal to 200. The data range is from 250 to 1,800.

Next, we simulate the selection of 2,000 samples of size 10 from the population and compute the sample mean for each sample. These sample means can then be graphed as a frequency histogram, as shown in Figure 6-6. This histogram represents the sampling distribution. It, too, is approximately normally distributed.

FIGURE 6-6

Approximated Sampling Distribution ($n = 10$)

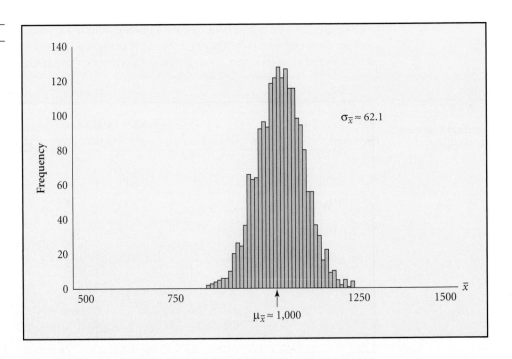

[3]The same task can be performed in Minitab using the **Calc–Random Data** option. However, you will have to generate each sample individually, which will take time.

We next compute the average of the 2,000 sample means and use it to approximate $\mu_{\bar{x}}$ as follows.

$$\mu_{\bar{x}} \approx \frac{\sum \bar{x}}{2,000} = \frac{2,000,178}{2,000} \approx 1,000$$

The mean of these sample means is approximately 1,000. This is the same as the population mean. We also approximate the standard deviation of the sample means as follows.

$$\sigma_{\bar{x}} \approx \sqrt{\frac{\sum(\bar{x} - \mu_{\bar{x}})^2}{2,000}} = 62.1$$

We see the standard deviation of the sample means is 62.1. This is much smaller than the population standard deviation, which is 200. The largest sample mean was just more than 1,212, and the smallest sample mean was just less than 775. Recall, however, that the population ranged from 250 to 1,800. The variation in the sample means always will be less than the variation for the population as a whole.

We have used this simulated example to illustrate how a sampling distribution is developed. However, in actual practice we only select one sample from the population, and we know this sample is subject to sampling error. The sample mean may be either larger or smaller than the population mean. Currently, we are assuming the population is normally distributed. Because the population forms a continuous distribution and has an uncountable number of values, we could not possibly obtain all possible samples from this population. As a result, we would be unable to construct the true sampling distribution. Figure 6-6 is an approximation based on 2,000 samples. Fortunately, an important statistical theorem exists that overcomes this obstacle: **Theorem 6-1**.

Theorem 6-1

If a population is normally distributed, with mean μ and a standard deviation σ, the sampling distribution of the sample mean $\bar{x}$ is also normally distributed with a mean equal to the population mean ($\mu_{\bar{x}} = \mu$) and a standard deviation equal to the population standard deviation divided by the square root of the sample size $\left(\sigma_{\bar{x}} = \frac{\sigma}{\sqrt{n}}\right)$.

In Theorem 6-1, the quantity $\sigma_{\bar{x}} = \frac{\sigma}{\sqrt{n}}$ is the *standard deviation of the sampling distribution*. Another term that is given to this is the *standard error of $\bar{x}$*, because it is the measure of the standard deviation of the potential sampling error.

Suppose we again use the simulated population shown in Figure 6-5, with $\mu = 1,000$ and $\sigma = 200$. We are interested in seeing what the sampling distribution will look like for different size samples. For example, if the sample size is 10 (as we simulated earlier), Theorem 6-1 indicates that the sampling distribution will have a mean equal to 1,000 and a standard deviation equal to

$$\sigma_{\bar{x}} = \frac{200}{\sqrt{10}} = 63.2$$

For the 2,000 random samples, the mean, $\bar{x}$, is almost exactly 1,000, and the standard deviation of the $\bar{x}$ values is 62.1, close to the theoretical value of 63.2.

If we were to take a random sample of 5, Theorem 6-1 indicates the sampling distribution would be normal, with a mean equal to 1,000 and a standard deviation equal to

$$\sigma_{\bar{x}} = \frac{200}{\sqrt{5}} = 89.4$$

For a sample size of 20, the sampling distribution will be centered at $\mu_{\bar{x}} = 1,000$, with a standard deviation equal to

$$\sigma_{\bar{x}} = \frac{200}{\sqrt{20}} = 44.7$$

FIGURE 6-7

Theorem 6-1 Examples

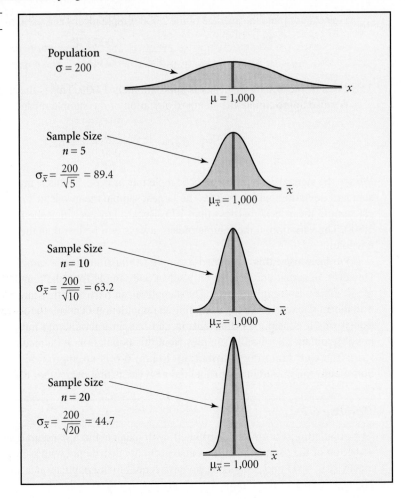

Notice, as the sample size is increased, the standard deviation of the sampling distribution is reduced. This means the potential for extreme sampling error is reduced when larger sample sizes are used. Figure 6-7 shows sampling distributions for sample sizes of 5, 10, and 20. When the population is normally distributed, the sampling distribution of $\bar{x}$ will always be normal and centered at the population mean. Only the spread in the distribution will change as the sample size changes.

The sampling distribution is composed of all possible sample means. Half the sample means will lie above the center of the sampling distribution and half will lie below. The relative distance that a given sample mean is from the center can be determined by *standardizing* the sampling distribution. As discussed in Chapter 5, a standardized value is determined by converting the value from its original units into a *z*-value. A *z*-value measures the number of standard deviations a value is from the mean. This same concept can be used when working with a sampling distribution. Equation 6-4 shows how the *z*-values are computed.

---

z-Value for Sampling Distribution of $\bar{x}$

$$z = \frac{\bar{x} - \mu}{\dfrac{\sigma}{\sqrt{n}}}$$

6-4

where:

$\bar{x}$ = Sample mean
μ = Population mean
σ = Population standard deviation
n = Sample size

Note, if the sample that is being selected is large relative to the size of the population (greater than 5 percent of the population size), and the sampling is being done without replacement, we need to modify how we compute the standard deviation of the sampling distribution and z-value using what is known as the **finite population correction factor** as shown in Equation 6-5.

---

z-Value Adjusted for the Finite Population Correction Factor

$$z = \frac{\bar{x} - \mu}{\dfrac{\sigma}{\sqrt{n}} \sqrt{\dfrac{N - n}{N - 1}}}$$

6-5

where:

$$N = \text{Population size}$$
$$n = \text{Sample size}$$

$$\sqrt{\frac{N - n}{N - 1}} = \text{Finite correction factor}$$

The finite population correction factor is used to calculate the standard deviation of the sampling distribution when the sampling is performed without replacement and when the sample size is greater than 5% of the population size.

EXAMPLE 6-2: FINDING THE PROBABILITY THAT $\bar{x}$ IS IN A GIVEN RANGE

Vextronix Manufacturing   Vextronix Manufacturing makes precision parts for the personal computer industry. One part is used in making the motor unit for PCs. When the production process is operating according to specifications, the diameter of the parts is normally distributed, with a mean equal to 1.5 inches and a standard deviation of 0.05 inches. Before shipping a large batch of these parts, Vextronix quality analysts have selected a random sample of 8 parts with the following diameters:

1.57	1.59	1.48	1.60	1.59	1.62	1.55	1.52

The analysts want to use these measurements to determine if the process is no longer operating within the specifications. The following steps can be used.

Step 1:   **Compute the mean for this sample.**

$$\bar{x} = \frac{\sum x}{n} = \frac{12.52}{8} = 1.565 \text{ inches}$$

Step 2:   **Define the sampling distribution for $\bar{x}$ using Theorem 6-1.**
Theorem 6-1 indicates that if the population is normally distributed, the sampling distribution for $\bar{x}$ will also be normally distributed, with

$$\mu_{\bar{x}} = \mu \text{ and } \sigma_{\bar{x}} = \frac{\sigma}{\sqrt{n}}$$

Thus, in this case, the mean of the sampling distribution should be 1.50 inches, and the standard deviation should be $\dfrac{0.05}{\sqrt{8}} = 0.0177$ inches

Step 3:   **Define the event of interest.**
Because the sample mean is $\bar{x} = 1.565$, which is greater than the mean of the sampling distribution, we want to find
$$P(\bar{x} \geq 1.565 \text{ inches}) = ?$$

Step 4:   **Convert the sample mean to a standardized z-value, using Equation 6-4.**

$$z = \frac{\bar{x} - \mu}{\dfrac{\sigma}{\sqrt{n}}} = \frac{1.565 - 1.50}{\dfrac{0.05}{\sqrt{8}}} = \frac{0.065}{0.0177} = 3.67$$

Step 5:   **Use the standard normal distribution table to determine the desired probability.**
$$P(z \geq 3.67) = ?$$
The standard normal distribution table in Appendix D does not show z-values as high as 3.67. This implies that $P(z \geq 3.67) \approx 0.00$. So, if the production process is working properly, there is virtually no chance that a random sample of eight items will have a mean diameter of 1.565 inches or greater. Because the analysts at Vextronix did find this sample result, there is a very good chance that something is wrong with the process.

THE CENTRAL LIMIT THEOREM

Theorem 6-1 applies when the population distribution is a normal (bell-shaped) distribution. Although there are many situations in business when this will be the case, there are also many situations when the population is not normal. For example, incomes in a region tend to be right-skewed. Some distributions, such as people's weight, are bimodal (a peak weight group for males and another peak weight group for females).

What does the sampling distribution of $\bar{x}$ look like when a population is not normally distributed? The answer is . . . it depends. It depends on what the shape of the population is and what size sample is selected. To illustrate, suppose we have a U-shaped population, such as the one in Figure 6-8, with mean = 14.00 and standard deviation equal to 3.00. Now, we select 3,000 simple random samples of size 3 and compute the mean for each sample. These $\bar{x}$ values are graphed in the histogram shown in Figure 6-9.

The number of all possible random samples of size 3 obtained from the population is, of course, considerably larger than 3,000. Therefore, we would not expect that these samples would produce exactly the same results as if we had actually taken all the possible random samples of size 3. However, the results would be reasonably close to the value that would be obtained for the average of all the possible means. The average of these 3,000 sample means is

$$\frac{\sum \bar{x}}{3,000} \approx \mu_{\bar{x}} = 14.02$$

Notice this value is approximately equal to the population mean of 14.00. Next we compute the standard deviation as

$$\sigma_{\bar{x}} \approx \sqrt{\frac{\sum(\bar{x} - \mu_{\bar{x}})^2}{3,000}} = 1.82$$

The standard deviation of the sampling distribution is less than the standard deviation for the population, which was 3.00. This will always be the case.

FIGURE 6-8

**Simulated Nonnormal
Population**

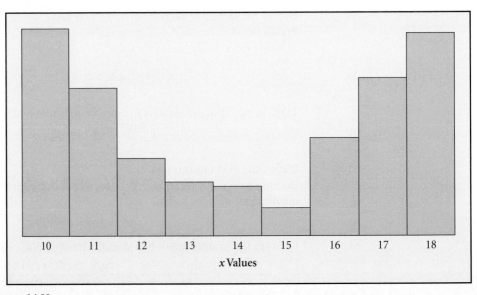

x Values

$\mu = 14.00$
$\sigma = 3.00$

F I G U R E 6 - 9

Frequency Distribution of
$\bar{x}$'s ($n = 3$)

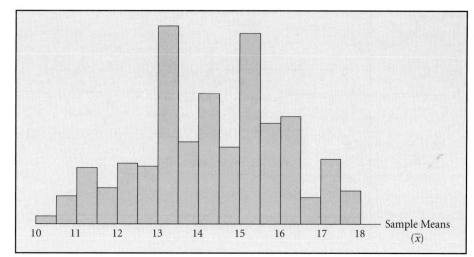

14.02 = Average of sample means
1.82 = Standard deviation of sample means

The frequency distribution of $\bar{x}$ values for the 3,000 samples of 3 looks different than the population distribution, which is U-shaped. Suppose we increase the sample size to 10 and take 3,000 samples from the same U-shaped population. The resulting frequency distribution of $\bar{x}$ values is shown in Figure 6-10. Now the frequency distribution looks very much like a normal distribution. The average of the sample means is still equal to 14.02, which is virtually equal to the population mean. The standard deviation for this sampling distribution is now reduced to 0.97.

This example is not a special case. Instead, it illustrates a very important statistical concept called the **Central Limit Theorem**.

Theorem 6-2: The Central Limit Theorem

For simple random samples of n observations taken from a population with mean μ and standard deviation σ, regardless of the population's distribution, provided the sample size is sufficiently large, the distribution of the sample means, $\bar{x}$, will be approximately normal with a mean equal to the population mean ($\mu_{\bar{x}} = \mu$) and a standard deviation equal to the population standard deviation divided by the square root of the sample size $\left(\sigma_{\bar{x}} = \dfrac{\sigma}{\sqrt{n}} \right)$. The larger the sample size, the better the approximation to the normal distribution.

F I G U R E 6 - 1 0

Frequency Distribution
($n = 10$)

14.02 = Average of sample means
0.97 = Standard deviation of sample means

FIGURE 6-11

**Central Limit Theorem
with Uniform Population
Distribution**

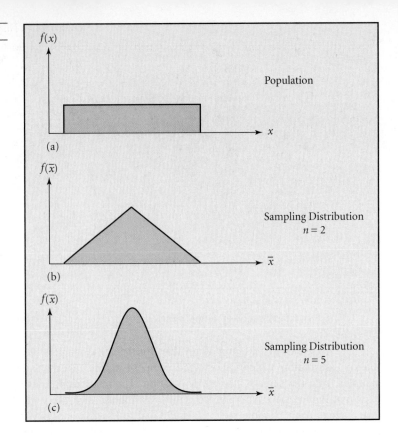

FIGURE 6-12

**Central Limit Theorem
with Triangular Population**

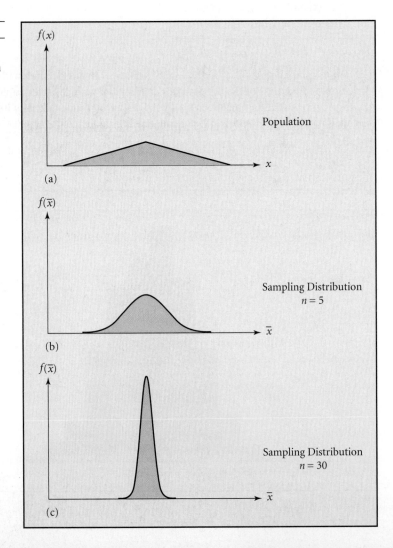

FIGURE 6-13

Central Limit Theorem with a Skewed Population

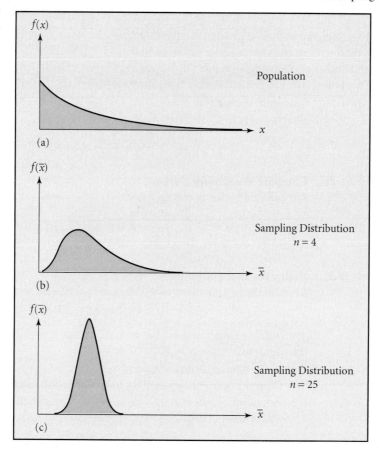

(a) Population

(b) Sampling Distribution $n = 4$

(c) Sampling Distribution $n = 25$

The Central Limit Theorem is very important because with it we know the shape of the sampling distribution even though we may not know the shape of the population distribution. The one catch is that the sample size must be "sufficiently large." What is a sufficiently large sample size?

The answer depends on the shape of the population. If the population is quite symmetric, then sample sizes as small as 2 or 3 will provide a normally distributed sampling distribution. If the population is highly skewed or otherwise irregularly shaped, the required sample size will be larger. Recall the example of the U-shaped population. The frequency distribution obtained from samples of 3 was shaped differently than the population, but not like a normal distribution. However, for samples of 10, the frequency distribution was a very close approximation to a normal distribution. Figures 6-11, 6-12, and 6-13 show some examples of the Central Limit Theorem concept. Simulation studies indicate that even for very strange-looking populations, samples of 25 to 30 produce sampling distributions that are approximately normal. Thus, *a conservative definition of a sufficiently large sample size is n ≥ 30.* The Central Limit Theorem is illustrated in the following examples.

XAMPLE 6-3: FINDING THE PROBABILITY THAT x̄ IS IN A GIVEN RANGE

Moline Insurance   Moline Insurance recently conducted a study of car damages. Past history has shown that the damage distribution is right-skewed, with $\mu = \$4,560$ and $\sigma = \$600$. A simple random sample of 100 automobile claim files was selected from the large population of claims in Moline's files. The dollar damages paid to repair the cars were recorded, as follows:

Insurance Payments for 100 Claims									
$4,483.95	$4,992.97	$3,906.07	$4,197.44	$5,718.97	$4,484.87	$3,800.40	$5,500.79	$4,402.45	$4,613.89
5,190.25	4,487.37	4,118.90	5,841.33	4,570.86	5,475.73	3,851.05	4,157.62	3,563.31	5,256.10
5,105.74	5,545.20	4,523.56	4,207.26	5,082.41	4,820.87	4,493.93	4,309.38	4,409.71	4,146.40
4,765.37	3,915.06	5,041.89	4,191.81	4,166.32	4,424.53	5,374.26	3,753.40	4,185.92	5,173.52
4,665.91	3,833.69	4,605.51	3,736.42	4,819.91	4,845.52	4,307.68	5,075.28	3,312.88	4,248.25
5,175.07	3,323.43	4,711.53	4,550.84	4,763.23	3,717.65	4,813.38	3,730.37	5,670.43	4,440.64
4,751.75	3,982.61	3,456.37	4,687.57	3,850.04	4,670.01	4,835.79	4,630.92	3,889.10	3,642.36
5,347.96	5,297.90	4,765.81	3,786.70	4,949.20	5,145.17	4,696.74	4,423.50	4,750.20	4,836.45
5,012.67	4,005.24	6,009.68	4,804.32	4,235.20	3,781.62	4,087.37	5,050.94	4,090.43	3,825.02
4,604.22	4,875.80	4,102.92	3,722.66	3,870.87	5,539.77	4,835.68	4,066.16	3,611.93	5,649.96

The company wishes to use this sample to help set its rate structure, but managers worry that the sampling error may be too large for this population. The company is interested in determining the probability of obtaining a sample with as much or more sampling error as obtained in this sample. This probability can be determined using the following steps.

Step 1: Calculate the sample mean.

The mean for this sample is

$$\bar{x} = \frac{\sum x}{100} = \$4{,}527.77$$

Step 2: Compute the sampling error.

The sampling error in this case is

$$\text{sampling error} = \bar{x} - \mu$$
$$= \$4{,}527.77 - \$4{,}560.00$$
$$= -\$32.23$$

Step 3: Define the event of interest.

Because the sample mean is less than the population mean, the event of interest is

$$P(\bar{x} \leq 4{,}527.77) = ?$$

The managers wish to know the probability of observing an $\bar{x} \leq \$4{,}527.77$, given that the population mean is $4,560.00.

Step 4: Define the sampling distribution.

The Central Limit Theorem allows us to define the sampling distribution even though the population is not normally distributed. Because the sample size is $n = 100$, we know the sampling distribution will be approximately normal, with

$$\mu_{\bar{x}} = \mu = \$4{,}560$$

and

$$\sigma_{\bar{x}} = \frac{\sigma}{\sqrt{n}} = \frac{600}{\sqrt{100}} = \$60$$

Step 5: Use the standard normal distribution to find the probability of interest.

To find $P(\bar{x} \leq \$4{,}527.77)$, we use the concepts introduced in Chapter 5 for finding probabilities with a normal distribution. We begin by converting to the standard normal distribution using Equation 6-4.

$$z = \frac{\bar{x} - \mu}{\dfrac{\sigma}{\sqrt{n}}} = \frac{4{,}527.77 - 4{,}560}{\dfrac{600}{\sqrt{100}}} = \frac{-32.23}{60} = -0.537$$

Now go to the standard normal table in Appendix D for $z = -0.54$. We find $P(-0.54 \leq z \leq 0) = 0.2054$. Subtract this from 0.50 to get the desired probability of 0.2946, as shown:

Insurance Claims Payout Distribution of the Sample Mean

0.2054

0.5000 − 0.2054 = 0.2946

z = −0.54   0.0
$\bar{x}$ = 4,527.77   μ = 4,560

Therefore, there is nearly a 30% chance of getting a sample mean as small or smaller than $4,527.77 from this population. Although the managers might want to look at other characteristics of the sample, this evidence suggests this sampling error is not unusual for the population of all claim values.

SUMMARY: SAMPLING DISTRIBUTION OF x̄

To find probabilities associated with a sampling distribution of $\bar{x}$ for samples of size n from a population with mean μ and standard deviation σ, use the following steps.

1. Compute the sample mean using

$$\bar{x} = \frac{\sum x}{n}$$

2. Define the sampling distribution.
If the population is normally distributed, the sampling distribution also will be normally distributed for any size sample. If the population is not normally distributed but the sample size is sufficiently large, the sampling distribution will be approximately normal. In either case, the sampling distribution will have:

$$\mu_{\bar{x}} = \mu \quad \text{and} \quad \sigma_{\bar{x}} = \frac{\sigma}{\sqrt{n}}.$$

3. Define the event of interest.
We are interested in finding the probability of some range of sample means, such as

$$P(\bar{x} \geq 25) =$$

4. Use the standard normal distribution to find the probability for the event of interest, using Equation 6-4 or 6-5 to convert the sample mean to a corresponding z-value.

$$z = \frac{\bar{x} - \mu}{\frac{\sigma}{\sqrt{n}}} \quad \text{or } z = \frac{\bar{x} - \mu}{\frac{\sigma}{\sqrt{n}}\sqrt{\frac{N-n}{N-1}}}$$

Then use the standard normal table to find the probability associated with the calculated z-value.

EXAMPLE 6-4: FINDING THE PROBABILITY THAT x̄ IS IN A GIVEN RANGE

Fairway Stores, Inc. Past sales records indicate that sales at the store are right-skewed, with a population mean of $12.50 per customer and a standard deviation of $5.50. The store manager has selected a random sample of 100 sales receipts. She is interested in determining the probability of getting a sample mean between $12.25 and $13.00 from this population. To find this probability, she can use the following steps.

Step 1: **Compute the sample mean.**
In this case, two sample means are being considered:
$$\bar{x} = \$12.25 \quad \text{and} \quad \bar{x} = \$13.00$$

Step 2: **Define the sampling distribution.**
The Central Limit Theorem can be used because the sample size is large enough ($n = 100$) to determine that the sampling distribution will be approximately normal (even though the population is right-skewed), with
$$\mu_{\bar{x}} = \$12.50 \quad \text{and} \quad \sigma_{\bar{x}} = \frac{\$5.50}{\sqrt{100}} = \$0.55$$

Step 3: **Define the event of interest.**
The manager is interested in:
$$P(\$12.25 \leq \bar{x} \leq \$13.00) = ?$$

Step 4: **Use the standard normal distribution to find the probability of interest.**
Assuming the population of sales records is quite large, we use Equation 6-4 to convert the sample means to corresponding z-values.

$$z = \frac{\bar{x} - \mu}{\frac{\sigma}{\sqrt{n}}} = \frac{12.25 - 12.50}{\frac{5.50}{\sqrt{100}}} = -0.46 \quad \text{and} \quad z = \frac{\bar{x} - \mu}{\frac{\sigma}{\sqrt{n}}} = \frac{13.00 - 12.50}{\frac{5.50}{\sqrt{100}}} = 0.91$$

From the standard normal table in Appendix D, the probability associated with $z = -0.46$ is 0.1772, and the probability for $z = 0.91$ is 0.3186. Therefore,

$$P(\$12.25 \leq \bar{x} \leq \$13.00) = P(-0.46 \leq z \leq 0.91) = 0.1772 + 0.3186 = 0.4958$$

There is nearly a 0.50 chance that the sample mean will fall in the range \$12.25 to \$13.00.

6-2: EXERCISES

Skill Development

6.11 A population is normally distributed, with a mean of 1,000 and a standard deviation equal to 200.
   a. Determine the probability that a random sample of size 5 selected from this population will have a sample mean less than 970.
   b. Referring to part a, suppose a second sample of size 10 is selected. What is the probability that this sample will have a mean that is less than 970?
   c. Why are the answers to parts a and b different? Discuss.

6.12 A population is known to have a mean equal to 6,000 and a standard deviation of 1,300. If a sample of size 50 is selected, what is the probability that the sample mean will be between 5,950 and 6,050? Does it matter what the distribution of the population is?

6.13 A population is normally distributed, with a mean of 400 and a standard deviation equal to 50.
   a. Determine the probability of selecting a single value from the population that exceeds 450.
   b. Calculate the probability of selecting a random sample of size 3 that has a sample mean that exceeds 450.
   c. Explain why the probabilities are different.

6.14 A population is thought to be normally distributed, with a mean of 500 and a standard deviation equal to 40. A sample of size 6 items is randomly selected from the population, with the following values:

570	430	600	520	480	500

Find the probability of getting a sample mean as large or larger than the one for these sample data.

6.15 A population is thought to be somewhat skewed, with a mean equal to 24.90 and a standard deviation of 1.30. A simple random sample of 40 items has been selected with the following values:

24.3	23.2	25.0	26.2	26.1	26.8	22.1	24.4	26.0	23.4
23.9	22.7	22.5	23.5	23.8	22.2	24.0	24.2	24.9	24.3
24.3	24.3	26.3	24.6	24.5	24.1	27.1	25.7	27.6	23.9
26.7	22.8	25.3	25.8	27.0	24.6	24.1	25.5	24.2	25.6

   a. What is the sampling error for this sample if you want to estimate the population mean?

   b. What is the probability of getting a sample mean as small or smaller than the one computed from this sample?

6.16 A population has a distribution of unknown shape. The mean of the population is 3,500, and the standard deviation is 600.
   a. If a sample of 100 values is selected randomly from this population, what is the probability that the sample mean will exceed 3,600?
   b. If a sample of 200 is selected from the population, what is the probability that the sample mean will exceed 3,600?
   c. Compare your answers to parts a and b and explain why the two probabilities are different.

6.17 A random sample of 100 items is selected from a population of size 350. What is the probability that the sample mean will exceed 200 if the population mean is 195 and the population standard deviation equals 20? (Hint: Use the finite correction factor, because the sample size is more than 5% of the population size.)

6.18 A population with a mean of 1.35 and a standard deviation of 0.40 is known to be very irregularly shaped. If a random sample of 49 items is selected from the population, calculate the probability that the sample mean will be less than 1.45

Business Applications

6.19 The Adam's Food King chain employs more than 3,000 people. The workers' ages are approximately normally distributed, with a mean of 31 years and a standard deviation of 4.3 years. The company is thinking of introducing a health-care package, and its insurance company wants to sample 25 workers before quoting a price.
   a. Calculate the probability that the sample of 25 will have an average age less than 31.
   b. Determine the value of the standard error associated with this sample.
   c. What can the insurance company do to reduce the standard error? Focus your answer on issues related to sampling concepts.

6.20 SeaFair Fashions relies on its sales force of 220 to do an initial screening of all new fashions. The company is bringing out a new line of swimwear and has invited 40 salespeople to its Orlando, Florida, home office. A issue of constant concern to the SeaFair sales office is the volume of orders generated by each salesperson. Last year the overall company average was $417,330, with a standard deviation of $45,285. (Hint: The finite correction factor, Equation 6-5, is required.)

a. Determine the probability the random sample of 40 will have a sales average less than $400,000.

b. What shape do you think the distribution of all possible sample means of 40 will have? Discuss.

c. Determine the value of the standard deviation of the distribution of the sample means of all possible samples of size 40.

d. How would the answers to parts a, b, and c change if the home office brought 60 salespeople to Orlando? Provide the respective answers for this sample size.

e. Each year SeaFair invites the sales personnel with sales greater than the 85th percentile to enjoy a complimentary vacation in Hawaii. Determine the smallest average salary for the sales personnel who were in Hawaii last year. (Assume the distribution of sales was normally distributed last year.)

6.21   A recent study by a midwestern university has concluded that the time adults spend watching television each week averages 14.6 hours, with a standard deviation of 4.3 hours.

a. Assuming these values are the population parameters, determine the probability that a sample of 100 adults from the population will average more than 15 hours of television per week. Does it seem likely that the university's conclusion concerning the population mean could be correct? Support your answer.

b. The university obtained three random samples of 100 adults, and each sample had an average greater than 15 hours. How likely is this assuming the university's conclusions about the population parameters are correct? Answer part a with this new information.

6.22   Draper, Inc., makes particleboard for the building industry. Particleboard is built by mixing wood chips and resins together, forming the mix into 4-feet-by-8-feet sheets, and pressing the sheets under extreme heat and pressure to form a 4-by-8 sheet that is used as a substitute for plywood. The strength of a particleboard is tied to the board's weight. Boards that are too light are brittle and do not meet the quality standard for strength. Boards that are too heavy are strong but are difficult for customers to use. The company knows that there will be variation in its boards' weight. Product specifications call for the weight per sheet to average 10 pounds, with a standard deviation of 1.75 pounds. During each shift, Draper employees select and weigh a random sample of 25 boards. The boards are thought to have a normally distributed weight distribution.

If the average of the sample slips below 9.60 pounds, an adjustment is made to the process to add more moisture and resins to increase the weight (and hopefully the strength).

a. Assuming that the process is operating correctly according to specifications, what is the probability that a sample will indicate that an adjustment is needed?

b. Assume the population mean weight per sheet slips to 9 pounds. Determine the probability that the sample will indicate an adjustment is not needed.

c. Assuming that 10 pounds is the mean weight, what should be the cutoff if the company wants no more than a 5% chance that a sample of 25 boards will have an average weight less than this cutoff?

6.23   Armstrong Windows makes windows for use in homes and commercial buildings. The standards for glass thickness call for the glass to average 0.375 inches, with a standard deviation of 0.050 inches. Suppose a random sample of $n = 50$ windows yields a sample mean of 0.392 inches.

a. What is the probability of $\bar{x} \geq 0.392$ if the windows meet the standards?

b. Based on your answer to part a, what would you conclude about the population of windows? Are they meeting the standards?

Advanced Business Applications

6.24   The Jordeen Beverage Company bottles soft drinks and distributes them in the St. Louis area. Every week, a Missouri state inspector comes to the plant (on randomly selected days during the week) to test whether the average fill in the cans and bottles is acceptable. The state inspector, in looking out for consumers, selects a random sample of cans and bottles from the plant inventory that day. Each can (or bottle) is supposed to contain 12 ounces, but there will always be a certain amount of inherent variability from can to can. If the mean of the sample of 50 cans is less than 11.98 ounces, the company is given a $1,000 citation and the state inspector comes back the next day and reinspects. The process continues until the company meets the standard.

Jordeen controls the mean fill per can with a machine adjustment. They always have this set at 12 ounces. The machine does put slightly different amounts into each can. The CD-ROM file called *Jordeen* contains the actual fill amounts for each of the 5,000 cans in inventory the day the state inspector arrives.

a. Assuming that the data represent the population of cans, compute the population mean fill and population standard deviation. (Note, if you are using Minitab, you will need to use the **Stack Columns** under the **Manip** menu item.)

b. Compute the probability that a sample mean from a random sample of 50 cans from this population will be less than 11.98 ounces.

c. Suppose the Jordeen managers wish to limit their chances of getting fined to no more than 5%. If the state will not change its procedure and assuming that the standard deviation in the fill amount can't be changed, what specifically must the company do to reach the 5% level? Discuss the ramifications of making this change, assuming that company fills 5,000 cans every week for 52 weeks a year.

d. Suppose the Jordeen managers are unwilling to adjust their average fill to any value higher than 12 ounces. Instead, they can purchase a new filling machine that will have an adjustable mean but also will have a different standard deviation in fill amount than the current machine. What would the new machine's standard deviation have to be if the company wants no more than a 5% chance of being fined and assuming that the average fill is exactly 12 ounces?

6.25   Open the CD-ROM file named *Fast100*. The second column contains total sales for the past four quarters for these 100 companies. Assume that these 100 companies represent the population of interest.
a. Compute the population mean and population standard deviation.
b. Develop a frequency distribution for these data using eight classes, and indicate whether the population data appear to be normally distributed.
c. Select a random sample of 30 companies from this population. Compute the mean sales for this sample of companies. If you were asked to write a report using these 30 companies that would have characteristics (such as the mean) similar to those of the population, would you use this sample? Why or why not? (Hint: Compute the probability of getting a sample mean as extreme or more extreme than the one you have. Remember to use the finite correction factor.)

6.26   Open the CD-ROM file called *Trucks*. This file contains data on trucks that have been weighed on two weigh scales: the in-ground scale at the Port of Entry (POE) and a scale that is located in the highway before the POE turnoff. This latter scale allows the trucks to be weighed as they move along the road and is referred to as a Weigh-in-Motion scale (WIM). Assuming that data for these 200 trucks represent the population of interest,

create a new variable that is the difference between front-axle WIM weight and front-axle POE weight.
a. Develop a frequency histogram for this new variable using six classes. Does this population distribution look approximately normally distributed? Describe the shape of the distribution.
b. Compute the population mean and population standard deviation for this new variable.
c. Select a random sample of 25 trucks. Compute the sample mean. What is the probability of getting a sample mean as extreme or more extreme than the one you have?

6.27   Referring to Exercise 6.26, suppose the data in the *Trucks* file represent a random sample from a bigger population of trucks rather than a population. Consider the new variable (difference between WIM front-axle and POE front-axle weights). Suppose the bigger population of all trucks has an average difference equal to 0 pounds with a standard deviation equal to 2,000 pounds. Suppose the objective is being met. Determine the probability that the random sample mean difference between WIM and POE front-axle weight will be as large or larger than the one you computed in Exercise 6.26. Discuss.

6.28   The CD-ROM file called *Cities* contains data on a random sample of 100 U.S. cities. Assume the population mean unemployment rate is 5%.
a. Calculate the probability of a sample of 100 cities having a mean unemployment rate as small or smaller than the one you have computed. (Hint: In your computation, substitute the sample standard deviation for σ.)
b. Based upon your calculation in part a, do you believe the population mean is the value it was assumed to be? Provide a rationale for your statement.

6-3 SAMPLING DISTRIBUTION OF A PROPORTION

WORKING WITH PROPORTIONS

In many instances, the objective of sampling is to estimate a population proportion. For instance, an accountant may be interested in determining the proportion of accounts payable balances that are correct. A production supervisor may wish to determine the percentage of product that is defect free. A marketing research department might want to know the proportion of potential customers who will purchase a particular product. In all these instances, the decision makers could select a sample, compute the sample proportion, and make their decision based on the sample results.

Sample proportions are subject to sampling error, just as are sample means. The concept of sampling distributions provides us a way to assess the potential magnitude of the sampling error for proportions in given situations.

Lincoln Research—Consider Lincoln Research, a market research firm that surveyed every customer in a certain region who purchased a specific brand of tires during the first week of March last year. The key question in the survey was: "Are you satisfied with the tires and service received at this tire store?"

The population size was 80 customers. The number of customers who answered "Yes" to the question was 72. The value of interest in this example is the **population proportion**. Equation 6-is used to compute a population proportion.

Population Proportion

The fraction of values in a population that have a specific attribute.

$$p = \frac{X}{N}$$

6-6

where:

p = Population proportion
X = Number of items in the population having the attribute
N = Population size

The proportion of customers in the population who are satisfied with the tires and service is

$$p = \frac{72}{80} = 0.90$$

Therefore, 90% of the population responded "Yes" to the survey question. This is the *parameter*. It is a measurement taken from the population. It is the "true value."

Now, suppose that the market research firm wishes to do a follow-up survey for a simple random sample of $n = 20$ of the customers. What fraction of this sample will be people who had previously responded "Yes" to the satisfaction question?

The answer depends on which sample is selected. There are many possible samples of 20 that could be selected from 80 people. However, the marketing research firm will select only one of these possible samples. At one extreme, suppose the 20 people selected for the sample included all 8 who answered "No" to the satisfaction question and 12 others who answered "Yes." The sample proportion is computed using Equation 6-7.

Sample Proportion

The fraction of items in a sample that have the attribute of interest.

$$\bar{p} = \frac{x}{n}$$

6-7

where:

$\bar{p}$ = Sample proportion
x = Number of items in the sample with the attribute
n = Sample size

For the tire store example, the sample proportion of "Yes" responses is

$$\bar{p} = \frac{12}{20} = 0.60$$

The sample proportion of "Yes" responses is 0.60, whereas the population proportion is 0.90. The difference between the sampling value and the population value is sampling error. Equation 6-8 is used to compute the sampling error involving a single proportion.

Single-Proportion Sampling Error

Sampling error = $\bar{p} - p$

6-8

where:

p = Population proportion
$\bar{p}$ = Sample proportion

Then for this extreme situation we get

Sampling error = $0.60 - 0.90 = -0.30$

If a sample on the other extreme had been selected and all 20 people came from the original list of 72 who had responded "Yes" in the original survey, the sample proportion would be

$$\bar{p} = \frac{20}{20} = 1.00$$

For this sample, the sampling error is

$$\text{Sampling error} = 1.00 - 0.90 = 0.10$$

Thus, the range of sampling error in this example is from -0.30 to 0.10. As with any sampling situation, you can expect some sampling error. The sample proportion will probably not equal the population proportion because the sample selected will not be a perfect mirror image of the population.

EXAMPLE 6-5: SAMPLING ERROR FOR A PROPORTION

Hewlett-Packard–Compaq Merger   As you may recall, in 2002 a proxy fight took place between the management of Hewlett-Packard (HP) and Walter Hewlett, the son of one of HP's founders, over whether the merger between HP and Compaq should be approved. Each outstanding share of common stock was allocated one vote. After the vote in March 2002, the initial tally showed that the proportion of shares in the approval column was 0.51. After the vote, a lawsuit was filed by a group led by Walter Hewlett, which claimed improprieties by the HP management team. Suppose the attorneys for the Hewlett faction randomly selected 40 shares from the millions of total shares outstanding. The intent was to interview the owners of these shares to determine whether they felt undue pressure to vote for the merger. Of these shares in the sample, 26 carried an "Approval" vote. The attorneys can use the following steps to assess the sampling error.

Step 1:   **Determine the population proportion.**
In this case, the proportion of votes cast in favor of the merger is
$$p = 0.51$$
This is the number of approval votes divided by the total number of shares.

Step 2:   **Compute the sample proportion using Equation 6-7.**
The sample proportion is

$$\bar{p} = \frac{x}{n} = \frac{26}{40} = 0.65$$

Step 3:   **Compute the sampling error using Equation 6-8.**
$$\text{Sampling error} = \bar{p} - p = 0.65 - 0.51 = 0.14$$

The proportion of "Approval" votes from the shares in this sample exceeds the population proportion by 0.14.

SAMPLING DISTRIBUTION OF $\bar{p}$

In many applications you will be interested in determining the proportion (p) of all items that possess a particular attribute. The best estimate of this population proportion will be $\bar{p}$, the sample proportion. However, any inference about how close your estimate is to the true population value will be based on the distribution of this sample proportion, $\bar{p}$, whose underlying distribution is the binomial. However, if the sample size is sufficiently large such that

$$np \geq 5 \quad \text{and} \quad n(1 - p) \geq 5$$

then the normal distribution can be used as a reasonable approximation to the discrete binomial distribution.[4] Providing we have a large enough sample size, the distribution of all possible sample proportions will be approximately normally distributed. In addition to being normally distributed, the sampling distribution will have a mean and standard error as indicated in Equations 6-9 and 6-10.

---

[4]An application of the Central Limit Theorem provides the rationale for this statement. Recall that $\bar{p} = \dfrac{x}{n}$ where x the sum of random variables (x_i) whose values are 0 and 1. Thus, $\dfrac{x}{n} = \dfrac{\sum x_i}{n}$. Therefore, $\bar{p}$ is in reality just a sample mean. Each of these x_i can be thought of as binomial random variables from a sample of size $n = 1$. Thus, they each have a mean $\mu = np = p$ and a variance of $\sigma^2 = np(1 - p) = p(1 - p)$. As we have seen from the Central Limit Theorem, the sample mean has an expected value of μ and a variance of $\dfrac{\sigma^2}{n}$. Thus, the sample proportion has an expected value of $\mu = p$ and variance of $\sigma^2 = \dfrac{p(1 - p)}{n}$.

Sampling Distribution of $\bar{p}$

$$\text{Mean} = \mu_{\bar{p}} = p \qquad \textbf{6-9}$$

and

$$\text{Standard error} = \sigma_{\bar{p}} = \sqrt{\frac{p(1-p)}{n}} \qquad \textbf{6-10}$$

where:

p = Population proportion
n = Sample size
$\bar{p}$ = Sample proportion

Heaton Manufacturing—Heaton Manufacturing makes Christmas ornaments that it ships to retailers throughout the United States. Heaton executives have observed that 15% of the ornaments, even when specially packed, are damaged before reaching the retailer. There appears to be no particular pattern to the damage. Whether one ornament breaks seems independent of whether any other ornament breaks.

Suppose that Heaton heard from a retail customer who claimed that 18% of the 500 ornaments she purchased were damaged. Assume the general damage rate of

$$p = 0.15$$

holds for the population of all ornaments. How likely is it that a sample of

$$n = 500$$

units will contain 18% or more broken items? To answer this question, we first check to determine if the sample size is sufficiently large. Because both

$$n(p) = 500(0.15) = 75 \geq 5 \text{ and } n(1-p) = 500(0.85) = 425 \geq 5$$

we can safely conclude that the sampling distribution of sample proportions will be approximately normal. Using Equations 6-9 and 6-10, we can compute the mean and standard error for the sampling distribution as follows.

$$\mu_{\bar{p}} = 0.15$$

and

$$\sigma_{\bar{p}} = \sqrt{\frac{(0.15)(0.85)}{500}} = 0.016$$

Equation 6-11 is used to convert the sample proportion to a standardized z-value.

---

z-Value for Proportions

$$z = \frac{\bar{p} - p}{\sigma_{\bar{p}}} \qquad \textbf{6-11}$$

where:

z = Number of standard errors $\bar{p}$ is from p
$\bar{p}$ = Sample proportion
$\sigma_{\bar{p}} = \sqrt{\frac{p(1-p)}{n}}$ = Standard error of the sampling distribution[5]
p = Mean of sample proportions

---

[5]If the sample size n is greater than 5% of the population size, the standard error of the sampling distribution should be computed using the finite population correction as $\sigma_{\bar{p}} = \sqrt{\frac{p(1-p)}{n}}\sqrt{\frac{N-n}{N-1}}$.

FIGURE 6-14

Standard Normal Distribution for Heaton Manufacturing

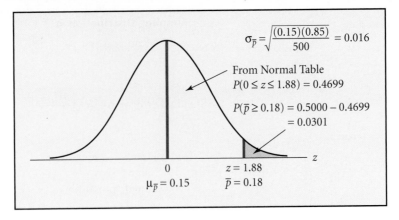

$$\sigma_{\bar{p}} = \sqrt{\frac{(0.15)(0.85)}{500}} = 0.016$$

From Normal Table
$P(0 \le z \le 1.88) = 0.4699$

$P(\bar{p} \ge 0.18) = 0.5000 - 0.4699 = 0.0301$

$z = 1.88$
$\bar{p} = 0.18$
$\mu_{\bar{p}} = 0.15$

From Equation 6-11 we get

$$z = \frac{\bar{p} - p}{\sigma_{\bar{p}}} = \frac{0.18 - 0.15}{\sqrt{\frac{(0.15)(0.85)}{500}}} = 1.88$$

Therefore the 0.18 damage rate reported by the customer is 1.88 standard deviations above the average rate of 0.15. Figure 6-14 illustrates that the chances of a damage rate of 0.18 or more is

$$P(\bar{p} \ge 0.18) = 0.0301$$

Because this is a very low probability, the Heaton managers might want to see if there was something unusual about how this shipment was packed.

SUMMARY: SAMPLING DISTRIBUTION OF p̄

To find probabilities associated with a sampling distribution for a single-population proportion, the following steps can be used.

1. Determine the population proportion, p, using:

$$p = \frac{x}{N}$$

2. Calculate the sample proportion using:

$$\bar{p} = \frac{x}{n}$$

3. Determine the mean and standard deviation of the sampling distribution using:

$$\mu_{\bar{p}} = p \quad \text{and} \quad \sigma_{\bar{p}} = \sqrt{\frac{p(1-p)}{n}}$$

4. Define the event of interest. For example:
$P(\bar{p} \ge 0.30) = ?$

5. If np and $n(1-p)$ are both ≥ 5, then convert $\bar{p}$ to a standardized z-value using:

$$z = \frac{\bar{p} - p}{\sigma_{\bar{p}}}$$

6. Use the standard normal distribution table in Appendix D to determine the required probability.

EXAMPLE 6-6: FINDING THE PROBABILITY THAT p̄ IS IN A GIVEN RANGE

The Daily Statesman The classified-advertisement manager for the *Daily Statesman* newspaper believes that the proportion of "apartment for rent" ads that are placed in the paper that result in a rental within two weeks is 0.80 or higher. She would like to make this claim as part of the paper's promotion of its classified section. Before doing this, she has selected a simple random sample of 100 "apartment for rent" ads. Of these, 73 resulted in a rental within the two-week period. To determine the probability of this result or something more extreme, she can use the following steps.

Step 1: **Determine the population proportion, p.**
The population proportion is believed to be $p = 0.80$, based upon the manager's experience.

Step 2: **Calculate the sample proportion.**
In this case, a sample of $n = 100$ ads was selected, with 73 having the attribute of interest. Thus,

$$\bar{p} = \frac{x}{n} = \frac{73}{100} = 0.73$$

Step 3: **Determine the mean and standard deviation of the sampling distribution.**
The mean of the sampling distribution is equal to p, the population proportion. So
$$\mu_{\bar{p}} = 0.80$$

The standard deviation of the sampling distribution for p is computed using:

$$\sigma_{\bar{p}} = \sqrt{\frac{p(1-p)}{n}} = \sqrt{\frac{0.80(1-0.80)}{100}} = 0.0400$$

Step 4: **Define the event of interest.**
In this case, because 0.73 is less than 0.80, we are interested in
$$P(\bar{p} \leq 0.73) = ?$$

Step 5: **If np and $n(1-p)$ are both ≥ 5, then convert $\bar{p}$ to a standardized z-value.**
Checking, we get
$$np = 100(0.80) = 80 \geq 5 \text{ and } n(1-p) = 100(0.20) = 20 \geq 5$$
then we convert p to a standardized z-value using:

$$z = \frac{\bar{p} - p}{\sigma_{\bar{p}}} = \frac{0.73 - 0.80}{\sqrt{\frac{0.80(1-0.80)}{100}}} = -1.75$$

Step 6: **Use the standard normal distribution table in Appendix D to determine the probability for the event of interest.**
We want

$$P(\bar{p} \leq 0.73) \quad \text{or} \quad P(z \leq -1.75)$$

From the normal distribution table for $z = -1.75$, we get 0.4599, which corresponds to the probability of a z-value between -1.75 and 0.0. To get the probability of interest, we subtract 0.4599 from 0.5000, giving 0.0401. There is only a 4% chance that a random sample of $n = 100$ would produce a sample proportion of $\bar{p} \leq 0.73$ if the population proportion is 0.80. She might want to use caution before making this claim.

6-3: EXERCISES

Skill Development

6.29 Assume the following data represent a population of 50 values. Values equal to 1 indicate that a particular attribute is present. A value equal to 0 indicates the attribute is not present.

1	1	1	1	1	1	1	1	0	0
0	1	1	0	0	1	1	1	0	1
0	1	1	1	1	1	1	1	1	0
1	1	1	1	1	1	1	0	1	1
0	1	1	1	1	1	1	1	1	1

a. Compute the population proportion.
b. A random sample of 15 items produced the following numbers: 1, 1, 1, 0, 0, 1, 0, 0, 1, 1, 0, 0, 0, 1, 0.

Compute the sample proportion and the sampling error present in your sample.
c. What is the range of extreme sampling error for a sample of 15 taken from this population?
d. How would the range of extreme sampling error change if the sample size was set to 30? Discuss the advantages of having a larger sample size.

6.30 Given a population in which the proportion of items with a desired attribute is $p = 0.25$, if a sample of 400 is taken:
a. What is the standard deviation of the sampling distribution of $\bar{p}$?
b. What is the probability the proportion of successes in the sample will be greater than 0.22?

6.31 Given a population in which the proportion of items with a desired attribute is $p = 0.65$, if a sample of 100 is taken:
a. Determine the probability the proportion of successes in the sample will be less than 0.63.
b. Referring to part a, suppose the sample size is increased to $n = 200$, what is the probability that the sample proportion will be less than 0.63? Discuss why the answers in parts a and b differ.

6.32 Given a population in which the proportion of items with a desired attribute is $p = 0.50$, if a sample of 200 is taken:
a. Find the probability the proportion of successes in the sample will be between 0.47 and 0.51.
b. Referring to part a, what would the probability be if the sample size were 100?

6.33 Thirty percent of the items in a population are known to possess a particular attribute. If a random sample of 60 items is selected, what is the probability that the sample proportion of items with the attribute will exceed 0.33?

6.34 Suppose 95% of the items in a population have a particular characteristic. Find the chance that a sample of 100 items will have fewer than 90 items with that same characteristic.

6.35 Given a population in which the probability of a success is $p = 0.40$, if a sample of 1,000 is taken:
a. Calculate the probability the proportion of successes in the sample will be less than 0.42.
b. What is the probability the proportion of successes in the sample will be greater than 0.44?

Business Applications

6.36 Tom Marley and Jennifer Griggs have recently started a marketing research firm in Jacksonville, Florida. They have contacted the Florida Democratic Party with a proposal to do all political polling for the party. Because they have just started their company, the state party chairman is reluctant to sign a contract without some test of their accuracy and has asked them to do a trial poll in a central Florida county known to have 60% registered Democratic Party voters. The poll itself had many questions. However, for the test of accuracy, only the proportion of registered Democrats was considered. Tom and Jennifer report back that from a random sample of 760 respondents, 395 were registered Democrats.
a. Determine the probability that such a random sample would result in 395 or fewer Democrats in the sample.
b. Based on your calculations in part a, would you recommend that the Florida Democratic Party (or anyone else for that matter) contract with the Marley/Griggs marketing research firm. Explain your answer.

6.37 A golf-equipment catalog company regularly inserts in the catalogs coupons that can be redeemed for merchandise in local businesses. Historically, 8% of the coupons are redeemed. Recently the company enclosed a new style of coupon in a sample of 300 catalogs. It then determined that 35 of these coupons were redeemed.

a. What is the probability that if the new coupon has the same redemption rate as the old, the company would find 35 or more new coupons redeemed in a sample of 300?
b. Based on the answer to part a, would you recommend adoption of the new coupon? Justify your answer.

6.38 Micron Electronics makes personal computers that are sold directly over the phone and the Internet. One of the most critical factors in the success of PC makers is how fast they can turn their inventory of parts. Faster inventory turns mean lower average inventory cost. Recently at a meeting, the vice president of manufacturing said that there is no reason to continue offering hard disk drives that have less than a 20 GB storage capacity because only 10% of Micron customers ask for the smaller hard disks. After much discussion and debate about the accuracy of the VP's figure, it was decided to sample 100 orders from the past week's sales. This sample revealed 14 requests for drives with less than 20 GB capacity.
a. Determine the probability of finding 14 or more requests like this if the VP's assertion is correct. Do you believe that the proportion of customers requesting hard drives with storage capacity is as small as 0.10? Explain.
b. Suppose a second sample of 100 customers is selected. This sample again yields 14 requests for a hard drive with less than 20 GB of storage. Combining this sample information with that found in part a, what conclusion would you now reach regarding the VP's 10% claim? Base your answer on probability.

6.39 One of the major video rental chains recently made a change in its rental policies, allowing movies to be rented for three nights instead of one. The marketing team that made this decision reasoned that at least 70% of the customers would return the movie by the second night anyway. A sample of 500 customers found 68% returned the movie before the third night.
a. Given the marketing team's estimate, what would be the probability of a sample result with 68% or fewer returns before the third night?
b. Based on your calculations, would you recommend the adoption of the new rental policy? Support your answer with statistical reasoning and calculations.

6.40 The file on your CD-ROM called *Patients* contains information for a random sample of geriatric patients. During a meeting, one hospital administrator indicated that 70% of the geriatric patients are males.
a. What is the sample proportion of male patients?
b. Assuming that the administrator is correct, what is the probability that a sample of this size would have a sample proportion as extreme or more extreme than the one you found in part a?
c. Would you conclude that the administrator's assertion concerning the proportion of male geriatric patients is correct? Justify your answer.

Advanced Business Applications

6.41 Referring to Exercise 6.40, the belief is that 80% of all geriatric patients are covered by Medicare (Code = CARE). Assuming that the data in the *Patients* file represents a random sample of all hospital geriatric patients,
a. What proportion of patients in the sample are covered by Medicare?
b. Determine probability of getting a sample proportion as extreme or more extreme than this one if the administrator's 80% figure is correct.
c. Based on the probability you computed in part b, what conclusion should the hospital administrator reach concerning the proportion of geriatric patients covered by Medicare? Discuss.

6.42 The data file *Trucks* contains a sample of 200 trucks that were weighed on two scales. The WIM (Weigh-in-Motion) scale weighs trucks as they drive down the highway. The POE scale weighs trucks while they are stopped in a port-of-entry station. The makers of the WIM scale believe that their scale will weigh heavier than the POE scale 60% of the time when gross weight is considered.
a. Create a new variable that has a value equal to 1 when the WIM gross weight is greater than POE gross weight, and 0 otherwise.
b. Determine the sample proportion of times the WIM gross weight exceeds the POE gross weight.
c. Based on this sample, what is the probability of finding a proportion less than that found in part b? For this calculation, assume the WIM maker's assertion is correct.
d. Based on the probability found in part c, what should the WIM maker conclude? Is his 60% figure reasonable?

6.43 Refer to Exercise 6.42. The *Trucks* file also contains data that indicate the speed the trucks were traveling when they crossed the WIM scale.
a. Determine the percentage of the trucks in the sample that were exceeding 55 mph when they crossed the WIM scale.
b. If the state highway patrol has indicated in the past that 30% of all trucks exceed the 55 mph speed limit on this section of highway, do the sample data tend to support or refute the highway patrol? (Hint: Compute the probability of getting the sample proportion equal to or more extreme than the one you computed. Base your response on this probability.)

6.44 Guidian Manufacturing supplies parts to Standard Generator, which incorporates the parts in its generators. Standard wishes to negotiate a contract with Guidian concerning the proportion of defective parts it receives. It wishes the defective rate to be no larger than 0.05. Guidian has established from past performance that its defective rate is 0.076.
a. Standard managers propose a way of checking to determine that the defective rate (*p*) does not exceed 0.05. They propose sampling 150 of the parts. If more than 5 are defective, they will conclude that $p > 0.05$ and cancel the contract. Calculate the probability that Standard will cancel the contract even if the defective rate is 0.05. After examining this probability, Guidian refuses to sign this contract and instead proposes that the contract only be cancelled if more than 10 are defective. Calculate the probability the contract isn't cancelled if the defective rate is what Guidian knows it to be (i.e., 0.076).
b. Write a report to both companies discussing the issues.

Summary and Conclusions

When a manager selects a sample, it is only one of many samples that could have been selected. Consequently the sample mean, $\bar{x}$, is only one of the many possible sample means that could have been found. There is no reason to believe that the single $\bar{x}$ value will equal the population mean, μ. The difference between $\bar{x}$ and μ is called sampling error. Because sampling error exists, decision makers must be aware of how the sample means are distributed in order to discuss the potential for extreme sampling error.

This chapter introduced two important theorems. These theorems describe the distribution of sample means taken from any population. The more important of these theorems is the Central Limit Theorem. The concepts of estimation and hypothesis testing depend heavily on the Central Limit Theorem. The important aspect of the Central Limit Theorem is that no matter how the population is distributed, if the sample size is large enough, the sampling distribution will be approximately normal.

The chapter also presented several new statistical terms, which are listed in the Key Terms section. Be sure you understand these concepts and how they apply to the material in this chapter. You will encounter these terms many times as you continue in this text.

EQUATIONS

Sampling Error of the Sample Mean
$$\text{Sampling error} = \bar{x} - \mu \qquad \textbf{6-1}$$

Population Mean
$$\mu = \frac{\sum x}{N} \qquad \textbf{6-2}$$

Sample Mean
$$\bar{x} = \frac{\sum x}{n} \qquad \textbf{6-3}$$

z-Value for Sampling Distribution of $\bar{x}$
$$z = \frac{\bar{x} - \mu}{\frac{\sigma}{\sqrt{n}}} \qquad \textbf{6-4}$$

z-Value Adjusted for the Finite Population Correction Factor
$$z = \frac{\bar{x} - \mu}{\frac{\sigma}{\sqrt{n}} \sqrt{\frac{N - n}{N - 1}}} \qquad \textbf{6-5}$$

Population Proportion

$$p = \frac{X}{N} \qquad \textbf{6-6}$$

Sample Proportion

$$\bar{p} = \frac{x}{n} \qquad \textbf{6-7}$$

Single-Proportion Sampling Error

$$\text{Sampling error} = \bar{p} - p \qquad \textbf{6-8}$$

Mean of the Sampling Distribution of $\bar{p}$

$$\text{Mean} = \mu_{\bar{p}} = p \qquad \textbf{6-9}$$

Standard Deviation of the Sampling Distribution of $\bar{p}$

$$\sigma_{\bar{p}} = \sqrt{\frac{p(1-p)}{n}} \qquad \textbf{6-10}$$

z-Value for Proportions

$$z = \frac{\bar{p} - p}{\sigma_{\bar{p}}} \qquad \textbf{6-11}$$

Key Terms

Central Limit Theorem, 242
Finite Population Correction Factor, 241
Parameter, 251

Population Proportion, 251
Sampling Distribution, 235
Sampling Error, 228

Simple Random Sample, 230
Theorem 6-1, 239
Unbiased Estimator, 236

CHAPTER EXERCISES

Conceptual Questions

6.45 Explain in your own words what is meant by the term *sampling distribution*.

6.46 Discuss why the sampling distribution will be less variable than the population distribution. Give a short example to illustrate your answer.

6.47 Discuss why the standard error of a sampling distribution is considered a measure of average sampling error.

6.48 Discuss (using your own examples) what effect the finite correction factor has on the computation of the standard error of the sampling distribution as the sample size gets small relative to the size of the population.

6.49 The Central Limit Theorem indicates that the sampling distribution of $\bar{x}$ will have a standard deviation of $\sigma_{\bar{x}} = \frac{\sigma}{\sqrt{n}}$.

Discuss why the sampling distribution of $\bar{x}$ should have less dispersion than the population distribution.

6.50 Under what conditions should the finite correction factor be used in determining the standard error of a sampling distribution?

6.51 A researcher has collected all possible samples of a size of 150 from a population and has listed the sample means for each of these samples.
a. If the average of the sample means is 450.55, what would be the numerical value of the true population mean? Discuss.
b. If the standard deviation of the sample means is 12.25, determine the standard deviation of the model from which the samples came. To perform this calculation, assume the population has a size of 1,250.

6.52 In Exercise 6.51, a researcher collected all possible samples of a given size and found that the average of the sample means was 450.55. The researcher recognized that the sample means will vary around the true population mean. Consequently, she found the standard deviation of the sample means to be 30.56.

a. Discuss this number. What term is used to describe this number?
b. Based on the 30.56 value, determine the population standard deviation.

6.53 Suppose we are told the sampling distribution developed from a sample of size 400, has a mean of 56.78, and has a standard error of 9.6. If the population is known to be normally distributed, what are the population mean and the population standard deviation? Discuss how these values relate to the values for the sampling distribution.

6.54 If a population is known to be normally distributed, what size sample is required to ensure that the sampling distribution is normally distributed?

6.55 Suppose a population is normally distributed. What is the probability of finding a sample mean, $\bar{x}$, that is greater than the population mean?

Business Applications

6.56 The Hardcone Baking Company recently performed a market study from a sample of 400. It asked people how much they spent on bakery products per week. The average of this sample was $3.45.
a. Calculate the probability that a sample of 400 would produce a sample mean exactly equal to $3.45.
b. Calculate the probability that two samples of 400 would both produce sample means of $3.45.
c. Review the answers to parts a and b. Is it reasonable to expect that another sample of size 400 would result in the same sample average? Discuss why or why not.

6.57 Recently, a school system in the Midwest performed a study of its students' performance on mathematics examinations. If the population of all examination scores is thought to be normally distributed, with a mean of 68 points and a standard deviation of 12 points,
a. What are the mean and standard deviation for the sampling distribution of $\bar{x}$ if the sample size is 100? Discuss why the sampling distribution has a smaller standard deviation that the population.

b. Suppose the school system takes a second sample of size 500. What is the relationship between the sampling distributions of the two sample means? Illustrate using graphs.

6.58 The time it takes a mechanic to tune an engine is known to be normally distributed, with a mean of 45 minutes and a standard deviation of 14 minutes.
  a. Determine the mean and standard error of a sampling distribution for a sample size of 20 tune-ups. Draw a picture of the sampling distribution.
  b. Calculate the largest sampling error you would expect to make in estimating the population mean with the sample size of 20 tune-ups.

6.59 The money spent by individuals for recreation in a particular target population is normally distributed.
  a. How much will the standard error be reduced if the sample size is doubled? Discuss.
  b. The z-value for a particular person's expenditure for recreation is 2.50. Determine the proportion of individuals who spend more on recreation than this individual.

6.60 Suppose the interest earned on savings accounts by individuals at a particular bank has a distribution that may be skewed to the right. The bank asserts that the population mean is $450 earned per year, with a standard deviation of $67.
  a. Describe the sampling distribution for a sample of size 100. Also show the sampling distribution in graphical form.
  b. An audit has been conducted on the bank's savings accounts. One hundred accounts were randomly sampled. The mean of the sample was $443. Do you believe the bank's assertion to be an exaggeration? Support your answer with calculation and statistical reasoning.

6.61 The population distribution for family incomes in the Canadian province of British Columbia is unknown, but it has a mean of $21,500 and a standard deviation of $1,700.
  a. A sample of size 200 is to be selected and the sample mean calculated. Describe the sampling distribution in terms of its general shape and descriptive measures.
  b. If the sample size were actually 60 instead of 200, how would the sampling distribution be affected? Illustrate with a graph, indicating the mean and standard error.
  c. What is the probability that a sample of 60 selected randomly from the population will have a mean equal to or greater than $21,300?

6.62 The Galusha CPA firm performs audits for the Alien Tool Company. As part of an audit, the accountant in charge selected a random sample of 300 accounts from the 2,000 accounts receivable on Alien's books. He was particularly interested in the average account balance.
  a. If the computer records indicate that the true average balance for all 2,000 accounts if $786.98, with a standard deviation of $356.75, describe the sampling distribution of the sample mean. (Hint: Use the finite correction factor.)
  b. Draw an illustration of the sampling distribution.
  c. Describe the sampling distribution for the mean if the accountant changes the sample size to 500 accounts. Also discuss why it is not necessary to know the shape of the population distribution.

d. The accountant's sample of 500 produced a mean of $795.20. If the computer records are correct with regard to the standard deviation of the account balances, do you believe the figure given for the average of the account balances? Support you answer with probability calculations and rationale.

6.63 The Chair Company repairs old furniture and restores it to "better than original" condition. Records indicate the time it takes to refinish and otherwise restore a standard dining room set is normally distributed, with a mean of 30 hours and a standard deviation of 5 hours. Recently a customer complained that he was charged too much for work performed. To settle the argument, the manager of the company offered the customer the following option. The company will select a random sample of past work performed on tables similar to the customer's table. If the sample mean based on five randomly selected work times turns out to be less than the time required for his table, the Chair Company will refund his money. If the mean of this sample turns out to be greater than or equal to his billed time, he will pay the company half again the amount of the bill.
  a. Taking into account the average and standard deviation of all work times on file, do you think the manager is wise to make such an offer if this customer's billed time was 26 hours? Discuss why or why not.
  b. What would be your response if the customer's billed time was 28 hours? Supply probability calculations and statistical reasoning to support your answer.

6.64 The Swim and Racquet Club is in the process of establishing a policy for how long a court may be reserved at any one time. The club pro has said that he thinks the average time required to complete a tennis match is 90 minutes, with a standard deviation of 10 minutes. To help make the policy, club managers have selected a random sample of 100 tennis matches and have determined that the mean time for completion is 75 minutes. The managers' spokesperson maintains that this data supports the club's pro and says the managers are preparing to put the maximum time to reserve a court to be 90 minutes. They argue that it is quite understandable that a sample of size 100 would produce a sample mean of 75 minutes. After all, 75 is only 1.5 standard deviations below the mean of 90 minutes.
  a. Calculate the probability that a sample mean of 75 or less would occur if the club pro were correct in his assessment of mean and standard deviation.
  b. Based on your answer to part a, does it appear that the 90-minute limit will be sufficient? Explain.

6.65 The Environmental Protection Agency (EPA) requires all U.S. automobile makers to test their cars for mileage in the city and on the highway. One company has indicated that a certain model will get 25 miles per gallon (mpg) in the city and 32 mpg on the highway. However, not all cars of a given model will get the same mileage; these mileage ratings are simply averages. Furthermore, because there is variation among cars, the manufacturer has discovered that the standard deviation is 3 mpg for city driving and 2 mpg for highway driving.
  a. Given this information, suppose the San Francisco Police Department has purchased a random sample of 64 cars from this company. The police officers have driven these cars exclusively in the city and have recorded

an average of 24.25 mpg. Based on this sample information, what would you conclude about the EPA city-driving average mileage rating for this car? Base your response on the probability of getting a sample mean of 24.25 mpg or less.

b. The police chief has asked his officers to drive the cars to Los Angeles and back to determine how the cars perform in highway driving. The 64 cars averaged 34 mpg. What can the chief conclude about the advertised highway mileage? Explain your answer.

Advanced Business Applications

6.66 The Sullivan Advertising Agency has determined that the average cost to develop a 30-second commercial is $20,000. The standard deviation is $3,000. Suppose a random sample of 50 commercials is selected and the average cost is $20,300.

a. What are the chances of finding a sample mean this high or higher?

b. Sullivan's has budgeted $2,250,000 to finance the development of its next 100 commercials. Is this a realistic figure? Determine the chances that Sullivan's will overrun their budget. (Assume the 100 commercials constitute a simple random sample.)

6.67 Referring to Exercise 6.66, suppose the Sullivan Advertising Agency is interested in establishing a pricing policy for prospective customers of 30-second commercials. Recall the mean cost is $20,000, with a standard deviation of $3,000.

a. What are the chances of a given commercial costing between $19,500 and $22,000?

b. What is the probability of a sample of 36 commercials having an average cost between $19,500 and $22,000? Explain why these probabilities are different.

6.68 The Baily Hill Bicycle Shop sells mountain bikes and offers a maintenance program to its customers. The manager has found the average repair bill during the maintenance program's first year to be $15.30, with a standard deviation of $7.00.

a. What is the probability a random sample of 40 customers will have a mean repair cost exceeding $16.00?

b. What is the probability the mean repair cost for a sample of 100 customers will be between $15.10 and $15.80?

c. The manager has decided to offer a Spring Special. He is aware of the mean and standard deviation for repair bills last year. Therefore, he has decided to randomly select and repair 50 bicycles for $14 each. He notes that this is not even one standard deviation below the mean price to make such repairs. He asks your advice. Is this a risky thing to do? Based on the probability of the mean repair bill being $14.00 or less, what would you recommend? Discuss.

6.69 As part of a marketing study, the Food King Supermarket chain has randomly sampled 150 customers. The average dollar volume purchased by the customers in this sample was $31.14.

Before sampling, the company assumed that the distribution of customer purchases had a mean of $30.00 and a standard deviation of $8.00. If these figures are correct, what is the probability of observing a sample mean of $31.14 or greater? What would this probability indicate to you concerning the assumed distribution of customer purchases?

6.70 The Bendbo Corporation has a total of 300 employees in its two manufacturing locations and the headquarters office. A study conducted five years ago showed the average commuting distance to work for Bendbo employees was 6.2 miles, with a standard deviation of 3 miles. Recently, a follow-up study based on a random sample of 100 employees indicated an average travel distance of 5.9 miles.

a. Assuming that the mean and standard deviation of the original study hold, what is the probability of obtaining a sample mean of 5.9 miles or less?

b. Based on this probability, do you think the average travel distance may have decreased?

c. A second random sample of 40 was selected. This sample produced a mean travel distance of 5.9 miles. If the mean for all employees is 6.2 miles and the standard deviation is 3 miles, what is the probability of observing a sample mean of 5.9 miles or less?

d. Discuss why the probabilities differ even though the sample results were the same in each case.

6.71 An automatic saw at a local lumber mill cuts 2-by-4s to an average length of 120 inches. However, because the saw is a mechanical device, not all the boards are 120 inches long. In fact, the distribution of lengths has a variance of 0.64. The saw operator took a sample of 36 boards.

a. If the saw is set correctly, what is the probability the average length of the sample boards is more than 120.2 inches?

b. What is the probability the sample mean length is less than 119.73 inches?

c. What should the saw operator conclude if she finds the sample to have an average length of 120.3 inches?

d. An order has been received for 1,000 2-by-4s. However, the purchaser has declared that he will refuse the shipment if any boards are more than 1.5 inches different than your stated average. Is this a good proposition for the lumber company? Support your opinion with statistical calculations and reasoning. You may have to make some assumptions to justify your calculations. Do so, but specify what they are.

6.72 The manager for quality control at Bixby Electronics recently reviewed a contract the company has with one of the suppliers of a particular component part. According to the contract, the defective rate in the components is to be no more than 7%. A large quantity of the components has just arrived at Bixby Electronics. As part of the regular receiving process, a random sample of 100 parts was selected. In this sample 12% of the parts were found to be defective.

a. What is the probability of 12% or more of the components being defective if the true percentage defective in the population is actually 7%?

b. Based on the probability you have computed, what should the quality control manager conclude about the entire shipment of components with respect to the 7% defective limit?

c. Calculate the value for control limits for the quality control procedure. The control limits are established at 3 standard deviations from the mean. (Assume $n = 100$.)

d. Determine the probability that a sample proportion from a sample of size 100 would be beyond the control limits if the true rate of defective items is 7%.

6.73 The Republican Election Committee maintains that 34% of the members of the AFL-CIO labor union are registered Republicans, but a random sample of 300 members shows a sample proportion of 28% registered Republicans.
   a. What statistical term is given to the difference between the 28% and the 34%?
   b. Also, how likely is it that a sample of this size would contain 28% or fewer Republicans if the 34% figure is correct?

6.74 The average of all accounts payable for a large national electronics firm has been determined to be $2,755, with a standard deviation of $375.
   a. Determine the probability that a random sample of 36 accounts payable would have a sample mean (1) greater than $2,850, (2) less than $2,700, or (3) between $2,650 and $2,750?
   b. Determine the largest accounts payable that the electronics firm has experienced. Assume that these accounts have a normal distribution.

6.75 Suppose it is thought that 45% of all computer users in Seattle have made at least one purchase using the Internet. You have just conducted a random sample of 49 computer users in Seattle and have found that 18 of them have made at least one purchase using the Internet.
   a. Does your sample proportion surprise you? How likely are you to see a sample proportion this small or smaller if the true population proportion is 0.45?
   b. Using your knowledge of the normal distribution, determine the maximum sampling error you could experience in such a sample.

6.76 The file *High Desert Banking* contains information regarding consumer, real estate, and small commercial loans made last year by the bank. Use your computer software to
   a. Construct a frequency histogram using eight classes for dollar values of loans made last year. Does the population distribution appear to be normally distributed?
   b. Compute the population mean for all loans made last year.
   c. Compute the population standard deviation for all loans made last year.
   d. Select a simple random sample of 36 loans. Compute the sample mean. By how much does the sample mean differ from the population mean? Use the Central Limit Theorem to determine the probability that you would have a sample mean this small or smaller and the probability that you would have a sample mean this large or larger.

6.77 Marketing research indicates that 37% of all customers of a nationwide pizza chain are college students.
   a. What is the probability that a random sample of 625 customers of the pizza chain would contain 250 or more people who are college students?
   b. A local pizzeria wishes to attract college students. The pizzeria advertises in the college newspaper that it will give a coffee mug displaying the local college's insignia to every customer who presents a student ID from that college on a certain Saturday. Normally the pizzeria has approximately 100 customers on Saturdays. If the pizzeria stocks 50 coffee mugs, determine the probability that it will have enough coffee mugs to give to the students if the advertisement doesn't work (i.e., doesn't attract a larger percentage of students). (Assume that the 100 customers constitutes a random sample of the population of customers.)

6.78 The file *Best-Companies* contains selected information from the 100 best companies for U.S. employees as determined by *Fortune* magazine. Use this file to perform the following:
   a. Calculate the average number of U.S. employees for all 100 companies.
   b. Calculate the population standard deviation for the variable number of U.S. employees.
   c. Select a simple random sample of 36 companies. Compute the average number of U.S. employees for the sample. Is the sample mean identical to the population mean? Would you expect it to be? Why or why not?
   d. Compute the standard error of the sampling distribution of the mean for a sample size of 36. Is this value larger than or smaller than the population standard deviation?
   e. What is the probability that for a sample of 36 you would get a sample mean that is at least 15,000 employees?

6.79 A sample of 500 business professionals found that 30% chose an airline based on price.
   a. If the population proportion of all business professionals who select an airline based on price is 0.27, then what is the probability that we would find a sample proportion of 0.30 or more?
   b. If the population proportion of all business professionals who select an airline based on price is 0.29, then what is the probability that we would find a sample proportion of 0.30 or more?
   c. If you had to decide whether the proportion of business professionals who select an airline based on price was at most 0.27 or greater than 0.27, what would you conclude? Justify your answer statistically.

6.80 When its ovens are working properly, the time required to bake fruit pies at Ellardo Bakeries is normally distributed, with a mean of 45 minutes and a standard deviation of 5 minutes. Yesterday, a random sample of 16 had an average baking time of 50 minutes.
   a. If Ellardo's ovens are working correctly, how likely is it that a sample of 16 pies would have an average baking time of 50 minutes or more?
   b. Would you recommend that Ellardo inspect its ovens to see if they are working properly? Justify your answer.

6.81 If the true proportion of home computer users who would purchase an additional telephone line for Internet use is 0.27, then what is the probability that a random sample of 500 computer users would produce a sample proportion between 0.25 and 0.29?

6.82 The CD-ROM file called *Cozine* contains data on weights of garbage trucks. Assume these data represent the population of interest. Suppose the landfill manager plans to select a random sample of 30 truck weights and from that will develop a report to the county commissioners.
   a. Determine the population mean and population standard deviation.

b. Develop a frequency histogram for these data.

c. Write a paragraph that describes the population.

d. Select a random sample of 30 weights. Compute the sample mean weight.

e. Compute the probability of getting a sample mean as extreme or more extreme than the one you calculated.

f. Based on the probability computed in part e, does it appear that this sample may have attributes, such as the mean, similar to those of the population, or is the sampling error too great? Discuss.

6.83 ● The Celltone company offers cell phone service with two plans for customers: Basic Plan and Business Plan.

When the owners first devised the idea of offering the two plans, they felt that 70% of all customers would select the Business Plan. The data file *Celltone* contains data for a random sample of 200 customers.

a. Compute the sample proportion of Business Plan customers.

b. What is the probability that a sample will contain a proportion as extreme or more extreme than the one computed in part a if the 70% figure is correct for the population?

c. Based on the result in part b, what conclusion should the owner reach about his assumption regarding Business Plan customers? Discuss.

CASE 6-A:

Carpita Bottling Company

Don Carpita owns and operates Carpita Bottling Company in Lakeland, Wisconsin. The company bottles soda pop and beer and distributes the products in the counties surrounding Lakeland.

The company has four bottling machines, which can be adjusted to fill bottles at any mean fill level between 2 ounces and 72 ounces. The machines exhibit some variation in actual fill from the mean setting. For instance, if the mean setting is 16 ounces, the actual fill may be slightly more or less than that amount.

Three of the four filling machines are relatively new, and their fill variation is not as great as that of the older machine. Don has observed that the standard deviation in fill for the three new machines is about 1% of the mean fill level when the mean fill is set at 16 ounces or less, and it is 0.5% of the mean at settings exceeding 16 ounces. The older machine has a standard deviation of about 1.5% of the mean setting regardless of the mean fill setting. However, the older machine tends to underfill bottles more than overfill, so the older machine is set at a mean fill slightly in excess of the desired mean to compensate for the propensity to underfill. For example, when 16-ounce bottles are to be filled, the machine is set at a mean fill level of 16.05 ounces.

The company can simultaneously fill bottles with two brands of soda pop using two machines, and it can use the other two machines to bottle beer. Although each filling machine has its own

warehouse and the products are loaded from the warehouse directly on a truck, products from two or more filling machines may be loaded on the same truck. However, an individual store almost always receives bottles on a particular day from just one machine.

On Saturday morning Don received a call at home from the J. R. Summers Grocery store manager. She was very upset because the shipment of 16-ounce bottles of beer received yesterday contained several bottles that were not adequately filled. The manager wanted Don to replace the entire shipment at once.

Don gulped down his coffee and prepared to head to the store to check out the problem. He started thinking how he could determine which machine was responsible for the problem. If he could at least determine whether it was the old machine or one of the new ones, he could save his maintenance people a lot of time and effort checking all the machines.

His plan was to select a sample of 64 bottles of beer from the store and measure the contents. Don figures that he might be able to determine, on the basis of the average contents, whether it is more likely that the beer was bottled by a new machine or by the old one.

The results of the sampling showed an average of 15.993 ounces. Now Don needs some help in determining whether a sample mean of 15.993 ounces or less is more likely to come from the new machines or the older machine.

CASE 6-B:

Truck Safety Inspection

The Idaho Department of Law Enforcement, in conjunction with the federal government, recently began a truck inspection program in Idaho. The current inspection effort is limited to an inspection of only those trucks that visually appear to have some defect when they stop at one of the weigh stations in the state. The proposed inspection program will not be limited to the trucks with visible defects, but it will potentially subject all trucks to a comprehensive safety inspection.

Jane Lund of the Department of Law Enforcement is in charge of the new program. She has stated that the ultimate objective of the new

truck inspection program is to reduce the number of trucks with safety defects operating in Idaho. Ideally, all trucks passing through, or operating within, Idaho would be inspected once a month, and substantial penalties would be applied to operators if safety defects were discovered. Ms. Lund is confident that such an inspection program would, without fail, reduce the number of defective trucks operating on Idaho's highways. However, each safety inspection takes about an hour, and because of limited money to hire inspectors, she realizes that all trucks cannot be inspected. She also knows it is unrealistic to have trucks wait to be inspected until trucks ahead of them have been checked. Such delays would cause problems with the drivers.

In meetings with her staff, Jane has suggested that before the inspection program begins, the number of defective trucks currently operating in Idaho should be estimated. This estimate can be compared with later estimates to see if the inspection program has been effective. To arrive at this initial estimate, Jane thinks that some sort of sampling plan to select representative trucks from the population for all trucks in the state must be developed. She has suggested that this sampling be done at the eight weigh stations near Idaho's borders, but she is unsure how to establish a statistically sound sampling plan that is practical to implement.

CASE 6-C:

Houston Nut and Candy Company

Bruce Houston wanted to get away from the office and start on a much-needed vacation that he and his family had been planning for some time. He really needed to get his packing done if they were going to make their 8:00 P.M. flight for Honolulu. But he also knew that he needed to get a potential problem straightened out before he left or he wouldn't be able to enjoy the sun and beaches of Hawaii.

Earlier in the day, Helen Stahl in quality assurance had dropped by his office with three e-mails she had received from customers in the past few days. The e-mail messages all contained essentially the same message: "Your gourmet mixed nuts contain too many peanuts!" Helen indicated that as far as she knew, there was nothing wrong with the production process. The company's standard calls for no more than 30% peanuts in the gourmet mix. Obviously, some cans will contain more, some less, but overall the proportion should not exceed 30%. The production line controls this by starting with fixed quantities of nuts that go into the storage vats that lead to the filling machine.

Helen assured Bruce that the vats started with 30% peanuts, 30% cashews, and 40% walnuts and other varieties. These nuts are thoroughly mixed and then the cans are filled. According to Helen, the contents of each can be considered a random sample of the total production.

While Helen waited in his office, Bruce called one of the unhappy customers to find out the basis of his complaint. This customer indicated that of the 345 nuts in a can, there were 125 peanuts when they would have expected no more than 103. A call to a second customer indicated that of 360 nuts in a can, 144 were peanuts. Bruce called the third customer and heard similar results.

After Helen left, Bruce decided to assign Helen three tasks. First he wanted her to determine the chances of other customers getting the results that were reported by the unhappy customers if the process proportion of peanuts was really 30%. Second, Bruce reasoned that if the vats started out with 30% peanuts, about half the cans would have more than 30% and half would have less than 30% by chance. He decided to have Helen open a random sample of 100 cans. For each can, she was to record whether the can contained more than 30% peanuts. Then, he wanted her to compute the probability of finding whatever result she recorded assuming that the proportion of cans with more than 30% peanuts was equal to 0.50. Finally, he wanted her to write him a short report summarizing the results along with suggestions for how they might improve things if improvement was needed. (The data file *Nuts* contains the results of the sample of 100 cans.)

Bruce e-mailed these instructions to Helen, shut off his lights, said good-bye to Gladys at the front desk, and headed for home.

General References

1. Albright, S. Christian, Wayne L. Winston, and Christopher Zappe, *Data Analysis and Decision Making with Microsoft Excel* (Pacific Grove, CA: Duxbury, 1999).
2. Berenson, Mark L., and David M. Levine, *Basic Business Statistics: Concepts and Applications*, 7th ed. (Upper Saddle River, NJ: Prentice Hall, 1999).
3. Cochran, William G., *Sampling Techniques*, 3rd ed. (New York: Wiley, 1977).
4. Dodge, Mark, and Craig Stinson, *Running Microsoft Excel 2000* (Redmond, WA: Microsoft Press, 1999).
5. Hogg, R. V., and Elliot A. Tanis, *Probability and Statistical Inference*, 5th ed. (Upper Saddle River, NJ: Prentice Hall, 1997).
6. Johnson, Richard A., and Dean W. Wichern, *Business Statistics: Decision Making with Data* (New York: Wiley, 1997).
7. *Microsoft Excel 2000* (Redmond, WA: Microsoft Corp., 1999).
8. *Minitab for Windows Version 13* (State College, PA: Minitab, 2000).

CHAPTER 7

Estimating Population Values

CHAPTER OUTCOMES

After studying the material in Chapter 7, you should be able to:

- Distinguish between a point estimate and a confidence interval estimate.
- Construct and interpret a confidence interval estimate for a single population mean using both the standard normal and *t* distributions.
- Determine the required sample size for estimating a single population mean.
- Establish and interpret a confidence interval estimate for a single population proportion.

WHY YOU NEED TO KNOW

Wherever you find yourself working, you may need to know population values (*parameters*) to help you make decisions. An accountant needs to know the percentage of accounts with correct balances. A marketing manager needs to know the average income in her target-market area. A manufacturing manager needs to know the average machine downtime in his plant. The programming manager at a major television network needs to know the percentage of people watching each of his shows so he can cancel the poor performers. A restaurant manager needs to know the percentage of customers who will order the daily special so she will know how many orders to have available.

In these cases and many others like them, decision makers need to know a population parameter. However, gaining access to an entire population is extremely expensive and time-consuming and, in many cases, infeasible. Therefore, an alternative approach is to select a sample from the population. The sample data are used to compute a desired statistic that forms an estimate of the corresponding population parameter.

Chapter 1 discussed various sampling techniques, including statistical and nonstatistical methods. Chapter 6 introduced the concepts of sampling error and sampling distributions. Chapter 7 builds on these concepts and introduces the steps needed to develop and interpret statistical estimations of various population values. The concepts introduced here will be very useful. You will undoubtedly need to estimate population parameters as a regular part of your managerial decision-making activities. In addition, you will receive estimates that other people have developed that you will need to evaluate before relying on them as inputs to your decision-making process. Was the sample size sufficiently large to provide valid estimates of the population parameter? How confident can I be that the estimate matches the population parameter of interest? These and similar questions can all be answered using the concepts and tools presented in this chapter.

7-1 POINT AND CONFIDENCE INTERVAL ESTIMATES FOR A POPULATION MEAN

POINT ESTIMATES AND CONFIDENCE INTERVALS

You, no doubt, have either been a respondent to, or have seen the results of a political poll taken during an election year. These polls attempt to determine the percentage of voters who will favor a particular candidate or a particular issue. For example, suppose a poll indicates that 62% of the people older than 18 in your state favor limiting property taxes to 1% of the market value of the property. The pollsters have not contacted every person in the state, but rather they have sampled only a relatively few people to arrive at the 62% figure. In statistical terminology, the 62% is the **point estimate** for the true population percentage of people who favor the property-tax limitation.

Point Estimate

A single number, determined from a sample, that is used to estimate the corresponding population parameter.

The Environmental Protection Agency (EPA) tests the mileage of automobiles sold in the United States. The resulting EPA mileage rating is actually a point estimate for the true average mileage of all cars of a given model.

Cost accountants study their company's production processes to determine product costs. Often the accountants select a sample of items and follow each one through a complete production process. The costs at each step in the process are measured and summed to determine the total cost. This figure is the point estimate for the true average cost of all the items produced. The point estimate is used in assigning a selling price to the finished product.

Which point estimator the decision maker uses depends on the population characteristic the decision maker wishes to estimate. However, regardless of the population value being estimated, we always expect **sampling error**.

Sampling Error

The difference between a value (a statistic) computed from a sample and the corresponding value (a parameter) computed from the population.

Chapter 6 discussed sampling error. We cannot eliminate sampling error, but we can deal with it in our decision process. For example, when cost accountants use $\bar{x}$, the average cost of a sample of items, to establish the average cost of production, the point estimate, $\bar{x}$, will most likely not equa the population mean, μ. But with $\bar{x}$ as their only information, they will have no way of determining how much in error it is.

To overcome this problem with point estimates, the most common procedure is to calculate an interval estimate known as a **confidence interval**.

Confidence Interval

An interval developed from sample values such that if all possible intervals of a given width were constructed, a percentage of these intervals, known as the confidence level, would include the true population parameter.

Lower Confidence Limit   **Upper Confidence**

Point
Estimate

An example will help to make this definition clear.

Excel and Minitab Tutorial

Nagel Beverage Company—The Nagel Beverage Company has recently installed a new soft-drink filling machine that allows the operator to adjust the mean fill quantity. However, no matter what the mean setting, the actual volume of the liquid in each can will vary. The machine has been carefully tested and is known to fill cans with a standard deviation of σ = 0.2 ounce.

The filling machine has been adjusted to fill cans at an average of 12 ounces. After running the machine for several hours, a simple random sample of 100 cans is selected and the volume of soda in each can is measured in the company's quality lab. Figure 7-1 shows the frequency histogram of the sample data. (The data are in a file on your CD-ROM called *Nagel-Beveragea*.) Notice that the distribution seems to be centered at a point higher than 12 ounces. The manager wishes to use the sample data to estimate the mean fill amount for all cans filled by this machine.

FIGURE 7-1

Excel Histogram for Nagel Beverage

Excel Instructions:
1. Open file: Nagel Beverage
2. Create bins (upper limit of each class).
3. Select Tools.
4. Select Histogram.
5. Define data and bins ranges.
6. Check Chart Output.

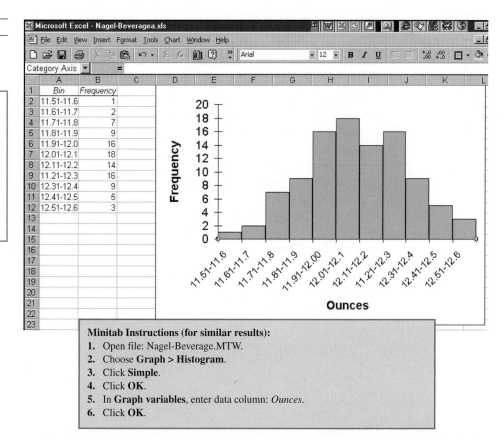

Minitab Instructions (for similar results):
1. Open file: Nagel-Beverage.MTW.
2. Choose **Graph > Histogram**.
3. Click **Simple**.
4. Click **OK**.
5. In **Graph variables**, enter data column: *Ounces*.
6. Click **OK**.

FIGURE 7-2

Sampling Distribution of $\bar{x}$

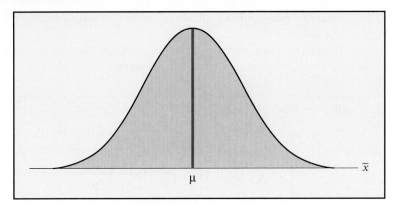

The sample mean computed from 100 cans is $\bar{x}$ = 12.09 ounces. This is the *point estimate* of the population mean, μ. Because of the potential for sampling error, the manager should not expect a particular $\bar{x}$ to equal μ. However, as discussed in Chapter 6, the Central Limit Theorem indicates that the distribution of all possible sample means will be approximately normally distributed around the population mean, as illustrated in Figure 7-2.

Although the sample mean is 12.09 ounces, the manager knows the true population mean may be higher or lower than this number. To account for the potential for sampling error, the manager can develop a *confidence interval estimate* for μ. This estimate will take the form:

Lower confidence limit   Upper confidence limit

$$\bar{x} = 12.09$$

The key now is to determine the upper and lower limits of the interval. The specific method for computing these values depends on whether the population standard deviation, σ, is known or unknown. We first take up the case in which σ is known.

CONFIDENCE INTERVAL ESTIMATE FOR THE POPULATION MEAN, σ KNOWN

There are two cases that must be considered. In the case in which the simple random sample is drawn from a normal distribution with a mean of μ and a standard deviation of σ, the sampling distribution of the sample mean is a normal distribution with a mean of μ and a standard deviation (or *standard error*) of $\sigma/\sqrt{n}$. This is true for any sample size.

The second case is that in which the population does not have a normal distribution. Chapter 6 addressed these specific circumstances. Recall that in such cases the Central Limit Theorem can be invoked if the sample size is sufficiently large ($n \geq 30$). In such cases, the sampling distribution is also a normal distribution, with a mean of μ and a standard deviation (standard error) of $\sigma/\sqrt{n}$.

In both cases, a confidence interval can be constructed from a basic probability statement. Consider the following equation, represented by Figure 7-3, concerning the standard normal distribution. Look at the standard distribution table for z = 1.96. The value there is .4750, which corresponds to $P(1.96 \leq z \leq 0)$. Then, likewise, $P(-1.96 \leq z \leq 0)$ = .4750. The sum of these two probabilities = .95. Thus we have the following:

$$P(-1.96 \leq z \leq 1.96) = 0.95$$

The probability 0.95 corresponds to a $1 - \alpha$ confidence level where $\alpha/2$ is the area in each tail of the distribution. In Figure 7-3, $\alpha/2$ = .025. Thus $z_{\alpha/2} = z_{.025} = 1.96$ and $-z_{\alpha/2} = -z_{.025} = -1.96$. The z-values have a normal distribution, with a mean of 0 and a standard deviation of 1. Therefore, this statement says that 95% of the z-values are within 1.96 standard deviations of their mean, 0. Given that the sampling distribution of $\bar{x}$ is also normally distributed, then 95% of the possible sample means must be within 1.96 standard errors of the population mean, μ. Because the standard error is

FIGURE 7-3

Critical Value for a 95% Confidence Interval

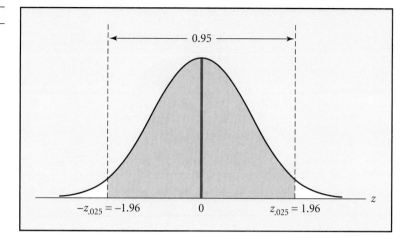

$\dfrac{\sigma}{\sqrt{n}}$, 95% of the sample means will be within $\pm 1.96\,\dfrac{\sigma}{\sqrt{n}}$ of the population mean, μ. Thus, 95% of all interval estimates formed as

$$\bar{x} - 1.96\,\frac{\sigma}{\sqrt{n}} \ \text{-----------------------} \ \bar{x} + 1.96\,\frac{\sigma}{\sqrt{n}}$$

will contain the population mean. Figure 7-4 illustrates this concept. This concept can be generalized to any probability by replacing the value 1.96 by the appropriate z-value. The z-value is referred to as the *critical value*.

Confidence Interval Calculation

All confidence interval estimates can be constructed using the same general format shown in Equation 7-1.

Confidence Interval General Format

Point estimate $\pm$ (Critical Value)(Standard Error)   **7-1**

The first step in developing a confidence interval estimate is to specify the **confidence level** that is needed to determine the critical value.

Confidence Level	*Confidence Coefficient*
A percentage less than 100 that corresponds to the percentage of all possible confidence intervals, based on a given sample size, that will contain the true population parameter.	The confidence level divided by 100%—that is, the decimal equivalent of a confidence level.

Suppose the Nagel Beverage manager specifies a 95% confidence level. This means the width of the interval estimate will be computed so that of all the possible confidence intervals that could be created from a given sample size, 95% will contain the true mean fill level for the population of all cans. The higher the confidence level, the better we feel about the one interval estimate that we will compute.

Once we decide on the confidence level, the next step is to determine the critical value. If the population standard deviation is known, and the population is normally distributed, or if the sample size is large enough to comply with the Central Limit Theorem requirements, the critical value is a z-value from the standard normal table. Equation 7-2 shows a modified form of the general format for a confidence interval.

Confidence Interval, General Format, σ Known

Point estimate $\pm z$ (Standard Error)   **7-2**

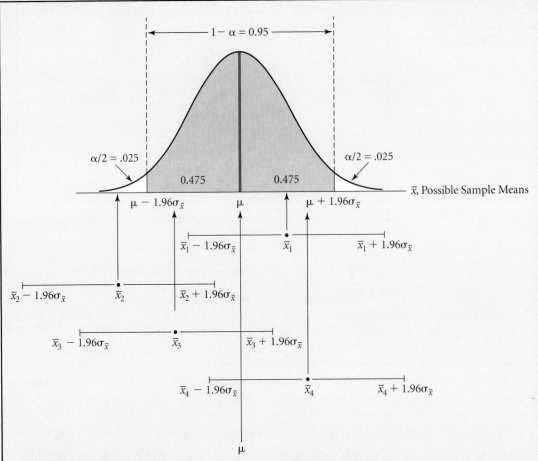

FIGURE 7-4 **Confidence Intervals from Selected Random Samples**

In Figure 7-3 you can see that the confidence coefficient defines an area that is the middle 95% of the distribution. Therefore, to find the z-value, divide the confidence coefficient by 2, giving:

$$\frac{0.95}{2} = 0.475$$

Then go to the standard normal table in Appendix D. Inside the table, where the probabilities are located, find the value that is as close to 0.475 as possible and determine the corresponding z-value. Here we find that the z-value that corresponds to a probability of 0.475 is 1.96:

$$P(0 \leq z \leq 1.96) = 0.475$$

A sample mean that falls within 1.96 standard deviations of the population mean will produce a 95% confidence interval that includes the population mean.

Note, instead of using the standard normal table, you can also find the critical z-value using Excel's **NORMSINV** function or Minitab's **Calc > Probability Distribution** command. In Excel, a probability equal to $\alpha/2$ is inserted where $(1 - \alpha)100\%$ is equal to the confidence level. For example, for a 95% confidence interval, $\alpha = 0.05$ and $\alpha/2 = 0.025$. The critical z-value is the absolute value of the function result. Then **NORMSINV(0.025)** $= -1.96$. The critical z is 1.96. Minitab requires the use of the cumulative probability equal to $1 - \alpha/2$. However, the same critical z is obtained.

The next step is to compute the standard error. In Chapter 6, you learned the standard error of the sampling distribution for $\bar{x}$ is $\frac{\sigma}{\sqrt{n}}$. Then Equation 7-3 is used to compute the confidence interval estimate of a single population mean.

Confidence Interval Estimate for μ, σ Known

$$\bar{x} \pm z_{\alpha/2} \frac{\sigma}{\sqrt{n}}$$ **7-3**

where:

$z_{\alpha/2}$ = Critical value from standard normal table for a $1 - \alpha$ confidence level
σ = Population standard deviation
n = Sample size

Nagel Beverage Company (continued)—Recall that the sample of 100 cans produced a sample mean of $\bar{x} = 12.09$ ounces and the Nagel manager knows that $\sigma = 0.2$ ounces. Thus, the 95% confidence interval estimate for the population mean is

$$\bar{x} \pm z_{.025} \frac{\sigma}{\sqrt{n}}$$
$$12.09 \pm 1.96 \frac{0.2}{\sqrt{100}}$$
$$12.09 \pm 0.039$$

12.051 ounces ------------------------ 12.129 ounces

Based on this sample information, the Nagel manager believes that the true mean fill for all cans is within the following range:

12.051 ounces   12.129 ounces

$\bar{x} = 12.09$ ounces

Because this interval does not contain the target mean of 12 ounces, the manager should conclude that the filling equipment is out of adjustment and is putting in too much soda, on average.

SUMMARY: CONFIDENCE INTERVAL ESTIMATE FOR μ WITH σ KNOWN

Computing a confidence interval estimate for the population mean when the population standard deviation is assumed known and either the population is normal or the sample size n is ≥ 30.

1. Define the population of interest and select a simple random sample of size n.

2. Specify the confidence level.

3. Compute the sample mean using:

$$\bar{x} = \frac{\sum x}{n}$$

4. Determine the standard error of the sampling distribution using:

$$\sigma_{\bar{x}} = \frac{\sigma}{\sqrt{n}}$$

5. Determine the critical value, z, from the standard normal table.

6. Compute the confidence interval estimate using:

$$\bar{x} \pm z_{\alpha/2} \frac{\sigma}{\sqrt{n}}$$

EXAMPLE 7-1: CONFIDENCE INTERVAL ESTIMATE FOR μ, σ KNOWN

Saint Regis Hospital   Administrators at Saint Regis Hospital wish to know the mean dollars spent on medical expenses for the patients who were admitted to the hospital during the previous year. To do this, they could use the following steps.

Step 1:   **Define the population of interest and select a simple random sample of size *n*.**
The population is all patients who were admitted to the hospital during the previous year. A simple random sample of 200 patients will be selected.

Step 2:   **Specify the confidence level.**
The administrators want to develop a 90% confidence interval estimate. Thus, 90% of all possible intervals will contain the population mean.

Step 3:   **Compute the sample mean.**

After the sample has been selected and the dollars spent on medical care last year have been recorded for each of the 200 people sampled, the sample mean is computed using:

$$\bar{x} = \frac{\sum x}{n}$$

Assume the sample mean is $5,230.

Step 4:   **Determine the standard error of the sampling distribution.**

Suppose past studies have indicated that the population standard deviation is

$$\sigma = \$500$$

Then the standard error of the sampling distribution is computed using:

$$\sigma_{\bar{x}} = \frac{\sigma}{\sqrt{n}} = \frac{\$500}{\sqrt{200}} = \$35.36$$

Step 5:   **Determine the critical value, z, from the standard normal table.**

Because the sample size is large, the Central Limit Theorem applies. The sampling distribution will be normally distributed, and the critical value will be a z-value from the standard normal distribution. The administrators want 90% confidence, so the z-value is determined by finding a probability in Appendix D corresponding to $\frac{0.90}{2} = 0.45$. We find 0.4495 and 0.4505, so the correct z-value is between $z = 1.64$ and $z = 1.65$. The critical value is $z = 1.645$.

Step 6:   **Compute the confidence interval estimate.**

The 90% confidence interval estimate for the population mean is

$$\bar{x} \pm z_{.05}\frac{\sigma}{\sqrt{n}}$$

$$\$5,230 \pm 1.645\frac{500}{\sqrt{200}}$$

$$\$5,230 \pm \$58.16$$

$$\$5,171.84 \text{ --------------------------------- } \$5,288.16$$

Thus, based on the sample results, with 90% confidence, the administrators at Saint Regis Hospital believe that the true population mean for dollars spent on medical care last year is between $5,171.84 and $5,288.16.

Special Message About Interpreting Confidence Intervals

There is a subtle distinction to be made here. Beginning students often wonder if it is permissible to say, "There is a 0.95 probability that the population mean is between $5,171.84 and $5,288.16." This may seem to be the logical consequence of constructing a confidence interval. However, we must be very careful to attribute probability only to random events or variables. Because the population mean is a fixed value, there can be no probability statement about the population mean. The confidence interval we have computed will either contain the population mean or it will not. If you were to produce all the possible confidence intervals using the mean of each possible sample from the population, 95% of these intervals would contain the population mean.

Impact of the Confidence Level on the Interval Estimate

Nagel Beverage (continued)—In the Nagel Beverage example, the manager specified a 95% confidence level. The resulting confidence interval estimate for the population mean was

$$\bar{x} \pm z_{.025}\frac{\sigma}{\sqrt{n}}$$

$$12.09 \pm 1.96\frac{0.2}{\sqrt{100}}$$

$$12.09 \pm 0.04$$

$$12.05 \text{ ounces } \text{ ------------------------ } 12.13 \text{ ounces}$$

The quantity, 0.04, on the right of the ± sign above is called the **margin of error**. This is illustrated in Equation 7-4. The margin of error defines the relationship between the sample mean and the population mean.

Margin of Error

The amount that is added and subtracted to the point estimate to determine the endpoints of the confidence interval.

Margin of Error for Estimating μ, σ Known

$$e = z_{\alpha/2} \frac{\sigma}{\sqrt{n}}$$

7-4

where:

$$e = \text{Margin of error}$$
$$z_{\alpha/2} = \text{Critical value}$$
$$\frac{\sigma}{\sqrt{n}} = \text{Standard error of the sampling distribution}$$

Now suppose the manager at Nagel is willing to settle for 80% confidence. This will impact the critical value. To determine the new value, divide 0.80 by 2, giving 0.40. Go to the standard normal table and locate a probability value (area under the curve) that is as close to 0.40 as possible. The corresponding z-value is 1.28.[1] The 80% confidence interval estimate is

$$\bar{x} \pm z_{0.10} \frac{\sigma}{\sqrt{n}}$$
$$12.09 \pm (1.28) \frac{0.2}{\sqrt{100}}$$
$$12.09 \pm 0.03$$
$$12.06 \text{ ounces} \text{ --------------------- } 12.12 \text{ ounces}$$

Based on this sample information and the 80% confidence interval, we believe that the true average fill level is between 12.06 ounces and 12.12 ounces.

By lowering the confidence level, the method used to produce the interval is less likely to contain the population mean. However, on the positive side, the margin of error has been reduced from 0.04 ounces to 0.03 ounces. For equivalent samples from a population:

1. If the confidence level is decreased, the margin of error is reduced.
2. If the confidence level is increased, the margin of error is increased.

The Nagel manager will need to decide which is more important, a higher confidence level or a lower margin of error.

EXAMPLE 7-2: IMPACT OF CHANGING THE CONFIDENCE LEVEL

DuVall Services   DuVall Services operates a garbage hauling company in a south Florida city. Each year, the company must apply for a new contract with the city. The contract is in part based on the pounds of garbage hauled. Part of the analysis that goes into contract development is an estimate of the mean pounds of garbage put out by each customer in the city. The city has asked for both 99% and 90% confidence interval estimates for the mean. The steps used to generate these estimates follow.

Step 1: **Define the population of interest and select a simple random sample of size *n*.**
The population is the collection of all of Duvall's customers, and a simple random sample of $n = 100$ customers is selected.

Step 2: **Specify the confidence level.**
The city requires 99% and 90% confidence interval estimates.

[1]You can also use Excel's NORMSINV function = NORMSINV(.10) = 1.281.

Step 3: **Compute the sample mean.**

After the sample has been selected and the pounds of garbage have been determined for each of the 100 customers sampled, the sample mean is computed using:

$$\bar{x} = \frac{\sum x}{n}$$

Suppose the sample mean is 40.78 pounds.

Step 4: **Determine the standard error of the sampling distribution.**

Suppose, from past years, the population standard deviation is known to be $\sigma = 12.6$ pounds. Then the standard error of the sampling distribution is computed using:

$$\sigma_{\bar{x}} = \frac{\sigma}{\sqrt{n}} = \frac{12.6}{\sqrt{100}} = 1.26 \text{ pounds}$$

Step 5: **Determine the critical value, z, from the standard normal table.**

First, the city wants a 99% confidence interval estimate so the z-value is determined by finding a probability in Appendix D corresponding to $\frac{0.99}{2} = 0.495$. The correct z-value is between $z = 2.57$ and $z = 2.58$. We split the difference to get the critical value: $z_{.005} = 2.575$. For 90% confidence, the critical z is determined to be 1.645.

Step 6: **Compute the confidence interval estimate.**

The 99% confidence interval estimate for the population mean is

$$\bar{x} \pm z_{.005} \frac{\sigma}{\sqrt{n}}$$
$$40.78 \pm 2.575 \frac{12.6}{\sqrt{100}}$$
$$40.78 \pm 3.24$$

37.54 pounds ---------------------------- 44.02 pounds

The margin of error at 99% confidence is ±3.24 pounds.
The 90% confidence interval estimate for the population mean is

$$\bar{x} \pm z_{.05} \frac{\sigma}{\sqrt{n}}$$
$$40.78 \pm 1.645 \frac{12.6}{\sqrt{100}}$$
$$40.78 \pm 2.07$$

38.71 pounds ---------------------------- 42.85 pounds

The margin of error is only 2.07 pounds when the confidence level is reduced from 99% to 90%. The margin of error will be smaller when the confidence level is smaller.

Lowering the confidence level is one way to reduce the margin of error. However, by examining Equation 7-4, you will note there are two other values that affect the margin of error. One of these is the population standard deviation. The more the population's standard deviation, σ, can be reduced, the smaller the margin of error will be. In a business environment, large standard deviations for measurements related to the quality of a product are not desired. In fact, corporations spend considerable effort to decrease the variation in their products either by changing their process or by controlling variables that cause the variation. Typically all avenues for reducing the standard deviation should be pursued before thoughts of reducing the confidence level are entertained.

Unfortunately, there are many situations in which reducing the population standard deviation is not possible. In these cases, another step that can be taken to reduce the margin of error is to increase the sample size. As you learned in Chapter 6, an increase in sample size reduces the standard error of the sampling distribution. This can be the most direct way of reducing the margin of error as long as obtaining an increased sample is not prohibitively costly or unattainable for other reasons.

Impact of the Sample Size on the Interval Estimate

Nagel Beverage (continued)—Suppose the Nagel Beverage Company production manager decided to increase the sample to 400 cans. This is a four-fold increase over the original sample size. We learned in Chapter 6 that an increase in sample size reduces the standard error of the sampling distribution because the standard error is computed as $\frac{\sigma}{\sqrt{n}}$. Thus, without adversely affecting his confidence level, the manager can reduce the margin of error by increasing his sample size.

Assume that the sample mean for the larger sample size also happens to be $\bar{x} = 12.09$ ounces. The new 95% confidence interval estimate is

$$12.09 \pm 1.96 \frac{0.2}{\sqrt{400}}$$

$$12.09 \pm 0.02$$

12.07 ounces -------------------- 12.11 ounces

Notice that by increasing the sample size to 400 cans, the margin of error is reduced from the original 0.04 ounces to 0.02 ounces. The production manager now believes that his sample mean is within ±.02 ounces of the true population mean.

He was able to reduce the margin of error without reducing the confidence level. However, the downside is that a sample of 400 cans instead of 100 cans will cost more money and take more time. That's the trade-off. Absent the possibility of reducing the population standard deviation, if he wants to reduce the margin of error, he must either reduce the confidence level or increase the sample size, or some combination of each. If he is unwilling to do so, he will have to accept the larger margin of error.

CONFIDENCE INTERVAL ESTIMATES FOR THE POPULATION MEAN, σ UNKNOWN

In the Nagel Beverage Company example, the manager was dealing with a filling machine that had a known standard deviation in fill volume. You may encounter situations in which the standard deviation is known. However, in most cases, if you do not know the population mean, you also will not know the standard deviation. When this occurs you need to make a minor, but important, modification to the confidence interval estimation process.

STUDENT'S *t*-DISTRIBUTION

When the population standard deviation is known, the sampling distribution of the mean has only one unknown parameter: its mean, μ. This is estimated by $\bar{x}$. However, when the population standard deviation is unknown, there are two unknown parameters, μ and σ, which must be estimated by $\bar{x}$ and s, respectively. This estimation doesn't affect the general format for a confidence interval, as shown earlier in Equation 7-1:

Point Estimate ± (Critical Value)(Standard Error)

However, not knowing the population standard deviation does affect the critical value. Recall that when σ is known and the population is normally distributed or the Central Limit Theorem applies, the critical value is a *z*-value taken from the standard normal table. But when σ is not known, the critical value is a *t*-value taken from a distribution called the **Student's *t*-distribution**.

Student's t-Distribution

A family of distributions that is bell-shaped and symmetric like the standard normal distribution but with greater area in the tails. Each distribution in the *t*-family is defined by its degrees of freedom. As the degrees of freedom increase, the *t*-distribution approaches the normal distribution.

Because the specific *t*-distribution chosen is based upon its *degrees of freedom*, it is important to understand what degrees of freedom means. Recall that the sample standard deviation is an estimate of the population's standard deviation and is defined as

$$s = \sqrt{\frac{\Sigma(x - \bar{x})^2}{n - 1}}$$

Therefore, if we wish to estimate the population standard deviation, we must first calculate the sample mean. The sample mean is itself an estimator of a parameter, namely the population mean. The sample mean is obtained from a sample of n randomly chosen (and, therefore, independent) data values. Once the sample mean has been obtained, there are only $n - 1$ independent pieces of data information left in the sample.

To illustrate, examine a sample of size $n = 3$ in which the sample mean is calculated to be 12. This implies that the sum of the three data values equals 36 (3×12). If you know that the first two data values are 10 and 8, respectively, then the third data value is determined to be 18. Similarly, if you know that the first two data values are 18 and 7, respectively, the third data value must be 11. You are free to choose any two of the three data values. In general, if you must estimate k parameters before you are able to estimate the population's standard deviation from a sample of n data values, you have the freedom to choose any $n - k$ data values before the remaining k values are determined. This value $n - k$ is called the **degrees of freedom**.

Degrees of Freedom

The number of independent data values available to estimate the population's standard deviation. If k parameters must be estimated before the population's standard deviation can be calculated from a sample of size n, the degrees of freedom are equal to $n - k$.

When the population is normally distributed, the t-value represents the number of standard errors $\bar{x}$ is from μ, as shown in Equation 7-5. Appendix F contains a table of standardized t-values that correspond to specified tail areas and different degrees of freedom. The t-table is used to determine the critical value when we do not know the population standard deviation. Note, in Equation 7-5, we use the sample standard deviation, s, to estimate the population standard deviation, σ. The fact that we are estimating σ is the reason the t-distribution is more spread out (i.e., has a larger standard deviation) than the normal distribution (see Figure 7-5). By estimating σ, we are introducing more uncertainty into the estimation process; therefore, to achieve the same level of confidence requires a larger number of standard deviations. As the sample size increases, our estimate of σ becomes better and the t-distribution converges to the z-distribution.

t-Value for $\bar{x}$

$$t = \frac{\bar{x} - \mu}{\dfrac{s}{\sqrt{n}}}$$

7-5

where:

$\bar{x}$ = Sample mean
μ = Population mean
s = Sample standard deviation
n = Sample size

FIGURE 7-5

t **Distribution and Normal Distribution**

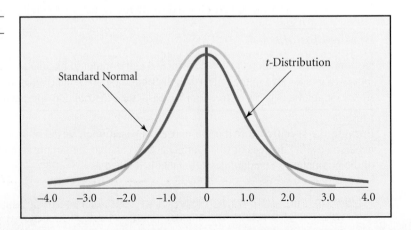

We should emphasize that the *t*-distribution is based on the assumption that the population is normally distributed. Although beyond the scope of this text, it can be shown that as long as the population is reasonably symmetric, the *t*-distribution can be used.

Excel and Minitab Tutorial

Heritage Software—Heritage Software, a maker of educational and business software, operates a service center in Tulsa, Oklahoma, where employees respond to customer calls about questions and problems with the company's software packages. Recently, a team of Heritage employees was asked to study the average length of time service representatives spend with customers. The team decided that a simple random sample of 25 calls would be collected and the population mean call time would be estimated based on the sample data. Not only did the team not know the average length of time, μ, but it also didn't know the standard deviation of length of service time, σ.

Table 7-1 shows the sample data for 25 calls, along with a box and whisker diagram. (These data are on your CD-ROM in a file called *Heritage*.) After examining the box and whisker diagram for the sample data and observing that the median is approximately equidistant between the first and third quartiles and that the whiskers extend about the same distance in each direction, the managers at Heritage Software are willing to assume the population of call times is approximately normal.[2]

Heritage's sample mean and standard deviation are

$$\bar{x} = 7.088 \text{ minutes}$$
$$s = 4.64 \text{ minutes}$$

If the managers need a single-valued estimate of the population mean, they would use the point estimate, $\bar{x} = 7.088$ minutes. However, they should realize that this point estimate is subject to sampling error. To take the sampling error into account, the managers can construct a confidence interval estimate. Equation 7-6 shows the formula for the confidence interval estimate for the population mean when the population standard deviation is unknown.

Confidence Interval Estimate for μ, σ Unknown

$$\bar{x} \pm t_{\alpha/2} \frac{s}{\sqrt{n}}$$

7-6

where:

$\bar{x}$ = Sample mean
$t_{\alpha/2}$ = Critical value from the *t*-distribution with $n - 1$ degrees of freedom for a $1 - \alpha$ level
s = Sample standard deviation
n = Sample size

TABLE 7-1

Sample Call Times for Heritage Software

7.1	11.6	12.4	8.5	0.4
13.6	1.7	11.0	6.1	11.0
1.4	16.9	3.7	3.3	0.8
3.6	2.6	14.6	6.1	6.4
1.9	7.7	8.8	6.9	9.1

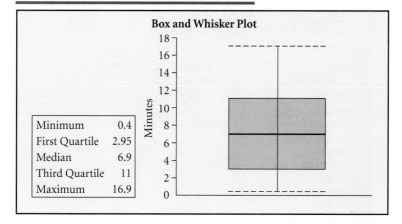

[2]Chapter 12 introduces a statistical technique called the goodness-of-fit test that can be used to test whether the sample data could have come from a normally distributed population. PHStat and Minitab contain box and whisker diagram features.

FIGURE 7-6

The Critical *t*-Value for Heritage Software

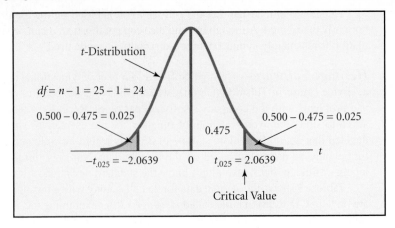

The first step is to specify the desired confidence level. For example, suppose the Heritage team specifies a

95% confidence level.

To get the critical *t*-value from the *t*-table in Appendix F, go to the top of the table to the row labeled *Conf. Level*. Locate the column headed 0.95. Next, go to the row corresponding to

$$n - 1 = 25 - 1 = 24 \text{ degrees of freedom.}$$

The critical *t*-value for 95% confidence and 24 degrees of freedom is

$$t_{\alpha/2} = 2.0639.$$

Figure 7-6 illustrates the *t*-distribution and the critical value. You can get the *t* critical value by using Excel's **TINV** function. For this example, enter **TINV(0.05,24)** to get 2.0639. (Note: The **TINV** function requires that α be used while the **NORMSINV** function requires $\alpha/2$.) You can also insert the cumulative probability 0.975 into Minitab's **Calc > Probability Distribution > *t*** command.

The Heritage team can now compute the 95% confidence interval estimate using Equation 7-6, as follows:

$$\bar{x} \pm t_{.025} \frac{s}{\sqrt{n}}$$

$$7.088 \pm 2.0639 \frac{4.64}{\sqrt{25}}$$

$$7.088 \pm 1.915$$

$$5.173 \text{ min.} \text{ ------------------------ } 9.003 \text{ min.}$$

FIGURE 7-7

Excel Output for the Heritage Example

Excel Instructions:
1. Open File: Heritage.xls
2. Click **Tools** tab.
3. Select **Data Analysis**.
4. Select **Descriptive Statistics**.
5. Define data range.
6. Check **Descriptive Statistics** and **Confidence Level**.

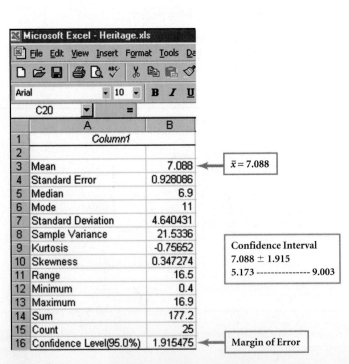

FIGURE 7-8

**Minitab Output for the
Heritage Example**

Minitab Instructions:
1. Open file: Heritage.MTW.
2. Choose **Stat > Basic Statistics > 1 − sample t**.
3. In **Samples in column**, enter data column.
4. Click **Options**.
5. In **Confidence level**, enter confidence level.
6. Click **OK. OK.**

Therefore, based on the random sample of 25 calls and the 95% confidence interval, the Heritage Software team has estimated the true average time per call to be between 5.173 minutes and 9.003 minutes.

Excel and Minitab have procedures for computing the confidence interval estimate of the population mean. The Excel output is shown in Figure 7-7. Note, the margin of error is printed. You will have to use it and the sample mean to compute the upper and lower limits. Figure 7-8 shows the results when Minitab is used to compute the 95% confidence interval estimate for the Heritage Company.

EXAMPLE 7-3: CONFIDENCE INTERVAL ESTIMATE FOR μ, σ UNKNOWN

Medlin & Associates   Medlin & Associates is a regional CPA firm located near Minneapolis. Recently a team conducted an audit for a discount chain. One part of the audit involved developing an estimate for the mean dollar error in total charges that occur during the checkout process. They wish to develop a 90% confidence interval estimate for the population mean. To do so, they can use the following steps.

Step 1:   Define the population and select a simple random sample of size n from the population.
In this case, the population consists of errors made in all customers' bills at the discount chain store in a given week. A simple random sample of $n = 20$ is selected, with the following data (Note: Positive values indicate that the customer was overcharged.)

$0.00	$1.20	$0.43	$1.00	$1.47	$0.83	$0.50	$3.34	$1.58	$1.46
−$0.36	−$1.10	$2.60	$0.00	$0.00	−$1.70	$0.83	$1.99	$0.00	$1.34

Step 2:   Specify the confidence level.
A 90% confidence interval estimate is desired.

Step 3:   Compute the sample mean and sample standard deviation.
After the sample has been selected and the billing errors have been determined for each of the 20 customers sampled, the sample mean is computed using:

$$\bar{x} = \frac{\sum x}{n} = \frac{\$15.41}{20} = \$0.77$$

The sample standard deviation is computed using:

$$s = \sqrt{\frac{\sum(x - \bar{x})^2}{n - 1}} = \sqrt{\frac{(0.00 - 0.77)^2 + (1.20 - 0.77)^2 + \cdots + (1.34 - 0.77)^2}{20 - 1}} = \$1.19$$

Step 4:   Determine the standard error of the sampling distribution.

Because the population standard deviation is unknown, the standard error of the sampling distribution is estimated using:

$$\sigma_{\bar{x}} \approx \frac{s}{\sqrt{n}} = \frac{1.194}{\sqrt{20}} = \$0.27$$

Step 5:   Determine the critical value for the desired level of confidence.

Because we do not know the population standard deviation and the sample size is reasonably small, the critical value will come from the *t*-distribution, providing we can assume that the population is normally distributed. A box and whisker diagram can give some insight about how the population might look.

Minimum	−1.7
First Quartile	0
Median	0.83
Third Quartile	1.47
Maximum	3.34

This diagram does not indicate that there is any serious skewness or other abnormality in the data, so we will continue with the normal distribution assumption.

Then the critical value for 90% confidence and $20 - 1 = 19$ degrees of freedom is found in the *t*-distribution table as $t = 1.7291$.

Step 6:   Compute the confidence interval estimate.

The 90% confidence interval estimate for the population mean is

$$\bar{x} \pm t_{.05} \frac{s}{\sqrt{n}}$$

$$0.77 \pm 1.7291 \frac{1.19}{\sqrt{20}}$$

$$0.77 \pm 0.46$$

$$\$0.31 \text{ -------------------------------- } \$1.23$$

Thus, based upon the sample data, with 90% confidence, the auditors can conclude that the population mean dollar error at the checkout is between $0.31 and $1.23.

Estimation with Larger Sample Sizes

We saw earlier that a change in sample size can affect the margin of error in a statistical estimation situation when the population standard deviation is known. This is also true in applications in which the standard deviation is not known. In fact, the effect of a change is compounded because the change in sample size affects both the calculation of the standard error and the critical value from the *t*-distribution.

The *t*-distribution table in Appendix F shows degrees of freedom up to 30 and then incrementally to 500. Observe that for any confidence level, as the degrees of freedom increase, the *t*-value gets smaller as it approaches a limit equal to the *z*-value from the standard normal table in Appendix D for the same confidence level. If you need to estimate the population mean with a sample size at least 30, a conventional option is to find the critical value in the *z*-table then use Equation 7-7 to develop the interval estimate.

Note: Anytime the population standard deviation, σ, is unknown and must be estimated using the sample standard deviation, s, the technically correct approach is to use the t-distribution to obtain the critical value. However, many authors suggest using Equation 7-7 when $n \geq 30$ based on the Central Limit Theorem.

Confidence Interval Estimate for the Mean, σ Unknown, Large Samples

$$\bar{x} \pm z_{\alpha/2} \frac{s}{\sqrt{n}} \qquad \qquad \textbf{7-7}$$

where:

$\bar{x}$ = Sample mean
$z_{\alpha/2}$ = Value from the standard normal distribution for a $1 - \alpha$ confidence level
s = Sample standard deviation
n = Sample size

A second option is to use Excel **TINV** function or Minitab's **Calc > Probability Distribution > t** command to get the critical t-value for any specified degrees of freedom and then use Equation 7-6.

You should have noticed that the format for confidence interval estimates for μ is essentially the same, regardless of whether the population standard deviation is known. The basic format is always

Point Estimate ± (Critical Value)(Standard Error)

Later in this chapter, we introduce estimation examples in which the population value of interest is p, the population proportion. Regardless of the parameter of interest, the same confidence interval format is used. In addition, the trade-offs between margin of error, confidence level, and sample size that were discussed in this section also apply to every other estimation situation.

SUMMARY: CONFIDENCE INTERVAL ESTIMATES FOR A SINGLE POPULATION MEAN

A confidence interval estimate for a single population mean can be developed using the following steps.

1. Define the population of interest and the variable for which you wish to estimate the population mean.

2. Determine the sample size and select a simple random sample.

3. Compute the confidence interval as follows, depending on the conditions that exist:

   ■ If σ is known and the population is normally distributed or the sample size is large ($n \geq 30$), use:

   $$\bar{x} \pm z_{\alpha/2} \frac{\sigma}{\sqrt{n}}$$

   ■ If σ is unknown, the sample size is small ($n < 30$), and we can assume that the population distribution is approximately normal, use:

   $$\bar{x} \pm t_{\alpha/2} \frac{s}{\sqrt{n}}$$

   ■ If σ is unknown, but the sample size is large ($n \geq 30$), use:

   $$\bar{x} \pm z_{\alpha/2} \frac{s}{\sqrt{n}}$$

7-1: EXERCISES

Skill Development

7.1 Assume a sample of size n has been obtained from a normal distribution. Determine the critical value from a t-distribution when you wish to estimate the population mean in each of the following cases:

a. Confidence coefficient = 0.95, $n = 26$
b. Confidence coefficient = 0.90, $n = 31$
c. Confidence coefficient = 0.98, $n = 15$
d. Confidence coefficient = 0.99, $n = 19$
e. Confidence coefficient = 0.80, $n = 21$
f. Confidence coefficient = 0.90, $n = 17$

7.2 Assuming that the population standard deviation is known, compute the critical values from the standard normal distribution table in each of the following cases:
a. Confidence coefficient = 0.95, $n = 31$
b. Confidence coefficient = 0.90, $n = 31$
c. Confidence coefficient = 0.98, $n = 15$
d. Confidence coefficient = 0.99, $n = 36$
e. Confidence coefficient = 0.88, $n = 56$
f. Confidence coefficient = 0.90, $n = 41$

7.3 Determine the 90% confidence interval estimate for the population mean.
a. $\bar{x} = 102.36, n = 17, \sigma = 1.26$
b. $\bar{x} = 56.33, n = 21, s = 22.4$

7.4 Determine the 95% confidence interval estimate for a population mean of a normal distribution, given the following information:
a. $\bar{x} = 13.56, n = 300, \sigma = 12.6$
b. $\bar{x} = 2.45, n = 31, s = 22.3$

7.5 For each of the following situations, determine the margin of error
a. Confidence coefficient = 0.98, $\bar{x} = 2.47, n = 12, \sigma = 6.58$
b. Confidence coefficient = 0.95, $\bar{x} = 13.9, n = 21, s = 2.33$
c. Confidence coefficient = 0.80, $\bar{x} = 114.7, n = 500, s = 15.6$

7.6 Determine the 99% confidence interval estimate for the population mean of a normal distribution given $n = 500$, $\sigma = 1.22$, and $\bar{x} = 34.6$.

7.7 Determine the margin of error for a confidence interval estimate for the population mean of a normal distribution, given the following information:
a. Confidence coefficient = 0.98, $n = 13, s = 15.68$
b. Confidence coefficient = 0.99, $n = 25, \sigma = 3.47$
c. Confidence coefficient = 0.98, standard error = 2.356

7.8 Determine the margin of error for a confidence interval estimate for the population mean of a normal distribution, given the following information:
a. Confidence coefficient = 0.80, $n = 11, s = 114.7$
b. Confidence coefficient = 0.98, $n = 3, s = 26.96$

7.9 Given the following data from a simple random sample for the population of interest, compute the 95% confidence interval estimate. (What assumption must be made about the population?)

114	97	107	101	84	84	85	66	108	76

7.10 The following data were collected in a simple random sample from a normally distributed population. Construct a 90% confidence interval estimate for the population mean.

11	14	10	12	11	11	12	12	15

Business Applications

7.11 Mortimor's is a nice, upscale restaurant specializing in seafood dishes. The owner is interested in estimating the mean dollars spent per table on appetizers. He has selected a simple random sample of 200 sales receipts from the past year's receipts and has calculated the mean and standard deviation for the dollar amount of each bill that was allocated to appetizers. These results are

$$\bar{x} = \$4.22 \qquad s = \$2.59$$

a. Based on these sample data, what is the point estimate for the mean amount spent on appetizers per table at Mortimor's?
b. Construct and interpret a 95% confidence interval estimate for the true mean amount spent per table on appetizers.

7.12 Presto Pizza delivers pizzas throughout its local market area at no charge to the customer. However, customers often tip the driver. The owner is interested in estimating the mean tip income per delivery. To do this, she has selected a simple random sample of 12 deliveries and has recorded the tips that were received by the drivers. These data are

$2.25	$2.50	$2.25	$2.00	$2.00	$1.50
$0.00	$2.00	$1.50	$2.00	$3.00	$1.50

a. Based on these sample data, what is the best point estimate to use as an estimate of the true mean tip per delivery?
b. Suppose the owner is interested in developing a 90% confidence interval estimate. Given the fact that the sample size is small and the population standard deviation is unknown, what distribution will be used to obtain the critical value?
c. Referring to part b, what assumption is required to use the specified distribution to obtain the critical value? Develop a box and whisker diagram to illustrate whether this assumption seems to be reasonably satisfied.
d. Referring to parts b and c, construct and interpret the 90% confidence interval estimate for the population mean.

7.13 The Traveler Rent-A-Car Company is interested in estimating the mean number of miles its cars are driven on a particular holiday. From the 23,000 cars it owns nationwide, analysts have selected a simple random sample of 200 cars on the holiday in question. The mileage for each car was recorded. The data computed from the sample data were

$$\bar{x} = 54.5 \text{ miles}$$
$$s = 14.0 \text{ miles}$$

a. Produce a 95% confidence interval estimate for the mean miles driven by all 23,000 vehicles owned by the company.

b. Traveler's vice president of operations received a report from the company's southwestern region. It indicated the region had rented 200 cars during the holiday and had received $2,500 in fees charged for mileage. Assume Traveler's charges 25 cents per mile as a mileage fee. On the basis of the confidence interval calculated in part a, would you say that the vice president should investigate the billing practices of the southwestern region? Support your opinion with statistical reasoning and logic.

c. Suppose the Traveler Rent-A-Car Company wishes to decrease the margin of error in the estimate for average miles driven per car per day. Discuss the three options available to the managers, and provide examples for each case that demonstrate that your options actually do decrease the margin of error.

7.14 The First National Bank is considering a survey of its customers to estimate the mean number of checks written per month. A sample of 360 customers was selected. The sample values were

$$\bar{x} = 33.4$$
$$s = 11.2$$

a. Provide a 90% confidence interval estimate for the mean number of checks written and interpret the estimate.

b. Suppose a clerical mistake was made in recording the number of customers who were surveyed and the actual sample size was 36, not 360. Recompute the 90% confidence interval estimate and compare it to the estimate developed in part a. Why are the estimates different even though the sample mean and standard deviation did not change?

7.15 Agri-Beef, Inc., is a large midwestern farming operation. The company has been a leader in employing statistical analysis techniques in its business. Recently, John Goldberg, operations manager, requested that a random sample of cattle be selected and fed a special diet. The cattle were weighed before the start of the new feeding program and at the end. John wished to estimate the average daily weight gain for cattle on the new program. Two hundred cattle were tested, and the sample results were

$$\bar{x} = 1.2 \text{ lb. per day gain}$$
$$s = 0.50 \text{ lb}$$

a. Obtain a 95% confidence interval estimate for the true average daily weight gain.

b. Provide a 90% confidence interval estimate for the true average daily weight gain.

c. Discuss the difference between the estimates found in parts a and b and indicate the advantages and disadvantages of each.

7.16 The Evergreen Company operates retail pharmacies in 10 eastern states. Recently, the company's internal audit department selected a random sample of 300 prescriptions filled throughout the system. The objective of the sampling was to estimate the average dollar value of all prescriptions filled by the company. The data collected were

$$\bar{x} = \$14.23$$
$$s = 3.00$$

a. Determine the 90% confidence interval estimate for the true average sales value for prescriptions filled. Interpret the interval estimate.

b. One of its retail outlets recently reported that it had monthly revenue of $7,392 from 528 prescriptions. Are such results to be expected? Do you believe that the retail outlet should be audited? Support your answer with calculations and logic.

7.17 Marine World–Africa USA is a facility located near San Francisco, California, where people can see animals from the ocean and from Africa on display and performing in shows. Customers pay for a full-day ticket. The management is interested in determining the average length of time customers actually spend at the park. They select a simple random sample of customers and ask them their arrival time as they leave the park, from which they determine the length of stay for each customer. A total of 144 customers were selected at random, and the sample results were

$$\bar{x} = 311 \text{ minutes}$$
$$s = 72 \text{ minutes}$$

a. Obtain a 90% confidence interval estimate for the mean time spent at the park. Interpret the interval estimate.

b. If park administration wishes to reduce the margin of error from that which you determined in part a, what options exist to do so? Discuss.

7.18 The Apex Entertainment Company owns and operates movie theaters in Wyoming. The president of the company is concerned that home videocassette recorders are hurting business because people can simply rent a movie and watch it at home. He has directed a staff member to estimate the mean number of movies rented by people in Wyoming in December. A phone survey involving a random sample of 300 homes was conducted, and the results were

$$\bar{x} = 2.4 \text{ movies}$$
$$s = 1.6 \text{ movies}$$

a. Develop and interpret the 95% confidence interval estimate for the true mean number of movies rented by people in Wyoming in December.

b. Develop and interpret a 90% confidence interval estimate for the mean number of movies rented per month. Discuss why the width of this interval is smaller than the one you constructed in part a.

7.19 A major American pharmaceutical company has randomly sampled 14 customers who have used one of their new painkilling drugs for two months. There is concern that the drug may elevate the user's heart rate. Each of the customers in the sample had their heart rate measured after using the drug for one week. All people in the sample had heart rates of 55 prior to taking the drug. The following data were recorded for the 14 customers:

50	70	60	70	90	72	50
80	85	55	66	70	80	40

a. Suppose that you have just started working in the marketing department of the pharmaceutical company. You were given the following instructions: "Based on these sample data, construct a 90% confidence interval estimate for the true mean heart rate for the company's drug customers. Interpret the estimate." Follow these instructions.

b. Referring to your answer in part a, can the estimate be applied to all potential drug customers? Explain why or why not.

c. Refer to your calculations in part a. (1) Was the concern expressed justified? Explain your answer. (2) If the average heart rate did increase, determine the probability that a sample mean at least as large as the one obtained in your sample could have been obtained assuming the beginning mean rate is 55.

7.20 The Simmons Furniture Company selected a random sample of nine sofas that were made at its Memphis factory. Each sofa was subjected to a test process that simulated people sitting on the cushions. The test requires that a heavy object be repeatedly dropped on the cushion until the fabric wears out. The following data reflect the number of drops that were recorded for each of the nine sofas:

13,356	12,742	15,345
9,459	10,634	14,309
14,098	11,245	12,652

a. Obtain a 95% confidence interval estimate for the mean number of drops until the sofa cushions wear out. Interpret the result.

b. Simmons wishes to advertise that the sofa fabric will last at least 20 years. If a sofa is sat upon an average of once a day, could Simmons justify their proposed advertisement? Explain your answer.

Advanced Business Applications

7.21 The Aims Investment Company is interested in estimating the average number of mutual funds its customers have in their portfolios. A random sample of investment customers is located in the CD-ROM file called *Aims*.

a. Based on the sample data, construct a 90% confidence interval estimate for the mean number of mutual funds for all their customers. Interpret this interval.

b. Suppose that the interval estimate that you computed in part a has a margin of error that is greater than Aims management wants. Discuss what options are open to Aims. What are the advantages and disadvantages of each option?

7.22 The Ecco Company makes electronics products for distribution throughout the world. As quality manager, you are interested in the warranty claims that are made by customers who have experienced problems with Ecco products. The CD-ROM file called *Ecco* contains data for a random sample of warranty claims.

a. You are to develop and interpret a 90% confidence interval estimate for the mean dollar claim.

b. Develop and interpret a 95% confidence interval estimate for the mean warranty claim amount for only those products that were made on the graveyard shift (shift 3 in the data file). There has been some concern within Ecco management that the graveyard shift's workmanship is not of the caliber of the other two shifts. Using the confidence interval you have calculated and any other statistical techniques required, address this issue.

7.23 Refer to Exercise 7.22. Ecco's quality control manager has been concerned with the source of what he believes to be high warranty claims at the Boise site. He believes that corrosion may be the source.

a. Develop and interpret a 95% confidence interval estimate for the mean warranty claim amount for products produced at the Boise site. Do this for each of the complaint sources (complaint codes 1 to 4). (You must produce four separate confidence intervals.) Now compute the 95% confidence interval estimate for mean warranty claims for Boise that were based on corrosion complaints. How do these two interval estimates compare?

b. Write a letter to the quality control manager that addresses his concern about the source of the high warranty claims. Identify, if possible, what complaint is producing the highest warranty claims. Discuss the implications of the four confidence intervals concerning the average warranty claims for each complaint type.

7.24 Clair's Deli serves many types of sandwiches, soups, and salads. All sandwiches are made fresh at the time of the order. Customers can eat inside at tables or use the drive-through window to order food to go. The manager is interested in estimating the mean time customers spend in the drive-through line. The CD-ROM file called *Clairs Deli* contains data from a simple random sample of 50 drive-through customers. These data, measured in minutes, are also shown here.

6.6	6.9	6.4	12.2	11.3
9.0	11.1	9.5	9.9	12.5
11.9	16.3	9.4	2.5	13.2
4.4	7.4	10.8	9.7	13.2
9.8	10.1	8.2	8.2	9.0
9.1	7.4	9.9	14.5	8.9
6.2	9.3	9.8	5.7	6.2
9.3	8.2	15.9	9.8	7.0
7.9	18.4	14.1	10.2	9.3
11.5	8.2	18.7	11.5	11.1

a. Develop a box and whisker diagram and discuss whether the sample data appear to come from a population that is approximately normally distributed.

b. Regardless of your conclusions in part a, develop and interpret a 95% confidence interval estimate for the mean time the customers wait in the drive-through line.

7-2 DETERMINING THE REQUIRED SAMPLE SIZE FOR ESTIMATING THE POPULATION MEAN

We have discussed the basic trade-offs that are present in all statistical estimations: the desire to have a high confidence level, a low margin of error, and a small sample size. The problem is these three objectives conflict. For a given sample size, a high confidence level will tend to generate a large margin of error. For a given confidence level, a small sample size will result in an increased margin of error. Reducing the margin of error requires either reducing the confidence level or increasing the sample size or both.

A common question from business decision makers who are planning an estimation application is, "How large a sample size do I really need?" To answer this question, we usually begin by asking a couple of questions of our own:

1. How much money do you have budgeted to do the sampling?
2. How much will it cost to select each item in the sample?

The answers to these questions provide the upper limit on the sample size that can be selected. For instance, if the decision maker indicates that she has a $2,000 budget for selecting the sample and the cost will be about $10 per unit to collect the sample, the sample size's upper limit is $2,000 ÷ $10 = 200 units.

Keeping in mind the estimation trade-offs discussed earlier, the issue should be fully discussed with the decision maker. For instance, is a sample of 200 sufficient to give the desired margin of error at a specified confidence level? Is 200 more than is needed to achieve the desired margin of error?

Therefore, before we can give a definite answer about what sample size is needed, the decision maker must specify her confidence level and a desired margin of error. Then the required sample size can be computed.

DETERMINING THE REQUIRED SAMPLE SIZE FOR ESTIMATING μ, σ KNOWN

Mission Valley Power Company—Consider the Mission Valley Power Company (MVP) in northwest Michigan, which has more than 6,000 residential customers. In response to a request by the Michigan Public Utility Commission, MVP needs to estimate the average kilowatts of electricity used by customers on February 1. The only way to get this number is to select a random sample of customers and take a meter reading after 5:00 P.M. on January 31 and again after 5:00 P.M. on February 1. The commission has specified that any estimate presented in the utility's report must be based on a 95% confidence level. Further, the margin of error must not exceed ±30 kilowatts. Given these requirements, what size sample is needed?

To answer this question, if the population standard deviation is known, we start with Equation 7-4, the equation for calculating the margin of error.

$$e = z_{\alpha/2} \frac{\sigma}{\sqrt{n}}$$

We next substitute into this equation the values we know. For example, the margin of error was specified to be

$$e = 30 \text{ kilowatts}$$

The confidence level was specified to be 95%. The z-value for 95% is 1.96. (Refer to the standard normal table in Appendix D.) This gives us

$$30 = 1.96 \frac{\sigma}{\sqrt{n}}$$

We need to know the population standard deviation. MVP might know this value from other studies that it has conducted in the past or from similar studies done by other utility companies. Assume for this example that σ, the population standard deviation, is 200 kilowatts. We can now substitute

$$\sigma = 200$$

into the equation for e, as follows,

$$30 = 1.96 \frac{200}{\sqrt{n}}$$

We now have a single equation with one unknown, n, the sample size. Doing the algebra to solve for n, we get

$$n = \left(\frac{1.96\,(200)}{30} \right)^2 = 170.73 \approx 171 \text{ customers}$$

Thus, to meet the requirements of the utility commission, a sample of $n = 171$ customers should be selected. Equation 7-8 is used to determine the required sample size for estimating a single population mean when σ is known.

Sample Size Requirement for Estimating μ, σ Known

$$n = \left(\frac{z_{\alpha/2}\,\sigma}{e} \right)^2 = \frac{z_{\alpha/2}^{2}\sigma^2}{e^2} \qquad \textbf{7-8}$$

where:

$z_{\alpha/2}$ = Critical value for the specified $1 - \alpha$ confidence level
e = Desired margin of error
σ = Population standard deviation

If MVP feels that the cost of sampling 171 customers will be too high, it might appeal to the commission to allow for a higher margin of error or a lower confidence level. For example, if the confidence level is lowered to 90%, the z-value is lowered to 1.645, as found in the standard normal table.[4]

We can now use Equation 7-8 to determine the revised sample-size requirement.

$$n = \frac{1.645^2 (200)^2}{30^2} = 120.27 \approx 121$$

MVP will need to sample only 121 (120.27 rounded up) customers for a confidence level of 90% rather than 95%.

EXAMPLE 7-4: DETERMINING THE REQUIRED SAMPLE SIZE, σ KNOWN

Gordon's Self-Service Gasoline   The general manager for Gordon's Self-Service Gasoline is interested in estimating the mean number of gallons of gasoline that are purchased by customers at his Kansas City location. He would like his estimate to be within plus or minus 0.50 gallons, and he would like the estimate to be at the 99% confidence level. Past studies have shown that the standard deviation for purchase amount is 4.0 gallons. To determine the required sample size, he can use the following steps.

Step 1:   Specify the desired margin of error.
The manager wishes to have his estimate be within ±0.50 gallons, so the margin of error is
$$e = 0.50 \text{ gallons}$$

---

[4]You can also use the Excel function, NORMSINV, to determine the z-value.

Step 2:   Determine the population standard deviation.
Based on other studies, the manager is willing to conclude that the population standard deviation is known. Thus,

$$\sigma = 4.0$$

Step 3:   Determine the critical value for the desired level of confidence.
The critical value will be a z-value from the standard normal table for 99% confidence. This is

$$z_{0.005} = 2.575$$

Step 4:   Compute the required sample size using Equation 7-8.
The required sample size is

$$n = \frac{z_{\alpha/2}^2 \sigma^2}{e^2} = \frac{2.575^2 4.0^2}{0.50^2} = 424.36 = 425 \text{ customers}$$

Note: The sample size is always rounded up to the next integer value.

DETERMINING THE REQUIRED SAMPLE SIZE FOR ESTIMATING μ, σ UNKNOWN

Equation 7-8 assumes that you know the population standard deviation. Although this may be the case in some situations, most likely we won't know the population standard deviation. To get around this problem, three approaches can be used. One is to use a value for σ that is considered to be at least as large as the true σ. This will provide a conservatively large sample size.

The second option is to select a **pilot sample**, a sample from the population that is used explicitly to estimate σ.

Pilot Sample

A sample taken from the population of interest of a size smaller than the anticipated sample size that is used to provide an estimate for the population standard deviation.

The third option is to use the range of the population to estimate the population's standard deviation. Recall the Empirical Rule in Chapter 3 and Chapter 6's examination of the normal distribution. Both sources suggest that $\mu \pm 3\sigma$ contains virtually all of the data values of a normal distribution. If this were the case, then $\mu - 3\sigma$ would be approximately the smallest number and $\mu + 3\sigma$ would be approximately the largest number. Remember that the Range = R = Maximum Value − Minimum Value. So, $R \approx (\mu + 3\sigma) - (\mu - 3\sigma) = 6\sigma$. We can, therefore, obtain an estimate of the standard deviation as

$$\sigma \approx \frac{R}{6}$$

We can also use a procedure that produces a larger estimate of the standard deviation, which will lead to a larger, more conservative sample size. This involves dividing the range by 4 instead of 6.

We seldom know the standard deviation of the population. However, very often we have a very good idea about the largest and smallest value of the population. Therefore, this third method can be used in many instances in which you do not wish to, or cannot, obtain a pilot sample or you are unable to offer a conjecture concerning a conservatively large value of the standard deviation.

EXAMPLE 7-5: DETERMINING THE REQUIRED SAMPLE SIZE σ UNKNOWN

Georgia Lumber Mill   Consider a Georgia lumber mill manager who wishes to know the average diameter of logs the mill cuts. Not only does she not know μ, she also does not know the population standard deviation. She wants a 90% confidence level and is willing to have a margin of error of 0.50 inch in estimating the true mean diameter. The required sample size can be determined using the following steps.

Step 1:   **Specify the desired margin of error.**
The manager wants the estimate to be within ±0.50 inch of the true mean. Thus,
$$e = 0.50$$

Step 2:   **Determine an estimate for the population standard deviation.**
The manager will select a pilot sample of $n = 20$ logs and measure the diameter of each. These values are

18.9	22.4	24.6	25.7	26.3	28.4	21.7	31.0	19.0	31.7
17.4	25.5	20.1	34.3	25.9	20.3	21.6	25.8	31.6	28.8

The estimate for the population standard deviation is the sample standard deviation for the pilot sample. This is computed using:
$$s = \sqrt{\frac{\sum(x - \bar{x})^2}{n - 1}} = \sqrt{\frac{(18.9 - 25.05)^2 + (22.4 - 25.05)^2 + \cdots + (28.8 - 25.05)^2}{20 - 1}} = 4.85$$

We will use
$$\sigma \approx 4.85$$

Step 3:   **Determine the critical value for the desired level of confidence.**
The critical value will be a z-value from the standard normal table. The 90% confidence level gives
$$z_{.05} = 1.645$$

Step 4:   **Calculate the required sample size using Equation 7-8.**
The required sample size is
$$n = \frac{z_{\alpha/2}^2 \sigma^2}{e^2} = \frac{(1.645^2)(4.85^2)}{0.50^2} = 254.61 = 255$$

The required sample size is 255, but we can use the pilot sample as part of this total. Thus, the net required sample size in this case is $255 - 20 = 235$.

7-2: EXERCISES

Skill Development

7.25 Suppose it is known that the population standard deviation is 40. If you wish to estimate the population mean using a 95% confidence interval estimate with a margin of error of ± 2.5, what sample size will be required?

7.26 If you wish to estimate a population mean and have your estimate be within ±0.25 of the true value and you wish to have a confidence level of 99%, what sample size will be required if the population standard deviation is known to be 1.20?

7.27 Suppose, as part of your job, you are asked to estimate a population mean using a 90% confidence interval and a margin of error of 60. What size sample is required if the following pilot sample is used to determine a value to use for the population standard deviation?

3,239	3,144	2,960	2,507	2,842
3,134	3,249	2,908	2,754	2,715

7.28 A sample size must be determined for estimating a population mean, given the confidence level is to be 90%, and the desired margin of error is 0.30. The largest value in the population is thought to be 15, and the smallest value is thought to be 5.
   a. Calculate the sample size required to estimate the population using a conservatively large sample size. (Hint: Use the range ÷ 4 option.)
   b. If a smaller sample size is desired (use the range ÷ 6 option), calculate the required sample size. Discuss why the answers in parts a and b are different.

7.29 The required sample size for estimating a population mean is to be calculated, given that the desired margin of error is 40 and a pilot sample of 30 items indicated a sample standard deviation of 900.
   a. Determine the required sample size if the confidence level is to be 90%.
   b. Increase the confidence level to 95% and determine the percentage change in the resulting sample size.

7.30 A sample size is required for estimating a population mean, given that the confidence level is to be 99%, the desired margin of error is 2, and a pilot sample of 50 items indicated a sample standard deviation of 46.5

Calculate the number of additional items that must be sampled to provide the required estimation of the population mean.

7.31 There are trade-offs that exist when estimating a single population mean.
a. For a given sample size, what must be done to decrease the margin of error?
b. What will be affected if the confidence level is to be increased for a given sample size?
c. How can the confidence level increase and the margin of error decrease at the same time?

7.32 The standard deviation of a population is thought to be somewhere in the interval (250, 300). The population mean is to be estimated using a confidence interval with a 90% confidence level. The desired margin of error is 20.
a. Calculate the required sample size using the smallest value of the standard deviation perceived to be possible.
b. Repeat the calculation in part a using the largest value of the standard deviation perceived to be possible.
c. Discuss why the sample size requirements would be greater when a population has a larger variation.

Business Applications

7.33 A study is being planned to estimate the mean number of inches that trees will grow per year in a forest. The analysts wish to have 90% confidence and want to estimate the mean within ±0.20 inch. A pilot study was conducted that showed a sample standard deviation equal to 0.80 inch. What size sample is needed for this study?

7.34 The Longmont Computer Leasing Company leases computers and peripherals such as laser printers. The printers have a counter that keeps track of the number of pages that are printed. The company wishes to estimate the mean number of pages that will be printed in a month on their leased printers. The plan is to select a random sample of printers and record the number on each printer's counter at the beginning of May. At the end of May, the number on the counter will be recorded again, and the difference will be the number of copies on that printer for the month. The company wants the estimate to be within ±100 pages of the true mean, with a 95% confidence level.
a. The standard deviation in pages printed is thought to be about 1,400 pages. How many printers should be sampled?
b. Suppose that the conjecture concerning the size of the standard deviation is off (plus or minus) by as much as 10%. What percentage change in the required sample size would this produce?

7.35 Arco Manufacturing makes electronic pagers. As part of the company's quality efforts, the company wishes to estimate the mean number of days the pager is used before repair is needed. A pilot sample of 40 pagers indicates a sample standard deviation of 200 days. The company wishes its estimate to have a margin of error of no more than 50 days, and the confidence level must be 95%.

a. Given this information, how many additional pagers should be sampled?
b. The pilot study was initiated because of the costs involved in sampling. Each sampled observation costs approximately $10 to obtain. Originally, it was thought that the population's standard deviation might be as large as 300. Determine the amount of money saved by obtaining the pilot sample. (Hint: Figure the total cost of obtaining the required samples for both methods.)

7.36 The Northwest Pacific Phone Company wishes to estimate the average number of minutes its customers spend on long-distance calls per month. The company wants the estimate made with 99% confidence and a margin of error of no more than 5 minutes.
a. A previous study indicated that the standard deviation for long-distance calls is 21 minutes per month. What should the sample size be?
b. Determine the required sample size if the confidence level were changed from 99% to 90%.
c. What would the required sample size be if the confidence level was 95% and the margin of error was 8 minutes?

7.37 The quality manager for a major automobile manufacturer is interested in estimating the mean number of paint defects in cars produced by the company. She wishes to have her estimate be within ± 0.10 of the true mean and wants 98% confidence in the estimate. The data in the CD-ROM file called *CarPaint* contains a pilot sample that was conducted for the purpose of determining a value to use for the population standard deviation. How many additional cars need to be sampled to provide the estimate required by the quality manager?

Advanced Business Applications

7.38 The quality manager at Ecco Company, a maker of back-up alarms for use on industrial vehicles such as forklifts, is interested in estimating the mean dollar volume for warranty claims for products made in Boise on the day shift. He has taken a pilot sample. The data for the pilot sample are in a CD-ROM file called *ECCO*.
a. Assuming that the manager wishes to estimate the mean warranty amount to within ±$8.00 with 90% confidence, how many additional claims must be selected to develop the estimate?
b. Suppose the sample size determined in part a is more than the manager is willing to use. What options are open to the manager? Discuss.
c. Referring to parts a and b, suppose the manager wishes to cut the total sample size in half. For each option available to the manger, show specifically what must be done to achieve the reduction in sample size.

7.39 The loan manager at High-Desert Bank wishes to estimate the mean loan amount for the commercial customers of his bank. A couple of weeks ago, an intern from the nearby college collected a random sample of customers (commercial and retail). These data are in a file called *High-Desert Bank*.

a. Use the data in this sample to develop a 95% confidence interval estimate for the population mean loan amount for commercial customers. The manager's promotion program had a goal of raising the average loan amount for commercial customers to $67,500. Has the manager reached this goal? Explain your answer.

b. Referring to part a, suppose the loan manager would like to maintain the 95% confidence interval but with a margin of error that is 40% of the existing margin of error. How many, if any, additional loan customers must be sampled?

c. Refer to parts a and b. Suppose the manager feels the new required sample size is too large but does not want to increase the margin of error, what must he do? Assume he wants to cut the required sample size by 15% of that found in part b, what specifically will be required? Discuss the impact of these trade-offs.

7.40   The state Department of Transportation is experimenting with a new scale for weighing trucks. This new scale is called a Weigh-in-Motion (WIM) scale because it weighs trucks while they are driving down the highway. The traditional method is a static scale that is at the port of entry (POE). The trucks pull into the scale, stop, and are weighed. The POE scale is assumed to provide accurate weights. The state has set up a test area on one stretch of highway. The WIM scale is located about a half-mile before the POE scale. A sample of trucks are weighed on the WIM scale and then on the POE scale. Some trucks were weighed in each of several months beginning in February. These data are in the file called *Trucks*.

a. Suppose that the department's objective is to estimate the mean difference between WIM gross weight and POE gross weight for those trucks that were weighed in February. (Note, February trucks have a Month Code = 2.) The estimate is to be based on a 95% confidence level. Using the sample data, develop this estimate and interpret it. (Hint: Compute a new variable that is WIM gross − POE gross.)

b. Referring to part a, suppose the department wants the margin of error reduced to no more than 50 pounds with 95% confidence. Using the sample data already collected as a pilot sample, how many more trucks would be needed to estimate the February mean difference? Comment on this result.

c. Suppose the department wishes to estimate the speed of vehicles crossing the WIM scale with 99% confidence and with a margin of error equal to ±1.5 mph. Use the data in the file as a pilot sample. How many additional trucks must be sampled to meet the estimation requirements?

7-3   ESTIMATING A POPULATION PROPORTION

The previous sections have illustrated the methods for developing confidence interval estimate when the population value of interest is the mean. However, you will encounter many situations in which the value of interest is the proportion of items in the population that possess a particular attribute. For example, you may wish to estimate the proportion of customers who are satisfied with the service provided by your company. The notation for the *population proportion* is p. The point estimate for p is the *sample proportion*, $\bar{p}$, which is computed using Equation 7-9.

Sample Proportion

$$\bar{p} = \frac{x}{n} \qquad \text{7-9}$$

where:

x = Number of occurrences
n = Sample size

In Chapter 6, we introduced the sampling distribution for proportions. We indicated then that when the sample size is sufficiently large [$np \geq 5$ and $n(1 - p) \geq 5$], the sampling distribution can be approximated by a normal distribution centered at p, with a standard error for $\bar{p}$ computed using Equation 7-10.

Standard Error for $\bar{p}$

$$\sigma_{\bar{p}} = \sqrt{\frac{p(1 - p)}{n}} \qquad \text{7-10}$$

where:

p = Population proportion
n = Sample size

CONFIDENCE INTERVAL ESTIMATE FOR A POPULATION PROPORTION

To develop the confidence interval estimate for a population proportion, p, we use Equation 7-1, the basic equation for establishing all confidence intervals:

$$\text{Point Estimate} \pm (\text{Critical Value})(\text{Standard Error})$$

Using Equations 7-9 and 7-10 as the point estimator and standard error, we find the confidence interval estimate for p in Equation 7-11.

Theoretical Confidence Interval Estimate for p

$$\bar{p} \pm z_{\alpha/2}\sqrt{\frac{p(1-p)}{n}} \qquad \textbf{7-11}$$

where:

$\bar{p}$ = Point estimate for p $\left(\bar{p} = \dfrac{x}{n}\right)$

n = Sample size

p = Population proportion

$z_{\alpha/2}$ = Critical value from the standard normal distribution for a $1 - \alpha$ confidence level

---

Equation 7-11 creates a conflict. We are trying to estimate p, yet the standard error requires that p be known. To overcome this, we must estimate the standard error by substituting the sample proportion, $\bar{p}$, for the population proportion, p. Therefore, the specific format for *confidence intervals involving the population proportion* is shown in Equation 7-12.

Confidence Interval Estimate for p

$$\bar{p} \pm z_{\alpha/2}\sqrt{\frac{\bar{p}(1-\bar{p})}{n}} \qquad \textbf{7-12}$$

where:

$\bar{p}$ = Sample proportion

n = Sample size

z = Critical value from the standard normal distribution for a $1 - \alpha$ confidence level

---

SUMMARY: DEVELOPING A CONFIDENCE INTERVAL ESTIMATE FOR A POPULATION PROPORTION

Here are the steps necessary to develop a confidence interval estimate for a population proportion.

1. Define the population of interest and the variable for which to estimate the population proportion.

2. Determine the sample size and select a simple random sample. Note, the sample must be large enough so that $np \geq 5$ and $n(1 - p) \geq 5$.

3. Specify the level of confidence and obtain the critical value from the standard normal distribution table.

4. Calculate $\bar{p}$, the sample proportion.

5. Construct the interval estimate using Equation 7-12.

$$\bar{p} \pm z_{\alpha/2}\sqrt{\frac{\bar{p}(1-\bar{p})}{n}}$$

EXAMPLE 7-6: CONFIDENCE INTERVAL FOR A POPULATION PROPORTION

Quick Lube   The Quick Lube Company operates a chain of oil-change outlets in several states. When a customer comes in for service, the date of service and the mileage on the car are recorded. A computer program tracks the customers, and when three months have almost passed, a reminder card is sent to the customer.

The marketing manager is interested in estimating the *proportion* of customers who return after getting a card. Of a simple random sample of 100 customers, 62 returned within one month after the card was mailed. A confidence interval estimate for the true population proportion is found using the following steps.

Step 1: **Define the population and the variable of interest.**
The population is all customers who have their oil changed at Quick Lube, and the variable of interest is the number who respond to a reminder card that is mailed to them.

Step 2: **Determine the sample size.**
A simple random sample of $n = 100$ customers receive cards. (Note, as long as $p \geq 0.05$, a sample size of 100 will meet the requirements that $np \geq 5$ and $n(1 - p) \geq 5$.

Step 3: **Specify the desired level of confidence and determine the critical value.**
Assuming that a 95% confidence level is desired, the critical value from the standard normal distribution table (Appendix D) will be $z = 1.96$.

Step 4: **Compute the point estimate based on the sample data.**
Equation 7-9 is used to compute the sample proportion.

$$\bar{p} = \frac{x}{n} = \frac{62}{100} = 0.62$$

Step 5: **Compute the confidence interval using Equation 7-12.**
The 95% confidence interval estimate is

$$\bar{p} \pm z_{.025} \sqrt{\frac{\bar{p}(1 - \bar{p})}{n}}$$

$$.62 \pm 1.96 \sqrt{\frac{.62(1 - .62)}{100}}$$

$$0.62 \pm 0.095$$

$$0.525 \text{ --------------------------- } 0.715$$

Using the sample of 100 customers and a 95% confidence interval, the manager estimates that the true percentage of customers who will respond to the reminder card will be between 52.5% and 71.5%.

DETERMINING THE REQUIRED SAMPLE SIZE FOR ESTIMATING A POPULATION PROPORTION

Changing the confidence level affects the interval width. Likewise, changing the sample size will affect the interval width. An increase in sample size will reduce the standard error and reduce the interval width. A decrease in the sample size will have the opposite effect. For many applications, decision makers would like to determine a required sample size before doing the sampling. As was the case for estimating the population mean, the required sample size in a proportion application is based on the desired margin of error, the desired confidence level, and the variation in the population. The **margin of error**, e, is computed using Equation 7-13.

Margin of Error for Estimating p

$$e = z_{\alpha/2} \sqrt{\frac{p(1 - p)}{n}}$$

7-13

where:

p = Population proportion
$z_{\alpha/2}$ = Critical value from standard normal distribution for a $1 - \alpha$ confidence level
n = Sample size

Equation 7-14 is used to determine the required sample size for a given confidence level and margin of error.

Sample Size for Estimating p

$$n = \frac{z_{\alpha/2}^2 p(1 - p)}{e^2}$$

7-14

where:

p = Value used to represent the population proportion
e = Desired margin of error
$z_{\alpha/2}$ = Critical value from standard normal distribution for a $1 - \alpha$ confidence level

Quick Lube (continued)—Referring to Example 7-6, recall that the marketing manager developed a confidence interval estimate for the proportion of customers who would respond to a reminder card. This interval was

$$0.62 \pm 1.96\sqrt{\frac{0.62(1-0.62)}{100}}$$
$$0.62 \pm 0.095$$
$$0.525 \text{----------------------------} 0.715$$

The margin of error in this situation is 0.095. Suppose the marketing manager wants the margin of error reduced to $e = \pm 0.04$ at a 95% confidence level. This will require an increase in sample size. To apply Equation 7-14, the margin of error and the confidence level are specified by the decision maker. However, the population proportion, p, is not something you can control. In fact, if you already knew the value for p, you wouldn't need to estimate it and the sample-size issue wouldn't come up.

Two methods overcome this problem. First, you can select a *pilot sample* and compute the sample proportion, $\bar{p}$, and substitute $\bar{p}$ for p. Then once the sample size is computed, the pilot sample can be used as part of the overall required sample.

Second, you can select a conservative value for p. The closer p is to 0.50, the greater is the variation because $p(1-p)$ is greatest when $p = 0.50$. For example, if the manager has reason to believe that the population proportion, p, will be about 0.60, he could use a value for p a little closer to 0.50—say, 0.55. If he doesn't have a good idea of what p is, he could conservatively use $p = 0.50$, which will give a sample size at least large enough to meet requirements.

Suppose the Quick Lube manager selects a pilot sample of $n = 100$ customers and sends these people cards. Further suppose $x = 62$ of these customers respond to the mailing. Then

$$\bar{p} = \frac{62}{100} = 0.62$$

is substituted for p in Equation 7-14. For a 95% confidence level, the z-value is

$$z = 1.96,$$

and the margin of error is equal to

$$e = 0.04.$$

Substitute these values into Equation 7-14 and solve for the required sample size.

$$n = \frac{1.96^2(0.62)(1-0.62)}{0.04^2} = 565.676 = 566$$

Because the pilot sample of 100 can be included, the Quick Lube manager needs to send out an additional 466 cards to randomly selected customers. If this is more than the company can afford or wishes to include in the sample, the margin of error can be increased or the confidence level can be reduced.

EXAMPLE 7-7: SAMPLE SIZE DETERMINATION FOR ESTIMATING p

The Newsday Times   The managing editor for the *The Newsday Times* paper is interested in estimating the proportion of the paper's customers who like the new design for the sports page. She wishes to develop a 90% confidence interval estimate and would like to have the estimate be within ± 0.05 of the true population proportion. To determine the required sample size, she can use the following steps.

Step 1:   Define the population of interest.
The population is all customers of the newspaper.

Step 2:   Determine the level of confidence and find the critical z-value using the standard normal distribution table.
The desired confidence level is 90%. The z-value for 90% confidence is the z-value that corresponds to $\frac{0.90}{2} = 0.45$. This is $z = 1.645$.

Step 3:   Determine the desired margin of error.
The editor wishes the margin of error to be 0.05.

Step 4:   Arrive at a value to use for _p_.
Two options can be used to obtain a value for _p_:

1. Use a pilot sample and compute _p_, the sample proportion. Use $\bar{p}$ to represent _p_.
2. Select a value for _p_ that is closer to 0.50 than you actually believe the value to be. If you have no idea what _p_ might be, use _p_ = 0.50 to give a conservatively large sample size.

In this case, suppose the editor has no idea what the _p_ is but wants to make sure that her sample is sufficiently large to meet her estimation requirements. Then she will use _p_ = 0.50.

Step 5:   Use Equation 7-14 to determine the sample size.

$$n = \frac{z_{\alpha/2}^2 p(1-p)}{e^2} = \frac{1.645^2(0.50)(1-0.50)}{0.05^2} = 270.6025 = 271$$

The editor should randomly survey 271 customers.

7-3: EXERCISES

Skill Development

7.41   Compute the 95% confidence interval estimate for _p_ based on a sample size of 400 when the sample proportion, $\bar{p}$, is equal to 0.30.

7.42   Determine the required sample size needed to estimate a population proportion when the desired margin of error is ±0.03, the confidence level is 95%, and _p_ is set at 0.50.

7.43   A sample of _n_ = 300 items has been randomly selected. Of these, 55 contain the attribute of interest. Based on this information, compute a 90% confidence interval estimate for the proportion of items in the population that have this attribute.

7.44   A simple random sample of 150 items provides a sample proportion having a specific attribute of 0.23.
   a. What is the point estimate for the population proportion having the attribute?
   b. Develop a 99% confidence interval estimate for the proportion of items in the population having the attribute.

7.45   A pilot sample of _n_ = 50 items reveals that 11 items have the attribute of interest. Using this information, determine how many more items must be sampled to obtain a confidence interval estimate for the population proportion if the confidence level is 98% and the margin of error is ±0.03.

7.46   A random sample of 900 items was selected from a population. The sample contained 750 items with a particular attribute.
   a. Based on the sample data, construct a 90% confidence interval estimate and interpret the estimate.
   b. Referring to your answer in part a, what size sample would be needed to cut the margin of error in half? (Hint: Use the 900 units as a pilot sample.)

7.47   Assume that we wish to have 95% confidence and a margin of error of ±0.03.
   a. What sample size is needed to estimate the population proportion if it is thought that _p_ will be approximately 0.70?

   b. Suppose that _p_ were 0.30 instead. How would this change the required sample size? Does this answer surprise you? Explain why the sample sizes came out as they did.

7.48   A sample of size 100 was selected from a population. Out of this sample, 47 had a particular attribute.
   a. Is the sample size large enough so that the sampling distribution of the sample proportion can be approximated with a normal distribution? Support your answer with calculations and reasons.
   b. Based on these sample data, construct and interpret the 95% confidence interval estimate for the population proportion.

7.49   A random sample of 300 items was selected from a population. Of this sample, 88 items possessed a desired attribute. Construct and interpret the 85% confidence interval estimate for the population proportion.

7.50   Assume that a decision maker wants to estimate a population proportion with 90% confidence and a margin of error of ±0.03. The decision maker has obtained a pilot sample of 10. This pilot sample's proportion is 0.50. What sample size will be sure to achieve the desired results? How many additional observations must the decision maker obtain?

7.51   Suppose a pilot sample of 50 items was selected and 22 items had the attribute of interest. How many more items must be sampled to develop a 90% confidence level with a 0.05 margin of error?

Business Applications

7.52   A bank in Midland, Texas, is interested in estimating the proportion of customers who have credit cards with one or more other banks. A simple random sample of 200 customers showed that 144 have these credit cards. If the bank wishes the estimate to be made with a 95% confidence level, what are the upper and lower limits of the confidence interval estimate?

7.53 An export–import shop in Seattle, Washington, recently sent a buyer to China to purchase glass dinnerware products from a company. The buyer is interested in estimating the proportion of the glassware that contains visual defects. A simple random sample of 130 items is selected, and 13 are found to have a visual defect.

    a. Based on this information, what is the 90% confidence interval estimate for the proportion of all products made by the company?

    b. Suppose the buyer would like to reduce the margin of error for the estimate found in part a, what options does he have? Discuss.

7.54 A survey of 499 women for the American Orthopedic Foot and Ankle Society revealed that 38% wear flats to work.

    a. Use this sample information to develop a 99% confidence interval for the population proportion of women who wear flats to work.

    b. Suppose the society wished to estimate the proportion of women who wear athletic shoes to work and the proportion of women who wear flats to work within a margin of error of 0.01 with 95% confidence. Determine the sample size required if only one sample is to be obtained.

7.55 Watson, Harris & Tonkin is a CPA firm in Columbus, Ohio. As part of an audit of a large retail company, the firm wishes to estimate the proportion of credit card accounts that are past due. They want this estimate to have a margin of error no greater than 0.03, and they wish to use a 95% confidence interval estimate.

    a. What size sample should they select if they have no idea what the percentage might be and they want to make sure the sample size is large enough to meet their requirements?

    b. Suppose that the sample size determined in part a is used and the sample proportion is 0.18. Construct the confidence interval estimate for the population.

    c. Referring to parts a and b, discuss why the margin of error obtained in the interval estimate is actually smaller than what the firm wanted.

7.56 A local radio station is interested in estimating the percentage of people in a target market who have a favorable impression of its morning show. The marketing department wishes to estimate this proportion within ±0.03 of the true population value and have a confidence level of 98%. A pilot sample of 40 people is selected, and the proportion in this sample with a favorable impression is 0.45. Based on this information, how many more people must be surveyed?

Advanced Business Applications

7.57 The corporate operations manager for the Phillips Oil Company has his staff working on a new service-station layout plan that would potentially alter the ratio of regular unleaded pumps to other gasoline pumps (premium, super premium, etc.) that are placed at a station. As part of the staff's analysis, they are interested in estimating the difference in the population proportion of customers who purchase unleaded regular gasoline in eastern states versus western states. They have considerably more experience with the eastern states. The proportion of customers who purchase unleaded regular gasoline in the eastern states is known to be 0.75. They have sampled 900 western-state customers; 643 of the western-state customers purchased regular unleaded gasoline.

    a. Using a 95% confidence level, determine the estimate for the population proportion of western-state customers who purchase unleaded regular.

    b. On the basis of this confidence interval, would you recommend that Phillips Oil use a different ratio of regular unleaded pumps in the western states than in the eastern states? Support your answer with the confidence interval and the logic that accompanies it.

    c. Referring to part a, what is the margin of error for the confidence interval?

    d. Discuss the options that exist to reduce the margin of error.

7.58 Most major airlines allow passengers to carry two pieces of luggage (of a certain maximum size) onto a plane. However, their studies show that the more carry-on bags passengers have, the longer it takes the plane to unload and load passengers. One regional airline is considering changing its policy to allow only one carry-on per passenger. Before doing so, it decided to collect some data. Specifically, a random sample of 1,000 passengers was selected. The passengers were observed and the number of bags carried on the plane was noted. Out of the 1,000 passengers, 345 had more than one bag.

    a. Based on this sample, develop and interpret a 95% confidence interval estimate for the proportion of the traveling population who would have been impacted if the "one-bag" limit had been in effect. Discuss your result.

    b. The domestic version of Boeing's 747 has a capacity for 568 passengers. Determine an interval estimate of the number of passengers you would expect to board the plane carrying more than one piece of luggage. Assume the plane is at its passenger capacity.

    c. Suppose the airline also noted whether the passengers were male or female. Out of the 1,000 passengers observed, 690 were males. Of this group, 280 had more than one bag. Using this data, obtain and interpret a 95% confidence interval estimate for the proportion of male passengers in the population who would have been affected by the one-bag limit. Discuss.

    d. Suppose the airline decides to conduct a survey of its customers to determine their opinion of the proposed one-bag limit. The plan calls for a random sample of customers on different flights to be given a short written survey to complete during the flight. One key question on the survey will be: "Do you approve of limiting the number of carry-on bags to a maximum of one bag?" Airline managers expect that only about 15% will say yes. Based on this assumption, what size sample should the airline take if it wants to develop a 95% confidence interval estimate for the population proportion who will say "yes" with a margin of error of ±0.02?

7.59 A major manufacturer of athletic footwear is considering a new marketing campaign directed at working women. The idea is to create the impression that athletic footwear is comfortable and appropriate to wear to work. Part of the motivation for this idea came from a survey of 499 women conducted for the American Orthopedic Foot and Ankle Society. This survey revealed that 23% wear athletic shoes to work.

    a. Use this information to develop a 90% confidence interval estimate for the population proportion of women who wear athletic shoes to work. Interpret your findings.

b. The mass media usually references the information contained in a confidence interval by reciting the point estimate for the parameter of interest, followed by a specification of the margin of error. Write a short description of the media release summarizing the confidence in part a.

c. Suppose the station manager can't afford to survey that many people and has indicated that the maximum sample size can be 300 people. Assuming that the sample size is cut to 300, without changing the confidence level, indicate specifically what must be changed and by how much.

Summary and Conclusions

By the time you have reached this point, you may be wondering how you are ever going to keep all these different estimation processes straight. If you try to memorize them, you probably won't be able to do it. However, if you develop an understanding of the basic logic of estimation, it is very manageable.

Remember, your first objective is to estimate a population value based on information from a sample. There are two types of estimates: point estimates and interval estimates. Point estimates are subject to potential sampling error. Point estimates are almost always different than the population value. A confidence interval estimate takes into account the potential for sampling error and provides a range within which we believe the true population value falls. There is a common format for all confidence interval estimates:

Point Estimate ± (Critical Value)(Standard Error)

The point estimate is at the center of the interval. The amount that we add and subtract to the point estimate is called the margin of error.

Although this format is always used, there are slightly different formulas that we use depending on what population value we are estimating and certain other conditions. You shouldn't try to memorize these formulas. Instead, you should focus on sorting out the characteristics of the situation at hand. Once you do that, you can locate the appropriate formula to determine the interval estimate. The key will be on correctly interpreting the results and applying these results to your decision situation.

Figure 7-9 contains a diagram that you should find useful as you work the problems and cases at the end of this chapter and later on when you encounter estimation applications in your work.

EQUATIONS

Confidence Interval General Format
Point Estimate ± (Critical Value)(Standard Error)   **7-1**

Confidence Interval General Format—σ Known
Point Estimate ± z(Standard Error)   **7-2**

Confidence Interval Estimate for μ, σ Known

$$\bar{x} \pm z_{\alpha/2} \frac{\sigma}{\sqrt{n}}$$ **7-3**

Margin of Error for Estimating μ, σ Known

$$e = z_{\alpha/2} \frac{\sigma}{\sqrt{n}}$$ **7-4**

t-Value for $\bar{x}$

$$t = \frac{\bar{x} - \mu}{\frac{s}{\sqrt{n}}}$$ **7-5**

Confidence Interval Estimate for μ, σ Unknown

$$\bar{x} \pm t_{\alpha/2} \frac{s}{\sqrt{n}}$$ **7-6**

Confidence Interval Estimate Approximation for μ, Large Samples, σ Unknown

$$\bar{x} \pm z_{\alpha/2} \frac{s}{\sqrt{n}}$$ **7-7**

Sample Size Requirement for Estimating μ, σ Known

$$n = \left(\frac{z_{\alpha/2}\sigma}{e}\right)^2 = \frac{z_{\alpha/2}^2 \sigma^2}{e^2}$$ **7-8**

Sample Proportion

$$\bar{p} = \frac{x}{n}$$ **7-9**

Standard Error for $\bar{p}$

$$\sigma_{\bar{p}} = \sqrt{\frac{p(1-p)}{n}}$$ **7-10**

Theoretical Confidence Interval Estimate for p

$$\bar{p} \pm z_{\alpha/2} \sqrt{\frac{p(1-p)}{n}}$$ **7-11**

Confidence Interval Estimate for p

$$\bar{p} \pm z_{\alpha/2} \sqrt{\frac{\bar{p}(1-\bar{p})}{n}}$$ **7-12**

FIGURE 7-9

Flow Diagram for Confidence Interval Estimation Alternatives

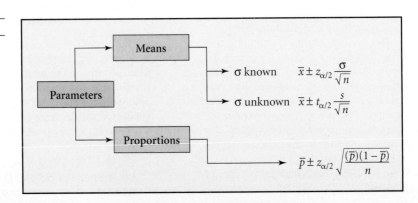

Margin of Error for Estimating p

$$e = z_{\alpha/2}\sqrt{\frac{p(1-p)}{n}} \qquad \textbf{7-13}$$

Sample Size for Estimating p

$$n = \frac{z_{\alpha/2}^2 p(1-p)}{e^2} \qquad \textbf{7-14}$$

Key Terms

Confidence Coefficient, 269
Confidence Interval, 267
Confidence Level, 269

Degrees of Freedom, 275
Margin of Error, 273
Pilot Sample, 287

Point Estimate, 266
Sampling Error, 266
Student's *t*-Distribution, 275

CHAPTER EXERCISES

Conceptual Questions

7.60 In a situation in which our objective is to estimate the population mean, if a small sample is used and the population standard deviation is unknown, we are hit with a "double whammy" when it comes to the margin of error. Explain what the double whammy is and why it occurs. (Hint: Consider the sources of variation in the margin of error.)

7.61 When a decision maker is interested in estimating a single population proportion, why is the margin of error greater when the sample proportion is near 0.50 for a given confidence level? (Note: If you have had a calculus class, you may wish to use the tools acquired there to prove the result. If not, a few sample calculations of the margin of error for various sample proportions should point the way.)

7.62 An insurance company in Iowa recently conducted a survey of its automobile-policy customers to estimate the mean miles these customers commute to work each day. The result based on a random sample of 300 policyholders indicated the population mean was between 3.5 and 6.7 miles. This interval estimate was constructed using 95% confidence.
  a. After receiving this result, one of the managers was overheard telling a colleague that 95% of all customers commute between 3.5 and 6.7 miles to work each day. How would you respond to this statement? Is it correct? Why or why not? Discuss.
  b. Another manager was overheard to say that he was 95% confident that the mean of the 300 policyholders was between 3.5 and 6.7. How would you respond to this statement? Is it correct? Why or why not? Discuss.

7.63 Referring to Exercise 7.62, suppose a third manager is overheard telling another colleague that there is a 95% chance that the true average commute for all policyholders is between 3.5 and 6.7 miles per day. Comment on this statement. Is it a correct statement? Discuss why or why not.

Business Applications

7.64 A survey of 619 working adults revealed that 38% of them favored allowing the federal government to invest a portion of the Social Security Trust Fund in the stock market (*USA Today*, July 27, 1998). Use this information to construct a 99% confidence interval for the proportion of working adults who favor such investments.

7.65 A random sample of 48 individuals who purchased items over the Internet revealed an average purchase amount of $178, with a standard deviation of $27. Use this sample information and a 95% confidence level to provide the following:
  a. a point estimate of the average purchase amount
  b. the margin of error of the point estimate you have provided
  c. an interval estimate for the population mean

7.66 Chambre Corporation makes a variety of products, including electrical surge protectors. They are considering developing a special model surge protector that will be mounted internally in a PC at the time of manufacture. However, before doing this, the company needs convincing data to make the sale to the computer makers. The company contracted with a national survey research firm to conduct a survey of PC owners to determine several issues related to PC ownership and the need for a surge protector. A key question on the survey asked the respondents to indicate the total value of the PCs that they had purchased most recently. The objective now is to develop a 95% confidence interval estimate for the mean value for all PCs owned in the market. The desired margin of error is not to exceed ±$100. A previous study has indicated that the standard deviation for PC value is approximately $300. Based on this, what size random sample should be taken? Explain why this required sample size is this small.

7.67 Suppose the survey research firm selected a simple random sample of 300 people for the purposes of estimating their mean weekly income and found the sample information was $\bar{x} = \$1,345.78$ and $s = \$257.90$.
  a. Compute the desired confidence interval estimate and interpret the estimate.
  b. Indicate what options exist to reduce the margin of error.
  c. Based on the sample information above, determine the smallest and largest prices being paid for a PC.
  d. What assumption about the distribution of the PC prices allows you to produce these estimates?

7.68 A U.S. senator has asked her staff to conduct a study to determine whether people would be in favor of raising the retirement age as a way to save the Social Security system.
  a. If you seek to have a 95% confidence interval for your estimate, with a margin of error of 4 percentage points, how large a sample should you select? Produce a conservatively high sample size.

b. Suppose when the survey was conducted in the senator's home state using the sample size determined in part a, 37.9% indicated that they would favor the proposal. Use this information to construct the confidence interval estimate. Interpret the estimate.

7.69 A company wishes to obtain the sample size required to determine a company's average ordering lead time to within 1 day with 95% confidence. If the standard deviation of lead times is known to be 7 days, determine the required sample size.

7.70 A random sample of 25 sports utility vehicles (SUVs) for the same year and model revealed the following miles per gallon (MPG) values:

12.40	13.00	12.60	12.10	13.10
13.00	12.00	13.10	11.40	12.60
9.50	13.25	12.40	10.70	11.70
10.00	14.00	10.90	9.90	10.20
11.00	11.90	9.90	12.00	11.30

Assume that the population distribution for MPG for this model year is normally distributed.
a. Use the sample results to develop a 95% confidence interval estimate for the population mean MPG.
b. Determine the average number of gallons of gasoline the SUVs described here would use to travel between Los Angeles and San Francisco, California—a distance of approximately 400 miles.
c. Another sample of the same size is to be obtained. If you know that the average MPG in the second sample will be larger than the one obtained in part a, determine the probability that the sample mean will be larger than the upper confidence limit of the confidence interval you calculated.

7.71 A travel agency would like to estimate the proportion of domestic travelers who select an airline based on the price of the ticket to the desired destination. If the travel agency would like to be 94% confident of being within ±4% of the true population proportion, then what size sample should they take? (Assume that they have no knowledge about what the proportion might be and want to make sure they have a large enough sample size to meet their needs.)

Advanced Business Applications

7.72 The Future-Vision Company is considering applying for a franchise to market satellite television dish systems in a Florida market area. As part of the company's research into this opportunity, staff in the New Acquisitions Department conducted a survey of 548 homes selected at random in the market area. They asked a number of questions on the survey. The data for some of the variables are in the CD-ROM file called *Future-Vision*. One key question asked whether the household was currently connected to cable TV.
a. Using the sample information, what is the 95% confidence interval estimate for the true proportion of households in the market area that subscribe to cable television?

b. Based on the sample data, develop a 95% confidence interval estimate for the mean income and interpret this estimate.

7.73 The Jordeen Bottling Company recently did an extensive sampling of its soft drink inventory in which 5,000 cans were sampled. Employees weighed each can and used weight to determine the fluid ounces in the cans. The data are in a file on your CD-ROM called *Jordeen*. Based on this sample data, should the company conclude that the mean volume is 12 ounces? Base your conclusion on a 95% confidence interval estimate and discuss.

7.74 A survey was taken to determine the average amount young professionals living in Denver have invested in stock mutual funds outside of retirement accounts. The survey results showed lower and upper confidence interval limits of $25,114 and $26,068. respectively. If the confidence interval was based on a sample size of 1,024 young professionals and a known population standard deviation of $7,543, then what is the confidence level for the estimate of the population mean amount invested?

7.75 A survey conducted by the NPD Group for Quaker Oats (*USA Today*) revealed that 70% of those people who use oatmeal as a cereal put something on it. Suppose this estimate was based on a sample of 1,024 people who eat oatmeal for breakfast.
a. Use the study's findings to calculate the 95% confidence interval for the true proportion of breakfast oatmeal eaters who put something on their oats.
b. Calculate the largest the margin of error could possibly be when estimating the proportion of oatmeal eaters who put something on it with the sample proportion given above.

7.76 A sample of 441 shoppers selected from people in San Luis Obispo, California, revealed that 76% made at least one purchase at a discount store last month.
a. Based on this sample information, what is the 90% confidence interval for the population proportion of shoppers who made at least one discount store purchase last month?
b. San Luis Obispo has a population of 35,000 people. It does not have a discount store. Therefore, shoppers travel outside of the city to buy at discount stores. Determine a 90% confidence interval for the number of shoppers who made at least one discount store purchase last month.

7.77 Open the CD-ROM file *High-Desert Banking*. Assume that these data reflect the population of all loans in the bank's portfolio.
a. Select a random sample of 49 loans. Use this sample to construct a 90% confidence interval for the population mean of all loans in the High Desert Bank's portfolio. (Hint: Remember to use the finite correction factor because the sample is large relative to the size of the population.)
b. Repeat this process nine more times, for a total of 10 samples, each of size 49.

c. Compute the actual population mean for all loans in the portfolio. How many of the 10 confidence intervals that you constructed contain the population mean? How many intervals would you expect to contain the true population mean in the long run?

7.78 💿 Paper-R-Us is a national distributor of printer and copier paper for commercial use. The data file called *Sales* contains the annual, year-to-date sales values for each of the company's customers. Suppose the internal audit department has decided to audit a sample of 36 of these accounts. However, before they actually conduct the in-depth audit (a process that involves tracking all transactions for each sampled account), they want to be sure that the sample they have selected is representative of the population.

a. Compute the population mean.
b. Use all the data in the population to develop a frequency distribution and histogram.
c. Calculate the proportion of accounts for customers in each region of the country.
d. Select a random sample of accounts. Develop a frequency distribution for this sample data. Compare this distribution to that of the population. (Hint: You might want to consider using relative frequencies for comparison purposes.)
e. Construct a 95% confidence interval estimate for the population mean sales per customer. Discuss how you would use this interval estimate to help determine whether the sample is a good representative of the population. (Hint: You may want to use the finite correction factor, because the sample is large relative to the size of the population.)
f. Use the information developed in parts a through e to draw a conclusion about whether the sample is a representative sample of the population. What other information would be desirable? Discuss.

7.79 In 1998, the University of Michigan conducted a study of college basketball players in the United States. A total of 758 people responded to the survey. Among these, 316 were female athletes. The study found that 546 athletes admitted to gambling since entering college. Of the females, 187 said they had gambled. Two hundred sixty-five of the respondents said they had placed bets on sports, and 266 of the male athletes said they had bet on sports. Finally, 22 of the male athletes admitted to providing inside information for gambling purposes, betting on a game in which they were playing, or shaving points for money. (Source: *Idaho Statesman* and Associated Press, January 12, 1999.)

a. Develop a 95% confidence interval estimate for the proportion of all athletes who have gambled on sports while in college. Interpret.
b. Develop a 99% confidence interval estimate for the proportion of male athletes who have gambled on sports while in college. Interpret.
c. Construct and interpret a 95% confidence interval estimate for the proportion of male students who have shaved points, provided inside information, or bet on their own game.

d. Based on your responses to parts a, b, and c, write a short report to the NCAA on the subject of gambling by student athletes.

7.80 The president of Morgan Fabrics, a nationwide manufacturer of fabric material for the garment industry, has recommitted the company to better serving its customers. One key measure of customer satisfaction is the proportion of on-time deliveries. The company did not use this measure in the past, so the president has no idea right now of what the company's past on-time delivery rate has been. To establish this benchmark, the customer service manager has sampled 400 customer orders from the past year. Of these, 310 showed that the delivery had reached the customer by the promised date. Use this sample data to construct a 90% confidence interval of the true proportion of on-time deliveries for this company. Interpret this interval and discuss whether you feel this will be a good benchmark against which they can compare their future on-time delivery performance.

7.81 💿 One of the major U.S. producers of household products recently surveyed 64 adults in order to estimate the proportion of adults who prefer mint-flavored toothpaste to plain toothpaste. The motive behind the survey was to aid in its production planning efforts. The results of the survey are contained in a file called *Toothpaste*.

a. Use this sample data to construct a 99% confidence interval of the population proportion of adults who prefer mint-flavored toothpaste. Explain how this might help the company plan its toothpaste production.
b. Suppose that you are the production manager for a relatively small toothpaste-manufacturing company. You only produce mint-flavored and plain toothpaste. You are trying to decide what proportion of each of these you should produce. You would like the proportion of production to match that of the consumers' preferences. You do, however, have a slightly larger profit margin on plain toothpaste. Determine the proportions of each type of toothpaste that you will produce. Support you answer with statistical reasoning related to the above confidence interval.

7.82 💿 The brokerage firm of Gallusha, Higgins & Morton is considering buying another brokerage firm in the Northeast. One factor that plays a part in the price it would be willing to pay for this firm is the cash balances of the current clients. The data file called *Gallusha* contains cash balance data as of a particular point in time for a sample of customers in the firm.

a. Assuming the population of cash account balances from which this sample was taken is normally distributed, construct a 95% confidence interval of the mean cash balance for all accounts for this firm.
b. Suppose that Gallusha representatives look at the confidence interval computed in part a and feel that the margin of error is too large. If they want to reduce the margin of error by 40%, what would be the required sample size, assuming that no change in confidence level takes place? (Hint: Use the sample standard deviation from part a in solving for the required sample size.)

CASE 7-A:

Duro Industries, Inc.

Rochelle Phillips was more nervous than she had been for a long time. Today was the day she would have to prepare an interim report to management on the new production process she had been testing at Duro Industries, Inc., a producer of bricks and paver blocks. Rochelle had started work at the company's Memphis plant right out of college and had worked her way up to assistant plant manager in charge of production during her 22 years with the company.

She knew her report could result in significant changes at Duro Industries. The company had been in business for 75 years and had established a solid regional reputation for quality and reliability in the manufacturing and delivery of its products. But the brick industry was changing rapidly. In addition to competition from other regional companies, Duro was facing increased competition from large foreign firms that were looking for ways to take Duro's best customers. Furthermore, there were fundamental changes underway in how brick companies managed their production processes.

Brick companies had traditionally relied on manual labor to move bricks through the manufacturing process. Duro was not different, employing hundreds of workers to help move bricks and paver blocks through the various manufacturing steps. But some foreign competitors, most notably Australian firms, were using vector drives to provide the precision motion control necessary to automatically move different quantities and configurations through the process accurately and repeatedly, with less manual labor than before. This produced both cost savings and faster production times. If domestic firms adopted the same technology, the resulting costs savings could give them a competitive advantage in price and delivery times over Duro.

The CEO of Duro had notified Rochelle that her plant would be expected to evaluate the feasibility of undertaking this new approach to moving product through the process. If successful, Rochelle would head up the implementation team at the other Duro facilities in the United States. She was concerned that the implementation would be difficult and expensive. Furthermore, she was uncertain whether the expenditure on the vector drives would have a quick enough payback. Duro was convinced that the company had to at least investigate the feasibility of such a process, and the company was initially interested in the productivity improvements that might arise from such a plan.

Rochelle contacted a company that produced electric motors and vector drives, and its consultants told her that it would be possible to set up an experiment that would allow her to estimate whether the new process could increase production. Rochelle began to plan for the test. She decided that once the new equipment was in place and the workers were trained in the new process, the experiment would run for 50 days. Each day's output would be recorded. The CD-ROM file called *Duro* contains the production output each day at the Memphis plant.

Rochelle needs to prepare a report that analyzes the data for the test period at the Memphis plant. The financial analysts at Duro headquarters believe the purchase can be justified if the equipment will lead to an average increase in production of at least 10,000 bricks per day. (Note, in Chapter 9, Rochelle will be asked to compare the output at the Memphis plant to that at a comparable plant in Birmingham, Alabama.)

CASE 7-B:

Management Solutions, Inc.

The round-trip to the "site" was just under 360 miles, which gave Fred Kitchener and Mike Kyte plenty of time to discuss the next steps in the project. The site is a rural stretch of highway in Idaho where two visibility sensors are located. The project is part of a contract Fred's company, Management Solutions, Inc., has with the state of Idaho and the Federal Highway Administration. Under the contract, among other things, Management Solutions is charged with evaluating the performance of a new technology for measuring visibility. The larger study involves determining whether visibility sensors can be effectively tied to electronic message signs that would warn motorists of upcoming visibility problems in rural areas.

Mike Kyte, a transportation engineer and professor at the University of Idaho, has been involved with the project as a consultant to Fred's company since the initial proposal. Mike is very knowledgeable about visibility sensors and traffic systems. Fred's expertise is in managing projects like this one, in which it is important to get people from multiple organizations to work together effectively.

As the pair headed back toward Boise from the site, Mike was more excited than Fred had seen him in a long time. Fred reasoned that the source of excitement was that they had finally been successful in getting solid data to compare the two visibility sensors in a period of low visibility. The previous day at the site had been very foggy. The Scorpion Sensor is a tested technology that Mike has worked with for some time in urban applications. However, it has never before been installed in such a remote location at this stretch of highway I-84, which connects Idaho and Utah. The other sensor produced by the Vanguard Company measures visibility in a totally new way using laser technology.

The data that had excited Mike so much were collected by the two sensors and fed back to a computer system at the port of entry near the test site. The measurements were collected every five minutes for the 24-hour day. As Fred took advantage of the 75 mph speed limit through southern Idaho, Mike kept glancing at the data on the printout he had made of the first few 5-minute time periods. The Scorpion system had not only provided visibility readings, but it also had provided other weather-related data, such as temperature, wind speed, wind direction, and humidity.

Mike's eyes went directly to the two visibility columns. Ideally, the visibility readings for the two sensors would be the same at any 5-minute period, but they weren't. After a few exclamations of surprise from Mike, Fred suggested that they come up with an outline for the report they would have to make from these data for the project team meeting next week. Both agreed that a full descriptive analysis of all the data, including graphs and numerical measures, was necessary. In addition, Fred wanted to use these early data to provide an estimate for the mean visibility provided by the two sensors. They agreed that estimates were needed for the day as a whole and also for only those periods when the Scorpion system showed visibility under 1.0 mile. They also felt that the analysis should look at the other weather factors, too, but they weren't sure just what was needed.

As the lights in the Boise Valley became visible, Mike agreed to work up a draft of the report, including a narrative based on the data in the CD-ROM file called *Visibility*. Fred said that he would set up the project team meeting agenda, and Mike could make the presentation. Both men agreed that the data were strictly a sample and that more low-visibility data would be collected when conditions occurred.

General References

1. Berenson, Mark L., and David M. Levine, *Basic Business Statistics Concepts and Applications*, 7th ed. (Upper Saddle River, NJ: Prentice Hall, 1999).
2. Dodge, Mark, and Craig, Stinson, *Running Microsoft Excel 2000* (Redmond, WA: Microsoft Press, 1999).
3. Hogg, Robert V., and Elliot A. Tanis, *Probability and Statistical Inference*, 5th ed. (Upper Saddle River, NJ: Prentice Hall, 1997).
4. Marx, Morris L., and Richard J. Larsen, *Mathematical Statistics and Its Applications*, 3rd ed. (Upper Saddle River, NJ: Prentice Hall, 2000).
5. *Microsoft Excel 2000* (Redmond, WA: Microsoft Corp., 1999).
6. *Minitab for Windows Version 13* (State College, PA: Minitab, 2000).
7. Siegel, Andrew F., *Practical Business Statistics*, 4th ed. (Burr Ridge, IL: Irwin, 2000).

CHAPTER 8

Introduction to Hypothesis Testing

CHAPTER OUTCOMES

After studying the material in Chapter 8, you should be able to:

- Formulate null and alternative hypotheses for applications involving a single population mean or proportion.
- Correctly formulate a decision rule for testing a null hypothesis.
- Know how to use the test statistic, critical value, and p-value approaches to test the null hypothesis.
- Know what Type I and Type II errors are.
- Compute the probability of a Type II error.

WHY YOU NEED TO KNOW

Chapter 7 introduced the steps required to estimate the value of a population mean or proportion based on data from a simple random sample. Based on those estimates, decision makers are able to draw inferences about a population without having to conduct a costly and time-consuming census. Estimation is required when the decision maker has no specific knowledge of a population value but seeks to gain that knowledge.

However, many times managers know what a population value should be because of a company policy or a contract specification, and they must be able to use sample information to determine whether the policy or contract specification is being satisfied. For instance, large metropolitan areas are required to report air pollution levels on a daily basis. They cannot possibly sample all the air in the metropolitan area, yet they are required to report whether the city's air quality meets federal standards. When CPA firms perform audits, they issue a final report stating whether the audited firm followed Generally Accepted Accounting Procedures. They are unable to audit every transac-

tion, so they must make the statement based on a sample of transactions. Even construction crews pouring foundations for large buildings need to determine whether the concrete meets specifications. Taking core samples (long cylinders cut from the poured foundation) and testing these samples does this. The core samples provide information that building inspectors and construction managers use to decide whether construction work can continue, or whether foundations must be further reinforced.

Imagine for a moment that you are the buyer for a company that makes home thermostats, which are used to regulate the heating and cooling systems in homes. A new producer of a major electronic component that is used in your thermostats claims that no more than 3% of its components will have a sensing error of two degrees or more. Before you buy 100,000 units, you might want to test the manufacturer's claim. Because you could not feasibly test each component, you would select a sample and use the sample information to decide whether to make the purchase.

This chapter introduces statistical techniques used to test claims about population values. All decision makers need to have a solid understanding of these techniques in order to use sample information effectively in their decision making.

8-1 HYPOTHESIS TESTS FOR MEANS

By now you know that information contained in a sample is subject to sampling error. The sample mean likely will not equal the population mean. Therefore, in situations in which you need to test a claim about a population mean by using the sample mean, you can't simply compare the sample mean to the claim and reject the claim if $\bar{x}$ and the claim are different. Instead, you need a testing procedure that incorporates the potential for sampling error.

Statistical hypothesis testing provides managers with a structured analytical method for making decisions of this type. It lets them make decisions in such a way that the probability of decision errors can be controlled, or at least measured. Even though statistical hypothesis testing does not eliminate the uncertainty in the managerial environment, the techniques involved often allow managers to identify and control the level of uncertainty.

The techniques presented in this chapter assume the data are selected using an appropriate statistical sampling process and that the data are interval or ratio level. In short, we assume we are working with good data.

FORMULATING THE HYPOTHESES

Null and Alternative Hypotheses

In hypothesis testing, two hypotheses are formulated. One is the **null hypothesis**.

> *Null Hypothesis*
>
> The statement about the population value that will be tested. The null hypothesis will be rejected only if the sample data provide substantial contradictory evidence.

The null hypothesis is represented by H_0 and should contain an equality sign, such as "=," "≤," or "≥." The second hypothesis is the **alternative hypothesis** (represented by H_A).

Alternative Hypothesis

The hypothesis that includes all population values not covered by the null hypothesis. The alternative hypothesis is deemed to be true if the null hypothesis is rejected.

Based on the sample data, we either reject H_0 or we do not reject H_0.

State Insurance Fund—The State Insurance Fund administers the workmen's compensation system. The agency is under legislative inquiry because of complaints from companies covered by the fund. The major objection is that the average processing time exceeds the legally mandated average of 25 days. The fund managers, however, believe they are within the 25-day average response, although they admit that some complicated claims may take longer.

Because the legislative committee has requested a quick reply, fund managers cannot gather information from all claims filed this year and, therefore, must formulate a response based on a sample of claims. As indicated earlier, when a decision is based on sample results, sampling error must be expected. Without considering the effect of sampling error, the managers can't simply say that if the sample mean is 25 days or less, then the population mean is also. Likewise, if the sample mean exceeds 25 days, that does not automatically indicate that the population mean exceeds 25 days.

To account for the potential sampling error, the managers need to formally test whether the sample mean supports the conclusion that the population mean is less than or equal to 25 days or the conclusion that the average time exceeds 25 days. The first step is to express these two possibilities using formal hypothesis-testing terms.

In this example, the status quo is that no change is needed and that the mean processing time is less than or equal to 25 days. If this is rejected and the data indicate that the mean processing time is greater than 25 days, the fund managers would need to change procedures. In this case, the null and alternative hypotheses are stated as:

Null hypothesis $H_0: \mu \leq 25$ days

Alternative hypothesis $H_A: \mu > 25$ days

where μ is the mean claim-processing time.

Determining the null and alternative hypotheses is often a difficult task for students. The null hypothesis represents the situation that is assumed to be true unless the evidence is strong enough to convince the decision maker it is not true. A common analogy is with a legal system, in which a defendant is assumed innocent unless the evidence convinces a jury that the person is guilty. A little bit of evidence is not sufficient. The proof must be substantial. In the case of the State Insurance Fund, the formulation for the null and alternative hypotheses puts the burden of proof on those filing the complaint. Unless the sample mean is "substantially" greater than 25 days, no action will be taken to change the system.

$\mathcal{E}$XAMPLE 8-1: FORMULATING THE NULL AND ALTERNATIVE HYPOTHESES

Student Work Hours   In today's economy, many university students work many hours, often full time, to help pay for the high costs of a college education. Suppose a university in the Midwest was considering changing its class schedule to accommodate students working long hours. The registrar has stated a change was needed because the mean number of hours worked by undergraduate students at the university is more than 20 per week. The following steps can be taken to establish the appropriate null and alternative hypotheses.

Step 1:   Determine the population value of interest.
In this case, the population value of interest is the mean hours worked, μ. The null and alternative hypotheses must be stated in terms of the population value.

Step 2:   Define the situation that is assumed to be true unless substantial information exists to suggest otherwise.
Because changing the class scheduling system would be expensive and time consuming, the assumption is made that the mean hours worked is less than or equal to 20

hours per week. Thus, the burden of proof is placed on the registrar to justify her claim that the mean exceeds 20 hours.

Step 3: **Formulate the null and alternative hypotheses.**
Keep in mind that the equality goes in the null hypothesis.

$$H_0: \mu \leq 20 \text{ hours}$$
$$H_A: \mu > 20 \text{ hours (claim)}$$

Example 8-2 illustrates another example of how the null and alternative hypotheses are formulated.

EXAMPLE 8-2: FORMULATING THE NULL AND ALTERNATIVE HYPOTHESES

Chips N' Snacks Company   The Chips N' Snacks Company produces several snack and food products that are sold in food stores throughout Colorado and New Mexico. The company uses an automatic filling machine to fill the sacks with the desired weight. For instance, when the company is running potato chips on the fill line, the machine is set to fill the sacks with 20 ounces. Thus, if the machine is working properly, the mean fill will be 20 ounces. Each hour, a sample of sacks is collected and weighed, and the technicians determine whether the machine is still operating correctly or whether it needs adjustment. The following steps can be used to establish the null and alternative hypotheses to be tested.

Step 1: **Determine the population value of interest.**
In this case, the population value of interest is the mean weight per sack, μ.

Step 2: **Define the situation that is assumed to be true unless substantial information exists to suggest otherwise.**
The status quo is that the machine is filling the sacks with the proper amount, which is $\mu = 20$ ounces. We will believe this to be true unless we find evidence to suggest otherwise. If such evidence exists, it means that the filling process needs to be adjusted.

Step 3: **Formulate the null and alternative hypotheses.**
Keep in mind that the equality goes in the null hypothesis.
The null and alternative hypotheses are

$$H_0: \mu = 20 \text{ ounces}$$
$$H_A: \mu \neq 20 \text{ ounces}$$

The Research Hypothesis

Another way to think about formulating the null and alternative hypotheses is to consider research applications. Companies such as Intel, Gillette, Dell Computers, and 3M continually bring out new and improved products. However, before introducing a new product, the companies want to be sure it is superior to the old product. They want sufficient evidence of the new product's superiority. The default position is that the existing product or process is at least as good as the new one. The burden of proof rests with the new idea. Only if the sample test results are substantially better for the new product or process will it be deemed superior. In these situations, when the decision maker has control over how the null and alternative hypotheses are stated, the alternative hypothesis should be the **research hypothesis**.

Research Hypothesis

The hypothesis the decision maker attempts to demonstrate to be true. Because this is the hypothesis deemed to be the most important to the decision maker, it will not be declared true unless the sample data strongly indicate that it is true.

If the research hypothesis forms the alternative hypothesis, a decision to reject the null hypothesis would indicate that there is statistical evidence to believe that the research hypothesis is true.

SUMMARY: FORMULATING THE NULL AND ALTERNATIVE HYPOTHESES

We find that some students have a difficult time formulating the null and alternative hypotheses. The previous discussion hopefully has clarified the process. However, we might offer the following suggestions and reminders.

1. The null and alternative hypotheses must be stated in terms of the population value of interest (e.g., μ or p).

2. The null hypothesis represents the status quo, it should contain an equality sign. It represents the condition that will be assumed to exist unless sufficient evidence is presented to show the condition has changed.

3. If you have a choice in formulating the null and alternative hypotheses, construct them so that the null hypothesis contains an equality sign and the alternative hypothesis contains what you wish to show. That way, if the null hypothesis is rejected, you have statistical support for your position.

4. In a research situation, construct the null and alternative hypotheses so that the burden of proof is placed on the research study. This means that the null hypothesis will be the status quo and the alternative will contain the "new" outcome.

You will encounter situations in which it may seem impossible to adhere to this broad set of rules. For instance, someone else may want the burden of proof to be placed on a claim containing an equality, such as $\mu \geq 20$. In such cases you must reason with the individual. For all continuous and many discrete variables, the chances that the population mean would equal exactly, say, 20 are so small that such an eventuality can be disregarded. The claim may be restated to be $\mu > 20$ without tainting the hypothesis test or the intent of the research.

Types of Statistical Errors

Because of the potential for extreme sampling error, two possible errors can occur when a hypothesis is tested: **Type I** and **Type II errors**. These errors show the relationship between what actually exists (a state of nature) and the decision made based on the sample information.

Type I Error	***Type II Error***
Rejecting the null hypothesis when it is, in fact, true.	*Failing to reject* the null hypothesis when it is, in fact, false.

Figure 8-1 shows the possible actions and states of nature associated with any hypothesis-testing application. As you can see, there are three possible outcomes: no error (correct decision), Type I error, and Type II error. *Only one of these outcomes will occur for a hypothesis test.* From Figure 8-1, if the null hypothesis is true and an error is made, it must be a Type I error. On the other hand, if the null hypothesis is false and an error is made, it must be a Type II error.

Many statisticians argue that you should never use the phrase "accept the null hypothesis." Instead you should use "*do not reject* the null hypothesis." Thus, the only two hypothesis-testing decisions would be *reject H_0* or *do not reject H_0*. This is why in a jury verdict to acquit a defendant, the verdict is "not guilty" rather than innocent. Just because the evidence is insufficient to convict does not necessarily mean that the defendant is innocent.

FIGURE 8-1

The Relationship Between Decisions and States of Nature

		State of Nature	
		Null Hypothesis True	Null Hypothesis False
Decision	Conclude Null True (Don't reject H_0)	Correct Decision	Type II Error
	Conclude Null False (Reject H_0)	Type I Error	Correct Decision

This thinking is appropriate when hypothesis testing is employed in situations in which some future action is not dependent on the results of the hypothesis test. However, in most business applications, the purpose of the hypothesis test is to direct the decision maker to take one action or another, based on the test results. For instance, in the State Insurance Fund example, if the sample data do not lead the managers to reject that $\mu \leq 25$ days, the fund managers will write a report to the legislature indicating that the customer assertions are not supported. Therefore, no changes will be made in the claims-evaluation process. Although they have "not rejected" the null hypothesis, their actions are consistent with what would have taken place if they had "accepted" the null hypothesis. So, in this text, when hypothesis testing is applied to decision-making situations, *not rejecting* the null hypothesis is essentially the same as *accepting* it.[1]

State Insurance Fund (continued)—In the State Insurance Fund hypothesis test, a Type I error would occur if the sample data led the managers to conclude that $\mu > 25$ days (H_0 is rejected) when the truth is that $\mu \leq 25$ days. The result would be that the managers would undertake an effort to change the system when no changes were required. This would be a costly waste of resources.

A Type II error would occur if the sample evidence led the managers to incorrectly conclude that $\mu \leq 25$ days (H_0 is not rejected) when the truth is the mean response time exceeds 25 days. The outcome is that nothing would be done to the system when changes were needed.

SIGNIFICANCE LEVEL AND CRITICAL VALUE

The objective of a hypothesis test is to use sample information to decide whether to reject the null hypothesis about a population parameter. How do decision makers determine whether the sample information supports or refutes the null hypothesis? The answer to this question is the key to understanding statistical hypothesis testing.

In hypotheses tests for a single population mean, the sample mean, $\bar{x}$, is used to test the hypotheses under consideration. Depending on how the null and alternative hypotheses are formulated, certain values of $\bar{x}$ will tend to support the null hypothesis, whereas other values will appear to contradict it. In the State Insurance Fund example, the null and alternative hypotheses were formulated as:

$$H_0: \mu \leq 25 \text{ days}$$
$$H_A: \mu > 25 \text{ days}$$

Values of $\bar{x}$ less than or equal to 25 days would tend to support the null hypothesis. By contrast, values of $\bar{x}$ greater than 25 days would tend to refute the null hypothesis. The larger the value of $\bar{x}$, the greater the evidence that the null hypothesis should be rejected. However, because we expect some sampling error, do we want to reject H_0 for any value of $\bar{x}$ that is greater than 25 days? Probably not. But should we reject H_0 if $\bar{x} = 26$ days, or $\bar{x} = 30$ days, or $\bar{x} = 35$ days? At what point do we stop attributing the result to sampling error?

In order to perform the hypothesis test we need to select a *cutoff* point that is the demarcation between rejecting and not rejecting the null hypothesis. Our *decision rule* is then

If $\bar{x} >$ cutoff, reject H_0
If $\bar{x} \leq$ cutoff, do not reject H_0

If $\bar{x}$ is greater than the cutoff, we will reject H_0 and conclude that the average processing time *does* exceed the mandated value of 25 days. If $\bar{x}$ is less than or equal to the cutoff, we will not reject H_0; in this case our test does not give evidence that the processing time exceeds 25 days.

Recall from the Central Limit Theorem (see Chapter 6) that, for large samples, the distribution of the possible sample means is approximately normal, with a center at the population mean μ. The null hypothesis in our example is $\mu \leq 25$ days. Figure 8-2 shows the sampling distribution for $\bar{x}$ assuming that $\mu = 25$. The shaded region on the right is called the *rejection region*. The area of the rejection region gives the probability of getting an $\bar{x}$ larger than the cutoff when μ is really 25, so it is the probability of making a Type I statistical error. This probability is called the **significance level** of the test and is given the symbol α.

---

[1]Whichever language you use, you should make an effort to understand both arguments and make an informed choice. If your instructor requests that you reference the action in a particular way, it would behoove you to follow the instructions. Having gone through this process ourselves, we prefer to state the choice as "don't reject the null hypothesis." This terminology will be used throughout this text.

FIGURE 8-2

Sampling Distribution of $\bar{x}$
for the State Insurance
Fund

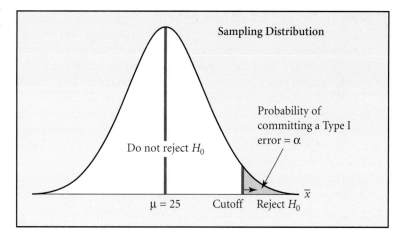

FIGURE 8-2

Sampling Distribution of $\bar{x}$
for the State Insurance
Fund

Significance Level

The maximum allowable probability of committing a Type I statistical error. The probability is denoted by the symbol α.

The decision maker carrying out the test specifies the significance level, α. The value of α is determined based on the costs involved in committing a Type I error. If making a Type I error is costly, we will want the probability of a Type I error to be small. If a Type I error is less costly, then we can allow a higher probability of a Type I error.

However, in determining α, we must also take into account the probability of making a Type II error, which is given the symbol β (*beta*). The two error probabilities, α and β, are inversely related.[2] That is, if we reduce α, then β will increase. Thus, in setting α, you must consider both sides of the issue.

Calculating the specific dollar costs associated with making the Type I and Type II errors is often difficult and may require a subjective management decision. Therefore, any two managers might well arrive at different alpha levels. However, in the end, the choice for alpha must reflect the decision maker's best estimate of the costs of these two errors.[3]

Having chosen a significance level α, the decision maker then must calculate the corresponding cutoff point, which is called a **critical value**.

Critical Value

The value of a statistic corresponding to a given significance level. This cutoff value determines the boundary between those samples resulting in a test statistic that leads to rejecting the null hypothesis and those that lead to a decision not to reject the null hypothesis.

HYPOTHESIS TEST FOR μ, σ KNOWN, LARGE SAMPLE

Calculating Critical Values

To calculate critical values corresponding to a chosen α, we need to know the sampling distribution of the sample mean $\bar{x}$. If our sample size n is large ($n \geq 30$) and we know the population standard deviation σ, then the sampling distribution of $\bar{x}$ is normal with mean equal to the population mean μ and standard deviation $\frac{\sigma}{\sqrt{n}}$. With this information we can calculate a critical z-value, called z_α, or a critical $\bar{x}$-value, called $\bar{x}_\alpha$. We illustrate both calculations in the State Insurance Fund example.

---

[2]The sum of alpha and beta may coincidently equal one. However, in general, the sum of these two error probabilities does not equal one.

[3]We will discuss Type II errors more fully later in this chapter. Contrary to the Type I situation in which we specify the desired alpha level, beta is computed based on certain assumptions. Methods for computing beta are shown later.

State Insurance Fund (continued)—Suppose the managers decide they are willing to incur a 0.10 probability of committing a Type I error. Assume also that the population standard deviation, σ, for processing claims is three days and the sample size is 64 claims. Given that the sample size is large ($n \geq 30$) and that the population standard deviation is known ($\sigma = 3$ days), we can state the critical value in two ways. First, we can establish the critical value as a z-value.

Figure 8-3 shows that if the rejection region on the upper end of the sampling distribution has an area of 0.10, the z-value from the standard normal table (or by using Excel's **NORMSINV** function or Minitab's **Calc > Probability Distributions** command) corresponding to the critical value is 1.28. Thus, $z_\alpha = 1.28$. If the sample mean lies more than 1.28 standard deviations above $\mu = 25$ days, H_0 should be rejected; otherwise we will not reject H_0.

Second, having found the critical value in terms of a z-value, we can express it in the same units as the sample mean. In the Insurance Fund example, we can calculate a critical $\bar{x}$ value, $\bar{x}_\alpha$, so that if $\bar{x}$ is greater than the critical value, we should reject H_0. If $\bar{x}$ is less than or equal to $\bar{x}_\alpha$, we should not reject H_0. Equation 8-1 shows how $\bar{x}_\alpha$ is computed. Figure 8-4 illustrates the use of Equation 8-1 for computing the critical value, $\bar{x}_\alpha$.

$\bar{x}_\alpha$ **for Hypothesis Tests, σ Known, Large Samples**

$$\bar{x}_\alpha = \mu + z_\alpha \frac{\sigma}{\sqrt{n}}$$

8-1

where:

μ = Hypothesized value for the population mean
z_α = Critical value from the standard normal distribution
σ = Population standard deviation
n = Sample size

If $\bar{x} > 25.48$ days, H_0 should be rejected and changes made in the process; otherwise, H_0 should not be rejected and the process should not be changed. Any sample mean between 25.48 and 25 days would be attributed to sampling error, and the null hypothesis would not be rejected. A sample mean of 25 or fewer will support the null hypothesis.

Decision Rules and Test Statistics

To conduct a hypothesis test, you can use two approaches. You can calculate a z-value and compare it to the critical value, z_α. Alternatively, you can calculate the sample mean, $\bar{x}$, and compare it to the critical value, $\bar{x}_\alpha$. It makes no difference which approach you use in establishing the critical value as long as you use the corresponding statistic to make your decision.

Suppose $\bar{x} = 26$ days. How we test the null hypothesis depends on the procedure we used to establish the critical value. First, using the z-value method, we establish the following decision rule.

Hypotheses

$$H_0: \mu \leq 25 \text{ days}$$
$$H_A: \mu > 25 \text{ days}$$
$$\alpha = 0.10$$

FIGURE 8-3

Determining the Critical Value as a z-Value

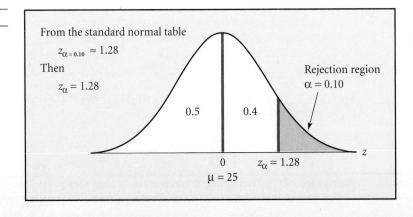

From the standard normal table
$z_{\alpha = 0.10} \approx 1.28$
Then
$z_\alpha = 1.28$

0.5   0.4

Rejection region
$\alpha = 0.10$

0 $z_\alpha = 1.28$
$\mu = 25$

z

FIGURE 8-4

Determining the Critical Value as an $\bar{x}$-Value, State Insurance Fund Example

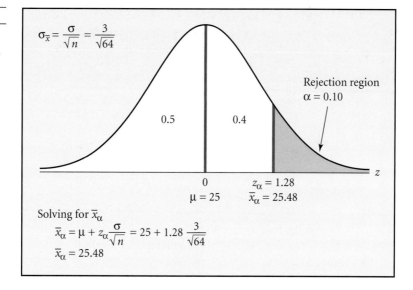

$$\sigma_{\bar{x}} = \frac{\sigma}{\sqrt{n}} = \frac{3}{\sqrt{64}}$$

0.5   0.4

Rejection region
$\alpha = 0.10$

0
$\mu = 25$

$z_\alpha = 1.28$
$\bar{x}_\alpha = 25.48$

Solving for $\bar{x}_\alpha$

$$\bar{x}_\alpha = \mu + z_\alpha \frac{\sigma}{\sqrt{n}} = 25 + 1.28 \frac{3}{\sqrt{64}}$$

$$\bar{x}_\alpha = 25.48$$

Decision Rule

If $z > z_\alpha$, reject H_0.
If $z \leq z_\alpha$, do not reject H_0.

where:

$$z_\alpha = 1.28$$

Recall that the number of claims tested is 64 and the population standard deviation is assumed known at 3 days. The calculated z-value is called the **test statistic**.

Test Statistic

A function of the sampled observations that provides a basis for testing a statistical hypothesis.

The z test statistic is computed using Equation 8-2.

---

z Test Statistic for Hypothesis Tests, σ Known, Large Samples

$$z = \frac{\bar{x} - \mu}{\frac{\sigma}{\sqrt{n}}}$$

8-2

where:

$\bar{x}$ = Sample mean
μ = Hypothesized value for the population mean
σ = Population standard deviation
n = Sample size

Applying Equation 8-2 we get:

$$z = \frac{\bar{x} - \mu}{\frac{\sigma}{\sqrt{n}}} = \frac{26 - 25}{\frac{3}{\sqrt{64}}} = 2.67$$

The sample mean is 2.67 standard deviations above the hypothesized mean. Because z is greater than the critical value

$$z = 2.67 > z_\alpha = 1.28,$$

we clearly

$$\text{reject } H_0.$$

Now we use the second approach, which established (see Figure 8-4) a decision rule, as follows.

Decision Rule

$$\text{If } \bar{x} > \bar{x}_\alpha, \text{ reject } H_0$$
$$\text{Otherwise, do not reject } H_0$$

then

$$\text{If } \bar{x} > 25.48 \text{ days, reject } H_0$$
$$\text{Otherwise, do not reject } H_0.$$

Then, because

$$\bar{x} = 26 > \bar{x}_\alpha = 25.48,$$

as before, we

$$\text{reject } H_0.$$

Note that the two methods yield the same conclusion, as they always will if you perform the calculations correctly. We have found that academic applications of hypothesis testing tend to use the z-value method, whereas organizational applications of hypothesis testing use the $\bar{x}$ approach.

You will often come across a different language used to express the outcome of a hypothesis test. For instance, a statement for the hypothesis test presented above would be "The hypothesis test was significant at an α (or significance level) of 0.10." This simply means that the null hypothesis was rejected using a significance level of 0.10.

$\mathcal{E}$XAMPLE 8-3: HYPOTHESIS TEST FOR μ, σ KNOWN, LARGE SAMPLE

Employee Commute Time   A study in southern California claimed that the mean commute time for all employees working in Orange County exceeds 40 minutes. This figure is higher than what has been assumed in the past. The plan is to test this claim using an alpha level equal to 0.05 and a sample size of $n = 100$ commuters. Based on previous studies, suppose that the population standard deviation is known to be $\sigma = 8$ minutes. The hypothesis test can be conducted using the following steps.

Step 1:   **Specify the population value of interest.**
The population value of interest is the mean commute time, μ.

Step 2:   **Formulate the null and alternative hypotheses.**
The new claim is that μ > 40. Because this is different from past studies, it will become the alternative hypothesis. Thus, the null and alternative hypotheses are

$$H_0: \mu \leq 40 \text{ minutes}$$
$$H_A: \mu > 40 \text{ minutes (claim)}$$

Step 3:   **Specify the significance level.**
The alpha level is specified to be 0.05.

Step 4:   **Construct the rejection region.**
Because we have a large sample and the population standard deviation is known, alpha is the area under the standard normal distribution to the right of the critical value. The critical z-value, z_α, is found by locating the z-value that corresponds to an area equal to $0.50 - 0.05 = 0.45$. The critical z-value from the standard normal table is 1.645.

Step 5:   **Compute the test statistic.**
Suppose that the sample of 100 commuters showed a sample mean of 43.5 minutes. Because the sample size is large and the population standard deviation is known to be 8 minutes, the test statistic is a z-value computed using:

$$z = \frac{\bar{x} - \mu}{\frac{\sigma}{\sqrt{n}}} = \frac{43.5 - 40}{\frac{8}{\sqrt{100}}} = 4.38$$

The sample mean is 4.38 standard deviations higher than the hypothesized mean.

Step 6: **Reach a decision.**

The decision rule is

If $z > 1.645$, reject H_0
Otherwise, do not reject.

Because $z = 4.38 > 1.645$, we reject H_0.

Step 7: **Draw a conclusion.**

Conclude that the mean commute distance does exceed 40 minutes.

p-Values

In addition to the two methods discussed previously, a third approach for conducting hypothesis tests also exists. This third approach uses a *p*-value instead of a critical value.

---

p-Value

The probability (assuming the null hypothesis is true) of obtaining a test statistic at least as extreme as the test statistic we calculated from the sample. The *p*-value is also known as the *observed significance level*.

If the calculated *p*-value is smaller than the probability in the rejection region (α), then the null hypothesis is rejected. If the calculated *p*-value is greater than or equal to α, then the hypothesis will not be rejected. The *p*-value approach is popular today because *p*-values are usually computed by statistical software packages, including Excel and Minitab. The advantage to reporting test results using a *p*-value is that it provides more information than simply stating whether the null hypothesis is rejected. The decision maker is presented with a measure of the degree of significance of the result (i.e., the *p*-value). This allows the reader the opportunity to evaluate the *extent* to which the data disagree with the null hypothesis, not just whether they disagree.

$\mathcal{E}$XAMPLE 8-4: HYPOTHESIS TEST USING p-VALUES, σ KNOWN, LARGE SAMPLE

Cardio-Fitness Club   The manager at the Cardio-Fitness Club believes that the recent remodeling project has greatly improved the club's appeal for members and that they now stay longer at the club per visit than before the remodeling. Studies show that the previous mean time per visit was 36 minutes, with a standard deviation equal to 11 minutes. A simple random sample of $n = 200$ visits is selected, and the current sample mean is 36.8 minutes. To test the manager's claim, and partially justify the remodeling project, using an alpha = 0.05 level, the following steps can be used.

Step 1: **Specify the population value of interest.**

The manager is interested in the mean time per visit, μ.

Step 2: **Formulate the null and alternative hypotheses.**

Based on the manager's claim that the current mean stay is longer than before the remodeling, the null and alternative hypotheses are

H_0: $\mu \leq 36$ minutes
H_A: $\mu > 36$ minutes (claim)

Step 3: **Specify the significance level.**

The alpha level specified for this test is $\alpha = 0.05$.

Step 4: **Compute the test statistic.**

Because the sample size is large and the population standard deviation is assumed known, the test statistic will be a *z*-value, which is computed as follows:

$$z = \frac{\bar{x} - \mu}{\dfrac{\sigma}{\sqrt{n}}} = \frac{36.8 - 36}{\dfrac{11}{\sqrt{200}}} = 1.0285 = 1.03$$

Step 5: **Calculate the p-value.**

In this example, the p-value is the probability of a z-value from the standard normal distribution being at least as large as 1.03. This is stated as:

$$p\text{-value} = p\,(z \geq 1.03)$$

From the standard normal distribution table in Appendix D:

$$P(z \geq 1.03) = 0.5000 - 0.3485 = 0.1515$$

Step 6: **Reach a decision.**

The decision rule is:

If p-value $< \alpha = 0.05$, reject H_0
Otherwise, do not reject H_0.

Because the p-value $= 0.1515 > \alpha = 0.05$, do not reject the null hypothesis.

Step 7: **Draw a conclusion.**

The difference between the sample mean and the hypothesized population mean is not large enough to attribute the difference to anything but sampling error.

Why do we need three methods to test the same hypothesis when they all give the same result? The answer is that we don't. However, you need to be aware of all three methods because you will encounter each in business situations. The p-value approach is especially important because many statistical software packages provide a p-value that you can use to test a hypothesis quite easily, and using a p-value means you don't need probability distribution tables. This text will use both test-statistic approaches, as well as the p-value approach to hypothesis testing.

TYPES OF HYPOTHESIS TESTS

Hypothesis tests are formulated as either one-tailed tests or two-tailed tests depending on how the null and alternative hypotheses are presented.

One-Tailed Test

A hypothesis test in which the entire rejection region is located in one tail of the sampling distribution. In a one-tailed test, the entire alpha level is located in one tail of the distribution.

For instance, in the State Insurance Fund application, the null and alternative hypotheses are:

Null hypothesis H_0: $\mu \leq 25$ days
Alternative hypothesis H_A: $\mu > 25$ days

This hypothesis test is one-tailed because the entire rejection region is located in the upper tail and the null hypothesis will be rejected only when the sample mean falls in the extreme upper tail of the sampling distribution (see Figure 8-5). In this application, it will take a sample mean substantially larger than 25 days in order to reject the null hypothesis.

Two-Tailed Test

A hypothesis test in which the entire rejection region is split into the two tails of the sampling distribution. In a two-tailed test, the alpha level is typically split evenly between the two tails.

In Example 8-2 involving the Chips N' Snack Company, the null and alternative hypotheses involving the mean fill of potato chip sacks is:

H_0: $\mu = 20$ ounces
H_A: $\mu \neq 20$ ounces

In this two-tailed hypotheses case, the null hypothesis will be rejected if the sample mean is extremely large (upper tail) or extremely small (lower tail). The alpha level would be split evenly between the two tails.

$\mathcal{S}$UMMARY: ONE-TAILED TEST FOR A HYPOTHESIS ABOUT A POPULATION MEAN, σ KNOWN, LARGE SAMPLES

To test the hypothesis, perform the following steps:

1. Specify the population value of interest.

2. Formulate the null hypothesis and the alternative hypothesis in terms of the population mean, μ.

3. Specify the desired significance level (α).

4. Construct the rejection region. (We strongly suggest you draw a picture showing where in the distribution the rejection region is located.)

5. Compute the test statistic.

$$\bar{x} = \frac{\sum x}{n}, z = \frac{\bar{x} - \mu}{\frac{\sigma}{\sqrt{n}}}, \text{ or the } p \text{ - value.}$$

6. Reach a decision. Compare the test statistic with $\bar{x}_\alpha, z_\alpha$, or α, respectively.

7. Draw a conclusion regarding the null hypothesis.

$\mathcal{E}$XAMPLE 8-5: ONE-TAILED HYPOTHESIS TEST FOR μ, σ KNOWN, LARGE SAMPLE

Elgin Heart Institute   The Elgin Heart Institute performs many open-heart surgery procedures. Recently research physicians at Elgin have developed a new heart bypass surgery procedure that they believe will reduce the average recovery time. The hospital board will not recommend the new procedure unless there is substantial evidence to suggest that it is better than the existing procedure. Records indicate that the current mean recovery rate for the standard procedure is 42 days, with a standard deviation of 5 days. To test whether the new procedure actually results in a lower mean recovery time, the procedure was performed on a random sample of 36 patients.

Step 1:   Specify the population value of interest.
We are interested in the mean recovery time, μ.

Step 2:   Formulate the null and alternative hypotheses.
$$H_0: \mu \geq 42$$
$$H_A: \mu < 42$$

Step 3:   Specify the desired significance level (α).
The researchers wish to test the hypothesis using a 0.05 level of significance.

Step 4:   Construct the rejection region.
This will be a one-tailed test, with the rejection region in the lower (left-hand) tail of the sampling distribution. The critical value is $-z_{0.05} = -1.645$. Therefore, the decision rule becomes:
If $z < -1.645$, reject H_0; otherwise, do not reject H_0.

Step 5:   Compute the test statistic.
For this example we will use z. Assume the sample mean, computed using $\bar{x} = \frac{\sum x}{n}$, is 40.2 days. Then

$$z = \frac{\bar{x} - \mu}{\frac{\sigma}{\sqrt{n}}} = \frac{40.2 - 42}{\frac{5}{\sqrt{36}}} = -2.16$$

Step 6:   Reach a decision. (See Figure 8-5.)
The decision rule is
$$\text{If } z < -1.645, \text{ reject } H_0$$
$$\text{Otherwise, do not reject.}$$
Because $-2.16 < -1.645$, reject H_0.

Step 7:   Draw a conclusion.
There is sufficient evidence to conclude that the new bypass procedure does result in a shorter average recovery period.

FIGURE 8-5

Elgin Heart Institute
Hypothesis Test

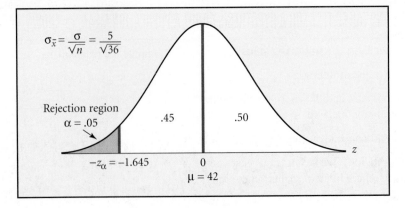

p-VALUE FOR TWO-TAILED TESTS

In the previous examples, the rejection region was located in one tail of the sampling distribution. In those cases, the null hypothesis was of the $\geq$ or $\leq$ format. However, sometimes the null hypothesis will be stated as a direct equality.

Cranston Peanuts—Consider the Cranston Peanut Company, which grows and packages salted and unsalted, unshelled peanuts in 16-ounce sacks. The company's filling process strives for an average fill amount equal to 16 ounces. Therefore, Cranston would test the following null and alternative hypotheses:

$$H_0: \mu = 16 \text{ ounces}$$
$$H_A: \mu \neq 16 \text{ ounces}$$

The null hypothesis will be rejected if the test statistic falls in either tail of the sampling distribution. The size of the rejection region is determined by α. Each tail has an area equal to $\alpha/2$.

The p-value for the two-tailed test is computed in a manner similar to that for a one-tailed test. First, determine the z test statistic as follows:

$$z = \frac{\bar{x} - \mu}{\frac{\sigma}{\sqrt{n}}}$$

Suppose for this situation, Cranston managers calculated a $z = 3.32$. Next, find $P(z > 3.32)$ using either the standard normal table in Appendix D, Excel's **NORMSDIST** function, or Minitab's **Calc > Probability Distributions** command. In this case, because $z = 3.32$ exceeds the table values, we will use Excel or Minitab to obtain

$$P(z \leq 3.32) = 0.9995.$$

Then

$$P(z > 3.32) = 1 - 0.9995 = 0.0005.$$

However, because this is a two-tailed hypothesis test, the p-value is found by multiplying the 0.0005 value by 2 (to account for the chance that our sample result could have been on either side of the distribution). This is

$$p\text{-value} = 2(0.0005) = 0.0010.$$

Assuming an alpha = 0.10 level, then since the

$$p\text{-value} = 0.0010 < \alpha = 0.10, \text{ we reject } H_0.$$

Figure 8-6 illustrates the two-tailed test for the Cranston Peanuts example.

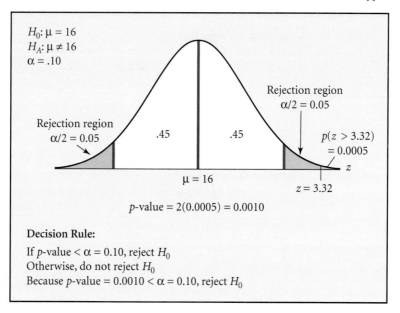

FIGURE 8-6

Two-Tailed Test—Cranston Peanut Example

$H_0: \mu = 16$
$H_A: \mu \neq 16$
$\alpha = .10$

Rejection region
$\alpha/2 = 0.05$

Rejection region
$\alpha/2 = 0.05$

.45   .45

$p(z > 3.32)$
$= 0.0005$

z

$\mu = 16$

$z = 3.32$

$p\text{-value} = 2(0.0005) = 0.0010$

Decision Rule:
If $p\text{-value} < \alpha = 0.10$, reject H_0
Otherwise, do not reject H_0
Because $p\text{-value} = 0.0010 < \alpha = 0.10$, reject H_0

SUMMARY: TWO-TAILED TEST FOR A HYPOTHESIS ABOUT A POPULATION MEAN, σ KNOWN

To conduct a two-tailed hypothesis test when the population standard deviation is known, you can perform the following steps.

1. Specify the population value of interest.

2. Formulate the null and alternative hypotheses in terms of the population mean, μ.

3. Specify the desired significance level, α.

4. Construct the rejection region.
   Determine the critical values for each tail, $z_{\alpha/2}$ and $-z_{\alpha/2}$, from the standard normal table. If needed, calculate $\bar{x}_{(\alpha/2)L}$ and $\bar{x}_{(\alpha/2)U}$.

Define the two-tailed decision rule using one of the following:

- If $z > z_{\alpha/2}$, or if $z < -z_{\alpha/2}$ reject H_0; otherwise, do not reject H_0.
- If, $\bar{x} < \bar{x}_{(\alpha/2)L}$, or $\bar{x} > \bar{x}_{(\alpha/2)U}$, reject H_0; otherwise, do not reject H_0.
- If $p\text{-value} < \alpha$, reject H_0; otherwise, do not reject H_0.

5. Compute the test statistic, $z = \dfrac{\bar{x} - \mu}{\frac{\sigma}{\sqrt{n}}}$, $\bar{x} = \dfrac{\sum x}{n}$ or find the p-value.

6. Reach a decision.

7. Draw a conclusion.

EXAMPLE 8-6: TWO-TAILED HYPOTHESIS TEST FOR μ, σ KNOWN

The Wilson Glass Company   The Wilson Glass Company has a contract to supply plate glass for home and commercial windows. The contract specifies that the mean thickness of the glass must be 0.375 inches. The standard deviation, σ, is known to be 0.05 inch. Before sending the first shipment, Wilson managers wish to test whether they are meeting the requirements by selecting a random sample of $n = 100$ thickness measurements.

Step 1:   **Specify the population value of interest.**
          The mean thickness of glass is of interest.

Step 2:   **Formulate the null and the alternative hypotheses.**
          The null and alternative hypotheses are:

$$H_0: \mu = 0.375 \text{ inch}$$
$$H_A: \mu \neq 0.375 \text{ inch}$$

Step 3:   **Specify the desired significance level (α).**
          The managers wish to test the hypothesis using an $\alpha = 0.05$.

Step 4: **Construct the rejection region.**
This is a two-tailed test. The critical values for the upper and lower tails are found in the standard normal table. These are:

$$-z_{\alpha/2} = -z_{0.05/2} = -z_{0.025} = -1.96$$

and

$$z_{\alpha/2} = z_{0.05/2} = z_{0.025} = 1.96$$

Define the two-tailed decision rule:
If $z > 1.96$, or if $z < -1.96$, reject H_0; otherwise, do not reject H_0.

Step 5: **Compute the test statistic.**
Select the random sample and calculate the sample mean.
Suppose that the sample mean for the random sample of 100 measurements is:

$$\bar{x} = \frac{\sum x}{n} = 0.378 \text{ inch}$$

The test statistic is

$$z = \frac{\bar{x} - \mu}{\frac{\sigma}{\sqrt{n}}} = \frac{0.378 - 0.375}{\frac{0.05}{\sqrt{100}}} = 0.60$$

Step 6: **Reach a decision.**
Because $-1.96 < z = 0.60 < 1.96$, do not reject the null hypothesis.

Step 7: **Draw a conclusion.**
The Wilson Company does not have sufficient evidence to conclude that they are not meeting the contract.

HYPOTHESIS TEST FOR μ WITH σ UNKNOWN, LARGE SAMPLE

In the previous examples, we assumed that the population standard deviation, σ, was known. However, in most business situations, the population standard deviation will not be known and will have to be estimated using the sample standard deviation, s. If the sample size is large ($n \geq 30$), the test statistic may be approximated as a z-value using Equation 8-3. Note, regardless of the shape of the population, if the sample size is large, the sampling distribution will be approximately normal.[4]

---

z Test Statistic for Hypothesis Tests for μ, σ Unknown, Large Sample

$$z = \frac{\bar{x} - \mu}{\frac{s}{\sqrt{n}}}$$

8-3

where:

$\bar{x}$ = Sample mean
μ = Hypothesized value for the population mean
s = Sample standard deviation $s = \sqrt{\dfrac{\sum(x - \bar{x})^2}{n - 1}}$
n = Sample size

---

*E*XAMPLE 8-7: HYPOTHESIS TEST FOR μ, σ UNKNOWN, LARGE SAMPLE

American Lighting Company   Engineers at the American Lighting Company recently developed a new three-way light bulb that they claim is more energy efficient than the company's current three-way bulb. They also claim that the new bulb will outlast the current bulb, which has

---

[4]Note: Anytime the population standard deviation, σ, is unknown and must be estimated using the sample standard deviation, s, the technically correct approach is to use the t-distribution as shown in Equation 8-4. However, many authors suggest using the z-distribution and Equation 8-3 when $n \geq 30$ based on the Central Limit Theorem.

an average lifetime of 700 hours. A random sample of 100 new light bulbs was selected, and the following sample results were reported:

$$\bar{x} = 702 \text{ hours} \qquad s = 15 \text{ hours}$$

To test the claim using an alpha = 0.10 level, you can use the following steps.

Step 1: **Specify the population value of interest.**
The company is interested in the mean life of the bulbs.

Step 2: **Formulate the appropriate null and alternative hypotheses.**
The company claimed the mean will exceed 700 hours. This is the research hypothesis, and the null and alternative hypotheses become

$$H_0: \mu \leq 700 \text{ hours}$$
$$H_A: \mu > 700 \text{ hours}$$

Step 3: **Specify the desired level of significance.**
The hypothesis test will be conducted using an alpha = 0.10 level.

Step 4: **Construct the rejection region.**
Because the sample size is large, the critical value can be approximated using a z-value from the standard normal distribution for a one-tailed test, with alpha = 0.10. The z-value from Appendix D is $z = 1.28$. The decision rule is

If $z > z_\alpha = 1.28$, reject H_0; otherwise, do not reject H_0.

Step 5: **Compute the test statistic using Equation 8-3.**
The test statistic is

$$z = \frac{\bar{x} - \mu}{\dfrac{s}{\sqrt{n}}} = \frac{702 - 700}{\dfrac{15}{\sqrt{100}}} = 1.33$$

Step 6: **Reach a decision.**
Because $z = 1.33 > 1.28 = z_\alpha$, we reject the null hypothesis.

Step 7: **Draw a conclusion.**
Conclude that the new bulb does have a higher mean life than the original.

HYPOTHESIS TEST FOR μ, σ UNKNOWN, SMALL SAMPLE

In Chapter 7, we introduced situations in which the objective was to estimate a population mean based on small sample sizes when the population standard deviation was unknown. In those cases, the t-distribution was used to determine the critical value, rather than the standard normal distribution. The same logic is used again, together with Equation 8-4, to compute the test statistic when testing hypotheses about a population mean for cases in which the sample size is small ($n < 30$) and σ is unknown.

---

t **Test Statistic for Hypothesis Test, σ Unknown, Small Sample**

$$t = \frac{\bar{x} - \mu}{\dfrac{s}{\sqrt{n}}}$$

8-4

where:

$\bar{x}$ = Sample mean

μ = Hypothesized value for the population mean

s = Sample standard deviation $s = \sqrt{\dfrac{\Sigma(x - \bar{x})^2}{n - 1}}$

n = Sample size

In order to employ the t-distribution, we must make the following assumption:

SSUMPTION   The population is normally distributed.

If the population from which the simple random sample is selected is approximately normal, the *t* test statistic computed using Equation 8-4 will be distributed according to a *t*-distribution with *n* − 1 degrees of freedom.

XAMPLE 8-8: HYPOTHESIS TEST FOR μ, σ UNKNOWN, SMALL SAMPLE

Dairy Fresh Ice Cream   The Dairy Fresh Ice Cream plant in Pittsburgh, Pennsylvania, uses a filling machine for its 64-ounce cartons. There is some variation in the actual amount of ice cream that goes into the carton. The machine can go out of adjustment and put a mean amount either less or more than 64 ounces in the cartons. To monitor the filling process, the production manager selects a simple random sample of 16 filled ice cream cartons each day. He can test whether the machine is still in adjustment using the following steps.

Step 1:   **Specify the population value of interest.**
The manager is interested in the mean amount of ice cream.

Step 2:   **Formulate the appropriate null and alternative hypotheses.**
The status quo is that the machine continues to fill ice cream cartons with a mean equal to 64 ounces. Thus, the null and alternative hypotheses are:

$$H_0: \mu = 64 \text{ ounces (Machine is in adjustment.)}$$
$$H_A: \mu \neq 64 \text{ ounces (Machine is out of adjustment.)}$$

Step 3:   **Specify the desired level of significance.**
The test will be conducted using an alpha level equal to 0.05.

Step 4:   **Construct the rejection region.**
We first produce a box and whisker plot for a rough check on the normality assumption. The sample data are

62.7	64.7	64.0	64.5	64.6	65.0	64.4	64.2
64.6	65.5	63.6	64.7	64.0	64.2	63.0	63.6

The box and whisker diagram is:

Minimum	62.7
First Quartile	63.6
Median	64.3
Third Quartile	64.7
Maximum	65.5

The box and whisker diagram does not indicate that the population distribution is unduly skewed. Thus, the normal distribution assumption is reasonable based on these sample data.

Now we determine the critical values from the *t*-distribution.

Based on the null and alternative hypotheses, this test is two-tailed. Thus, we will split the alpha into two tails and determine the critical value from the *t*-distribution with *n* − 1 degrees of freedom. Using Appendix F, the critical *t* for $\alpha/2 = 0.025$, and 16 − 1 = 15 degrees of freedom is $t = \pm 2.1315$.

The decision rule for this two-tailed test is

If $t < -2.1315$ or $t > 2.1315$, reject H_0
Otherwise, do not reject H_0.

Step 5:   **Compute the test statistic using Equation 8-4.**
The sample mean is

$$\bar{x} = \frac{\sum x}{n} = \frac{1{,}027.3}{16} = 64.2$$

The sample standard deviation is

$$s = \sqrt{\frac{\sum(x - \bar{x})^2}{n - 1}} = 0.72$$

The test statistic is

$$t = \frac{\bar{x} - \mu}{\frac{s}{\sqrt{n}}} = \frac{64.2 - 64}{\frac{0.72}{\sqrt{16}}} = 1.11$$

Step 6:   **Reach a decision.**
Because $t = 1.11$ is not less than -2.1315 and not greater than 2.1315, we do not reject the null hypothesis.

Step 7:   **Draw a conclusion.**
Based on these sample data, the company has no reason to believe that the filling machine is out of adjustment.

EXAMPLE 8-9: TESTING THE HYPOTHESIS FOR μ, σ UNKNOWN, SMALL SAMPLE SIZE

The Qwest Company   The Qwest Company operates service centers in various cities where customers can call to get answers to questions about their bills. Previous studies indicate that the distribution of time required for each call is normally distributed, with a mean equal to 540 seconds. Company officials have selected a random sample of 16 calls and wish to determine whether the mean call time is now fewer than 540 seconds after a training program given to call-center employees.

Step 1:   **Specify the population value of interest.**
The mean call time is the population value of interest.

Step 2:   **Formulate the null and alternative hypotheses.**
The null and alternative hypotheses are

$$H_0: \mu \geq 540 \text{ seconds}$$
$$H_A: \mu < 540 \text{ seconds}$$

Step 3:   **Specify the significance level.**
The test will be conducted at the 0.01 level of significance. Thus, $\alpha = 0.01$.

Step 4:   **Construct the rejection region.**
Because this is a one-tailed test and the rejection region is in the lower tail, the critical value from the t-distribution with $16 - 1 = 15$ degrees of freedom is $-t_\alpha = -t_{.01} = -2.6025$.

Step 5:   **Compute the test statistic.**
The sample mean for the random sample of 16 calls is $\bar{x} = \frac{\sum x}{n} = 510$ seconds, and

the sample standard deviation is $s = \sqrt{\frac{\sum(x - \bar{x})^2}{n - 1}} = 45$ seconds. Assuming that the

population distribution is approximately normal, the test statistic is

$$t = \frac{\bar{x} - \mu}{\frac{s}{\sqrt{n}}} = \frac{510 - 540}{\frac{45}{\sqrt{16}}} = -2.67$$

Step 6:   **Reach a decision.**
Because $t = -2.67 < -2.6025$, the null hypothesis should be rejected.

Step 7:   **Draw a conclusion.**
Qwest can conclude that the mean time for service calls has been reduced below 540 seconds.

Using the *t*-Distribution with Large Sample Sizes

Examples 8-8 and 8-9 illustrate how the *t*-distribution is used when testing a null hypothesis about a single population mean when the population standard deviation is unknown and the sample size is small. Example 8-7 illustrated the hypothesis testing approach when the population standard deviation is unknown but the sample size is large. We used a *z* test statistic, because for large sample sizes, there is little difference between the *t* and the *z* values. We also use the *z* in these situations because the *t* table is limited with respect to the degrees of freedom covered. However, you should be aware that any time the population standard deviation is unknown, the *t*-distribution can be used as long as the population is approximately normally distributed. As the next example illustrates, software such as Excel and Minitab will typically use the *t*-distribution.

Excel and Minitab Tutorial

Franklin Tire Company—The Franklin Tire Company recently conducted a test on a new tire design to determine whether the company could make the claim that the mean tire mileage would exceed 60,000 miles. The test was conducted in Alaska. A simple random sample of 100 tires was tested, and the number of miles each tire lasted until it no longer met the federal government minimum tread thickness was recorded. Figure 8-7 shows some of the sample data in an Excel spreadsheet format and a box and whisker diagram. The data (shown in thousands of dollars) are in the CD-ROM file called *Franklin*.

The null and alternative hypotheses to be tested are

$$H_0: \mu \le 60$$
$$H_A: \mu > 60$$
$$\alpha = 0.05$$

Excel does not have a special procedure for testing hypotheses for single population means. However, the Excel add-ins software called PHStat on the CD-ROM that accompanies this text has the necessary hypothesis-testing tools. Figure 8-8a and Figure 8-8b show the Excel PHStat and the Minitab outputs.[5]

We denote the critical value of an upper (lower) tail test with a significance level of α as t_α $(-t_\alpha)$. The critical value for $\alpha = 0.05$ and 99 degrees of freedom is $t_\alpha = 1.66$. Using the critical value approach, the decision rule is

If the test statistic > $1.66 = t_\alpha$, reject H_0; otherwise, do not reject H_0.

The sample mean, based on a sample of 100 tires is $\bar{x} = 60.17$ (60,170 miles), and the sample standard deviation is $s = 4.701$ (4,701 miles). The *t* test statistics shown in Figures 8-8a and 8-8b are computed as follows:

$$t = \frac{\bar{x} - \mu}{\dfrac{s}{\sqrt{n}}} = \frac{60.17 - 60}{\dfrac{4.701}{\sqrt{100}}} = 0.3616$$

FIGURE 8-7

Tires Test Data for Franklin Tire Company

Excel Instructions:
1. Open file: Franklin.xls
2. Select **PHStat**.
3. Select **Box and Whisker Plot**.
4. Define **Data Range**.
5. Select **5-Number Summary**.

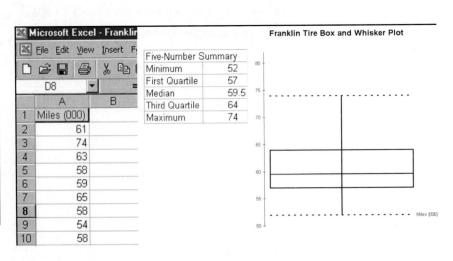

FIGURE 8-8A

Excel (PHStat) Output for Franklin Tire Hypothesis Test Results

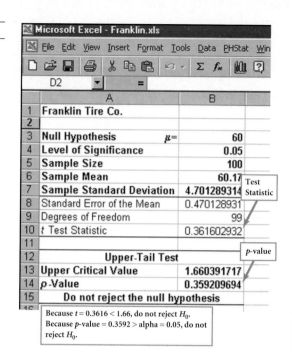

Because

$$t = 0.3616 < 1.66 = t_\alpha,$$

we

do not reject the null hypothesis.

Thus, based upon the sample data, the evidence is insufficient to conclude that the new tires have an average life exceeding 60,000 miles. Based on this test, the company would not be justified in making the claim.

Franklin managers could also use the *p*-value approach to test the null hypothesis because the output shown in Figures 8-8a and 8-8b provide the *p*-value. In this case, the *p*-value = 0.3592. The decision rule for a test is

If *p*-value $< \alpha$ reject H_0; otherwise, do not reject H_0.

Because

$$p\text{-value} = 0.3592 > 0.05 = \alpha,$$

we do not reject the null hypothesis. This is the same conclusion we reached using the critical value approach.

FIGURE 8-8B

Minitab Output for Franklin Tire Hypothesis Test Results

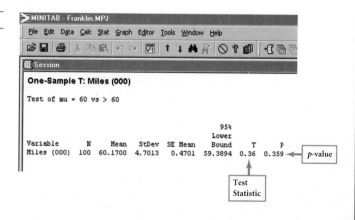

SUMMARY: ONE- OR TWO-TAILED TESTS FOR μ, σ UNKNOWN, SMALL SAMPLE

1. Specify the population value of interest, μ.

2. Formulate the null hypothesis and the alternative hypothesis.

3. Specify the desired significance level (α).

4. Construct the rejection region.

If it is a two-tailed test, determine the critical values for each tail, $t_{\alpha/2}$ and $-t_{\alpha/2}$, from the t-distribution table. If the test is a one-tailed test, find either t_α or $-t_\alpha$, depending on the tail of the rejection region. Degrees of freedom are $n - 1$. If desired, the critical t-values can be used to find the appropriate $\bar{x}_\alpha$ or the $\bar{x}_{\alpha/2}$ and $\bar{x}_{\alpha/2}$ values.

Define the decision rule.

a. If the test statistic falls into the rejection region, reject H_0; otherwise, do not reject H_0.

b. If the p-value is less than α, reject H_0; otherwise, do not reject H_0.

5. Assuming that the population is approximately normal, compute the test statistic.

Select the random sample and calculate the sample mean, $\bar{x} = \dfrac{\Sigma x}{n}$, and the sample standard deviation,

$s = \sqrt{\dfrac{\Sigma(x - \bar{x})^2}{n - 1}}$. Then calculate

$$t = \frac{\bar{x} - \mu}{\dfrac{s}{\sqrt{n}}} \text{ or } p\text{-value}$$

6. Reach a decision.

7. Draw a conclusion.

This section has introduced the basic concepts of hypothesis testing. There are several ways to test a null hypothesis. Each method will yield the same result, however computer software such as Minitab and Excel show the p-values automatically. Therefore, decision makers increasingly use the p-value approach.

8-1: EXERCISES

Skill Development

8.1 For each of the following claims, list the appropriate null and alternative hypotheses:
a. The mean is larger than 20.
b. The mean equals 50.
c. The mean is at least 35.
d. The mean is more than 87.
e. The mean is at most 6.

8.2 Determine the p-values associated with the following test statistics for a two-tailed test.
a. $z = 2.97$
b. $z = 1.98$
c. $z = 3.01$
d. $z = 4.58$
e. $z = -1.58$

8.3 Given the following null and alternative hypotheses,

$$H_0: \mu \leq 200$$
$$H_A: \mu > 200$$
$$\alpha = 0.05$$

and

$$\bar{x} = 204.50 \qquad \sigma = 45.00 \qquad n = 200$$

a. Establish the appropriate decision rule for $\bar{x}$ and z.
b. Indicate the appropriate decision based on the sample information and each of the decision rules.
c. Which of the hypotheses will not be declared true unless the sample data strongly indicate that it is true?

8.4 Given the following null and alternative hypotheses,

$$H_0: \mu \leq 24.78$$
$$H_A: \mu > 24.78$$
$$\alpha = 0.03$$

and

$$\bar{x} = 24.85 \qquad \sigma = 9.00 \qquad n = 50$$

a. Establish the appropriate decision rule for the p-value and z.
b. Indicate the appropriate decision based on the sample information and each of the decision rules.

8.5 Given the following null and alternative hypotheses,

$$H_0: \mu \geq 4{,}000$$
$$H_A: \mu < 4{,}000$$
$$\alpha = 0.05$$

and

$$\bar{x} = 3{,}980 \qquad s = 205 \qquad n = 100$$

a. Establish the appropriate decision rule.
b. Indicate the appropriate decision based on the sample information, using both the p-value and $\bar{x}$.
c. Provide the two research hypotheses that could have produced the null and alternative hypotheses in this problem.

8.6 Determine the p-values associated with the following test statistic for an upper-tail test.
a. $z = 1.45$
b. $z = 2.33$

c. $z = -1.87$
d. $z = 0$
e. $z = -4.59$

8.7 For each of the following, indicate which of the two errors associated with hypothesis testing could occur.
a. The null hypothesis was rejected.
b. The null hypothesis was not rejected.
c. The null hypothesis, in reality, was true.
d. The alternative hypothesis, in reality, was true.

8.8 Given the following null and alternative hypotheses,

$$H_0: \mu = 1,346$$
$$H_A: \mu \neq 1,346$$
$$\alpha = 0.05$$

and

$$\bar{x} = 1,338 \qquad \sigma = 90 \qquad n = 64$$

a. Establish the appropriate decision rule based on z as a test statistic.
b. Indicate the appropriate decision based on the sample information and the decision rule.
c. Given the decision you reached, which of the two types of errors associated with hypothesis tests could you have made?

8.9 Determine the p-value for each of the following hypothesis scenarios:
a. $H_0: \mu = 1,346$ versus $H_A: \mu \neq 1,346$ and $z = 2.36$.
b. $H_0: \mu \geq 4,000$ versus $H_A: \mu < 4,000$ and $z = -1.85$.
c. $H_0: \mu \leq 24.78$ versus $H_A: \mu > 24.78$ and $z = 0.84$
d. $H_0: \mu \leq 200$ versus $H_A: \mu > 200$ and $z = -2.06$ (be careful here).

8.10 Determine the critical value(s), z_α (or $\pm z_{\alpha/2}$), for each of the following situations.
a. $\alpha = 0.05$, upper-tail test
b. $\alpha = 0.025$, upper-tail test
c. $\alpha = 0.01$, lower-tail test
d. $\alpha = 0.05$, two-tailed test
e. $\alpha = 0.10$, two-tailed test

8.11 Given the following null and alternative hypotheses,

$$H_0: \mu = 4,450$$
$$H_A: \mu \neq 4,450$$
$$\alpha = 0.1$$

and

$$\bar{x} = 4,475.6 \qquad s = 940 \qquad n = 30$$

a. Establish the appropriate decision rule in terms of $\bar{x}$.
b. Indicate the appropriate decision based on the sample information and the decision rule.

Business Applications

8.12 Peterson Automotive is the Honda automobile dealership in a western U.S. city. They recently stated in an advertisement that Honda owners average more than 85,000 miles before trading in or selling their Hondas. To test this, an independent agency selected a simple random sample of 80 Honda owners who have either traded or sold their Hondas and determined the number of miles on the cars when the owners parted with them. They plan to test Peterson's claim at the alpha = 0.05 level.
a. State the appropriate null and alternative hypotheses.
b. If the sample mean is 86,200 miles and the sample standard deviation is 12,000 miles, what conclusion should be reached about the claim?

8.13 The director of a state agency claims that the average starting salary for clerical employees in the state is less than $30,000 per year. To test this claim, she has collected a simple random sample of 100 starting salaries of clerks from across the state and found that the sample mean is $29,750.
a. State the appropriate null and alternative hypotheses.
b. Assuming the population standard deviation is known to be $2,500 and the significance level for the test is 0.05, what is the critical value?
c. Referring to your answer in part b, what conclusion should be reached with respect to the null hypothesis?
d. Referring to your answer in part c, which of the two statistical errors might have been made in this case? Explain.

8.14 A telemarketing company located in Los Angeles has established a guideline that states that the average time for each completed call should be 4 minutes or less. Recently the operations manager was concerned that calls were taking too long. The operations manager did not wish to assert that the calls were taking too long if the sample data did not strongly indicate this. A sample of 12 calls was selected and the following times (in seconds) were recorded.

| 194 | 278 | 302 | 140 | 245 | 234 | 268 | 208 | 102 | 190 | 220 | 255 |

a. Construct the appropriate null and alternative hypotheses.
b. Based on the sample data, what should the operations manager conclude? Test at the 0.10 significance level.
c. Suppose you wished to conduct the test in part b using $\bar{x}$ as the test statistic. Calculate the critical value, $\bar{x}_\alpha$.

8.15 A mail-order business prides itself in its ability to fill customers' orders in six calendar days or fewer, on the average. Periodically, the operations manager selects a random sample of customer orders and determines the number of days required to fill the orders. Based on this sample information, he decides whether the desired standard is being met. He will assume that the average number of days to fill customers' orders is six or fewer unless the data suggest strongly otherwise.
a. Establish the appropriate null and alternative hypotheses.
b. On one occasion when a sample of 40 customers was selected, the average number of days was 6.65, with a sample standard deviation of 1.5 days. Can the

operations manager conclude that his mail-order business is achieving its goal? Use a significance level of 0.025 to answer this question.

c. Calculate the p-value for this test. Conduct the test using this p-value.

d. The operations manager wishes to monitor the efficiency of his mail-order service often. Therefore, he does not wish to repeatedly calculate z-values to conduct the hypothesis tests. Obtain the critical value, $\bar{x}_\alpha$, so that the manager can simply compare the sample mean to this value to conduct the test. Use $\bar{x}$ as the test statistic to conduct the test.

8.16　The makers of Mini-Oats Cereal have an automated packaging machine that can be set at any targeted fill level between 12 and 32 ounces. Every box of cereal is not expected to contain exactly the targeted weight, but the average of all boxes filled should. At the end of every shift (8 hours), 16 boxes are selected at random and the mean and standard deviation of the sample are computed. Based on these sample results, the production control manager determines whether the filling machine needs to be readjusted or it remains all right to operate. Use $\alpha = 0.05$.

a. Establish the appropriate null and alternative hypotheses to be tested for boxes that are supposed to have an average of 24 ounces.

b. At the end of a particular shift during which the machine was filling 24-ounce boxes of Mini-Oats, the sample mean of 16 boxes was 24.32 ounces, with a standard deviation of 0.70 ounce. Assist the production control manager in determining if the machine is achieving its targeted average.

c. Why do you suppose the production control manager would prefer to make this hypothesis test a two-tailed test? Discuss.

d. Conduct the test using a p-value as the test statistic.

e. Considering the result of the test, which of the two types of errors in hypothesis testing could you have made?

8.17　Bowman Electronics sells electronic components for car stereos. They claim that the average life of a component exceeds 4,000 hours. To test this claim, they have selected a random sample of $n = 12$ of their components and have traced the life between installation and failure. The following data were obtained:

1,973	4,838	3,805	4,494	4,738	5,249
4,459	4,098	4,722	5,894	3,322	4,800

a. State the appropriate null and alternative hypotheses.

b. Assuming that the test is to be conducted using a 0.05 level of significance, what conclusion should be reached based on these sample data? Be sure to examine the required normality assumption.

8.18　The makers of a new home furnace system claim that if the furnace is installed, homeowners will observe an aver-

age fuel bill of less than $80.00 per month during January if their house has between 2,200 and 2,400 square feet of heated living space. A consumer agency plans to test this claim by taking a random sample of homes of this size where the new furnace has just been installed.

a. (1) Suppose the consumer agency conducts this test and declares that the manufacturer's claim is not correct. Would you expect the manufacturer to take legal action?

(2) Suppose, now, that the consumer agency states that the manufacturer's claim is correct. Would you expect the same type and magnitude of consequences?

(3) Taking your answers to (1) and (2), determine the research hypothesis for the consumer agency's test.

b. Establish the appropriate null and alternative hypotheses.

c. If the desired significance level for the test is 0.05, what should be concluded about the company's claim if the following sample results are observed?

$$\bar{x} = \$78.60 \qquad s^2 = 625 \qquad n = 64$$

Use the p-value to conduct this hypothesis test.

Advanced Business Applications

8.19　The Cell Tone Company sells cellular phones and airtime in several northwestern states. At a recent meeting, the marketing manager stated that the average age of Cell Tone customers is under 40 years. This came up in conjunction with a proposed advertising plan that is to be directed toward a young audience. Before actually completing the advertising plan, Cell Tone decided to randomly sample customers. Among the questions asked in the survey of 50 customers in the Jacksonville, Florida, area was the customers' ages. The age data are available in the CD-ROM file called *Cell Phone Survey*

a. Based on the statement made by the marketing manager, formulate the appropriate null and alternative hypotheses.

b. The marketing manager must support his statement concerning average customer age in an upcoming board meeting. Using a significance level of 0.10 provide this support for the marketing manager.

c. Consider the result of the hypothesis test you conducted in part b. Which of the two types of hypothesis test errors could you have committed? How could you discover if you had, indeed, made this error?

8.20　Reconsider Exercise 8.19.

a. Calculate the critical value, $\bar{x}_\alpha$.

b. Determine the p-value and conduct the test using the p-value.

c. Note that the sample data lists the customers' ages to the nearest year.

(1) If we denote a randomly selected customer's age (to the nearest year) as x_i, is x_i a continuous or discrete random variable? (2) Is it possible that x_i has a normal distribution? (3) Consider your answer to (1) and (2) and the fact that $\bar{x}$ must have a nor-

mal distribution to facilitate the calculation in part b. Does this mean that the calculation you have performed in part b is inappropriate? Explain your answer.

8.21 🔘 The Haines Lumber Company makes plywood for the furniture industry. One product it makes is $\frac{3}{4}$-inch oak veneer panels. It is very important that the panels conform to specifications. One specification calls for the panels to be made to an average thickness of 0.75 inch. Each hour, 5 panels are selected at random and measured. After 20 hours, a total of 100 panels have been measured. These data are in the CD-ROM file called *Haines*.

a. Formulate the appropriate null and alternative hypotheses relative to the thickness specification.

b. Based on the sample data, what should the company conclude about the status of its product meeting the thickness specification? Test at a significance level of 0.01. Discuss your results in a report to the production manager.

c. The production manager has looked at the results of your test. He wishes to repeat this sampling process and wants a rule to compare future $\bar{x}$ values. Furnish this information to the manager.

d. The manager wishes to know what error in part b could have been made. He also wishes to know how you could be certain whether such an error could have been made. Provide this information to the manager.

8.22 🔘 The Wilson Company uses a great deal of water in the process of making industrial milling equipment. To comply with the federal clean-water laws, it has a water purification system that all wastewater goes through before being discharged into a settling pond on the company's property. To determine whether the company is complying with federal requirements, sample measures are taken every so often. One requirement is that the average pH level not exceed 7.4. A sample of 95 pH measures has been taken. The data for these measures are shown in the file *Wilson Water*.

a. Considering the requirement for pH level, state the appropriate null and alternative hypotheses.

b. Discuss why it is appropriate to form the hypotheses with the federal standard as the alternative hypothesis.

c. Based on the sample data of pH level, what should the company conclude about its current status on meeting the federal requirement? Test the hypothesis at the 0.05 level. Discuss your results in a memo to the company's environmental relations manager.

8-2 HYPOTHESIS TESTS FOR PROPORTIONS

So far this chapter has focused on hypothesis tests about a single population mean. Although many decision problems involve a test of a population mean, there are also cases in which the value of interest is the population proportion. For example, a production manager might consider the proportion of defective items produced on an assembly line in order to determine whether the line should be restructured. Likewise, a life insurance salesperson's performance assessment might include the proportion of existing clients who renew their policies.

TESTING A HYPOTHESIS ABOUT A SINGLE POPULATION PROPORTION

The basic concept of hypothesis testing for proportions is the same as for means.

1. The null and alternative hypotheses are stated in terms of a population parameter, now p instead of μ, and the sample statistic becomes $\bar{p}$ instead of $\bar{x}$.
2. The null hypothesis should be a statement concerning the parameter that includes the equality.
3. The significance level of the hypothesis again determines the size of the rejection region.
4. The test can be one- or two-tailed, depending on how the alternative hypothesis is formulated.

First American Bank and Title—The internal auditors at First American Bank and Title Company routinely test the bank's system of internal controls. Recently, the audit manager examined the documentation on the bank's 22,500 outstanding automobile loans. The bank's procedures require that the file on each auto loan account contain certain specific documentation, such as a list of applicant assets, statement of monthly income, list of liabilities, and certificate of automobile insurance. If an account contains all the required documentation, then it complies with bank procedures.

The audit manager has established a 1% noncompliance rate as the bank's standard. If more than 1% of the 22,500 loans do not have appropriate documentation, then the internal controls are not effective and the bank needs to improve the situation. The audit staff does not have enough time to examine all 22,500 files to determine the noncompliance rate. As a result, the audit staff selects a random sample of 600 files, examines them, and determines the number of files not in compliance with bank documentation requirements. The sample findings will tell the manager if the bank is exceeding the 1% noncompliance rate for the population of all 22,500 loan files. The manager will not act unless the noncompliance rate exceeds 1%. The default position is that the internal controls are effective. Thus, the null and alternative hypotheses are

$$H_0: p \leq 0.01 \text{ (Internal Controls Are Effective)}$$
$$H_A: p > 0.01 \text{ (Internal Controls Are Not Effective)}$$

Suppose the sample of 600 accounts uncovered 9 files with inadequate loan documentation. The question is whether 9 out of 600 is sufficient to conclude that the bank has a problem. To answer this question statistically, we need to recall a lesson from Chapter 6.

REQUIREMENT

The sample size, n, is large such that $np \geq 5$ and $n(1 - p) \geq 5$.

If this requirement is satisfied, the sampling distribution is approximately normal with mean $= p$ and standard deviation $= \sqrt{\dfrac{p(1 - p)}{n}}$.

The bank's auditors have a general policy of performing these tests with a significance level of

$$\alpha = 0.02.$$

They are willing to reject a true null hypothesis 2% of the time. In this case, if a Type I statistical error is committed, the internal controls will be considered ineffective when, in fact, they are working as intended.

Once the null and alternative hypotheses and the significance level have been specified, we can formulate the decision rule for this test. Figure 8-9 shows how the decision rule is developed. Notice the critical value, $\bar{p}_\alpha$, is 2.05 standard deviations above $p = 0.01$. Thus, if the sample proportion, $\bar{p}$, exceeds

$$\bar{p}_\alpha = 0.0182,$$

the null hypothesis should be rejected.

Because there were 9 deficient files in the sample of 600 files, this means that

$$\bar{p} = 9/600 = 0.015.$$

Because

$$\bar{p} = 0.015 < 0.0182 = \bar{p}_\alpha$$

the null hypothesis H_0 should not be rejected, based on these sample data. Therefore, the auditors will conclude the system of internal controls is working effectively.

FIGURE 8-9

Decision Rule for First American Bank and Title Example

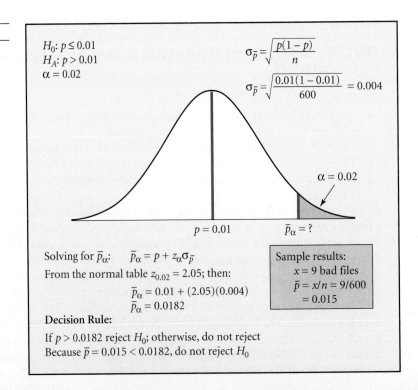

$H_0: p \leq 0.01$
$H_A: p > 0.01$
$\alpha = 0.02$

$\sigma_{\bar{p}} = \sqrt{\dfrac{p(1-p)}{n}}$

$\sigma_{\bar{p}} = \sqrt{\dfrac{0.01(1-0.01)}{600}} = 0.004$

$\alpha = 0.02$

$p = 0.01$ $\bar{p}_\alpha = ?$

Solving for $\bar{p}_\alpha$: $\bar{p}_\alpha = p + z_\alpha \sigma_{\bar{p}}$
From the normal table $z_{0.02} = 2.05$; then:

$$\bar{p}_\alpha = 0.01 + (2.05)(0.004)$$
$$\bar{p}_\alpha = 0.0182$$

Sample results:
$x = 9$ bad files
$\bar{p} = x/n = 9/600$
$= 0.015$

Decision Rule:

If $p > 0.0182$ reject H_0; otherwise, do not reject
Because $\bar{p} = 0.015 < 0.0182$, do not reject H_0

Alternatively, we could have based the test on a test statistic (z) with a standardized normal distribution. This test statistic is calculated using Equation 8-5.

---

z Test Statistic for Proportions

$$z = \frac{\bar{p} - p}{\sqrt{\dfrac{p(1-p)}{n}}}$$

8-5

where:

$\bar{p}$ = Sample proportion
p = Hypothesized population proportion
n = Sample size

The z-value for this test statistic is

$$z = \frac{0.015 - 0.01}{0.004} = 1.25.$$

As was established in Figure 8-9, the critical value,

$$z_\alpha = 2.05.$$

We reject the null hypothesis only if $z > z_\alpha$. Because

$$z = 1.25 < 2.05$$

we

don't reject the null hypothesis.

This, of course, was the same conclusion we reached when we used $\bar{p}$ as the test statistic. Both test statistics must yield the same decision.

SUMMARY: TESTING HYPOTHESES ABOUT A SINGLE POPULATION PROPORTION

1. Specify the population value of interest.

2. Formulate the null and alternative hypotheses.

3. Specify the significance level for testing the null hypothesis.

4. Construct the rejection region.
    For a one-tail test, determine the critical value, z_α, from the standard normal distribution table or

$$\bar{p}_\alpha = p + z_\alpha \sqrt{\frac{p(1-p)}{n}}$$

For a two-tail test, determine the critical values

$$\pm z_{\alpha/2} \text{ or } \bar{p}_{\alpha/2} = p \pm z_{\alpha/2}\sqrt{\frac{p(1-p)}{n}}$$

5. Compute the test statistic, $\bar{p} = \dfrac{x}{n}$ or $z = \dfrac{\bar{p} - p}{\sqrt{\dfrac{p(1-p)}{n}}}$

6. Reach a decision by comparing z to z_α or $\bar{p}$ to $\bar{p}_\alpha$.

7. Draw a conclusion.

EXAMPLE 8-10: TESTING HYPOTHESES FOR SINGLE POPULATION PROPORTIONS

Season Ticket Sales   A major university is considering increasing the season ticket prices for basketball games. The athletic director is concerned that some people will terminate their ticket orders if this change occurs. If more than 10% of the season ticket orders would be terminated, the AD does not want to implement the changes. To test this, a random sample of ticket holders are surveyed and asked what they would do if the prices were increased.

Step 1:   **Specify the population value of interest.**
        The parameter of interest is the population proportion.

Step 2:   **Formulate the null and alternative hypotheses.**
        The null and alternative hypotheses are

$$H_0: p \leq 0.10$$
$$H_A: p > 0.10$$

Step 3:　Specify the significance level.
The alpha level for this test is $\alpha = 0.05$.

Step 4:　Construct the rejection region.
The critical value from the standard normal table for this upper-tailed test is $z_\alpha = z_{.05} = 1.645$.
The decision rule is

If $z > 1.645$, reject H_0; otherwise, do not reject.

Step 5:　Compute the test statistic.
The random sample of $n = 100$ season ticket holders showed that 14 would cancel their ticket orders if the price change were implemented. The sample proportion is

$$\bar{p} = \frac{x}{n} = \frac{14}{100} = 0.14$$

$$z = \frac{\bar{p} - p}{\sqrt{\dfrac{p(1-p)}{n}}} = \frac{0.14 - 0.10}{\sqrt{\dfrac{0.10(1-0.10)}{100}}} = 1.33$$

Step 6:　Reach a decision.
Because $z = 1.33 < 1.645$, do not reject H_0.

Step 7:　Draw a conclusion.
Based on the sample data, the athletic director does not have sufficient evidence to conclude that more than 10% of the season ticket holders will cancel their ticket orders.

8-2: EXERCISES

Skill Development

8.23　Calculate the critical values for the following situations:
a. $H_A: p > 0.4$, $n = 150$, $\alpha = 0.05$
b. $H_A: p < 0.7$, $n = 200$, $\alpha = 0.10$
c. $H_A: p \neq 0.85$, $n = 100$, $\alpha = 0.10$

8.24　Given the following null and alternative hypotheses,

$$H_0: p = 0.20$$
$$H_A: p \neq 0.20$$

test the null hypothesis based on a random sample of 100, where $p = 0.23$.
a. Use the p-value approach to test the hypothesis. State the decision rule.
b. Use z as the test statistic to test the hypothesis. Assume an $\alpha = 0.05$ level. Be sure to show clearly the decision rule.

8.25　Given the following null and alternative hypotheses,

$$H_0: p = 0.70$$
$$H_A: p \neq 0.70$$

test the null hypothesis based on a random sample of 100, where $\bar{p} = 0.64$. Assume an $\alpha = 0.07$ level. Use the p-value approach to test the hypothesis. Be sure to show clearly the decision rule.

8.26　Given the following null and alternative hypotheses,

$$H_0: p \leq 0.45$$
$$H_A: p > 0.45$$

test the null hypothesis based on a random sample of $n = 500$, where $\bar{p} = 0.49$. Assume an $\alpha = 0.05$ level. Use the critical value approach to test the hypothesis. Be sure to show clearly the decision rule.

8.27　Given the following null and alternative hypotheses,

$$H_0: p \leq 0.24$$
$$H_A: p > 0.24$$

test the null hypothesis based on a random sample of $n = 100$, where $\bar{p} = 0.27$. Assume an $\alpha = 0.05$ level.
a. Use $\bar{p}_\alpha$ as the test statistic to test the hypothesis. Be sure to show clearly the decision rule.
b. Use z as the test statistic to test the hypothesis.

8.28　Given the following null and alternative hypotheses,

$$H_0: p \geq 0.50$$
$$H_A: p < 0.50$$

test the null hypothesis based on a random sample of 200, where $\bar{p} = 0.47$. Use $\alpha = 0.10$.
a. Use the p-value approach to test the hypothesis. State the decision rule.
b. Use $\bar{p}_\alpha$ as the test statistic to conduct the test of hypothesis.

Business Applications

8.29　The College of Business at a state university has a computer-literacy requirement for all graduates: Students must show proficiency with a spreadsheet software package and with a word-processing software package. To assess whether students are computer literate, a test is given at the end of each semester. The test is designed so that at least 70% of all students who have taken a special microcomputer course will pass the test. Suppose that, in a random sample of 100 students who have recently finished the microcomputer course, 63 pass the proficiency test.

a. Using a significance level of 0.05, what conclusions should the administrators make regarding the difficulty of the test?

b. Describe a Type II error in the context of this problem.

8.30 A shopping center developer claims in a presentation to a potential client that at least 40% of the adult female population in a community visit the mall one or more times a week. To test this claim, the developer selected a random sample of 100 households with an adult female present and asked if they visit the mall at least one day per week. Thirty-eight of the 100 respondents replied "yes" to the question.

Based on the sample data and a significance level of 0.05, what should be concluded about the developer's claim? Show the decision rule and your analysis clearly.

8.31 A large number of complaints have been received in the past six months regarding airlines losing fliers' baggage. The airlines claim the problem is much smaller than newspaper articles have indicated. In fact, one airline spokesman claimed that fewer than 1% of all bags fail to arrive at their destinations with the passengers. To test this claim, 800 bags were randomly selected at various airports in the United States when they were checked with this airline. Of these, 6 failed to reach their destinations when their owners arrived.

a. Is this sufficient evidence to support the airline spokesman's claim? Test using a significance level of 0.05. Discuss.

b. Estimate the proportion of bags that fail to arrive at the proper destinations using a technique for which 95% confidence applies.

8.32 Evan Huntsman & Associates owns and operates a lawn maintenance service in Trenton, New Jersey. The company is considering expanding into a nearby community. The managers believe that the proportion of homes in this new community that are currently using a professional lawn service is less than 0.40. To test this, the company plans to select a simple random sample of 120 homes and interview the homeowners to determine their lawn care status.

a. State the appropriate null and alternative hypotheses.

b. Using a significance level of 0.05, conduct the hypothesis test, assuming that 45 of those interviewed indicated that they are already using a lawn service. Discuss your results.

8.33 Suppose that at your university, administrators believe that the proportion of students preferring to take classes at night exceeds 0.30. To test this, a simple random sample of 200 students is selected, and 66 indicate that they prefer night classes.

a. State the appropriate null and alternative hypotheses.

b. If an alpha level equal to 0.10 is used, conduct the hypothesis test and discuss your results.

8.34 A major issue facing many states is whether to legalize casino gambling. Suppose the governor of one state believes that more than 55% of the state's registered voters would favor some form of legal casino gambling. However, before backing a proposal to allow such gambling, the governor instructed his aides to conduct a statistical test on the issue. To do this, the aides hired a consulting firm to survey a simple random sample of 300 voters. Of these 300 voters, 175 actually favor legalized gambling.

a. State the appropriate null and alternative hypotheses.

b. Assuming that a significance level of 0.05 is used, what conclusion should the governor reach based on these sample data? Discuss.

8.35 In a March 2002 article, *Golf Digest* reported on a survey in which 300 golfers were asked their views about the impact of new technologies on the game of golf. Before the study, a group of United States Golf Association officials believed that 50% or fewer of golfers believed that professional golfers should have different equipment rules than amateurs. The survey found 67% did not favor different equipment rules.

a. If the claim made by the USGA is to be tested, what should be the null and alternative hypotheses?

b. Based on the sample data and an alpha level equal to 0.05, use the *p*-value approach to conduct the hypothesis test.

Advanced Business Applications

8.36 The AJ Fitness Center has surveyed 1,214 of its customers. Of particular interest is whether more than 60% of the customers who express overall service satisfaction with the club (represented by codes 4 or 5) are female. If this is not the case, the promotions director feels she must initiate new exercise programs that are designed specifically for women. Should the promotions director initiate the new exercise programs? Support your answer with the relevant hypothesis test, utilizing a *p*-value to perform the test. The data are found in the CD-ROM file *AJ Fitness* ($\alpha = 0.05$).

8.37 A computer manufacturer has a dial-up 800 number that customers can use to call for help with problems related to their computer. The service manager expects that the proportion of calls that will be answered within 5 minutes exceeds 0.80. Recently a survey was conducted of 70 calls. The data file *Customer Service* contains the evaluation (Yes or No) on whether the call was answered within 5 minutes.

a. State the appropriate null and alternative hypotheses.

b. Carry out the hypothesis test using a significance level of 0.10. Show the decision rule and the result of the test.

c. Construct a 90% confidence interval for the proportion of calls that were answered in 5 minutes. Do you see any relationship between the confidence interval you constructed and the test you conducted in part b? State any generalization you may determine.

8.38 ● At the annual meeting of the Golf Equipment Manufacturers' Association, a speaker made the claim that fewer than 30% of all golf clubs being used by non-professional United States Golf Association members are knockoffs. These knockoffs are clubs that look very much like the more-expensive originals, such as Big Bertha drivers, but they are actually nonauthorized copies that are sold at a very reduced rate. This claim prompted the association to conduct a study to see if the speaker was correct. A random sample of 400 golfers was selected from the USGA. The players were called and asked to indicate the brand of clubs that they used, along with several other questions. Data were collected from 294 golfers. Based on the response to club brand, a determination was made about whether the clubs were "original" or a "copy." The data are in a CD-ROM file called *Golf Survey*.

a. Based on the sample data, what conclusion should be reached if the hypothesis is tested at a significance level of 0.05? Show the decision rule.

b. Determine whether a Type I or Type II error for this hypothesis test would be more severe. Given your determination, would you advocate raising or lowering the significance level for this test? Explain your reasoning.

8.39 ● Referring to Exercise 8.38, one of the USGA officials has stated that the use of knockoff golf clubs is greater among the high-handicap players. He went on to say that at least 40% of all golfers with handicaps 20 and above use unauthorized copies. This claim will be accepted unless the sample data indicate strongly that it is incorrect. Use the data in the file *Golf Survey* to test this claim.

a. Confirm that the sample proportion's distribution can be approximated by a normal distribution.

b. Based on the sample data and a significance level of 0.05, what should the USGA conclude about the use of knockoff clubs by the high-handicap golfers? Is the official's statement justified?

8-3 TYPE II ERRORS

Sections 8-1 and 8-2 provided several examples that illustrated how hypotheses and decision rules for tests of the population mean are formulated. In these examples, we determined the critical values by first specifying the significance level, alpha: the maximum allowable probability of committing a Type I error. As we indicated, if the cost of committing a Type I error is high, the decision maker will want to specify a small significance level.

This logic provides a basis for establishing the critical value for the hypothesis test. However, it ignores the possibility of committing a Type II error. Recall that a Type II error occurs if a false null hypothesis is accepted. The probability of a Type II error is given the symbol β, the Greek letter beta. We discussed in Section 8-1 that α and β are inversely related. That is, if we make α smaller, β will increase. However, the two are not proportional. A case in point: cutting α in half will not necessarily double β.

CALCULATING BETA

Once α has been specified for a hypothesis test involving a particular sample size, β cannot also be specified. Rather, the β value is fixed, and all the decision maker can do is calculate it. However, β is not a single value. Because a Type II error occurs when a false null hypothesis is accepted (refer to Figure 8-1), there is a β value for each possible population value for which the null hypothesis is false. To calculate beta, we must first specify a "what if" value for the true population value. Then, β is computed conditional on that population value being true. Keep in mind that β is computed before the sample is taken, so its value is not dependent on the sample outcome.

For instance, if the null hypothesis is the mean income for a population is equal to or greater than \$30,000, then β could be calculated for any value of μ less than \$30,000. We would get a different β for each value of μ. An example will help clarify this concept.

American Lighting Company—Recall Example 8-7, in which the American Lighting Company had developed a new light bulb to last more than 700 hours on average. If a hypothesis test could confirm this, the company would use the "greater than 700 hour" claim in its advertising. The null and alternative hypotheses are:

$$H_0: \mu \leq 700 \text{ hours}$$
$$H_A: \mu > 700 \text{ hours}$$

Therefore, the null hypothesis is false for all possible values of $\mu > 700$ hours. Thus, for each of the infinite number of possibilities, a value of β can be determined. (Note: σ is assumed to be 15 hours.)

FIGURE 8-10

Beta Calculation for True
$\mu = 701$

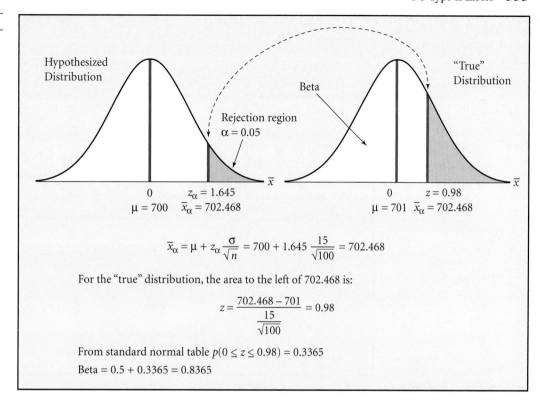

$$\bar{x}_\alpha = \mu + z_\alpha \frac{\sigma}{\sqrt{n}} = 700 + 1.645 \frac{15}{\sqrt{100}} = 702.468$$

For the "true" distribution, the area to the left of 702.468 is:

$$z = \frac{702.468 - 701}{\frac{15}{\sqrt{100}}} = 0.98$$

From standard normal table $p(0 \le z \le 0.98) = 0.3365$
Beta $= 0.5 + 0.3365 = 0.8365$

Figure 8-10 shows how β is determined if the value of μ selected from H_A is 701 hours. By specifying the significance level to be 0.05 and a sample size of 100 bulbs, the chance of committing a Type II error is approximately 0.8365. This means that if the true population mean is 701 hours, there is nearly an 84% chance that the sampling plan American Lighting is using will not reject the assumption that the mean is 700 hours or less.

Figure 8-11 shows that if the "what if" mean value ($\mu = 704$) is farther from the hypothesized mean ($\mu = 700$), beta becomes smaller. The greater the difference between the mean specified in H_0 and the mean selected from H_A, the easier it is to tell the two apart, and the less likely we are to not reject the null hypothesis when it is actually false. Of course the opposite is also true. As the mean selected from H_A moves increasingly closer to the mean specified in H_0, the harder it is for the hypothesis test to distinguish between the two.

FIGURE 8-11

Beta Calculation for True
$\mu = 704$

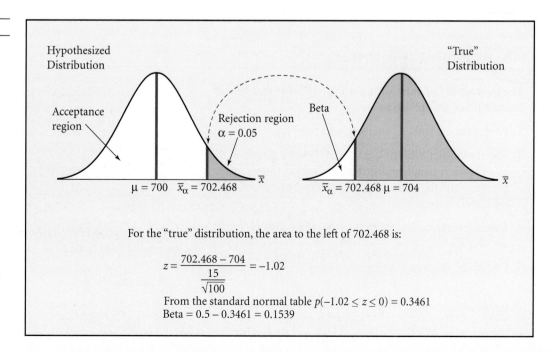

For the "true" distribution, the area to the left of 702.468 is:

$$z = \frac{702.468 - 704}{\frac{15}{\sqrt{100}}} = -1.02$$

From the standard normal table $p(-1.02 \le z \le 0) = 0.3461$
Beta $= 0.5 - 0.3461 = 0.1539$

FIGURE 8-12

**Beta Calculation for True
μ and $n = 500$**

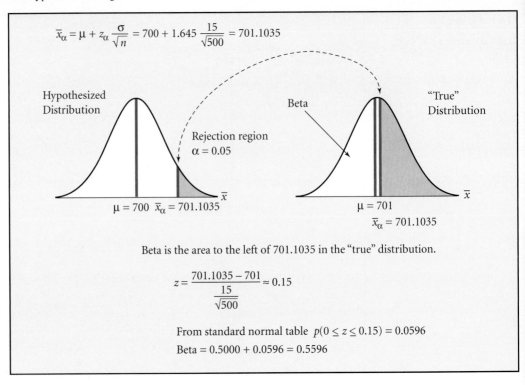

$$\bar{x}_\alpha = \mu + z_\alpha \frac{\sigma}{\sqrt{n}} = 700 + 1.645 \frac{15}{\sqrt{500}} = 701.1035$$

Hypothesized Distribution

Rejection region $\alpha = 0.05$

Beta

"True" Distribution

$\mu = 700$ $\bar{x}_\alpha = 701.1035$

$\mu = 701$
$\bar{x}_\alpha = 701.1035$

Beta is the area to the left of 701.1035 in the "true" distribution.

$$z = \frac{701.1035 - 701}{\frac{15}{\sqrt{500}}} \approx 0.15$$

From standard normal table $p(0 \le z \le 0.15) = 0.0596$

Beta $= 0.5000 + 0.0596 = 0.5596$

CONTROLLING ALPHA AND BETA

Ideally, we want both alpha and beta to be as small as possible. Although we can set alpha at any desired level, for a specified sample size and standard deviation, the calculated value of beta depends on the population mean chosen from the alternative hypothesis and the significance level. For a specified sample size, reducing alpha will increase beta. However, we can control the size of both alpha and beta if we are willing to increase the sample size.

The American Lighting Company planned to take a sample of 100 light bulbs. In Figure 8-10, we showed that beta = 0.8365 when the "true" population mean was 701 hours. This is a very large probability and would be unacceptable to the company. However, if the company is willing to incur the cost associated with a sample size of 500 bulbs, the probability of a Type II error could be reduced to 0.5596, as shown in Figure 8-12. This is a big improvement and is due to the fact that the standard error $\left(\frac{\sigma}{\sqrt{n}} \right)$ is reduced because of the increased sample size.

SUMMARY: CALCULATING BETA

The probability of committing a Type II error can be calculated using the following steps.

1. Formulate the null and alternative hypotheses.

2. Specify the significance level. (Hint: Draw a picture of the hypothesized sampling distribution showing the rejection region(s) and the acceptance region found by specifying the significance level.)

3. Determine the critical value, z_α, from the standard normal distribution.

4. Determine the critical value, $\bar{x}_\alpha = \mu + z_\alpha \frac{\sigma}{\sqrt{n}}$ for an

upper-tail test, or $\bar{x}_\alpha = \mu - z_\alpha \frac{\sigma}{\sqrt{n}}$ for a lower-tail test.

5. Specify the stipulated value for μ, the population mean for which you wish to compute β.

6. Compute the test statistic based on the stipulated population mean as:

$$z = \frac{\bar{x}_\alpha - \mu}{\frac{\sigma}{\sqrt{n}}}$$

7. Use the standard normal table to find β, the probability associated with "accepting" the null hypothesis when it is false.

EXAMPLE 8-10: COMPUTING BETA

Wright Tax Assistance, Inc.   Wright Tax Assistance, Inc., a major income tax preparation company, has claimed its clients save an average of more than $200 each by using the company's services. A consumer's group plans to randomly sample 64 customers to test this claim. The standard deviation of the amount saved is assumed to be $100. Before testing, the consumer's group is interested in knowing the probability that they will mistakenly conclude that the mean savings is less than or equal to $200 when, in fact, it does exceed $200, as the company claims. To find beta if the true population mean is $210, the company can use the following steps.

Step 1:   **Specify the null and alternative hypotheses.**
The null and alternative hypotheses are

$$H_0: \mu \le \$200$$
$$H_A: \mu > \$200$$

Step 2:   **Specify the significance level.**
The one-tailed hypothesis test will be conducted using $\alpha = 0.05$.

Step 3:   **Determine the critical value, z_α, from the standard normal distribution.**
The critical value from the standard normal is $z_\alpha = z_{0.05} = 1.645$.

Step 4:   **Calculate the critical value.**

$$\bar{x}_\alpha = \mu + z_\alpha \frac{\sigma}{\sqrt{n}} = 200 + 1.645 \frac{100}{\sqrt{64}} = 220.56$$

Thus, the null hypothesis will be rejected if $\bar{x} > 220.56$.

Step 5:   **Specify the stipulated value for μ.**
The null hypothesis is false for all values greater than $200. What is beta if the stipulated mean is $210?

Step 6:   **Compute the test statistic based on the stipulated population mean.**
The test statistic based on stipulated population mean is

$$z = \frac{\bar{x}_\alpha - \mu}{\frac{\sigma}{\sqrt{n}}} = \frac{220.56 - 210}{\frac{100}{\sqrt{64}}} = 0.84$$

Step 7:   **Determine beta.**
From the standard normal table, the probability associated with $z = 0.84$ is 0.2995. Then $\beta = 0.5000 + 0.2995 = 0.7995$. There is a 0.7995 probability that the hypothesis test will lead the consumer agency to mistakenly believe that the mean tax savings is less than or equal to $200 when, in fact, the mean savings is $210.

POWER OF THE TEST

In the previous examples, we have been concerned about the chance of making a Type II error. We would like beta to be as small as possible. If the null hypothesis is false, we want to reject it. Another way to look at this is that we would like the hypothesis test to have a high probability of rejecting a false hypothesis. This concept is expressed by what is called the **power** of the test.

Power

The probability that the hypothesis test will reject the null hypothesis when the null hypothesis is false.

When the alternative hypothesis is true, the power of the test is computed using Equation 8-6.

Power

Power $= 1 - \beta$

8-6

8-3: EXERCISES

Skill Development

8.40 You are given the following null and alternative hypotheses:

$$H_0: \mu \leq 4{,}000$$
$$H_A: \mu > 4{,}000$$
$$\alpha = 0.05$$

a. If the population mean is 4,004, determine the value of beta. Assume that the population standard deviation is known to be 20 and the sample size is 40.
b. Referring to part a, calculate the power of the test.
c. Referring to parts a and b, what could be done to increase power and reduce beta if the true population mean is 4,004? Discuss.
d. Indicate clearly the decision rule that would be used to test the null hypothesis and determine what decision should be made if the sample mean were 4,002.

8.41 You are given the following null and alternative hypotheses:

$$H_0: \mu = 1.20$$
$$H_A: \mu \neq 1.20$$
$$\alpha = 0.10$$

a. If the true population mean is 1.25, determine the value of beta. Assume the population standard deviation is known to be 0.50 and the sample size is 60.
b. Referring to part a, calculate the power of the test.
c. Referring to parts a and b, what could be done to increase power and reduce beta when the true population mean is 1.25? Discuss.
d. Indicate clearly the decision rule that would be used to test the null hypothesis and determine what decision should be made if the sample mean were 1.23.

8.42 You are given the following null and alternative hypotheses:

$$H_0: \mu \geq 88$$
$$H_A: \mu < 88$$
$$\alpha = 0.10$$

a. If the true population mean is 86, determine the value of beta. Assume that the population standard deviation is known to be 12 and the sample size is 64.
b. Referring to part a, calculate the power of the test.
c. Referring to parts a and b, what could be done to increase power and reduce beta when the true population mean is 86? Discuss.
d. Indicate clearly the decision rule that would be used to test the null hypothesis and determine what decision should be made if the sample mean were 85.66.

8.43 You are given the following null and alternative hypotheses:

$$H_0: \mu \geq 4{,}350$$
$$H_A: \mu < 4{,}350$$
$$\alpha = 0.05$$

a. If the true population mean is 4,345, determine the value of beta. Assume the population standard deviation is known to be 200 and the sample size is 100.
b. Referring to part a, calculate the power of the test.
c. Referring to parts a and b, what could be done to increase power and reduce beta when the true population mean is 4,345? Discuss.
d. Indicate clearly the decision rule that would be used to test the null hypothesis and determine what decision should be made if the sample mean were 4,337.50.

8.44 You are given the following null and alternative hypotheses:

$$H_0: \mu \leq 256$$
$$H_A \mu > 256$$
$$\alpha = 0.05$$

a. If the true population mean is 260, determine the value of beta. Assume the population standard deviation is known to be 40 and the sample size is 100.
b. Referring to part a, calculate the power for this test.
c. Suppose that the true mean is 262. Determine the value of the power and beta. Indicate why these values changed compared with those found in parts a and b.
d. Suppose the true population mean is 260, but the alpha level for the test is 0.10 rather than 0.05, what will be the impact on the beta value? Will power increase or decrease?

Business Applications

8.45 The Arrow Tire and Rubber Company plans to warranty its new mountain bike tire for 12 months. However, before it does this, the company wants to be sure that the mean lifetime of the tires is at least 18 months under normal operations. It will put the warranty in place unless the sample data strongly suggest that the mean lifetime of the tires is less than 18 months. The company plans to test this statistically using a random sample of tires. The test will be conducted using an alpha level of 0.03.
a. If the population mean is actually 16.5 months, determine the probability the hypothesis test will lead to incorrectly accepting the null hypothesis. Assume that the population standard deviation is known to be 2.4 months and the sample size is 60.
b. If the population mean is actually 17.3, calculate the chance of committing a Type II error. This is a specific example of a generalization relating the probability of committing a Type II error and the parameter being tested. State this generalization.
c. Without calculating the probability, state whether the probability of a Type II error would be larger or smaller than that calculated in part b if you were to calculate it for a hypothesized mean of 15 months. Justify your answer.
d. Suppose the company decides to increase the sample size from 60 to 100 tires. What can you expect to happen to the probabilities calculated previously?

8.46 The union negotiations between labor and management at the Stone Container paper mill in Minnesota hit a snag when management asked labor to take a cut in health insurance coverage. As part of its justification, management claimed that the average amount of insurance claims filed by union employees did not exceed $250 per employee. The union's chief negotiator requested that a sample of 100 employees' records be selected and that this claim be tested statistically. The claim would be accepted if the sample data did not strongly suggest otherwise. The significance level for the test was set at 0.10.

a. State the null and alternative hypotheses.

b. Before the sample was selected, the negotiator was interested in knowing the power of this test if the mean amount of insurance claims was $260. (Assume the standard deviation in claims is $70, as determined in a similar study at another plant location.) Calculate this probability for the negotiator.

c. Referring to part b, how will the power of the test change if alpha = 0.05 is used?

d. Suppose alpha is left at 0.10, but the standard deviation of the population is $50 rather than $70, what will be the power of the test? State the generalization that explains the relationship between the answers to parts b and d.

e. Referring to part d, based on the probability computed, if you were the negotiator, would you be satisfied with the sampling plan in this situation? Explain why or why not. What steps could be taken to improve the sampling plan?

8.47   The makers of Mini-Oats Cereal have an automated packaging machine that can be set at any targeted fill level between 12 and 32 ounces. At the end of every shift (8 hours), 16 boxes are selected at random and the mean and standard deviation of the sample are computed. Based on these sample results, the production control manager determines whether the filling machine needs to be readjusted or whether it remains all right to operate. Previous data suggest the fill level has a normal distribution, with a standard deviation of 0.65 ounces. Use $\alpha = 0.05$. The test is a two-sided test to determine if the mean fill level is equal to 24 ounces.

a. Calculate the probability that the test procedure will detect that the average fill level is not equal to 24 ounces when in fact it equals 24.5 ounces.

b. On the basis of your calculation in part a, would you suggest a change in the test procedure? Explain what change you would make and the reasons you would make this change.

8.48   The Wainwright Lawn and Garden Company's marketing manager believes that the average income for the company's customers is less than $30,000. This claim was made by the manager as he defended his selection of brands aimed at lower-income customers. To verify the claim, a simple random sample of 400 customers was selected and a survey was conducted to determine income levels. It is assumed that σ is equal to $4,000. The significance level is 0.10. If the actual mean income is $29,800, determine the probability that the test will mistakenly lead the managers to "accept" the null hypothesis.

Summary and Conclusions

This chapter has introduced the fundamentals of hypothesis testing. The concepts presented in this chapter provide decision makers with tools for using sample information to decide whether a given null hypothesis should be rejected.

In this chapter we have concentrated on examples of sample hypothesis tests involving a single population mean and a population proportion. In subsequent chapters you will see that the hypothesis testing methodology is basically the same for all situations. The central issue is always to determine whether the sample information tends to support or refute the null hypothesis.

We have emphasized the importance of recognizing that when a hypothesis is tested, an error might occur. Type I and Type II statistical errors have been discussed. We have shown how to calculate the probability of committing each type of error for applications involving a single population mean.

You have probably noticed that the statistical estimation techniques discussed in Chapter 7 and hypothesis testing have much in common. Both estimation and hypothesis testing are used extensively by business decision makers. Estimation procedures are most useful when decision makers have little or no idea of the value of a population parameter and are primarily interested in determining these values. On the other hand, hypothesis testing is used when a claim about a population value needs to be tested. Estimation and hypothesis testing are the central components of statistical inference and will be used throughout the remaining chapters of this text. Figure 8-13 on the next page is a flow diagram that should help you determine which hypothesis testing procedure to use in various situations. Note: Figure 8-13 assumes a right-tailed hypothesis test. Table 8-1 provides a matrix format to help you determine which statistical tools to apply in specific situations.

EQUATIONS

$\bar{x}_\alpha$ for Hypothesis Tests, σ Known, Large Samples

$$\bar{x}_\alpha = \mu + z_\alpha \frac{\sigma}{\sqrt{n}} \qquad \textbf{8-1}$$

z Test Statistic for Hypothesis Tests for μ, σ Known

$$z = \frac{\bar{x} - \mu}{\frac{\sigma}{\sqrt{n}}} \qquad \textbf{8-2}$$

z Test Statistic for Hypothesis Tests for μ, σ Unknown, Large Samples

$$z = \frac{\bar{x} - \mu}{\frac{s}{\sqrt{n}}} \qquad \textbf{8-3}$$

t Test Statistic for Hypothesis Tests for μ, σ Unknown

$$t = \frac{\bar{x} - \mu}{\frac{s}{\sqrt{n}}} \qquad \textbf{8-4}$$

z Test Statistic for Proportions

$$z = \frac{\bar{p} - p}{\sqrt{\frac{p(1-p)}{n}}} \qquad \textbf{8-5}$$

Power

$$\text{Power} = 1 - \beta \qquad \textbf{8-6}$$

FIGURE 8-13

**Deciding Which Hypothesis
Testing Procedure to Use**

	Population Mean μ	Population Proportion p
TABLE 8-1 **Statistic**	$\bar{x} = \dfrac{\sum x}{n}$	$\bar{p} = \dfrac{X}{n}$

TABLE 8-1

Statistical Inference Tools—One Sample Situations

	Population Mean μ	Population Proportion p
Confidence Interval	σ **known:** $\bar{x} \pm z_{\alpha/2}\dfrac{\sigma}{\sqrt{n}}$ σ **unknown, $n \geq 30$** $\bar{x} \pm z_{\alpha/2}\dfrac{s}{\sqrt{n}}$ σ **unknown, $n < 30$** $\bar{x} \pm t_{\alpha/2}\dfrac{s}{\sqrt{n}}$	$\bar{p} \pm z\sqrt{\dfrac{\bar{p}(1-\bar{p})}{n}}$
Hypotheses	**Example** $H_0: \mu \leq 200$ $H_A: \mu > 200$	**Example** $H_0: p \geq 0.60$ $H_A: p < 0.60$
Test Statistic	σ **known:** $z = \dfrac{\bar{x}-\mu}{\dfrac{\sigma}{\sqrt{n}}}$ σ **unknown, $n \geq 30$** $z = \dfrac{\bar{x}-\mu}{\dfrac{s}{\sqrt{n}}}$ σ **unknown, $n < 30$** $t = \dfrac{\bar{x}-\mu}{\dfrac{s}{\sqrt{n}}}$	$z = \dfrac{\bar{p}-p}{\sqrt{\dfrac{p(1-p)}{n}}}$

Key Terms

Alternative Hypothesis, 305
Critical Value, 309
One-Tailed Test, 314
Null Hypothesis, 304

p-Value, 313
Power, 335
Research Hypothesis, 306
Significance Level, 309

Two-Tailed Test, 314
Test Statistic, 311
Type I Error, 307
Type II Error, 307

CHAPTER EXERCISES

Conceptual Questions

8.49 Discuss the two types of statistical errors that can occur when a hypothesis is tested. Illustrate what you mean by using a business example for each.

8.50 Discuss the issues that a decision maker should consider when determining the significance level to use in a hypothesis test.

8.51 What is meant by the term *critical value* in a hypothesis-testing situation? Illustrate what you mean with a business example.

8.52 Discuss why it is necessary to use an estimate of the standard error for a confidence interval but not for a hypothesis test concerning a population proportion.

8.53 What is the maximum probability of committing a Type I error called? How is this probability determined? Discuss.

8.54 Recall that the power of the test is the probability that the null hypothesis is rejected when H_0 is false. Explain whether power is definable if the given parameter is the value specified in the null hypothesis.

8.55   Examine the test statistic used in testing a population proportion. Why is it impossible to test the hypothesis that the population proportion equals zero using such a test statistic? Try to determine a way that such a test could be conducted.

8.56   The Oasis Chemical Company develops and manufactures pharmaceutical drugs for distribution and sale in the United States. The pharmaceutical business can be very lucrative when useful and safe drugs are introduced into the market. Whenever the Oasis research lab considers putting a drug into production, the company must establish the following sets of null and alternative hypotheses:

Set 1	Set 2
H_0: The drug is safe.	H_0: The drug is effective.
H_A: The drug is not safe.	H_A: The drug is not effective.

Take each set of hypotheses separately.
a. Discuss the considerations that should be made in establishing alpha and beta.
b. For each set of hypotheses, describe what circumstances would suggest that a Type I error would be of more concern.
c. For each set of hypotheses, describe what circumstances would suggest that a Type II error would be of more concern.

Business Applications

8.57   The Ohio State Tax Commission attempts to set up payroll-tax withholding tables so that by the end of a year, an employee's income-tax withholding is about $100 below his or her actual income tax owed to the state. The commission director claims that when all the Ohio tax returns are in, the average additional payment will be less than $100.

A random sample of 50 accounts revealed, on average, an additional payment of $114, with a sample standard deviation of $50.
a. Testing at a significance level of 0.10, do the sample data refute the director's claim?
b. Determine the largest sample mean (with the same sample size and standard deviation) that would fail to refute the director's claim.

8.58   The TSR Testing Service prepares real estate license examinations for several states. Wisconsin officials are considering hiring this company to devise a test for their real estate brokers' license requirements. Wisconsin requires that the average test score be exactly 70 points. In order to evaluate the test prepared by TSR Testing, Wisconsin officials selected a random sample of 60 potential brokers and administered the exam. They found that the mean score was 68.55 points.
a. State the appropriate null and alternative hypotheses.
b. Assuming that the true standard deviation is 10 points and the hypothesis is to be tested at a significance level of 0.08, on the basis of the sample data, should the Wisconsin officials consider requiring TSR to restructure its test? Describe what a Type II error would be in the context of this problem.

8.59   The Cherry Hill Growers Association operates a fruit warehouse in California. Because of the volume of cherries that arrive at the warehouse during the picking season, the growers have agreed that instead of weighing each box of cherries, they would assume that the average box weighs 20 pounds. The total weight is then simply the number of boxes times 20 pounds.

Past studies have shown that the standard deviation of weight from box to box is 0.5 pound. Suppose the warehouse manager has decided to select a random sample of 70 boxes of cherries from a particular grower's crop. He suspects that the grower may be underfilling the boxes and is concerned about detecting this, if it is the case. He is not concerned if the average box contains more than 20 pounds.
a. Would the warehouse manager be justified in concluding that underfilling of the boxes is occurring if the sample mean is 19.62? Use a significance level of 0.05.
b. Determine the probability that a sample mean less than or equal to 19.62 would be obtained from a sample of size 70 if the population mean were 20 pounds. What is the statistical term for the value you calculated?
c. Discuss which type of hypothesis testing error would be more important to the warehouse manager.
d. Discuss which type of error would be more important to the grower.

8.60   The Lazer Company has a contract to produce a part for Boeing Corporation that must have an average diameter of 6 inches and a standard deviation of 0.10 inch. Lazer has developed a process that will meet the specifications with respect to the standard deviation, but it is still trying to meet the mean specifications. A test run (considered a random sample) of parts was produced and the company wishes to determine whether this latest process that produced the sample will produce parts meeting the requirement of average diameter equal to 6 inches.
a. Specify the appropriate null and alternative hypotheses.
b. Develop the decision rule assuming that the sample size is 200 parts and the significance level is 0.01.
c. What should Lazer conclude if the sample mean diameter for the 200 parts is 6.03 inches? Discuss.

8.61   Tom Morgan operates a gas station in a suburban area of Boston. He is thinking of installing a mechanism on his self-service pumps that will not allow more than 10 gallons to be pumped without having the pump restarted. He hopes this will cut down on theft without making honest customers angry.

The marketing representative for the new mechanism claims that if Tom's station is typical, the average fill-up is no more than 10 gallons. Tom has decided to select a random sample of 200 customers and test to determine whether the marketing representative's claim is true. He is willing to accept the claim unless the data strongly indicate that it is not true.
a. If the sample results show a mean of 10.32 gallons per fill-up, with a sample standard deviation of 2.9 gallons, what should Tom conclude about the population mean? Use a significance level of 0.05. Discuss your results.
b. Calculate a 95% confidence interval for the average fill-up.

8.62   The owners of Fit and Trim, a fitness and diet club, would like to advertise that their clients lose more than 10 pounds on average during their first three months of membership at the club. A sample resulted in the following summary statistics:

$$\bar{x} = 10.9 \text{ lb.}$$
$$s = 0.4 \text{ lb.}$$
$$n = 20$$

a. If the desired significance level is 0.05, what should be concluded about this claim if the above results are observed? Be sure to first set up the appropriate decision rule.

b. What assumption(s) must you make about the population's distribution so that your results in part a are valid?

8.63 The personnel manager for a large airline has claimed that, on the average, workers are asked to work no more than 3 hours overtime per week. Past studies show the standard deviation in overtime hours per worker to be 1.2 hours.

Suppose union negotiators wish to test this claim by sampling payroll records for 250 employees. They believe that the personnel manager's claim is untrue, but they want to base their conclusion on the sample results.

a. State the null and alternative hypotheses, and discuss the meaning of Type I and Type II errors in the context of this case.

b. Establish the appropriate decision rule if the union wishes to have no more than a 0.01 chance of a Type I error.

c. The payroll records produced a sample mean of 3.15 hours. Do the union negotiators have a basis for a grievance against the airline? Support your answer with a relevant statistical procedure.

8.64 A major U.S. tire manufacturer has developed a new design that will allow an owner to drive on a punctured tire for some miles without having to stop and change the tire. The R&D engineers claim that the average miles should exceed 50. However, they do not wish to assert this claim to the public if the sample data indicate otherwise. To conduct a test, a sample of 25 tires is selected with the following results:

$$\bar{x} = 51.05$$
$$s = 14.2$$

a. State the appropriate null and alternative hypotheses.

b. What conclusion should the company reach, assuming they want to test the hypothesis with a significance level of 0.05?

8.65 At a recent meeting of the budget committee at the Winter Corporation, the marketing manager made a pitch for a larger department budget by stating that more money was needed in advertising to improve the company's image. This prompted the company president to establish a task force to measure public opinion about the company.

This task force planned to use a well-established instrument for measuring public perception of companies such as Winter. Past studies using this particular instrument indicate that a company should receive at least an average 40-point overall rating to consider that it has a positive image in the public eye. They will assume that the company's image is positive unless the sample data indicate otherwise.

The task force randomly sampled 300 people within the market area and found that the average rating received was 38.98, with a sample standard deviation of 5.3 points.

a. Establish the appropriate null and alternative hypotheses.

b. Assuming that the test is to be conducted with a significance level equal to 0.10, what conclusion should the Winter Corporation reach about its average company rating by all the members of the population? Discuss.

c. Reflect on Type I and Type II errors in the context of this problem. Which of these do you think would be of most importance to the task force? Explain your reasoning.

8.66 A major U.S. tire manufacturer has developed a new design that will allow the owner to drive on a punctured tire for several miles without having to change the tire. The R&D department head claims that more than 90% of the tires will last for more than 30 miles before needing to be changed. However, he wishes to test this claim before going public with the statement. A simple random sample of 100 tires with punctures revealed that 93 lasted longer than 30 miles.

a. State the appropriate null and alternative hypotheses.

b. What conclusion should the department head reach, based on the sample data, if the test is to be conducted using an alpha level equal to 0.05?

8.67 In a recent management-union negotiating process at a large, national, tire manufacturing company, one of the points made by management was that the average number of dollars in health-care benefits used per worker was $417 per year or less. It also indicated that the standard deviation was $200 per employee. Assuming that the standard deviation figure was correct, the union decided to select a random sample of 100 employee health records and test to determine whether the management assertion was correct. It planned to test at a significance level of 0.05.

a. Set up the correct null and alternative hypotheses.

b. Discuss why this hypothesis test is considered a one-tailed hypothesis test.

c. If the sample mean for the 100 workers was $433, what should the union conclude about the claim made by management? Discuss.

8.68 The Bell Corporation is a parent corporation that franchises automobile lube-and-oil-change centers around the United States. The standard set forth by Bell is that the average time to lube and change oil in a car is 10 minutes or less.

Periodically, Bell representatives visit the franchises and perform a compliance test on this standard. They randomly select 15 cars (without the local operator's knowledge) and record how long it takes to service each car. Then, based on the sample mean, they will determine whether the franchise is operating within the standard.

a. Establish the appropriate null and alternative hypotheses.

b. Determine the decision rule, assuming that the company performs the compliance test using a significance level of 0.05.

c. Determine if the franchise is operating within its standard if the sample average service time is 10.30 minutes and standard deviation = 2.0 minutes.

8.69 The maker of Quick Lite, ready-to-light charcoal briquettes, bases its claim to fame on the premise that its product, on average, will ignite within three tries. A consumer-awareness group would like to test the charcoal maker's claim and reach its own opinion about the product.

A sample of 20 buyers was asked to use the charcoal and record how many times it took before the briquettes caught fire. The sample revealed that an average of 3.15 tries, with a sample standard deviation of 0.2, was the norm.

a. Testing at a significance level of 0.05, decide what the consumer group should conclude about Quick Lite's claim.

b. Which type of error associated with hypothesis tests would the consumer-awareness group be most interested in avoiding? Explain your reasoning.

8.70 A manufacturer of computer monitors claims that its product will last at least 50 weeks on average without needing repairs. The Quast Corporation is considering purchasing a great many of these computer monitors. However, it does not wish to purchase the computer monitors if the manufacturer's claim is untrue. A Quast data-processing manager has determined that, given the price of the monitor and the total dollars involved, Quast should ask for some quality control records from the manufacturer.

Suppose the manufacturer produces records of a random sample of 30 monitors. The average time before the first breakdown was 48 weeks, with a standard deviation equal to 12 weeks.

a. Establish the appropriate null and alternative hypotheses.

b. Determine the appropriate decision rule and indicate whether the sample information justifies rejecting the manufacturer's claim. Use a significance level of 0.05.

c. Discuss the ramifications of this decision and the potential costs of being wrong.

d. Which type of hypothesis test error would Quast be most interested in avoiding? Explain your reasons.

Advanced Business Applications

8.71 The Softsoap Company recently developed a new soap product designed for use in automatic washing machines. The marketing department would like to claim in its advertisements that the new soap will save the average homeowner at least 10 ounces of soap per month. Before setting up the advertising plan, it decided to test the product in a random sample of 70 homes for a period of one month. The selected homeowners were asked to record how much soap they had used the previous month. Then they were asked to keep track of their soap usage with the new Softsoap product, while keeping their washing procedures the same as before the test.

a. Establish the null and alternative hypotheses to be tested, considering the objectives of the marketing department.

b. Assuming that the population standard deviation is known to be 3 ounces saved per month, what is the decision rule for the hypothesis test if the test is to be conducted with a significance level of 0.10?

c. Suppose the sample shows that the average savings is 9.5 ounces. What conclusion should the Softsoap marketing department reach with respect to its desired advertising claim? Discuss.

d. With respect to the decision reached in part c, comment on which statistical error may have been committed and what it would mean to the Softsoap Company.

8.72 The Rainbow Company operates coin-operated candy machines in Lincoln, Nebraska. When the company started using the so-called "talking" machines, it expected daily revenue per machine to exceed $63, on the average. Suppose a sample of 100 machines was selected in the Lincoln area over a period of time after the new machines were installed and the average revenue per machine was $66.05 with a standard deviation of $12.40.

a. Formulate the appropriate null and alternative hypotheses for this situation.

b. Establish the critical value and decision rule using the z-value approach, assuming the significance level is 0.05.

c. Determine if the Rainbow Company's expectations have been met.

d. If the average daily revenue were in fact $63, determine the probability that the sample mean would be at most $66.05. Give the statistical term that refers to the probability calculated.

8.73 ⊙ The Inland Empire Food Store Company has stated in its advertising that the average shopper will save more than $3.00 per week by shopping at Inland stores. A consumer group has decided to test this assertion by sampling 50 shoppers who currently shop at other stores. It selects the customers and then notes each item purchased at their regular store. These same items are then priced at an Inland store, and the total bill is compared. The data in a file called *Inland Foods* on the CD-ROM reflect savings at Inland for the 50 shoppers. Those cases in which the bill was higher at Inland are marked with a minus sign.

a. Set up the appropriate null and alternative hypotheses to test Inland's claim.

b. Using a significance level of 0.05, develop the decision rule and test the hypothesis. Can Inland Empire support its advertising claim?

c. Which type of hypothesis error would the consumer group be most interested in controlling? Which type of hypothesis error would the company be most interested in controlling? Explain your reasoning.

8.74 The Falcon Speed-Reading Course advertises that the average increase in reading speed for graduates of the course is more than 200 words per minute.

a. What should an independent reviewer conclude if a sample of 15 graduates showed an average improvement of 210 words per minute, with a standard deviation equal to 40? Test at the significance level of 0.10.

b. Consider the facts that you do not know the population's standard deviation and that the sample size is small. What assumption must you make concerning the population to validate your analysis in part a?

c. Suppose the sample standard deviation is 20 words per minute rather than 40. Assuming that the sample mean and the significance level are unchanged, what conclusion should be reached with respect to the speed-reading course offered by Falcon?

d. Discuss why the change in standard deviation would have this effect on the conclusion reached, considering that the sample mean did not change.

8.75 The Cajun King restaurant manager is thinking about running a coupon advertisement in the local newspaper offering a free soft drink with the purchase of a meal. He hopes that more than 30% of the coupons will be redeemed. Before running the ad, he has a student group at a local high school distribute 200 coupons to a random sample of homes in the market area. Seventy-four coupons are redeemed.

a. What should the owner conclude concerning his preconception of the redemption rate, assuming that the test is based on a significance level of 0.10? Be sure to state the appropriate null and alternative hypotheses.

b. Construct a 90% confidence interval for the proportion of coupons that will be redeemed. Suppose it costs the owner of Cajun King 10 cents for each free soft drink and that he distributes 5,000 coupons. Determine the minimum and maximum cost of the free drink offer to the owner.

8.76 A story ran recently in a major newspaper that claimed that more than 70% of all employees call in sick at least one time a year when they are not actually sick. The story described this as a way for employees to get extra vacation days. Suppose a follow-up study is conducted in which 400 employees are selected at random and asked (confidentially) to indicate whether they had called in sick when they were not sick during the past year. A total of 292 employees admit that they had done this.

a. State the appropriate null and alternative hypotheses to test the claim made in the newspaper story.

b. Based on the sample data and a significance level of 0.05, what should be concluded about the newspaper's claim? Use the *p*-value approach to test the hypothesis.

8.77 Assuming the data in the CD-ROM file *Cities* is a random sample of cities in the United States, use this data to test an economist's claim that the average of 1998 white-collar earnings in U.S. cities was less than $25,000. Testing at a significance level of 0.05, do these sample data support or refute this contention? Discuss your results.

8.78 Referring to Exercise 8.77, the same economist has claimed that the average manufacturing salary in U.S. cities in 1998 exceeded $26,100. Based on the sample data, can this claim be supported or refuted at a significance level of 0.05? Discuss your conclusion.

8.79 A market research company was recently hired to conduct a survey of cell phone owners to determine whether the Nokia brand had a market share greater than 35%. Use the sample data contained in the file *Cell Phone Survey* to reach a conclusion, using a significance level of 0.05. Be sure to state the null and alternative hypotheses.

8.80 A study was conducted by the State Transportation Department to determine whether a weigh-in-motion (WIM) scale could be used in place of the static scale currently used at port-of-entry (POE) locations across the state. The WIM scale weighs trucks as they drive over a scale, rather than making them stop at a POE to be weighed. It is thought that the mean speed of trucks crossing the WIM scale would be less than the posted speed limit of 65 miles per hour.

a. Based on the sample data in the file *Trucks*, what conclusion can be reached concerning the preconception about the average speed? Test at an $\alpha = 0.10$.

b. A published report indicates the WIM scale average truck length on the state highway exceeds 60 feet. Based on the sample data, can this claim be supported or refuted? Test at an $\alpha = 0.05$.

c. Compute a new variable that is the difference between X_7 and X_4. It is thought that, if the WIM scale were effective, the average difference would be 0. Based on these sample data, what can be concluded? Test at an $\alpha = 0.05$.

CASE 8-A:

Campbell Brewery, Inc., Part 1

Don Campbell and his younger brother, Edward, purchased Campbell Brewery from their father in 1983. The brewery makes and bottles beer under two labels and distributes it throughout the Southwest. Since purchasing the brewery, Don has been instrumental in modernizing operations.

One of the latest acquisitions is a filling machine that can be adjusted to fill at any average fill level desired. Because the bottles and cans filled by the brewery are exclusively the 12-ounce size, when they received the machine Don set the fill level to 12 ounces and left it that way. According to the manufacturer's specifications, the machine will fill bottles or cans around the average, with a standard deviation of 0.15 ounce.

Don just returned from a brewery convention in which he attended a panel discussion related to problems with filling machines. One brewery representative discussed a problem her company had. It failed to learn that its machine's average fill went out of adjustment until several months later, when its cost accounting department reported some problems with beer production in bulk not matching output in bottles and cans. It turns out that the machine's average fill had increased from 12 ounces to 12.07 ounces. With large volumes of production, this deviation meant a substantial loss in profits.

Another brewery reported the same type of problem, but in the opposite direction. Its machine began filling bottles with slightly less than 12 ounces on the average. Although the consumers could not detect the shortage in a given bottle, the state and federal agencies responsible for checking the accuracy of packaged products discovered the problem in their testing and substantially fined the brewery for the underfill.

These problems were a surprise to Don Campbell. He had not considered the possibility that the machine might go out of adjustment and pose these types of problems. In fact, he became very concerned because the problems of losing profits and potentially being fined by the government were ones that he wished to avoid, if possible. After the convention, Don and Ed decided to hire a consulting firm with expertise in these matters to assist them in setting up a procedure for monitoring the performance of the filling machine.

The consultant suggested that they set up a sampling plan in which once a month they would sample some number of bottles and measure their volumes precisely. If the average of the sample deviated too much from 12 ounces, they would shut the machine down and make the necessary adjustments. Otherwise, they would let the filling process continue. The consultant identified two types of problems that could occur from this sort of sampling plan:

1. They might incorrectly decide to adjust the machine when it was not really necessary to do so.
2. They might incorrectly decide to allow the filling process to continue when, in fact, the true average had deviated from 12 ounces.

After carefully considering what the consultant told them, Don indicated that he wanted no more than a 0.02 chance of the first problem occurring because of the costs involved. He also decided that if the true average fill had slipped to 11.99 ounces, he wanted no more than a 0.05 chance of not detecting this with his sampling plan. He wanted to avoid problems with state and federal agencies. Finally, if the true average fill had actually risen to 12.007 ounces, he wanted to be able to detect this 98% of the time with his sampling plan. Thus, he wanted to avoid the lost profits that would result from such a problem.

In addition, Don needs to determine how large a sample size is necessary to meet his requirements.

General References

1. Berenson, Mark L., and David M. Levine, *Basic Business Statistics Concepts and Applications*, 7th ed. (Upper Saddle River, NJ: Prentice Hall, 1999).
2. Dodge, Mark, and Craig Stinson, *Running Microsoft Excel 2000* (Redmond, WA: Microsoft Press, 1999).
3. Hogg, Robert V., and Elliot A. Tanis, *Probability and Statistical Inference*, 5th ed. (Upper Saddle River, NJ: Prentice Hall, 1997).
4. Marx, Morris L., and Richard J. Larsen, *Mathematical Statistics and Its Applications*, 3rd ed. (Upper Saddle River, NJ: Prentice Hall, 2000).
5. *Microsoft Excel 2000* (Redmond, WA: Microsoft Corp., 1999).
6. *Minitab for Windows Version 13* (State College, PA: Minitab, 2000).
7. Siegel, Andrew F., *Practical Business Statistics*, 4th ed. (Burr Ridge, IL: Irwin, 2000).

CHAPTER 9

Estimation and Hypothesis Testing for Two Population Parameters

CHAPTER OUTCOMES

After studying the material in Chapter 9, you should be able to:

- Discuss the logic behind, and demonstrate the techniques for, using sample data to test hypotheses and develop interval estimates about the difference between two population means for both independent and paired samples.
- Carry out hypothesis tests and establish interval estimates, using sample data, for the difference between two population proportions.

WHY YOU NEED TO KNOW

Chapter 8 introduced the concepts of hypothesis testing and illustrated its application through examples involving a single population parameter. However, in many business decision-making situations, managers must decide between two or more alternatives. For example, farmers must decide which of several brands and types of wheat to plant. Fleet managers in large companies must decide which model and make of car to purchase next year. Airlines must decide whether to purchase replacement planes from Boeing or Airbus. When deciding on a new advertising campaign, a company may need to evaluate proposals from competing advertising agencies. Hiring decisions may require a personnel director to select one employee from a list of applicants. Production managers are often confronted with decisions concerning whether to change a production process or leave it alone. Each day consumers purchase a product from among several competing brands.

The difficulty in such situations is that the decision maker must make the decision based on limited (sample) information. Fortunately, there are statistical tools that can help decision makers use sample information to compare different populations (alternative choices). In this chapter, we introduce these tools and techniques by discussing methods that can be used to make statistical comparisons between two populations. Later, we will discuss some methods to extend this comparison to more than two populations. Whether we are discussing cases involving two populations or those with more than two populations, the techniques we present are all extensions of the statistical tools involving a single population parameter introduced in Chapters 7 and 8.

9-1 ESTIMATION FOR TWO POPULATION MEANS

In this section, we build on the concepts introduced in Chapters 7 and 8 and examine situations in which we are interested in the difference between two population means. We look first at the case where our samples from the two populations are **independent**.

Independent Samples

Samples selected from two or more populations in such a way that the occurrence of values in one sample has no influence on the probability of the occurrence of values in the other sample(s).

We will introduce techniques for estimating the difference between two population means in the following situations:

1. The population standard deviations are known and the samples are large and independent.
2. The population standard deviations are unknown and the samples are large and independent.
3. The population standard deviations are unknown and the samples are small and independent.
4. The samples are not independent.

ESTIMATING THE DIFFERENCE BETWEEN TWO MEANS WHEN σ_1 AND σ_2 ARE KNOWN, LARGE INDEPENDENT SAMPLES

Recall that in our Chapter 7 discussion of estimation involving a single population mean we introduced procedures that applied when the population standard deviation was assumed to be known. The standard normal distribution z-values were used in establishing the critical value and developing the interval estimate. The general format for a confidence interval estimate is shown in Equation 9-1. This same format applies when we are interested in estimating the difference between two population means.

Confidence Interval, General Format

$$\text{Point Estimate} \pm (\text{Critical Value})(\text{Standard Error})$$ **9-1**

You will often be interested in estimating the difference between two population means. For instance, you may wish to estimate the difference in mean starting salaries between males and females, the difference in mean production in union and nonunion factories, or the difference in mean service times at two different fast-food businesses. In these situations, the best point estimate for $\mu_1 - \mu_2$ is

$$\text{Point Estimate} = \bar{x}_1 - \bar{x}_2$$

When large independent samples are selected ($n_1 \geq 30$ and $n_2 \geq 30$) and when the population standard deviations are known, the critical value will be a z-value from the standard normal table for the desired level of confidence. Under these same conditions, Equation 9-2 gives the standard error of the sampling distribution.

Standard Error of $\bar{x}_1 - \bar{x}_2$ When σ_1 and σ_2 Are Known

$$\sigma_{\bar{x}_1 - \bar{x}_2} = \sqrt{\frac{\sigma_1^2}{n_1} + \frac{\sigma_2^2}{n_2}}$$

9-2

where:

$$\sigma_1^2 = \text{variance of population 1}$$
$$\sigma_2^2 = \text{variance of population 2}$$
$$n_1 \text{ and } n_2 = \text{sample sizes from populations 1 and 2}$$

Then the confidence interval estimate for the difference between the two population means when σ_1 and σ_2 are known is given by Equation 9-3.

Confidence Interval Estimate for $\mu_1 - \mu_2$ When σ_1 and σ_2 Are Known, Large Independent Samples

$$(\bar{x}_1 - \bar{x}_2) \pm z_{\alpha/2} \sqrt{\frac{\sigma_1^2}{n_1} + \frac{\sigma_2^2}{n_2}}$$

9-3

$\mathcal{E}$XAMPLE 9-1: CONFIDENCE INTERVAL ESTIMATE FOR $\mu_1 - \mu_2$ WHEN σ_1 AND σ_2 ARE KNOWN, LARGE INDEPENDENT SAMPLES

Crawford & Associates   Crawford & Associates was recently retained to survey customers of one of the nation's largest food chains to estimate the difference in mean time spent in the store per visit between men and women shoppers. Previous studies indicate that the standard deviation is 11 minutes for males and 16 minutes for females. To develop a 95% confidence interval estimate, the following steps are taken.

Step 1:   Define the population value of interest.
In this case, the company is interested in estimating the difference in mean time spent in the store between males and females. The measure of interest is $\mu_1 - \mu_2$.

Step 2:   Specify the desired confidence level and determine the critical value.
The interval estimate will be developed using a 95% confidence interval. Because the population standard deviations are known, the critical value is a z-value from the standard normal table. The critical value is

$$z_{\alpha/2} = z_{0.025} = 1.96.$$

Step 3:   Select independent samples from the two populations and compute the point estimate.
The company has selected simple random samples of 100 males and 100 females at different times in different stores owned by the food chain. The resulting sample means are

Males: $\bar{x}_1 = 34.5$ minutes   Females: $\bar{x}_2 = 42.4$ minutes

The point estimate is

$$\bar{x}_1 - \bar{x}_2 = 34.5 - 42.4 = -7.9 \text{ minutes}$$

Women spent 7.9 minutes longer, on average, shopping at the stores.

Step 4:   **Develop the confidence interval estimate using Equation 9-3.**

$$(\bar{x}_1 - \bar{x}_2) \pm z_{\alpha/2} \sqrt{\frac{\sigma_1^2}{n_1} + \frac{\sigma_2^2}{n_2}}$$

$$-7.9 \pm 1.96 \sqrt{\frac{11^2}{100} + \frac{16^2}{100}}$$

$$-7.9 \pm 3.8056$$

The 95% confidence interval estimate for the difference in mean time spent in the chain's food stores between men and women is

$$-11.7056 \text{ minutes} \text{ -----------------} -4.0944 \text{ minutes}$$

Thus, based on the sample data, women spend on average between 4.09 and 11.71 minutes more at the food stores.

ESTIMATING THE DIFFERENCE BETWEEN TWO MEANS WHEN σ_1 AND σ_2 ARE UNKNOWN, LARGE INDEPENDENT SAMPLES

In most situations in which we need to estimate the difference between two population means, we will not know the values for the two population standard deviations. Instead, we will estimate σ_1 and σ_2 using s_1 and s_2, computed from samples selected from the two populations. If the samples are large enough (n_1 and $n_2 \geq 30$), the confidence interval estimate for the difference between the two population means is computed using Equation 9-4.

Confidence Interval Estimate for $\mu_1 - \mu_2$ When σ_1 and σ_2 Are Unknown, Large Independent Samples

$$(\bar{x}_1 - \bar{x}_2) \pm z_{\alpha/2} \sqrt{\frac{s_1^2}{n_1} + \frac{s_2^2}{n_2}} \qquad \text{9-4}$$

$\mathcal{E}$**XAMPLE 9-2:** CONFIDENCE INTERVAL ESTIMATE FOR $\mu_1 - \mu_2$ WHEN σ_1 AND σ_2 ARE UNKNOWN, LARGE INDEPENDENT SAMPLES

Holland Realty   The lead broker at Holland Realty is interested in estimating the mean difference in the number of days that homes stay on the market before selling in San Francisco versus Atlanta. To do this, he has selected a simple random sample of 60 homes in each city. The following steps can be used to estimate the difference between the two population means.

Step 1:   **Specify the population value of interest.**
The objective here is to estimate the difference in the mean times houses stay on the market in the two cities. The parameter of interest is $\mu_1 - \mu_2$.

Step 2:   **Specify the desired confidence level and determine the critical value.**
The broker wishes to have a 99% confidence interval estimate. Because the samples are large, the critical value will be a z-value from the standard normal distribution. The critical z-value is

$$z_{\alpha/2} = z_{0.005} = 2.575.$$

Step 3:   **Select independent samples from the two populations and compute the point estimate.**
Because the broker has selected simple random samples of 60 homes in San Francisco and 60 in Atlanta, the samples are independent. The resulting sample means and sample standard deviations are

San Francisco: $\bar{x}_1 = 39.4$ days   Atlanta: $\bar{x}_2 = 36.1$ days
$s_1 = 5$ days $s_2 = 4.3$ days

The point estimate is $\bar{x}_1 - \bar{x}_2 = 39.4 - 36.1 = 3.3$ days.

Step 4: **Develop the confidence interval estimate using Equation 9-4.**

$$(\bar{x}_1 - \bar{x}_2) \pm z_{\alpha/2}\sqrt{\frac{s_1^2}{n_1} + \frac{s_2^2}{n_2}}$$

$$3.3 \pm 2.575\sqrt{\frac{5^2}{60} + \frac{4.3^2}{60}}$$

$$3.3 \pm 2.192$$

Thus, the 99% confidence interval estimate for the difference in mean times that homes spend on the market in San Francisco and Atlanta is

1.108 days ---------------------- 5.492 days

ESTIMATING THE DIFFERENCE BETWEEN TWO MEANS WHEN σ_1 AND σ_2 ARE UNKNOWN, SMALL INDEPENDENT SAMPLES

In Chapter 7, you learned that when estimating a single population mean when the population standard deviation is unknown and the sample sizes are small, the critical value is a t-value from the t-distribution. This is also the case when you are interested in estimating the difference between two population means, if three conditions hold:

- The populations are normally distributed.
- The populations have equal variances.
- The samples are independent.

The following application illustrates how a confidence interval estimate is developed using the t-distribution.

Retirement Investing—A major political issue for the past decade has focused on the long-term future of the U.S. Social Security system. Many people who have entered the workforce in the past 20 years believe the system will not be solvent when they retire, so they are actively investing in their own retirement accounts. One investment alternative is a tax-sheltered annuity (TSA) marketed by life insurance companies. Certain people, depending on occupation, qualify to invest part of their paychecks in a TSA and pay no federal income tax on this money until it is withdrawn. While the money is invested, the insurance companies invest it in either stock or bond portfolios. A second alternative open to many people is a plan known as a 401(k), in which employees contribute a portion of their paychecks to purchase stocks, bonds, or mutual funds. In some cases, employers match all or part of the employee contributions. In many 401(k) systems, the employees can control how their funds are invested.

A recent study in North Carolina was interested in estimating the difference in mean annual contributions for individuals covered by the two plans [TSA or 401(k)]. A simple random sample of 15 people from the population of adults who are eligible for a TSA investment was selected. A second sample of 15 people was selected from the population of adults in North Carolina who have 401(k) plans. The variable of interest is the dollar amount of money invested in the retirement plan during the previous year. Specifically, we are interested in estimating $\mu_1 - \mu_2$ using a 95% confidence interval estimate where:

μ_1 = Mean dollars invested by the TSA-eligible population during the past year
μ_2 = Mean dollars invested by the 401(k)-eligible population during the past year

The sample results are

TSA-Eligible	401(k)-Eligible
$n_1 = 15$	$n_2 = 15$
$\bar{x}_1 = \$2,119.70$	$\bar{x}_2 = \$1,777.70$
$s_1 = \$709.70$	$s_2 = \$593.90$

Before applying the t-distribution, we need to determine whether the assumptions are likely to be satisfied. First, the samples are considered independent because the amount invested by one group should have no influence on the amount invested by the other.

FIGURE 9-1

**Investment Study—Sample
Information**

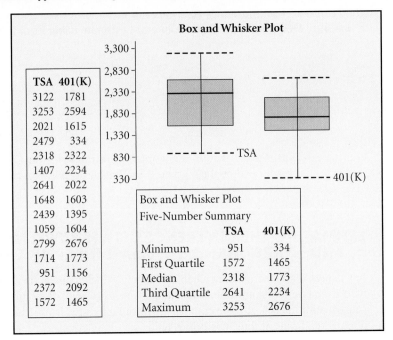

Next, Figure 9-1 shows the sample data and the box and whisker diagrams for the two samples. These diagrams exhibit characteristics that are reasonably consistent with those that might be associated with normal distributions and approximately equal variances. While using a box and whisker plot to check the *t*-distribution assumptions may seem to be imprecise, fortunately studies have shown the *t*-distribution to be applicable even when there are small violations of the assumptions. This is particularly the case when the sample sizes are approximately equal.[1]

Equation 9-5 can be used to develop the confidence interval estimate for the difference between two population means when you have small independent samples.[2]

Confidence Interval Estimate for $\mu_1 - \mu_2$ When σ_1 and σ_2 Are Unknown, Small Independent Samples

$$(\bar{x}_1 - \bar{x}_2) \pm t_{\alpha/2}s_p\sqrt{\frac{1}{n_1} + \frac{1}{n_2}}$$

9-5

where:

$$s_p = \sqrt{\frac{(n_1 - 1)s_1^2 + (n_2 - 1)s_2^2}{n_1 + n_2 - 2}} = \text{pooled standard deviation}$$

$t_{\alpha/2}$ = critical *t*-value from the *t*-distribution, with degrees of freedom equal to $n_1 + n_2 - 2$

To use Equation 9-5, we must compute the pooled standard deviation, s_p. If the equal-variance assumption holds, then both s_1^2 and s_2^2 are estimators of the same population variance, σ^2. To only use one of these, say s_1^2, to estimate σ^2 would be disregarding the information obtained from the other sample. To use the average of s_1^2 and s_2^2, if the sample sizes were different, would ignore the fact that more information about σ^2 is obtained from the sample having the larger sample size. We therefore, use a weighted average of s_1^2 and s_2^2, denoted as s_p^2 to estimate σ^2, where the weights are

---

[1]Chapter 10 introduces a statistical procedure for testing whether two populations have equal variances. Chapter 12 provides a statistical procedure for testing whether a population is normally distributed.

[2]Note: Anytime the population standard deviations are unknown, the technically correct approach is to use the *t*-distribution as shown in Equation 9-5. However many authors suggest using the *z*-distribution and Equation 9-4 when both n_1 and $n_2 \geq 30$ based on the Central Limit Theorem.

the degrees of freedom associated with each sample. The square root of s_p^2 is known as the *pooled standard deviation* and is computed using:

$$s_p = \sqrt{\frac{(n_1 - 1)s_1^2 + (n_2 - 1)s_2^2}{n_1 + n_2 - 2}}$$

Notice that the sample size we have available to estimate σ^2 is $n_1 + n_2$. However, to produce s_p, we must first calculate s_1^2 and s_2^2. This requires that we estimate μ_1 and μ_2 using $\bar{x}_1$ and $\bar{x}_2$, respectively. The degrees of freedom are equal to the sample size minus the parameters estimated before the variance estimate is obtained. Therefore, our degrees of freedom must equal $n_1 + n_2 - 2$.

For the retirement investing example, the pooled standard deviation is:

$$s_p = \sqrt{\frac{(n_1 - 1)s_1^2 + (n_2 - 1)s_2^2}{n_1 + n_2 - 2}} = \sqrt{\frac{(15 - 1)(709.7)^2 + (15 - 1)(593.9)^2}{15 + 15 - 2}} = 654.37$$

The critical t-value for

$$n_1 + n_2 - 2 = 15 + 15 - 2 = 28$$

degrees of freedom and 95% confidence is

$$t_{\alpha/2} = 2.0484.$$

Now we can develop the interval estimate using Equation 9-5.

$$(\bar{x}_1 - \bar{x}_2) \pm t_{\alpha/2} s_p \sqrt{\frac{1}{n_1} + \frac{1}{n_2}}$$

$$(2119.70 - 1777.70) \pm 2.0484(654.37) \sqrt{\frac{1}{15} + \frac{1}{15}}$$

$$342 \pm 489.45$$

Thus, the 95% confidence interval estimate for the difference in mean dollars for people who invest in a TSA versus those who invest in a 401(k) is

$$-\$147.45 \text{ ------------------ } \$831.45$$

The fact that this interval crosses zero indicates that there may be no difference in the mean investment by the two groups of investors.

ℰXAMPLE 9-3: CONFIDENCE INTERVAL ESTIMATE FOR $\mu_1 - \mu_2$ WHEN σ_1 AND σ_2 ARE UNKNOWN, SMALL INDEPENDENT SAMPLES

Sneva Pharmaceutical Research The head of research and development at Sneva Pharmaceutical Research is interested in estimating the difference between males and females with respect to the mean time from when a patient takes a new medication until the medication can be detected in the blood. A simple random sample of six males and eight females participated in the study. The estimate can be developed using the following steps.

Step 1: **Define the population value of interest.**
The objective here is to estimate the difference in mean time between males and females with respect to the speed at which the medication reaches the blood. The parameter of interest is $\mu_1 - \mu_2$.

Step 2: **Select independent samples from the two populations, verify that the assumptions are satisfied, and compute the point estimate.**
The research lab has selected simple random samples of six males and eight females. Because the impact of the medication in one person does not influence the impact in another person, the samples are independent. The resulting sample means and sample standard deviations are

Males: $\bar{x}_1 = 13.6$ minutes   Females: $\bar{x}_2 = 11.2$ minutes

$s_1 = 3.1$ minutes $s_2 = 5.0$ minutes

Although not shown here, the box and whisker diagrams were not inconsistent with the normal distribution and equal variance assumptions.

Step 3:   **Compute the point estimate.**

The point estimate is

$$\bar{x}_1 - \bar{x}_2 = 13.6 - 11.2 = 2.4 \text{ minutes.}$$

Step 4:   **Specify the desired confidence level and determine the critical value.**

The research manager wishes to have a 95% confidence interval estimate. Because the samples are small, the critical value will be a t-value from the t-distribution as long as the population variances are equal and the populations are normally distributed.

Because we have established that the assumptions are reasonable in this case, we can use the t-distribution to obtain the critical value. The critical t for 95% confidence and $6 + 8 - 2 = 12$ degrees of freedom is

$$t_{\alpha/2} = 2.1788.$$

Step 5:   **Develop a confidence interval using Equation 9-5.**

$$(\bar{x}_1 - \bar{x}_2) \pm t_{\alpha/2} s_p \sqrt{\frac{1}{n_1} + \frac{1}{n_2}}$$

where:

$$s_p = \sqrt{\frac{(n_1 - 1)s_1^2 + (n_2 - 1)s_2^2}{n_1 + n_2 - 2}} = \sqrt{\frac{(6 - 1)3.1^2 + (8 - 1)5^2}{6 + 8 - 2}} = 4.31$$

Then the interval estimate is

$$2.4 \pm 2.1788(4.31)\sqrt{\frac{1}{6} + \frac{1}{8}}$$

$$2.4 \pm 5.0715$$

$$-2.6715 \text{ ------------------------------- } 7.4715$$

Because the interval crosses zero, the research manager cannot conclude that a difference exists between males and females with respect to the mean time needed for the medication to be detected in the blood.

What If the Population Variances Are Not Equal?

If you have reason to believe that the population variances are substantially different, Equation 9-5 is not appropriate for computing the confidence interval. Instead of computing the pooled standard deviation as part of the confidence interval formula, we use Equation 9-6.

Confidence Interval for the Difference Between Two Means When σ_1 and σ_2 Are Unknown and Not Equal, Small Independent Samples

$$(\bar{x}_1 - \bar{x}_2) \pm t_{\alpha/2} \sqrt{\frac{s_1^2}{n_1} + \frac{s_2^2}{n_2}} \qquad \text{9-6}$$

where:

$t_{\alpha/2} = t$-value from the t-distribution with degrees of freedom computed using:

$$df = \frac{(s_1^2/n_1 + s_2^2/n_2)^2}{\left(\dfrac{(s_1^2/n_1)^2}{n_1 - 1} + \dfrac{(s_2^2/n_2)^2}{n_2 - 1} \right)}$$

INTERVAL ESTIMATION FOR PAIRED SAMPLES

The previous examples in this section introduced the methods by which decision makers can estimate the difference between the means for two populations when the two samples are independent. In each example, the samples were independent because the sample values from one population did not have the potential to influence the probability that values would be selected from the second population.

However, there are instances in business in which you would want to use **paired samples** to control for sources of variation that might otherwise distort the conclusions of a study.

Paired Samples

Samples that are selected in such a way that values in one sample are matched with the values in the second sample for the purpose of controlling for extraneous factors. Another term for paired samples is dependent samples.

Testing Engine Oil

—A major oil company wanted to estimate the difference in average mileage for cars using a regular engine oil compared with cars using a synthetic-oil product. The company used a paired-sample approach to control any variation in mileage arising because of different cars and drivers. A random sample of 10 motorists (and their cars) was selected. Each car was filled with gasoline, the oil was drained and new, regular oil was added. The car was driven 200 miles on a specified route. The car then was filled with gasoline and the miles per gallon were computed. After the 10 cars completed this process, the same steps were performed using synthetic oil. Because the same cars and drivers tested both types of oil, the miles-per-gallon measurements for synthetic oil and regular engine oil will most likely be related. The two samples are not independent, but are instead considered paired samples. Thus, we will compute d, the **paired difference** between the values from each sample, using Equation 9-7.

Paired Difference

$$d = x_1 - x_2$$

9-7

where:

d = Paired difference

x_1 and x_2 = Values from sample 1 and 2, respectively

FIGURE 9-2

Excel Worksheet for Engine Oil Study

Excel Instructions:
1. Open file: Engine Oil.xls

Figure 9-2 shows the Excel spreadsheet for this engine oil study with the paired differences computed. The data are in the file on your CD-ROM called *Engine-Oil*.

The first step to develop the interval estimate is to compute the *mean paired difference*, $\bar{d}$, using Equation 9-8. This value is the best point estimate for the population mean paired difference, μ_d.

Point Estimate for the Population Mean Paired Difference, μ_d

$$\bar{d} = \frac{\sum_{i=1}^{n} d_i}{n}$$

9-8

where:

d_i = ith paired difference value

n = Number of paired differences

Using Equation 9-8, we determine $\bar{d}$ as follows.

$$\bar{d} = \frac{\sum d}{n} = \frac{22.7}{10} = 2.27$$

The next step is to compute the sample *standard deviation for the paired differences* using Equation 9-9.

Sample Standard Deviation for Paired Differences

$$s_d = \sqrt{\frac{\sum_{i=1}^{n} (d_i - \bar{d})^2}{n-1}}$$

9-9

where:

$d_i = i$th paired difference
$\bar{d} = $ Mean paired difference

The sample standard deviation for the paired differences is

$$s_d = \sqrt{\frac{\sum (d - \bar{d})^2}{n-1}} = \sqrt{\frac{172.8}{10-1}} = 4.38$$

Assuming that the population of paired differences is normally distributed, the confidence interval estimate for the population mean paired difference is computed using Equation 9-10.

Confidence Interval Estimate for Population Mean Paired Difference, μ_d

$$\bar{d} \pm t_{\alpha/2} \frac{s_d}{\sqrt{n}}$$

9-10

where:

$t_{\alpha/2} = $ Critical t-value from t-distribution with $n-1$ degrees of freedom
$\bar{d} = $ Sample mean paired difference
$s_d = $ Sample standard deviation of paired differences
$n = $ Number of paired differences (sample size)

For a 95% confidence interval with $10 - 1 = 9$ degrees of freedom, we use a critical t from the t-distribution of

$$t_{\alpha/2} = 2.2622$$

The interval estimate obtained from Equation 9-10 is

$$\bar{d} \pm t_{\alpha/2} \frac{s_d}{\sqrt{n}}$$

$$2.27 \pm 2.2622 \frac{4.38}{\sqrt{10}}$$

$$2.27 \pm 3.13$$

$$-.86 \text{ mpg} \text{ -------------------------- } 5.40 \text{ mpg}$$

EXAMPLE 9-4: CONFIDENCE INTERVAL ESTIMATE FOR μ_d

Golf Ball Testing   Technology has done more to change golf than possibly any other sport in recent years. Titanium woods and irons and new golf ball designs have impacted professional and amateur golfers alike. A maker of golf balls has developed a new ball technology and is interested in estimating the mean difference in driving distance for this new ball versus its existing best-seller. To conduct the test, the developers selected six professional golfers and had each golfer hit each ball one time. Here are the steps necessary to develop a confidence interval estimate for the mean paired difference.

Step 1:   **Define the population value of interest.**
Because the same golfers hit each golf ball, the company is controlling for the variation in the golfers' ability to hit a golf ball. The samples are paired, and the population value of interest is μ_d, the mean paired difference in distance. We assume that the population of paired differences is normally distributed.

Step 2: **Specify the desired confidence level and determine the appropriate critical value.** For a 95% confidence interval, the critical value is a t-value from the t-distribution with $n - 1 = 5$ degrees of freedom. From the t-table, we get
$$t_{\alpha/2} = 2.5706$$

Step 3: **Collect the sample data and compute the point estimate, $\bar{d}$, and the standard deviation, s_d.**
The sample data, paired differences, are shown as follows.

Golfer	Existing Ball	New Ball	d
1	278	285	−7
2	299	301	−2
3	280	276	4
4	295	300	−5
5	268	273	−5
6	301	299	2

The point estimate is computed using Equation 9-8.

$$\bar{d} = \frac{\sum d}{n} = \frac{-13}{6} = -2.17 \text{ yards}$$

The standard deviation for the paired differences is computed using Equation 9-9.

$$s_d = \sqrt{\frac{\sum(d - \bar{d})^2}{n - 1}} = 4.36 \text{ yards}$$

Step 4: **Compute the confidence interval estimate using Equation 9-10.**

$$\bar{d} \pm t_{\alpha/2} \frac{s_d}{\sqrt{n}}$$
$$-2.17 \pm 2.5706 \frac{4.36}{\sqrt{6}}$$
$$-2.17 \pm 4.58$$
$$-6.75 \text{ yards} \text{----------------} 2.41 \text{ yards}$$

The key in deciding whether to use paired samples is to determine whether a factor exists that might adversely influence the results of the estimation. In the engine-oil test example, we controlled for potential outside influence by using the same cars to test both oils. In Example 9-4, we controlled for golfer ability by having the same golfers hit both golf balls. If you determine that there is no need to control for an outside source of variation, then independent samples should be used, as discussed earlier in this section.

9-1: EXERCISES

Skill Development

9.1 Given the following information:
$$n_1 = 100 \quad n_2 = 150$$
$$\bar{x}_1 = 50 \quad \bar{x}_2 = 65$$
$$s_1 = 6 \quad s_2 = 8$$

a. Determine the 90% confidence interval estimate for the difference between population means. Interpret the estimate.
b. Determine the 98% confidence interval estimate for the difference between population means. Interpret the estimate.

c. What are the advantages and disadvantages of using a higher confidence level to estimate the difference between the two population means?

9.2 Given the following information:

$$n_1 = 25 \qquad n_2 = 25$$
$$\bar{x}_1 = 0.145 \qquad \bar{x}_2 = 0.107$$
$$s_1 = 0.06 \qquad s_2 = 0.08$$

a. Determine the 90% confidence interval estimate for the difference between population means. Interpret the estimate.
b. Determine the 95% confidence interval estimate for the difference between population means. Interpret the estimate.
c. How would the answers to parts a and b differ if the sample sizes were doubled? Discuss what factors affect your answer.

9.3 You are given the following results of a paired difference test:

$$\bar{d} = 344$$
$$s_d = 34$$
$$n = 23$$

a. Construct and interpret a 95% confidence interval estimate for the paired difference in mean values.
b. Construct and interpret a 90% confidence interval estimate for the paired difference in mean values.
c. Discuss why the two estimates are different. What are the advantages and disadvantages of using a lower confidence level?

9.4 You are given the following results of a paired difference test:

$$\bar{d} = -4.6$$
$$s_d = 0.25$$
$$n = 16$$

a. Construct and interpret a 99% confidence interval estimate for the paired difference in mean values.
b. Construct and interpret a 90% confidence interval estimate for the paired difference in mean values.
c. The variances of the two dependent samples are $s_1^2 = 0.060$ and $s_2^2 = 0.065$. Calculate a 90% confidence interval as though the samples were obtained independently. Comment on any differences you see in the two intervals obtained in parts b and c.

9.5 Given the following information:

Sample 1	Sample 2
$n_1 = 36$	$n_2 = 45$
$s_1 = 32$	$s_2 = 80$
$\bar{x}_1 = 2{,}456$	$\bar{x}_2 = 2{,}460$

a. Develop a 90% confidence interval estimate for the difference in the population means.
b. Develop a 98% confidence interval estimate for the difference in the population means.

9.6 Given the following information:

Sample 1	Sample 2
$n_1 = 25$	$n_2 = 20$
$s_1 = 20$	$s_2 = 24$
$\bar{x}_1 = 430$	$\bar{x}_2 = 405$

a. Develop a 95% confidence interval estimate for the difference in the population means.
b. Develop a 99% confidence interval estimate for the difference in the population means.

Business Applications

9.7 Wilson Construction and Concrete Company is known as a very progressive company that is willing to try new ideas to improve its products and service. One of the key factors of importance in concrete work is the time it takes for the concrete to "set up." The company is considering a new additive that can be put in concrete mix to help reduce the set-up time. Before going ahead with the additive, the company tested it against the current additive. To do this, 14 batches of concrete were mixed using each of the additives. The following results were observed:

Old Additive	New Additive
$\bar{x} = 17.2$ hours	$\bar{x} = 15.9$ hours
$s = 2.5$ hours	$s = 1.8$ hours

a. Use these sample data to construct a 90% confidence interval estimate for the difference in mean set-up time for the two concrete additives. On the basis of the confidence interval produced, do you agree that the new additive helps reduce the set-up time for cement? Explain your answer.
b. Assuming that the new additive is slightly more expensive than the old additive, do the data support switching to the new additive if the managers of the company are primarily interested in reducing average set-up time?

9.8 A random sample of 256 credit unions that offer credit cards revealed that the average annual fee charged by credit union was $12.56, with a standard deviation of $2.33. A random sample of 225 federally chartered bank offering credit cards showed that the average annual fee was $22.48, with a standard deviation of $6.18.
a. Construct 90% and 95% confidence interval estimates for the true difference in means between the annual fees charged by credit unions and federally chartered banks.
b. Could the federally chartered banks be accused of having an average annual fee that is $10 more than that of credit unions? Support your answer using your knowledge of probability and statistics.

9.9 ● The ECCO company makes back-up alarms for equipment such as forklifts. As its quality manager, you are concerned about how large the difference is in average warranty claims for products made at the Boise location versus the Atlanta location. Sample warranty data are contained in a file called *ECCO* on your CD-ROM. Develop a 98% confidence interval estimate for the difference in mean warranty amounts for the two locations. Interpret your results. Do these results suggest that the manager needs to focus on one location or the other? Discuss.

9.10 The CD-ROM file *Banks* contains data on a sample of U.S. banks. You are asked to develop a 95% confidence interval estimate for the difference in mean number of employees per bank for banks that had profits greater than $1 billion versus those that had profits less than $1 billion. (Data listed under "Profits" in the data file are in units of thousands of dollars.) Interpret your results. Do these data provide evidence to suggest that there is a difference between the two groups of banks? Discuss. (Hint: You may need to reorganize the data prior to developing the interval estimate.)

9.11 The marketing manager for the Capital Credit Union is considering developing an advertising campaign directed at female credit card customers. However, before continuing, she wants to know what the difference in average credit card balances is between male and female customers. She asked the database manager to select a random sample of 300 customers. These data are in the CD-ROM file *Capital*.
a. Use the sample data to construct a 95% confidence interval estimate for the difference in mean credit card balances for males and females.
b. Interpret the interval estimate and write a business letter to the marketing manager discussing the conclusions that could be reached from this estimate.

9.12 Freedom Hospital is in the midst of contract negotiations with its resident physicians. There has been a lot of discussion about the hospital's ability to pay and the way patients are charged. The doctors' negotiator recently mentioned that the geriatric charge system does not make sense and there may be a difference in the way males are charged versus females. To look into this, the hospital has collected a random sample of patient data for 138 patients. The data are in a CD-ROM file called *Patients*. The operations manager wants to use this data to develop an estimate for the difference in average charges between males and females.
a. Construct a 95% confidence interval estimate for the difference in average charges. What does this imply about how male and female patients are charged? Is there anything to what the negotiator is saying? Discuss.
b. The manager is now interested in estimating the difference between average charges for male and female patients, but only for patients who have Medicare as their principal payer. Construct the 95% confidence interval estimate. Is there a difference in how male and female patients are charged for this group?

Advanced Applications

9.13 The CD-ROM file *Cities* contains a random sample of cities in the United States. Use this sample data to estimate the difference in average SAT scores for city versus suburban dwellers. (Hint: Are the samples independent or paired?)
a. Compute the point estimate for the difference in mean SAT scores. On the basis of this point estimate alone, could you conclude that there are as many as 150 points of difference in the average SAT scores for those living in the suburbs? Explain your answer.
b. Based on the sample data, calculate a 95% confidence interval estimate for the difference between mean SAT scores for city versus suburban dwellers. On the basis of this confidence interval alone, could you conclude that there are as many as 150 points of difference in the average SAT scores for those living in the suburbs? Explain your answer.
c. Referring to part b, suppose the confidence level is changed to 80%. What is the impact on the interval estimate? Discuss why this impact occurred.

9.14 The owner of Fortee Bakery is interested in determining the difference between mean purchase amounts per customer at his two locations. To estimate the difference, he has selected a random sample of 50 customer receipts at each location. The following data are available:

Location 1	Location 2
$\bar{x} = \$5.26$	$\bar{x} = \$6.19$
$s = \$0.89$	$s = \$1.05$

a. What is the point estimate for the difference between mean purchase amounts at the two locations? Comment on the advantages and disadvantages of using a point estimate only in this case?
b. Assuming that the owner wishes to develop a 95% confidence interval estimate for the difference in mean purchase amounts, what will the standard error be?
c. Compute the 95% confidence interval estimate. Determine if there is a difference in the average purchase amounts per customer at his two locations.
d. Referring to parts c and d, suppose the owner wishes to reduce the margin of error, what are his options? Discuss.

9.15 Two companies that manufacture batteries for electronics products have submitted their products to an independent testing agency. The agency tested 200 of each company's batteries and recorded the length of time the batteries lasted before failure. The following results were determined:

Company A	Company B
$\bar{x} = 41.5$ hours	$\bar{x} = 39.0$ hours
$s = 3.6$	$s = 5.0$

a. Based on these data, determine the 95% confidence interval to estimate the difference in average lives of the batteries for the two companies. Do these data indicate that one company's batteries will outlast the other company's batteries on average? Explain.

b. Suppose the manufacturers of each of these batteries wished to warranty their batteries. One small company to which they both ship batteries receives shipments of 200 batteries weekly. If the average length of time to failure of the batteries is less than a specified number, the manufacturer will refund the company's purchase price of that set of batteries. What value should each manufacturer set if they wish to refund money to at most 5% of the shipments?

9.16 Referring to Exercise 9-7, suppose Wilson's managers repeat the test with 14 more batches of concrete, using each additive. They then combined the information from the two tests, giving a sample size of 28 batches. The following results were observed.

Old Additive	New Additive
$\bar{x} = 18.4$ hours	$\bar{x} = 15.2$ hours
$s = 2.9$ hours	$s = 1.6$ hours

a. Use these sample data to construct a 90% confidence interval estimate for the difference in mean set-up time for the two concrete additives. On the basis of this confidence interval, do you agree that the new additive helps reduce the set-up time for cement? Explain your answer.

b. Compare this interval with the one computed in Exercise 9-7. Discuss why the standard error for the estimate is lower when the samples are combined.

c. Assuming that the new additive is slightly more expensive than the old additive, do the data support switching to the new additive if the managers of the company are primarily interested in reducing average set-up time?

9-2 HYPOTHESIS TESTS FOR THE DIFFERENCE BETWEEN TWO POPULATION MEANS

You will encounter many business situations such as those illustrated in Section 9-1, in which you will be interested in the difference between two population means. However, you will also encounter many other situations that will require you to test whether two populations have equal means, or whether one population mean is larger (smaller) than another. These hypothesis-testing applications are just an extension of the hypothesis-testing process introduced in Chapter 8 for a single population mean. They also build directly on the estimation process introduced in Section 9-1.

In this section, we will introduce hypothesis-testing techniques for the difference between two population means in the following situations:

1. The population standard deviations are known and the samples are large and independent.
2. The population standard deviations are not known and the sample sizes are large and independent.
3. The population standard deviations are unknown and the sample sizes are small and independent.
4. The samples are not independent.

SUMMARY: THE HYPOTHESIS-TESTING PROCESS

The hypothesis-testing process for tests involving two population means introduced in this section is essentially the same as for a single population mean. The process is composed of the following steps:

1. Specify the population value of interest.

2. Formulate the appropriate null and alternative hypotheses. The null hypothesis should contain the equality. Possible formats for testing whether two populations have equal means are

$H_0: \mu_1 - \mu_2 = 0.0$ $H_0: \mu_1 - \mu_2 \leq 0.0$ $H_0: \mu_1 - \mu_2 \geq 0.0$

$H_A: \mu_1 - \mu_2 \neq 0.0$ $H_A: \mu_1 - \mu_2 > 0.0$ $H_A: \mu_1 - \mu_2 < 0.0$

two-tailed test   one-tailed test   one-tailed test

3. Specify the significance level (α) for testing the hypothesis. Alpha is the maximum probability of committing a Type I statistical error.

4. Construct the rejection region and develop the decision rule.

5. Compute the test statistic. Of course, you must first select simple random samples from each population and compute the sample means.

6. Reach a decision. Apply the decision rule to determine whether to reject the null hypothesis. Note that you can also compute the p-value and compare it to α.

7. Draw a conclusion.

The logic of all hypothesis tests is that if the sample value (statistic) is "substantially" different from the hypothesized population value (parameter), the null hypothesis should be rejected. If the sample values are consistent with the hypothesized population value, the null hypothesis will not be rejected. Two possible errors can occur:

Type I Error: Rejecting H_0 when it is true. (Alpha error)

Type II Error: Not rejecting H_0 when it is false. (Beta error)

The probability of a Type I error is controlled by the decision maker by the choice of α. Recall from Section 8-3 that α and β are inversely related. If we reduce α, β is increased, assuming everything else remains constant.

The remainder of this section presents examples of hypothesis tests under different situations.

TESTING FOR $\mu_1 - \mu_2$ WHEN σ_1 AND σ_2 ARE KNOWN, LARGE INDEPENDENT SAMPLES

In Section 9-1, we said that *independent samples* occur when the samples from the two populations are taken in such a way that the values in one sample are in no way influenced by the values in the second sample. In special cases in which the population standard deviations are known and the samples are independent, the test statistic is a z-value computed using Equation 9-11.

---

z Test Statistic for $\mu_1 - \mu_2$ When σ_1 and σ_2 Are Known, Large Independent Samples

$$z = \frac{(\bar{x}_1 - \bar{x}_2) - (\mu_1 - \mu_2)}{\sqrt{\dfrac{\sigma_1^2}{n_1} + \dfrac{\sigma_2^2}{n_2}}}$$

9-11

If the calculated z-value using Equation 9-11 exceeds the critical z-value from the standard normal distribution, the null hypothesis is rejected. Example 9-5 illustrates the use of this test statistic.

EXAMPLE 9-5: HYPOTHESIS TEST FOR $\mu_1 - \mu_2$ WHEN σ_1 AND σ_2 ARE KNOWN, LARGE INDEPENDENT SAMPLES

Phillips Systems   Phillips Systems is an Ohio-based company that makes parts for the automotive industry. One part is a bolt used in the engine manifold system. The company has two machines that make these bolts. It is well established that the standard deviation for bolts made by machine one is 0.025 inches and the standard deviation for machine two is 0.034 inches. At question is whether machine 2 also provides bolts with higher average diameters. To test this, you can use these steps.

Step 1: **Specify the population value of interest.**
This is $\mu_1 - \mu_2$, the difference in population means.

Step 2: **Formulate the appropriate null and alternative hypotheses.**
We are interested in determining whether the mean diameter for machine two exceeds that for machine one. The following null and alternative hypotheses are specified:

$$H_0: \mu_1 - \mu_2 \geq 0.0$$
$$H_A: \mu_1 - \mu_2 < 0.0$$

Step 3: **Specify the significance level for the test.**
The test will be conducted using alpha = 0.05.

Step 4: **Determine the rejection region and state the decision rule.**
Because the population standard deviations are assumed to be known, the critical value is a z-value from the standard normal distribution. This test is a one-tailed lower-tail test, with $\alpha = 0.05$. From the standard normal distribution, the critical z-value is

$$z_{0.05} = -1.645$$

The decision rule is

If $z < -1.645$, reject the null hypothesis;
Otherwise, do not reject the null hypothesis.

Alternatively, you can state the decision rule in terms of a p-value, as follows:

If p-value $< \alpha = 0.05$, reject the null hypothesis;
Otherwise, do not reject the null hypothesis.

Step 5:   Compute the test statistic.

Select simple random samples from the two populations and compute the sample means. A simple random sample of 100 bolts is selected from machine one's production, and another simple random sample of 100 bolts is selected from machine two. The samples are independent because the diameters of bolts made by one machine can in no way influence the diameter of bolts made by the other machine. The means computed from the samples are

$$\bar{x}_1 = 0.501 \text{ inches and } \bar{x}_2 = 0.509 \text{ inches}$$

The test statistic is obtained using Equation 9-11.

$$z = \frac{(\bar{x}_1 - \bar{x}_2) - (\mu_1 - \mu_2)}{\sqrt{\dfrac{\sigma_1^2}{n_1} + \dfrac{\sigma_2^2}{n_2}}}$$

$$z = \frac{(0.501 - 0.509) - 0}{\sqrt{\dfrac{0.025^2}{100} + \dfrac{0.034^2}{100}}} = -1.90$$

Step 6:   Reach a decision.

Applying the decision rule,

Because $z = -1.90 < -1.645$, reject the null hypothesis.

Step 7:   Draw a conclusion.

There is statistical evidence to conclude that the bolts made by machine two have a larger mean diameter than those made by machine one.

Using p-values

The z test statistic computed in Example 9-5 indicates the difference in sample means is 1.90 standard errors below the hypothesized difference of zero. Because this falls below the z critical level of -1.645, the null hypothesis was rejected. You could have also tested this hypothesis using the p-value approach introduced in Chapter 8. The p-value for this one-tailed test is the probability of a z-value in a standard normal distribution being less than -1.90. From the standard normal table, the probability associated with $z = -1.90$ is 0.4713. Then the p-value is

$$p\text{-value} = 0.5000 - 0.4713 = 0.0287$$

The decision rule to use with p-values is

If p-value $< \alpha = 0.05$, reject the null hypothesis;
Otherwise, do not reject the null hypothesis.

Because

$$p\text{-value} = 0.0287 < \alpha = 0.05,$$

reject the null hypothesis and conclude that the population means are different.

TESTING $\mu_1 - \mu_2$ WHEN σ_1 AND σ_2 ARE UNKNOWN, LARGE INDEPENDENT SAMPLES

In most hypothesis-testing situations involving two population means, you will not know the population standard deviations. When this occurs, a slight modification in the hypothesis-testing process is required. Specifically, if the sample sizes are large (n_1 and $n_2 \geq 30$), the test statistic for testing whether the population means are equal is a z-value computed using Equation 9-12.

z Test Statistic for $\mu_1 - \mu_2$ When σ_1 and σ_2 Are Unknown, Large Independent Samples

$$z = \frac{(\bar{x}_1 - \bar{x}_2) - (\mu_1 - \mu_2)}{\sqrt{\dfrac{s_1^2}{n_1} + \dfrac{s_2^2}{n_2}}}$$

9-12

The only difference between the test statistics in Equation 9-11 and 9-12 is that when the population standard deviations are unknown, the sample standard deviations (or variances) are used in computing the test statistic. Note that Equation 9-12 is used when the sample sizes are large. We have suggested that both n_1 and n_2 should be at least 30.

$\mathcal{E}$XAMPLE 9-6: HYPOTHESIS TEST FOR $\mu_1 - \mu_2$ WHEN σ_1 AND σ_2 ARE UNKNOWN, LARGE INDEPENDENT SAMPLES

Manchester Cellular   Manchester Cellular marketing executives are interested in determining whether there is a difference in mean income for their male and female cell phone customers. They will conduct a test using random samples of 200 males and 100 females. The following steps can be used to conduct the test.

Step 1:   **Specify the population value of interest.**
We are interested in determining if a difference exists in mean income for males (population 1) and females (population 2).

Step 2:   **Formulate the appropriate null and alternative hypotheses.**
The following null and alternative hypotheses are specified:

$$H_0: \mu_1 - \mu_2 = 0.0$$
$$H_A: \mu_1 - \mu_2 \neq 0.0$$

Step 3:   **Specify the significance level for the test.**
The test will be conducted using $\alpha = 0.05$.

Step 4:   **Construct the rejection region.**
Even though the population standard deviations are unknown, because the sample sizes are large, the critical value is a z-value from the standard normal distribution. This test is a two-tailed test, with $\alpha = 0.05$. From the standard normal distribution, the critical z-values for both tails of the distribution are

$$-z_{0.025} = -1.96 \quad \text{and} \quad z_{0.025} = 1.96.$$

The decision rule is

If $z < -1.96$ or $z > 1.96$, reject the null hypothesis;
Otherwise, do not reject the null hypothesis.

Alternatively, you can state the decision rule in terms of a p-value, as follows:

If p-value $< \alpha = 0.05$, reject the null hypothesis;
Otherwise, do not reject the null hypothesis.

Step 5:   **Compute the test statistic.**
A simple random sample of 200 males is selected, and another simple random sample of 100 females is selected. The incomes for these customers are determined. The samples are independent because the incomes of one group can in no way influence the incomes of the other group. The means computed from the samples are

$$\bar{x}_1 = \$43,390 \quad \text{and} \quad \bar{x}_2 = \$42,400.$$

Because we do not know the population standard deviations, these values are also computed from the sample data and are

$$s_1 = \$7,300 \quad \text{and} \quad s_2 = \$8,200.$$

Using Equation 9-12, the test statistic is

$$z = \frac{(\bar{x}_1 - \bar{x}_2) - (\mu_1 - \mu_2)}{\sqrt{\dfrac{s_1^2}{n_1} + \dfrac{s_2^2}{n_2}}}$$

$$z = \frac{(\$43,390 - \$42,400) - 0}{\sqrt{\dfrac{\$7,300^2}{200} + \dfrac{\$8,200^2}{100}}} = 1.022$$

Step 6:   Reach a decision.
Because $z = 1.022 < 1.96$, do not reject the null hypothesis.

Step 7:   Draw a conclusion.
There is no statistical evidence to conclude that mean incomes differ between male and female customers.

TESTING $\mu_1 - \mu_2$ WHEN σ_1 AND σ_2 ARE UNKNOWN, SMALL INDEPENDENT SAMPLES

In Section 9-1 we showed that to develop a confidence interval estimate for the difference between two population means when the standard deviations are unknown and the sample sizes are small (n_1 or $n_2 < 30$), we used the t-distribution to obtain the critical value. As you might suspect, this same approach is taken for hypothesis-testing situations. Equation 9-13 shows the t-test statistic that will be used when σ_1 and σ_2 are unknown and the samples are small.

---

t Test Statistic for $\mu_1 - \mu_2$ When σ_1 and σ_2 Are Unknown, Small Independent Samples

$$t = \frac{(\bar{x}_1 - \bar{x}_2) - (\mu_1 - \mu_2)}{s_p\sqrt{\dfrac{1}{n_1} + \dfrac{1}{n_2}}}, \qquad df = n_1 + n_2 - 2 \qquad\qquad \textbf{9-13}$$

where:

$\bar{x}_1$ and $\bar{x}_2$ = Sample means from populations 1 and 2
$\mu_1 - \mu_2$ = Hypothesized difference
n_1 and n_2 = Sample sizes from the two populations
s_p = Pooled standard deviation

The test statistic in Equation 9-13 is based on three assumptions:

SSUMPTIONS

1.   Each population has a normal distribution.[3]
2.   The two population variances, σ_1^2 and σ_2^2, are equal.
3.   The samples are independent.

Notice that in Equation 9-13 we are using the pooled estimate for the common population standard deviation that we developed in Section 9-1.

Retirement Investing—Recall the earlier example discussing a recent study in North Carolina involving retirement investing. The leaders of the study are interested in determining whether there is a difference in mean annual contributions for individuals covered by tax-sheltered annuities (TSA) and those with 401(k) retirement programs. A simple random sample of 15 people from the population of adults who are eligible for a TSA investment was selected. A second sample of 15 people was selected from the population of adults in North Carolina who have 401(k) plans. The variable of interest is the dollar amount of money invested in the retirement plan during the previous year.

---

[3]In Chapter 12 we will introduce a technique called the goodness-of-fit test, which we can use to test whether the sample data come from a population that is normally distributed.

Specifically, we are interested in testing the following null and alternative hypotheses:

$$H_0: \mu_1 - \mu_2 = 0.0$$
$$H_A: \mu_1 - \mu_2 \neq 0.0$$

μ_1 = Mean dollars invested by the TSA-eligible population during the past year
μ_2 = Mean dollars invested by the 401(k)-eligible population during the past year

The leaders of the study select a significance level of $\alpha = 0.05$. Refer to Figure 9-1 on page 350 for the sample data and the box and whisker diagrams.

The sample results are

TSA-Eligible	401(k)-Eligible
$n_1 = 15$	$n_2 = 15$
$\bar{x}_1 = \$2{,}119.70$	$\bar{x}_2 = \$1{,}777.70$
$s_1 = \$709.70$	$s_2 = \$593.90$

Because the investments by individuals with TSA accounts is in no way influenced by investments by individuals with 401(k) accounts, the samples are considered independent. The box and whisker diagrams shown earlier in Figure 9-1 are consistent with what might be expected if the populations have equal variances and are approximately normally distributed.

We are now in a position to complete the hypothesis test to determine whether the mean dollar amount invested by TSA employees is equal to the mean amount invested by 401(k) employees. We first determine the critical value from the t-distribution table in Appendix F (or use Excel's **TINV** function or Minitab's **Calc > Probability Distributions** command) with degrees of freedom equal to

$$n_1 + n_2 - 2 = 15 + 15 - 2 = 28,$$

and alpha = 0.05 for the two-tailed test. The appropriate t-value is

$$t_{\alpha/2} = 2.0484.$$

To continue the hypothesis test, we compute the pooled standard deviation.

$$s_p = \sqrt{\frac{(n_1 - 1)s_1^2 + (n_2 - 1)s_2^2}{n_1 + n_2 - 2}} = \sqrt{\frac{(15 - 1)(709.7)^2 + (15 - 1)(593.9)^2}{15 + 15 - 2}} = 654.37$$

Note that the pooled standard deviation is partway between the two sample standard deviations. Now, keeping in mind that the hypothesized difference between μ_1 and μ_2 is zero, we compute the t test statistic using Equation 9-15, as follows.

$$t = \frac{(\bar{x}_1 - \bar{x}_2) - (\mu_1 - \mu_2)}{s_p\sqrt{\dfrac{1}{n_1} + \dfrac{1}{n_2}}} = \frac{(2{,}119.70 - 1{,}777.70) - 0.0}{654.37\sqrt{\dfrac{1}{15} + \dfrac{1}{15}}} = 1.4313$$

This indicates that the difference in sample means is 1.4313 standard errors above the hypothesized difference of zero. Because

$$t = 1.4313 < t_{\alpha/2} = 2.0484,$$

the null hypothesis should not be rejected.

The difference in sample means is attributed to sampling error. Figure 9-3 summarizes this hypothesis test. Based on the sample data, there is no statistical justification to believe that the mean annual investment by individuals who are eligible for the tax-sheltered annuity option is different than for those individuals who are eligible for the 401(k) plan.

Excel and Minitab Tutorial

SUV Vehicle Mileage—Both Excel and Minitab have procedures for performing the necessary calculations to test hypotheses involving two population means. Consider a national car rental company that is interested in testing to determine whether there is a difference in mean mileage for sport-utility vehicles (SUVs) driven in town versus those driven on the highway. Based on its experience with regular automobiles, the company believes the mean highway mileage will exceed the mean city mileage.

To test this belief, the company has randomly selected 25 SUV rentals driven only on the highway and another random sample of 25 SUV rentals driven only in the city. The vehicles were filled with 14 gallons of gasoline. The company then asked each customer to drive their car until it ran out of gasoline. At that point, the elapsed miles were noted and the miles per gallon (mpg) were

FIGURE 9-3

Hypothesis Test for the
Equality of the Two
Population Means for the
North Carolina Investment
Study

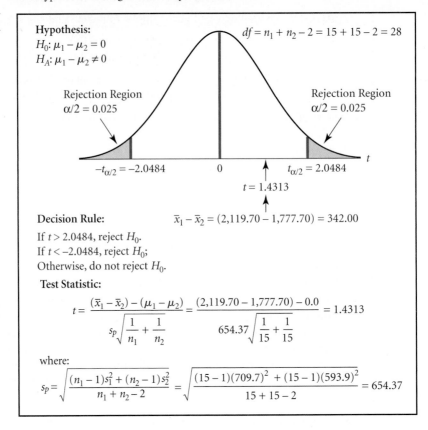

FIGURE 9-3

**Hypothesis Test for the
Equality of the Two
Population Means for the
North Carolina Investment
Study**

Hypothesis:
$H_0: \mu_1 - \mu_2 = 0$
$H_A: \mu_1 - \mu_2 \neq 0$

$df = n_1 + n_2 - 2 = 15 + 15 - 2 = 28$

Rejection Region
$\alpha/2 = 0.025$

Rejection Region
$\alpha/2 = 0.025$

$-t_{\alpha/2} = -2.0484$ 0 $t_{\alpha/2} = 2.0484$

$t = 1.4313$

Decision Rule: $\bar{x}_1 - \bar{x}_2 = (2{,}119.70 - 1{,}777.70) = 342.00$

If $t > 2.0484$, reject H_0.
If $t < -2.0484$, reject H_0;
Otherwise, do not reject H_0.

Test Statistic:

$$t = \frac{(\bar{x}_1 - \bar{x}_2) - (\mu_1 - \mu_2)}{s_p\sqrt{\dfrac{1}{n_1} + \dfrac{1}{n_2}}} = \frac{(2{,}119.70 - 1{,}777.70) - 0.0}{654.37\sqrt{\dfrac{1}{15} + \dfrac{1}{15}}} = 1.4313$$

where:

$$s_p = \sqrt{\frac{(n_1 - 1)s_1^2 + (n_2 - 1)s_2^2}{n_1 + n_2 - 2}} = \sqrt{\frac{(15 - 1)(709.7)^2 + (15 - 1)(593.9)^2}{15 + 15 - 2}} = 654.37$$

recorded. For their trouble, the customers received free use of the SUV and a coupon valid for one week's free rental. The results of the experiment are contained in the CD-ROM file *Mileage*.

Both Excel and the PHStat add-ins that accompany this text contain procedures for performing the calculations we will need to determine whether the manager's belief about SUV highway mileage can be justified. We first formulate the null and alternative hypotheses to be tested.

$$H_0: \mu_1 - \mu_2 \leq 0.0$$
$$H_A: \mu_1 - \mu_2 > 0.0$$

Population 1 represents highway mileage, and Population 2 represents city mileage. The test is conducted using a significance level of $0.05 = \alpha$.

Figure 9-4 shows the descriptive statistics for the two independent samples.

FIGURE 9-4

**Excel Output—SUV
Mileage Descriptive
Statistics**

Microsoft Excel - Mileage.xls

File Edit View Insert Format Tools Data PHStat Window Help

Arial   10   B I U

A1   = Highway Mileage

	A	B	C	D
1	Highway Mileage		City Mileage	
2				
3	Mean	19.6468	Mean	16.146
4	Standard Error	0.85938907	Standard Error	1.088235881
5	Median	19.54	Median	16.62
6	Mode	#N/A	Mode	#N/A
7	Standard Deviation	4.296945349	Standard Deviation	5.441179406
8	Sample Variance	18.46373933	Sample Variance	29.60643333
9	Kurtosis	-0.417874222	Kurtosis	-0.722382196
10	Skewness	0.19290028	Skewness	-0.382880482
11	Range	15.66	Range	18.43
12	Minimum	12.27	Minimum	5.89
13	Maximum	27.93	Maximum	24.32
14	Sum	491.17	Sum	403.65
15	Count	25	Count	25

FIGURE 9-5A

Excel Output (PHStat Add-in) Box and Whisker Diagram—SUV Mileage Test

Excel Instructions:
1. Open file: Mileage.xls
2. Select **PHStat tab**.
3. Select **Box and Whisker Plot**.
4. Define data range (both columns).
5. Check **Multiple Groups—Unstacked**.

FIGURE 9-5A

Excel Output (PHStat Add-in) Box and Whisker Diagram—SUV Mileage Test

Excel Instructions:
1. Open file: Mileage.xls
2. Select **PHStat tab**.
3. Select **Box and Whisker Plot**.
4. Define data range (both columns).
5. Check **Multiple Groups—Unstacked**.

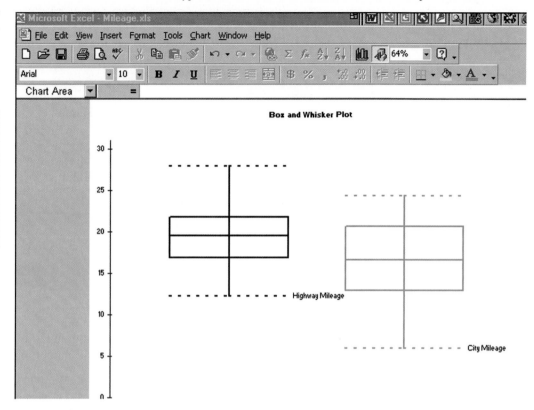

Figure 9-5a displays the box and whisker diagrams for the two samples, and Figure 9-5b shows the Minitab boxplot diagrams. Based on these diagrams, the normal distribution and equal variance assumptions appear reasonable. We will proceed with the test of means assuming normal distributions and equal variances and use Equation 9-13.

Both Excel and Minitab have procedures for carrying out this hypothesis test. Figure 9-6a and Figure 9-6b show the outputs from these procedures. The mean highway mileage is 19.6468 mpg, whereas the mean for city driving is 16.146. At issue is whether this difference in sample means $(19.6468 - 16.146 = 3.5008 \text{ mpg})$ is sufficient to conclude the population means are not equal. The one-tail t critical value for alpha $= 0.05$ is shown in Figure 9-6a to be

$$t_\alpha = 1.6772.$$

FIGURE 9-5B

Minitab Output Boxplot Diagrams—SUV Mileage Test

Minitab Instructions:
1. Open file: Mileage.MTW.
2. Choose **Graph > Boxplot**.
3. Under **Multiple Ys**, select **Simple**.
4. Click **OK**.
5. In **Graph variables**, enter data columns.
6. Click **OK**.

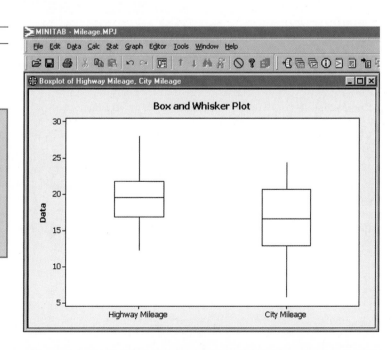

FIGURE 9-6A

Excel Output—SUV
Mileage *t*-Test for Two
Population Means

Excel Instructions:
1. Select **Tools** tab.
2. Select t-test: **Two-Sample** Assuming Equal **Variances**.
3. Define data ranges.
4. Set Hypothesized Mean Difference to 0.0.
5. Set alpha at 0.05.

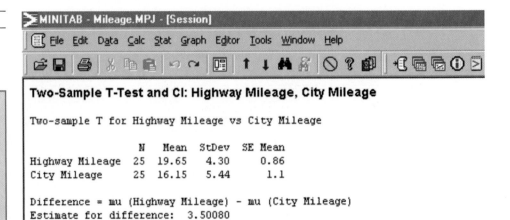

	A	B	C
1	t-Test: Two-Sample Assuming Equal Variances		
2			
3		Highway Mileage	City Mileage
4	Mean	19.6468	16.146
5	Variance	18.46373933	29.60643333
6	Observations	25	25
7	Pooled Variance	24.03508633	
8	Hypothesized Mean Difference	0	
9	df	48	
10	t Stat	2.524640028	
11	P(T<=t) one-tail	0.007470767	
12	t Critical one-tail	1.677224191	
13	P(T<=t) two-tail	0.014941533	
14	t Critical two-tail	2.01063358	

Figures 9-6a and 9-6b show that the "*t*-Stat" value from Excel and the *t*-value from Minitab, which are the calculated test statistics (or *t*-values, based on Equation 9-13), are equal to

$$t = 2.525$$

(rounded to 2.52 in Minitab). This means that the difference in sample means (3.5008 mpg) is 2.525 (2.52) standard errors above the hypothesized difference of zero. Because the test statistic

$$t = 2.525 > t_\alpha = 1.6772,$$

we reject the null hypothesis. Thus, the sample data do provide sufficient evidence to conclude that mean SUV highway mileage exceeds mean SUV city mileage, and this study confirms the expectations of the rental company managers.

The outputs shown in Figures 9-6a and 9-6b also provide the *p*-value for the one-tailed test, which can also be used to test the null hypothesis. Recall, if the calculated *p*-value is less than alpha, the null hypothesis should be rejected. The decision rule is

If *p*-value < 0.05, reject H_0;
Otherwise, do not reject H_0.

FIGURE 9-6B

Minitab Output—SUV
Mileage *t*-Test for Two
Population Means

Minitab Instructions:
1. Open file: Mileage.MTW.
2. Choose **Stat > Basic Statistics > 2-Sample t**.
3. Choose **Samples in different columns**.
4. In **First**, enter the first data column.
5. In **Second**, enter the other data column.
6. Check **Assume equal variances**.
7. Click **Options** and enter $1 - \alpha$ in **Confidence level**.
8. In **Alternative**, choose *greater than*.
9. Click **OK. OK.**

Two-Sample T-Test and CI: Highway Mileage, City Mileage

Two-sample T for Highway Mileage vs City Mileage

	N	Mean	StDev	SE Mean
Highway Mileage	25	19.65	4.30	0.86
City Mileage	25	16.15	5.44	1.1

Difference = mu (Highway Mileage) - mu (City Mileage)
Estimate for difference: 3.50080
95% lower bound for difference: 1.17507
T-Test of difference = 0 (vs >): T-Value = 2.52   P-Value = 0.007   DF = 48
Both use Pooled StDev = 4.9026

The p-value for the one-tailed test is 0.00747. Because $0.00747 < 0.05$, the null hypothesis is rejected. This is the same conclusion as the one we reached using the test statistic approach.

$\mathcal{E}$XAMPLE 9-7: HYPOTHESIS TEST FOR $\mu_1 - \mu_2$ WHEN σ_1 AND σ_2 ARE UNKNOWN, SMALL INDEPENDENT SAMPLES

Color Printer Ink Cartridges   An Associated Press news story out of Brussels, Belgium, on May 16, 2002, indicated the European Union was considering a probe of computer makers after consumers complained that they were being overcharged for ink cartridges. Companies such as Cannon, Hewlett-Packard, and Epson are the printer market leaders and make most of their printer-related profits by selling replacement ink cartridges. Suppose an independent test agency wishes to conduct a test to determine whether name-brand ink cartridges generate more color pages on average than competing generic ink cartridges. The test can be conducted using the following steps:

Step 1:   **Specify the population value of interest.**
We are interested in determining whether the mean number of pages printed by name-brand cartridges (population 1) exceeds the mean pages printed by generic cartridges (population 2).

Step 2:   **Formulate the appropriate null and alternative hypotheses.**
The following null and alternative hypotheses are specified:

$$H_0: \mu_1 - \mu_2 \leq 0.0$$
$$H_A: \mu_1 - \mu_2 > 0.0$$

Step 3:   **Specify the significance level for the test.**
The test will be conducted using $\alpha = 0.05$.
When the population standard deviations are unknown and the sample sizes are small, the critical value is a t-value from the t-distribution if the populations are assumed to be normally distributed.
A simple random sample of 10 users was selected, and the users were given a name-brand cartridge. A second sample of 8 users was given generic cartridges. Both groups used their printers until the ink ran out. The number of pages printed was recorded. The samples are independent because the pages printed by users in one group did not in any way influence the pages printed by users in the second group. The means computed from the samples are

$$\bar{x}_1 = 322.5 \text{ pages} \quad \text{and} \quad \bar{x}_2 = 298.3 \text{ pages.}$$

Because we do not know the population standard deviations, these values are computed from the sample data and are

$$s_1 = 48.3 \text{ pages} \quad \text{and} \quad s_2 = 53.3 \text{ pages.}$$

Suppose previous studies have shown that the number of pages printed by both types of cartridge tend to be approximately normal with equal variances.

Step 4:   **Construct the rejection region.**
Based on a one-tailed test with $\alpha = 0.05$, the critical value is a t-value from the t-distribution with $10 + 8 - 2 = 16$ degrees of freedom. From the t-table, the critical t-value is

$$t_{0.05} = 1.7459.$$

The decision rule is

If $t > 1.7459$, reject the null hypothesis;
Otherwise, do not reject the null hypothesis.

Step 5:   **Compute the test statistic using Equation 9-13.**

$$t = \frac{(\bar{x}_1 - \bar{x}_2) - (\mu_1 - \mu_2)}{s_p \sqrt{\dfrac{1}{n_1} + \dfrac{1}{n_2}}}$$

The pooled standard deviation is

$$s_p = \sqrt{\frac{(n_1 - 1)s_1^2 + (n_2 - 1)s_2^2}{n_1 + n_2 - 2}} = \sqrt{\frac{(10 - 1)48.3^2 + (8 - 1)53.3^2}{10 + 8 - 2}} = 50.55$$

Then the t-test statistic is

$$t = \frac{(322.5 - 298.3) - 0.0}{50.55 \sqrt{\frac{1}{10} + \frac{1}{8}}} = 1.0093$$

Step 6:   Reach a decision.
Because

$$t = 1.0093 < t_{\alpha/2} = 1.7459,$$

do not reject the null hypothesis.

Step 7:   Draw a conclusion.
Based on these sample data, there is insufficient evidence to conclude that the mean number of pages produced by name-brand ink cartridges exceeds the mean for generic cartridges.

What If the Population Variances Are Not Equal?

In the previous examples, we assumed that the population variances were equal, and we carried out the hypothesis test for two population means using Equation 9-13. Even in cases where the population variances are not equal, the t-test as specified in Equation 9-13 is appropriate as long as the sample sizes are equal. However, if the sample sizes are not equal and if the sample data lead us to suspect that the variances are not equal, the t test statistic must be approximated using Equation 9-14. In cases where the variances are not equal, the degrees of freedom are computed using Equation 9-15.[4]

---

t Test Statistic for $\mu_1 - \mu_2$ When Population Variances Are Not Equal

$$t = \frac{(\bar{x}_1 - \bar{x}_2) - (\mu_1 - \mu_2)}{\sqrt{\frac{s_1^2}{n_1} + \frac{s_2^2}{n_2}}} \qquad \text{9-14}$$

Degrees of Freedom for t Test Statistic When Population Variances Are Not Equal

$$\frac{(s_1^2/n_1 + s_2^2/n_2)^2}{\left(\frac{(s_1^2/n_1)^2}{n_1 - 1} + \frac{(s_2^2/n_2)^2}{n_2 - 1}\right)} \qquad \text{9-15}$$

HYPOTHESIS TESTING FOR PAIRED SAMPLES

In Section 9-1, we discussed the difference between independent and paired samples. As we indicated, there will be instances when paired samples can be used to control for an outside source of variation. For instance in Example 9-7 involving the ink cartridges, the original test of whether name-brand cartridges yield a higher mean number of printed pages than generic cartridges involved different users for the two types of cartridges, so the samples were independent. However, different users may use more or less ink as a rule; therefore, we could control for that source of variation by having a sample of people use both types of cartridges in a paired test format.

If a paired sample experiment is used, the test statistic is computed using Equation 9-16.

---

[4]Chapter 10 introduces a statistical procedure for testing whether two populations have equal variances.

t-Test Statistic for Paired Sample Test

$$t = \frac{\bar{d} - \mu_d}{\frac{s_d}{\sqrt{n}}} \qquad df = (n-1) \qquad\qquad 9\text{-}16$$

where:

$$\bar{d} = \text{Mean paired difference} = \frac{\sum d}{n}$$

μ_d = Hypothesized population mean paired difference

$$s_d = \text{Sample standard deviation for paired differences} = \sqrt{\frac{\sum (d - \bar{d})^2}{n-1}}$$

n = Number of paired values in the sample

EXAMPLE 9-8: HYPOTHESIS TEST FOR μ_d, PAIRED SAMPLES

Color Printer Ink Cartridges   Referring to Example 9-7, suppose the experiment regarding ink cartridges is conducted differently. Instead of having different samples of users use name-brand and generic cartridges, the test is done using paired samples. This means that the same people will use both types of cartridges, and the pages printed in each case will be recorded. The test under this paired sample scenario can be conducted using the following steps. Six randomly selected people have agreed to participate.

Step 1:   **Specify the population value of interest.**
In this case we will form paired differences by subtracting the generic pages from the name-brand pages. We are interested in determining whether name-brand cartridges produce more printed pages, on average, than generic cartridges, so we would expect the paired difference to be positive. We assume that the paired differences are normally distributed.

Step 2:   **Formulate the null and alternative hypotheses.**
The null and alternative hypotheses are

$$H_0: \mu_d \le 0.0$$
$$H_A: \mu_d > 0.0$$

Step 3:   **Specify the significance level for the test.**
The test will be conducted using $\alpha = 0.01$.

Step 4:   **Construct the rejection region.**
The critical value is a t-value from the t-distribution, with alpha = 0.01 and $6 - 1 = 5$ degrees of freedom. The critical value is

$$t_{0.01} = 3.3649.$$

The decision rule is

If $t > 3.3649$, reject the null hypothesis;
Otherwise, do not reject the null hypothesis.

Step 5:   **Compute the test statistic.**
Select the random sample and compute the mean and standard deviation for the paired differences.
In this case a random sample of six people tests each type of cartridge. The following data and paired differences were observed:

Printer User	Name-Brand	Generic	d
1	306	300	6
2	256	260	−4
3	402	357	45
4	299	286	13
5	306	290	16
6	257	260	−3

The mean paired difference is

$$\bar{d} = \frac{\Sigma d}{n} = \frac{73}{6} = 12.17$$

The standard deviation for the paired differences is

$$s_d = \sqrt{\frac{\Sigma (d - \bar{d})^2}{n - 1}} = 18.02$$

The test statistic is calculated using Equation 9-16.

$$t = \frac{\bar{d} - \mu_d}{\frac{s_d}{\sqrt{n}}} = \frac{12.17 - 0.0}{\frac{18.02}{\sqrt{6}}} = 1.6543$$

Step 6:   **Reach a decision.**
Because $t = 1.6543 < t_\alpha = 3.3649$, do not reject the null hypothesis.

Step 7:   **Draw a conclusion.**
Based on these sample data, there is insufficient evidence to conclude that name-brand ink cartridges produce more pages on average than generic brands.

9-2: EXERCISES

Skill Development

9.17   Given two independent samples with the following information:

Item	Sample 1	Sample 2
1	19.6	21.3
2	22.1	17.4
3	19.5	19.0
4	20.0	21.2
5	21.5	20.1
6	20.2	23.5
7	17.9	18.9
8	23.0	22.4
9	12.5	14.3
10	19.0	17.8

Based on these samples, test at the 0.10 significance level whether the true average difference is 0.

9.18   The following sample data have been collected from two independent samples from two populations. The claim is that the second population mean will exceed the first population mean.

Sample 1	Sample 2
12	9
21	18
12	16
11	17
11	13
13	7
12	12
9	17

a. State the appropriate null and alternative hypotheses.
b. Based on the sample data, what should you conclude about the null hypothesis? Test using an $\alpha = 0.05$. Perform the test using both a critical value and a p-value.

9.19   Given the following null and alternative hypotheses:

$$H_0: \mu_1 - \mu_2 \geq 0$$
$$H_A: \mu_1 - \mu_2 < 0$$

and this sample information:

Sample 1	Sample 2
$n_1 = 16$	$n_2 = 25$
$s_1 = 32$	$s_2 = 30$
$\bar{x}_1 = 2{,}456$	$\bar{x}_2 = 2{,}460$

a. Develop the appropriate decision rule, assuming a significance level of 0.05 is to be used.
b. Use the appropriate test to determine whether the two populations have equal means.

9.20   Given the following null and alternative hypotheses:

$$H_0: \mu_1 - \mu_2 = 0$$
$$H_A: \mu_1 - \mu_2 \neq 0$$

and the following sample information:

Sample 1	Sample 2
$n_1 = 25$	$n_2 = 20$
$s_1 = 20$	$s_2 = 24$
$\bar{x}_1 = 430$	$\bar{x}_2 = 405$

a. Develop the appropriate decision rule, assuming a significance level of 0.05 is to be used.

b. Test the null hypothesis and indicate whether the sample information leads you to reject or fail to reject the null hypothesis. Use the test-statistic approach.

9.21 Given the following null and alternative hypotheses:

$$H_0: \mu_1 - \mu_2 = 0$$
$$H_A: \mu_1 - \mu_2 \neq 0$$

and the following sample information:

Sample 1	Sample 2
$n_1 = 125$	$n_2 = 120$
$s_1 = 31$	$s_2 = 38$
$\bar{x}_1 = 130$	$\bar{x}_2 = 105$

a. Develop the appropriate decision rule, assuming a significance level of 0.05 is to be used.
b. Test the null hypothesis and indicate whether the sample information leads you to reject or fail to reject the null hypothesis. Use the test-statistic approach.

9.22 Given the following null and alternative hypotheses:

$$H_0: \mu_1 - \mu_2 \leq 0$$
$$H_A: \mu_1 - \mu_2 > 0$$

and the following sample information:

Sample 1	Sample 2
$n_1 = 75$	$n_2 = 80$
$s_1 = 2.20$	$s_2 = 2.644$
$\bar{x}_1 = 5.30$	$\bar{x}_2 = 5.10$

a. Develop the appropriate decision rule, assuming a significance level of 0.05 is to be used.
b. Test the null hypothesis and indicate whether the sample information leads you to reject or fail to reject the null hypothesis.

9.23 The following sample data have been collected from a paired sample from two populations. The claim is that the first population mean will be at least as large as the mean of the second population. This claim will be assumed to be true unless the data strongly suggest otherwise.

Sample 1	Sample 2
4.4	3.7
2.7	3.5
1.0	4.0
3.5	4.9
2.8	3.1
2.6	4.2
2.4	5.2
2.0	4.4
2.8	4.3

a. State the appropriate null and alternative hypotheses.
b. Based on the sample data, what should you conclude about the null hypothesis? Test using $\alpha = 0.10$. Test using both a critical value and a p-value.

c. Calculate a 90% confidence interval for the difference in the population means. Are the results from the confidence interval consistent with the outcome of your hypothesis test? Explain.

9.24 The following sample data have been collected from a paired sample from two populations. The claim is that the first population mean will exceed the second population mean.

Sample 1	Sample 2
50	38
47	44
44	38
48	37
40	43
36	44
43	31
46	38
72	39
40	54
55	41
38	40

a. State the appropriate null and alternative hypotheses.
b. Based on the sample data, what should you conclude about the null hypothesis? Test at a significance level of 0.01.
c. Suppose these samples had been obtained independently. Conduct the test and determine if the results would be different.

Business Applications

9.25 The State College registrar is interested in determining whether female students exceed male students by more than one credit hour taken during a term. She has selected a random sample of 60 males and 60 females and has observed the following sample information:

Male	Female
$\bar{x} = 13.24$ credits	$\bar{x} = 14.65$ credits
$s = 1.2$ credits	$s = 1.56$ credits

Provide the registrar with the information she is seeking by performing a hypothesis test based on a 0.05 significance level.

9.26 The marketing manager for a major retail grocery chain is wondering about the location of the stores' dairy products. She believes that the mean amount spent by customers on dairy products per visit is higher in stores in which the dairy section is in the central part of the store, compared with stores that have the dairy section at the rear. To consider relocating the dairy products, the manager feels that the increase in the mean amount spent by customers must be more than 25 cents. To determine whether relocation is justified, her staff selected a random sample of 25 customers at stores in which the dairy section is central in the store. A second sample of 25 customers was selected in stores with the dairy section at the rear of the store. The following sample results were observed:

Central Dairy	Rear Dairy
$\bar{x}_1 = \$3.74$	$\bar{x}_2 = \$3.26$
$s_1 = \$0.87$	$s_2 = \$0.79$

a. Conduct a hypothesis test with a significance level of 0.05 to determine if the manager should relocate the dairy products in those stores displaying their dairy products in the rear.

b. If a statistical error associated with hypothesis testing were made in this hypothesis test, what error could it have been? Explain.

9.27 The makers of ink cartridges for color ink-jet printers have developed a new system for storing the ink. They think the new system will result in a longer lasting product. In order to determine whether this is the case, a test was developed in which a sample of 35 of the new cartridges was selected. They were put in a printer, and test pages were run until the cartridge was empty. The same thing was done for a sample of 32 —original cartridges. The following data were observed:

New Cartridge	Existing Cartridge
$\bar{x}_1 = 288$ pages	$\bar{x}_2 = 279$ pages
$s_1 = 16.3$ pages	$s_2 = 15.91$ pages

a. Based on the sample data and a significance level equal to 0.10, determine if the new system will result in a longer lasting product. Write a short statement that discusses the results of the test.

b. Calculate a 90% confidence interval for the difference between these two population means. Are the results of the hypothesis test consistent with the confidence interval you produced? Explain.

9.28 The managers of a regional bank in Florida believe that customers who regularly use their ATM cards (regular is defined as at least one time per week) are more profitable to the bank overall than customers who do not regularly use their ATM cards. A sample of 200 of the bank's customers in each category was selected. An accounting was performed to determine the 1999 profit generated from each customer. The following sample data were observed?

Regular ATM	Non-ATM Users
$\bar{x}_1 = \$142.76$	$\bar{x}_2 = \$133.19$
$s_1 = \$30.31$	$s_2 = \$33.92$

a. Using an alpha level equal to 0.05, what conclusion should the bank's managers reach based on the sample data? Discuss your results in a short written statement.

b. Calculate a 95% confidence interval for the difference of the average profit produced by these two

groups. If you were one of the bank's managers, which of the two (hypothesis test or confidence interval) statistical inference procedures would you prefer in this situation? Explain.

9.29 ● The First Night Stage Company operates a small nonprofit theater group in Milwaukee, Wisconsin. Each year the company markets Christmas candy to help fund its operations. This year, it has obtained the help of a marketing research company in the city. This company has proposed two different candy brochures. Brochure B costs an average of 35 cents more to produce than brochure A. The theater group is trying to determine which brochure will produce the higher sales. To determine this, a random sample of 20 people was selected to receive brochure A and another random sample of 20 people was selected to receive brochure B. The sales data (including sales tax) are contained in the CD-ROM file called *First-Night*.

a. Based on these sample data, which brochure should the First Night Company adopt? Use $\alpha = 0.01$ for whatever statistical inference techniques you use.

b. Referring to the statistical inference techniques you used in part a, what assumptions are required?

9.30 ● The California State Highway Patrol recently conducted a study on a stretch of interstate highway south of San Francisco to determine whether the mean speed for California vehicles exceeded the mean speed for out-of-state vehicles. It would consider any average hike of more than 5 mph to be a significant increase in speed. A total of 140 California cars were included in the study, whereas 75 out-of-state cars were included. Radar was used to measure speed. The CD-ROM file called *Speed-Test* contains the data collected by the California Highway Patrol.

a. Determine the research hypothesis. Specify the alternative and null hypotheses that would be derived from the research hypothesis.

b. Using a significance level equal to 0.10, would the average speed of California drivers be considered to be "significantly higher" by the California Highway Patrol? Use both the *p*-value and critical value to perform the test. Are the conclusions consistent?

c. Discuss the results of this test in a short written statement.

9.31 ● For years there has been a debate about whether children who are in child care facilities while their parents work experience negative effects. A recent study, discussed in the March 1999 issue of *Developmental Psychology*, of 6,000 children found "no permanent negative effects caused by their mothers' absence." In fact, the study indicated that there might be some positive benefits from the day care experience. To investigate this premise, a nonprofit organization called Child Care Connections conducted a small study in which children were observed playing in a neutral setting (not at home or at a day care center). Over a period of 20 hours of observation, 15 children who did not go to day care and 21 children who had spent much time in day care were observed. The variable of interest was the total minutes of play in which each child was actively interacting with other students. Child Care Connections leaders hoped to show that the children who had been in day care would have a higher mean time in interactive situations than the stay-at-home children. The CD-ROM file called *Children* contains the study results.

a. Test the hypothesis that the children who had been in day care had a higher mean time in interactive situations than the stay-at-home children. Use a significance level of 0.05.

b. Based on the outcome of the hypothesis test, which statistical error might have been committed?

Advanced Applications

9.32   A regional airport is considering the purchase of a new visibility sensor system to be used in conjunction with air traffic control equipment. The managers have narrowed the choices down to two suppliers: Vangaurd and Scorpion. To help make the final selection, the two suppliers agreed to participate in a test. The two sensors were temporarily installed side by side at the airport. Visibility readings from each sensor were recorded on 5-minute intervals for a 24-hour period. The resulting data are in a CD-ROM file called *Visibility*.

a. Discuss whether the samples can be treated as independent, or if they are in fact paired samples. Be sure to state your reasoning.

b. Perform the hypothesis test using a *p*-value, assuming that samples are independent, and using a significance level of 0.05. Discuss the results.

c. Perform the hypothesis test assuming that the samples are paired. Use a significance level of 0.05 and discuss your results. How does the conclusion compare with the one reached in part b?

9.33   The Sunbeam Corporation makes a wide variety of appliances for the home. One product is a digital blood pressure gauge. For obvious reasons, the blood pressure readings made by the monitor need to be accurate. When a new model is being designed, one of the steps is to test it. To do this, a sample of people is selected. Each person has his or her systolic blood pressure taken by a highly respected physician. They then immediately have their systolic blood pressure taken using the Sunbeam monitor. If the mean blood pressure is the same for the monitor as that determined by the physician, then the monitor passes the test.

In a recent test, 15 people were randomly selected to be in the sample. The blood pressure readings for these people using both methods are contained in the data file called *Sunbeam*.

Physician	Monitor
112	126
109	108
139	116
141	123
120	138
99	123
128	119
118	122
116	116
120	118
111	114
123	108
114	130
121	123
132	127

a. Based on the sample data and a significance level equal to 0.05, what conclusion should the Sunbeam engineers reach regarding the latest blood pressure monitor? Discuss your answer in a short written statement.

b. Consider the context of this problem. Does it make sense to you that any deviation from the equality between the mean blood pressure readings would be of interest? Examine the data to determine a, perhaps, more reasonable criterion.

c. Calculate a 95% confidence interval for the paired difference between the two mean blood pressure readings. Based on your criterion of part b, would you consider the Sunbeam blood pressure monitor to be a good substitute for a doctor's blood pressure reading? Explain.

d. Comment on whether it would be possible to reach a different conclusion using a paired sample test versus a test assuming independent samples. Why could this happen?

9-3 ESTIMATION AND HYPOTHESIS TESTS FOR TWO POPULATION PROPORTIONS

The previous section illustrated the methods for testing hypotheses involving two population means. There are many business situations in which these methods can be applied. However, there are other instances involving two populations in which the measures of interest are not the population means. For example, Chapter 8 introduced the methodology for testing hypotheses involving a single population proportion. This section extends that methodology to tests involving hypotheses about the difference between two population proportions. First, we will look at a confidence interval estimation involving two population proportions.

ESTIMATING THE DIFFERENCE BETWEEN TWO POPULATION PROPORTIONS

V. C. Elroy Agency—Advertising agencies spend a significant amount of time determining whether proposed advertisements will appeal to different market segments before the ads run on national media. Recently, the V. C. Elroy Agency in Chicago developed an advertising campaign for a national fast-food chain. Among the many issues the ad managers were interested in was the difference in how appealing males and females would find the ads.

Obviously, there was no way to gauge the attitudes of the entire population of men and women who would eventually see or hear the ads. Instead, the Elroy agency showed the ad campaign to a random sample of 425 men and 370 women. In the results that follow, the variable x indicates the number in the sample who said they liked the campaign.

Men	Women
$n_1 = 425$	$n_2 = 370$
$x_1 = 240$	$x_2 = 196$

Based on these sample data, the sample proportions are

$$\bar{p}_1 = \frac{240}{425} = 0.565 \text{ and } \bar{p}_2 = \frac{196}{370} = 0.530.$$

The point estimate for the difference in population proportions is

$$\bar{p}_1 - \bar{p}_2 = 0.565 - 0.530 = 0.035.$$

So, the single best estimate for the difference in the proportion of men versus women who liked the ad campaign is 0.035. However, all point estimates are subject to sampling error. A confidence interval estimate for the difference in population proportions can be developed using Equation 9-17, providing the sample sizes are sufficiently large. A rule of thumb for "sufficiently large" is that, as with hypothesis testing, $n\bar{p}$ and $n(1 - \bar{p})$ are greater than or equal to 5 for both samples.

Confidence Interval Estimate for $p_1 - p_2$

$$(\bar{p}_1 - \bar{p}_2) \pm z_{\alpha/2} \sqrt{\frac{(\bar{p}_1)(1 - \bar{p}_1)}{n_1} + \frac{(\bar{p}_2)(1 - \bar{p}_2)}{n_2}} \qquad \textbf{9-17}$$

where:

$\bar{p}_1$ = Sample proportion from population 1
$\bar{p}_2$ = Sample proportion from population 2
$z_{\alpha/2}$ = Critical value from the standard normal table

---

The Elroy managers can substitute the sample results into Equation 9-17 to establish a 95% confidence interval estimate, as follows.

$$(.565 - .530) \pm 1.96 \sqrt{\frac{(.565)(1 - .565)}{425} + \frac{(.530)(1 - .530)}{370}}$$

$$0.035 \pm 0.069$$

$$-0.034 \text{ ------------------------- } 0.104$$

Thus, based on the sample data and using a 95% confidence interval, the managers estimate that the true difference in proportion of males versus females who like the ad campaign is between -0.034 and 0.104. At one extreme, 3.4% more females like the ad than males. At the other extreme, 10.4% more males like the ad than females. Because zero is included in the interval, there may be no difference between males and females based on these data. Consequently, the managers are not able to conclude that one group or the other has a stronger preference for the fast-food ad campaign.

HYPOTHESIS TESTS FOR THE DIFFERENCE BETWEEN TWO POPULATION PROPORTIONS

Excel and Minitab Tutorial

Pomona Fabrications—Pomona Fabrication, Inc., produces handheld hair dryers that several major retailers sell as in-house brands. A critical component of a handheld hair dryer is the motor-heater unit, which accounts for most of the dryer's cost and also for most of the product's reliability problems. Product reliability is important to Pomona because the company offers a 1-year warranty. Of course, Pomona is also interested in reducing production costs.

Ponoma's research and development department has recently created a new motor-heater unit with fewer parts than the current unit, which would lead to a 15% cost savings per hair dryer. However, the company's vice president of product development is unwilling to authorize the new component unless it is more reliable than the current motor-heater.

The research and development department has decided to test samples of both units to see which motor-heater is more reliable. Two hundred fifty units of each type will be tested under conditions that simulate one year's use, and the proportion of each type that fails within that time will be recorded. This leads to the formulation of the following null and alternative hypotheses:

$$H_0: p_1 - p_2 \geq 0.0$$
$$H_A: p_1 - p_2 < 0.0$$

where:

p_1 = Population proportion of new dryer type that fails in simulated one-year period
p_2 = Population proportion of existing dryer type that fails in simulated one-year period

The null hypothesis states that the new motor-heater is no better than the old, or current, motor-heater. The alternative states that the new unit has a smaller proportion of failures within one year than the current unit. In other words, the alternative states that the new unit is more reliable. The company wants clear evidence before changing units. If the null hypothesis is rejected, the company will conclude that the new motor-heater unit is more reliable than the old unit and should be used in producing the hair dryers. To test the null hypothesis, we can use the test statistic approach.

The test statistic is based on the sampling distribution of $\bar{p}_1 - \bar{p}_2$. In Chapter 6 we showed that when $np \geq 5$ and $n(1 - p) \geq 5$, the sampling distribution of the sample proportion is approximately normally distributed, with a mean equal to p and a variance equal to $\dfrac{p(1 - p)}{n}$.

Likewise, in the two-sample case, the sampling distribution of $\bar{p}_1 - \bar{p}_2$ will also be approximately normal if

SSUMPTIONS

$$n_1 p_1 \geq 5, \; n_1(1 - p_1) \geq 5, \; n_2 p_2 \geq 5, \quad \text{and} \quad n_2(1 - p_2) \geq 5$$

Because p_1 and p_2 are unknown, we substitute the sample proportions, $\bar{p}_1$ and $\bar{p}_2$, to determine whether the sample size requirements are satisfied.

The mean of the sampling distribution of $\bar{p}_1 - \bar{p}_2$ is the difference of the population proportions, $p_1 - p_2$. The variance is, however, the sum of the variances, $\dfrac{p_1(1 - p_1)}{n_1} + \dfrac{p_2(1 - p_2)}{n_2}$.

Because the test is conducted using the assumption that the null hypothesis is true, we assume that $p_1 = p_2 = p$ and estimate their common value, p, using a pooled estimate, as shown in Equation 9-18. The z test statistic for the difference between two proportions is given as Equation 9-19.

Pooled Estimator for Overall Proportion

$$\bar{p} = \frac{n_1 \bar{p}_1 + n_2 \bar{p}_2}{n_1 + n_2} = \frac{x_1 + x_2}{n_1 + n_2}$$ 9-18

where:

x_1 and x_2 = number from samples 1 and 2 with the characteristic of interest

---

z Test Statistic for Difference between Population Proportions

$$z = \frac{(\bar{p}_1 - \bar{p}_2) - (p_1 - p_2)}{\sqrt{\bar{p}(1 - \bar{p})\left(\dfrac{1}{n_1} + \dfrac{1}{n_2}\right)}}$$ 9-19

where:

$(p_1 - p_2)$ = Hypothesized difference in proportions from populations 1 and 2, respectively

$\bar{p}_1$ and $\bar{p}_2$ = Sample proportions for samples selected from populations 1 and 2

$\bar{p}$ = Pooled estimator for the overall proportion for both populations combined

The reason for taking a weighted average in Equation 9-18 is to give more weight to the larger sample. Note that the numerator is the total number of items with the characteristic of interest in the two samples, and the denominator is the total sample size. Again, the pooled estimator, $\bar{p}$, is used when the null hypothesis is that there is no difference between the population proportions.

Assume that Pomona is willing to use a significance level of 0.05 and that 55 of the new motor-heaters and 75 of the originals failed the one-year test. Figure 9-7 illustrates the decision-rule development and the hypothesis test. As you can see, Pomona should reject the null hypothesis based on the sample data. Thus, the firm should conclude that the new motor-heater is more reliable than the old one. Because the new one is also less costly, the company should now use the new unit in the production of hair dryers.

The p-value approach to hypothesis testing could also have been used to test Pomona's hypothesis. In this case, the calculated value of the test statistic, $z = -2.04$, results in a p-value of 0.0207 $(0.5 - 0.4793)$ from the standard normal table. Because this p-value is smaller than the significance level of 0.05, we would reject the null hypothesis. Remember, whenever your p-value is smaller than the alpha value, your sample contains evidence to reject the null hypothesis.

Both Minitab and the PHStat add-ins to Excel contain procedures for performing hypothesis tests involving two population proportions. Figures 9-8a and 9-8b show the PHStat output and the Minitab output for the Pomona example. The output contains both the z test statistic and the p-value. As we observed from our manual calculations, the difference in sample proportions is sufficient to reject the null hypothesis that there is no difference in population proportions.

FIGURE 9-7

Hypothesis Test of Two Population Proportions for Pomona Fabrications

$H_0: p_1 - p_2 \geq 0$
$H_A: p_1 - p_2 < 0$
$n_1 = 250, n_2 = 250$
$x_1 = 55, x_2 = 75$
$\bar{p}_1 = 55/250 = 0.22$
$\bar{p}_2 = 75/250 = 0.30$

Rejection Region
$\alpha = 0.05$

$-z_\alpha = -1.645$ 0 z

Decision Rule:

If $z < -1.645$, reject H_0.
If $z \geq -1.645$, do not reject H_0.

Test Statistic:

$$z = \frac{(\bar{p}_1 - \bar{p}_2) - (p_1 - p_2)}{\sqrt{\bar{p}(1 - \bar{p})\left(\frac{1}{n_1} + \frac{1}{n_2}\right)}} = \frac{(0.22 - 0.30) - 0}{\sqrt{0.26(1 - 0.26)\left(\frac{1}{250} + \frac{1}{250}\right)}} = -2.04$$

where:

$$\bar{p} = \frac{250(0.22) + 250(0.30)}{250 + 250} = \frac{55 + 75}{500} = 0.26$$

Since $z = -2.04 < -1.645$, reject H_0.

FIGURE 9-8A

Excel (PHStat) Output of the Two Proportions Test for Pomona Fabrications

Excel (PHStat) Instructions:
1. Click on the PHStat tab.
2. Select the **Two-Sample Tests** option.
3. Select **Z Test for Differences in Two Proportions**.
4. Enter sample size and number of occurrences for each population.

	A	B
1	Pomona	
2		
3	Hypothesized Difference	0
4	Level of Significance	0.05
5	Group 1	
6	Number of Successes	55
7	Sample Size	250
8	Group 2	
9	Number of Successes	75
10	Sample Size	250
11	Group 1 Proportion	0.22
12	Group 2 Proportion	0.3
13	Difference in Two Proportions	-0.08
14	Average Proportion	0.26
15	Z Test Statistic	-2.039118476
16		
17	Lower-Tail Test	
18	Lower Critical Value	-1.644853
19	p-Value	0.020719034
20	Reject the null hypothesis	

$z = -2.039 < -1.645$
Reject the null hypothesis.

EXAMPLE 9-9: HYPOTHESIS TEST FOR THE DIFFERENCE BETWEEN TWO POPULATION PROPORTIONS

Gregston Ticketing   Gregston Ticketing is evaluating two suppliers of a scanning system it is considering purchasing. Both scanners are designed to detect forged tickets for sporting events. High quality scanners and printers and home computers have made forged tickets an increasing industry problem. The company is interested in determining whether there is a difference in the proportion of forged tickets detected by the two suppliers. To conduct this test, use the following steps.

Step 1:   Specify the population value of interest.
In this case, the population value of interest is the population proportion of detected forged tickets. At issue is whether there is a difference between the two suppliers in terms of the proportion of forged tickets detected.

FIGURE 9-8B

Minitab Output of the Two Proportions Test for

Minitab Instructions:
1. Choose **Stat > Basic Statistics >2 Proportions**.
2. Choose **Summarized data**.
3. In **First**, enter Trials and Events for sample 1. (e.g., 250 and 55).
4. In **Second**, enter Trials and Events for sample 2. (e.g., 250 and 75).
5. Select **Options**. Insert $1 - \alpha$ in **Confidence level**.
6. In **Alternative**, select *less than*.
7. Check **Use pooled estimate of p for test**.
8. Click **OK. OK**.

MINITAB - PomonaFab.MPJ

File Edit Data Calc Stat Graph Editor Tools Window Help

Test and CI for Two Proportions

```
Sample   X    N   Sample p
1       55  250  0.220000
2       75  250  0.300000


Difference = p (1) - p (2)
Estimate for difference:  -0.08
95% upper bound for difference:  -0.0157369
Test for difference = 0 (vs < 0):  Z = -2.04  P-Value = 0.021
```

$z = -2.04 < -1.645$
Reject the null hypothesis.

Step 2: **Formulate the appropriate null and alternative hypotheses.**
The null and alternative hypotheses are

$$H_0: p_1 - p_2 = 0.0$$
$$H_A: p_1 - p_2 \neq 0.0$$

Step 3: **Specify the significance level.**
The test will be conducted using an $\alpha = 0.02$.

Step 4: **Construct the rejection region.**
For a two-tailed test, the critical values for each side of the distribution are

$$-z_{0.02/2} = -2.33 \text{ and } z_{0.02/2} = 2.33.$$

The decision rule based on the z test statistic is:

If $z < -2.33$ or $z > 2.33$, reject the null hypothesis;

Otherwise, do not reject the null hypothesis.

Step 5: **Compute the z test statistic using Equation 9-19 and apply it to the decision rule.**
Two hundred known forged tickets will be randomly selected and scanned by systems from each supplier. For supplier one, 186 forgeries are detected, and for supplier two, 168 are detected. The sample proportions are

$$\bar{p}_1 = \frac{x_1}{n_1} = \frac{186}{200} = 0.93 \qquad \bar{p}_2 = \frac{x_2}{n_2} = \frac{168}{200} = 0.84$$

The test statistic is then calculated using Equation 9-19.

$$z = \frac{(\bar{p}_1 - \bar{p}_2) - (p_1 - p_2)}{\sqrt{\bar{p}(1 - \bar{p})\left(\dfrac{1}{n_1} + \dfrac{1}{n_2}\right)}}$$

where:

$$\bar{p} = \frac{n_1 \bar{p}_1 + n_2 \bar{p}_2}{n_1 + n_2} = \frac{200(0.93) + 200(0.84)}{200 + 200} = 0.885 \qquad \text{(see Equation 9-18)}$$

Then:

$$z = \frac{(0.93 - .084) - 0.0}{\sqrt{0.885(1 - 0.885)\left(\dfrac{1}{200} + \dfrac{1}{200}\right)}} = 2.8211$$

Step 6: **Reach a decision.**
Because $z = 2.8211 > z_{\alpha/2} = 2.33$, reject the null hypothesis.

Step 7: **Draw a conclusion.**
The difference between the two sample proportions does provide sufficient evidence to allow us to conclude a difference exists between the two suppliers.

9-3: EXERCISES

9.34 Note the following null and alternative hypotheses:

$$H_0: p_1 = p_2$$
$$H_A: p_1 \neq p_2$$

and this sample information:

Sample 1	Sample 2
$n_1 = 100$	$n_2 = 100$
$x_1 = 30$	$x_2 = 34$

Using an $\alpha = 0.05$ and the sample information, what should be concluded with respect to the null and alternative hypotheses? Conduct the hypothesis test using a p-value approach. Be sure to clearly show the decision rule.

9.35 Given the following null and alternative hypotheses:

$$H_0: p_1 - p_2 = 0.05$$
$$H_A: p_1 - p_2 \neq 0.05$$

and this sample information:

Sample 1	Sample 2
$n_1 = 200$	$n_2 = 150$
$x_1 = 87$	$x_2 = 80$

Using an $\alpha = 0.10$ and the sample information, what should be concluded with respect to the null and alternative hypotheses? Be sure to clearly show the decision rule.

9.36 Given the following null and alternative hypotheses:

$$H_0: p_1 - p_2 \geq 0.0$$
$$H_A: p_1 - p_2 < 0.0$$

and this sample information:

Sample 1	Sample 2
$n_1 = 100$	$n_2 = 100$
$x_1 = 70$	$x_2 = 75$

a. Based on $\alpha = 0.05$ and the sample information, what should be concluded with respect to the null and alternative hypotheses? Be sure to clearly show the decision rule.
b. Calculate a 95% confidence interval for the difference between the two population proportions.
c. Compare the standard error obtained in the confidence interval to that in the test statistic. Why are these two standard errors different?

9.37 Given the following null and alternative hypotheses:

$$H_0: p_1 - p_2 \leq 0.0$$
$$H_A: p_1 - p_2 > 0.0$$

and this sample information:

Sample 1	Sample 2
$n_1 = 60$	$n_2 = 80$
$x_1 = 30$	$x_2 = 24$

a. Based on $\alpha = 0.02$ and the sample information, what should be concluded with respect to the null and alternative hypotheses? Be sure to clearly show the decision rule.
b. Calculate the p-value for this hypothesis test. Based on the p-value, would the null hypothesis be rejected? Support your answer with calculations and/or reasons.

9.38 The following information was obtained from samples of two populations:

Population 1	Population 2
$n_1 = 300$	$n_2 = 400$
$x_1 = 88$	$x_2 = 136$

a. Determine if the sample sizes are large enough so that the sampling distribution of the difference between the sample proportions is approximately normally distributed.
b. Calculate and interpret an 80% confidence interval estimate for the difference between the two population proportions.

Business Applications

9.39 Recently a nationwide television network commissioned a polling service to poll homeowners across the United States. Among the issues to be addressed in the survey was whether there is a difference in the proportions of households that watch a national news broadcast depending on whether the household is headed by a man or a woman. The study surveyed 1,200 households. In 745 of these, the head of household was listed as a man. In the others, the household head was a woman. The survey results showed that 62% of the households headed by men tuned into a national network news program, whereas 49% of those homes headed by women did so.
a. Can the distribution of the difference between the sample proportions of households headed by men and women that tune into a national network news program be approximated by a normal distribution? Provide calculations and reasons for your answer.
b. Based on these data, what could the network conclude overall? State the null and alternative hypotheses, and test at a significance level equal to 0.05.

9.40 The United Way raises money for community charity activities. Recently in one community, the fund-raising committee was concerned with whether there is a difference in the proportion of employees who give to the United Way, depending on whether their employer is a private business or a government agency. A random sample of people who had been contacted about contributing last year was selected. Of those contacted, 70 worked for a private business and 50 worked for a government agency. Of the 70 private-sector employees, 22 had contributed some amount to United Way, and 19 of the government employees in the sample had contributed.
a. Based on these sample data and $\alpha = 0.05$, what should be concluded? Be sure to show the decision rule.
b. Construct a 95% confidence interval for the difference between the proportion of private-business and government-agency employees who contribute to United Way. Do the hypothesis test and the confidence interval produce compatible results? Explain and give reasons for your answer.

9.41   Most major airlines allow passengers to carry two pieces of luggage (of a certain maximum size) onto the plane. However, their studies show that the more carry-on baggage passengers have, the longer it takes the plane to unload and load passengers. One regional airline is considering changing its policy to allow only one carry-on per passenger. Before doing so, it decided to collect some data. Specifically, a random sample of 1,000 passengers was selected. The passengers were observed, and the number of bags each carried onto the plane was counted. The passengers are divided into two groups: those with fewer than two bags and those with two or more bags. Suppose 404 passengers had fewer than two bags each. Of these, 181 people responded "yes" to a question about whether the airline should limit the number of bags to one. Of those in the group with two bags, 123 indicated "yes" to the question. Using this information, construct and interpret a 95% confidence interval estimate for the difference in proportion of "yes" responses for the two groups. Do you find the results surprising?

Advanced Applications

9.42   ● Vintner Mortgage Company in Chicago, Illinois, markets residential and commercial loans to customers in the region. Recently, the company's board of directors asked whether the company had experienced a difference in the proportion of loan defaults between residential and commercial customers. To answer this question, company officials selected a random sample of 200 residential loans and 105 commercial loans that had been issued before 1995. The loans were analyzed to determine their status. A loan that was still being paid was labeled "Active," whereas a default loan was labeled "Default." The resulting data are in a CD-ROM file called *Vintner*.

a. Based on the sample data and a significance level equal to 0.05, does there appear to be a difference in the proportion of loan defaults between residential and commercial customers?

b. Prepare a short response to the Vintner board of directors. Include a graph of the data that supports your statistical analysis in your report.

c. Consider the outcome of the hypothesis test in part a. In the last five audits, 10 residential and 10 commercial customers were selected. In three of the audits, there were more residential than commercial loan defaults. Determine the probability of such an occurrence.

Summary and Conclusions

The process of using sample information to reach conclusions about the population from which the sample was selected is used extensively in business decision making. This inferential analysis takes on two forms: estimation and hypothesis testing. Chapter 7 introduced the fundamentals of statistical estimation. There we discussed how to formulate and interpret confidence interval estimates for a variety of population values involving one and two populations.

Chapter 8 introduced hypothesis testing in which we were interested in a single population value. It presented the basic concepts and discussed the types of statistical errors that can be made when a hypothesis is tested using sample information. In Chapter 9, we have extended the discussion of hypothesis testing to situations involving two populations. We specifically looked at situations in which the difference between two population means was the issue of concern. In some instances, the samples from the two populations are considered independent. In other cases, to control for potential sources of variation, we paired the samples and used a paired-sample test to determine whether the population means were different.

In addition to tests about the difference in population means, this chapter introduced hypothesis testing for the difference in two population proportions.

You may have difficulty in determining which procedure to use in a given situation. Figure 9-9 shows a flow diagram that you might find useful. As you work the problems at the end of the chapter, you might use this diagram to help you sort through the options.

EQUATIONS

Confidence Interval Format

Point Estimate ± (Critical Value)(Standard Error)   **9-1**

Standard Error of $\bar{x}_1 - \bar{x}_2$ When σ_1 and σ_2 Are Known

$$\sigma_{\bar{x}_1 - \bar{x}_2} = \sqrt{\frac{\sigma_1^2}{n_1} + \frac{\sigma_2^2}{n_2}}$$ **9-2**

Confidence Interval Estimate for $\mu_1 - \mu_2$ When σ_1 and σ_2 Are Known, Large Independent Samples

$$(\bar{x}_1 - \bar{x}_2) \pm z_{\alpha/2}\sqrt{\frac{\sigma_1^2}{n_1} + \frac{\sigma_2^2}{n_2}}$$ **9-3**

Confidence Interval Estimate for $\mu_1 - \mu_2$ When σ_1 and σ_2 Are Unknown, Large Independent Samples

$$(\bar{x}_1 - \bar{x}_2) \pm z_{\alpha/2}\sqrt{\frac{s_1^2}{n_1} + \frac{s_2^2}{n_2}}$$ **9-4**

Confidence Interval Estimate for $\mu_1 - \mu_2$ When σ_1 and σ_2 Are Unknown, Small Independent Samples

$$(\bar{x}_1 - \bar{x}_2) \pm t_{\alpha/2}s_p\sqrt{\frac{1}{n_1} + \frac{1}{n_2}}$$ **9-5**

FIGURE 9-9

**Estimation and Hypothesis
Testing Flow Diagram**

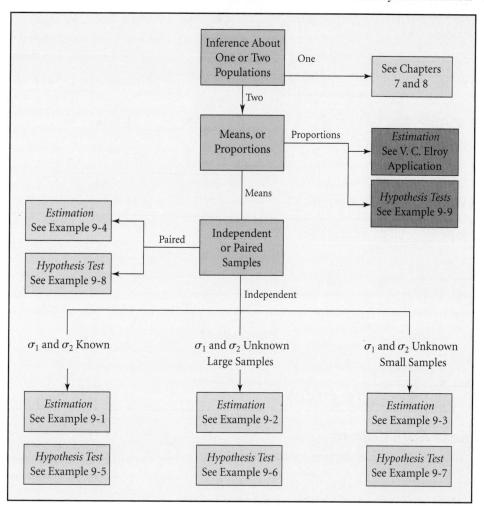

Confidence Interval Estimate for $\mu_1 - \mu_2$ When σ_1 and σ_2 Are Unknown and Not Equal, Small Independent Samples

$$(\bar{x}_1 - \bar{x}_2) \pm t_{\alpha/2} \sqrt{\frac{s_1^2}{n_1} + \frac{s_2^2}{n_2}} \qquad \textbf{9-6}$$

Paired Difference

$$d = x_1 - x_2 \qquad \textbf{9-7}$$

Point Estimate for the Population Mean Paired Difference, μ_d

$$\bar{d} = \frac{\sum_{i=1}^{n} d_i}{n} \qquad \textbf{9-8}$$

Sample Standard Deviation for Paired Differences

$$s_d = \sqrt{\frac{\sum_{i=1}^{n} (d_i - \bar{d})^2}{n - 1}} \qquad \textbf{9-9}$$

Confidence Interval Estimate for Population Mean Paired Difference, μ_d

$$\bar{d} \pm t_{\alpha/2} \frac{s_d}{\sqrt{n}} \qquad \textbf{9-10}$$

z Test Statistic for $\mu_1 - \mu_2$ When σ_1 and σ_2 Are Known, Large Independent Samples

$$z = \frac{(\bar{x}_1 - \bar{x}_2) - (\mu_1 - \mu_2)}{\sqrt{\frac{\sigma_1^2}{n_1} + \frac{\sigma_2^2}{n_2}}} \qquad \textbf{9-11}$$

z Test Statistic for $\mu_1 - \mu_2$ When σ_1 and σ_2 Are Unknown, Large Independent Samples

$$z = \frac{(\bar{x}_1 - \bar{x}_2) - (\mu_1 - \mu_2)}{\sqrt{\frac{s_1^2}{n_1} + \frac{s_2^2}{n_2}}} \qquad \textbf{9-12}$$

t Test Statistic for $\mu_1 - \mu_2$ When σ_1 and σ_2 Are Unknown, Small Independent Samples

$$t = \frac{(\bar{x}_1 - \bar{x}_2) - (\mu_1 - \mu_2)}{s_p \sqrt{\frac{1}{n_1} + \frac{1}{n_2}}}, \qquad df = n_1 + n_2 - 2 \qquad \textbf{9-13}$$

t Test Statistic for $\mu_1 - \mu_2$ When Population Variances Are Not Equal

$$t = \frac{(\bar{x}_1 - \bar{x}_2) - (\mu_1 - \mu_2)}{\sqrt{\frac{s_1^2}{n_1} + \frac{s_2^2}{n_2}}} \qquad \textbf{9-14}$$

Degrees of Freedom for t Test Statistic When Population Variances Are Not Equal

$$\frac{(s_1^2/n_1 + s_2^2/n_2)^2}{\left(\dfrac{(s_1^2/n_1)^2}{n_1 - 1} + \dfrac{(s_2^2/n_2)^2}{n_2 - 1}\right)} \qquad \text{9-15}$$

t Test Statistic for Paired Sample Test

$$t = \frac{\bar{d} - \mu_d}{\dfrac{s_d}{\sqrt{n}}} \qquad df = (n - 1) \qquad \text{9-16}$$

Confidence Interval Estimate for $p_1 - p_2$

$$(\bar{p}_1 - \bar{p}_2) \pm z_{\alpha/2}\sqrt{\frac{(\bar{p}_1)(1 - \bar{p}_1)}{n_1} + \frac{(\bar{p}_2)(1 - \bar{p}_2)}{n_2}} \qquad \text{9-17}$$

Pooled Estimator for Overall Proportion

$$\bar{p} = \frac{n_1\bar{p}_1 + n_2\bar{p}_2}{n_1 + n_2} = \frac{x_1 + x_2}{n_1 + n_2} \qquad \text{9-18}$$

z Test Statistic for Difference Between Population Proportions

$$z = \frac{(\bar{p}_1 - \bar{p}_2) - (p_1 - p_2)}{\sqrt{\bar{p}(1 - \bar{p})\left(\dfrac{1}{n_1} + \dfrac{1}{n_2}\right)}} \qquad \text{9-19}$$

Key Terms

Independent Samples, 346

Paired Samples, 353

CHAPTER EXERCISES

Business Applications

9.43 Recently at a sales meeting of the Fitness Service Company, the statement was made that there is no difference in the average whole life insurance coverage for clients in the two states. Managers decided a test of this statement should be made because the conclusion could affect the sales promotion that was being planned.

To test the claim, a random sample of 65 clients was selected from Wisconsin and another sample of 85 clients was selected from Ohio. The sample was analyzed, with these results:

Wisconsin	Ohio
$\bar{x}_1 = \$58,740$	$\bar{x}_2 = \$54,900$
$s_1 = \$24,800$	$s_2 = \$27,920$

Assuming that a significance level equal to 0.05 is used, based on the sample data, what should the Fitness Service Company conclude? Conduct the hypothesis test using a p-value approach. Discuss.

9.44 A book publisher claims that undergraduates are more likely to buy used textbooks than graduate students. The publisher's marketing department selected two random samples of 200 undergraduate students and 100 graduate students, respectively, at Arizona State University. The students were asked whether they had purchased a used textbook this term. Of the undergraduates, 138 said "yes," whereas 59 of the graduates said "yes."
a. Using a significance level of 0.05, what should the publisher conclude?
b. Based on the results of this survey, should the publisher extend its conclusions to all undergraduates and graduates at any university? Discuss.

9.45 A college official claimed that there is no difference between athletes and nonathletes in terms of the proportion of credits taken that apply toward graduation. To test this two random samples were selected. First a random sample of 200 courses taken by athletes was selected. Of these 144 were judged to count toward the degree of the person taking the course. The second sample consisted of 500 courses taken by nonathletes. Of these, 402 were deemed to apply toward the graduation requirements of the students involved. Using a significance level equal to 0.05 what conclusion should be reached about the official's claim regarding athletes and nonathletes?

9.46 Hamilton Bank & Trust operates banks throughout Wisconsin. Management is very concerned about making sure that a standard of quality service is achieved. For instance, they are interested in whether there is a difference in standard deviation in service times for customers who use the drive-up window versus those who go inside to the teller windows.

One branch in Madison recently was the subject of evaluation. A sample of 13 drive-up customers was selected, and a sample of 9 inside-counter customers was selected. The time (in minutes) it took each customer to be served was recorded. The following statistics were computed from the sample data.

Drive-Up	Walk-In
$\bar{x}_1 = 8.5$	$\bar{x}_2 = 8.4$
$s_1 = 2.0$	$s_2 = 1.2$

Suppose the managers are also interested in testing whether there is a difference in average time it takes to service the two types of customers. State the appropriate nu and alternative hypotheses and test using $\alpha = 0.05$. Based on part a, comment on the validity of this latter test concerning the population means.

9.47 Last year the city of Bellingham in Selina County, Georgia, undertook a campaign to consolidate the city and county governments. The premise was that proportionately more people in the city would favor the concept than in the outlying county area. This was because the county residents might expect a tax increase from the consolidation even though the proponents of the plan promised a tax reduction in the long run. A polling agency was hired to conduct a study of this issue. It randomly selected 100 people in the city and 75 people in the county. It found 62 city dwellers favored the idea and 36 county residents favored the plan. Based on the sample results, what should be concluded about the proportions favoring the consolidation when the city residents are compared with the county residents? Use a significance level of 0.10.

9.48 A local restaurant is interested in determining whether the dollar amount of lunches ordered by males has greater variability than those ordered by females. To conduct the test, random samples of 25 males and 25 females were selected from people who had lunch during the last month. The following statistics were computed from the sample data:

Males	Females
$\bar{x}_1 = \$12.40$	$\bar{x}_2 = \$8.92$
$s_1 = \$2.50$	$s_2 = \$1.34$

Suppose the manager is also interested in determining whether there is a significant difference in the average dollar amount spent on lunch between men and women. The manager believes that only a difference of $1.00 or more would be considered significant. State the appropriate null and alternative hypotheses and test using $\alpha = 0.05$.

9.49 The owners of Campbell Electronics decided to place an advertisement on television to be shown three times during a live broadcast of the local university's football game. They hope that their average sales per day would increase so that they would recoup the cost of the advertisements during any seven randomly selected days after the football game. The advertisements cost a total of $3,500. The sales for each of the seven days after the ad was placed were to be compared with the sales for the seven days immediately before the ad ran. The following data, representing the total dollar sales each day, were collected:

Sales Before the Ad	Sales After the Ad
$1,765	$2,045
1,543	2,456
2,867	2,590
1,490	1,510
2,800	2,850
1,379	1,255
2,097	2,255

a. What assumptions must be made about the population distributions in order to test the hypothesis using the t-distribution?

b. Based on the sample data, what conclusions should be reached with respect to average sales before versus after the advertisement?

9.50 The Wilcox Company sells breakable china through a mail-order system that has been very profitable. One of its major problems is freight damage. Wilcox insures the items at shipping, but the inconvenience to the customer when a piece gets broken can cause the customer not to place another order in the future. Thus, packaging is important to Wilcox.

In the past, the company has purchased two different packaging materials from two suppliers. The assumption was that there would be no difference in proportion of damaged shipments resulting from use of either packaging material. The sales manager recently decided a study of this issue should be done. Therefore, a random sample of 300 orders using shipping material 1 and a random sample of 250 orders using material 2 were pulled from the files. The number of damaged parcels, x, was recorded for each material, as follows:

Material 1	Material 2
$n_1 = 300$	$n_2 = 250$
$x_1 = 19$	$x_2 = 12$

a. Is the normal distribution a good approximation for the distribution of the difference between the sample proportions? Provide support for your answer.
b. Based on the sample information and an alpha = 0.03 level, what should the Wilcox Company conclude?

9.51 The makers of Hot Mix Chili in Houston, Texas, have a product that, by seasoning standards, is one of the hottest on the market. They have marketed this product under the assumption that there is no difference between men and women in their preference for spicy foods. The marketing manager decided that she would test this assumption by taking two samples of 280 men and 280 women, respectively, and letting them taste Hot Mix Chili and a milder variety offered by a competitor. The people were asked to select which chili they liked better based on the seasoning. The results showed that 81 men preferred Hot Mix Chili and 74 women preferred Hot Mix Chili.
a. Determine if the sample difference of the proportion of women and men who prefer Hot Mix Chili can be properly approximated with a normal distribution.
b. Using a significance level of 0.10, what conclusions should the marketing manager reach based on these sample data?

Advanced Applications

9.52 Bach Photographs has studios in two locations. Among the factors the owner is interested in monitoring is whether the mean value in customer orders per day for the two locations is the same. A random sample of 11 days' orders for the two locations showed the following data:

Location A			Location B		
$444	$478	$501	$233	$127	$230
200	400	350	299	250	300
167	250	300	800	340	400
300	600		780	370	

The owner wishes to know the difference between the average amount in customer orders per day for the two locations. He has no idea what this difference might be. What procedure would you use under these circumstances? Explain your reasoning.

9.53   The manager of a local engine repair service is considering mailing out a large number of discount coupons. Two types of coupons would be mailed. The first offers discounts on engine tune-ups. The second offers discounts on brake work. Before doing the mass mailing, a sample of 90 potential customers was selected to receive the tune-up coupon, and a sample of 90 potential customers received the brake-work coupon. A total of 11 engine tune-up coupons were redeemed, and 15 brake-work coupons were redeemed. The owner is interested in determining whether this sample information indicates that there will be a difference in the proportion of coupons of the two types that will be redeemed after the mass mailing is sent.

a. Based on the sample data and a significance level equal to 0.05, what conclusion should the owner reach? Conduct the hypothesis test using the *p*-value approach.

b. Discuss in terms that the shop owner can understand what Type I and Type II errors are as they relate to this situation. Also discuss the relative costs associated with each type of error. Which type of error might have been committed in this case?

9.54   U.S. automakers have been criticized in some circles for the poor quality of U.S. cars when compared with their foreign competitors. In fact, one trade publication has indicated that the percentage of U.S.-made cars having serious mechanical troubles within two years from purchase is greater than that for foreign cars after five years of ownership. If this allegation were to be substantiated, it would be a severe blow to the U.S. automakers' efforts to contradict their poor quality image. To test this claim, a random sample of 60 U.S.-car owners and another sample of 70 foreign-car owners were selected. It found that 12 owners of U.S. cars had severe mechanical problems within the first two years, and 13 foreign-car owners had severe mechanical problems within the first five years of ownership.

a. Discuss what a Type I and a Type II error would be in this situation, and provide an assessment of the relative costs of each.

b. Based on a significance level of 0.02, what conclusion should be reached? Discuss.

9.55   The makers of Bounce Back glass backboards for basketball gymnasiums have claimed that their board is more durable, on the average, than the leading backboard made by Swoosh Company. Products Testing Services of Des Moines, Iowa, was hired to verify this claim. It selected a random sample of 50 backboards of each type and subjected the boards to a pressure test to determine how much weight is needed to break each company's backboard. The following results were determined from the testing process:

Swoosh	Bounce Back
$\bar{x}_1 = 653$ lbs	$\bar{x}_2 = 691$ lbs
$s_1 = 112$ lbs	$s_2 = 105$ lbs

a. Assuming that the more pounds it takes to break the backboard, the better it is, state the appropriate null and alternative hypotheses.

b. At a significance level of 0.01, what conclusion should be reached with respect to the claim made by the Bounce Back Company? Discuss.

c. Suppose the hypothesis test were conducted at a significance level of 0.10, instead of 0.01. Would this change the conclusion reached based on the sample data? If so, discuss why; if not, discuss why not.

9.56   The Barton Family Bakery makes and sells a variety of specialty breads at its Fifth Street location. The production scheduler believes that white bread outsells wheat bread. Specifically, he believes that the average number of white loaves sold per day exceeds the average number for wheat bread. To test this, a sample of past days' sales was selected. The data are contained in the CD-ROM file called *Bakery*.

a. Based on the sample data, what conclusions should the production manager reach about the sales of white and wheat bread? Test the hypothesis using a significance level of 0.05.

b. Discuss your results in a report that uses appropriate graphs.

9.57   The Capital Bank marketing department has recently conducted a study of a sample of the bank's customers. At issue is whether there is a difference between the mean credit card balance between female and male customers. If they find that the two groups differ, they will target the lower group with a marketing campaign designed to increase their use of the credit card. The sample data for this study are in the CD-ROM file called *Capital*.

Based on the sample data, what conclusion should the Capital Bank reach about the mean balances for males and females? Test using a significance level of 0.05.

9.58   The makers of a new chemical fertilizer claim that hay yields will average 0.40 tons more per acre if its fertilizer is used than if the leading brand is used. The agricultural testing service at Oregon State University was retained to test this claim. A random sample of 52 acre-sized plots was selected, and the new fertilizer was applied. A second sample of 40 acre-sized plots was selected, and the leading fertilizer was used. The following sample data (in tons per acre) were observed:

Current Leading Brand	New Product
$n_1 = 40$	$n_2 = 52$
$\bar{x}_1 = 4.3$ tons/acre	$\bar{x}_2 = 5.2$ tons/acre
$s_1 = 0.8$ tons	$s_2 = 0.7$ tons

a. If alpha is set at 0.05, what conclusion should be reached with respect to the claim made by the makers of the new fertilizer? Discuss.

b. Determine the largest significance level at which this test could indicate the new hay yields would average more than 0.40 tons per acre more if this fertilizer were used than if the leading brand is used.

9.59   In planning for graduation, the university graduation chairperson based her seat assignments on the assumption that the proportion of undergraduates attending would exceed the proportion of graduate students attending. A member of the graduation committee suggested that before making firm plans, they should survey students to see whether the assumption of the chairperson is correct. A sample of 80 undergraduates showed that 46 planned to attend, whereas a sample of 60 graduate students showed 26 planned to attend.

a. Based on the sample data, what conclusions should the committee reach concerning the proportion of graduate and undergraduates who plan to attend the ceremony? Assume they plan to test the hypothesis using a significance level of 0.05. Discuss.

b. Suppose there are 2,000 undergraduates and 500 graduates who are eligible to graduate. Determine the number of seats that should be reserved for the graduate and undergraduate students. Explain your answer.

CASE 9-A:

Green Valley Assembly Company

The Green Valley Assembly Company assembles consumer electronics products for manufacturers that need temporary extra production capacity. As such, it has periodic product changes. Because the products Green Valley assembles are marketed under the label of well-known manufacturers, high quality is a must.

Tom Bradley of the Green Valley personnel department has been very impressed by recent research concerning job-enrichment programs. In particular, he has been impressed with the increases in quality that seem to be associated with these programs. However, some studies have shown no significant increase in quality, and they imply that the money spent on such programs has not been worthwhile.

Tom has talked to Sandra Hansen, the production manager, about instituting a job-enrichment program in the assembly operation at Green Valley. Sandra was somewhat pessimistic about the potential, but she agreed to introduce the program. The plan was to implement the program in one wing of the plant and continue with the current method in the other wing. The procedure was to be in effect for six months. After that period, a test would be made to determine the effectiveness of the job-enrichment program.

After the six-month trial period, a random sample of employees from each wing produced the following output measures:

OLD	JOB-ENRICHED
$n_1 = 50$	$n_2 = 50$
$\bar{x}_1 = 11/hr$	$\bar{x}_2 = 9.7/hr$
$s_1 = 1.2/hr$	$s_2 = 0.9/hr$

Both Sandra and Tom wonder whether the job-enrichment program has affected production output. They would like to use these sample results to determine whether the average output has changed and to determine whether the employees' consistency has been affected by the new program.

A second sample from each wing was selected. The measure was the quality of the products assembled. In the "old" wing, 79 products were tested and 12% were found to be defectively assembled. In the "job-enriched" wing, 123 products were examined and 9% were judged defectively assembled.

With all these data, Sandra and Tom are beginning to get a little confused. However, they realize that there must be some way to use the information in order to make a judgment about the effectiveness of the job-enrichment program.

CASE 9-B:

U-Need-It Rental Agency

Richard Fundt has operated the U-Need-It rental agency in a northern Wisconsin city for the past five years. One of the biggest rental items has always been chainsaws; lately, the demand for these saws has increased dramatically. Richard buys chainsaws at a special industrial rate and then rents them for $10 per day. The chainsaws are used an average of 50 to 60 days per year. Although Richard makes money on any chainsaw, he obviously makes more on those saws that last the longest.

Richard worked for a time as a repairperson and can make most repairs on the equipment he rents, including chainsaws. However, he would also like to limit the time he spends making repairs. U-Need-It is currently stocking two types of saws: North Woods and Accu-Cut. Richard has an impression that one of the models, Accu-Cut, does not seem to break down as much as the other. Richard presently has 8 North Woods saws and 11 Accu-Cut

saws. He decides to keep track of the number of hours each is used between major repairs. He finds the following values, in hours:

ACCU-CUT		NORTH WOODS	
48	46	48	78
39	88	44	94
84	29	72	59
76	52	19	52
41	57		
24			

The North Woods sales representative has stated that the company may be raising the price of its saws in the near future. This will make them slightly more expensive than the Accu-Cut models. However, the prices have tended to move with each other in the p

General References

1. Berenson, Mark L., and David M. Levine, *Basic Business Statistics Concepts and Applications*, 7th ed. (Upper Saddle River, NJ: Prentice Hall, 1999).

2. Cryer, Jonathan D., and Robert B. Miller, *Statistics for Business: Data Analysis and Modeling*, 2nd ed. (Belmont, CA: Duxbury Press, 1994).

3. Johnson, Richard A. and Dean W. Wichern, *Business Statistics: Decision Making with Data* (New York: John Wiley & Sons, 1997).

4. Larsen, Richard J., Morris L. Marx, and Bruce Cooil, *Statistics for Applied Problem Solving and Decision Makir* (Pacific Grove, CA: Duxbury Press, 1997).

5. *Microsoft Excel 2000* (Redmond, WA: Microsoft Corp., 1999).

6. *Minitab for Windows Version 13* (State College, PA: Minitab, 2000).

7. Siegel, Andrew F., *Practical Business Statistics*, 4th ed. (Burr Ridge, IL: Irwin, 2000).

CHAPTER 10

Hypothesis Tests for One and Two Population Variances

CHAPTER OUTCOMES

After studying the material in Chapter 10, you should be able to:

- Formulate and carry out hypothesis tests for a single population variance.
- Formulate and carry out hypothesis tests for the difference between two population variances.

WHY YOU NEED TO KNOW

Chapters 8 and 9 introduced the concepts of hypothesis testing for one and two population means and proportions. There are also business situations where decision makers must reach a conclusion about the value of a single population variance, or about the relationship between two population variances. For example, knowing that a machine fills soda bottles with a specific average fill rate may not be enough. The manager must also be concerned about the variability in the fill rate. If the machine is too variable, then some bottles may be underfilled and will cause problems with consumers who believe they have been cheated. If the machine overfills the bottles, then soda is wasted and unnecessary costs are incurred in the bottling process. The manager in this case must monitor both the average fill and the variation in the fill of the bottling

process. A manager may also be required to decide if there is a difference in the variability of sales between two different sales territories, or if the output of one production process is more or less variable than another. Just as we have tools and techniques for tests involving population means and proportions, we also have tools and techniques for testing a single population variance and two population variances. In this chapter we discuss methods that can be used to make inferences concerning one and two population variances. The techniques presented in this chapter will also introduce new distributions that will be used in later chapters of the textbook. When reading this chapter keep in mind that the techniques discussed here are extensions of the hypothesis testing concepts introduced in Chapters 8 and 9.

10-1 HYPOTHESES TESTS FOR A SINGLE POPULATION VARIANCE

In the previous two chapters, we concentrated on examples involving population means or proportions. However, in many cases you will be as interested in the spread of a population as in its central location. For instance, military planes designed to penetrate enemy defenses have a ground-following radar system. The radar tells the pilot exactly how far the plane is above the ground. A radar unit that is correct *on the average* is useless if the readings are distributed widely around the average value. Many airport shuttle systems have stopping sensors to deposit passengers at the correct spot in a terminal. A sensor that, *on the average*, lets passengers off at the correct point could leave many irritated people long distances up and down the track. Therefore, many product specifications involve both an average value and some limit on the dispersion that the individual values can have. For example, the specification for a steel push pin may be an average length of 1.78 inches plus or minus 0.01 inch. A company using these pins would be interested in both the average length and how much these pins vary in length.

Usually when we think of measuring variation, the standard deviation is used as the measure because it is measured in the same units as the mean. Ideally, in the ground-following radar example, we would want to test to see whether the standard deviation exceeds a certain level, as determined by the product specifications. Unfortunately, there is no statistical test that directly tests the standard deviation. However, there is a test called the chi-square test that can be used to test the population variance. We can convert any standard deviation application into one involving the variance, as shown in the following example.

CHI-SQUARE TEST FOR A ONE POPULATION VARIANCE

H & L Machines—H & L Machines services copy machines. Looking at past records and manufacturer recommendations, the company determined the mean service time for a properly trained staff working on a Kodak Image Source 85 should be 2 hours, with a standard deviation not to exceed 0.5 hour. Past data indicate that the 2-hour average is being achieved. However, variability may be excessive. The service schedule is built around the assumptions of $\mu = 2$ hours and $\sigma = 0.5$ hour. If the service-time standard deviation exceeds 0.5 hour, the service schedule gets disrupted.

The service manager has decided to select a sample of service calls and use the sample data to determine whether the service-time standard deviation exceeds 0.5 hour. The methodology for conducting such a test is generally the same as for testing a population mean or proportion.

Ideally, the manager would like to test the following null and alternative hypotheses.

$$H_0: \sigma \leq 0.5$$
$$H_A: \sigma > 0.5$$

Because there is no statistical technique for directly testing hypotheses about a population standard deviation, she will use a test for a population variance. We first convert the standard deviation to a variance by squaring the standard deviation, and then restate the null and alternative hypotheses as follows:

$$H_0: \sigma^2 \leq 0.25$$
$$H_A: \sigma^2 > 0.25$$

As with all hypothesis tests, the decision to reject or accept the null hypothesis will be based on the value computed from the sample. In testing hypotheses about a single population variance, the appropriate sample value is s^2, the *sample variance*.

To test a null hypothesis about a population variance, we compare s^2 with the hypothesized population variance, σ^2. To do this, we need to standardize the distribution of the sample variance in much the same way as we used the z-distribution and the t-distribution when testing hypotheses about the population mean.

SSUMPTION

If the random sample is from a normally distributed population, the distribution for the standardized sample variance is a *chi-square distribution*.

The chi-square distribution is a continuous distribution of a standardized random variable, computed by using Equation 10-1.

Chi-Square Test for a Single Population Variance

$$\chi^2 = \frac{(n-1)s^2}{\sigma^2}$$

10-1

where:

χ^2 = Standardized chi-square variable
n = Sample size
s^2 = Sample variance
σ^2 = Hypothesized variance

Examining Equation 10-1, you will note that this test statistic can be rewritten as

$$\chi^2 = \frac{(n-1)s^2}{\sigma^2} = \frac{(n-1)\frac{\Sigma(x-\bar{x})^2}{n-1}}{\sigma^2} = \frac{\Sigma(x-\bar{x})^2}{\sigma^2} = \Sigma\left(\frac{x-\bar{x}}{\sigma}\right)^2$$

If the sample is obtained from a normal distribution, the last expression inside the parentheses is essentially a z-value. Recall that $z = \frac{x-\mu}{\sigma}$. Therefore, χ^2 is the sum of squared z-values. When a z-value from a normal distribution is squared, it produces a chi-squared variable with one degree of freedom. The sum of n independent chi-squared variables is also a chi-squared random variable with n degrees of freedom. Here, however, we must estimate the population mean using the sample mean (because μ is unknown) before we estimate the population variance using s^2. You may recall from the discussion concerning degrees of freedom in Chapter 7 that this reduces the degrees of freedom by one. Therefore, the distribution of χ^2 is a chi-squared distribution with $n-1$ degrees of freedom.

The central location and shape of the chi-square distribution depends only on the degrees of freedom, $n-1$. Figure 10-1 illustrates chi-square distributions for various degrees of freedom. Note that as the degrees of freedom increase, the chi-square distribution becomes more symmetrical.

Returning to the H & L Machines example, suppose the dispatch manager took a sample of 20 service calls and found a variance of 0.33 hours squared. Figure 10-2 illustrates the hypothesis test at a significance level of 0.10.

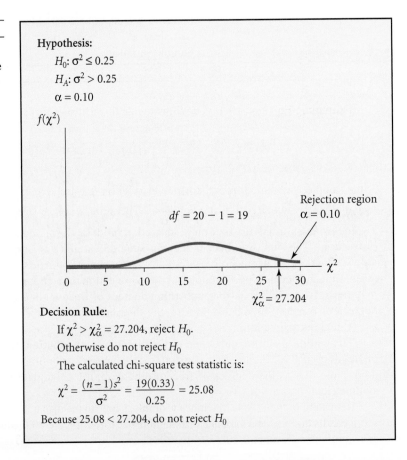

FIGURE 10-1

Chi-Square Distributions

Appendix G contains a table of chi-square values for various probabilities and degrees of freedom. The use of the chi-square table is similar to the use of the t-distribution table. For example, to find the critical value, χ^2_α, for the H & L Machines example, determine the

$$\text{degrees of freedom, } n - 1 = 20 - 1 = 19, \text{ and}$$
$$\text{the desired significance level, } 0.10.$$

Now go to the chi-square table under the column headed 0.10 and find the χ^2 value in this column that intersects the row corresponding to the appropriate degrees of freedom. You should find the critical value of $\chi^2_\alpha = 27.204$.

As you can see in Figure 10-2, the chi-square test statistic, calculated using Equation 10-1, is

$$\chi^2 = 25.08.$$

This falls to the left of the rejection region, meaning the manager should not reject the null hypothesis based on these sample data. Thus, based on these results, there is insufficient evidence to conclude that the service representatives should complete their service calls with a standard deviation of more than 0.5 hours.

FIGURE 10-2

Chi-square Test for One Population Variance for the H & L Machines Example

Hypothesis:

$H_0: \sigma^2 \leq 0.25$

$H_A: \sigma^2 > 0.25$

$\alpha = 0.10$

$f(\chi^2)$

$df = 20 - 1 = 19$

Rejection region
$\alpha = 0.10$

χ^2

0   5   10   15   20   25   30

$\chi^2_\alpha = 27.204$

Decision Rule:

If $\chi^2 > \chi^2_\alpha = 27.204$, reject H_0.

Otherwise do not reject H_0

The calculated chi-square test statistic is:

$$\chi^2 = \frac{(n-1)s^2}{\sigma^2} = \frac{19(0.33)}{0.25} = 25.08$$

Because 25.08 < 27.204, do not reject H_0

SUMMARY: HYPOTHESES TESTS FOR A POPULATION VARIANCE

1. Specify the population value of interest.

2. Formulate the null and alternative hypotheses in terms of σ^2, the population variance.

3. Specify the level of significance for the hypothesis test.

4. Construct the rejection region.

    Obtain the critical value, χ^2_α, from the chi-square distribution table.

5. Compute the test statistic.
    Select a random sample and compute the sample variance,

$$s^2 = \frac{\Sigma(x - \bar{x})^2}{n - 1}$$

    Based on the sample variance, $\chi^2 = \frac{(n - 1)s^2}{\sigma^2}$

6. Reach a decision.

7. Draw a conclusion.

EXAMPLE 10-1: HYPOTHESES TESTS FOR A POPULATION VARIANCE

Abo Manufacturing Company   One specification listed in the contract between the Abo Manufacturing Company and its customers concerns the variability in the diameter of the part being supplied. Before shipping a batch of parts, Abo employees take a random sample of 20 parts from the batch and test to see whether the standard deviation exceeds the 0.05-inch specification. This can be done using the following steps.

Step 1:   Specify the population value of interest.
The variability in the diameter of a part is the value of interest.

Step 2:   Specify the null and alternative hypotheses.
The null and alternative hypotheses must be stated in terms of the population variance, so we convert the specification, $\sigma = 0.05$, to the variance, $\sigma^2 = 0.0025$. The null and alternative hypotheses are

$$H_0: \sigma^2 \leq 0.0025$$
$$H_A: \sigma^2 > 0.0025$$

Step 3:   Specify the significance level.
The hypothesis test will be conducted using $\alpha = 0.05$.

Step 4:   Construct the rejection region.
The critical value from the chi-square distribution with $20 - 1 = 19$ degrees of freedom and 0.05 level of significance is

$$\chi^2_\alpha = \chi^2_{0.05} = 30.1435$$

The decision rule is stated as:

If $\chi^2 > \chi^2_{0.05} = 30.1435$, reject H_0; otherwise, do not reject.

Step 5:   Compute the test statistic.
The random sample of $n = 20$ parts gives a sample variance for part diameter of

$$s^2 = \frac{\Sigma(x - \bar{x})^2}{n - 1} = 0.0108.$$

The test statistic is

$$\chi^2 = \frac{(n - 1)s^2}{\sigma^2} = \frac{(20 - 1)0.0108}{0.0025} = 82.08$$

Step 6:   Reach a decision.
Because $\chi^2 = 82.08 > 30.1435$, reject the null hypothesis.

Step 7:   Draw a conclusion.
Conclude that the variance of the population does exceed the 0.0025 limit. The company appears to have a problem with its product variation.

10-1: EXERCISES

Skill Development

10.1 Find the critical value of the chi-square distribution for each of the following situations:
a. H_A: $\sigma^2 > 0.25$, $n = 10$, $\alpha = 0.05$
b. H_A: $\sigma^2 > 20$, $n = 20$, $\alpha = 0.025$
c. H_A: $\sigma^2 \neq 0.25$, $n = 10$, $\alpha = 0.10$

10.2 Determine the p-value for each of the following situations:
a. H_A: $\sigma^2 > 0.25$, $n = 10$,
and test statistic $\chi^2 = 16.919$
b. H_A: $\sigma^2 > 13$, $n = 21$,
and test statistic $\chi^2 = 35.0196$
c. H_A: $\sigma^2 \neq 7.80$, $n = 23$,
and test statistic $\chi^2 = 35.1725$

10.3 Given the following null and alternative hypotheses,
$$H_0: \sigma^2 \leq 12$$
$$H_A: \sigma^2 > 12$$
a. Test if $n = 13$, $s = 4.5$, and $\alpha = 0.10$. Be sure to show the decision rule.
b. Test if $n = 30$, $s^2 = 21$, and $\alpha = 0.05$. Show the decision rule.

10.4 Given the following null and alternative hypotheses,
$$H_0: \sigma^2 \leq 40$$
$$H_A: \sigma^2 > 40$$
a. Test if $n = 10$, $s = 7$, and $\alpha = 0.05$. Be sure to show the decision rule.
b. Test if $n = 30$, $s^2 = 54$, and $\alpha = 0.10$. Show the decision rule.

10.5 Given the following null and alternative hypotheses,
$$H_0: \sigma^2 \leq 300$$
$$H_A: \sigma^2 > 300$$
a. Test if $n = 20$, $s = 20$, and $\alpha = 0.05$. Be sure to show the decision rule.
b. Test if $n = 15$, $s^2 = 367$, and $\alpha = 0.10$. Show the decision rule.

Business Applications

10.6 TranCo operates the city bus service for a large southern city. One of the keys to satisfying bus riders is that the buses run on schedule. One important part of this requires that the variation in travel time for the bus route be controlled. Suppose on one particular bus route, the company wants the standard deviation in travel time to be no greater than 2 minutes. To test this, a random sample of 15 trips is selected.
a. State the appropriate null and alternative hypotheses. (Remember, there is not a test procedure for testing the standard deviations directly.)
b. Assuming that the company wishes to test the null hypothesis in part a using a significance level equal to 0.05, what conclusion should be reached if the sample standard deviation is 2.86 minutes? Discuss your result.

10.7 One dimension of quality for a city fire department is the time it takes from when a call for help arrives until a crew is on the scene. Two aspects of this quality measure are important: the mean time to arrival and the variance of time to arrival. Suppose the fire chief wishes the variance for response time to be no greater than 2,025 seconds squared.
a. State the appropriate null and alternative hypotheses.
b. Assume that a simple random sample of 20 calls results in a sample variance of 3,000 seconds squared. Based on this sample value and a significance level equal to 0.10, what should the chief conclude? Discuss.

10.8 The Hagluud Corporation manufactures paint and stain products for interior and exterior home and commercial applications. The new "Apple Wood Stain" product is thought to be a real improvement over some of the company's previous products. One criterion of a quality stain is the consistency of coverage per gallon. Hagluud hopes the standard deviation of the new stain will not exceed 20 square feet per gallon. The company R&D Department will assume the standard deviation does not exceed 20 square feet unless the data strongly suggest otherwise. To test this, they selected a random sample of 12 gallons and found the following coverage in square feet:

245	302	240	280	255	300	290	240	300	270	230	300

Perform a hypothesis test to determine if the consistency of coverage for the stain is as desired by Hagluud's R&D Department. Write one paragraph for the manager stating your conclusions concerning the stain's coverage consistency.

10.9 Airlines face the challenging task of keeping their planes on schedule. One key measure is the number of minutes a plane deviates from the targeted arrival time. Ideally, the measure for each arrival will be zero minutes, indicating that the plane arrived exactly on time. However, experience indicates that even under the best of circumstances there will be inherent variability. Suppose one major airline has set standards that require its planes to arrive, on average, on time, with a standard deviation not to exceed 2 minutes. To determine whether these standards are being met, each month the airline selects a random sample of 12 airplane arrivals and determines the number of minutes early or late each flight is. For last month, the times, rounded to the nearest minute, are

3	−7	4	2	−2	5	11	−3	4	6	−4	1

a. State the appropriate null and alternative hypotheses for testing the standard regarding the mean value. Test the hypothesis using a significance level equal to 0.05. What assumption will be required?
b. State the appropriate null and alternative hypotheses regarding the standard deviation. Use the sample data to conduct the hypothesis test with $\alpha = 0.05$.
c. Discuss the results of both tests. What should the airline conclude regarding its arrival standards? What factors could influence the arrival times of flights?

10.10 A software design firm has recently developed a prototype educational computer game for children. One of the important factors in the success of a game such as this is the time it takes a child to play the game. Two factors are important: the mean time it takes to play and the variability in time required from child to child. Experience indicates that the mean time should be 10 minutes or less, and the standard deviation should not exceed 4 minutes. The company decided to test this prototype with 10 children selected at random from the local school district. The following values represent the time (rounded to the nearest minute) each child spent completing the game.

9	14	11	8	13	15	11	10	7	12

a. The software developers will assume the mean time to completion of the game is 10 minutes or less unless the data strongly suggest otherwise. State the appropriate null and alternative hypotheses for testing the requirement regarding the mean value.

b. Referring to part a, test the hypothesis using a significance level equal to 0.10. What assumption will be required?

c. The software developers will assume the standard deviation of the time to completion of the game does not exceed 4 minutes unless the data strongly suggest otherwise. State the appropriate null and alternative hypotheses regarding the standard deviation. Use the sample data to conduct the hypothesis test with a significance level = 0.10.

Advanced Business Applications

10.11 The Fillmore Institute has established a service designed to help charities increase the amount of money they collect from their direct mail solicitations. Its consulting is aimed at increasing the mean dollar amount returned from each giver and also at reducing the variation in amount contributed from giver to giver. The Badke Foundation collects money for heart disease research. Over the past eight years, records show that the average contribution per returned envelope is $14.25, with a standard deviation of $6.44. Badke Foundation directors decided to try the Fillmore services on a test basis. They used the recommended letters and other request materials and sent out 1,000 requests. From these, 166 were returned. The data showing the dollars returned per giver are in the CD-ROM file *Badke*.

Based on the sample data, what conclusions should the Badke Foundation reach regarding the Fillmore consulting services? Use appropriate hypothesis tests with a significance level = 0.05 to reach your conclusions. (Hint: Use Excel's ChiInv function or Minitab's Calc > Probability Distributions command to obtain the critical value for the chi-square distribution.)

10-2 HYPOTHESIS TESTS FOR TWO POPULATION VARIANCES

F-TEST FOR TWO POPULATION VARIANCES

The previous section introduced a method for testing hypotheses involving a single population standard deviation. Recall that in order to conduct the test, we had to first convert the standard deviation to the variance. Then we used the chi-square distribution to determine whether the sample variance led us to reject the null hypothesis. However, decision makers are often faced with decision problems involving two population standard deviations. Although there is no hypothesis test that directly tests standard deviations, there is a procedure that can be used to test whether two populations have equal variances. We can formulate null and alternative hypotheses of the following forms. Note, the three different forms are equivalent and may be used interchangeably, depending on your preference.

Two-Tailed Test	Upper One-Tailed Test	Lower One-Tailed Test
Format 1		
$H_0:\ \sigma_1^2 - \sigma_2^2 = 0$	$H_0:\ \sigma_1^2 - \sigma_2^2 \leq 0$	$H_0:\ \sigma_1^2 - \sigma_2^2 \geq 0$
$H_A:\ \sigma_1^2 - \sigma_2^2 \neq 0$	$H_A:\ \sigma_1^2 - \sigma_2^2 > 0$	$H_A:\ \sigma_1^2 - \sigma_2^2 < 0$
Format 2		
$H_0:\ \sigma_1^2 = \sigma_2^2$	$H_0:\ \sigma_1^2 \leq \sigma_2^2$	$H_0:\ \sigma_1^2 \geq \sigma_2^2$
$H_A:\ \sigma_1^2 \neq \sigma_2^2$	$H_A:\ \sigma_1^2 > \sigma_2^2$	$H_A:\ \sigma_1^2 < \sigma_2^2$
Format 3		
$H_0:\ \dfrac{\sigma_1^2}{\sigma_2^2} = 1$	$H_0:\ \dfrac{\sigma_1^2}{\sigma_2^2} \leq 1$	$H_0:\ \dfrac{\sigma_1^2}{\sigma_2^2} \geq 1$
$H_A:\ \dfrac{\sigma_1^2}{\sigma_2^2} \neq 1$	$H_A:\ \dfrac{\sigma_1^2}{\sigma_2^2} > 1$	$H_A:\ \dfrac{\sigma_1^2}{\sigma_2^2} < 1$

In order to test a hypothesis involving two population variances, we first compute the sample variances. We then compute the test statistic shown as Equation 10-2.

F Test Statistic for Testing Whether Two Populations Have Equal Variances

$$F = \frac{s_i^2}{s_j^2} \quad (df: D_1 = n_i - 1 \quad \text{and} \quad D_2 = n_j - 1)$$

10-2

where:

n_i = Sample size from ith population

n_j = Sample size from jth population

s_i^2 = Sample variation from the ith population

s_j^2 = Sample variation from the jth population

Analyzing this test statistic requires that we introduce the F-distribution. Although it is beyond the scope of this book, statistical theory shows the F-distribution is equal to the ratio of two independent chi-square distributions. Like the chi-square and the t-distributions, the appropriate F-distribution is determined by its degrees of freedom. However, the F-distribution has two degrees of freedom, D_1 and D_2, that depend on the sample sizes for the variances in the numerator and denominator, respectively, in Equation 10-2.

In order to apply the F-distribution to test whether two population variances are equal, the following assumptions must be made:

SSUMPTIONS

- The populations are normally distributed.
- The sample variances are independent.

Independent sample variances will occur when the sample data are obtained in such a way that the values in one sample are in no way influenced by the values in the second sample.

Independent Samples

Samples selected from two or more populations in such a way that the occurrence of values in one sample has no influence on the probability of the occurrence of values in the other sample(s).

The test statistic shown in Equation 10-2 is formed as the ratio of two sample variances. There are two key points to remember when formulating this ratio.

1. For a two-tailed test, always place the larger sample variance in the numerator. This will make the calculated F-value greater than 1.0 and push the F-value toward the upper tail of the F-distribution.
2. For the one-tailed test, look to the alternative hypothesis. For the population that is *predicted* (based on the alternative hypothesis) to have the larger variance, place that sample variance in the numerator.

The following applications and examples will illustrate the specific methods used for testing for a difference between two population variances.

E. Coli Bacteria Testing—Recent years have seen several national scares involving contaminated meat carrying *E. coli* bacteria. The recommended preventative measure is to cook the meat at a required temperature. However, different meat patties cooked for the same amount of time will have different final internal temperatures because of variations in the patties and variations in burner temperatures. A regional fast-food chain will replace its current burners with one of two new digitally controlled models.

The chain's purchasing agents have arranged to sample 11 batches of meat cooked by burner model 1 and 13 batches of meat cooked by burner model 2 to learn if there is a difference in temperature variation between the two models. If a difference exists, the chain's managers have decided to select the model that provides the smaller variation in final internal meat temperature. Ideally they would like a test that compares standard deviations, but no such test exists. Instead they must convert the standard deviations to variances. The hypotheses are

Hypotheses:

$$H_0: \sigma_1^2 = \sigma_2^2$$
$$H_A: \sigma_1^2 \neq \sigma_2^2$$

The null and alternative hypotheses are formulated as a two-tailed test. Intuitively, you might reason that if the two population variances are actually equal, the sample variances should be approximately equal also. That would mean that the ratio of the two sample variances should be approximately one. We will reject the null hypothesis if one sample variance is significantly larger than the other and if the ratio of sample variances is significantly greater than one. The managers will use a significance level of $\alpha = 0.10$.

The next step is to collect the sample data. Figure 10-3 shows the sample data and the box and whisker diagram. The assumption of independence is met because the two burners were used to cook different meat patties and the temperature measures are not related. The box and whiskers diagrams provide no evidence to suggest that the distributions are highly skewed, so the assumption that populations are normally distributed seems reasonable.

The sample variances are computed using Equation 10-3.

Sample Variance

$$s^2 = \frac{\Sigma(x - \bar{x})^2}{n - 1}$$

10-3

where:

$$\bar{x} = \frac{\Sigma x}{n} = \text{Sample mean}$$
$$n = \text{Sample size}$$

Based on the sample data shown in Figure 10-3, the sample variances are:

$$s_1^2 = 6.7 \quad \text{and} \quad s_2^2 = 2.5.$$

The null hypothesis is that the two population variances are equal, making this a two-tailed test. Thus, we form the test statistic using Equation 10-3 by placing the larger sample variance in the numerator. Thus, the calculated F-value is

$$F = \frac{s_1^2}{s_2^2} = \frac{6.7}{2.5} = 2.68$$

If the calculated F-value exceeds the critical value, then the null hypothesis is rejected. The critical F-value is determined by locating the appropriate F-distribution table for the desired alpha level and the correct degrees of freedom. This requires the following thought process:

1. If the test is two-tailed, use the table corresponding to $\alpha/2$. For example, if $\alpha = 0.10$ for a two-tailed test, the appropriate F table is the one with the upper tail equal to 0.05.

FIGURE 10-3

E. Coli **Bacteria Testing**

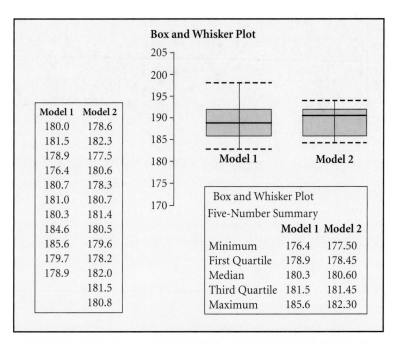

2. If the test is one-tailed, use the F table corresponding to the significance level. If $\alpha = 0.05$ for a one-tailed test, use the table with the upper-tail area equal to 0.05.

In this example, the test is two-tailed and α is 0.10. Thus, we go to the F-distribution table in Appendix H for the upper-tail area equal to 0.05.

The next step is to determine the appropriate degrees of freedom. In Chapter 7, we showed that the degrees of freedom of any test statistic are equal to the number of independent data values available to estimate the population variance. We lose one degree of freedom for each parameter we are required to estimate. For both the numerator and denominator in Equation 10-2, we must estimate the population mean using $\bar{x}$ before we calculate s^2. In each case, we lose one degree of freedom. Therefore, we have two distinct degrees of freedom, D_1 and D_2, where D_1 is equal to the sample size for the variance in the numerator of the F test statistic minus one ($n_1 - 1$) and D_2 is equal to the sample size for the variance in the denominator minus one ($n_2 - 1$). Recall that for a two-tailed test, the larger sample variance is placed in the numerator. In this example, burner 1 has the larger sample variance, so model 1 is placed in the numerator with a sample size of 11 so $D_1 = 11 - 1 = 10$ and $D_2 = 13 - 1 = 12$.

Locate the page of the F table corresponding to the desired upper-tail area. In this text we have three options (0.05, 0.025, and 0.01). The F table is arranged in columns and rows. The columns correspond to the D_1 degrees of freedom, and the rows correspond to the D_2 degrees of freedom. For this example, the critical F-value at the intersection of $D_1 = 10$ and $D_2 = 12$ degrees of freedom is 2.753. If you prefer you can use Excel's **FINV** function or Minitab's **Calc > Probability Distributions** command to determine the critical F-value.[1]

Figure 10-4 summarizes the hypothesis test. Note that the decision rule is

If the calculated $F > 2.753$, reject H_0;
Otherwise, do not reject H_0.

Because the F-value $= 2.68 < 2.753$, the conclusion is that the null hypothesis is not rejected based on these sample data; that is, we cannot conclude that there is a difference in the population variances.

FIGURE 10-4

F-Test for the *E. Coli* Example

Hypothesis:

$H_0: \sigma_1^2 = \sigma_2^2$

$H_A: \sigma_1^2 \neq \sigma_2^2$

$\alpha = 0.10$

$f(F)$

$df\!: D_1 = 10, D_2 = 12$

Rejection Region
$\alpha/2 = 0.05$

$F_{\alpha/2} = 2.753$

F

Decision Rule:

If $F > 2.753$, reject H_0;

Otherwise, do not reject H_0.

The F-test is

$$F = \frac{s_1^2}{s_2^2} = \frac{6.7}{2.5} = 2.68$$

Because $F = 2.68 \leq F_{\alpha/2} = 2.753$, do not reject H_0.

Note: The right-hand tail of the F-distribution always contains an area of $\alpha/2$ if the hypothesis is two-tailed.

[1]The FINV function is = FINV(.05,10,12) = 2.753.

XAMPLE 10-2: TWO-TAILED TEST FOR TWO POPULATION VARIANCES

Airport Security   Since the September 11 tragedy in New York City, airport security has been tightened substantially around the world. The federal government has taken over the management of airport security in U.S. airports, and private security companies have been replaced by federal employees. Suppose that the security manager at O'Hare airport in Chicago is concerned about the waiting time for passengers required to pass through security checks before being admitted to the departure gates. Of particular interest is whether there is a difference in the variability of waiting time at concourses A and B. The following steps can be used to test to determine whether there is a difference in population variances.

Step 1:   **Specify the population value of interest.**
The population value of interest is the variation in waiting times at the two concourses.

Step 2:   **Formulate the appropriate null and alternative hypotheses.**
Because we are interested in determining if a difference exists in variances and because neither concourse is predicted to have a higher variance, the test will be two-tailed, and the hypotheses are established as:

$$H_0: \sigma_A^2 = \sigma_B^2$$
$$H_A: \sigma_A^2 \neq \sigma_B^2$$

Step 3:   **Specify the level of significance.**
The test will be conducted using an alpha = 0.02 level.

Step 4:   **Construct the rejection region.**
Select simple random samples from each population of interest, determine whether the assumptions have been satisfied, and compute the test statistic.

Random samples of 25 passengers from Concourse A and 31 passengers from Concourse B were selected and the waiting time for each passenger was recorded. There is no connection between the two samples, so the assumption of independence is satisfied. The stem and leaf diagrams do not dispute the assumption of normality.

Stem and Leaf Display for Concourse A Stem unit: 1			Stem and Leaf Display for Concourse B Stem unit: 1	
Statistics		8 | 9	**Statistics**	4 | 7
Sample Size	25	9 | 0	Sample Size 31	5 |
Mean	14.58191	10 | 2 3 7 9	Mean 16.24597	6 | 3
Median	14.15696	11 | 9	Median 15.77023	7 |
Std. Deviation	3.765897	12 | 2 4	Std. Deviation 4.785841	8 |
Minimum	8.889582	13 | 2	Minimum 4.70353	9 |
Maximum	22.16486	14 | 0 0 2 2	Maximum 24.37963	10 | 8
		15 | 5 6 9		11 | 1 4 7
		16 | 2		12 | 2 4
		17 | 0 4		13 |
		18 | 2 4		14 | 2 2 2 8
		19 |		15 | 1 3 7 8
		20 | 8		16 |
		21 | 5		17 | 0 5
		22 | 2		18 | 3 6
				19 | 0 1 3 3
				20 | 4
				21 | 8 8
				22 | 1 4 9
				23 |
				24 | 4

To determine the critical value from the F-distribution, we can use either Excel's FINV function, Minitab's **Calc > Probability Distributions** command, or the F table in Appendix H. The degrees of freedom are D_1 = numerator sample size − 1, and D_2 = denominator sample size − 1. As shown in the statistics section of the stem and leaf display, Concourse B has the larger standard deviation, thus we get:

$$D_1 = n_B - 1 = 31 - 1 = 30 \quad \text{and} \quad D_2 = n_A - 1 = 25 - 1 = 24$$

Then for $\alpha/2 = 0.01$, we get a critical $F = 2.577$. The null hypothesis is rejected if $F > F_{\alpha/2} = 2.577$. Otherwise, do not reject the null hypothesis.

Step 5:   Compute the test statistic.

The test statistic is formed by the ratio of the two sample variances. Because this is a two-tailed test, the large sample variance is placed in the numerator.

$$F = \frac{4.786^2}{3.766^2} = 1.615$$

Step 6:   Reach a decision.

Compare the test statistic to the critical value and reach a conclusion with respect to the null hypothesis.

Because $F = 1.615 < F_{\alpha/2} = 2.577$, do not reject the null hypothesis.

Step 7:   Draw a conclusion.

There is no reason to conclude that there is a difference in the variability of waiting time at concourses A and B.

Excel and Minitab Tutorial

Bank ATM Machines—One-tailed tests on two population variances are performed much like two-tailed tests. Consider the systems development group for a midwestern bank, which has developed a new software algorithm for its ATM machines. Although reducing average transaction time is an objective, the systems programmers also want to reduce the variability in transaction speed. They believe the standard deviation for transaction time will be less with the new software (population 2) than it was with the old algorithm (population 1). For their analysis, the programmers have performed 7 test runs using the original software and 11 test runs using the new system. Although the managers want to determine the standard deviation of transaction time, they must perform the test as a test of variances because no method exists for testing standard deviations directly. Thus, the null and alternative hypotheses are

$$H_0: \quad \sigma_1^2 \le \sigma_2^2 \quad \text{or} \quad \sigma_1^2 - \sigma_2^2 \le 0$$
$$H_A: \quad \sigma_1^2 > \sigma_2^2 \quad \text{or} \quad \sigma_1^2 - \sigma_2^2 > 0$$

The hypothesis is to be tested using a significance level of $\alpha = 0.01$.

In order to use the F-test to test whether these sample variances come from populations with equal variances, we need to make sure that the sample variances are independent and the populations are approximately normally distributed. Because the test runs using the two algorithms were unique, the variances are independent. The following box and whisker plots give no reason to indicate that, based on these small samples, the populations are not approximately normal.

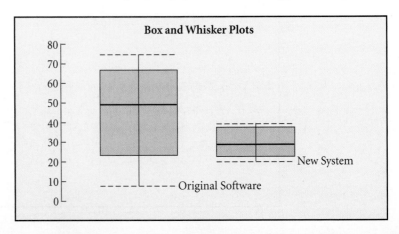

Excel Instructions:
1. Open file: ATM.xls
2. Click on **Tools**.
3. Select **Data Analysis**.
4. Select **F-Test Two Sample for Variances**.
5. Define data ranges.
6. Indicate significance level = 0.01.

	A	B	C	D	E	F
1	Original Software	New System		F-Test Two-Sample for Variances		
2	38.9	22.8				
3	23.2	20			Original Software	New System
4	49.2	26.5		Mean	46.55714286	29.8
5	66.8	37.9		Variance	612.6761905	51.494
6	65.5	27.2		Observations	7	11
7	74.6	39.6		df	6	10
8	7.7	34.1		F	11.89801123	
9		39.4		P(F<=f) one-tail	0.000473972	
10		20.9		F Critical one-tail	5.38580025	
11		30.3				
12		29.1				

Because the calculated $F = 11.898 > F_{.01} = 5.39$, we reject the null hypothesis and conclude that the variance for population 1 exceeds the population 2 variance.

Figure 10-5a and Figure 10-5b illustrate the one-tailed hypothesis test for this situation using a significance level of 0.01. Recall that in a two-tailed test, placing the largest sample variance in the numerator and the smallest variance in the denominator forms the *F*-ratio. In a one-tailed test, we look to the alternative hypothesis to determine which sample variance should go in the numerator. In this example, population 1 (the original software) is thought to have the larger variance. Then the sample variance from population 1 forms the numerator, regardless of the size of the sample variances. Excel and Minitab correctly compute the calculated *F*-ratio.

If you are performing the test manually, the *F*-ratio needs to be formed correctly for two reasons. First, the correct *F*-ratio will be computed. Second, the correct degrees of freedom will be used to determine the critical value to test the null hypothesis. In this one-tailed example, the numerator represents population 1, and the denominator represents population 2. This means that the degrees of freedom are

$$D_1 = n_1 - 1 = 7 - 1 = 6 \quad \text{and} \quad D_2 = n_2 - 1 = 11 - 1 = 10.$$

Using the *F*-distribution table in Appendix H, Minitab's **Calc > Probability Distributions** command, or Excel's **FINV** function, you can determine

$$F_{0.01} = 5.39$$

for this one-tailed test with a $\alpha = 0.01$.

The sample data for the test runs are in a CD-ROM file called *ATM*. The sample variances are

$$s_1^2 = 612.68$$
$$s_2^2 = 51.49$$

Thus, the calculated *F*-ratio is

$$F = \frac{612.68}{51.49} = 11.898$$

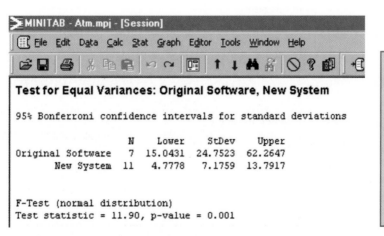

Minitab Instructions:
1. Open file: ATM.MTW.
2. Choose **Stat > Basic Statistics > 2 Variances**.
3. Select **Samples in different columns**, enter one data column in **First** and another in **Second**.
4. Click on **Options**.
5. In **Confidence Level**, enter $1 - \alpha$.
6. Click OK. OK.

Excel and Minitab have a procedure for performing this test. As shown in Figures 10-5a and 10-5b, the calculated

$$F = 11.898 > F_{0.01} = 5.39,$$

so the null hypothesis,

$$H_0, \text{ is rejected.}$$

Based on the sample data, the systems programmers have evidence to support their claim that the new ATM algorithm will result in reduced transaction-time variability.

There are many business decision-making applications in which you will need to test whether two populations have equal variances.

EXAMPLE 10-3: ONE-TAILED TEST FOR TWO POPULATION VARIANCES

Thomas Supply   Thomas Supply has a contract to assemble component parts that will be used by a leading maker of personal computers. One critical part is available from two suppliers, and Thomas will purchase from supplier 1 because its parts are less expensive, if the variation in thickness is less than or equal to that for supplier 2. The following steps can be used to conduct a test for the two suppliers.

Step 1:   Specify the population value of interest.
Thomas Supply is concerned with the variation in thickness. Therefore, the population parameter of interest is the variance, σ^2.

Step 2:   Formulate the appropriate null and alternative hypotheses.
Because Thomas managers are concerned with whether supplier 1's variance will exceed that of supplier 2, the test will be one-tailed, and the null and alternative hypotheses are formed as follows:

$$H_0: \sigma_1^2 \leq \sigma_2^2$$
$$H_A: \sigma_1^2 > \sigma_2^2$$

Step 3:   Specify the significance level.
The test will be conducted using an alpha level equal to 0.05.

Step 4:   Construct the rejection region.
Based on sample sizes of 11 parts from each supplier, the critical value for a one-tailed test with alpha = 0.05 and $D_1 = 10$ and $D_2 = 10$ degrees of freedom is 2.98. The null hypothesis is rejected if $F > F_\alpha = 2.98$. Otherwise, do not reject the null hypothesis.

Step 5:   Compute the test statistic.
A simple random sample of 11 parts was selected from each supplier with the sample variances of

$$s_1^2 = 0.799 \quad \text{and} \quad s_2^2 = 0.547.$$

The assumptions of independence and normal populations are believed to be satisfied in this case.

The test statistic is an F-ratio formed by placing the variance that is predicted to be larger (as shown in the alternative hypothesis) in the numerator. Supplier 1 is predicted to have the larger variance in the alternative hypothesis. Thus the test statistic is:

$$F = \frac{0.799}{0.547} = 1.4607$$

Step 6:   Reach a decision.
Because $F = 1.4607 < 2.98 = F_{0.05}$, do not reject the null hypothesis.

Step 7:   Draw a conclusion.
Based on the sample data, there is insufficient evidence to conclude that the variance of part thickness from supplier 1 is greater than that for supplier 2. Therefore, Thomas will continue to purchase from supplier 1.

Additional *F*-test Considerations:

Recall that in Chapter 9, the *t*-test for the difference between two population means with independent samples assumed that the two populations have equal variances. Often times, decision makers use the *F*-test introduced in this section to test whether the assumption of equal variances is satisfied. However, studies have shown that the *F*-test may not be particularly effective in detecting certain differences in population variances that can adversely affect the *t*-test. Therefore, other tests for equality of variances such as the Aspen-Welch test may be preferred as preliminary tests to the *t*-test for two population means. (See the Markowski reference at the end of this chapter.)

10-2: EXERCISES

Skill Development

10.12 Find the appropriate critical *F*-value, F_α, from the *F*-distribution table for each of the following assuming one-tailed tests:
   a. $D_1 = 10, D_2 = 14, \alpha = 0.05$
   b. $D_1 = 8, D_2 = 8, \alpha = 0.01$
   c. $D_1 = 14, D_2 = 10, \alpha = 0.05$

10.13 Find the appropriate critical *F*-value, F_α, from the *F*-distribution table for each of the following assuming one-tailed tests:
   a. $D_1 = 16, D_2 = 14, \alpha = 0.01$
   b. $D_1 = 5, D_2 = 12, \alpha = 0.05$
   c. $D_1 = 16, D_2 = 20, \alpha = 0.01$

10.14 Given the following null and alternative hypotheses:

$$H_0: \sigma_1^2 = \sigma_2^2$$
$$H_A: \sigma_1^2 \neq \sigma_2^2$$

and the following sample information:

Sample 1	Sample 2
$n_1 = 11$	$n_2 = 21$
$S_1 = 19$	$S_2 = 23$

   a. If $\alpha = 0.02$, state the decision rule for the hypothesis.
   b. Test the hypothesis and indicate whether the null hypothesis should be rejected.
   c. If you are able to obtain it from suitable computer software, determine the *p*-value for this hypothesis test. Otherwise, place a bound on the *p*-value using Appendix H.

10.15 Given the following null and alternative hypotheses:

$$H_0: \sigma_1^2 \leq \sigma_2^2$$
$$H_A: \sigma_1^2 > \sigma_2^2$$

and the following sample information:

Sample 1	Sample 2
$n_1 = 15$	$n_2 = 11$
$S_1 = 230$	$S_2 = 210$

   a. If $\alpha = 0.05$, state the decision rule for the hypothesis.
   b. Test the hypothesis and indicate whether the null hypothesis should be rejected.

10.16 Given the following null and alternative hypotheses:

$$H_0: \sigma_1^2 \leq \sigma_2^2$$
$$H_A: \sigma_1^2 > \sigma_2^2$$

and the following sample information:

Sample 1	Sample 2
$n_1 = 13$	$n_2 = 21$
$s_1^2 = 1,450$	$s_2^2 = 1,320$

   a. If $\alpha = 0.05$, state the decision rule for the hypothesis.
   b. Test the hypothesis and indicate whether the null hypothesis should be rejected.

10.17 Given the following null and alternative hypotheses:

$$H_0: \sigma_1^2 \leq \sigma_2^2$$
$$H_A: \sigma_1^2 > \sigma_2^2$$

and the following sample information:

Sample 1	Sample 2
$n_1 = 21$	$n_2 = 13$
$s_1^2 = 345.7$	$s_2^2 = 745.2$

   a. If $\alpha = 0.01$, state the decision rule for the hypothesis. (Be careful to pay attention to the alternative hypothesis to construct this decision rule.)
   b. Test the hypothesis and indicate whether the null hypothesis should be rejected.

10.18 You are given two random samples with the following information:

Item	Sample 1	Sample 2
1	19.6	21.3
2	22.1	17.4
3	19.5	19.0
4	20.0	21.2
5	21.5	20.1
6	20.2	23.5
7	17.9	18.9
8	23.0	22.4
9	12.5	14.3
10	19.0	17.8

a. Based on these samples, test at $\alpha = 0.10$ whether the true difference in population variances is equal to zero.

b. If you are able to obtain it from suitable computer software, determine the p-value for this hypothesis test. Otherwise, place a bound on the p-value using Appendix H.

Business Applications

10.19 The McBurger Company operates fast-food stores throughout the United States and in 14 other countries. Management is very concerned about making sure that a standard of quality service is achieved. For instance, they are interested in whether there is a difference in standard deviation in service times for customers who use the drive-through window versus those who go inside to the service counter.

The McBurger store in Knoxville, Tennessee, was recently analyzed. A sample of 13 drive-through customers was selected, and a sample of 9 inside-counter customers was selected. The time (in minutes) it took each customer to be served was recorded. The following statistics were computed from the sample data.

Drive-Through	Walk-In
$\bar{x} = 4.5$	$\bar{x} = 4.0$
$s = 2.0$	$s = 1.2$

Based on a significance level of 0.10, determine if there is a difference in standard deviation in service times for customers who use the drive-through window versus those who go inside to the service counter.

10.20 A national TV telethon committee is interested in determining whether males' donations have greater variability in amount than females' donations. To test this, random samples of 25 males and 25 females were selected from people who donated during last year's telethon. The following statistics were computed from the sample data:

Males	Females
$\bar{x} = \$12.40$	$\bar{x} = \$8.92$
$s = \$2.50$	$s = \$1.34$

Based on a significance level of 0.05, does it appear that donations by males have greater variability than donations by females?

10.21 💿 The First Night Stage Company operates a small nonprofit theater group in Milwaukee, Wisconsin. Each year the Company solicits donations to help fund its operations. This year, it obtained the help of a marketing research company in the city. This company's representatives proposed two different solicitation brochures. They are interested in determining

whether there is a difference in the standard deviation of dollars returned between the two brochures. To test this, a random sample of 20 people was selected to receive brochure A, and another random sample of 20 people was selected to receive brochure B. The data are contained in the CD-ROM file *First-Night*. Based on these sample data, what should the First Night Company conclude about the two brochures with respect to their variability? Test using a significance level of 0.02. Use both the p-value and critical-value approaches.

10.22 💿 The Celltone Company is in the business of providing cellular phone coverage. Recently it conducted a study of its customers who have purchased either the "Basic Plan" or the "Business Plan" service. At issue is the number of minutes of use by the customers during the midnight to 7:00 A.M. time period, Monday through Friday, over a four-week period. The belief by Celltone managers is that the standard deviation in minutes used by Business Plan customers will be less than that for Basic Plan customers. Data for this study are in the CD-ROM file *Celltone*. Assume that the managers wish to test this using a 0.05 level of significance.

Determine if the standard deviation in minutes used by Business Plan customers is less than that for the Basic Plan customers, using an alpha level equal to 0.05.

Advanced Applications

10.23 The Fister Corporation makes ribbons for computer printers. It is currently considering changing from its current ribbon to a new ribbon expected to last just as long, on the average, as the current ribbon. However, the new ribbon is thought to be more consistent in terms of how long it will last.

To test this claim, random samples of 21 current and 17 new ribbons were selected and tested on the company's quality-testing equipment. The following results (measured in tens of thousands of characters) were recorded.

Current	New
$n = 21$	$n = 17$
$s = 3.45$	$s = 2.87$

Be sure to state clearly the null hypothesis, alternative hypothesis, and decision rule. Test the hypotheses using $\alpha = 0.05$. Also discuss the results.

10.24 As purchasing agent for the Horner-Williams Company, you have primary responsibility for securing high-quality raw materials at the best possible price. One particular material that the Horner-Williams Company uses a great deal is aluminum. After careful study, you have been able to reduce the prospective vendors to two. It is unclear whether these two vendors produce aluminum that is equally durable.

To compare durability, the recommended procedure is to put pressure on an aluminum sample until it cracks. The vendor whose aluminum requires the greatest average pressure will be judged to be the one that provides the most durable product.

To carry out this test, 14 pieces of aluminum from vendor 1 and 14 pieces from vendor 2 are selected at random. The following results in pounds per square inch were noted.

Vendor 1	Vendor 2
$n_1 = 14$	$n_2 = 14$
$\bar{x}_1 = 2{,}345$ psi	$\bar{x}_2 = 2{,}411$ psi
$s_1 = 300$	$s_2 = 250$

Before testing the hypothesis about difference in population means, suppose the purchasing agent for the company is concerned about whether the assumption of equal population variances is satisfied.

a. Based on the sample data, what would you tell him if you tested at the significance level of 0.10?
b. Would your conclusion differ if you tested at the significance level of 0.02? Discuss.
c. What would be the largest significance level that would cause the null hypothesis to be rejected?

10.25 The production control manager at Ashmore Manufacturing is interested in determining whether there is a difference in standard deviation of product diameter for part #XC-343 for units made at the Trenton, New Jersey, plant versus those made at the Atlanta, Georgia, plant. The Trenton plant is highly automated and thought to provide better quality control. Thus, the parts produced there should be less variable than those made in Atlanta.

A random sample of 15 parts was selected from those produced last week at Trenton. The standard deviation for these parts was 0.14 inch. A sample of 13 parts was selected from those made in Atlanta. The sample standard deviation for these parts was 0.202 inch.

a. Based on these sample data, is there sufficient evidence to conclude that the Trenton plant produces parts that are less variable than those of the Atlanta plant? Test using $\alpha = 0.05$.
b. Consider the scenario in which the Trenton plant is discovered to have a smaller variability than the Atlanta plant. Management, on this basis, decides that they must expend a large amount of money to upgrade the machinery in Atlanta. Suppose also that, in reality, the difference in the observed variability between the two plants is a result of sampling error. Under these conditions, specify the type of error associated with this hypothesis test. How would you modify the hypothesis procedure to guard against such an error?

Summary and Conclusions

There are many business situations where the decision maker must reach a conclusion about a single population variance or about the relationship between two population variances. Chapter 10 introduced two hypothesis tests, the first using the chi-square distribution for testing a single population variance and the second using the F-distribution for testing the relationship between two population variances. Together, these procedures provide the decision maker with powerful tools for making inferences concerning one and two population variances. Combining the techniques presented in Chapter 10 with the hypothesis testing procedures in Chapters 8 and 9 gives the decision maker useful techniques for testing population parameters for one and two populations. Furthermore, Chapter 10 introduced two probability distributions, the chi-square distribution and the F-distribution. The chi-square distribution will again be used in Chapter 12 where goodness of fit and contingency analysis are discussed. The F-distribution will be used extensively in the analysis of variance and regression analysis chapters.

EQUATIONS

Chi-Square Test for a Single Population Variance

$$\chi^2 = \frac{(n-1)s^2}{\sigma^2} \qquad \textbf{10-1}$$

F Test Statistic for Testing Whether Two Populations Have Equal Variances

$$F = \frac{s_i^2}{s_j^2} \; (df = D_1 = n_i - 1 \quad \text{and} \quad D_2 = n_j - 1) \quad \textbf{10-2}$$

Sample Variance

$$s^2 = \frac{\Sigma(x - \bar{x})^2}{n - 1} \qquad \textbf{10-3}$$

Key Term

Independent Samples, 394

CHAPTER EXERCISES

Business Applications

10.26 Maher Saddles, Inc. produces bicycle seats. Among the many seats produced by the company is a seat for the high-end mountain bicycle market. Maher is interested in knowing whether changes to the production process will reduce the variability in the assembly time for this bicycle seat, as measured by the standard deviation for assembly times. Before changes were made to the production process the standard deviation of assembly times was 3.27 minutes. To evaluate whether the changes made to the production process are effective in reducing the variability in assembly times, Maher produced 36 seats using the new production methods and found the sample standard deviation to be 3.12 minutes. Based on the sample results, and using a significance level of 0.05, can Maher conclude that the new production methods have reduced the variation in the seat's assembly time?

10.27 A medical research group is investigating what differences might exist between the two pain killing drugs, Azerlieve and Zynumbic. The researchers have already established that there is no difference between the two drugs in terms of the average amount of time required before the drugs take effect. However, they are also interested in knowing if there is any difference between the variability of time until pain relief occurs. A random sample of 24 patients using Azerlieve and 32 patients using Zynumbic yielded the following results:

Azerlieve	Zynumbic
$n_1 = 24$	$n_2 = 32$
$s_1 = 37.5$ sec	$s_2 = 41.3$ sec

At the 0.05 level of significance, can the researchers conclude that there is a significant difference in the effect time variability between the two drugs?

10.28 Marsha and Greg operate two jewelry stores in Denver, one located downtown and one located in a suburban mall. While both stores report approximately the same average monthly sales figures, Marsha and Greg would like to know if the downtown store has higher variability in monthly sales than the suburban mall store. A random sample of 36 monthly sales reports from the downtown store and 39 monthly sales reports from the suburban store produced the following results:

Downtown	Mall
$n_1 = 36$	$n_2 = 39$
$s_1 = \$687$	$s_2 = \$521$

Based on the sample data, can Marsha and Greg conclude that the downtown store has greater variability in monthly sales than their suburban mall store? Conduct your analysis using a level of significance of 0.10.

10.29 In the production of its Nutty Toffee, Cordum Candies must carefully control the temperature of its cooking process. If there is too much variation in the cooking temperature then the taste and consistency of the toffee is compromised. Historically the standard deviation of the cooking temperature has been 0.90° F. A random sample of 27 batches of toffee was selected yesterday and the standard deviation of the temperature was computed to be 1.15° F. At the 0.05 level of significance does the sample data support the conclusions that there has been an increase in the variability of the toffee cooking temperature?

10.30 The production control supervisor at a fish cannery in Alaska is concerned with the variability in the fill rates for cans of salmon. The current canning process for 12 oz cans of salmon has a standard deviation in the fill rate of 0.05 oz. Following changes to the canning process the production control supervisor samples 36 12-oz cans of salmon and computes a sample standard deviation of 0.04 oz. Based on these sample results can the production control supervisor conclude that the production process changes have reduced the variability in the fill rate for 12-oz cans of salmon? Use a level of significance of 0.10.

10.31 Ozarka Lumber uses two types of saws to cut 2-x-6 boards. Both saws cut to the correct dimension on the average, but there is variability in the cutting process. A random sample of 29 2-x-6 boards cut using Saw 1 and 33 2-x-6 boards cut using Saw 2 produced the following results:

Saw 1	Saw 2
$n_1 = 29$	$n_2 = 33$
$s_1 = 0.0061$	$s_2 = 0.00593$

At the 0.10 level of significance can Ozarka conclude that there is more variability in the length of 2-x-6 boards cut using Saw 1 than in 2-x-6 boards cut using Saw 2?

10.32 The Automotive Research Group (ARG) provides independent testing for a variety of automobile-related products. Recently, ARG tested two gasoline additives that are designed to increase the average miles per gallon for automobiles that use the additive. The additives had similar effects on mean miles per gallon, but ARG is interested in determining if there is a difference in the variability between the two additives. Random samples of automobiles using the additives were selected and the following results were reported:

Additive 1	Additive II
$n_1 = 30$	$n_2 = 30$
$s_1 = 1.53$ miles	$s_2 = 0.98$ miles

Based on the sample results, can ARG conclude that there is a significant difference in the variability between the two additives? Conduct the analysis at the 0.05 level of significance.

10.33 Crestline Bank has instituted a new check clearing procedure. Historically, the bank's standard deviation in the number of checks cleared daily has been 29.2. Crestline is interested in knowing if the new check clearing procedure has reduced the variation in the number of checks cleared each day as measured by the standard deviation. A sample standard deviation of 22.8 was computed based on a random sample of 45 days checks. Based on this sample result, can Crestline conclude that the variation in the num-

10.42 Jason Enterprises produces two different products, Product 1 and Product 2. Among the concerns of the production engineers is whether there is less variation in the production of Product I than in Product II. The data file *Jason Enterprises* contains the time in minutes required to produce the two products using three different production processes: Current, Cellular, and Flex-Flow. Assuming that the data in the file *Jason Enterprises* is a random sample of the times required to produce the two products, conduct the appropriate statistical test to determine whether there is less variation in the production time required for Product 1 than for Product 2 for the Current production process. Use a level of significance of 0.05.

10.43 Hypos, a marketer of computer games, sells its products online (using the Internet), by telephone, through the mail (catalog), and through the company's retail stores. Assume that the file *Hypos* contains a random sample of the dollar sales of computer games for the different sales channels. The marketing department is interested in understanding more about the buying decisions of its customers.
a. Based on the sample of Internet sales, can Hypos conclude that the variability in Internet sales as measured by the standard deviation is less than $10.00 per order? Use a level of significance of 0.05 to conduct the appropriate test. Be sure to state a conclusion that answers Hypos' question.
b. Based on the sample data for Phone/Catalog sales and In-Store sales can Hypos conclude that there is a difference in the variability of sales between the two sales channels? Use a level of significance of 0.05 to conduct the appropriate statistical analysis. State your conclusion in terms of the marketing issue of interest.

10.44 Phone Solutions provides assistance to users of a personal finance software package. Users of the software call Phone Solutions with their questions and trained consultants provide answers and information. One concern that Phone Solutions must deal with is the staffing of its call centers. As a part of the staffing issues Phone Solutions

seeks to reduce the average variability in the amount of time that a consultant spends on each caller. A study of this issue is currently being undertaken by the operations managers of Phone Solutions three call centers. Each call center manager has randomly sampled 50 days of calls and the collected times, in minutes, are in the file *Phone Solutions*.
a. Call Center 1 has set the goal that the average variation in phone calls, measured in standard deviation of the length of phone calls in minutes, should be less than 3.5 minutes. Using the data in the *Phone Solutions* file, can the operations manager of Call Center 1 conclude that her consultants are meeting the goal? Use a level of significance of 0.10.
b. Can the managers conclude that there is greater variability in the average length of phone calls for Call Center 3 than for Call Center 2? Use a level of significance of 0.10 to conduct the appropriate test.

10.45 To determine whether there is a difference between the average variation in computer usage by college major, the manager of the computer laboratories at a state university in North Dakota randomly sampled observations from the computer records kept in the computer laboratories. When students enter a computer laboratory they must enter a code that indicates their college: (1) for Engineering; (2) for Arts and Sciences; and (3) for Business. A computer then keeps track of each student's start and stop time. At the end of the semester the computer laboratory manager randomly selected the 155 records contained in the file labeled *Lab-Time* from all the students who used the computer laboratories that semester.
a. Based on the sample data is there evidence to conclude at the 0.05 level of significance that the variability in computer lab usage as measured by the standard deviation is greater than 1.5 minutes for Business students?
b. Based on the sample data is there evidence to conclude at the 0.05 level of significance that there is greater variability in usage for Arts and Sciences than for Engineering students?

General References

1. Berenson, Mark L., and David M. Levine, *Basic Business Statistics Concepts and Applications*, 7th ed. (Upper Saddle River, NJ: Prentice Hall, 1999).
2. Cryer, Jonathan D., and Robert B. Miller, *Statistics for Business: Data Analysis and Modeling*, 2nd ed. (Belmont, CA: Duxbury Press, 1994).
3. Duncan, Acheson, J., *Quality Control and Industrial Statistics*, 5th Edition (Burr Ridge, IL: Irwin, 1986).
4. Johnson, Richard A. and Dean W. Wichern, *Business Statistics: Decision Making with Data* (New York: John Wiley & Sons, 1997).
5. Larsen, Richard J., Morris L. Marx, and Bruce Cooil, *Statistics for Applied Problem Solving and Decision Making* (Pacific Grove, CA: Duxbury Press, 1997).
6. Markowski, Carol, and Edmund Markowski, *Conditions for the Effectiveness of a Preliminary Test of Variance*, The American Statistician, November, 1990, No. 4, pp. 322–326.
7. *Microsoft Excel 2000* (Redmond, WA: Microsoft Corp., 1999).
8. *Minitab for Windows Version 13* (State College, PA: Minitab, 2000).
9. Siegel, Andrew F., *Practical Business Statistics*, 4th ed. (Burr Ridge, IL: Irwin, 2000).

CHAPTER 11

Analysis of Variance

CHAPTER OUTCOMES

After studying the material in Chapter 11, you should be able to:

- Recognize situations that call for the use of analysis of variance.
- Understand the basic logic of analysis of variance.
- Be aware of several different analysis of variance designs and understand when to use each.
- Perform a single-factor hypothesis test using analysis of variance manually and with the aid of Excel or Minitab software.
- Conduct and interpret post-analysis of variance pairwise comparisons procedures.
- Recognize when randomized blocks analysis of variance is useful and be able to perform randomized blocks analysis.
- Perform two-factor analysis of variance tests with replications using Excel or Minitab and interpret the output.

WHY YOU NEED TO KNOW

Chapters 8, 9, and 10 introduced the basics of hypothesis testing. By now you should understand that, regardless of the population parameter in question, hypothesis-testing steps are basically the same.

1. Specify the population value of interest.
2. Formulate the null and alternative hypothesis.
3. Specify the level of significance.
4. Determine a decision rule defining the rejection and "acceptance" regions.
5. Select a random sample of data from the population(s). Compute the appropriate sample statistic(s). Finally, calculate the test statistic.
6. Reach a decision. Reject the null hypothesis, H_0, if the sample statistic falls in the rejection region; otherwise, do not reject the null hypothesis. If the test is conducted using the p-value approach, H_0 is rejected whenever the p-value is smaller than the significance level; otherwise H_0 is not rejected.
7. Draw a conclusion. State the result of your hypothesis test in the context of the exercise or analysis of interest.

Chapter 8 focused on hypothesis tests involving a single population. Chapter 9 expanded the hypothesis-testing process to include applications in which differences between two populations are involved. However, you will encounter many instances involving more than two populations. For example, the vice pres-

ident of operations at Farber Rubber, Inc., oversees production at Farber's six different U.S. manufacturing plants. Because each plant uses slightly different manufacturing processes, the vice president needs to know if there are any differences in average strength of the products produced at the different plants.

Similarly, *Golf Digest*, a major publisher of articles about golf, might wish to determine which of five major brands of golf balls have the highest mean distance off the tee. The Environmental Protection Agency (EPA) might conduct a test to determine if there is a difference in the average miles-per-gallon performance of cars manufactured by the Big Three U.S. automobile producers. In each of these cases, testing a hypothesis involving more than two population means could be required.

This chapter introduces a tool called analysis of variance (ANOVA), which can be used to test whether there are differences among three or more population means. There are several ANOVA procedures, depending on the type of test that is being conducted. Our aim in this chapter is to introduce you to the basics of ANOVA and to illustrate how to use Microsoft Excel or Minitab to help conduct hypothesis tests involving three or more population parameters. You will almost certainly need either to apply ANOVA in future decision-making situations or to interpret the results of an ANOVA study performed by someone else. Thus, you need to be familiar with this powerful statistical tool.

11-1 ONE-WAY ANALYSIS OF VARIANCE

In Chapter 9 we introduced the t-test for testing whether two populations have equal means when the samples from the two populations are independent. However, you will often encounter situations in which you are interested in determining whether three or more populations have equal means. To conduct this test you will need a new tool called *analysis of variance (ANOVA)*. There are many different analysis of variance designs to fit different situations. The simplest ANOVA design is **one-way analysis of variance**.

One-Way Analysis of Variance

An analysis of variance design in which independent samples are obtained from k levels of a single factor for the purpose of testing whether the k levels have equal means.

THE LOGIC BEHIND ONE-WAY ANOVA

Bayhill Marketing Company—The Bayhill Marketing Company is a full-service marketing and advertising firm in San Francisco, California. Although Bayhill provides many different marketing services, one of its most lucrative is coupon design. Companies that wish to increase sales often mail coupons to potential customers in their marketing areas. These companies hope that people will redeem them and overall sales will increase. Bayhill's account managers help client companies design their coupons for maximum effectiveness. Of course, some coupon designs are more effective than others.

For example, a major greeting card company wants to work with Bayhill in developing a coupon offer for its "Special Events" card set. The card company has negotiated a deal with the American Express credit card company to include its coupon in every American Express cardholder's monthly statement. Now the company must decide what the coupon should offer and how it will look to maximize its effectiveness. Coupon effectiveness can be determined by the percentage of coupon redeemed or by the dollar value of the greeting card sets purchased with a redeemed coupon.

Through a series of meetings with the client and focus-group sessions with potential customers Bayhill has developed four coupon designs. Bayhill has arranged with American Express to test thes

TABLE 11-1				

Bayhill Marketing Company Coupon Order Data

	COUPON DESIGN			
Customer	**1**	**2**	**3**	**4**
1	$ 4.10	$ 6.90	$ 4.60	$12.50
2	5.90	9.10	11.40	7.50
3	10.45	13.00	6.15	6.25
4	11.55	7.90	7.85	8.75
5	5.25	9.10	4.30	11.15
6	7.75	13.40	8.70	10.25
7	4.78	7.60	10.20	6.40
8	6.22	5.00	10.80	9.20
				Grand Mean
Mean	$ 7.00	$ 9.00	$ 8.00	$ 9.00	$8.25
Variance	7.341	8.423	7.632	5.016	

Note: Data are dollar value of card sets ordered with each coupon.

designs by sending out 200 of each coupon type to randomly selected cardholders. Bayhill will then select a random sample from redeemed coupons and determine the dollar value of greeting card sets purchased with each coupon. Table 11-1 shows the data for a sample of eight redemptions for each design. The values in the table are the dollar values of greeting card sets ordered by each customer.

In this example, we are interested in whether the different coupon designs result in different order sizes. In other words, we are trying to determine if "coupon designs" are one of the possible causes of the variation in the dollar value of the card sets ordered (the response variable). In this case, coupon design is called a **factor**.

Factor

A quantity under examination in an experiment as a possible cause of variation in the response variable.

The *single factor* of interest is coupon design. This factor has four categories, measurements, or strata, called **levels**.

Levels

The categories, measurements, or strata of a factor of interest in the current experiment.

These four levels are the four designs: 1, 2, 3, and 4. Because we are using only one factor here, each dollar value of card sets ordered is associated with only one level (that is, with coupon design—type 1, 2, 3, or 4), as you can see in Table 11-1. Each level is a population of interest.

The null and alternative hypotheses to be tested are

$$H_0: \mu_1 = \mu_2 = \mu_3 = \mu_4$$
$$H_A: \text{At least two of the population means are different.}$$

The experimental design producing the data for this experiment is called a **completely randomized design**.

Completely Randomized Design

An experiment is completely randomized if it consists of the independent random selection of observations representing each level of one factor.

The appropriate statistical tool for conducting the hypothesis test related to this experimental design is ANOVA. Because this ANOVA addresses an experiment with only one factor, it is a one-way ANOVA, or a one-factor ANOVA. Because the sample size for each coupon design (level) is the same, the experiment has a **balanced design**.

Balanced Design

An experiment has a balanced design if the factor levels have equal sample sizes.

ANOVA tests the null hypothesis that three or more populations have the same mean. The test is based on three assumptions:

SSUMPTIONS

1. All populations are normally distributed.
2. The population variances are equal.
3. The observations are independent—that is, the occurrence of any one individual value does not affect the probability that any other observation will occur.

If the null hypothesis is true, the populations have identical distributions. If so, the sample means for random samples from each population should be close in value. The basic logic of ANOVA is the same as the two-sample t-test introduced in Chapter 9: The null hypothesis should be rejected only if the sample means are substantially different.

You may be surprised to learn that the hypothesis test for equality of the population means is in fact an F-test involving two variances. To show you what we mean, consider that in Chapter 6 we showed that the distribution of sample means for a sample of size n taken from a normally distributed population has a standard deviation, $\sigma_{\bar{x}} = \dfrac{\sigma}{\sqrt{n}}$. From this, the variance of the $\bar{x}$ values is $\sigma_{\bar{x}}^2 = \dfrac{\sigma^2}{n}$.

Figure 11-1 illustrates what the sampling distribution of $\bar{x}$ values would look like. If the null hypothesis is true, the sample means from each population can be thought of as values coming from the sampling distribution in Figure 11-1. The average value of the sample means would be an estimate for μ, the mean of the sampling distribution. Likewise, the variation in the sample means would be the estimate for the variance of the sampling distribution, $\sigma_{\bar{x}}^2$.

If, as assumed, the populations have the same variance, σ^2, we can solve for σ^2 as:

$$n\sigma_{\bar{x}}^2 = \sigma^2$$

where n is the common sample size from each population. Consider the data in Table 11-1. The sample means are shown for sample sizes of eight. Also shown is the average of the sample means, 8.25. Then the estimate for $\sigma_{\bar{x}}^2$ is

$$s_{\bar{x}}^2 = \frac{(7 - 8.25)^2 + (9 - 8.25)^2 + (8 - 8.25)^2 + (9 - 8.25)^2}{4 - 1} = 0.91667$$

It follows that an estimate of σ^2 is

$$n\left(s_{\bar{x}}^2\right) = 8(0.91667) = 7.333$$

This value is referred to as the *between-levels (or treatments) estimate of* σ^2, and it is based on the premise that the null hypothesis is true and the means of the respective populations are equal.

Another approach to estimating the common variance, σ^2, is to use a pooled estimate. Because we assume that all k populations have the same variance, the average of the population variances is equal to the common population variance:

$$\sigma^2 = \frac{\sigma_1^2 + \sigma_2^2 + \cdots + \sigma_k^2}{k} = \frac{\sigma^2 + \sigma^2 + \cdots + \sigma^2}{k} = \frac{k\sigma^2}{k}$$

FIGURE 11-1

Sampling Distribution of $\bar{x}$

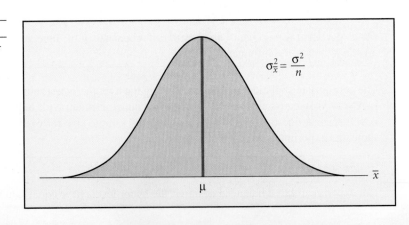

FIGURE 11-2

Variation in Sample Means

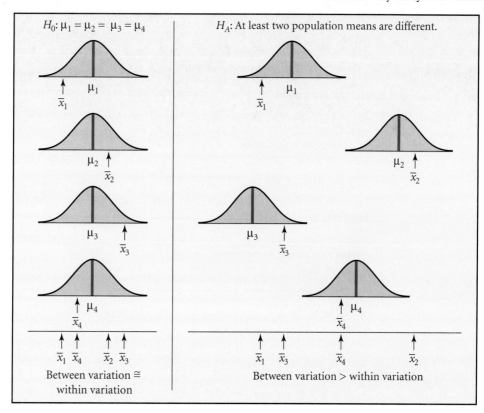

$H_0: \mu_1 = \mu_2 = \mu_3 = \mu_4$

H_A: At least two population means are different.

Between variation $\cong$ within variation

Between variation $>$ within variation

However, each population variance is a measure of the variation within that specific population and is not dependent on whether the means of the populations are equal. Thus, given equal sample sizes from each population, the *within-levels estimate of* σ^2 is

$$s^2 = \frac{s_1^2 + s_2^2 + \cdots + s_k^2}{k}$$

Based on the data in Table 11-1 for the Bayhill Marketing Company, the within-levels estimate for σ^2 is

$$s^2 = \frac{7.341 + 8.423 + 7.632 + 5.016}{4} = 7.103$$

Now, we have two estimates for the same population variance. The two estimates should have approximately the same value if the null hypothesis of equal means is true. However, if the populations have unequal means, the *between-levels estimate* for σ^2 will be greater than the *within-levels estimate* because the sample means will tend to differ substantially from one another. This is illustrated in Figure 11-2.

Thus, to test whether the population means are equal, we actually compare these two variance estimates. As we learned in Chapter 10, the *F*-distribution is used to test whether two variances are equal. As we will illustrate shortly, in ANOVA, the *F*-ratio is formed by taking the ratio of the between level estimate over the within level estimate. If this *F*-ratio gets too large, the null hypothesis of equal means is rejected.

PARTITIONING THE SUM OF SQUARES

Refer again to the sample data in Table 11-1. In order to understand the logic of ANOVA, you should take note of several things about the data. First, the dollar values of the orders are different throughout the data table. Some values are higher; others are lower. Thus, variation exists across all customer orders. This variation is called the **total variation** in the data.

Total Variation

The aggregate dispersion of the individual data values across the various factor levels is called the *total variation* in the data.

Next, within any particular coupon design (i.e., factor levels), not all customers ordered the same dollar value of greeting card sets. For instance, within level 1, order size ranged from $4.10 to $11.55. Similar differences occur within the other levels. The variation within each factor level is called the **within-sample variation**.

Within-Sample Variation

The dispersion that exists among the data values within a particular factor level is called the *within-sample variation*.

Finally, the sample means for the four coupon designs are not all equal. Thus, variation exists between the four designs' averages. This variation between the factor levels is referred to as the **between-sample variation**.

Between-Sample Variation

Dispersion among the factor sample means is called the *between-sample variation*.

Recall that the sample variance is computed as:

$$s^2 = \frac{\Sigma(x - \bar{x})^2}{n - 1}$$

The sample variance is the sum of squared deviations from the sample mean divided by its degrees of freedom. When all the data from all the samples are included, s^2 is the estimator of the *total variation*. The numerator of this estimator is called the *total sum of squares* (SST) and can be partitioned into the sum of squares associated with the estimators of the between-sample variation and the within-sample variation, as shown in Equation 11-1.

Partitioned Sum of Squares

$$SST = SSB + SSW$$

        11-1

where:

SST = Total Sum of Squares
SSB = Sum of Squares Between
SSW = Sum of Squares Within

After separating the sum of squares, they are divided by their degrees of freedom to produce the respective variance estimators previously discussed. If the between-sample portion of the total variation is large relative to the within-sample variation, the ANOVA procedure will lead us to reject the null hypothesis and conclude the population means are different. The question is: How can we determine at what point any difference is statistically significant?

THE ANOVA ASSUMPTIONS

Bayhill Marketing Company (continued)—Recall that Bayhill is testing whether the four coupon designs generate orders of equal average dollar value. The null and alternative hypotheses are

$$H_0: \mu_1 = \mu_2 = \mu_3 = \mu_4$$
H_A: At least two population means are different.

Before we jump into the ANOVA calculations, recall the three basic assumptions of ANOVA:

1. All populations are normally distributed.
2. The population variances are equal.
3. The sampled observations are independent.

Figure 11-3 demonstrates the first two assumptions. The populations are normally distributed and the spread (variance) is the same for each population. However, in this case, the populations

FIGURE 11-3

Normal Populations with Equal Variances and Unequal Means

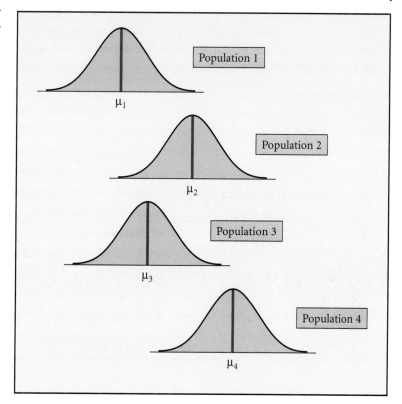

have different means—and the null hypothesis is false. Figure 11-4 demonstrates the same assumptions but in a case in which the population means are equal; therefore, the null hypothesis is true.

You can do a rough check to determine whether the normality assumption is satisfied by developing graphs of the sample data from each population. Histograms are probably the best tool for checking the normality assumption, but they require a fairly large sample size. The stem and leaf and box and whisker diagrams are good alternatives when sample sizes are smaller. If the graphical

FIGURE 11-4

Normal Populations with Equal Variances and Means

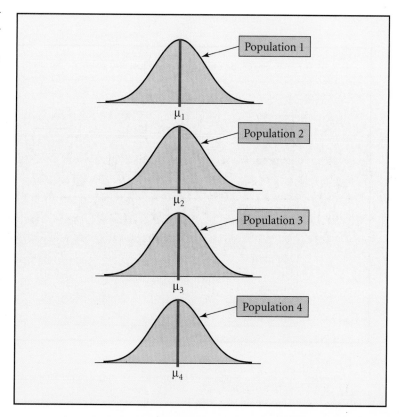

tools show diagrams that are consistent with a normal distribution, then that evidence suggests the normality assumption is satisfied.[1] Figure 11-5 illustrates the box and whisker diagram for the Bayhill data. Note, when the sample sizes are very small, as they are here, the graphical techniques may not be very effective.

In Chapter 10, you learned how to test whether two populations have equal variances using the F-test. To determine whether the second assumption is satisfied, we can hypothesize that all the population variances are equal:

$$H_0: \sigma_1^2 = \sigma_2^2 = \cdots = \sigma_k^2$$
$$H_A: \text{Not all variances are equal.}$$

To test whether this null hypothesis should be rejected, we form the F test statistic using Equation 11-2.

F Test Statistic

$$F_{max} = \frac{s_{max}^2}{s_{min}^2}$$

11-2

where:

$$s_{max}^2 = \text{Largest sample variance}$$
$$s_{min}^2 = \text{Smallest sample variance}$$

We can use the F-value computed using Equation 11-2 to test whether the variances are equal by comparing the calculated F to a critical value from a distribution known as *Hartley's F_{max} distribution*, which appears in Appendix I.[2] For the Bayhill example, the computed variance for each of the four samples is

$$s_1^2 = 7.341 \quad s_2^2 = 8.423 \quad s_3^3 = 7.632 \quad s_4^2 = 5.016$$

Using Equation 11-2, we compute the F_{max} value as

$$F_{max} = \frac{8.423}{5.016} = 1.679$$

FIGURE 11-5

Box and Whisker Diagram—Bayhill Marketing Company

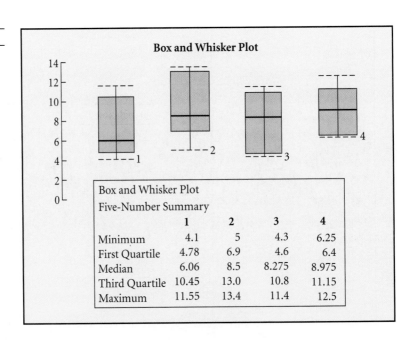

Box and Whisker Plot

Box and Whisker Plot
Five-Number Summary

	1	2	3	4
Minimum	4.1	5	4.3	6.25
First Quartile	4.78	6.9	4.6	6.4
Median	6.06	8.5	8.275	8.975
Third Quartile	10.45	13.0	10.8	11.15
Maximum	11.55	13.4	11.4	12.5

---

[1]Chapter 12 introduces a goodness-of-fit approach to testing whether sample data come from a normally distributed population.

[2]Other tests for equal variances exist. For example, Minitab has a procedure that uses Bartlett and Levine's test.

This value is now compared to the critical F_α from the table in Appendix I for $\alpha = 0.05$, with $k = 4$ and $\bar{n} - 1 = 7$ degrees of freedom. The value, k, is the number of populations ($k = 4$). The value $\bar{n}$ is the average sample size, which equals 8 in this example. If $\bar{n}$ is not an integer value, then set $\bar{n}$ equal to the integer portion of the computed $\bar{n}$. If $F_{max} > F_\alpha$, reject the null hypothesis of equal variances. If $F_{max} \leq F_\alpha$, do not reject. From the Hartley's F_{max} distribution table, the critical $F = 8.44$. Because $F_{max} = 1.679 \leq 8.44$, the null hypothesis of equal variances is not rejected.[3]

If you are unsure whether you meet the ANOVA assumptions or if your tests indicate that you do not, Chapter 16 introduces an alternative ANOVA procedure called the Kruskal-Wallis one-way ANOVA, which does not require these restrictive assumptions. However, for the examples presented in this chapter, we will consider the ANOVA assumptions to be satisfied.

APPLYING ONE-WAY ANOVA

Although the previous discussion covers the essence of ANOVA, to determine whether the null hypothesis should be rejected requires that we actually determine values of the estimators for the total variation, between-sample variation, and within-sample variation. Most ANOVA tests are done using a computer, but we will illustrate the manual computational approach once. Because software such as Excel and Minitab can be used to perform all calculations, future examples will be done using the computer. The software packages will do all the computations while we focus on interpreting the results.

Bayhill Marketing Company (continued)—Now we are ready to perform the necessary one-way ANOVA computations for the Bayhill example. Recall from Equation 11-1 that we can partition the total sum of squares into two components:

$$SST = SSB + SSW$$

The *total sum of squares* is computed as shown in Equation 11-3.

Total Sum of Squares

$$SST = \sum_{i=1}^{k} \sum_{j=1}^{n_i} (x_{ij} - \bar{\bar{x}})^2$$

11-3

where:

SST = Total sum of squares
k = Number of populations (treatments)
n_i = Sample size from population i
x_{ij} = jth measurement from population i
$\bar{\bar{x}}$ = Grand mean (mean of all the data values)

Equation 11-3 is not as complicated as it appears. Manually applying Equation 11-3 to the Bayhill data shown in Table 11-1 on page 409 (grand mean = $\bar{\bar{x}} = 8.25$), we can compute SST as follows.

$$SST = (4.10 - 8.25)^2 + (5.90 - 8.25)^2 + (10.45 - 8.25)^2 + \cdots + (9.20 - 8.25)^2$$
$$SST = 220.88$$

Thus, the sum of the squared deviations of all values from the grand mean is 220.88. Equation 11-3 can also be restated as:

$$SST = \sum_{i=1}^{k} \sum_{j=1}^{n_i} (x_{ij} - \bar{\bar{x}})^2 = (N - 1)s^2$$

where s^2 is the sample variance for all data combined, and N is the sum of the combined sample sizes.

---

[3]Hartley's F_{max} test is very dependent on the populations being normally distributed and should not be used if the populations' distributions are skewed. Note also in Hartley's F_{max} table, $c = k$ and $v = \bar{n} - 1$.

We now need to determine how much of this total sum of squares is due to between-sample sum of squares and how much is due to within-sample sum of squares. The between-sample portion is called the *sum of squares between* and is found using Equation 11-4.

Sum of Squares Between

$$SSB = \sum_{i=1}^{k} n_i(\bar{x}_i - \bar{\bar{x}})^2$$

11-4

where:

SSB = Sum of squares between samples
k = Number of populations
n_i = Sample size from population i
$\bar{x}_i$ = Sample mean from population i
$\bar{\bar{x}}$ = Grand mean

We can use Equation 11-4 to manually compute the sum of squares between for the Bayhill data, as follows.

$$SSB = 8(7 - 8.25)^2 + 8(9 - 8.25)^2 + 8(8 - 8.25)^2 + 8(9 - 8.25)^2$$
$$SSB = 22$$

Once both the SST and SSB have been computed, the *sum of squares within* (also called the sum of squares error, SSE) is easily computed using Equation 11-5. The sum of squares within can also be computed directly using Equation 11-6.

Sum of Squares Within
$$SSW = SST - SSB$$

11-5

or

Sum of Squares Within

$$SSW = \sum_{i=1}^{k}\sum_{j=1}^{n_i}(x_{ij} - \bar{x}_i)^2$$

11-6

where:

SSW = Sum of squares within samples
k = Number of populations
n_i = Sample size from population i
$\bar{x}_i$ = Sample mean from population i
x_{ij} = jth measurement from population i

TABLE 11-2

One-Way ANOVA Table: The Basic Format

SOURCE OF VARIATION	SS	df	MS	F-RATIO
Between samples	SSB	$k-1$	MSB	$\dfrac{MSB}{MSW}$
Within samples	SSW	$N-k$	MSW	
Total	SST	$N-1$		

where:

k = Number of populations
N = Sum of the sample sizes from all populations
df = Degrees of freedom
MSB = Mean square between = $\dfrac{SSB}{k-1}$

MSW = Mean square within = $\dfrac{SSW}{N-k}$

	SOURCE OF VARIATION	SS	df	MS	F-RATIO
TABLE 11-3	Between samples	22.00	3	7.3333	$\dfrac{7.3333}{7.10286} = 1.03244$
One-Way ANOVA Table for the Bayhill Marketing Co.	Within samples	198.88	28	7.10286	
	Total	220.88	31		

where:

$$MSB = \text{Mean square between} = \frac{SSB}{k-1} = \frac{22}{3} = 7.3333$$

$$MSW = \text{Mean square within} = \frac{SSW}{N-k} = \frac{198.88}{28} = 7.10286$$

For the Bayhill example, the *SSW* is

$$SSW = 220.88 - 22.00$$
$$= 198.88$$

These computations are the essential first steps in performing the ANOVA test to determine whether the population means are equal. Table 11-2 illustrates the ANOVA table format that is used to conduct the test.

The format shown in Table 11-2 is the standard ANOVA table layout. For the Bayhill example, we substitute the numerical values for *SSB*, *SSW*, and *SST*, and complete the ANOVA table, as shown in Table 11-3.

The Mean Square column contains the *MSB* (mean square between-samples) and the *MSW* (mean square within-samples).[4] These values are computed by dividing the sum of squares by their respective degrees of freedom, as shown in Table 11-3. They are actually the estimates of the respective variances that we computed earlier.

Restating the null and alternative hypotheses for the Bayhill example:

H_0: $\mu_1 = \mu_2 = \mu_3 = \mu_4$
H_A: At least one pair of populations has different means.

Glance back at Figures 11-3 and 11-4. If the null hypothesis is true (that is, all the means are equal—Figure 11-4), *MSW* and *MSB* will be equal, except for the presence of sampling error. However, the more the sample means differ (Figure 11-3), the larger the *MSB* becomes. As the *MSB* increases, it will tend to get larger than the *MSW*. When this difference gets too large, we will conclude that the population means must not be equal, and the null hypothesis will be rejected. But how do we determine what "too large" is? How do we know when the difference is due to more than just sampling error?

To answer these questions, recall from Chapter 10 and from the development in "The Logic Behind the One-Way ANOVA" that the *F*-distribution is used to test whether two populations have the same variance. In the ANOVA test, if the null hypothesis is true, the ratio of *MSB* over *MSW* forms an *F*-distribution with $D_1 = k - 1$ and $D_2 = N - k$ degrees of freedom. If the calculated *F*-ratio in Table 11-3 gets too large, the null hypothesis is rejected.

Figure 11-6 illustrates the hypothesis test for a significance level of 0.05. Because the calculated *F*-ratio = 1.03244 is less than the critical *F* = 2.95 from the *F*-table with 3 and 28 degrees of freedom, the null hypothesis cannot be rejected. The *F*-ratio indicates that the between-levels estimate and the within-levels estimate are not different enough to conclude that the population means are significantly different. This means there is insufficient statistical evidence to conclude that any one of the four coupon designs will generate higher average dollar values of orders than any of the other four designs. Therefore, the choice of which coupon design to use can be based on other factors, such as printing cost.

---

[4]*MSW* is also known as the *mean square for error* (*MSE*).

FIGURE 11-6

Bayhill Company Hypothesis Test

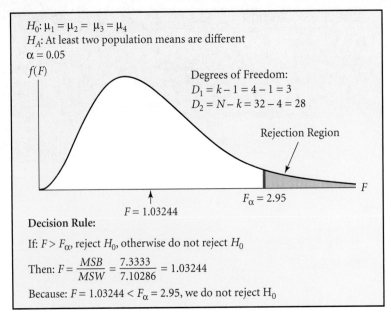

H_0: $\mu_1 = \mu_2 = \mu_3 = \mu_4$
H_A: At least two population means are different
$\alpha = 0.05$

$f(F)$

Degrees of Freedom:
$D_1 = k - 1 = 4 - 1 = 3$
$D_2 = N - k = 32 - 4 = 28$

Rejection Region

$F_\alpha = 2.95$

$F = 1.03244$

F

Decision Rule:

If: $F > F_\alpha$, reject H_0, otherwise do not reject H_0

Then: $F = \dfrac{MSB}{MSW} = \dfrac{7.3333}{7.10286} = 1.03244$

Because: $F = 1.03244 < F_\alpha = 2.95$, we do not reject H_0

EXAMPLE 11-1: ONE-WAY ANALYSIS OF VARIANCE

Westfall Relocation Company   The Westfall Relocation Company, located in Denver, Colorado, contracts with major corporations forced to lay off employees. Westfall provides a variety of services, including job searches, specialized training, and resume development. Westfall then bills the corporation for the services. It currently operates in three regions: west, southwest, and northwest. Recently, Westfall's general manager questioned whether the company's mean billing amount differed by region. To determine this, the following steps can be performed.

Step 1:   **Specify the parameter(s) of interest.**
The parameter of interest is the mean dollars billed in each region.

Step 2:   **Formulate the null and alternative hypotheses.**
The appropriate null and alternative hypotheses are

$$H_0: \mu_W = \mu_{SW} = \mu_{NW}$$
H_A: Not all populations have the same mean.

Step 3:   **Specify the significance level (α) for testing the hypothesis.**
The test will be conducted using an $\alpha = 0.05$.

Step 4:   **Select independent simple random samples from each population, and compute the sample means and the grand mean.**
There are three regions. Simple random samples of employees served in these regions have been selected: 10 in the west, 8 in the southwest, and 12 in the northwest. The following sample data were collected:

West	Southwest	Northwest
$3,700	$3,300	$2,900
2,900	2,100	4,300
4,100	2,600	5,200
4,900	2,100	3,300
4,900	3,600	3,600
5,300	2,700	3,300
2,200	4,500	3,700
3,700	2,400	2,400
4,800		4,400
3,000		3,300
		4,400
		3,200

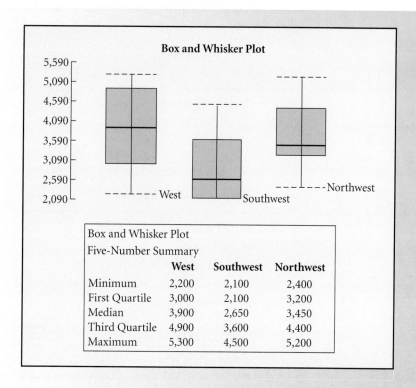

Box and Whisker Plot
Five-Number Summary

	West	Southwest	Northwest
Minimum	2,200	2,100	2,400
First Quartile	3,000	2,100	3,200
Median	3,900	2,650	3,450
Third Quartile	4,900	3,600	4,400
Maximum	5,300	4,500	5,200

Step 5: **Check to see that the normality and equal variance assumptions have been satisfied.**
Because of the small sample size, the box and whisker diagram is used.

As long as we assume that the populations are normally distributed, Hartley's F_{max} test can be used to test whether the three populations have equal variances. The test statistic is

$$F_{max} = \frac{s_{max}^2}{s_{min}^2}$$

The three variances are computed using:

$$s_W^2 = \frac{\sum(x - \bar{x})^2}{n - 1} = 1{,}062{,}778 \quad s_{SW}^2 = 695{,}535.7 \quad s_{NW}^2 = 604{,}242.4$$

$$\text{Hartley's } F_{max} = \frac{1{,}062{,}778}{604{,}242.4} = 1.7589$$

From the F_{max} table in Appendix I, the critical value for $\alpha = 0.05$, $c = 3$, and $v = 9$ ($v = \bar{n} - 1$) is 5.34. Because $1.7589 \leq 5.34$, we conclude that the population variances could be equal.

Step 6: **Construct the rejection region.**
The F critical value from the F-distribution table in Appendix H for $D_1 = 2$ and $D_2 = 27$ degrees of freedom is a value between 3.316 and 3.403. The exact value $F = 3.354$ can be found using Excel's **FINV** function or Minitab's **Calc > Probability Distributions** command.

The decision rule is

If $F > 3.354$, reject the null hypothesis;
Otherwise, do not reject the null hypothesis.

Step 7: **Compute the test statistic.**
The sample means are

$$\bar{x}_W = \frac{\sum x}{n} = \frac{\$39{,}500}{10} = \$3{,}950 \qquad \bar{x}_{SW} = \frac{\$23{,}300}{8} = \$2{,}912.50$$

$$\bar{x}_{NW} = \frac{\$44{,}000}{12} = \$3{,}666.67$$

The grand mean is the mean of the data from all samples combined:

$$\bar{\bar{x}} = \frac{\sum\sum x}{N} = \frac{\$3,700 + \$2,900 + \cdots + \$3,200}{30} = \frac{\$106,800}{30} = \$3,560$$

Compute the total sum of squares, sum of squares between, and sum of squares within, and complete the ANOVA table.

Total Sum of Squares

$$SST = \sum_{i=1}^{k}\sum_{j=1}^{n_i}(x_{ij} - \bar{\bar{x}})^2 = 26,092,000$$

Sum of Squares Between

$$SSB = \sum_{i=1}^{k} n_i(\bar{x}_i - \bar{\bar{x}})^2 = 5,011,583$$

Sum of Squares Within

$$SSW = SST - SSB = 21,080,417$$

The ANOVA table is

Source of Variation	SS	df	MS	F-Ratio
Between samples	5,011,583	2	2,505,792	$\frac{2,505,792}{780,756.2} = 3.2094$
Within samples	21,080,417	27	780,756.2	
Total	26,092,000	29		

Step 8:   Reach a decision.
Because the F test statistic = $3.2094 < F_\alpha = 3.354$, we do not reject the null hypothesis based on these sample data.

Step 9:   Draw a conclusion.
We are not able to detect a difference in the mean billing per customer by region.

Excel and Minitab Tutorial

Hydronics Corporation—The Hydronics Corporation makes and distributes health products Currently the company's research department is experimenting with two new herb-based weight loss-enhancing products. To gauge their effectiveness, researchers at the company conducted a tes using 300 human subjects over a six-week period. All the people in the study were between 30 anc 40 pounds overweight.

One-third of the subjects were randomly selected to receive a placebo—in this case, a pill con taining only vitamin C. One-third of the subjects were randomly selected and given Product 1. The remaining 100 people received Product 2. The subjects did not know which pill they had been assigned. Each person was asked to take the pill regularly for six weeks and otherwise observe his o her normal routine. At the end of six weeks, the subjects' weight loss was recorded. The company was hoping to find statistical evidence that at least one of the products is an effective weight-loss aid

The CD-ROM file *Hydronics* shows the study data. Positive values indicate that the subject los weight, whereas negative values indicate that the subject gained weight during the six-week stud period. As often happens in studies involving human subjects, people drop out. Thus, at the end o six weeks, only 89 placebo subjects, 91 Product 1 subjects, and 83 Product 2 subjects with vali data remained. Consequently, this experiment resulted in an unbalanced design. (Note, though, one way ANOVA applies to both balanced and unbalanced designs.)

The null and alternative hypotheses to be tested using a significance level of 0.05 are

$H_0: \mu_1 = \mu_2 = \mu_3$
$H_A:$ At least two population means are different.

The experimental design is completely randomized. The factor is diet supplement, which has thre levels: placebo, Product 1, and Product 2. We will use a significance level of

$$\alpha = 0.05$$

FIGURE 11-7A

Excel Output: Hydronics Weight Loss ANOVA Results

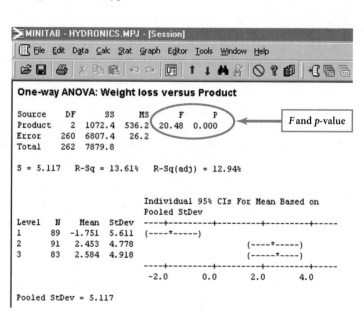

Excel Instructions
1. Open file: Hydronics.xls
2. Select **Tools**.
3. Click on **Data Analysis**.
4. Select **ANOVA: Single Factor**.
5. Define data range.
6. Specify alpha level.

Figure 11-7a and Figure 11-7b show the Excel and Minitab analysis of variance results. The top section of the Excel ANOVA and the bottom section of the Minitab ANOVA output in Figure 11-7b provide descriptive information for the three levels. The ANOVA table is the other half of the output. These tables look like the one we generated manually in the Bayhill example. However, Excel and Minitab also compute the p-value. In addition, Excel displays the critical value, F-critical, from the F-distribution table. Thus, you can test the null hypothesis by comparing the calculated F to the F-critical or by comparing the p-value to the significance level.

The decision rule is

$$\text{If } F > F_\alpha = 3.03, \text{ reject } H_0;$$
$$\text{Otherwise, do not reject } H_0.$$

or

$$\text{If } p\text{-value} < \alpha, \text{ reject } H_0;$$
$$\text{Otherwise, do not reject } H_0.$$

Because

$$F = 20.48 > F_\alpha = 3.03 \text{ (or because } p\text{-value} = 5.51 \text{ E-09} < \alpha = 0.05)$$

we reject the null hypothesis

FIGURE 11-7B

Minitab Output: Hydronics Weight Loss ANOVA Results

Minitab Instructions:
1. Open file: Hydronics.MTW.
2. Choose **Stat > ANOVA > One-way**.
3. In **Response**, enter data column, *Loss*.
4. In **Factor**, enter factor level column, *Program*.
5. Click **OK**.

and conclude there is a difference in the mean weight loss for people on the three treatments. At least two of the populations have different means. The top portion of Figure 11-7a shows the descriptive measures for the sample data. For example, the subjects who took the placebo actually gained an average of 1.75 pounds. Subjects on Product 1 lost an average of 2.45 pounds, and subjects on Product 2 lost an average of 2.58 pounds.

The Tukey-Kramer Procedure for Multiple Comparisons

What does this conclusion imply about which treatment results in greater weight loss? One approach for answering this question is to use confidence interval estimates for all possible pairs of population means, based on the pooling of the two relevant sample variances, as introduced in Chapter 9.

$$s_p = \sqrt{\frac{(n_1 - 1)s_1^2 + (n_2 - 1)s_2^2}{n_1 + n_2 - 2}}$$

These confidence intervals are constructed using the formula also given in Chapter 9, Equation 9-5:

$$(\bar{x}_1 - \bar{x}_2) \pm t_{\alpha/2} \ s_p \sqrt{\frac{1}{n_1} + \frac{1}{n_2}}$$

It uses a weighted average of only the two sample variances corresponding to the two sample means in the confidence interval. However, in the Hydronics example, we have three samples, and thus three variances involved. If we were to use the pooled standard deviation, s_p shown here, we would be disregarding one-third of the information available to estimate the common population variance. Instead, we use confidence intervals based on the pooled standard deviation obtained from the square root of MSW. This is the square root of the weighted average of all (three in this example) sample variances. This is preferred to the interval estimate shown here because we are assuming that each of the three sample variances is an estimate of the common population variance.

A superior method for testing which populations have different means after the one-way ANOVA has led us to reject the null hypothesis is called the *Tukey-Kramer procedure for multiple comparisons*. To understand why the Tukey-Kramer procedure is superior, we introduce the concept of an **experiment-wide error rate**.

Experiment-Wide Error Rate

The proportion of experiments in which at least one of the set of confidence intervals constructed does not contain the true value of the population parameter being estimated.

The Tukey-Kramer procedure is based on the simultaneous construction of confidence intervals for all differences of pairs of treatment means. In this example, there are three different pairs of means ($\mu_1 - \mu_2, \mu_1 - \mu_3, \mu_2 - \mu_3$). The Tukey-Kramer procedure simultaneously constructs three different confidence intervals for a specified confidence level, say 95%. Intervals that do not contain zero imply that a difference exists between the associated population means.

Suppose we repeat the study a large number of times. Each time, we construct the Tukey-Kramer 95% confidence intervals. The Tukey-Kramer method assures us that in 95% of these experiments, the three confidence intervals constructed will include the true difference between the population means, $\mu_i - \mu_j$. In 5% of the experiments, at least one of the confidence intervals will not contain the true difference between the population means. Thus in 5% of the situations, we would make at least one mistake in our conclusions about which populations have different means. This proportion of errors (0.05) is known as the experiment-wide error rate.

For a 95% confidence interval, the Tukey-Kramer procedure controls the experiment-wide error to a 0.05 level. However, because we are concerned with only this one experiment (with one set of sample data), the error rate associated with any one of the three confidence intervals is actually less than 0.05.

The Tukey-Kramer procedure allows us to simultaneously examine all pairs of populations *after* the ANOVA test has been completed without increasing the true alpha level.[5] Because these comparisons are made after the ANOVA *F*-test, the procedure is called a post-test procedure.

The first step in using the Tukey-Kramer procedure is to compute the absolute differences between each pair of sample means. Using the results shown in Figure 11-7a, we get the following differences.

$$|\bar{x}_1 - \bar{x}_2| = |-1.75 - 2.45| = 4.20$$
$$|\bar{x}_1 - \bar{x}_3| = |-1.75 - 2.58| = 4.33$$
$$|\bar{x}_2 - \bar{x}_3| = |2.45 - 2.58| = 0.13$$

The Tukey-Kramer procedure requires us to compare these absolute differences to the *critical range* that is computed using Equation 11-7.

Tukey-Kramer Critical Range

$$\text{Critical Range} = q_\alpha \sqrt{\frac{MSW}{2}\left(\frac{1}{n_i} + \frac{1}{n_j}\right)} \qquad \textbf{11-7}$$

where:

q_α = Value from studentized range table (Appendix J), with $D_1 = k$ and $D_2 = N - k$ degrees of freedom for the desired level of α [k = number of groups or factor levels, and N = total number of data values from all populations (levels) combined]

MSW = Mean square within

n_i and n_j = Sample sizes from populations (levels) i and j, respectively

---

A critical range is computed for each pairwise comparison, but if the samples sizes are equal, only one critical-range calculation is necessary because the quantity under the radical in Equation 11-7 will be the same for all comparisons. If the calculated pairwise comparison value is greater than the critical-range value, we conclude the difference is significant.

The q value from the studentized range table in Appendix J for a significance level equal to

$$\alpha = 0.05$$

and

$$k = 3 \text{ and } N - k = 260 \text{ degrees of freedom}$$

is approximately

$$q_\alpha = 3.31$$

For $D_2 = N - k = 260$ degrees of freedom, we use the row labeled ∞. Then, for the placebo versus Product 1 comparison,

$$n_1 = 89 \text{ and } n_2 = 91$$

We use Equation 11-7 to compute the critical range, as follows:

$$\text{Critical Range} = q_\alpha \sqrt{\frac{MSW}{2}\left(\frac{1}{n_i} + \frac{1}{n_j}\right)}$$

$$\text{Critical Range} = 3.31\sqrt{\frac{26.18}{2}\left(\frac{1}{89} + \frac{1}{91}\right)} = 1.785$$

Because

$$|\bar{x}_1 - \bar{x}_2| = 4.20 > 1.785$$

we conclude that

$$\mu_1 \neq \mu_2$$

[5]There are a variety of other methods for performing multiple-comparison tests in ANOVA.

TABLE 11-4

Hydronics Pairwise Comparisons—Tukey-Kramer Test

	$|\bar{x}_i - \bar{x}_j|$	CRITICAL RANGE	SIGNIFICANT?
Placebo vs. Product 1	4.20	1.785	Yes
Placebo vs. Product 2	4.33	1.827	Yes
Product 1 vs. Product 2	0.13	1.818	No

The mean weight loss for the placebo group is not equal to the mean for the Product 1 group. Table 11-4 summarizes the results for the three pairwise comparisons.

From the table we see that Product 1 and Product 2 both offer significantly higher average weight loss than the placebo. However, the sample data do not indicate a difference in the average weight loss between Product 1 and Product 2.

EXAMPLE 11-2: THE TUKEY-KRAMER PROCEDURE FOR MULTIPLE COMPARISON

Excel and Minitab Tutorial

Digitron, Inc. Digitron, Inc., makes disc brakes for automobiles. Digitron's R&D department recently tested four brake systems to determine if there is a difference in the average stopping distance among them. Forty identical mid-sized cars were driven on a test track. Ten cars were fitted with Brake A, 10 with Brake B, and so forth. An electronic, remote switch was used to apply the brakes at exactly the same point on the road. The number of feet required to bring the car to a full stop was recorded. The data are in the CD-ROM file *Digitron*. Because we care to determine only whether the four brake systems have the same or different mean stopping distances, the test is a one-way (single factor) test with four levels and can be completed using the following steps.

Step 1: **Specify the parameter(s) of interest.**
The parameter of interest is the mean stopping distance for each brake type. The company is interested in knowing whether a difference exists in mean stopping distance for the four brake types.

Step 2: **Formulate the appropriate null and alternative hypotheses.**
The appropriate null and alternative hypotheses are

$$H_0: \mu_1 = \mu_2 = \mu_3 = \mu_4$$
$$H_A: \text{At least two population means are different.}$$

Step 3: **Specify the significance level for the test.**
The test will be conducted using $\alpha = 0.05$.

Step 4: **Select independent simple random samples from each population.**

Step 5: **Check to see that the normality and equal-variance assumptions have been satisfied.**
Because of the small sample size, the box and whisker diagram is used.

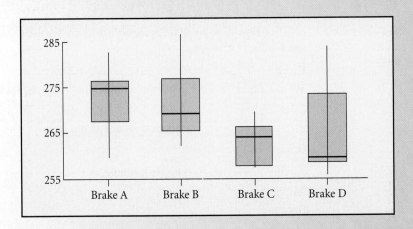

The box plots indicate some skewness in the samples and question the assumption of equality of variances. However, if we assume that the populations are normally distributed, Hartley's F_{max} test can be used to test whether the four populations have equal variances. The test statistic is

$$F_{max} = \frac{s_{max}^2}{s_{min}^2}$$

The four variances are computed using $s_1^2 = \dfrac{\Sigma(x - \bar{x})^2}{n - 1} = 49.9001$

$$s_1^2 = 49.9001 \quad s_2^2 = 61.8557 \quad s_3^2 = 21.7356 \quad s_4^2 = 106.4385$$

Hartley's $F_{max} = \dfrac{106.4385}{21.7356} = 4.8970$

From the F_{max} table in Appendix I, the critical value for alpha = 0.05, $k = 4$, and $\bar{n} - 1 = 9$ is 6.31. Because $4.8970 < 6.31$, we conclude that the population variances could be equal. We might perform other confirmatory tests, such as the chi-square goodness-of-fit test, to determine if the populations have normal distributions. However, of the two assumptions, equality of variances is the most pressing concern. Because we have concluded that the population variances are equal, we proceed with the analysis.

Step 6:   Determine the decision rule.

Because $k - 1 = 3$ and $N - k = 36$, $F_\alpha = 2.866$. The decision rule is

If the calculated $F > F_\alpha = 2.866$, reject H_0, or
If the p-value $< \alpha = 0.05$, reject H_0;
Otherwise, do not reject H_0.

Step 7:   Use Excel or Minitab to construct the ANOVA table.

Figure 11-8 shows the Excel output for the ANOVA.

Step 8:   Reach a decision.

From Figure 11-8, we see that

$$F = 3.89 > F_\alpha = 2.866, \text{ and}$$
$$p\text{-value} = 0.0167 < 0.05.$$

We reject the null hypothesis.

Step 9:   Draw a conclusion.

We conclude that not all population means are equal. But which systems are different? Is one system superior to all the others?

FIGURE 11-8

Excel One-Way ANOVA Output for the Digitron Example

Excel Instructions:
1. Open file: Digitron.xls
2. Click on **Tools** tab.
3. Select **Data Analysis** option.
4. Select **ANOVA: Single Factor**.
5. Enter significance level and data ranges.

Minitab Instructions (for similar results):
1. Open file: Digitron.MTW.
2. Choose **Stat > ANOVA > One-way**.
3. In **Response**, enter data column, *Distance*.
4. In **Factor**, enter factor level column, *Brake*.
5. Click **OK**.

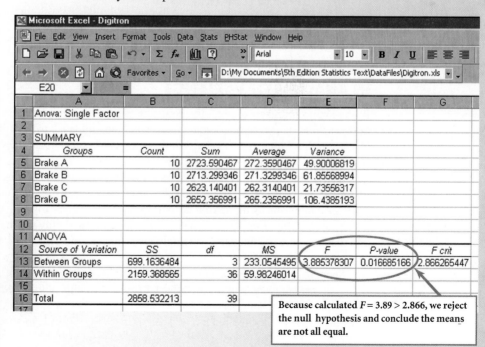

Anova: Single Factor						
SUMMARY						
Groups	*Count*	*Sum*	*Average*	*Variance*		
Brake A	10	2723.590467	272.3590467	49.90006819		
Brake B	10	2713.299346	271.3299346	61.85568994		
Brake C	10	2623.140401	262.3140401	21.73556317		
Brake D	10	2652.356991	265.2356991	106.4385193		
ANOVA						
Source of Variation	*SS*	*df*	*MS*	*F*	*P-value*	*F crit*
Between Groups	699.1636484	3	233.0545495	3.885378307	0.016685166	2.866265447
Within Groups	2159.368565	36	59.98246014			
Total	2858.532213	39				

Because calculated $F = 3.89 > 2.866$, we reject the null hypothesis and conclude the means are not all equal.

Step 10: **Use the Tukey-Kramer test to determine which populations have different means.**
Because we have rejected the null hypothesis of equal means, we need to perform a post-ANOVA multiple comparison test. Using Equation 11-7 to construct the critical range to compare to the absolute differences in all possible pairs of sample means. The critical range is[6]

$$\text{Critical Range} = q_\alpha \sqrt{\frac{MSW}{2}\left(\frac{1}{n_i} + \frac{1}{n_j}\right)} = 3.79 \sqrt{\frac{59.98}{2}\left(\frac{1}{10} + \frac{1}{10}\right)}$$

Critical Range = 9.282

Only one critical range is necessary because all of the sample sizes are equal. If any pair of sample means has an absolute difference, $|\bar{x}_i - \bar{x}_j|$, greater than the critical range, we can infer that a difference exists in those population means. The possible pairwise comparisons (part of a family of comparisons called *contrasts*) are

Contrast	Conclusions
$|\bar{x}_1 - \bar{x}_2| = |272.359 - 271.3299| = 1.029 < 9.282$	
$|\bar{x}_1 - \bar{x}_3| = |272.359 - 262.314| = 10.045 > 9.282$	$\mu_1 \neq \mu_3$
$|\bar{x}_1 - \bar{x}_4| = |272.359 - 265.2357| = 7.123 < 9.282$	
$|\bar{x}_2 - \bar{x}_3| = |271.3299 - 262.314| = 9.016 < 9.282$	
$|\bar{x}_2 - \bar{x}_4| = |271.3299 - 265.2357| = 6.094 < 9.282$	
$|\bar{x}_3 - \bar{x}_4| = |262.314 - 265.2357| = 2.922 < 9.282$	

Therefore, based on the Tukey-Kramer procedure, we can infer that population 1 (brake system A) and population 3 (brake system C) have different mean stopping distances. Because short stopping distances are preferred, system C would be preferred over system A, but no other differences are supported by these sample data. For the other contrasts, the difference between the two sample means is insufficient to conclude that a difference in population means exists.

FIXED EFFECTS VERSUS RANDOM EFFECTS IN ANALYSIS OF VARIANCE

In the Digitron brake example, the company was testing four brake systems. These were the only brake systems under consideration. The ANOVA was intended to determine whether there was a difference in these four brake systems only. In the Hydronics weight loss example, the company was interested in determining whether there was a difference in mean weight loss for two supplements and the placebo. In the Bayhill example involving coupon designs, the company narrowed its choices to four different designs, and the ANOVA test was used to determine whether there was a difference in means for these four designs only.

Thus, in each of these examples, the inferences extend only to the factor levels being analyzed, and the levels are assumed to be the only levels of interest. This type of test is called a *fixed effects analysis of variance test*.

Suppose in the Bayhill coupon example that instead of paring the list of possible coupons to a final four, the company had simply selected a random sample of four coupon designs from all possible coupon designs being considered. In that case, the factor levels included in the test would be a random sample of the possible levels. Then, if the ANOVA leads to rejecting the null hypothesis, the

[6]The q-value from the studentized range table with alpha = 0.05 and degrees of freedom equal to $k = 4$ and $N - k = 36$ must be approximated using degrees of freedom 4 and 40 because the table does not show degrees of freedom of 4 and 36. This value is 3.79.

conclusion applies to all possible coupon designs. The assumption is the possible levels have a normal distribution and the tested levels are a random sample from this distribution. When the factor levels are selected through random sampling, the analysis of variance test is called a *random effects test*.

11-1: EXERCISES

Skill Development

11.1 Respond to each of the following questions using this partially completed one-way ANOVA table.

Source of Variation	SS	df	MS	F-Ratio
Between samples	1,745			
Within samples		240		
Total	6,504	246		

a. How many different populations are being considered in this analysis?
b. Fill in the ANOVA table with the missing values.
c. State the appropriate null and alternative hypotheses.
d. Based on the ANOVA F-test, what conclusion should be reached regarding the null hypothesis? Test using a significance level of 0.01.

11.2 Respond to each of the following questions using this partially completed one-way ANOVA table.

Source of Variation	SS	df	MS	F-Ratio
Between samples		3		
Within samples	405			
Total	888	31		

a. How many different populations are being considered in this analysis?
b. Fill in the ANOVA table with the missing values.
c. State the appropriate null and alternative hypotheses.
d. Based on the ANOVA F-test, what conclusion should be reached regarding the null hypothesis? Test using an $\alpha = 0.05$ level.

11.3 Given the following sample data:

Item	Group 1	Group 2	Group 3
1	10.1	8.2	13.7
2	9.3	6.1	12.2
3	11.4	8.6	12.4
4	12.0	9.5	11.6
5	13.5	10.3	13.1
6	12.8	10.4	15.1

a. State the appropriate null and alternative hypotheses for determining whether a difference exists in the average value for the three populations.
b. Compute the sum of squares-between for the sample data.
c. Compute the sum of squares within for the sample data.
d. Based on the computations in parts b and c, develop the ANOVA table and test the null hypothesis using $\alpha = 0.05$. Use the test-statistic approach.

11.4 Given the following sample data:

Item	Group 1	Group 2	Group 3	Group 4
1	20.9	28.2	17.8	21.2
2	27.2	26.2	15.9	23.9
3	26.6	21.6	18.4	19.5
4	22.1	29.7	20.2	17.4
5	25.3	30.3	14.1	
6	30.1	25.9		
7		23.8		

a. Based on the computations for the within- and between-sample variations, develop the ANOVA table and test the appropriate null hypothesis using an $\alpha = 0.05$. Use the p-value approach.
b. Use the Tukey-Kramer procedure to determine which populations have different means. Use $\alpha = 0.05$.

Business Applications

11.5 The Green-Checker Cab Company operates 12 taxis in Seattle, Washington. The manager is interested in determining whether there is a difference in average fares collected for the day, swing, and graveyard shifts. To test whether a difference exists, she has collected a random sample of 10 observations from each shift. The following summary values have been computed from the sample data:

$$SST = 156.764 \ SSB = 55.600$$

a. Develop the appropriate ANOVA table to reach the determination of interest to the manager. Test the hypothesis using an $\alpha = 0.05$.
b. How would your conclusion change if you used a significance level of 0.01? Discuss why this change would occur.

11.6 Channel 9 television in Colville, Washington, recently conducted a study of television news viewers. One item of interest to Channel 9 management was whether the average age of viewers watching Channel 9 was the same as for the other two stations in Colville. The sample included 24 viewers of each station, with $SST = 2,903.27$ and $SSW = 713.56$.

Using a significance level of 0.05, what should Channel 9 conclude about the average ages of news viewers of the three stations? Discuss.

11.7 The Savouy Corporation recently purchased a bicycle manufacturing plant formerly owned by the American Traveling Company. American had been outfitting its bikes with tires produced by the Leach Corporation. Savouy management is considering whether to stay with Leach tires or to change to another brand. Three other brands are being considered, all of which cost about the same as the Leach tire. The criterion for tire selection will be average tread life.

Samples of 20 have been selected from the Leach tires and from brands A, B, and C. The following results were found:

$$\bar{x}_{Leach} = 111 \text{ hours} \quad \bar{x}_A = 126 \text{ hours}$$
$$\bar{x}_B = 100 \text{ hours} \quad \bar{x}_C = 105 \text{ hours}$$
$$SST = 19,620$$

(Note that the sample means represent the mean hours of use until the tread was reduced to a specified level, at which time the tires were discarded.)

Based on the sample data and using $\alpha = 0.05$ level, what conclusion should the Savouy Corporation reach regarding the different brands of bicycle tires? Discuss.

Advanced Applications

11.8 Suppose as part of your job you are responsible for installing emergency lighting in a series of state office buildings. Bids have been received from four manufacturers of battery-operated emergency lights. The costs are about equal, so the decision will be based on the length of time the lights last before failing. A sample of four lights from each manufacturer has been tested, with the following values (time in hours) recorded for each manufacturer:

Type A	Type B	Type C	Type D
1,024	1,270	1,121	923
1,121	1,325	1,201	983
1,250	1,426	1,190	1,087
1,022	1,322	1,122	1,121

a. Using a significance level equal to 0.01, what conclusion should you reach about the four manufacturer's battery-operated emergency lights? Explain.

b. If the test conducted in part a reveals that the null hypothesis should be rejected, what manufacturer should be used to supply the lights? Is there one or more manufacturers that you can eliminate based on these data? Use the appropriate test for multiple comparisons. Discuss.

11.9 A large metropolitan police force is considering changing from full-size cars to intermediates. The police force sampled cars from each of three manufacturers. The number of cars sampled represents the number the manufacturer was able to provide for the test. Each car was driven for 5,000 miles, and the operating cost per mile was computed. The operating costs, in cents per mile, for the cars are provided in the CD-ROM file *Police*.

a. Perform an analysis of variance on these data. Assume an alpha level of 0.05. Do the experimental data provide evidence that the average operating costs per mile for the three types of police cars are different? Use a p-value approach.

b. Referring to part a, based on the sample data and the appropriate test for multiple comparisons, what con-clusions should be reached concerning which type of car the police force should adopt? Discuss and prepare a report to the police chief.

c. Provide an estimate for the maximum and minimum differences in average savings per year if the police chief chooses the "best" versus the "worst" car, using operating costs as a criterion. Assume that police cars are driven 30,000 miles a year. Use a 90% confidence interval.

11.10 A nationwide moving company is considering five different types of nylon tie-down straps. The purchasing department randomly selected straps from each company and determined their breaking strengths in pounds. The sample data are contained in the CD-ROM file called *Nylon*.

a. (1) Determine if the variance of the breaking strength measurements for each of the companies can be considered equal. Use a significance level of 0.05. (2) State any additional assumptions you would need to make to justify the use of a one-way ANOVA procedure to determine that the mean strength of the aluminum was the same for each vendor. (3) Construct histograms for the data for each company. Do these samples appear to have come from normal distributions? Explain your reasons.

b. Based on your analysis, with a Type I error rate of 0.05, can you conclude that a difference in breaking strengths exists among the types of nylon ropes?

c. Based on the sample data, make a recommendation regarding which company should be selected based on mean strength of the nylon straps. Discuss in a report to the purchasing manager.

11.11 A leading brewer of beer is considering five different types of advertising displays for a new low-calorie beer. Each display type is tested in five different randomly selected stores. A total of 25 stores are in the sample. The mean monthly sales figures (in dollars) and variances for each type of display are as follows:

Display Type	Sample Mean	Sample Variance
A	98	100.75
B	77	83.00
C	84	64.75
D	103	144.35
E	91	101.00

a. Based on these sample data, can the brewery conclude that it makes a difference which type of display is used? Test using a significance level of 0.05. (Hint: Use the means and variances to determine the SSB and SSW values.)

b. Comment on the sampling method used for this study. Specifically, address any assumptions that are violated and are necessary for the ANOVA to be valid.

c. Use the Tukey-Kramer procedure to determine which display type is preferred. Discuss your conclusions in a short report to the marketing manager.

11-2 RANDOMIZED COMPLETE BLOCK ANALYSIS OF VARIANCE

Section 11-1 introduced one-way ANOVA for testing hypotheses involving three or more population means. This ANOVA method is appropriate as long as we are interested in analyzing one factor at a time and we select independent random samples from the populations. For instance, Example 11-2 involving brake assembly systems at the Digitron Corporation (Figure 11-8) illustrated a situation in which we were interested in only one factor: type of brake assembly system. The measurement of interest was the stopping distance with each brake system. To test the hypothesis that the four brake systems were equal with respect to average stopping distance, four groups of the same make and model cars were assigned to each brake system independently. Thus, the one-way ANOVA design was appropriate.

There are, however, situations in which another factor affects the observed response in a one-way design. Often this additional factor is unknown. This is the reason for randomization within the experiment. However, there are also situations in which we know the factor that is impinging on the response variable of interest. Chapter 9 introduced the concept of paired samples and indicated that there are instances when you will want to test for differences in two population means by controlling for sources of variation that might adversely affect the analysis. For instance, in the Digitron example, we might be concerned that, even though we used the same make and model of car in the study, the cars themselves may interject a source of variability that could affect the result. To control for this, we could use the concept of *paired samples* by using the same 10 cars for each of the four brake systems. When an additional factor with two or more levels is involved, a design technique called *blocking* can be used to eliminate its effect on the statistical analysis of the main factor of interest.

RANDOMIZED COMPLETE BLOCK ANOVA

Excel and Minitab Tutorial

Citizen's State Bank—At Citizen's State Bank, homeowners can borrow money against the equity they have in their homes. To determine equity the bank values the home and subtracts the mortgage balance. The maximum loan is 90% of the equity.

The bank outsources the home appraisals to three companies: Allen & Associates, Heist Appraisal, and Appraisal International. The bank managers know that appraisals are not exact. Some appraisal companies may overvalue homes on average, whereas others might undervalue homes.

Bank managers wish to test the hypothesis that there is no difference in the average house appraisal among the three different companies. The managers could select a random sample of homes for Allen & Associates to appraise, a second sample of homes for Heist Appraisal to work on, and a third sample of homes for Appraisal International. One-way ANOVA would be used to compare the sample means. Obviously a problem could occur if, by chance, one company received larger, higher-quality homes located in better neighborhoods than the other companies. This company's appraisals would naturally be higher on average, not because it tended to appraise higher, but because the homes were simply more expensive.

Citizen's State Bank officers need to control for the variation in size, quality, and location of homes to fairly test that the three companies' appraisals are equal on the average. To do this, they select a random sample of properties and have each company appraise the same properties. In this case, the properties are called *blocks*, and the test design is called a *randomized complete block design*.

The data in Table 11-5 were obtained when each appraisal company was asked to appraise the same five properties. The bank managers wish to test the following hypothesis.

$$H_0: \mu_1 = \mu_2 = \mu_3$$
$$H_A: \text{At least two populations have different means.}$$

The randomized block design requires the following assumptions:

ASSUMPTIONS

1. The populations are normally distributed.
2. The populations have equal variances.
3. The observations within samples are independent.

You can check these assumptions using graphical methods (e.g., histograms and box and whisker diagrams) and the Hartley's *F*-test if you have sufficient sample sizes from each population.

Because the managers have chosen to have the same properties appraised by each company (block on property), the samples are not independent, and a method known as *randomized complete block ANOVA* must be employed to test the hypothesis. This method is similar to the one-way

TABLE 11-5

Citizen's State Bank Property Appraisals (in thousands of dollars)

	APPRAISAL COMPANY			
Property (Block)	Allen & Associates	Heist Appraisal	Appraisal International	Block Mean
1	78	82	79	79.67
2	102	102	99	101.00
3	68	74	70	70.67
4	83	88	86	85.67
5	95	99	92	95.33
Factor Level Mean	85.2	89	85.2	86.47 = Grand Mean

ANOVA in Section 11-1. However, there is one more source of variation to be accounted for, the block variation. As was the case in Section 11-1, we must find estimators for each source of variation. Identifying the appropriate sums of squares and then dividing each by its degrees of freedom does this. As was the case in the one-way ANOVA, the sums of squares are obtained by partitioning the total sum of squares (SST). However, in this case the *SST* is divided into three components instead of two, as shown in Equation 11-8.

Sum of Squares Partitioning for Randomized Complete Block Design

$$SST = SSB + SSBL + SSW$$ **11-8**

where:

SST = Total sum of squares
SSB = Sum of squares between factor levels
$SSBL$ = Sum of squares between blocks
SSW = Sum of squares within levels

Both *SST* and *SSB* are computed just as we did with one-way ANOVA, using Equations 11-3 and 11-4. The *sum of squares for blocking (SSBL)* is computed using Equation 11-9.

Sum of Squares for Blocking

$$SSBL = \sum_{j=1}^{b} k(\bar{x}_j - \bar{\bar{x}})^2$$ **11-9**

where:

k = Number of levels for the factor
b = Number of blocks
$\bar{x}_j$ = The mean of the *j*th block
$\bar{\bar{x}}$ = Grand mean

Finally, the *sum of squares within (SSW)* is computed using Equation 11-10. This sum of squares is what remains (the residual) after the variation for all known factors has been removed. This residual sum of squares may be due to the inherent variability of the data, measurement error, or other unidentified sources of variation. Therefore, the sum of squares within is also known as the sum of squares of error, *SSE*.

Sum of Squares Within

$$SSW = SST - (SSB + SSBL)$$ **11-10**

The effect of computing *SSBL* and subtracting it from *SST* in Equation 11-9 is that *SSW* is reduced. Also, if the corresponding variation in the blocks is significant, the variation within the factor levels will be significantly reduced. This can make it easier to detect a difference in the population means if such a difference actually exists. If it does, the estimator for the within variability will in all likelihood be reduced and, thus, the denominator for the *F* test statistic will be smaller. This will pro-

SOURCE OF VARIATION	SS	df	MS	F-RATIO
Between blocks	SSBL	$b - 1$	MSBL	$\dfrac{MSBL}{MSW}$
Between samples	SSB	$k - 1$	MSB	$\dfrac{MSB}{MSW}$
Within samples	SSW	$(k - 1)(b - 1)$	MSW	
Total	SST	$N - 1$		

TABLE 11-6

Basic Format for the Randomized Block ANOVA Table

where:

k = Number of levels
b = Number of blocks
df = Degrees of freedom
N = Combined sample size
MSB = Mean square between = $\dfrac{SSB}{k - 1}$
$MSBL$ = Mean square blocking = $\dfrac{SSBL}{b - 1}$
MSW = Mean square within = $\dfrac{SSW}{(k - 1)(b - 1)}$

Note: Some randomized block ANOVA tables put SSB first, followed by $SSBL$.

duce a larger F test statistic, which will more likely lead to rejecting the null hypothesis. This will depend, of course, on the relative size of $SSBL$ and the respective changes in the degrees of freedom.

Table 11-6 shows the completely randomized block ANOVA table format and equations for degrees of freedom, mean squares, and F-ratios. As you can see, we now have two F-ratios. The reason for this is that we test not only to determine whether the population means are equal, but also to obtain an indication of whether the blocking was necessary by examining the ratio of the mean square for blocks to the mean square within.

Although you could manually compute the necessary values for the randomized block design, both Excel and Minitab contain a procedure that will do all the computations and build the ANOVA table. The Citizen's State Bank appraisal data are included in your data diskette in the file *Citizens*. (Note that the first column contains labels for each block.)

Figures 11-9a and 11-9b show the ANOVA output. Using Excel or Minitab to perform the computations frees the decision maker to focus on interpreting the results. Note that Excel refers to the randomized block ANOVA as Two-Factor ANOVA without replication. Minitab refers to randomized block ANOVA as Two-Way ANOVA.

The main issue is to determine whether the three appraisal companies differ in average appraisal values. The primary test is

H_0: $\mu_1 = \mu_2 = \mu_3$
H_A: At least two populations have different means.
$\alpha = 0.05$

Using the output presented in Figures 11-9a and 11-9b, you can test this hypothesis two ways. First, we can use the F-distribution approach. Figure 11-10 shows the results of this test. Based on the sample data, we reject the null hypothesis and conclude that the three appraisal companies do not provide equal average values for properties.

The second approach to testing the null hypothesis is the p-value approach. The decision rule in an ANOVA application for p-values is

If p-value $< \alpha$, reject H_0;
Otherwise, do not reject H_0.

In this case,

$\alpha = 0.05$

and the p-value in Figure 11-9a is 0.0103. Because

$p\text{-value} = 0.0103 < \alpha = 0.05$

we

reject the null hypothesis

Both the F-distribution approach and the p-value approach give the same result, as they must.

FIGURE 11-9A

Excel Output: Citizen's State Bank Analysis of Variance

Excel Instructions:
1. Open file: Citizens.xls
2. Click on the **Tools** tab.
3. Select the **Data Analysis** option.
4. Select **ANOVA: Two-Factor Without Replication**.
5. Specify the data range.
6. Determine the desired alpha level.

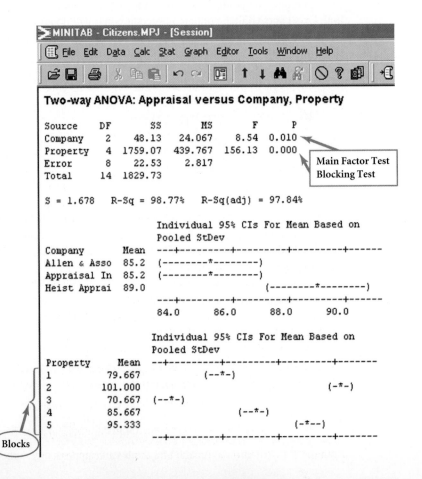

Microsoft Excel - Citizens

	A	B	C	D	E	F	G
1	Anova: Two-Factor Without Replication						
2							
3	SUMMARY	Count	Sum	Average	Variance		
4	1	3	239	79.66667	4.333333		
5	2	3	303	101	3		
6	Blocks 3	3	212	70.66667	9.333333		
7	4	3	257	85.66667	6.333333		
8	5	3	286	95.33333	12.33333		
9							
10	Allen & Associates	5	426	85.2	182.7		
11	Heist Appraisal	5	445	89	136		
12	Appraisal International	5	426	85.2	126.7		
13							
14							
15	ANOVA						
16	Source of Variation	SS	df	MS	F	P-value	F crit
17	Rows	1759.067	4	439.7667	156.1302	1.27E-07	3.837854
18	Columns	48.13333	2	24.06667	8.544379	0.010338	4.458968
19	Error	22.53333	8	2.816667			
20	Within						
21	Total	1829.733	14				

Blocking Test
Main Factor Test

FIGURE 11-9B

Minitab Output: Citizen's State Bank Analysis of Variance

Minitab Instructions:
1. Open file: Citizens.MTW.
2. Choose **Stat > ANOVA > Two-way**.
3. In **Response**, enter the data column (*Appraisal*).
4. In **Row Factor**, enter main factor indicator column (*Company*) and select **Display Means**.
5. In **Column Factor**, enter the block indicator column (*Property*) and select **Display Means**.
6. Choose **Fit additive model**.
7. Click **OK**.

MINITAB - Citizens.MPJ - [Session]

Two-way ANOVA: Appraisal versus Company, Property

Source	DF	SS	MS	F	P
Company	2	48.13	24.067	8.54	0.010
Property	4	1759.07	439.767	156.13	0.000
Error	8	22.53	2.817		
Total	14	1829.73			

Main Factor Test
Blocking Test

S = 1.678   R-Sq = 98.77%   R-Sq(adj) = 97.84%

```
                          Individual 95% CIs For Mean Based on
                          Pooled StDev
Company        Mean   ---+---------+---------+---------+------
Allen & Asso   85.2   (---------*---------)
Appraisal In   85.2   (---------*---------)
Heist Apprai   89.0                        (---------*---------)
                      ---+---------+---------+---------+------
                      84.0      86.0      88.0      90.0
```

```
                          Individual 95% CIs For Mean Based on
                          Pooled StDev
Property       Mean   --+---------+---------+---------+-------
1             79.667              (--*-)
2            101.000                               (-*-)
3             70.667  (--*-)
4             85.667                  (--*-)
5             95.333                            (-*--)
                      --+---------+---------+---------+-------
```

Blocks

FIGURE 11-10

Appraisal Company Hypothesis Test for Citizens State Bank

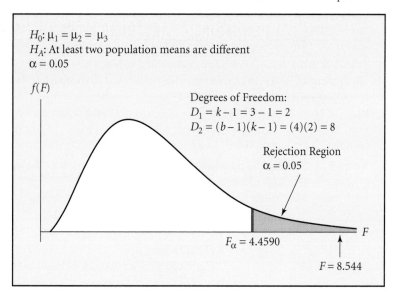

Was Blocking Necessary?

Before we take up the issue of determining which company provides the highest mean property values, we need to discuss one other issue. Recall that the bank managers chose to control for variation between properties by having each appraisal company evaluate the same five properties. This restriction is called blocking, and the properties are the blocks. The ANOVA output in Figure 11-9a contains information that allows us to test whether blocking was necessary.

If the blocking was necessary, it would mean that appraisal values are in fact influenced by the particular property being appraised. The blocks then form a second factor of interest, and we formulate a secondary hypothesis test for this factor, as follows.

$$H_0: \mu_{b1} = \mu_{b2} = \mu_{b3} = \mu_{b4} = \mu_{b5}$$
$$H_A: \text{Not all block means are equal.}$$

Note that we are using μ_{bj} to represent the mean of the jth block.

It seems only natural to use a test statistic that consists of the ratio of the mean square for blocks to the mean square within. However, certain (randomization) restrictions placed on the complete block design make this proposed test statistic invalid from a theoretical-statistics point of view. As an approximate procedure, however, the examination of the ratio *MSBL/MSW* is certainly reasonable. If it is large, it implies that the blocks had a large effect on the response variable and that they were probably helpful in improving the precision of the F-test for primary factor's means.[7] In performing the analysis of variance, we may also conduct a pseudo-test to see whether the average appraisals for each property are equal. If the null hypothesis is "rejected," we have an indication that the blocking is necessary and the randomized block design is justified. However, we should be careful to present this only as an indication and not a precise test of hypothesis for the blocks. The output in Figure 11-9a provides the F-value and p-value for this pseudo-test to determine if the blocking was a necessity. Because $F = 156.1302 > F_\alpha = 3.837$, we definitely have an indication that the blocking design was necessary.

If a hypothesis test indicates blocking is not necessary, the chance of a Type II error for the primary hypothesis has been unnecessarily increased by the use of blocking. The reason is that by blocking we not only partition the sum of squares, we also partition the degrees of freedom. Therefore, the denominator of *MSW* is decreased, and *MSW* will most likely increase. If blocking isn't needed, the *MSW* will tend to be relatively larger than if we had run a one-way design with independent samples. This can lead to failing to reject the null hypothesis for the primary test when it actually should have been rejected.

Therefore, if blocking is indicated to be unnecessary, follow these rules:

1. If the primary H_0 is rejected, proceed with your analysis and decision making. There is no concern.
2. If the primary H_0 is not rejected, redo the study without using blocking. Run a one-way ANOVA with independent samples.

---

[7]Many authors argue that the randomization restriction imposed by using blocks means that the F-ratio really is a test for the equality of the block means plus the randomization restriction. For a summary of this argument and references, see Montgomery, D. C., *Design and Analysis of Experiments*, 4th ed. (New York: John Wiley & Sons, 1997) pp. 175–176.

EXAMPLE 11-3: PERFORMING A RANDOMIZED BLOCK ANALYSIS OF VARIANCE

Fresh & Fun Inc.   Fresh & Fun is a new fast-food chain with three outlets in a midwestern community. The franchise owner is interested in determining if the service quality at the three is the same. She has developed a test in which she selected 14 people who were asked to eat at each of the three fast-food outlets. The order of visits to the three outlets was randomized, but each customer visited each outlet one time. After each visit, each customer rated the service on a scale of 1 to 1,000, with 1,000 being the highest rating. A randomized block analysis of variance test can be performed using the following steps.

Step 1: **Specify the parameter of interest and formulate the appropriate null and alternative hypotheses.**

The parameter of interest is the mean customer-service rating for each outlet, and the question is whether there is a difference between the mean ratings at the three outlets. The appropriate null and alternative hypotheses are

$$H_0: \mu_1 = \mu_2 = \mu_3$$
$$H_A: \text{At least two populations have different means.}$$

In this case, the franchise owner wants to control for variation in customer standards by having the same customers visit each outlet. The ratings will be independent because the rating assigned by one customer does not influence the ratings assigned by other customers. Here the customers are the blocks.

Step 2: **Select simple random samples from each population, check the normality and equal-variance assumptions, and compute treatment means, block means, and the grand mean.**

The following sample data were observed:

Customer	Outlet 1	Outlet 2	Outlet 3	Block Means
1	830	647	630	702.33
2	743	840	786	789.67
3	652	747	730	709.67
4	885	639	617	713.67
5	814	943	632	796.33
6	733	916	410	686.33
7	770	923	727	806.67
8	829	903	726	819.33
9	847	760	648	751.67
10	878	856	668	800.67
11	728	878	670	758.67
12	693	990	825	836.00
13	807	871	564	747.33
14	901	980	719	866.67
Treatment Means	793.57	849.50	668.00	770.36 = grand mean

Step 3: **Compute the sums of squares and complete the ANOVA table.**

Four sums of squares are required:

Total Sum of Squares (Equation 11-3)

$$SST = \sum_{i=1}^{k} \sum_{j=1}^{n_i} (x_{ij} - \bar{\bar{x}})^2 = 614,641.6$$

Sum of Squares Between (Equation 11-4)

$$SSB = \sum_{i=1}^{k} n_i (\bar{x}_i - \bar{\bar{x}})^2 = 241,912.7$$

Sum of Squares Blocking (Equation 11-9)

$$SSBL = \sum_{j=1}^{b} k(\bar{x}_j - \bar{\bar{x}})^2 = 116,605$$

Sum of Squares Within (Equation 11-10)

$$SSW = SST - (SSB + SSBL) = 256{,}123.90$$

The ANOVA table is (see Table 11-6 format):

Source	SS	df	MS	F-Ratio
Between blocks	116,605.0	13	8,969.6	0.9105
Between samples	241,912.7	2	120,956.4	12.279
Within samples	256,123.9	26	9,850.9	
Total	614,641.6	41		

Step 4:   **Specify the level of significance for conducting the tests.**
The tests will be conducted using an $\alpha = 0.05$.

Step 5:   **Test to determine whether blocking is effective.**
Fourteen people were used to evaluate and rate customer service. These constitute the blocks, so if blocking is effective, the mean rating across the three fast-food outlets will not be the same for all 14 customers. The null and alternative hypotheses are

$$H_0\colon \mu_1 = \mu_2 = \mu_3 = \ldots = \mu_{14}$$
$$H_A\colon \text{Not all means are equal (blocking is effective).}$$

As shown in Step 3, the F test statistic to test this null hypothesis is formed by:

$$F = \frac{MSBL}{MSW} = \frac{8{,}969.6}{9{,}850.9} = 0.9105$$

The F-critical from the F-distribution, with alpha $= 0.05$ and $D_1 = 13$ and $D_2 = 26$ degrees of freedom, can be approximated using the F-distribution table in Appendix H as

$$F_{\alpha = .05} \approx 2.15$$

The exact F-critical can be found using the **FINV** function in Excel or the **Calc > Probability Distributions** command in Minitab as $F = 2.119$. Then, because

$$F = 0.9105 < F_{\alpha = .05} = 2.119, \text{ do not reject the null hypothesis}$$

This means that based on these sample data we cannot conclude that blocking was effective.

Step 6:   **Conduct the main hypothesis test to determine whether the treatments have equal means.**
We have three outlet locations. At issue is whether the mean service rating is equal for the three outlets. The appropriate null and alternative hypotheses are

$$H_0\colon \mu_1 = \mu_2 = \mu_3$$
$$H_A\colon \text{At least two populations have different means.}$$

As shown in the ANOVA table in step 3, the F test statistic for this null hypothesis is formed by:

$$F = \frac{MSB}{MSW} = \frac{120{,}956.4}{9{,}850.9} = 12.279$$

The F-critical from the F-distribution, with alpha $= 0.05$ and $D_1 = 2$ and $D_2 = 26$ degrees of freedom, can be approximated using the F-distribution table in Appendix H as

$$F_{\alpha = .05} \approx 3.40$$

The exact F-critical can be found using the **FINV** function in Excel or the **Calc > Probability Distributions** command in Minitab as $F = 3.369$. Then, because

$$F = 12.279 > F_{\alpha = .05} = 3.369, \text{ reject the null hypothesis}$$

Even though in step 5 we concluded that blocking was not effective, the sample data still lead us to reject the primary null hypothesis and conclude that the three outlets do not all have the same mean service rating.

FISHER'S LEAST SIGNIFICANT DIFFERENCE TEST

An analysis of variance test can be used to test whether the populations of interest have different means. However, even if the null hypothesis of equal population means is rejected, the ANOVA does not specify which population means are different. In Section 11-1, we showed how the Tukey–Kramer multiple comparisons procedure is used to determine where the population differences occur for a one-way ANOVA design. Likewise, *Fisher's least significant difference test* is one test for multiple comparisons that we can use for a randomized block ANOVA design.

If the primary null hypothesis has been rejected, then we can compare the absolute differences in sample means from any two populations to the *least significant difference (LSD)*, as computed using Equation 11-11.

Fisher's Least Significant Difference

$$LSD = t_{\alpha/2} \sqrt{MSW} \sqrt{\frac{2}{b}}$$

11-11

where:

$t_{\alpha/2}$ = One-tailed value from student's t-distribution for
$\frac{\alpha}{2}$ and $(k-1)(b-1)$ degrees of freedom
MSW = Mean square within from ANOVA table
b = Number of blocks
k = Number of levels of the main factor

EXAMPLE 11-4: APPLYING FISHER'S LEAST SIGNIFICANT DIFFERENCE TEST

Fresh & Fun Inc. Recall that in Example 11-3 the franchise operators for the three Fresh & Fun fast-food outlets used a randomized block ANOVA design to conclude that three outlets do not all have the same mean customer-service rating. To determine which populations have different means, you can use the following steps.

Step 1: **Compute the *LSD* statistic using Equation 11-11.**

$$LSD = t_{\alpha/2} \sqrt{MSW} \sqrt{\frac{2}{b}}$$

Using a significance level equal to 0.05, the t-critical for $(3-1)(14-1) = 26$ degrees of freedom is

$$t_{.05/2} = 2.0555$$

The mean square within from the ANOVA table (see Example 11-3, step 3) is
$$MSW = 9,850.9$$

The *LSD* is

$$LSD = t_{\alpha/2} \sqrt{MSW} \sqrt{\frac{2}{b}} = 2.0555\sqrt{9,850.9}\sqrt{\frac{2}{14}} = 77.1092$$

Step 2: **Compute the sample means from each population.**

$$\bar{x}_1 = \frac{\sum x}{n} = 793.57 \quad \bar{x}_2 = \frac{\sum x}{n} = 849.50 \quad \bar{x}_3 = \frac{\sum x}{n} = 668$$

Step 3: **Form all possible contrasts by finding the absolute differences between all pairs of sample means. Compare these to the LSD value.**

Absolute Difference	Comparison	Conclusion
$\lvert \bar{x}_1 - \bar{x}_2 \rvert = \lvert 793.57 - 849.50 \rvert = 55.93$	$55.93 < 77.1092$	
$\lvert \bar{x}_1 - \bar{x}_3 \rvert = \lvert 793.57 - 668 \rvert = 125.57$	$125.57 > 77.1092$	$\mu_1 \neq \mu_3$
$\lvert \bar{x}_2 - \bar{x}_3 \rvert = \lvert 849.50 - 668 \rvert = 181.50$	$181.50 > 77.1092$	$\mu_2 \neq \mu_3$

We infer, based on the sample data, that the mean customer-service rating for outlet 1 exceeds the mean for outlet 3, and the mean for outlet 2 exceeds the mean for outlet 3.

11-2: EXERCISES

Skill Development

11.12 The following data were collected for a randomized block ANOVA design with four populations and eight blocks:

	Group 1	Group 2	Group 3	Group 4
Block 1	56	44	57	84
Block 2	34	30	38	50
Block 3	50	41	48	52
Block 4	19	17	21	30
Block 5	33	30	35	38
Block 6	74	72	78	79
Block 7	33	24	27	33
Block 8	56	44	56	71

a. State the appropriate null and alternative hypotheses for both groups and blocks.
b. Construct the appropriate ANOVA table.
c. Using a significance level equal to 0.05, can you conclude that blocking was necessary in this case? Use a test-statistic approach.
d. Based on the data and a significance level equal to 0.05, is there a difference in population means for the four groups? Use a p-value approach.
e. If you found that a difference exists in part d, use the LSD approach to determine which populations have different means.

11.13 The following data were collected for a randomized block ANOVA design with three groups and 10 blocks:

	Group 1	Group 2	Group 3
Block 1	67	56	60
Block 2	45	42	41
Block 3	61	53	51
Block 4	30	29	24
Block 5	44	42	38
Block 6	85	84	81
Block 7	44	36	30
Block 8	67	56	59
Block 9	99	77	56
Block 10	35	60	67

a. Construct the appropriate ANOVA table.

b. Using a significance level equal to 0.05, can you conclude that blocking was effective in this case?
c. Based on the data and a significance level equal to 0.05, is there a difference in population means for the four groups?
d. If you found that a difference exists in part c, use the LSD approach to determine which populations have different means.

11.14 A randomized block ANOVA was performed, and the following partially completed ANOVA table is available:

Source of Variation	SS	df	MS	F-Ratio
Between blocks	4,560	7		
Between samples	8,900	3		
Within samples	___	—		
Total	23,400			

a. How many populations are being tested? How many blocks were used?
b. Using a significance level equal to 0.05, what conclusion have you reached about whether blocking was necessary in this case? Be sure to state the appropriate null and alternative hypotheses.
c. What conclusion should be reached with respect to the primary null hypothesis? Test using a significance level equal to 0.05. Be sure to state the appropriate null and alternative hypotheses.
d. Given your results in part c, is it appropriate to perform a post-ANOVA multiple comparison test to determine which populations have different means? Discuss. If so, conduct the appropriate test and discuss the results.

11.15 A randomized block ANOVA was performed and the following partially completed ANOVA table is available:

Source of Variation	SS	df	MS	F-Ratio
Between blocks		14	2464.2857	
Between samples		6		
Within samples	56,900	—		
Total	133,100			

a. How many populations are being tested?

b. How many blocks were used in this analysis of variance?
c. What is the calculated F-value for testing whether blocking was effective?
d. Based on your response to part c, using an alpha equal to 0.05, what conclusion have you reached about whether blocking was effective in this case? Be sure to state the appropriate null and alternative hypotheses.
e. What is the calculated F-value for testing the main hypothesis?
f. Based on your response to part e, what conclusion should be reached with respect to the primary null hypothesis? Test using an alpha level equal to 0.05. Be sure to state the appropriate null and alternative hypotheses.

11.16 A complete randomized block ANOVA has been performed on four populations using a three-blocks data set. It produces the following summary statistics: $SSBL = 25.667$, $SSB = 38.50$, $SSW = 5.333$, $\bar{x}_1 = 9.40$, $\bar{x}_2 = 9.425$, $\bar{x}_3 = 9.725$, and $\bar{x}_4 = 9.95$.
a. Without determining whether blocks should be included in the model, you are requested to conduct a completely randomized ANOVA on this data. Produce the ANOVA table for this experiment.
b. Turning now to the randomized block design, determine if the blocks should be used in this model.
c. If you determined in part b that the blocks should be included in the design, conduct a hypothesis test that the main factor's means are all equal to each other. If you concluded that blocks were not necessary, determine which of the main factor's means differ.
d. Use Fisher's LSD procedure to determine which of the main factor's means differ.

Business Application

11.17 Weekly cash sales records have been collected for four drive-in restaurants in Topeka, Kansas, for a six-week period. The following data were collected and are also contained in the CD-ROM file *Topeka*.

Week	Drive-in 1	2	3	4
1	$1,430	$ 980	$1,780	$2,300
2	2,200	1,400	2,890	2,680
3	1,140	1,200	1,500	2,000
4	880	1,300	1,470	1,900
5	1,670	1,300	2,400	2,540
6	990	550	1,600	1,900

a. If the assumptions of a one-way ANOVA design are satisfied in this case, what should be concluded about the average sales at the four drive-in restaurants in Topeka? Use a significance level of 0.05.
b. Discuss whether you think the assumptions of a one-way ANOVA are satisfied in this case and indicate why or why not. If they are not, what design is appropriate? Discuss.
c. Perform a randomized block ANOVA test using a significance level of 0.05 to determine whether the mean sales for the four drive-ins are equal.

d. Comment on any differences between these results and those in part a.
e. Suppose blocking was necessary and the researcher chose not to use blocks. Discuss what impact this could have on the results of the ANOVA.
f. Use Fisher's LSD procedure to determine which, if any, drive-ins have different true average weekly sales.

Advanced Applications

11.18 There are three commercial tax-preparation offices in Benbde, Minnesota. The local Better Business Bureau has been receiving some complaints that one of the offices does not understand tax law well enough to provide expert advice. The complaints state that to safeguard itself, the preparing office overstates the tax due by the payer and thus avoids later problems with the IRS.
The Better Business Bureau has decided to invest several hundred dollars in grant money to test the claim. It has selected eight people at random and has asked that they allow each of the three offices to prepare their taxes using the same information. The following data show the tax bills as figured by each office. The data are also located in the CD-ROM file *Tax-test*.

Return	Office 1	Office 2	Office 3
1	4,376.20	5,100.10	4,988.03
2	5,678.45	6,234.23	5,489.23
3	2,341.78	2,242.60	2,121.90
4	9,875.33	10,300.30	9,845.60
5	7,650.20	8,002.90	7,590.88
6	1,324.80	1,450.90	1,356.89
7	2,345.90	2,356.90	2,345.90
8	15,468.75	16,080.78	15,376.70

a. Discuss why the Better Business Bureau set this test up as a randomized block design. Why did it think it was important to have all three offices do the returns for each of the eight people?
b. Test to determine whether the blocking was necessary in this situation. Use a significance level of 0.01. State the null and alternative hypotheses.
c. Based on the sample data, can the Better Business Bureau conclude that there is a difference in the mean taxes due on tax returns? Test using a significance level of 0.01. State the appropriate null and alternative hypotheses.
d. Referring to part c, if you did conclude that a difference exists, use Fisher's LSD approach to determine which office has the highest mean tax due.

11.19 In a local community there are three grocery chain stores. The three have been carrying out a spirited advertising campaign in which each claims to have the lowest prices. A local news station recently sent a reporter to the three stores to check prices on several items. She found that for certain items each store had the lowest price. This survey didn't really answer the question for consumers. Thus, the station set up a test in which 20 shoppers were given different lists of grocery items and were sent to each of the three chain stores. The sales receipts from each of the three stores were recorded in the CD-ROM file called *Groceries*.

a. Why should this price test be conducted using the design that the television station used? What was it attempting to achieve by having the same shopping lists used at each of the three grocery stores?

b. Based on a significance level of 0.05 and these sample data, test to determine whether blocking was nec-

essary in this example. State the null and alternative hypotheses. Use a test-statistic approach.

c. Based on these sample data, can you conclude the three grocery stores have different sample means? Test using a significance level of 0.05. State the appropriate null and alternative hypotheses. Use a *p*-value approach.

d. Based on the sample data, which store has the highest average prices? Use Fisher's LSD test if appropriate.

11-3 TWO-FACTOR ANALYSIS OF VARIANCE WITH REPLICATION

Section 11-2 introduced an ANOVA procedure called the randomized complete block ANOVA. This method is used when we are interested in testing whether the means for the populations (levels) for a factor of interest are equal and we want to control for potential variation due to a second factor. The second factor is called the blocking factor. Consider again the Citizens State Bank property appraisal example, in which the bank was interested in determining whether the mean property valuation was the same for three different appraisal companies. The company used the same five properties to test each appraisal company in an attempt to reduce any variability that might exist due to the properties involved in the test. The properties were the blocks in that example, but we were not really interested in knowing whether the mean appraisal was the same for all properties. The single factor of interest was the appraisal companies.

However, you will encounter many situations in which there are actually two or more factors of interest in the same study. In this section, we limit our discussion to situations involving only two factors. The technique that is used when we wish to analyze two factors is called *two-factor ANOVA with replications*.

TWO-FACTOR ANOVA WITH REPLICATIONS

Excel and Minitab Tutorial

Fly High Airlines—Like other major U.S. airlines, Fly High Airlines is concerned because many of its Frequent Flier program members have accumulated large quantities of free miles.[8] The airline worries that at some point in the future there will be a big influx of customers wanting to use their miles, and the airline will have difficulty satisfying all the requests at once. Thus, Fly High recently conducted an experiment in which three methods for redeeming frequent flier miles were offered to a sample of 16 customers. Each customer had accumulated more than 100,000 frequent flier miles. The customers were equally divided into four age groups. The variable of interest was the number of miles redeemed by the customers during the six-week trial. Table 11-7 shows the number of miles redeemed for each person in the study. These data are also contained in the *Fly High* file on your CD-ROM.

TABLE 11-7

Fly High Airlines Frequent Flier Miles Data

	CASH OPTION	VACATION	SHOPPING
Under 25 years	30,000	40,000	25,000
	0	25,000	25,000
	25,000	0	75,000
	0	0	5,000
25 to 40 years	60,000	40,000	30,000
	0	25,000	25,000
	0	5,000	50,000
	25,000	25,000	0
41 to 60 years	40,000	25,000	25,000
	25,000	50,000	50,000
	25,000	0	0
	0	25,000	0
Over 60 years	0	45,000	30,000
	5,000	25,000	25,000
	25,000	0	25,000
	50,000	50,000	50,000

[8]Name changed at request of the airline.

Method 1 offered cash inducements to use miles. Method 2 offered discount vacation options, and method 3 offered access to a discount-shopping program through the Internet. The airline wants to know the number of miles redeemed under each redemption offer and whether the age of the customer mattered.

A *two-factor ANOVA* design is the appropriate method in this case because the airline has two factors of interest. Factor A (arbitrarily assigned) is the redemption offer type with three levels. Factor B is the age group of each customer with four levels. As shown in Table 11-7, there are $3 \times 4 = 12$ cells in the study and four customers in each cell. The measurements are called *replications* because we get four measurements (miles redeemed) at each combination of redemption offer (Factor A) level and age level (Factor B).

Two-factor ANOVA follows the same logic as all other ANOVA designs. Each factor of interest introduces variability into the experiment. As was the case in Sections 11-1 and 11-2, we must find estimators for each source of variation. Identifying the appropriate sums of squares and then dividing each by its degrees of freedom does this. As was the case in the one-way ANOVA, the total sum of squares (*SST*) can be partitioned into four parts.

1. One part is due to differences in the levels of Factor A (SS_A).
2. Another part is due to the levels of Factor B (SS_B).
3. Another part is due to the *interaction* between Factor A and Factor B (SS_{AB}). (We will discuss the concept of interaction between factors later.)
4. The final component making up the total sum of squares is the sum of squares due to the inherent random variation in the data (*SSE*).

Figure 11-11 illustrates this partitioning concept. The variations due to each of these components will be estimated using the respective *mean squares* obtained by dividing the sums of squares by their degrees of freedom. If the variation accounted for by Factor A and Factor B is large relative to the error variation, we will tend to conclude that the factor levels have different means.

Table 11-8 illustrates the format of the two-factor ANOVA. Three different hypotheses can be tested from the information in this ANOVA table. First, for Factor A (redemption options), we have

$$H_0: \mu_{A1} = \mu_{A2} = \mu_{A3}$$
$$H_A: \text{Not all means are equal.}$$

For factor B (age levels):

$$H_0: \mu_{B1} = \mu_{B2} = \mu_{B3} = \mu_{B4}$$
$$H_A: \text{Not all means are equal.}$$

Test to determine whether interaction exists between the two factors:

$$H_0: \text{Factors A and B do not interact to affect the mean response.}$$
$$H_A: \text{Factors A and B do interact.}$$

Here are the necessary assumptions for the two-factor ANOVA.

ASSUMPTIONS

1. The population values for each combination of pairwise factor levels are normally distributed.
2. The variances for each population are equal.
3. The samples are independent.

FIGURE 11-11

Two-Factor ANOVA— Partitioning of Total Sums of Squares

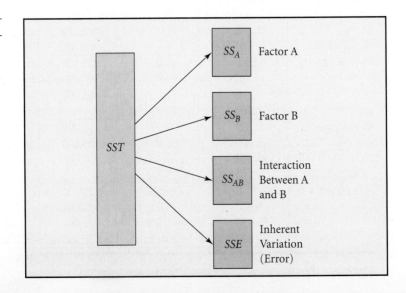

	SOURCE OF VARIATION	SS	df	MS	F-RATIO
TABLE 11-8	Factor A	SS_A	$a - 1$	MS_A	$\dfrac{MS_A}{MSE}$
Basic Format of the Two-Factor ANOVA Table	Factor B	SS_B	$b - 1$	MS_B	$\dfrac{MS_B}{MSE}$
	AB interaction	SS_{AB}	$(a - 1)(b - 1)$	MS_{AB}	$\dfrac{MS_{AB}}{MSE}$
	Error	SSE	$N - ab$	MSE	
	Total	SST	$N - 1$		

where:

a = Number of levels of factor A

b = Number of levels of factor B

N = Total number of observations in all cells

$$MS_A = \text{Mean square factor A} = \frac{SS_A}{a - 1}$$

$$MS_B = \text{Mean square factor B} = \frac{SS_B}{b - 1}$$

$$MS_{AB} = \text{Mean square interaction} = \frac{SS_{AB}}{(a - 1)(b - 1)}$$

$$MSE = \text{Mean square within} = \frac{SSE}{N - ab}$$

Although all the necessary values to complete Table 11-8 could be computed manually using the equations shown in Table 11-9, this would be a time-consuming task for even a small example because the equations for the various sum-of-squares values are quite complicated. Instead, you will want to use Excel or Minitab to perform the two-factor ANOVA.

Interaction Explained

Before we share the ANOVA results for the Fly High Airlines example, a few comments regarding the concept of *factor interaction* are needed. Consider our example involving the two factors: miles redemption-offer type and age category of customer. The response variable is the number of miles redeemed in the six weeks after the offer. Suppose one redemption-offer type is really better and results in a higher average miles being redeemed. If there is no interaction between age and offer type, then customers of all ages will have uniformly higher average miles redeemed for this offer type compared with the other offer types. If another offer type yields lower average miles, then if there is no interaction, all age groups receiving this offer type will redeem uniformly lower miles on average than the other offer types. Figure 11-12 illustrates a situation with no interaction between the two factors.

However, if interaction exists between the factors, we would see a graph similar to the one shown in Figure 11-13. Interaction would be indicated if one age group redeemed higher average miles than the other age groups with one program but lower average miles than the other age groups on the other mileage-redemption programs. In general, interaction occurs if the differences in the averages of the response variable for the various levels of one factor, say Factor A, are not the same for each level of the other factor, say Factor B. The general idea is that interaction between two factors means that the effect due to one of them is not uniform across all levels of the other factor.

Another example in which potential interaction might exist occurs in plywood manufacturing, where thin layers of wood called veneer are glued together to form plywood. One of the important quality attributes of plywood is its strength. However, plywood is made from different species of wood (pine, fir, hemlock, etc.), and different types of glue are available. If some species of wood work better (stronger plywood) with certain glues, whereas other species work better with different glues, we say that the wood species and the glue type interact.

TABLE 11-9

Two-Factor ANOVA Equations

Total Sum of Squares

$$SST = \sum_{i=1}^{a}\sum_{j=1}^{b}\sum_{k=1}^{n'} (x_{ijk} - \bar{\bar{x}})^2 \qquad \textbf{11-12}$$

Sum of Squares Factor A

$$SS_A = bn'\sum_{i=1}^{a} (\bar{x}_{i..} - \bar{\bar{x}})^2 \qquad \textbf{11-13}$$

Sum of Squares Factor B

$$SS_B = an'\sum_{j=1}^{b} (\bar{x}_{.j.} - \bar{\bar{x}})^2 \qquad \textbf{11-14}$$

Sum of Squares Interaction Between Factors A and B

$$SS_{AB} = n'\sum_{i=1}^{a}\sum_{j=1}^{b} (\bar{x}_{ij.} - \bar{x}_{i..} - \bar{x}_{.j.} + \bar{\bar{x}})^2 \qquad \textbf{11-15}$$

Sum of Squares Error

$$SSE = \sum_{i=1}^{a}\sum_{j=1}^{b}\sum_{k=1}^{n'} (x_{ijk} - \bar{x}_{ij.})^2 \qquad \textbf{11-16}$$

where:

$$\bar{\bar{x}} = \frac{\displaystyle\sum_{i=1}^{a}\sum_{j=1}^{b}\sum_{k=1}^{n'} x_{ijk}}{abn'} = \text{grand mean}$$

$$\bar{x}_{i..} = \frac{\displaystyle\sum_{j=1}^{b}\sum_{k=1}^{n'} x_{ijk}}{bn'} = \text{mean of each level of factor A}$$

$$\bar{x}_{.j.} = \frac{\displaystyle\sum_{i=1}^{a}\sum_{k=1}^{n'} x_{ijk}}{an'} = \text{mean of each level of factor B}$$

$$\bar{x}_{ij.} = \sum_{k=1}^{n'} \frac{x_{ijk}}{n'} = \text{mean of each cell}$$

a = Number of levels of factor A
b = Number of levels of factor B
n' = Number of replications in each cell

FIGURE 11-12

Differences Between Factor-Level Mean Values: No Interaction

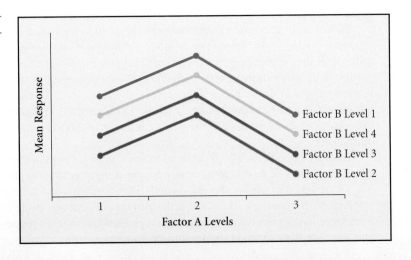

FIGURE 11-13

Differences Between Factor-Level Mean Values: Interaction Present

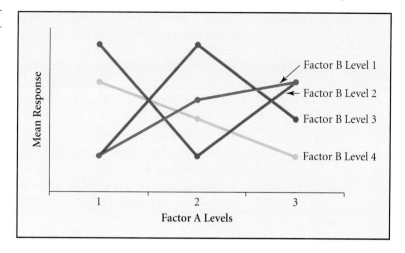

FIGURE 11-13

Differences Between Factor-Level Mean Values: Interaction Present

If interaction is suspected, it should be accounted for by subtracting the interaction term (SS_{AB}) from the total sum-of-squares term in the ANOVA, as shown in Table 11-8. From a strictly arithmetic point of view, the effect of computing SS_{AB} and subtracting it from SST is that SSE is reduced. Also, if the corresponding variation due to interaction is significant, the variation within the factor levels will be significantly reduced. This can make it easier to detect a difference in the population means if such variability actually exists. If it does, the estimator for the error variability, in all likelihood, will be reduced, and the denominator for the F test statistic will be smaller. This will produce a larger F test statistic, which will more likely lead to the rejection of the null hypothesis. This will improve your chances of finding a difference in the Factor A and Factor B mean values, if such a difference exists. This will depend, of course, on the relative size of SS_{AB} and the respective changes in the degrees of freedom. We will comment later, however, on the appropriateness of testing the factor hypotheses if interaction is present. *Note that in order to measure the interaction effect, the sample size for each combination of Factor A and Factor B must be two or greater.*

Excel and Minitab contain a data analysis tool for performing two-factor ANOVA with replications, and they will compute the different sums-of-squares and complete the ANOVA table. However, Excel requires that the data be organized in a special way, as shown in Figure 11-14.[9] (Note, the first row must contain the names for each level of Factor A. Also, column 1 contains the Factor B level names. These must be in the row corresponding to the first sample item for each Factor B level.)

FIGURE 11-14

Excel Data Format for Two-Factor ANOVA—Fly High Airline

Excel Instructions
1. Open file: Fly High.xls

	A	Cash Option	Vacation	Shopping
1		Cash Option	Vacation	Shopping
2	under 25 years	30,000	40,000	25,000
3		0	25,000	25,000
4		25,000	0	75,000
5		0	0	5,000
6	25-40 years	60,000	40,000	30,000
7		0	25,000	25,000
8		0	5,000	50,000
9		25,000	25,000	0
10	41-60 years	40,000	25,000	25,000
11		25,000	50,000	50,000
12		25,000	0	0
13		0	25,000	0
14	over 60 years	0	45,000	30,000
15		5,000	25,000	25,000
16		25,000	0	25,000
17		50,000	50,000	50,000

Factor A Names

Factor B Names

[9]Minitab uses the same data input format for two-factor ANOVA as for randomized block ANOVA.

The Excel two-factor ANOVA output for this example is actually too big to fit on one screen. The top portion of the printout shows summary information for each cell, including means and variances (see Figure 11-15). At the bottom of the output (scroll down) is the ANOVA table shown in Figure 11-16a. Figure 11-16b shows the Minitab output. Excel changes a few labels. For example, Factor A (the miles redemption options) is now referred to as *Columns*. Factor B (age groups) is referred to as *Sample*. In Figures 11-16a and 11-16b, we see all the information necessary to test whether the three redemption offers (factor A) result in different mean miles redeemed.

$$H_0: \mu_{A1} = \mu_{A2} = \mu_{A3}$$
$$H_A: \text{Not all means are equal.}$$
$$\alpha = 0.05$$

Both the p-value and F-distribution approaches can be used. Because

$$p\text{-value (columns)} = 0.561 > \alpha = 0.05$$

the null hypothesis H_0 is not rejected.

(Also, $F = 0.587 < F_\alpha = 3.259$; the null hypothesis is not rejected).

This means the test data do not indicate that a difference exists between the average amount of mileage redeemed for the three types of offers. None seems superior to the others.

We can also test to determine if age level makes a difference in frequent flier miles redeemed.

$$H_0: \mu_{B1} = \mu_{B2} = \mu_{B3} = \mu_{B4}$$
$$H_A: \text{Not all means are equal.}$$
$$\alpha = 0.05$$

In Figure 11-16a, we see that the

$$p\text{-value} = 0.8796 > \alpha = 0.05$$
$$(\text{Also, } F = 0.2232 < F_\alpha = 2.866)$$

Thus, the null hypothesis is not rejected.

The test data don't indicate that customer age significantly influences the average number of frequent flier miles that will be redeemed.

Finally, we can also test for interaction. The null hypothesis is that no interaction exists. The alternative is that interaction does exist between the two factors. The ANOVA table in Figure 11-16b shows a p-value of 0.939, which is greater than $\alpha = 0.05$. Based on these data, interaction between the two factors does not appear to exist. This would indicate that the differences in the average mileage redeemed between the various age categories are the same for each redemption-offer type.

FIGURE 11-15

Excel Output (Part 1) for Two-Factor ANOVA—Fly High Airlines Example

Excel Instructions
1. Open file: Fly High.xls.
2. Click on the **Tools** tab.
3. Select **Data Analysis > Two Factor with Replication**.
4. Specify the data range.
5. Specify the rows for each sample.
6. Determine the desired alpha level.

	A	B	C	D	E
1	Anova: Two-Factor With Replication				
2					
3	SUMMARY	Cash Option	Vacation	Shopping	Total
4	*under 25 years*				
5	Count	4	4	4	12
6	Sum	55000	65000	130000	250000
7	Average	13750	16250	32500	20833.33333
8	Variance	256250000	389583333.3	891666666.7	494696969.7
9					
10	*25-40 years*				
11	Count	4	4	4	12
12	Sum	85000	95000	105000	285000
13	Average	21250	23750	26250	23750
14	Variance	806250000	206250000	422916666.7	396022727.3
15					
16	*41-60 years*				
17	Count	4	4	4	12
18	Sum	90000	100000	75000	265000
19	Average	22500	25000	18750	22083.33333
20	Variance	275000000	416666666.7	572916666.7	352083333.3
21					
22	*over 60 years*				

FIGURE 11-16A

Excel Output (Part 2) for Two-Factor ANOVA—Fly High Airlines Example

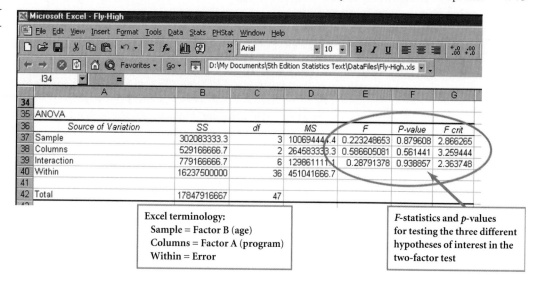

Excel terminology:
  Sample = Factor B (age)
  Columns = Factor A (program)
  Within = Error

F-statistics and *p*-values for testing the three different hypotheses of interest in the two-factor test

A CAUTION ABOUT INTERACTION

In this example, the sample data indicate that no interaction between factors A and B is present. Based on the sample data, we were unable to conclude that the three redemption offers resulted in different average frequent flier miles redeemed. Finally, we were unable to conclude that a difference in average miles redeemed occurred over the four different age groups.

The appropriate approach is to begin by testing for interaction. If the interaction null hypothesis is not rejected, proceed to test factor A and factor B hypotheses. However, if we conclude that interaction is present between the two factors, hypothesis tests for factors A and B generally *should not* be performed. The reason is that findings of significance for either factor might be due only to interactive effects when the two factors are combined, and not to the fact that the levels of the factor differ significantly. It is also possible that interactive effects might mask differences between means of one of the factors for at least some of the levels of the other factor. If significant interaction is present, the experimenter may conduct a one-way ANOVA to test the levels of one of the factors, for example, factor A, using only one level of the other factor, factor B.

Thus, when conducting hypothesis tests for a two-factor ANOVA:

1. Test for interaction.
2. If interaction is present, conduct a one-way ANOVA to test the levels of one of the factors using only one level of the other factor.[10]
3. If no interaction is found, test factor A and factor B.

FIGURE 11-16B

Minitab Output for Two-Factor ANOVA—Fly High Airlines Example

Minitab Instructions:
1. Open file: Fly High.MTW.
2. Choose **Stat > ANOVA > Two-way**.
3. In **Response**, enter the data column (*Value*).
4. In **Row Factor**, enter main factor indicator column (*Redemption Option*).
5. In **Column Factor**, enter the block indicator column (*Age*).
6. Click **OK**.

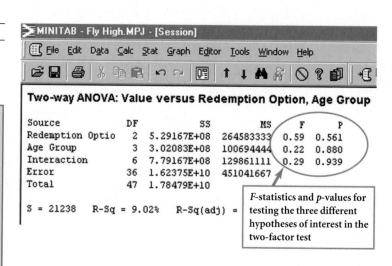

F-statistics and *p*-values for testing the three different hypotheses of interest in the two-factor test

[10]There are, however, some instances in which the effects of the factors provide important and meaningful information even though interaction is present. See Cox, D. R., *Planning of Experiments* (New York: John Wiley and Sons, 1992) pp. 107–108.

OPTIONAL CD-ROM TOPIC Experimental Design and Tukey's Method of Multiple Comparison

If the hypothesis tests for factor A or factor B lead to rejection of the null hypothesis that the means are equal, you may be interested in performing a post test to determine which populations have different means. Several techniques are available to make such a determination. One such technique, called Tukey's method for multiple comparison, can be used. For more about this go to the CD-ROM.

11-3: EXERCISES

Skill Development

11.20 A two-factor ANOVA design with replication has been performed. Factor A has four levels, whereas Factor B has three levels. There are five replications in each cell of the experiment.

a. Determine the number of degrees of freedom for the Factor A and Factor B components of the experiment.

b. Explain what is meant by the phrase "degrees of freedom."

c. Determine the degrees of freedom associated with the interactive component.

d. How many total degrees of freedom are there in this study?

11.21 Consider the following data for a two-factor experiment:

		Factor A		
		Level 1	Level 2	Level 3
Factor B	Level 1	33	30	21
		31	42	30
		35	36	30
	Level 2	23	30	21
		32	27	33
		27	25	18

a. Based on the sample data, do Factors A and B have significant interaction? State the appropriate null and alternative hypotheses and test using a significance level of 0.05.

b. Based on these sample data, can you conclude that the levels of Factor A have equal means? Test using a significance level of 0.05.

c. Do the data indicate that the levels of Factor B have different means? Test using a significance level equal to 0.05.

d. If you rejected the null hypothesis in either part b or part c, use Tukey's method to determine which levels have different means. (See the CD-ROM topic.)

11.22 Consider a two-factor experiment that generated the following sample data:

		Factor A				
		Level 1	Level 2	Level 3	Level 4	Level 5
Factor B	Level 1	203	200	191	188	185
		201	212	200	186	197
		205	206	200	190	191
		193	200	191	178	185
		202	197	203	187	182
		197	195	188	182	180
	Level 2	155	173	178	168	154
		177	195	200	221	178
		201	219	224	189	193
		189	207	198	191	156
		168	186	177	202	177
		190	208	199	214	168

a. Based on the sample data, do Factors A and B have significant interaction? State the appropriate null and alternative hypotheses and test using a significance level of 0.05.

b. Based on these sample data, can you conclude that the levels of Factor A have equal means? Test using a significance level of 0.05.

c. Do the data indicate that the levels of Factor B have different means? Test using a significance level equal to 0.05.

d. If you rejected the null hypothesis in either part b or part c, use Tukey's method to determine which levels have different means. (See the CD-ROM topic.)

11.23 Consider the following partially completed two-factor ANOVA table, which is an outgrowth of a study in which Factor A has three levels and Factor B has four levels. The number of replications was 11 in each cell.

Source of Variation	SS	df	MS	F-Ratio
Factor A				17.6309
Factor B				
AB interaction	33.2			
Error	952.7			
Total	1675.3			

a. Complete the ANOVA table.

b. Based on the sample data, can you conclude that the two factors have significant interaction? Test using a significance level equal to 0.05.

c. Based on the sample data, should you conclude that the means for Factor A differ across the four levels? State the appropriate null and alternative hypotheses and test using an alpha = 0.05 level.

d. Based on the sample data, should you conclude that the means for Factor B differ across the three levels? State the appropriate null and alternative hypotheses and test using an alpha = 0.05 level.

11.24 Consider the following partially completed two-factor ANOVA table, which is an outgrowth of a study in which Factor A has 4 levels and Factor B has 3 levels. The number of replications was 11 in each cell.

Source of Variation	SS	df	MS	F-Ratio
Factor A	345.1			
Factor B				
AB interaction	1123.2			
Error	256.7			
Total	1987.3			

a. Complete the analysis of variance table.

b. Based on the sample data, can you conclude that the two factors have significant interaction? Test using a significance level equal to 0.05.

c. Based on the sample data and the results of part b, should you conclude that the means for Factor A differ across the four levels or that the means for Factor B differ across the three levels? Discuss.

d. Considering the outcome of part b, determine what can be said concerning the differences of the levels of factors A and B. Use a significance level of 0.10 for any hypothesis tests required. Provide a rationale for your response to this question.

Business Application

11.25 💿 A national automotive repair service is interested in studying the effect of automobile manufacturer and vehicle model on the time required to complete a brake-replacement job involving all four wheels. The study was limited to the "Big Three" U.S. manufacturers (Ford, General Motors, and Chrysler) and to two models (passenger cars and sport-utility vehicles). Five vehicles of each model and manufacturer were tested, and the time required to complete each brake job was recorded. The data are contained in the CD-ROM file *Brake-Test*. Note, the manufacturer name has been disguised at the repair company's request.

a. Plot the mean brake-change time for each manufacturer for each of the model types. Looking at the graphs, what conclusions do you reach about the interaction between model type and manufacturer? Discuss.

b. Based on the sample data, is there interaction between manufacturer and model type? Test using a significance level equal to 0.05. Discuss the meaning of this result as it relates to this study.

c. Based on the sample data, can you conclude that a difference exists in mean brake-repair times for passenger cars versus SUVs? Test using a significance level equal to 0.05, and state the appropriate null and alternative hypotheses.

d. What conclusions should the automobile repair company make regarding the brake-repair times for the three manufacturers? Conduct this test using the p-value approach to hypothesis testing.

e. (1) If appropriate, use the Tukey procedure for multiple comparisons with an experiment-wide significance level of 0.05. Discuss. (2) If not appropriate, explain why this is so.

Advanced Applications

11.26 💿 A maker of commercial fertilizer for agricultural use has recently conducted a study of the effect of fertilizer mix and water quantity on the yield (in bushels per acre) for wheat. Three one-acre plots were planted with the same brand of wheat seed for each of three fertilizer mixes and four levels of water quantity. The resulting sample data are in the CD-ROM file *Wheat-Test*.

	Mix A	Mix B	Mix C
Water Quantity 1	87	67	89
	78	77	78
	92	58	92
Water Quantity 2	55	60	70
	67	55	67
	60	48	82
Water Quantity 3	101	90	104
	98	87	110
	89	98	98
Water Quantity 4	67	54	78
	87	67	81
	70	56	79

a. Plot the mean wheat production for each fertilizer level for each of the water quantities. Looking at the graphs, what conclusions do you reach about the interaction between fertilizer mix and water quantity? Discuss.

b. Based on the sample data, is there interaction between fertilizer mix and water quantity? Test using a significance level equal to 0.05. Discuss the meaning of this result as it relates to this study. Use a p-value approach.

c. Based on the sample data, can you conclude that a difference exists in mean wheat production across the different fertilizer levels? Test using a significance level equal to 0.05, and state the appropriate null and alternative hypotheses.

d. Do the sample data indicate that there is a difference in mean wheat production across the four water quantities? Use a significance level equal to 0.05, and state the appropriate null and alternative hypotheses. Use a p-value approach.

e. If appropriate, use the Tukey procedure to make this determination. Use an experiment-wide significant level equal to 0.05.

11.27 Mt. Jumbo Plywood Company makes plywood for use in furniture production. The first major step in the plywood process is the peeling of the logs into thin layers of veneer. A lathe that rotates the logs through a knife that peels the log into layers $\frac{3}{8}$-inch thick conducts the peeling process. Ideally, when a log is reduced to a 4-inch core diameter, the lathe releases the core and a new log is loaded onto the lathe. However, a problem called "spin-outs" occurs if the lathe kicks out a core that has more than 4 inches remaining. This wastes wood and costs the company money.

Before going to the lathe, the logs are conditioned in a water-filled vat that is heated to warm the logs. The company is concerned that improper log conditioning may lead to excessive spin-outs. Two factors are believed to effect the core diameter: the vat temperature and the time the logs spend in the vat prior to peeling. The lathe supervisor has recently conducted a test during which logs were peeled at several combinations of temperature and time. The sample data for this experiment are in the CD-ROM file *MtJumbo*. The data are the core diameters in inches.

a. Based on the sample data, is there an interaction between water temperature and vat hours? Test using a significance level of 0.01. Discuss what interaction would mean in this situation. Use a p-value approach.

b. Based on the sample data, is there a difference in mean core diameter at the three water temperatures? Test using a significance level of 0.01.

c. Do the sample data indicate a difference in mean core diameter across the three vat times analyzed in this study? Use a significance level of 0.10. Use a p-value approach.

d. Based on the sample data, and considering that the closer the mean core diameter is to 4 inches the better, what recommendations would you have for Mt. Jumbo Plywood based on this study? If appropriate, use the Tukey procedure to conduct the post-ANOVA tests. Use an experiment-wide significance level of 0.05.

Summary and Conclusions

Chapter 11 has illustrated through a wide variety of examples that there are many instances in business in which we are interested in testing to determine whether three or more populations have equal means. The technique for performing such tests is called analysis of variance. ANOVA is an extension of the two-sample t-test procedure introduced in Chapter 9. The basic logic is that if the sample means tend to be substantially different, then the hypothesis of equal means is rejected.

Depending upon the experimental design employed, there are different hypothesis tests that must be used. The most elementary of these experimental designs is the one-way design, which is used to test whether three or more populations have equal mean values when the samples from the populations are considered to be independent. If we need to control for an outside source of variation (analogous to forming paired samples in Chapter 9), we can use the randomized complete block design. If there are two factors of interest and we wish to test to see whether the levels of each separate factor have equal means, then a two-factor design with replications is used.

Regardless of which method is used, if the null hypothesis of equal means is rejected, methods exist to determine which pairs of populations have different means. Methods such as the Tukey-Kramer, Fisher's LSD method, and the Tukey method all allow us to examine all possible contrasts without expanding the experiment-wide significance level.

Analysis of variance is actually an array of statistical techniques used to test hypotheses related to these (and more) experimental designs. By completing this chapter, you will have been introduced to some of the most popular ANOVA techniques.

EQUATIONS

Partitioned Sum of Squares
$$SST = SSB + SSW \qquad \text{11-1}$$

F Test Statistic
$$F_{max} = \frac{s^2_{max}}{s^2_{min}} \qquad \text{11-2}$$

Total Sum of Squares
$$SST = \sum_{i=1}^{k} \sum_{j=1}^{n_i} (x_{ij} - \bar{\bar{x}})^2 \qquad \text{11-3}$$

Sum of Squares Between
$$SSB = \sum_{i=1}^{k} n_i (\bar{x}_i - \bar{\bar{x}})^2 \qquad \text{11-4}$$

Sum of Squares Within
$$SSW = SST - SSB \qquad \text{11-5}$$
or
$$SSW = \sum_{i=1}^{k} \sum_{j=1}^{n_i} (x_{ij} - \bar{x}_i)^2 \qquad \text{11-6}$$

Tukey-Kramer Critical Range
$$\text{Critical Range} = q_\alpha \sqrt{\frac{MSW}{2} \left(\frac{1}{n_i} + \frac{1}{n_j} \right)} \qquad \text{11-7}$$

Sum of Squares Partitioning for Randomized Complete Block Design
$$SST = SSB + SSBL + SSW \qquad \text{11-8}$$

Sum of Squares for Blocking
$$SSBL = \sum_{j=1}^{b} k(\bar{x}_j - \bar{\bar{x}})^2 \qquad \text{11-9}$$

Sum of Squares Within
$$SSW = SST - (SSB + SSBL) \qquad \text{11-10}$$

Fisher's Least Significant Difference
$$LSD = t_{\alpha/2} \sqrt{MSW} \sqrt{\frac{2}{b}} \qquad \text{11-11}$$

Total Sum of Squares

$$SST = \sum_{i=1}^{a}\sum_{j=1}^{b}\sum_{k=1}^{n'}(x_{ijk} - \bar{\bar{x}})^2 \quad \textbf{11-12}$$

Sum of Squares Factor A

$$SS_A = bn'\sum_{i=1}^{a}(\bar{x}_{i..} - \bar{\bar{x}})^2 \quad \textbf{11-13}$$

Sum of Squares Factor B

$$SS_B = an'\sum_{j=1}^{b}(\bar{x}_{.j.} - \bar{\bar{x}})^2 \quad \textbf{11-14}$$

Sum of Squares Interaction Between Factors A and B

$$SS_{AB} = n'\sum_{i=1}^{a}\sum_{j=1}^{b}(\bar{x}_{ij.} - \bar{x}_{i..} - \bar{x}_{.j.} + \bar{\bar{x}})^2 \quad \textbf{11-15}$$

Sum of Squares Error

$$SSE = \sum_{i=1}^{a}\sum_{j=1}^{b}\sum_{k=1}^{n'}(x_{ijk} - \bar{x}_{ij.})^2 \quad \textbf{11-16}$$

Key Terms

CHAPTER EXERCISES

Conceptual Questions

11.28 Explain in your own terms the logic of analysis of variance.

11.29 Discuss why in some circumstances it is appropriate to use the randomized complete block design. Give an example other than those discussed in the text in which this design could be used.

11.30 In a randomized complete block's ANOVA, the conclusion might be reached that blocking is not necessary.
a. What does this imply to the decision maker?
b. Why can this happen?
c. What should be done if it does happen? Discuss.

11.31 Consider some decision-making situations in your major and describe two or more in which tests of three or more population means are important.

11.32 Discuss in your own words each of the following:
a. Within-group variation
b. Between-group variation
c. Total sum of squares
d. Degrees of freedom

11.33 A one-way analysis of variance has just been performed. The conclusion reached is that the null hypothesis stating that the population means are equal has not been rejected. What would you expect the Tukey-Kramer procedure for multiple comparisons to show if it were performed for all pairwise comparisons? Discuss.

11.34 A one-way and a randomized complete block's ANOVA have been conducted on the same set of data.
a. Explain the relative sizes of both analysis of variances' sum of squares and degrees of freedom.
b. If the randomized complete block's ANOVA concluded that blocking was unnecessary, what would you expect to be the relative size of SSB in the two ANOVAs? Explain your answer.

c. When blocking is used unnecessarily, what impact does this have on the components of the ANOVA? Support your answer with reasons.

11.35 In any of the multiple-comparison techniques (Tukey-Kramer, LSD, etc.), the estimate of the within-sample variance uses data from the entire experiment. However, if one were to do a two-sample t-test to determine if there were a difference between any two means, the estimate of the population variances would only include data from the two specific samples under consideration. Explain this seeming discrepancy.

Business Applications

11.36 In an effort to improve the academic preparation of junior-high school students in the Dallas–Fort Worth metroplex, a group of concerned parents examined the number of hours per week spent doing homework by ninth-grade boys and girls attending public, private (nonreligious), and religious junior-high schools in the area. A random sample of 15 boys and 15 girls from the three types of schools were monitored during the semester and the average number of weekly hours that each spent doing homework was recorded. The data are in the CD-ROM file *Homework*.

The parents would like to know if the type of school makes a difference in the amount of hours students spend on homework. They would also like to determine if there is a difference in the average number of hours spent on homework by boys and girls.
a. Is there a significant interaction effect between the type of school and each student's gender? Justify and explain your answer.
b. At the 0.05 level of significance, is there evidence of a difference in the average number of hours spent on homework by type of school? Does one type of school require significantly fewer hours of homework per week? If so, identify the type of school.

c. At the 0.05 level of significance, is there a difference in the average number of hours spent on homework by gender?

11.37 Jason Enterprises produces two different products. The demand for the products is high, and Jason is concerned with meeting demand in a responsive manner. To help the company meet demand faster, Jason Enterprises is considering changing the layout of its production facilities. It is currently evaluating two new layouts—a cellular configuration and a flexible flow production layout—in addition to maintaining its current production process. To determine if any benefit is achieved from the new layouts, Jason Enterprises examined the amount of time needed to produce its two products using each of the three production-process alternatives. The times (in minutes) required to complete assembly of each finished product using the different layouts are displayed in the CD-ROM file *Jason Enterprises*.

a. Is the interaction between type of product and type of production process significant? Again, establish the appropriate null and alternative hypotheses and conduct the test at the 0.01 level of significance.

b. Is it possible to determine if there are significant differences due to the type of product being assembled or to the type of production process? If so, establish the appropriate null and alternative hypotheses for this question and conduct the test for a significant effect at the 0.01 level of significance. Use the test-statistic approach. If not, explain.

c. How might Jason Enterprises use the information from the tests you have conducted to better manage its business? Should Jason Enterprises select a single product process for both of the products it produces, or would it be to Jason's advantage to tailor the production process to the type of product? Comment and justify your answer.

11.38 Chip-O-Rama bakes and sells different types of cookies. Its managers are interested in testing whether there is an effect due to the type of cookie chip and whether margarine or butter is used in cookie dough. The company invited 30 randomly selected groups of cookie lovers to their test center and asked them to eat as many cookies as they wanted of four different types (chocolate chip, white chocolate chip, butterscotch chip, and peanut butter chip) made with either butter or margarine. The company then measured the average number of cookies of each type eaten. The results are shown in the CD-ROM file *Chip-O-Rama*.

a. Does there appear to be an interaction effect?

b. At the 0.05 level of significance, is there a significant difference in the average number of cookies eaten with respect to butter or margarine?

c. At the 0.05 level of significance, is there a significant difference in the average number of cookies eaten by type of cookie chip?

d. How could Chip-O-Rama use the information from this experiment in its bakery operations?

11.39 Gordon Manufacturing produces golf balls. Recently, Gordon developed a golf ball made from a space-age material. This new golf ball promises greater distance off the tee. To test Gordon Manufacturing's claim, a test was set up to measure the average distance of four different golf balls (the New Gordon, Competitor 1, Competitor 2, and Competitor 3) hit by a driving machine using three different types of drivers (Driver 1, Driver 2, and Driver 3). The results (rounded to the nearest yard) are listed in the CD-ROM file *Gordon*. Conduct a test to determine if there are significant differences due to type of golf ball.

a. Does there appear to be interaction between type of golf ball and type of driver?

b. Conduct a test to determine if there is a significant effect due to the type of driver used.

c. How could the results of the tests conducted be used by Gordon Manufacturing?

11.40 The materials planning group at Selser Industries is responsible for managing the inventory for all component parts and subassemblies used in the manufacturer of the firm's products. Because the group monitors more than 100,000 stock keeping units (SKUs), they must use a computer to assist them in their inventory control efforts. For example, the group uses the computer to calculate the requirements for all component parts of the firm's production plans. These material requirements planning (MRP) calculations are time-consuming, and Selser is currently evaluating six MRP software packages to determine if there are significant differences in the time required by each to calculate materials requirements. Each software package was installed on Selser's computer and used to calculate the material requirements for a random sample of production plans. The results that were reported are included in the CD-ROM file *Selser*.

a. (1) Determine if the variances in the time required by different software packages to calculate materials requirements can be considered equal. Use a significance level of 0.05. (2) Assume the distributions of the time required by different software packages to calculate materials requirements are normal. Comment on whether you would be justified in using a one-way ANOVA procedure to determine that the times required by different software packages to calculate materials requirements were the same.

b. At the 0.01 level of significance, would the materials planning group conclude that the software package makes a difference in the average time required to calculate the material plans? Use the test-statistic approach.

c. (1) At the 0.01 level of significance, is there evidence to conclude that Accumat calculates material requirements plans faster than Explode? (2) Is it possible to identify a clear winner on the basis of speed of calculation, or will Selser need to examine other criteria to decide on the "best" package?

Advanced Applications

11.41 PhoneEx provides call center services for many different companies. A large increase in its business has made it necessary to establish a new call center. One of four cities will be selected: Little Rock, Wichita, Tulsa, and Memphis. The new center will employ approximately 1,500 workers and PhoneEx will transfer 75 managers from its Omaha center to the new location. One concern in the choice of where to locate the new center is the cost of housing for the managers who will be moving there. To help determine whether significant housing-cost differences exist across the competing sites, PhoneEx has asked a real estate broker in each city to randomly select a list of 33 homes between 5 and 15 years old and ranging in size between 1,975 and 2,235 square feet. The prices (in dollars) that were recorded for each city are contained in the CD-ROM file *PhoneEx*.

a. At the 0.05 level of significance, is there evidence to conclude that average price of houses between 5 and 15 years old and ranging in size between 1,975 and 2,235 square feet is not the same in the four cities? Use the *p*-value approach.

b. At the 0.05 level of significance, is there a difference in average housing price between Wichita and Little Rock? Between Little Rock and Tulsa? Between Tulsa and Memphis?

c. Determine the sample size required to estimate the average housing price in Wichita to within $500 with a 95% confidence level. Assume the required parameters' estimates are sufficient for this calculation.

11.42   GroBros, a regional grocery store chain located in the intermountain West, is considering upgrading to a new series of price scanners for its checkout lanes. Although scanners can save checkers a great deal of time, scanners will sometimes misread an item's price code. Before investing in one of three new systems, GroBros would like to determine if there is a difference in scanner accuracy. To investigate possible differences, 30 shopping baskets were randomly selected from customers at the Boise store. The 30 baskets differed from each other in the number and types of items each contained. The items in each basket were then scanned by the three new scanners under consideration, as well as by the scanner type used in all GroBros stores, at a specially designed scanner set up for the analysis. Each item was also checked manually, and a count was kept of the number of scanning errors made by each scanner for each basket. Each of the scannings was repeated 30 times, and the average number of scanning errors was determined. The sample data are in the CD-ROM file *GroBros*.

a. What type of experimental design did GroBros use to test for differences among scanners? Why was this type of design selected?

b. State the primary hypotheses of interest for this test.

c. At the 0.01 level of significance, is there a difference in the average number of errors among the four different scanners?

d. (1) Is there a difference in the average number of errors by shopping basket? (2) Was GroBros correct in blocking by shopping basket?

e. If you determined that there is a difference in the average number of errors among the four different scanners, identify where those differences exist.

f. Do you think that GroBros should upgrade from its existing scanner to Scanner A, Scanner B, or Scanner C? What other factors may it want to consider before making a decision?

11.43   Phone Solutions provides assistance to users of a personal-finance software package. Users call Phone Solutions with their questions, and trained consultants provide answers and information. One concern that Phone Solutions must deal with regularly is the staffing of its call centers. If the centers are understaffed, callers seeking help must wait for long periods before reaching a consultant. Many callers are unwilling to wait for more than a couple of minutes before hanging up. If the centers are over-staffed, some consultants will be idle for a large part of their shift. Phone Solutions has invested heavily in a technology to help route calls to each of its three centers so that a uniform number of calls is being handled at each center each day. However, the number of calls can differ depending on the day. Also, if one center takes a great deal more time to handle each caller's request, then there will be a need to redirect calls and perhaps personnel, so that a more-uniform usage pattern across centers is maintained. Phone Solutions has collected data on the average lengths of phone calls (in minutes) for the three centers on 50 randomly selected days. These sample data are in the CD-ROM file *Phone Solutions*.

Phone Solutions would like to determine if there is a difference in the average lengths of phone calls among the three call centers.

a. State the null and alternative hypotheses of interest to Phone Solutions.

b. Is there an effect due to the day a call is made? Was Phone Solutions right in using this experimental design?

c. At the 0.05 level of significance, is there sufficient evidence to conclude that there is a difference in the average lengths of calls by call center?

d. If there is a difference in the average length of a call to a center, which center takes the greatest amount of time to handle calls?

e. What might Phone Solutions do to equalize the amount of time across centers?

11.44   In order to determine whether differences exist in grocery prices charged by three supermarket chains located in a small city in the southwestern United States, a consumer group purchased a "typical" shopping basket of groceries from each of the three stores every week for 26 weeks. The typical basket of groceries was the same for all three stores in any week. The price for each basket by store for each of the 26 weeks is shown in the CD-ROM file Grocery Store.

a. (1) Determine if the variance in the average price paid for the typical shopping basket among the three stores is equal. Use a significance level of 0.05. (2) Assume that the distributions of the average prices paid for the typical shopping basket among the three stores are normal. Comment on whether you would be justified if you were to use a one-way ANOVA procedure.

b. At the 0.05 level of significance, is there evidence of a significant difference in the average price paid for the typical shopping basket among the three stores?

c. Which pairs of stores differ in the average price of the typical shopping basket? Does one store clearly appear to be more expensive than the others? If so, which store?

d. Are there significant differences in the price of the shopping basket from week to week?

11.45   To determine whether there is a difference in average weekly hours of computer usage by college major, the manager of the computer laboratories at a state university in North Dakota randomly samples 155 observations from computer records kept at the lab. When entering the lab, student computer users must enter a code that indicates their college: (1) for Engineering; (2) for Arts and Sciences; and (3) for Business. The computer then keeps track of each student's start and stop time. At the end of the semester, the lab manager randomly selected the 155 records contained in the CD-ROM file *Lab-Time*.

a. State the null and alternative hypotheses of interest to the computer laboratory manager.
b. At the 0.01 level of significance, is there a significant difference in the average hours of weekly laboratory use by major?
c. What is the *p*-value for the test you conducted in part b?
d. If the average weekly amount of computer usage were actually the same for Engineering and Business, determine the probability that a difference in the sample means as large or larger than observed would occur. Assume the estimates for the relevant population parameters obtained in this problem are sufficient for this purpose.

11.46 Hypos, a marketer of computer games, is interested in determining whether there is a difference in the average dollar amount spent on its games. It wishes to know if this difference depends on whether the customer places an order online (using the Internet), over the telephone, by mail (catalog), or in one of the company's retail stores. Hypos hopes to use this information to determine how best to advertise and market its products. The VP of marketing for Hypos randomly selected sales receipts from Internet orders, phone and catalog orders, and in-store sales. These data are contained in the CD-ROM file *Hypos*.

a. Based on the sample data, what would be your conclusion about the average purchase amounts by customers from the different sources at the 0.01 level of significance?
b. If you concluded that differences in population means differ, identify which pairs of means differ.
c. How could Hypos use this information in its marketing and advertising programs?

CASE 11-A:

Consumer Information Association

Yolanda Carson is a newly hired research assistant for the Consumer Information Association. The association is a non-profit group whose major purpose is to supply information necessary to help consumers make better-informed decisions. Yolanda has been assigned to work with the group studying consumer practices in the banking industry.

Yolanda is aware of studies that indicate that the interest banks charge for loans is related to demographic factors such as the size of the city in which the banks are located and whether the state allows branch banks. She has been asked to determine whether there is a difference in consumer loan charges between major sections of the country.

Yolanda has been assured the cooperation of the American Banking Institute and has been given access to any data the institute has. However, she knows that loan charges may depend on many factors, and she feels compelled to study banks firsthand. In particular, she has decided to randomly select banks in all parts of the country and to apply for an automobile loan at each bank selected. She has decided to make the test during two time periods six months apart.

Because consumer interest rates have been changing rapidly lately, Yolanda has recorded all rates in terms of the prime rate plus a certain percentage. (The prime rate is the rate large banks charge their largest corporate customers.) In the first test, Yolanda found the following values charged. These data are also contained in the data file *Consumer Interest*.

NORTHEAST	SOUTHEAST	MIDWEST	WEST
3.2	2.7	3.4	3.7
2.9	2.9	3.5	3.6
2.8	3.0	2.9	3.6
3.5	2.0	3.7	3.9
3.4	2.8	3.4	4.0
4.0	2.5	3.5	3.8
3.2	2.7	3.0	3.4
	2.9		3.8

The executive director of the Consumer Information Association will be holding a news conference in a few days to discuss the work the organization has been doing. He would like to be able to cite Yolanda's study as an example of its services.

CASE 11-B:

West Coast Bell System

James Todd is the recently appointed director of employee benefits for West Coast Bell, a regional telephone system. The West Coast Bell medical-benefits system insures more than 60,000 employees and dependents. Over the last five years its medical costs have been increasing by more than 20% annually. James knows that many companies, when facing these annual increases, have tried to pass some of the medical costs to their employees, generally by

increasing the deductible allowance for each treatment visit. He has decided to look into the possibility of developing a managed-care network. Managed-care networks are a recent development in health care. They involve a company contracting with a group of physicians and hospitals to provide a variety of health care services. The company monitors the cost of the care provided to its employees and holds discussions with those whose costs are high. In some cases, the relationship between the company and either a hospital or physician will be terminated. Some companies using managed-care networks have held their health care cost increases to less than one-third of the previous levels.

James has recently read a study that reported on the cost of an outpatient procedure that determines the extent to which a patient's arteries are closed. One hospital in Kansas City charged more than $5,000 for the operation, whereas a second, also in Kansas City, charged less than $3,000. James decided to use this operation to determine whether categories of hospitals tended to charge less for this procedure. The four categories of hospitals he identified were university-related, religious-affiliated, municipally owned, and profit-making. He contacted 10 hospitals on the West Coast in each category, asking what they charged for this operation. Not all responded, and some who did provided data that could not readily be compared with that provided by the majority of respondents. The reported costs are shown here and are also contained in the CD-ROM file *Hospitals*.

UNIVERSITY-RELATED	RELIGIOUS-AFFILIATED	MUNICIPALLY-OWNED	PRIVATELY-HELD
$6,120	$4,010	$4,320	$5,100
5,960	3,770	4,650	4,920
6,300	3,960	4,575	5,200
6,500	3,620	4,440	5,345
6,250	3,280	4,900	4,875
6,695	3,680	4,560	5,330
6,475	3,350	4,610	5,415
6,250	3,250	4,850	5,150
6,880	3,400		5,380
6,550			

James plans to prepare a report on this study for presentation to the West Coast Bell committee on health and benefits.

General References

1. Berenson, Mark L., and David M. Levine, *Basic Business Statistics: Concepts and Applications*, 7th ed. (Upper Saddle River, NJ: Prentice Hall, 1999).
2. Bowerman, Bruce L., and Richard T. O'Connell, *Linear Statistical Models: An Applied Approach*, 2nd ed. (Belmont, CA: Duxbury Press, 1990).
3. Cox, D. R., *Planning of Experiments*, (New York: John Wiley & Sons, 1992).
4. Cryer, Jonathan D., and Robert B. Miller, *Statistics for Business: Data Analysis and Modeling*, 2nd ed. (Belmont, CA: Duxbury Press, 1994).
5. *Microsoft Excel 2000* (Redmond, WA: Microsoft Corp., 1999).
6. *Minitab for Windows Version 13* (State College, PA: Minitab, 2000).
7. Montgomery, D. C., *Design and Analysis of Experiments*, 4th ed. (New York: John Wiley & Sons, 1997).
8. Neter, John, Michael H. Kutner, Christopher J. Nachtsheim, and William Wasserman, *Applied Linear Statistical Models*, 4th ed. (Homewood, IL: Richard D. Irwin, 1996).
9. Searle, S. R., and R. F. Fawcett (1970). "Expected Mean Squares in Variance Component Models Having Finite Populations." *Biometrics*, Vol. 26, pp. 243–254.

CHAPTERS 7-11

Special Review Section

This review section, which is presented using block diagrams and flowcharts, is intended to help you tie together the material from several key chapters. This section is not a substitute for reading and studying the chapters covered by the review. However, you can use this review material to add to your understanding of the individual topics in the chapters.

CHAPTERS 7 TO 11

Statistical inference is the process of reaching conclusions about a population based on a random sample selected from the population. Chapters 7 to 11 introduced the fundamental concepts of statistical inference involving two major categories of inference, *estimation and hypothesis testing*. These chapters have covered a fairly wide range of different situations that for beginning students can sometimes seem overwhelming. The following diagrams will hopefully help you better identify which specific estimation or hypothesis-testing technique to use in a given situation. These diagrams form something resembling an expert system that you should be able to use as a guide through the estimation and hypothesis-testing processes.

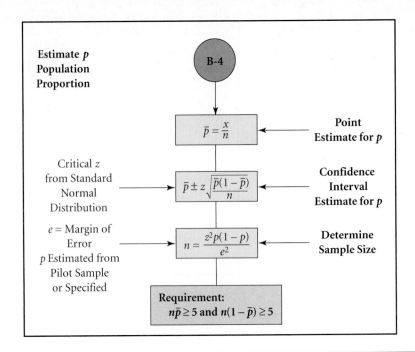

Estimate p Population Proportion

B-4

$\bar{p} = \dfrac{x}{n}$ — **Point Estimate for p**

Critical z from Standard Normal Distribution → $\bar{p} \pm z \sqrt{\dfrac{\bar{p}(1-\bar{p})}{n}}$ ← **Confidence Interval Estimate for p**

e = Margin of Error
p Estimated from Pilot Sample or Specified → $n = \dfrac{z^2 p(1-p)}{e^2}$ ← **Determine Sample Size**

Requirement:
$n\bar{p} \geq 5$ and $n(1-\bar{p}) \geq 5$

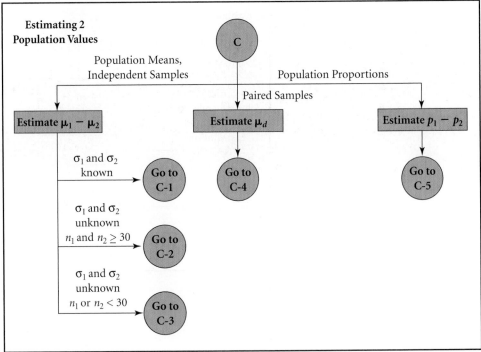

Estimating 2 Population Values

C

Population Means, Independent Samples

Population Proportions

Paired Samples

Estimate $\mu_1 - \mu_2$ Estimate μ_d Estimate $p_1 - p_2$

σ_1 and σ_2 known → Go to C-1

σ_1 and σ_2 unknown n_1 and $n_2 \geq 30$ → Go to C-2

σ_1 and σ_2 unknown n_1 or $n_2 < 30$ → Go to C-3

Go to C-4

Go to C-5

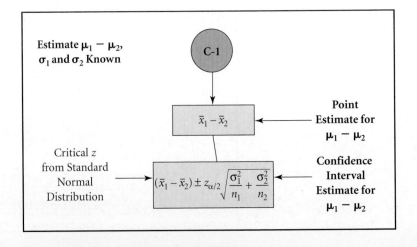

Estimate $\mu_1 - \mu_2$, σ_1 and σ_2 Known

C-1

$\bar{x}_1 - \bar{x}_2$ — **Point Estimate for $\mu_1 - \mu_2$**

Critical z from Standard Normal Distribution → $(\bar{x}_1 - \bar{x}_2) \pm z_{\alpha/2} \sqrt{\dfrac{\sigma_1^2}{n_1} + \dfrac{\sigma_2^2}{n_2}}$ ← **Confidence Interval Estimate for $\mu_1 - \mu_2$**

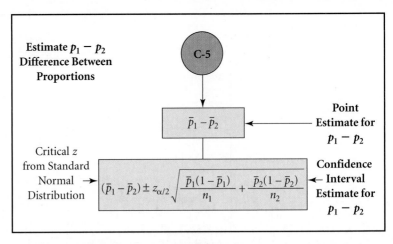

Estimate $p_1 - p_2$ Difference Between Proportions

C-5

Point Estimate for $p_1 - p_2$

$$\bar{p}_1 - \bar{p}_2$$

Critical z from Standard Normal Distribution

$$(\bar{p}_1 - \bar{p}_2) \pm z_{\alpha/2} \sqrt{\frac{\bar{p}_1(1-\bar{p}_1)}{n_1} + \frac{\bar{p}_2(1-\bar{p}_2)}{n_2}}$$

Confidence Interval Estimate for $p_1 - p_2$

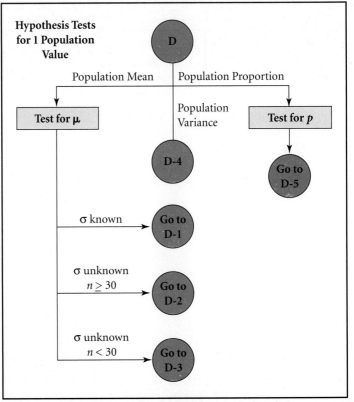

Hypothesis Tests for 1 Population Value

D

Population Mean

Population Proportion

Test for μ

Population Variance

Test for p

D-4

Go to D-5

σ known → Go to D-1

σ unknown $n \geq 30$ → Go to D-2

σ unknown $n < 30$ → Go to D-3

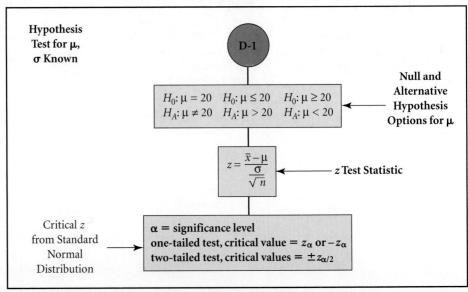

Hypothesis Test for μ, σ Known

D-1

Null and Alternative Hypothesis Options for μ

$H_0: \mu = 20$ $H_0: \mu \leq 20$ $H_0: \mu \geq 20$
$H_A: \mu \neq 20$ $H_A: \mu > 20$ $H_A: \mu < 20$

$$z = \frac{\bar{x} - \mu}{\frac{\sigma}{\sqrt{n}}}$$

z Test Statistic

Critical z from Standard Normal Distribution

α = significance level
one-tailed test, critical value = z_α or $-z_\alpha$
two-tailed test, critical values = $\pm z_{\alpha/2}$

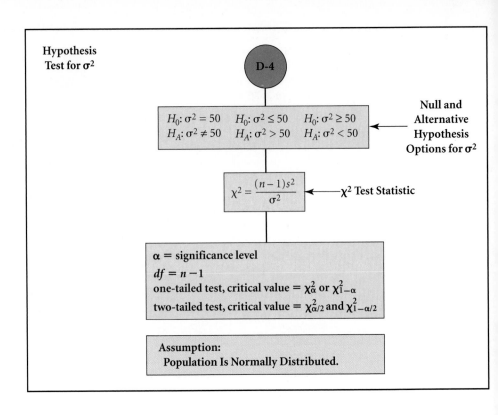

Hypothesis Test for σ^2

D-4

H_0: $\sigma^2 = 50$ H_0: $\sigma^2 \leq 50$ H_0: $\sigma^2 \geq 50$
H_A: $\sigma^2 \neq 50$ H_A: $\sigma^2 > 50$ H_A: $\sigma^2 < 50$

Null and Alternative Hypothesis Options for σ^2

$$\chi^2 = \frac{(n-1)s^2}{\sigma^2}$$

χ^2 Test Statistic

α = significance level
$df = n - 1$
one-tailed test, critical value = χ^2_α or $\chi^2_{1-\alpha}$
two-tailed test, critical value = $\chi^2_{\alpha/2}$ and $\chi^2_{1-\alpha/2}$

Assumption:
Population Is Normally Distributed.

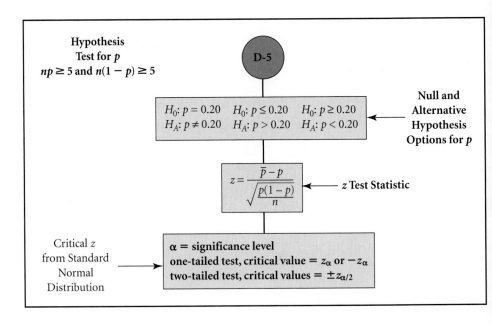

Hypothesis Test for p
$np \geq 5$ and $n(1-p) \geq 5$

D-5

H_0: $p = 0.20$ H_0: $p \leq 0.20$ H_0: $p \geq 0.20$
H_A: $p \neq 0.20$ H_A: $p > 0.20$ H_A: $p < 0.20$

Null and Alternative Hypothesis Options for p

$$z = \frac{\bar{p} - p}{\sqrt{\dfrac{p(1-p)}{n}}}$$

z Test Statistic

Critical z from Standard Normal Distribution

α = significance level
one-tailed test, critical value = z_α or $-z_\alpha$
two-tailed test, critical values = $\pm z_{\alpha/2}$

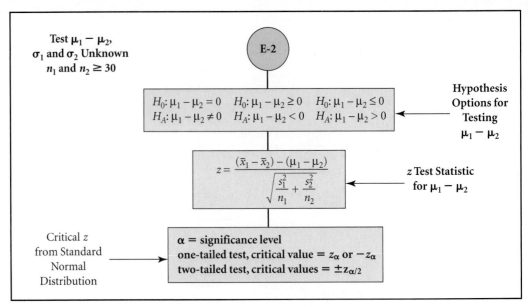

Test $\mu_1 - \mu_2$,
σ_1 and σ_2 Unknown
n_1 and $n_2 \geq 30$

E-2

$H_0: \mu_1 - \mu_2 = 0$ $H_0: \mu_1 - \mu_2 \geq 0$ $H_0: \mu_1 - \mu_2 \leq 0$
$H_A: \mu_1 - \mu_2 \neq 0$ $H_A: \mu_1 - \mu_2 < 0$ $H_A: \mu_1 - \mu_2 > 0$

Hypothesis Options for Testing $\mu_1 - \mu_2$

$$z = \frac{(\bar{x}_1 - \bar{x}_2) - (\mu_1 - \mu_2)}{\sqrt{\dfrac{s_1^2}{n_1} + \dfrac{s_2^2}{n_2}}}$$

z Test Statistic for $\mu_1 - \mu_2$

Critical z from Standard Normal Distribution

α = significance level
one-tailed test, critical value = z_α or $-z_\alpha$
two-tailed test, critical values = $\pm z_{\alpha/2}$

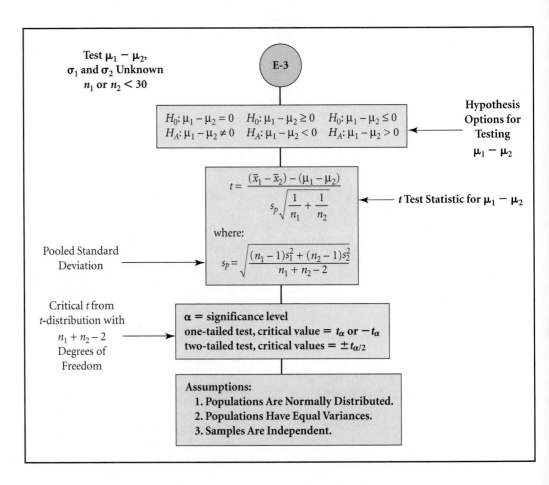

Test $\mu_1 - \mu_2$,
σ_1 and σ_2 Unknown
n_1 or $n_2 < 30$

E-3

$H_0: \mu_1 - \mu_2 = 0$ $H_0: \mu_1 - \mu_2 \geq 0$ $H_0: \mu_1 - \mu_2 \leq 0$
$H_A: \mu_1 - \mu_2 \neq 0$ $H_A: \mu_1 - \mu_2 < 0$ $H_A: \mu_1 - \mu_2 > 0$

Hypothesis Options for Testing $\mu_1 - \mu_2$

$$t = \frac{(\bar{x}_1 - \bar{x}_2) - (\mu_1 - \mu_2)}{s_p \sqrt{\dfrac{1}{n_1} + \dfrac{1}{n_2}}}$$

where:

$$s_p = \sqrt{\frac{(n_1 - 1)s_1^2 + (n_2 - 1)s_2^2}{n_1 + n_2 - 2}}$$

t Test Statistic for $\mu_1 - \mu_2$

Pooled Standard Deviation

Critical t from t-distribution with $n_1 + n_2 - 2$ Degrees of Freedom

α = significance level
one-tailed test, critical value = t_α or $-t_\alpha$
two-tailed test, critical values = $\pm t_{\alpha/2}$

Assumptions:
1. Populations Are Normally Distributed.
2. Populations Have Equal Variances.
3. Samples Are Independent.

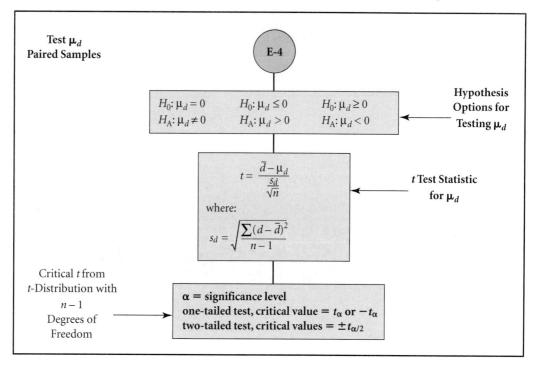

Test μ_d
Paired Samples

E-4

Hypothesis Options for Testing μ_d

$H_0: \mu_d = 0$ $H_0: \mu_d \leq 0$ $H_0: \mu_d \geq 0$
$H_A: \mu_d \neq 0$ $H_A: \mu_d > 0$ $H_A: \mu_d < 0$

t Test Statistic for μ_d

$$t = \frac{\bar{d} - \mu_d}{\frac{s_d}{\sqrt{n}}}$$

where:

$$s_d = \sqrt{\frac{\sum(d - \bar{d})^2}{n-1}}$$

Critical t from t-Distribution with $n-1$ Degrees of Freedom

α = significance level
one-tailed test, critical value = t_α or $-t_\alpha$
two-tailed test, critical values = $\pm t_{\alpha/2}$

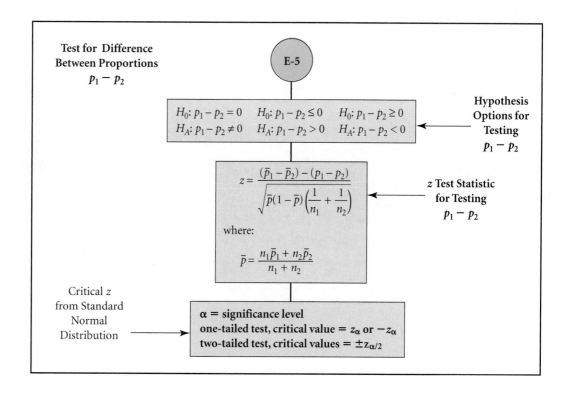

Test for Difference Between Proportions $p_1 - p_2$

E-5

Hypothesis Options for Testing $p_1 - p_2$

$H_0: p_1 - p_2 = 0$ $H_0: p_1 - p_2 \leq 0$ $H_0: p_1 - p_2 \geq 0$
$H_A: p_1 - p_2 \neq 0$ $H_A: p_1 - p_2 > 0$ $H_A: p_1 - p_2 < 0$

z Test Statistic for Testing $p_1 - p_2$

$$z = \frac{(\bar{p}_1 - \bar{p}_2) - (p_1 - p_2)}{\sqrt{\bar{p}(1 - \bar{p})\left(\frac{1}{n_1} + \frac{1}{n_2}\right)}}$$

where:

$$\bar{p} = \frac{n_1 \bar{p}_1 + n_2 \bar{p}_2}{n_1 + n_2}$$

Critical z from Standard Normal Distribution

α = significance level
one-tailed test, critical value = z_α or $-z_\alpha$
two-tailed test, critical values = $\pm z_{\alpha/2}$

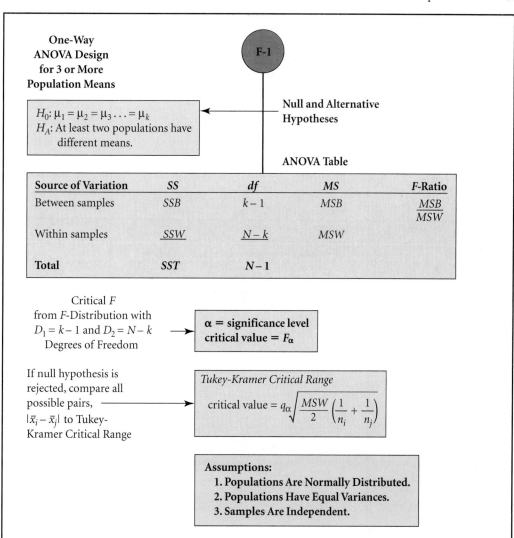

One-Way ANOVA Design for 3 or More Population Means

F-1

$H_0: \mu_1 = \mu_2 = \mu_3 \ldots = \mu_k$
H_A: At least two populations have different means.

Null and Alternative Hypotheses

ANOVA Table

Source of Variation	SS	df	MS	F-Ratio
Between samples	SSB	$k-1$	MSB	$\dfrac{MSB}{MSW}$
Within samples	SSW	$N-k$	MSW	
Total	**SST**	**$N-1$**		

Critical F from F-Distribution with $D_1 = k-1$ and $D_2 = N-k$ Degrees of Freedom

α = significance level
critical value = F_α

If null hypothesis is rejected, compare all possible pairs, $|\bar{x}_i - \bar{x}_j|$ to Tukey-Kramer Critical Range

Tukey-Kramer Critical Range

critical value $= q_\alpha \sqrt{\dfrac{MSW}{2}\left(\dfrac{1}{n_i}+\dfrac{1}{n_j}\right)}$

Assumptions:
1. Populations Are Normally Distributed.
2. Populations Have Equal Variances.
3. Samples Are Independent.

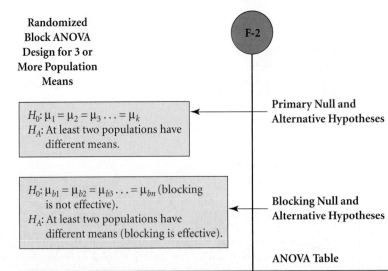

Randomized Block ANOVA Design for 3 or More Population Means

F-2

$H_0: \mu_1 = \mu_2 = \mu_3 \ldots = \mu_k$
H_A: At least two populations have different means.

Primary Null and Alternative Hypotheses

$H_0: \mu_{b1} = \mu_{b2} = \mu_{b3} \ldots = \mu_{bn}$ (blocking is not effective).
H_A: At least two populations have different means (blocking is effective).

Blocking Null and Alternative Hypotheses

ANOVA Table

Source of Variation	SS	df	MS	F-Ratio
Between blocks	SSBL	$b - 1$	MSBL	$\dfrac{MSBL}{MSW}$
Between samples	SSB	$k - 1$	MSB	$\dfrac{MSB}{MSW}$
Within samples	$\underline{SSW}$	$\underline{(k-1)(b-1)}$	MSW	
Total	SST	$N - 1$		

Critical F from F-Distribution

α = significance level
Blocking critical value = F_α
$df = D_1 = b - 1$ and $D_2 = (k - 1)(b - 1)$
Primary critical value = F_α, $df = D_1 = k - 1$ and $D_2 = (k - 1)(b - 1)$

Assumptions:
1. Populations Are Normally Distributed.
2. Populations Have Equal Variances.
3. Observations Within Samples Are Independent.

If null is rejected, compare all $|\bar{x}_i - \bar{x}_j|$ to Fisher's

$$LSD = t_{\alpha/2}\sqrt{MSW}\sqrt{\frac{2}{b}}$$

Two-Factor ANOVA Design with Replications

F-3

Factor A Null and Alternative Hypotheses

H_0: $\mu_{A1} = \mu_{A2} = \mu_{A3} \ldots = \mu_{Ak}$
H_A: Not all means are equal.

Factor B Null and Alternative Hypotheses

H_0: $\mu_{B1} = \mu_{B2} = \mu_{B3} \ldots = \mu_{Bn}$
H_A: Not all means are equal.

H_0: Factors A and B do not interact to affect the mean response.
H_A: Factors A and B do interact.

Null and alternative hypotheses for testing whether the two factors interact

ANOVA Table

Source of Variation	SS	df	MS	F-Ratio
Factor A	SS_A	$a-1$	MS_A	$\dfrac{MS_A}{MSE}$
Factor B	SS_B	$b-1$	MS_B	$\dfrac{MS_B}{MSE}$
AB Interaction	SS_{AB}	$(a-1)(b-1)$	MS_{AB}	$\dfrac{MS_{AB}}{MSE}$
Error	SSE	$N-ab$	MSE	
Total	SST	$N-1$		

α = significance level
Factor A critical value = F_α, $df = D_1 = a-1$ and $D_2 = N-ab$
Factor B critical value = F_α, $df = D_1 = b-1$ and $D_2 = N-ab$
Interaction critical value = F_α, $df = D_1 = (a-1)(b-1)$ and $D_2 = N-ab$

Assumptions:
1. The Population Values for Each Combination of Pairwise Factor Levels Are Normally Distributed.
2. The Variances for Each Population Are Equal.
3. The Samples Are Independent.

NOTE: Blocking is viewed as a restriction on randomization. Two-factor ANOVA has two (perhaps equally important) factors.

USING THE FLOW DIAGRAMS

Example Problem: A travel agency in Florida is interested in determining whether there is a difference in the total out-of-pocket costs incurred by customers on two major cruise lines. To test this, she has selected a simple random sample of 20 customers who have taken cruise line I and has asked these people to track their costs over and above the fixed price of the cruise. She did the same for a second simple random sample of 15 people who took cruise line II.

You can use the flow diagrams to direct you to the appropriate statistical tool.

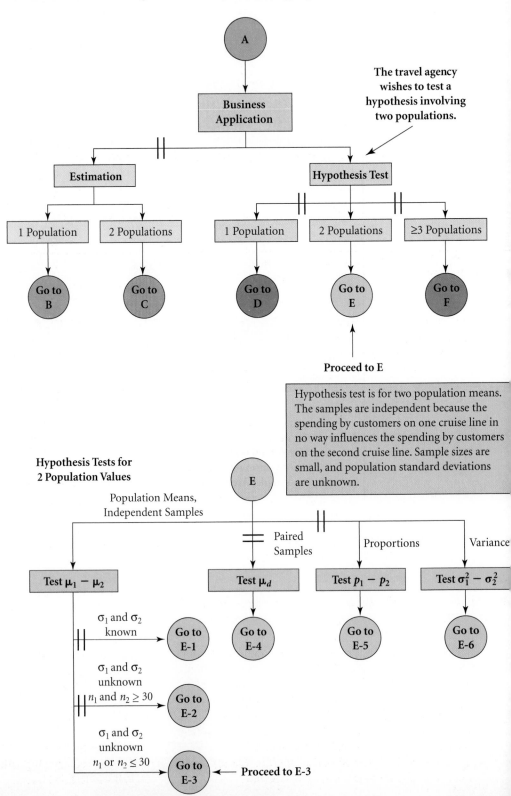

At E-3, we determine the null hypothesis to be

$$H_0: \mu_1 - \mu_2 = 0$$
$$H_A: \mu_1 - \mu_2 \neq 0$$

Next, we establish the test statistic as

$$t = \frac{(\bar{x}_1 - \bar{x}_2) - (\mu_1 - \mu_2)}{s_p \sqrt{\dfrac{1}{n_1} + \dfrac{1}{n_2}}}$$

where:

$$s_p = \sqrt{\frac{(n_1 - 1)s_1^2 + (n_2 - 1)s_2^2}{n_1 + n_2 - 2}}$$

Finally, the critical value is a t-value from the t-distribution with $20 + 15 - 2 = 33$ degrees of freedom. Note, if the degrees of freedom are not shown in the t table, use Excel's **TINV** or use Minitab to determine the t-value.

Thus, by using the flow diagrams and answering a series of basic questions, you should be successful in identifying the statistical tools required to address any problem or application covered in Chapters 7 to 11. You are encouraged to apply this process to the application problems and projects listed here.

EXERCISES

Integrative Application Problems

SR.1 Brandon Outdoor Advertising supplies neon signs to retail stores. A major complaint from their clients is that letters in the signs can burn out and leave the signs looking silly, depending on which letters stop working. The primary cause of neon letters not working is the failure of the starter unit attached to each letter. Starter units fail primarily based on turn-on/turn-off cycles. The present unit bought by Brandon averages 1,000 cycles before failure. A new manufacturer has approached Brandon claiming to have a model that is superior to the present unit. Brandon is skeptical but agrees to sample 50 starter units. It says it will buy from the new supplier if the sample results indicated the new unit is better. The sample of 50 gives the following values:

> Sample mean = 1,010 cycles
> Sample standard deviation = 48 cycles

Would you recommend changing suppliers?

SR.2 PestFree Chemicals has developed a new fungus preventative that may have a significant market among potato growers. Unfortunately, the actual extent of the fungus problem in any year depends on rainfall, temperature, and many other factors. To test the new chemical, PestFree has used it on 500 acres of potatoes and has used the leading competitor on an additional 500 acres. At the end of the season, 120 acres treated by the new chemical show significant levels of fungus infestation, whereas 160 of the acres treated by the leading chemical show significant infestation.

Do these data provide statistical proof that the new product is superior to the leading competitor?

SR.3 Last year Tucker Electronics decided to try to do something about turnover among assembly line workers at its several plants. It implemented two trial personnel policies, one based on an improved hiring policy and the other based on increasing worker responsibility. These policies were put into effect at two different plants, with the following results:

	Plant 1	Plant 2
	Improved Hiring	*Increased Responsibility*
Workers in trial group	800	900
Turnover proportion	0.05	0.09

Do these data provide evidence that there is a difference between the turnover rates for the two trial policies?

SR.4 A Big 10 University has been approached by Wilson Sporting Goods. Wilson has developed a football designed specifically for practice sessions. Wilson would like to claim the ball will last for 500 practice hours before it needs to be replaced. Wilson has supplied six balls for use during spring and fall practice. The following data has been gathered on the time used before the ball must be replaced.

Hours	
551	511
479	435
440	466

Do you see anything wrong with Wilson claiming the ball will last 500 hours?

SR.5 The management of a chain of movie theaters believes the average weekend attendance at their downtown theater is greater than at their suburban theater. The following sample results were found from their accounting data.

	Downtown	Suburban
Number of weekends	11	10
Average attendance	855	750
Sample variance	1,684	1,439

Do these data provide sufficient evidence to indicate there is a difference in average attendances? The company is also interested in whether there is a significant difference in the variability of attendance.

SR.6 A large mail-order company has placed an order for 5,000 thermal-powered fans to sit on wood-burning stoves from a supplier in Canada, with the stipulation that no more than 2% of the units will be defective. To check the shipment, the company tests a random sample of 400 fans and finds 11 defective. Should this sample evidence lead the company to conclude the supplier has violated the terms of the contract?

SR.7 A manufacturer of automobile shock absorbers is interested in comparing the durability of its shocks with that of its two biggest competitors. To make the comparison, a set of one each of the manufacturer's and of the competitor's shocks were randomly selected and installed on the rear wheels of each of six randomly selected cars of the same type. After the cars had been driven 20,000 miles, the strength of each test shock was measured, coded, and recorded.

Car number	Manufacturer's	Competitor 1	Competitor 2
1	8.8	9.3	8.6
2	10.5	9.0	13.7
3	12.5	8.4	11.2
4	9.7	13.0	9.7
5	9.6	12.0	12.2
6	13.2	10.1	8.9

Do these data present sufficient evidence to conclude there is a difference in the mean strength of the two types of shocks after 20,000 miles?

SR.8 AstraZeneca is the maker of the stomach medicine Prilosec, which is the second-best-selling drug in the world. Recently the company has come under close scrutiny concerning the cost of their medicines. The company's internal audit department selected a random sample of 300 prescriptions issued for Prilosec. They wished to characterize how much is being spent on this medicine. In the sample, the mean price per 20 milligram tablet of Prilosec was $2.70. The sample had a standard deviation of $0.30. Determine an estimate that will characterize the average range of values charged for a tablet of Prilosec.

SR.9 A manufacturer of PC monitors is interested in the effects that the type of glass and the type of phosphor used in the manufacturing process have on the brightness of the monitors. The director of research and development has received anecdotal evidence that the type of glass does not affect the brightness of the monitor as long as phosphor type 2 is used. However, the evidence seems to indicate that the type of glass does make a difference if two other phosphor types are used. Here are data to validate this anecdotal evidence.

Glass Type	Phosphor Type		
	1	2	3
1	279	307	287
	254	313	290
	297	294	285
2	243	253	252
	245	232	236
	267	223	278

Conduct a procedure to verify or repudiate the anecdotal evidence.

SR.10 The Vilmore Corporation is considering two word processors for its PCs. One factor that will influence its decision is the ease of use in preparing a business report. Consequently, Jody Vilmore selected a random sample of nine typists from the clerical pool and asked them to type a typical report using both word processors. The typists then were timed (in seconds) to determine how quickly they could type one of the frequently used forms. The results were as follows.

Typist	Processor 1	Processor 2
1	82	75
2	76	80
3	90	70
4	55	58
5	49	53
6	82	75
7	90	80
8	45	45
9	70	80

Jody wishes to have an estimate of the smallest and biggest differences that might exist in the average time required for typing the business form using the two processors. Provide this information.

SR.11 The research department of an appliance manufacturing firm has developed a solid-state switch for its blender that the department claims will reduce the percentage of appliances being returned under the one-year full warranty by from 3% to 6%. To determine if the claim can be supported, the testing department selects a group of the blenders manufactured with the new switch and the old switch and subjects them to a normal year's worth of wear. Out of 250 blenders tested with the new switch, nine would have been returned. Sixteen would have been returned out of the 250 blenders with the old switch. Use a statistical procedure to verify or refute the department's claim.

SR.12   The Ecco Company makes electronics products for distribution throughout the world. As a member of the quality department, you are interested in the warranty claims that are made by customers who have experienced problems with Ecco products. The file on your CD-ROM called *Ecco* contains data for a random sample of warranty claims. Large warranty claims not only cost the company money but also provide adverse publicity. The quality manager has asked you to provide her with a range of values that would represent the percentage of warranty claims filed for more than $300. Provide this information for your quality manager.

Term Project Assignment

Investigate whether there are differences in grocery prices for three or more stores in your city.

  a. Specify the type of testing procedure you will use.
  b. What type of experimental design will be used? Why?
  c. Develop a "typical" market basket of at least 10 items that you will price-check. Collect price data on these items at three or more different stores that sell groceries.
  d. Analyze your price data using the testing procedure and experimental design you specified in parts 1 and 2.
  e. Present your findings in a report. Did you find differences in average prices of the "market basket" across the different grocery stores?

CHAPTER 12

Goodness-of-Fit Tests and Contingency Analysis

CHAPTER OUTCOMES

After studying the material in Chapter 12, you should be able to:

- Utilize the chi-square goodness-of-fit test to determine whether data from a process fit a specified distribution.
- Set up a contingency analysis table and perform a chi-square test of independence.

WHY YOU NEED TO KNOW

The previous 11 chapters have introduced a wide variety of statistical techniques that are frequently used in business decision making. We have discussed numerous descriptive tools and techniques, as well as large-sample estimation and hypothesis tests for one and two populations, small-sample estimation and hypothesis tests using the *t*-distribution, and analysis of variance. However, as we have often mentioned, these statistical tools are limited to use under those conditions for which they were originally developed. For example, the large-sample tests based on the standard normal distribution assume that the data can be measured at least at the interval level. The small-sample tests that employ the *t*-distribution assume that the sampled populations are normally distributed.

In those situations in which the conditions just mentioned are not satisfied, we suggest using nonparametric statistics. Several of the more widely used nonparametric techniques will be discussed in Chapter 16. These procedures will be shown to be generally the nonparametric equivalent of the classical procedures discussed in previous chapters. The obvious questions when faced with a realistic decision-making situation are "Which test do I use? Should I consider a nonparametric test?" These questions are generally followed by a second question: "Do the data come from a normal distribution?" But recall that

we have also described situations involving data from Poisson or binomial distributions. How do we know which distribution applies to our situation? Fortunately, a statistical technique called *goodness-of-fit* exists that can help us answer this question. Using goodness-of-fit tests, we can decide whether a set of data comes from a specific hypothesized distribution.

You will also encounter many business situations in which the level of data measurement for the variable of interest is either nominal or ordinal, not interval or ratio. For example, a bank may use a code to indicate whether a customer is a good or poor credit risk. The bank may also have data for these customers that indicate, by a code, whether each person is buying or renting a home. The loan officer may be interested in determining whether credit-risk status is independent of home ownership. Because both credit risk and home ownership are qualitative, or categorical, variables, their measurement level is nominal and the previously introduced statistical techniques cannot be used to analyze this problem. We, therefore, need a new statistical tool to assist the manager in reaching an inference about the customer population. That statistical tool is contingency analysis. Contingency analysis is a widely used tool for analyzing the relationship between qualitative variables, one that decision makers in all business areas find helpful for data analysis.

12-1   INTRODUCTION TO GOODNESS-OF-FIT TESTS

Many of the statistical procedures introduced in earlier chapters require that the sample data come from populations that are normally distributed. For example, when we use the *t*-distribution in confidence interval estimation or hypothesis testing about one or two population means, the population(s) of interest is (are) assumed to be normally distributed. The analysis of variance *F*-test introduced in Chapter 11 is based on the assumption that the populations are normally distributed. But how can you determine whether these assumptions are satisfied? In other instances, you may wish to employ a particular probability distribution to help solve a problem related to an actual business process. In order to solve the problem, you may find it necessary to know whether the actual data from the process fit the probability distribution being considered. In such instances, a statistical technique known as a *goodness-of-fit test* can be used.

The term goodness-of-fit aptly describes the technique. Suppose a major retail department store believes that the proportion of customers who use each of the four entrances to the store is the same. This would mean that customer arrivals are *uniformly* distributed across the four entrances. Suppose a sample of 1,000 customers is observed entering the store and the entrance (A, B, C, or D) selected by each customer is recorded. Table 12-1 shows the results of the sample.

TABLE 12-1

Customer Door Entrance Data

ENTRANCE	NUMBER OF CUSTOMERS
A	260
B	290
C	230
D	220

If the manager's assumption about the entrances being used uniformly holds and if there was no sampling error involved, we would expect one-fourth of the customers, or 250, to enter through each door. When we allow for the potential of sampling error, we would still expect close to 250 customers entering through each entrance. The question is, how "good is the fit" between the sample data in Table 12-1 and the expected number of 250 people at each entrance? At what point do we no longer believe that the differences between what is actually observed at each entrance and what we expected can be attributed to sampling error? If these differences get too big, we will reject the uniformity assumption and conclude that customers prefer some entrances to others.

CHI-SQUARE GOODNESS-OF-FIT TEST

The *chi-square goodness-of-fit test* can be used to determine whether the sample data come from any hypothesized distribution. Consider the following application.

Vista Health Guard—Vista Health Guard, a Pennsylvania health clinic with 25 offices, is open seven days a week. The operations manager was recently hired from a similar position at a smaller chain of clinics in Florida. She is naturally concerned that the level of staffing—physicians, nurses, and other support personnel—be balanced with patient demand.

Currently, the staffing level is balanced Monday through Friday, with reduced staffing on Saturday and Sunday. Her predecessor explained that patient demand is fairly level throughout the week and about 25% less on weekends, but the new manager suspects that the staff members want to have weekends free. Although she was willing to operate with this schedule for a while, she has decided to study patient demand to see whether the assumed demand pattern still applies.

The operations manager requested a sample of 20 days for each day of the week that showed the number of patients on each of the sample days. A portion of those data follows:

DAY	PATIENT COUNT
Monday, May 6	325
Monday, October 7	379
Tuesday, July 2	456
Monday, July 15	323
Wednesday, April 3	467
etc.	etc.

TABLE 12-2

Patient Count Data for the Vista Health Guard Example

DAY	TOTAL PATIENT COUNT
Sunday	4,502
Monday	6,623
Tuesday	8,308
Wednesday	10,420
Thursday	11,032
Friday	10,754
Saturday	4,361
Total	56,000

For the 140 days observed, the total count was 56,000 patients. The total patient counts for each day of the week are shown in Table 12-2 and are graphed in Figure 12-1.

Recall that the previous operations manager at Vista Health Guard based his staffing on the premise that from Monday to Friday the patient count remained essentially the same and on Saturdays and Sundays it went down 25%. If this is so, how many of the 56,000 patients would we expect on Monday? How many on Tuesday, and so forth? To figure out this demand, we determine weighting factors by allocating four units each to days Monday through Friday and three units each (representing the 25% reduction) to Saturday and Sunday. The total number of units is then $(5 \times 4) + (2 \times 3) = 26$. The percentage of total patients expected on each weekday is $4/26 = 0.154$, or 15.4%, and the percentage expected on a weekend day is $3/26 = 0.115$, or 11.5%. The expected number of patients on a weekday is $0.154 \times 56,000 = 8,624$, and the expected number on each weekend day is $0.115 \times 56,000 = 6,440$.

FIGURE 12-1

Graph of Actual Frequencies for Vista Health Guard

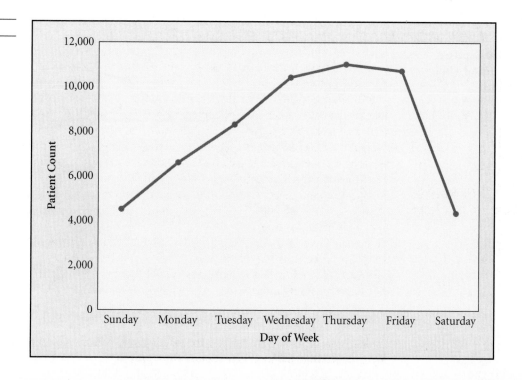

Figure 12-2 shows a graph with the actual sample data and the expected values. With exception of what might be attributed to sampling error, if the distribution claimed by the previous operations manager is correct, the actual frequencies for each day of the week should fit quite closely with the expected frequencies. As you can see in Figure 12-2, the actual data and the expected data do not match perfectly. However, is the difference enough to warrant a change in staffing patterns? The situation facing Vista Health Guard is one for which a number of statistical tests have been developed. One of the most frequently used is the chi-square goodness-of-fit test. What we need to examine is how well the sample data fit the hypothesized distribution. The following null and alternative hypotheses can represent this:

H_0: The patient demand distribution is evenly spread through the weekdays and 25% lower on the weekend.

H_A: The patient demand follows some other distribution.

Equation 12-1 is the equation for the chi-square goodness-of-fit test statistic. The logic behind this test is based on determining how far the actual *observed frequency* is from the *expected frequency*. Because we are interested in whether a difference exists, positive or negative, we remove the effect of negative values by squaring the differences. In addition, how important this difference is really depends on the magnitude of the expected frequency (e.g., a difference of 5 is more important if the expected frequency is 10 than if the expected frequency is 1,000), so we divide the squared difference by the expected frequency. Finally, we sum these difference ratios for all days. This sum is a statistic that has an approximate chi-square distribution.

Chi-Square Goodness-of-Fit Test Statistic

$$\chi^2 = \sum_{i=1}^{k} \frac{(o_i - e_i)^2}{e_i}$$

12-1

where:

o_i = Observed cell frequency for category i
e_i = Expected cell frequency for category i
k = Number of categories

The χ^2 statistic is distributed approximately as a chi-square only if the sample size is large.

FIGURE 12-2

Actual and Expected Frequencies for Vista Health Guard

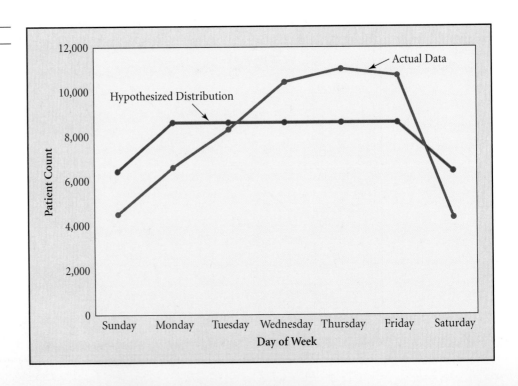

SPECIAL NOTE

A sample size of at least 30 is sufficient in most cases provided that none of the expected frequencies is too small.

This issue of expected cell frequencies will be expanded upon later. If the calculated chi-square statistic gets large, this is evidence to suggest the fit of the actual data to the hypothesized distribution is not good, and the null hypothesis should be rejected.

Figure 12-3 shows the hypothesis test process and results for this chi-square goodness-of-fit test. Note that the degrees of freedom for the chi-square test are equal to $k - 1$, where k is the number of categories or observed cell frequencies. In this example, we have 7 categories corresponding to the days of the week, so the degrees of freedom are $7 - 1 = 6$. The critical value of 12.592 is found in Appendix G for an upper-tail test with 6 degrees of freedom and a significance level of 0.05.

As Figure 12-3 indicates, $\chi^2 = 3{,}302.7 > 12.592$, so the null hypothesis is rejected and we should conclude that the demand pattern does not match the previously defined distribution. The data in Figure 12-3 indicate that demand is heavier than expected Wednesday through Friday and less than expected on the other days. The operations manager would now most likely wish to increase staffing on Wednesday, Thursday, and Friday to more closely approximate current demand patterns.

FIGURE 12-3

Chi-Square Goodness-of-Fit Test for Vista Health Guard

Hypotheses:

H_0: Patient demand is evenly spread through the weekdays and is 25% lower on weekends.
H_A: Patient demand follows some other distribution.
$\alpha = 0.05$

	Total Patient Count	
	Observed	Expected
Day	o_i	e_i
Sunday	4,502	6,440
Monday	6,623	8,624
Tuesday	8,308	8,624
Wednesday	10,420	8,624
Thursday	11,032	8,624
Friday	10,754	8,624
Saturday	4,361	6,440
Total	56,000	56,000

Test Statistic:

$$\chi^2 = \Sigma \frac{(o - e)^2}{e} = \frac{(4{,}502 - 6{,}440)^2}{6{,}440} + \frac{(6{,}623 - 8{,}624)^2}{8{,}624} + \cdots + \frac{(4{,}361 - 6{,}440)^2}{6{,}440}$$

$$\chi^2 = 583.2 + 464.3 + \cdots + 671.2$$

$$= 3{,}302.7$$

$df = k - 1 = 7 - 1 = 6$

Rejection Region

$\alpha = 0.05$

$\chi^2_\alpha = 12.592$

Decision Rule:

If $\chi^2 > 12.592$, reject H_0
Otherwise, do not reject H_0
Because $3{,}302.7 > 12.592$, reject H_0

EXAMPLE 12-1: CHI-SQUARE GOODNESS-OF-FIT TEST

California Port of Entry   When entering California, motorists are required to pass through a port-of-entry inspection station, where their vehicles are inspected to see whether fruit is being brought into the state. The state is concerned about fruit that might be infested with fruit flies and other insects. Full inspections are done on a random basis. One port of entry has five vehicle lanes. The manager wants to do a full inspection on the same number of vehicles in each lane each week. A goodness-of-fit test can be conducted to determine whether this objective is being met using the following steps:

Step 1:   **Formulate the appropriate null and alternative hypotheses.**
Because the number of inspections is supposed to be the same across the five inspection lanes, the following null and alternative hypotheses are formed:

H_0: Distribution of inspections is uniform across the five lanes.
H_A: Distribution of inspections is not uniform.

Step 2:   **Specify the significance level.**
The test will be conducted using $\alpha = 0.05$.

Step 3:   **Determine the critical value.**
The critical value for the goodness-of-fit test is a chi-square value from the chi-square distribution, with $k - 1 = 5 - 1 = 4$ degrees of freedom and $\alpha = 0.05$ is 9.4877.

Step 4:   **Collect the sample data and compute the chi-square test statistic.**
The manager collected data for a random sample of five weeks. The following data represent the number of inspections that were performed in each lane.

Lane	1	2	3	4	5
Inspections	358	402	578	403	380

A total of 2,120 inspections were performed during the sampled weeks. Under the hypothesis of a uniform distribution, 20% of this total (424) should be performed at each lane. This is the expected cell frequency.
Equation 12-1 is used to form the test statistic based on these sample data.

$$\chi^2 = \Sigma \frac{(o - e)^2}{e} = \frac{(358 - 424)^2}{424} + \frac{(402 - 424)^2}{424} + \frac{(578 - 424)^2}{424} + \frac{(403 - 424)^2}{424} + \frac{(380 - 424)^2}{424}$$
$$= 72.956$$

Step 5:   **Reach a decision.**
The decision rule is

If $\chi^2 > 9.4877$, reject H_0;
Otherwise, do not reject H_0.

Because $\chi^2 = 72.956 > 9.4877$, reject the null hypothesis.

Step 6:   **Draw a conclusion.**
We conclude that the inspections are not occurring equally across the five lanes.

Excel and Minitab Tutorial

Woodtrim Products, Inc.—Woodtrim Products, Inc., makes wood moldings, door frames, and window frames. It purchases lumber from mills throughout New England and eastern Canada. The first step in the production process is to rip the lumber into narrower strips. Different widths are used for different products. For example, wider pieces with no imperfections are used to make door and window frames. Once an operator decides on the appropriate width, that information is locked into a computer, and a ripsaw automatically cuts the board to the desired size. The manufacturer claims that the ripsaw cuts an average deviation of zero from target and that the differences from target will be normally distributed, with a standard deviation of 0.01 inch.

Woodtrim has recently become concerned that the ripsaw may not be cutting to the manufacturer's specifications because operators at other machines downstream in the production process are finding excessive numbers of ripped pieces that are too wide or too narrow.

FIGURE 12-4

Woodtrim Products Test Data

Excel Instructions:
1. Open file: Woodtrim.xls

	A	B	C	D
1	Sample	Actual Width	Target Width	Difference
2	1	2.870	2.875	-0.005
3	2	2.863	2.875	-0.012
4	3	2.885	2.875	0.010
5	4	2.872	2.875	-0.003
6	5	2.891	2.875	0.016
7	6	2.893	2.875	0.018
8	7	2.868	2.875	-0.007
9	8	2.861	2.875	-0.014
10	9	2.889	2.875	0.014

A quality improvement team (QIT) has started to investigate the problem. Team members selected a random sample of 300 boards just as they came off the ripsaw. To provide a measure of control, the only pieces sampled in the initial study had stated widths of $2\frac{7}{8}$ (2.875) inches. Each piece's width was measured halfway from its end. A portion of the data and the differences between the target 2.875 inches and the actual measured width are shown in Figure 12-4. The full data set is contained in the CD-ROM file *Woodtrim*. The team can use these data and the chi-square goodness-of-fit testing procedure to test the following null and alternative hypotheses:

H_0: The differences are normally distributed, with $\mu = 0$ and $\sigma = 0.01$.
H_A: The differences are not normally distributed, with $\mu = 0$ and $\sigma = 0.01$.

This example differs slightly from the previous examples because the hypothesized distribution is continuous rather than discrete. Thus, we organize the data into a grouped-data frequency distribution (see Chapter 2), as shown in Figure 12-5. Our choice of classes requires careful consideration. The chi-square goodness-of-fit test compares the actual cell frequencies with the expected cell frequencies. The test statistic from Equation 12-1,

$$\chi^2 = \Sigma \frac{(o - e)^2}{e}$$

FIGURE 12-5

Excel Results—Goodness-of-Fit Test for the Woodtrim Example

	J	K	L	M	N
1	Class	o Observed Frequency	Normal Distribution Probability	e Expected Frequency	(o-e)²/e
2	less than -0.02	0	0.02275	6.83	6.825
3	-0.02 and under -0.01	42	0.13591	40.77	0.037
4	-0.01 and under 0.00	133	0.34134	102.40	9.142
5	0.00 and under 0.01	75	0.34134	102.40	7.333
6	0.01 and under 0.02	47	0.13591	40.77	0.951
7	0.02 and over	3	0.02275	6.83	2.144
8	Total	300			
9					
10				Total =	26.432
11				p-value	0.0001

Excel Instructions:
1. Open file: Woodtrim.xls (see Figure 12-4).
2. Define Classes (column J).
3. Determine observed frequencies [i.e., cell K4 formula is =COUNTIF(D2:D301,"<0.0") − SUM(K2:K3)].
4. Determine normal distribution probabilities, assuming the mean = 0.0 and st.dev. = 0.01 [i.e., cell L4 formula is =NORMDIST(0,0,0.01,TRUE) − SUM(L$2:L3)]
5. Determine expected frequencies by multiplying normal probability by the same size (n = 300).
6. Compute values for chi-square in column N [cell N5 formula is =(K5 − M5)^2/M5].
7. Sum column N to get chi-square statistic.
8. Find p-value using CHITEST function [cell N11 formula is =CHITEST(K2:K7,M2:M7)].

is approximately chi-square distributed if the expected cell frequencies are large. Because the expected cell frequencies are used in computing the test statistic, the general recommendation is that the goodness-of-fit test be performed only when all expected cell frequencies are at least 5. If any of the cells have expected frequencies less than 5, the cells should be combined in a meaningful way such that the expected frequencies are at least 5. We have chosen to use $k = 6$ classes. The number of classes is your choice. Although Excel and Minitab do not have a tool for performing a chi-square goodness-of-fit test directly, we can perform the test using Excel functions and formulas and Minitab commands. (Both the Excel and Minitab tutorials on the CD-Rom take you through the specific steps required to complete this example.) Figure 12-5 shows the normal distribution probabilities, expected cell frequencies, and the chi-square calculation. The calculated chi-square statistic is $\chi^2 = 26.43$. The p-value associated with $\chi^2 = 26.43$ and $6 - 1 = 5$ degrees of freedom is 0.0001. Therefore, because p-value = 0.0001 is less than any reasonable level of significance, we reject the null hypothesis and conclude the ripsaw is not currently meeting the manufacturer's specification. The saw errors are not normally distributed with mean equal to zero and a standard deviation equal to 0.01.

Note that in this case, because the null hypothesis specified both the mean and the standard deviation, the normal distribution probabilities were computed using these values. However, if either or both had not been specified, the sample values would be used in the probability computation. You would lose one additional degree of freedom for each parameter that was estimated from the sample data. This is true any time sample values are specified in place of values in the hypothesis.

Minitab has a procedure for performing a goodness-of-fit test for a normal distribution. In fact, it offers three different approaches, none of which are exactly the chi-square approach just outlined. Figure 12-6 shows the Minitab results for the Woodtrim example. Consistent with our other Minitab and Excel results, this output illustrates that the null hypothesis of normality should be rejected because the p-value < 0.01.

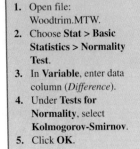

FIGURE 12-6

Minitab Output—Test of Normal-Distributed Ripsaw Cuts for the Woodtrim Example

Minitab Instructions:
1. Open file: Woodtrim.MTW.
2. Choose **Stat > Basic Statistics > Normality Test**.
3. In **Variable**, enter data column (*Difference*).
4. Under **Tests for Normality**, select **Kolmogorov-Smirnov**.
5. Click **OK**.

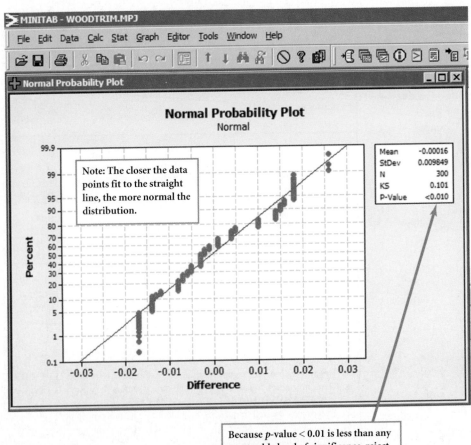

Because p-value < 0.01 is less than any reasonable level of significance, reject the null hypothesis of normality.

EXAMPLE 12-2: GOODNESS-OF-FIT TEST

Cushing Supply   Cushing Supply makes component parts used in the automobile industry. For some time, shipping workers have been inspecting 10 parts from every day's production before shipping. If two or more of the parts are defective, they do a complete inspection on the day's parts to sort the defective from the good parts. If they find one or fewer, they go ahead and ship the parts without further analysis. The contract calls for at most 10% of the parts to be defective. At issue is whether Cushing managers can evaluate this sampling plan using a binomial distribution with $n = 10$ and $p = 0.10$. To test this, a goodness-of-fit test can be performed using the following steps.

Step 1:   **State the appropriate null and alternative hypothesis.**
In this case, the null and alternative hypotheses are

H_0: Distribution of defects is binomial, with $n = 10$ and $p = 0.10$.
H_A: Distribution is not binomial.

Step 2:   **Specify the level of significance.**
The test will be conducted using $\alpha = 0.02$.

Step 3:   **Determine the critical value.**
The critical value depends on the number of degrees of freedom and the level of significance. The degrees of freedom will be equal to $k - 1$, where k is the number of categories for which observed and expected frequencies will be recorded. In this case, the managers have set up the following groups:

Defects: 0   1   2   3 and over

Therefore, $k = 4$, and the degrees of freedom are $4 - 1 = 3$. The critical chi-square value found in Appendix G is 9.8374.

Step 4:   **Collect the sample data and compute the chi-square test statistic using Equation 12-1.**
The company selected a simple random sample of 100 days from past production records and recorded the number of defects for each day when the sample of 10 items was inspected. The following table shows the computations for the chi-square statistic.

Defects	o Observed Defects	Binomial Probability $n = 10$, $p = .10$	e Expected Frequency	$\dfrac{(o_i - e_i)^2}{e_i}$
0	30	0.3487	34.87	0.680152
1	40	0.3874	38.74	0.040981
2	20	0.1937	19.37	0.02049
3 and over	10	0.0702	7.02	1.265014
Total	100			2.006638

The calculated chi-square test statistic is $\chi^2 = 2.006638$.

Step 5:   **Reach a decision.**
Because this is less than the critical value of 9.8374, we do not reject the null hypothesis.

Step 6:   **Draw a conclusion.**
The binomial distribution may be the appropriate distribution to describe the company's sampling plan.

12-1: EXERCISES

Skill Development

2.1   Use the chi-square goodness-of-fit test to determine whether the number of phone calls coming in to a radio talk show is Poisson distributed with a mean of 5 per hour. The following data, selected over a period of 100 hours, show the frequency distribution for the number of calls in a given hour.

Number of Calls	Frequency
0	0
1	2
2	4
3	10
4	7
5	14
6	11
7	13
8	5
9	10
10	5
11	5
12	7
13	4
14	3
	Total 100

Test at the $\alpha = 0.05$ level. Given your test results, which type of hypothesis error could you have committed?

12.2 The following data reflect the choices of majors by a sample of 200 incoming freshmen students.

Major	Number of Students
Liberal Arts	44
Engineering	30
Education	26
Business	45
Sciences	55

Using a significance level of 0.05, is there sufficient evidence to conclude that the distribution of major choices is not uniform?

12.3 The following data reflect the vehicle mileage (mpg) for a sample of 100 four-wheel-drive trucks. Based on these sample data, can you assume the population data are normally distributed? Test using an $\alpha = 0.05$ level.

12.8	8.9	15.0	19.1	18.8	20.9	5.3	13.1	18.4	9.7
11.2	7.2	6.6	10.1	10.9	5.5	11.7	12.4	14.5	12.5
12.7	12.5	19.4	13.7	13.3	11.9	21.9	17.5	23.5	11.4
20.6	7.6	16.2	17.6	21.7	13.7	11.9	16.7	12.5	17.0
8.2	10.6	7.9	12.5	13.9	14.1	12.7	22.8	7.0	11.1
3.7	19.8	8.9	11.4	17.0	15.9	17.5	16.4	8.5	9.5
16.8	15.3	10.2	13.0	14.5	16.2	14.6	10.4	21.5	15.9
14.3	17.3	17.4	11.5	10.3	18.4	9.2	7.8	16.8	16.6
22.8	19.8	19.2	14.5	14.0	15.8	13.9	9.8	6.9	17.3
15.8	16.5	14.9	9.9	19.0	12.8	10.6	10.7	12.3	12.2

12.4 The following table represents increases in ACT scores for students using a computer-based tutorial.

Increase in Score	Number
less than 20	20
20 < 30	60
30 < 40	100
40 < 50	90
50 < 60	80
60 < 70	50

Use a chi-square goodness-of-fit test to determine if the data come from a normal distribution with a mean of 40 and a standard deviation of 10. Test at $\alpha = 0.05$.

12.5 Refer to Exercise 12.3.
a. Use a chi-square goodness-of-fit test to determine if the data provided are a sample from a uniform distribution. Use the classes $(-\infty, \bar{x} - 3s)$, $(\bar{x} - 3s, \bar{x} - 2s)$, $(\bar{x} - 2s, \bar{x} - s)$, $(\bar{x} - s, \bar{x})$, $(\bar{x}, \bar{x} + s)$, $(\bar{x} + s, \bar{x} + 2s)$, $(\bar{x} + 2s, \bar{x} + 3s)$, and $(\bar{x} + 3s, \infty)$.
b. Compare the results of this test with the results from Exercise 12.3.

12.6 Daily sales volumes in dollars have been grouped as follows. Can you conclude that the sales are uniformly distributed? Test at $\alpha = 0.05$.

Sales	Frequency
$500 and under $1,000	40
$1,000 and under $1,500	63
$1,500 and under $2,000	55
$2,000 and under $2,500	50
$2,500 and under $3,000	61

12.7 The following data reflect the number of customers who use an ATM machine per hour. The claim is that the hourly usage rate is Poisson distributed with a mean equal to 5 per hour.

9	7	8	7	8
4	8	5	8	9
11	7	7	8	8
8	11	8	8	12
7	11	8	8	11
9	9	8	9	8
7	6	8	6	12
8	5	7	10	7
7	5	9	8	9
7	7	9	7	8

a. State the appropriate null and alternative hypotheses
b. Using an $\alpha = 0.10$ level, what conclusion should be reached about the population distribution based on the sample data?

Business Applications

12.8 The Baltimore Steel and Pipe Company recently developed a new pipe product for a customer. According to specifications, the pipe is supposed to have an average outside diameter of 2.00 inches, with a standard deviation equal to 0.10 inch, and the distribution of outside diameters is supposed to be normally distributed. Before going into full-scale production, the company selected a random sample of 30 sections of pipe from the initial test run. The following data were recorded.

Pipe Section	Diameter (Inches)	Pipe Section	Diameter (Inches)
1	2.04	16	1.96
2	2.13	17	1.89
3	2.07	18	1.99
4	1.99	19	2.13
5	1.90	20	1.90
6	2.06	21	1.91
7	2.19	22	1.95
8	2.01	23	2.18
9	2.05	24	1.94
10	1.98	25	1.93
11	1.95	26	2.08
12	1.90	27	1.82
13	2.10	28	1.94
14	2.02	29	1.96
15	2.11	30	1.81

a. Using a significance level of 0.01, perform the appropriate test.
b. Based on these data, should the company conclude that it is meeting the product specifications? Explain your reasoning.

12.9 The airport manager at the Sacramento, California, airport recently conducted a study of passengers departing from the airport. A random sample of 100 passengers was selected. The data are in the CD-ROM file *Airline Passengers*. An earlier study showed the following usage by airline:

Delta	20%
Horizon	10%
Northwest	10%
Skywest	3%
Southwest	25%
United	32%

a. If the manager wishes to determine whether the airline-usage pattern has changed from that reported in the earlier study, state the appropriate null and alternative hypotheses.
b. Based on the sample data, what should be concluded? Test using a significance level of 0.01.

Advanced Applications

12.10 A pharmaceutical company is planning to market a drug that is supposed to help reduce blood pressure. The company claims that if the drug is taken properly, the amount of blood pressure loss will be normally distributed, with a mean equal to 10 points on the diastolic reading and a standard deviation equal to 4.0. One hundred patients were administered the drug, and data were collected showing the reductions in blood pressure at

the end of the test period. The data are located in the CD-ROM file *Blood Pressure*.
a. Using a goodness-of-fit test and a significance level equal to 0.05, what conclusion should be reached with respect to the distribution of diastolic-blood-pressure reduction? Discuss.
b. Conduct a hypothesis test to determine if the standard deviation for this population could be considered to be 4.0. Use a significance level of 0.10.
c. Given the results of the two tests in parts a and b, is it appropriate to construct a confidence interval for the mean based on a normal distribution with a population standard deviation of 4.0? Explain your answer.
d. If appropriate, construct a 99% confidence interval for the mean reduction in blood pressure. Based on this confidence interval, does an average diastolic loss of 10 seem reasonable for this procedure? Explain your reasoning.

12.11 The owners of Clair's Deli are considering remodeling their facility to include a drive-through window. There is room for three cars in the drive-through line if they build it. However, they are concerned that the capacity may be too low during their busy hours between 11:00 A.M. and 1:30 P.M. One of the factors they need to know is the distribution of the length of time it takes to fill an order for cars coming to the drive-through. In order to collect this information, the owners have received permission from another deli in a nearby town to collect some data at that deli's drive-through. The data in the CD-ROM file *Clair's Deli* reflect the service time per car.

Based on these sample data, is there sufficient evidence to conclude that the distribution of service time is not normally distributed? Test using the chi-square distribution and an $\alpha = 0.05$ level.

12.12 Again, working with the Clair's Deli data from Exercise 12.11, the number of cars that arrive in each 10-minute period is another factor that will determine whether the deli will have the capacity to handle the drive-through business. In addition to studying the service times, the owners also counted the number of cars that arrived at the deli in the nearby town in a sample of 10-minute time periods. These data are shown as follows:

3	2	0
2	3	3
3	3	3
0	2	3
0	3	3
1	1	0
2	4	9
1	2	4
2	1	1
4	1	3

Based on these data, is there evidence to conclude that the arrivals are not Poisson distributed? State the appropriate null and alternative hypotheses and test using a significance level of 0.02.

12-2 INTRODUCTION TO CONTINGENCY ANALYSIS

In Chapters 8 and 9 you were introduced to hypothesis tests involving one and two population proportions. Although these techniques are useful in many cases, you will also encounter many situations involving multiple population proportions. For example, a major mutual fund company offers six different mutual funds. The president of the company may wish to determine if the proportion of customers selecting each mutual fund is related to the four sales regions in which the customers reside. A hospital administrator who collects service-satisfaction data from patients might be interested in determining whether there is a significant difference in patient rating by hospital department. A personnel manager for a large corporation might be interested in determining whether there is a relationship between level of employee job satisfaction and job classification. In each of these cases, the proportions relate to characteristic categories of the variable of interest. The six mutual funds, four sales regions, hospital departments, and job classifications are the specific categories.

These situations involving categorical data call for a new statistical tool known as *contingency analysis* to help make decisions when multiple proportions are involved. Contingency analysis can be used when a level of data measurement is either nominal or ordinal and the values are determined by counting the number of occurrences in each category.

2 × 2 CONTINGENCY TABLES

Dalgarno Photo, Inc.—Dalgarno Photo, Inc., gets much of its business from taking photographs for college yearbooks. Dalgarno hired a first-year MBA student to develop the survey it mailed to 850 yearbook representatives at the colleges and universities in its market area. The representatives were unaware that Dalgarno Photo had developed the survey.

The survey asked about the photography and publishing activities associated with yearbook development. For instance, what photographer and publisher services did the schools use, and what factors were most important in selecting services? The survey instrument contained 30 questions, which were coded into 137 separate variables.

Among his many interests in this study, Dalgarno's marketing manager questioned whether funding source and gender of the yearbook editor were related in some manner. To analyze this issue, we examine these two variables more closely. Source of university funding is a categorical variable, coded as follows:

1 = Private funding
2 = State-funded

TABLE 12-3

Contingency Table for Dalgarno Photo

GENDER	SOURCE OF FUNDING		
	Private	State	
Male	14	43	57
Female	141	23	164
	155	66	221

Of the 221 respondents who provided data for this variable, 155 came from privately funded colleges or universities and 66 were from publicly funded institutions.

The second variable, sex of the yearbook editor, is also a categorical variable, with two response categories, coded as follows:

1 = Male
2 = Female

Of the 221 responses to the survey, 164 were from females and 57 were from males.

In cases in which the variables of interest are both categorical and the decision maker is interested in determining whether a relationship exists between the two, a statistical technique known as contingency analysis is useful. We first set up a two-dimensional table called a **contingency table**. The contingency table for these two variables is shown in Table 12-3.

Contingency Table

A table used to classify sample observations according to two or more identifiable characteristics. It is also called a *crosstabulation table*.

Table 12-3 shows that 14 of the respondents were males from schools that are privately funded. The numbers at the extreme right and along the bottom are called the *marginal frequencies*. For example, 57 respondents were males, and 155 respondents were from privately funded institutions.

The issue of whether there is a relationship between responses to these two variables is formally addressed through a hypothesis test, in which the null and alternative hypotheses are stated as follows

TABLE 12-4

Contingency Table for Dalgarno Photo

GENDER	SOURCE OF FUNDING		
	Private	State	
Male	$o_{11} = 14$ $e_{11} = 39.98$	$o_{12} = 43$ $e_{12} = 17.02$	57
Female	$o_{21} = 141$ $e_{21} = 115.02$	$o_{22} = 23$ $e_{22} = 48.98$	164
	155	66	221

H_0: Gender of yearbook editor is independent of the college's funding source.

H_A: Gender of yearbook editor *is not* independent of the college's funding source.

If the null hypothesis is true, the population proportion of yearbook editors from private institutions who are males should be equal to the proportion of male editors from state-funded institutions. These two proportions should also equal the population proportion of male editors without regard to a school's funding source. To illustrate, we can use the sample data to determine the sample proportion of male editors as follows:

$$P_M = \frac{\text{Number of male editors}}{\text{Number of respondents}} = \frac{57}{221}$$
$$= 0.2579$$

Then, if the null hypothesis is true, we would expect 25.79% of the 155 privately funded schools, or 39.98 schools, to have a male yearbook editor. We would also expect 25.79% of the 66 state-funded schools, or 17.02, to have male yearbook editors. (Note that the expected numbers need not be integer values. Note also that the sum of expected frequencies in any column or row add to the marginal frequency.) We can use this reasoning to determine the expected number of respondents in each cell of the contingency table, as shown in Table 12-4.

You can simplify the calculations needed to produce the expected values for each cell. Note that the first cell's expected value, 39.98, was obtained by the following calculation:

$$e_{11} = 0.2579(155) = 39.98$$

However, because the probability, 0.2579, is calculated by dividing the row total, 57, by the grand total, 221, the calculation can be represented as

$$e_{11} = \frac{(\text{Row total})(\text{Column total})}{\text{Grand total}} = \frac{(57)(155)}{221} = 39.98$$

As a further example, we can calculate the expected value for the next cell in the same row. The expected number of male yearbook editors in state-funds schools is

$$e_{12} = \frac{(\text{Row total})(\text{Column total})}{\text{Grand total}} = \frac{(57)(66)}{221} = 17.02$$

Keep in mind that the row and column totals (the marginal frequencies) must be the same for the expected values as for the observed values. Therefore, when there is only one cell left in a row or a column for which you must calculate an expected value, you can obtain it by subtraction. So, as an example, the expected value, e_{12}, could have been calculated as

$$e_{12} = 57 - 39.98 = 17.02$$

Allowing for sampling error, we would expect the actual frequencies in each cell to approximately match the corresponding expected cell frequencies when the null hypothesis is true. The greater the difference between the actual and the expected frequencies, the more likely the null hypothesis of independence is false and should be rejected. The statistical test to determine whether the sample data support or refute the null hypothesis is given by Equation 12-2. Do not be confused by the double summation in Equation 12-2; it merely indicates that all rows and columns must be used in calculating χ^2. As was the case in the goodness-of-fit tests, the degrees of freedom are the number of independent data values obtained from the experiment. In any given row, once you know $c - 1$ of the data values, the remaining data value is determined. For instance, once you know that 14 of the 57 male editors were from privately funded institutions, you know that 43 were from state-funded institutions.

Chi-Square Contingency Test Statistic

$$\chi^2 = \sum_{i=1}^{r} \sum_{j=1}^{c} \frac{(o_{ij} - e_{ij})^2}{e_{ij}} \quad \text{with } df = (r-1)(c-1) \qquad \text{12-2}$$

where:

$$o_{ij} = \text{Observed frequency in cell } (i, j)$$
$$e_{ij} = \text{Expected frequency in cell } (i, j)$$
$$r = \text{Number of rows}$$
$$c = \text{Number of columns}$$

Similarly, once $r - 1$ data values in a column are known, the remaining data value is determined. Therefore, the degrees of freedom are obtained by the expression $(r-1)(c-1)$.

Figure 12-7 presents the hypotheses and test results for this example. As was the case in the goodness-of-fit tests, the test statistic has a distribution that can be approximated by the chi-square

FIGURE 12-7

Chi-Square Contingency Analysis Test for Dalgarno Photo

Hypotheses:

H_0: Gender of yearbook editor is independent of college's funding source.
H_A: Gender of yearbook editor is not independent of college's funding source.
$\alpha = 0.05$

	Private	Public
Male	$o_{11} = 14$ $e_{11} = 39.98$	$o_{12} = 43$ $e_{12} = 17.02$
Female	$o_{21} = 141$ $e_{21} = 115.02$	$o_{22} = 23$ $e_{22} = 48.98$

Test Statistic:

$$\chi^2 = \sum_{i=1}^{r} \sum_{j=1}^{c} \frac{(o_{ij} - e_{ij})^2}{e_{ij}} = \frac{(14 - 39.98)^2}{39.98} + \frac{(43 - 17.02)^2}{17.02}$$
$$+ \frac{(141 - 115.02)^2}{115.02} + \frac{(23 - 48.98)^2}{48.98} = 76.19$$

$f(\chi^2)$

$df = (r-1)(c-1) = (1)(1) = 1$

$\chi^2 = 3.8415$

χ^2

Decision Rule:

If $\chi^2 > 3.8415$, reject H_0
Otherwise, do not reject H_0
Because $76.19 > 3.8415$, reject H_0

distribution if the expected values are larger than 5. Note that the calculated chi-square statistic is compared to the tabled value of chi-square for an $\alpha = 0.05$ and degrees of freedom $= (2 - 1)(2 - 1) = 1$. Because $\chi^2 = 76.19 > 3.8415$, the null hypothesis of independence should be rejected. Dalgarno Photo representatives should conclude that the sex of the yearbook editor and each school's source of funding are not independent. By examining the data in Figure 12-7, you can see that private schools are more likely to have female editors, whereas state schools are more likely to have male yearbook editors.

EXAMPLE 12-3: 2×2 CONTINGENCY ANALYSIS

Barger Advertising   Before releasing a major advertising campaign to the media, Barger Advertising runs a test on the material. Recently, it randomly called 100 people and asked them to listen to a commercial that was slated to run nationwide on the radio. At the end of the commercial, the respondents were asked to name the company that was in the ad. The company is interested in determining whether there is a relationship between gender and a person's ability to recall the company name. To test this, the following steps can be used.

Step 1:   **Specify the null and alternative hypotheses.**
The company is interested in testing whether a relationship exists between gender and recall ability. Here are the appropriate null and alternative hypotheses.

H_0: Ability to correctly recall the company name is independent of gender.
H_A: Recall ability and gender are not independent.

Step 2:   **Determine the significance level.**
The test will be conducted using a 0.01 level of significance.

Step 3:   **Determine the critical value.**
The critical value for this test will be the chi-square value, with $(r - 1)(c - 1) = (2 - 1)(2 - 1) = 1$ degree of freedom with an $\alpha = 0.01$. From Appendix G, the critical value is 6.6349.

Step 4:   **Collect the sample data and compute the chi-square test statistic using Equation 12-2.**
The following contingency table shows the results of the sampling.

	Female	Male	Total
Correct Recall	33	25	58
Incorrect Recall	22	20	42
Total	55	45	100

The expected cell frequencies are determined by multiplying the row total by the column and dividing by the overall sample size. For example, for the cell corresponding to female and correct recall, we get:

$$\text{Expected} = \frac{58 \times 55}{100} = 31.90$$

The expected cell values for all cells are

	Female	Male	Total
Correct Recall	$o = 33$	$o = 25$	58
	$e = 31.90$	$e = 26.10$	
Incorrect Recall	$o = 22$	$o = 20$	42
	$e = 23.10$	$e = 18.9$	
Total	55	45	100

The test statistic is computed using Equation 12-2.

$$\chi^2 = \sum_{i=1}^{r}\sum_{j=1}^{c}\frac{(o_{ij} - e_{ij})^2}{e_{ij}}$$

$$= \frac{(33 - 31.9)^2}{31.9} + \frac{(25 - 26.10)^2}{26.10} + \frac{(22 - 23.10)^2}{23.10} + \frac{(20 - 18.9)^2}{18.9} = 0.20$$

Step 5:   **Reach a decision.**
Because $\chi^2 = 0.20 < 6.6349$, do not reject the null hypothesis.

Step 6:   **Draw a conclusion.**
Based on the sample data there is no reason to believe that being able to recall the name of the company in the ad is related to gender.

Excel and Minitab Tutorial

$r \times c$ CONTINGENCY TABLES

Benton Industries—Benton Industries manufactures carpets and draperies in the Atlanta area. It pays market wages, provides competitive benefits, and offers attractive options for employees in an effort to create a satisfied workforce and reduce turnover. Recently, however, several supervisors have complained that employee absenteeism is becoming a problem. In response to these complaints, the human resources manager studied a random sample of 500 employees. One aim of this study was to determine whether there is a relationship between absenteeism and marital status. Absenteeism during the past year was broken down into three levels:

1. zero absences
2. 1 to 5 absences
3. over 5 absences

Marital status was divided into four categories:

1. single   2. married

3. divorced   4. widowed

Table 12-5 shows the contingency table for the sample of 500 employees. The table is also shown in the CD-ROM file *Benton*. The null and alternative hypotheses to be tested are

H_0: Absentee behavior is independent of marital status.
H_A: Absentee behavior is *not* independent of marital status.

As with 2×2 contingency analysis, the test for independence can be made using the chi-square test, where the expected cell frequencies are compared to the actual cell frequencies and the test statistic shown as Equation 12-2 is used. The logic of the test says that if the actual and expected frequencies closely match, then the null hypothesis of independence is not rejected. However, if the actual and expected cell frequencies are substantially different overall, the null hypothesis of independence is rejected. The calculated chi-square statistic is compared to a table critical value for the desired significance and degrees of freedom equal to $(r - 1)(c - 1)$.

The expected cell frequencies are determined assuming that the row and column variables are independent. This means, for example, that the probability of a married person being absent more than 5 days during the year is the same as the probability of any employee being absent more than 5 days. An easy way to compute the expected cell frequencies, e_{ij}, is given by Equation 12-3.

TABLE 12-5

Contingency Table for Benton Industries

Marital Status	ABSENTEE RATE			
	Zero	1–5	Over 5	Row Totals
Single	84	82	34	200
Married	50	64	36	150
Divorced	50	34	16	100
Widowed	16	20	14	50
Column Total	200	200	100	500

$$\textbf{Expected Cell Frequencies}$$
$$e_{ij} = \frac{(i\text{th Row total}) \, (j\text{th Column total})}{\text{Total sample size}}$$

12-3

For example, the expected cell frequency for row 1, column 1 is

$$e_{11} = \frac{(200)(200)}{500} = 80$$

and the expected cell frequency for row 2, column 3 is

$$e_{23} = \frac{(100)(150)}{500} = 30$$

Figures 12-8a and 12-8b show the completed contingency table with the actual and expected cell frequencies. The calculated chi-square test value is computed as follows:

$$\chi^2 = \sum_{i=1}^{r} \sum_{j=1}^{c} \frac{(o_{ij} - e_{ij})^2}{e_{ij}}$$
$$= \frac{(84-80)^2}{80} + \frac{(82-80)^2}{80} + \dots + \frac{(20-20)^2}{20} + \frac{(14-10)^2}{10}$$
$$= 10.88$$

The degrees of freedom are $(r-1)(c-1) = (4-1)(3-1) = 6$. You can use the chi-square table in Appendix G to get the chi-square critical value for $\alpha = 0.05$ and 6 degrees of freedom, or you can use Minitab's **Probability Distributions** command or Excel's **CHIINV** function (CHIINV(0.05,6) = 12.5916). Because the calculated chi-square value (10.88) shown in Figure 12-8a is less than 12.5916, we cannot reject the null hypothesis. Based on these sample data, there is *insufficient evidence* to conclude that absenteeism and marital status are not independent.

CHI-SQUARE TEST LIMITATIONS

The chi-square distribution is only an approximation for the true distribution for contingency analysis. We use the chi-square approximation because the true distribution is impractical to compute in most instances. However, the approximation (and, therefore, the conclusion reached) is quite good when all expected cell frequencies are at least 5.0. When expected cell frequencies drop below 5.0, the calculated chi-square value tends to be inflated and may inflate the true probability of Type I error beyond the stated significance level. As a rule, if the null hypothesis is not rejected, you do not need to worry when the expected cell frequencies drop below 5.0.

FIGURE 12-8A

Excel Output—Benton Industries Contingency Analysis Test

Excel Instructions:
1. Open file: Benton.xls
2. Compute expected cell frequencies using Excel formula.
3. Compute chi-square statistic using Excel formula.

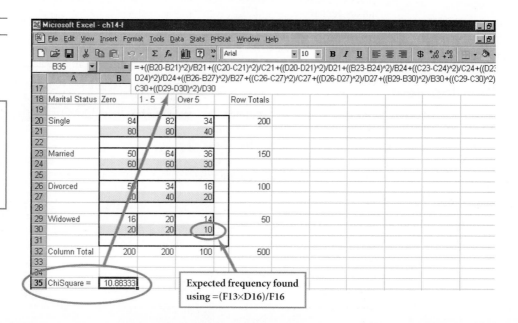

FIGURE 12-8B

**Minitab Output—Benton
Industries Contingency
Analysis Test**

Minitab Instructions:
1. Open file: Benton.MTW.
2. Choose **Stat > Tables >
   Chi-Square Test**.
3. In **Columns containing
   the table**, enter data
   columns.
4. Click **OK**.

```
MINITAB - BENTON.MPJ - [Session]

File  Edit  Data  Calc  Stat  Graph  Editor  Tools  Window  Help

Expected counts are printed below observed counts
Chi-Square contributions are printed below expected counts

            Zero    1-5   Over 5   Total
        1     84      82      34      200
            80.00   80.00   40.00
            0.200   0.050   0.900

        2     50      64      36      150
            60.00   60.00   30.00
            1.667   0.267   1.200

        3     50      34      16      100
            40.00   40.00   20.00
            2.500   0.900   0.800

        4     16      20      14       50
            20.00   20.00   10.00
            0.800   0.000   1.600

Total      200     200     100      500

Chi-Sq = 10.883,  DF = 6,  P-Value = 0.092
```

There are two alternatives that can be used to overcome the small expected-cell-frequency problem. The first is to increase the sample size. This may increase the marginal frequencies in each row and column enough to increase the expected cell frequencies. The second option is to combine the categories of the row and/or column variables. If you do decide to group categories together, there should be some logic behind the resulting categories. You don't want to lose the meaning of the results through poor groupings. You will need to examine each situation individually to determine whether the option of grouping classes to increase expected cell frequencies makes sense.

12-2: EXERCISES

Skill Development

12.13 A survey has been conducted at a local company in which various questions about the workplace environment were asked. Two of the questions are listed as follows:

1. Do you mind if people smoke in the office area?
   _____Yes _____No
2. Do you smoke? _____Yes _____No

Shown is a random sample of 30 responses that came back on these two variables.

   Construct a contingency table and perform the appropriate test to determine whether the responses to questions 1 and 2 are independent. Test using a significance level equal to 0.05.

Respondent (R)	Question 1 (Q1)	Question 2 (Q2)	R	Q1	Q2	R	Q1	Q2
1	Yes	No	11	No	No	21	No	Yes
2	Yes	Yes	12	No	No	22	Yes	Yes
3	No	Yes	13	No	Yes	23	Yes	No
4	No	Yes	14	Yes	No	24	Yes	No
5	No	No	15	Yes	Yes	25	No	Yes
6	Yes	No	16	Yes	Yes	26	Yes	Yes
7	Yes	No	17	No	Yes	27	Yes	No
8	Yes	Yes	18	No	No	28	No	No
9	No	No	19	No	Yes	29	Yes	No
10	Yes	No	20	Yes	No	30	Yes	No

12.14 Referring to Exercise 12.13, suppose 200 people in the company respond to the survey and the following contingency table is constructed from the responses.

Do You Care About Smoking in the Office?	Do You Smoke? Yes	No
Yes	11	139
No	29	21

Based on these data, is attitude about smoking in the office independent of whether an individual smokes? Use the chi-square test and test at an $\alpha = 0.10$ level. Discuss the results.

12.15 Jack O'Connell, chief of officials for the National Basketball Association, reviews films of all games to evaluate calls made by the referees. Jack rates each call "good" or "bad." For games played during a one-week period, Jack found the following distribution of calls for two officials:

Call	Official A	Official B
Good	463	518
Bad	51	38

a. Do these data indicate that the proportion of bad calls is the same for each official?
b. Test the data using a chi-square statistic with an $\alpha = 0.05$.
c. Compare the test in part b with the z-test for the difference between two population proportions. Determine the relationship between the two test statistics.

12.16 Develop a data-collection form on which you can collect measurements for two variables from students in one of your other classes (not this statistics course). The two variables are GPA and number of hours per week spent working at a paying job. Obtain a sample size of at least 25 students, and assume that these responses represent a random sample of all students at your college or university. Using the sample data that you have collected, apply contingency analysis to determine whether GPA is independent of number of hours worked. Break GPA into four categories and hours worked into five categories. Test at an $\alpha = 0.05$ level.

12.17 A contingency analysis table has been constructed from data obtained in a phone survey of customers in a market area in which respondents were asked to indicate whether they owned a domestic or foreign car and whether they were a member of a union. The following contingency table is provided.

Car	Union Yes	No
Domestic	155	470
Foreign	40	325

a. Use the chi-square approach to test whether type of car owned (domestic or foreign) is independent of union membership. Test using an $\alpha = 0.05$ level.
b. Calculate the p-value for this hypothesis test.

12.18 In a recent study of college graduates, it was hypothesized that income was independent of number of different employers a person had worked for since graduation. The data collected were as follows:

Income Level	1	2	3	4	5 or more
Under $20,000	3	4	3	2	3
$20,000–$30,000	5	3	7	3	2
$30,000–$40,000	2	5	3	6	1
$40,000–$50,000	1	7	9	3	4
Over $50,000	1	3	11	7	4

Assuming that these data reflect observed frequencies, what can be concluded about the hypothesis? Test at an $\alpha = 0.05$ level.

Business Applications

12.19 A study of automobile drivers was conducted to determine whether the number of traffic citations issued during a three-year period was independent of the sex of the driver. The following data were collected.

Citations Issued	Sex of Driver Male	Female
0	240	160
1	80	40
2	32	18
3	11	9
Over 3	5	4

a. Using an $\alpha = 0.05$ level, determine whether the two variables are independent.
b. A friend of yours claims to know a person who was included in the study. He says his friend had more than one citation during the study period. Calculate the probability that your friend's acquaintance is a female.

12.20 A bank in Midvale, Wisconsin, recently did a study of its customers to determine whether the number of transactions in a checking account was independent of the marital status of the customer. The following data were obtained.

Marital Status	0–10	11–20	21–30	31–40	Over 40
Single	13	23	19	20	11
Married	6	15	33	45	27
Divorced	4	19	22	20	15
Other	2	11	8	5	2

a. Based on these data, what should the bank conclude? Test at an $\alpha = 0.05$ level.
b. (1) Are there any cells that have expected values smaller than 5? (2) Suggest an appropriate way to combine cells in a meaningful way so that the expected cell frequencies are at least 5. (3) Repeat part a using the reconstructed contingency table.

c. Given the decision reached in part a, was it necessary to implement the procedure indicated in part b? When is it unnecessary to combine cells even though some of them have expected values smaller than 5?

12.21 In a recent labor negotiation, union officials collected data from a sample of union members regarding how long they had been with the company and how long they would be willing to stay out on strike if a strike were called. The following data were collected.

Time with Company	Strike-Length Toleration		
	Under 1 Week	1–4 Weeks	Over 4 Weeks
Under 1 year	23	6	3
1–2 years	19	15	8
2–5 years	20	23	19
5–10 years	4	21	29
Over 10 years	2	5	18

a. Based on these data, can the union conclude that strike-length toleration is independent of time with the company? Test at the $\alpha = 0.05$ level.

b. Consider two groups: those employed with the company at most 5 years, and those employed with the company more than 10 years. Do the data suggest that the proportion of employees who would be willing to stay out on strike for at least a week is larger for the first group? Conduct an appropriate hypothesis test to determine this.

12.22 The table here classifies a stock's price change as up, down, or no change for both today's and yesterday's prices. Price changes were examined for 100 days. A financial theory states that stock prices follow what is called a "random walk." This means, in part, that the price change today for a stock must be independent of yesterday's price change. Test the hypothesis that daily stock-price changes for this stock are independent. Let $\alpha = 0.05$.

Price Change Today	Price Change Previous Day		
	Up	No Change	Down
Up	14	16	12
No Change	6	8	6
Down	16	14	8

12.23 An AceCo Precision Products metal-fabrication shop operates three shifts. The accompanying data give the distribution of accidents among the three shifts by type of accident.

Shift	Accident Type	
	Behavior-Based	Equipment-Related
Day	270	80
Swing	190	25
Graveyard	96	24

Test the hypothesis that shift and accident type are unrelated. Let $\alpha = 0.01$.

12.24 A random sample of 980 heads of households was taken from the customer list for State Bank and Trust. Those sampled were asked to classify their own attitudes and their parents' attitudes toward borrowing money, as follows:

A: Borrow only for real estate and car purchases.
B: Borrow for short-term purchases such as appliances and furniture.
C: Never borrow money.

The following table indicates the responses from those in the study.

		Respondent		
		A	B	C
Parent	A	240	80	20
	B	180	120	40
	C	180	80	40

a. Test the hypothesis that the respondents' borrowing habits are independent from what they believe their parents' attitudes to be. Let $\alpha = 0.01$.

b. Calculate a 99% confidence interval for the difference between the proportion of respondents who never borrow money and whose parents never borrowed money and the proportion of respondents who never borrow money and whose parents borrowed money for short-term purchases. (Hint: See the discussion of the difference between two population proportions in Chapter 9). Are the results of this confidence interval compatible with the conclusion you reached in part a?

12.25 A major appliance manufacturer provides four washing machine models: standard, deluxe, superior, and XLT. The marketing manager has recently conducted a study on the purchasers of the washing machines. The study recorded the model of appliance purchased and the credit account balance of each customer at the time of purchase. The sample data are in the table here. Based on these data, is there evidence of a relationship between the account balance and the model of washer purchased? Use a significance level of 0.02. Conduct the test using a p-value approach.

Credit Balance	Washer Model Purchased			
	Standard	Deluxe	Superior	XLT
Under $200	10	16	40	5
$200–$800	8	12	24	15
Over $800	16	12	16	30

Advanced Applications

12.26 ECCO (Electronic Controls Company) makes back-up alarms that are used on such equipment as forklifts and delivery trucks. The quality manager recently performed a study involving a random sample of 100 warranty claims. One of the questions the manager wanted to answer was whether there is a relationship between the type of warranty complaint and the plant at which an alarm was made. The data are in the CD-ROM file *ECCO*.

a. Calculate the expected values for the cells in this analysis. Suggest a way in which cells can be combined to assure that the expected value of each cell is at least 5 so that as many level combinations of the two variables as possible are retained.

b. Using a significance level of 0.01, conduct a relevant hypothesis test and provide an answer to the manager's question.

12.27 Referring to Exercise 12.26, can the quality control manager conclude that the type of warranty problem is independent of the shift on which an alarm was manufactured? Test using a significance level of 0.05. Discuss your results.

Summary and Conclusions

This chapter has introduced two very useful statistical tools: goodness-of-fit tests and contingency analysis. Goodness-of-fit testing is used when a decision maker wishes to determine whether sample data come from a population having specific characteristics. The goodness-of-fit procedure that was introduced in this chapter is the chi-square goodness-of-fit test. This test relies on the idea that if the distribution of the sample data is substantially different from the hypothesized population distribution, then the population distribution from which these sample data came must not be what was hypothesized. The chi-square goodness-of-fit test is most effective when the sample data have been organized into a grouped frequency distribution.

Contingency analysis is a frequently used statistical tool that allows the decision maker to test whether responses to two variables are independent. Market researchers, for example, use contingency analysis on survey research data when at least one of the variables of interest is categorical. For instance, marketers may be interested in determining whether attitude about the quality of their company's product is independent of the gender of a customer. By using contingency analysis and the chi-square contingency test,

they can make this determination based on a sample of customers. If either or both of the variables are continuous in nature, they must be recoded before contingency analysis can be performed. Most software can facilitate this recoding process.

EQUATIONS

Chi-Square Goodness-of-Fit Test Statistic

$$\chi^2 = \sum_{i=1}^{k} \frac{(o_i - e_i)^2}{e_i} \qquad \textbf{12-1}$$

Chi-Square Contingency Test Statistic

$$\chi^2 = \sum_{i=1}^{r} \sum_{j=1}^{c} \frac{(o_{ij} - e_{ij})^2}{e_{ij}} \quad \text{with } df = (r-1)(c-1) \textbf{ 12-2}$$

Expected Cell Frequencies

$$e_{ij} = \frac{(i\text{th Row total})\,(j\text{th Column total})}{\text{Total sample size}} \qquad \textbf{12-3}$$

Key Term

CHAPTER EXERCISES

Conceptual Questions

12.28 Go to the library and locate a journal article using either contingency analysis or a goodness-of-fit test. Discuss the article, paying particular attention to the reasoning behind using the particular statistical test.

12.29 Go to the library and find a marketing research book (or borrow one from a friend). Does it discuss either of the tests considered in this chapter? If yes, outline the discussion. If no, determine where in the text such a discussion would be appropriate.

12.30 In some of the problems in this chapter, we have asked you to provide analysis for a 2 × 2 contingency table. In addition, you were asked to conduct a hypothesis test concerning two populations' proportions on the same data. Discuss the relative merits of these two procedures for analyzing 2 × 2 contingency tables.

Business Applications

12.31 Linda Stevens, the manager of Arlington Super Discount, always keeps four checkout stands open. However, she frequently notices lines for registers 1 and 2. She is not sure whether the layout of the store channels customers into these registers or whether the checkout clerks in these lines are simply slower than the other two.

Linda kept a record of which stands 2,000 shoppers chose for checkout. The shoppers checked out of the four stands according to the following pattern:

Stand 1	Stand 2	Stand 3	Stand 4
677	550	402	371

a. Based on these data, can Linda conclude that an equal number of shoppers are likely to use each of the stands? (Use an $\alpha = 0.05$.)

b. A friend suggested that you could just as well conduct four hypothesis tests that the proportion of customers visiting each stand is equal to one-fourth. Discuss the merits of this suggestion.

12.32 A manufacturer of packaged food has decided to market a new cake mix. This venture is rather risky because the new mix will compete with three established brands. The production manager argues that quality will sell the new mix. The marketing manager states that the average consumer cannot tell the difference between brands and that the critical factor in selling the mix will be the advertising campaign.

To test the marketing manager's contention, the four types of cakes were baked under equal conditions. Shoppers were randomly stopped in several supermarkets and were asked to sample each cake and indicate which of the four tasted the best. The cake that was tasted first was randomly determined. The following data show how many shoppers rated each brand the tastiest:

Brand			
A	B	C	New
37	23	27	41

Which contention do these data support? Use a Type I error rate of 0.01.

12.33 Cooper Manufacturing, Inc., of Dallas, Texas, has a contract with the U.S. Air Force to produce a part for a new fighter plane being manufactured. The part is a bolt that has specifications requiring that the length be normally distributed, with a mean of 3.05 inches and a standard deviation of 0.015 inch. As part of the company's quality control efforts, each day Cooper's engineers select a random sample of 100 bolts produced that day and carefully measure the bolts to determine whether the production is within specifications. The following data were collected yesterday.

Length (Inches)	Frequency
Under 3.030	5
3.030 and under 3.035	16
3.035 and under 3.040	7
3.040 and under 3.050	20
3.050 and under 3.060	36
3.060 and under 3.065	8
Over 3.065	8

Based on these sample data, what should Cooper's engineers conclude about the production output if they test using an $\alpha = 0.01$? Discuss.

12.34 The Cooper Company discussed in Exercise 12.33 has a second contract with a private firm for which it makes fuses for an electronic instrument. The quality control department at Cooper periodically selects a random sample of 5 fuses and tests each fuse to determine whether it is defective. Based on these findings, the production process is either shut down (if too many defectives are observed) or allowed to run. The quality control department believes that the sampling process follows a binomial distribution, and it has been using the binomial distribution to compute the probabilities associated with the sampling outcomes.

The contract allows for at most 5% defectives. The head of quality control recently compiled a list of the sampling results for the past 300 days, in which 5 fuses were tested each day, with the following frequency distribution for the number of defectives observed. She is concerned that the binomial distribution with a sample size of 5 and a probability of defectives of 0.05 may not be appropriate.

Number of Defectives	Frequency
0	209
1	33
2	43
3	10
4	5
5	0

a. Calculate the expected values for the cells in this analysis. Suggest a way in which cells can be combined to assure that the expected value of each cell is at least 5 so that as many level combinations of the two variables as possible are retained.
b. Using a significance level of 0.10, what should the quality control manager conclude based on these sample data? Discuss.

12.35 Ralph Rogers has developed a highly successful practice as an acupuncture specialist. Ralph's success is built on his money-back guarantee. If his treatment wears off, he will treat you again. His accountant, in trying to set up an allowance for the future-visits account, hypothesizes that whether a patient will demand a retreatment is related to the price of the original treatment. The following data show the relationship between price and return treatment:

		Price		
		High	Medium	Low
	In less than 2 years	46	53	56
Retreatment	In 2–5 years	83	75	92
	None in 5 years	127	119	149

a. What should the accountant conclude regarding the hypothesis? (Use $\alpha = 0.05$.)
b. What factors that the accountant apparently has not considered might be important to the analysis?

12.36 A regional cancer treatment center has had success treating localized cancers with a linear accelerator. Although admissions for further treatment nationally average 1.1 per patient per year, the center's director thinks that readmissions with the new treatment are Poisson distributed, with a mean of 1.2 per patient per year. He has collected the following data on a random sample of 300 patients:

Readmissions Last Year	Patients
0	139
1	87
2	48
3	14
4	8
5	1
6	1
7	0
8	2
	300

a. Adjust the data so you can test the director's claim using a test statistic whose sampling distribution can be approximated by a chi-square distribution.

b. Assume the Type I error rate is to be controlled at 0.05. Do you agree with the director's claim? Why? Conduct a statistical procedure to support your opinion.

12.37 The J. Scholten CPA firm performed a study of last year's income-tax business. In one part of the study, the accountants collected data on their clients' gross taxable incomes and the associated tax payments. These data are shown in the following table, where, for example, there are 50 clients whose gross incomes were below $10,000 and who paid $3,000 or less in taxes.

Gross Income	Taxes			
	$0-$3,000	$3,001–$5,000	$5,001–10,000	Over $10,000
$0–$10,000	50	0	0	0
$10,001–$20,000	42	30	0	0
$20,001–$40,000	40	65	33	28
Over $40,000	28	52	47	39

a. Based on these data, can Scholten conclude that its clients' gross incomes are independent of the income taxes paid? Test at $\alpha = 0.05$.

b. If the taxes paid and income earned are not independent, then based on an examination of the data, what conclusions do you reach? Discuss.

12.38 Scholten also studied the time its accountants took to complete each client's tax return and related this time to the taxes paid by the client. Scholten managers were interested in determining whether a relationship exists between these two variables or whether they could consider the two variables independent. The following data are available.

No. Work Hours	Taxes			
	$0–$3,000	$3,001–$5,000	$5,001–$10,000	Over $10,000
0–2	52	55	30	27
0–4	47	55	30	31
Over 4	35	37	55	35

Based on these data, what should the Scholten firm conclude? Use $\alpha = 0.10$.

Advanced Applications

12.39 The State Transportation Department recently conducted a study of motorists in Idaho. Two main factors of interest were whether a vehicle was insured with liability insurance and whether the driver was wearing a seatbelt. A random sample of 100 cars was stopped at various locations throughout the state. The data are in the CD-ROM file *Liabins*.

a. Based on the sample data, can the investigators conclude that the distribution of the time drivers have lived in Idaho is normally distributed? Test using an appropriate goodness-of-fit test at an $\alpha = 0.05$ level.

b. Construct a 95% confidence interval for the average time drivers have lived in Idaho.

12.40 Assume that you are preparing a speech for a trade conference and intend to use information from the *Cities* file. At one point in your speech, you would like to provide an estimate of mean population growth rates between 1990 and 1995. However, based on your knowledge of estimation, you know that because the population standard deviation is unknown, you must be able to assume that the distribution of growth rates is normally distributed.

a. Using an $\alpha = 0.10$ level, would you be justified in making the normal distribution assumption?

b. Based on your answer to part a, if appropriate, develop a 95% confidence interval estimate for the mean population growth rate between 1990 and 1995. Interpret your result.

12.41 Refer to the speech preparation discussed in Exercise 12.40. Using contingency analysis, can you consider the cities' labor market stress index to be statistically independent of 1998 unemployment rate?

a. Break each variable into appropriate categories. Produce two equally spaced intervals for the labor-market stress index by dividing the maximum and minimum values and give three equally spaced intervals for the unemployment rate.

b. Conduct the hypothesis test to determine if you can consider the cities' labor-market stress index to be statistically independent. Use an $\alpha = 0.02$.

12.42 Refer to the data in the *Cities* file discussed in Exercise 12.40.

a. Break the variables, labor-market stress index and 1998 unemployment rate, into a different set of categories: three equal-sized intervals for the stress index and four for the unemployment rate. Conduct the test again.

b. Did the results change this time? Discuss why it is possible for the contingency analysis results to differ depending on how the categories are formed for a continuous random variable.

12.43 Data were recently collected on several variables for the 100 fastest-growing companies in the United States. The data are in the CD-ROM file *Fast100*. A recent claim made in a major business publication stated that the mean P/E ratio exceeds 25.0 for all growth companies. Assuming that these data represent a random sample of companies:

a. Test to determine whether the distribution of P/E ratios is normally distributed. Use $\alpha = 0.05$ level to test the hypothesis.

b. If the result in part a warrants doing so, conduct the appropriate hypothesis test for the claim made by the business publication. Use $\alpha = 0.05$ to conduct the test.

12.44 Referring to Exercise 12.43, can you conclude that stock price is independent of the exchange on which a stock is traded? Break the stock price into four categories determined by the quartiles, and test at an $\alpha = 0.10$ level.

12.45 Referring to Exercise 12.44, is the annual 3- to 5-year growth rate for companies in this study described by a uniform distribution? Test using an appropriate goodness-of-fit method using $\alpha = 0.05$ level.

CASE 12-A:

American Oil Company

Chad Williams sat back in his airline seat to enjoy the hour flight between Los Angeles and Oakland, California. The hour would give him time to reflect on his upcoming trip to Australia and the work he had been doing the past week in Los Angeles.

Chad is one man on a six-man crew employed by the American Oil Company to literally walk the earth searching for oil. His college degrees in geology and petroleum engineering landed him the job with American, but he never dreamed he would be doing the exciting work he now does. Chad and his crew spend several months in special locations around the world using highly sensitive electronic equipment for oil exploration.

The upcoming trip to Australia is one that Chad has been looking forward to since it was announced that his crew would be going there to search the Outback for oil. In preparation for the trip, the crew has been in Los Angeles at American's engineering research facility working on some new equipment that will be used in Australia.

Chad's thoughts centered on the problem he was having with a particular component part on the new equipment. The specifications called for 200 of the components, with each having a diameter of between 0.15 and 0.18 inch. The only available supplier of the component manufactures the components in New Jersey to specifications calling for normally distributed output, with a mean of 0.16 inch and a standard deviation of 0.02 inch.

Chad faces two problems. First, he is unsure that the supplier actually does produce parts with means of 0.16 inch and standard deviations of 0.02 inch according to a normal distribution. Second, if the parts are made to specifications, he needs to determine how many components to purchase if enough acceptable components are to be received to make two oil exploration devices.

The supplier has sent Chad the following data for 330 randomly selected components. Chad believes that the supplier is honest and that he can rely on the data.

DIAMETER (INCH)	FREQUENCY
Under 0.14	5
0.14 and under 0.15	70
0.15 and under 0.16	90
0.16 and under 0.17	105
0.17 and under 0.18	50
Over 0.18	10
Total	330

Chad needs to have a report ready for Monday indicating whether he believes the supplier delivers at its stated specifications and, if so, how many of the components American should order to have enough acceptable components to outfit two oil exploration devices.

CASE 12-B:

Bentford Electronics, Part 1

On Saturday morning, Jennifer Bentford received a call at her home from the production supervisor at Bentford Electronics Plant 1. The supervisor indicated that she and the supervisors from Plants 2, 3, and 4 had agreed that something must be done to improve company morale and, thereby, increase the production output of their plants. Jennifer Bentford, president of Bentford Electronics, agreed to set up a Monday morning meeting with the supervisors to see if they could arrive at a plan for accomplishing these objectives.

By Monday each supervisor had compiled a list of several ideas, including a four-day work week and interplant competitions of various kinds. A second meeting was set for Wednesday to discuss the issue further.

Following the Wednesday afternoon meeting, Jennifer Bentford and her plant supervisors agreed to implement a weekly contest called the NBE Game of the Week. The plant producing the most each week would be considered the NBE Game of the Week winner and would receive 10 points. The second-place plant would receive 7 points, and the third- and fourth-place plants would receive 3 points and 1 point, respectively. The contest would last 26 weeks. At the end of that period, a $200,000 bonus would be divided among the employees in the four plants proportional to the total points accumulated by each plant.

The announcement of the contest created a lot of excitement and enthusiasm at the four plants. No one complained about the rules because the four plants were designed and staffed to produce equally.

At the close of the contest, Jennifer Bentford called the supervisors into a meeting, at which time she asked for data to determine whether the contest had significantly improved productivity. She indicated that she had to know this before she could authorize a second contest. The supervisors, expecting this response, had put together the following data:

UNITS PRODUCED (4 PLANTS COMBINED)	BEFORE-CONTEST FREQUENCY	DURING-CONTEST FREQUENCY
0–2,500	11	0
2,501–8,000	23	20
8,001–15,000	56	83
15,001–20,000	15	52
	105 days	155 days

Jennifer examined the data and indicated that it looked like the contest was a success, but she wanted to base her decision to continue the contest on more than just an observation of the data. "Surely there must be some way to statistically test the worthiness of this contest," Jennifer stated. "I have to see the results before I will authorize the second contest."

General References

1. Berenson, Mark L., and David M. Levine, *Basic Business Statistics: Concepts and Applications*, 7th ed. (Upper Saddle River, NJ: Prentice Hall, 1999).

2. Conover, W. J., *Practical Nonparametric Statistics*, 3rd ed. (New York: Wiley, 1999).

3. Marasculio, Leonard, and M. McSweeney, *Nonparametric and Distribution Free Methods for the Social Sciences* (Monterey, CA: Brooks/Cole, 1977).

4. *Microsoft Excel 2000* (Redmond, WA: Microsoft Corp. 1999).

6. *Minitab for Windows Version 13* (State College, PA: Minitab, Inc., 2000).

CHAPTER 13

Introduction to Linear Regression and Correlation Analysis

CHAPTER OUTCOMES

After studying the material in Chapter 13, you should be able to:

- Calculate and interpret the simple correlation between two variables.
- Determine whether the correlation is significant.
- Calculate the simple linear regression equation for a set of data and know the basic assumptions behind regression analysis.
- Determine whether a regression model is significant.
- Calculate and interpret confidence intervals for the regression coefficients.
- Recognize regression analysis applications for purposes of prediction and description.
- Recognize some potential problems if regression analysis is used incorrectly.
- Recognize several nonlinear relationships between two variables and be able to introduce the appropriate transformation to apply linear regression analysis.

WHY YOU NEED TO KNOW

Although some business situations involve only one variable, others require decision makers to consider the relationship between two or more variables. For example, an investment broker might be interested in the relationship between stock prices and the dividends issued by a publicly traded company. A marketing manager would be interested in examining the relationship between product sales and the amount of money spent on advertising. Finally, consider a real estate appraiser who is interested in determining the fair market value of a home or business. He would begin by collecting data on a sample of "comparable properties" that have sold recently. In addition to the selling price, he would collect data on other factors, such as the size and age of the property. He might then analyze the relationship between the price and the other variables and use this relationship to determine an appraised price for the property in question.

Simple linear regression and correlation analysis, which are introduced in this chapter, are statistical techniques the broker, marketing director, and appraiser will need in their analysis. These techniques are important to decision makers who need to determine the relationship between two variables. In Chapter 14, we will extend the discussion to include three or more variables. Regression analysis and correlation analysis are two of the most often applied statistical tools for business decision making.

13-1 SCATTER PLOTS AND CORRELATION

In those situations in which you are interested in analyzing the relationship between two variables, the **scatter plot**, or *scatter diagram*, introduced in Chapter 2 is very useful.

Scatter Plot

A two-dimensional plot showing the values for the joint occurrence of two variables. The scatter plot may be used to graphically represent the relationship between two variables. It is also known as a scatter diagram.

Figure 13-1 shows scatter plots that depict several potential relationships between values of a dependent variable, *y*, and an independent variable, *x*. A **dependent** (or *response*) **variable** is the variable whose variation we wish to explain. An **independent** (or *explanatory*) **variable** is a vari-

---

FIGURE 13-1 **Two-Variable Relationships**

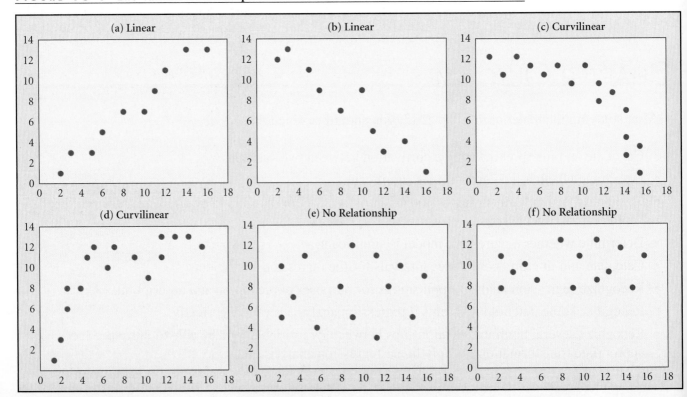

able used to explain variation in the dependent variable. The independent variable may or may not have random variation, but it is not of primary interest. In Figure 13-1, (a) and (b) are examples of strong *linear* relationships between x and y. This means that for each unit change in the independent variable, x, the corresponding change in the dependent variable, y, will tend to be a fairly consistent amount. Note that this systematic change in y can be positive (y increases as x increases) or negative (y decreases as x increases). The degree of linearity exhibited depends on the degree of consistency in the change of the y variable when the independent variable, x, changes.

Figures 13-1 (c) and (d) illustrate situations in which the relationship between the x and y variable are nonlinear. There are many possible nonlinear relationships that can occur. The scatter plot is very useful for visually identifying the nature of the relationship.

Figures 13-1 (e) and (f) show examples in which there is no identifiable relationship between the two variables. This means that as x increases, y sometimes increases and sometimes decreases but with no particular pattern.

CORRELATION VERSUS REGRESSION

In analyzing the relationship between two variables, there are two basic models that we can use, depending on the conditions under which the data are collected. These models are the subjects of this chapter. The first model is referred to as the *regression model*, in which the relationship between x and y assumes that the x variable takes on known values specifically selected from all the possible values for x. The y variable is a random variable observed at the different levels of x.

The second model is referred to as the *correlation model* and is used in applications in which both the x and the y variables are considered to be random variables. These two models, regression versus correlation, arise in practice by the way in which the data are obtained. Consider models that might apply to the relationship between the amount of daily sunscreen sold, y, as a function of the day's high temperature, x. We could select a random sample of 36 days and record the amount of sunscreen sold and the day's maximum temperature. In this case, the measurements obtained for both variables are observations from a joint distribution of x and y. An analysis of these data would be done using the correlation model approach.

Suppose instead that we decide to collect data for days with maximum temperatures of 75, 80, 85, 90, 95, and 100. We would measure the amount of daily sunscreen sold (y) for several randomly chosen days in which the maximum temperature is at each of these preselected temperatures. That is, we might pick six days at random from a population of days that have a maximum temperature of 75 degrees and observe the amount of sunscreen sold, and so on. Now each observation of y is from the distribution of y for a fixed x value. The analysis of these data would be done using the regression model approach.

We stress the two types of sampling because there are important differences in what can be estimated using these two methods. As we will illustrate later in this chapter, when the data have been collected at specific levels of the x variable, as was suggested in the second situation, our estimates for the y variable will be conditional on the value of x we are using.[1]

THE CORRELATION COEFFICIENT

In addition to analyzing the relationship between two variables graphically, we can also measure the strength of the linear relationship between two variables using a measure called the **correlation coefficient**. We introduced this concept in Chapter 4.

Correlation Coefficient

A quantitative measure of the strength of the linear relationship between two variables. The correlation ranges from -1.0 to $+1.0$. A correlation of ± 1.0 indicates a perfect linear relationship, whereas a correlation of 0 indicates no linear relationship.

---

[1]See Neter et al., *Applied Linear Statistical Models*, 4th ed., p. 85, and Draper, N. R., and Smith, H., *Applied Regression Analysis*, 3rd ed., p. 89, for more discussion on this subject.

The correlation coefficient for two variables can be estimated from sample data using Equation 13-1 or the algebraic equivalent, Equation 13-2.[2]

Sample Correlation Coefficient

$$r = \frac{\sum(x - \bar{x})(y - \bar{y})}{\sqrt{[\sum(x - \bar{x})^2][\sum(y - \bar{y})^2]}}$$

13-1

or the algebraic equivalent:

$$r = \frac{n\sum xy - \sum x \sum y}{\sqrt{[n(\sum x^2) - (\sum x)^2][n(\sum y^2) - (\sum y)^2]}}$$

13-2

where:

r = Sample correlation coefficient
n = Sample size
x = Value of the independent variable
y = Value of the dependent variable

The sample correlation coefficient computed using Equations 13-1 and 13-2 is called the *Pearson Product Moment Correlation*. The sample correlation coefficient, r, can range from a perfect positive correlation, +1.0, to a perfect negative correlation, −1.0. A perfect correlation is one in which a given change in the value of the x variable is accompanied by a specific uniform amount of change in the y variable. Graphically, the x,y points will plot on a straight line. If two variables have no linear relationship, the correlation between them is 0 and there is no linear relationship between the change in x and y. Consequently, the more the correlation differs from 0.0, the stronger the linear relationship between the two variables. The sign of the correlation coefficient indicates the direction of the relationship, but it does not aid in determining the strength.

Figure 13-2 illustrates some examples of correlation between two variables. Note for the correlation coefficient to equal plus or minus 1.0, all the (x,y) points form a perfectly straight line. The

FIGURE 13-2 Correlation Between Two Variables

[2]Refer to Section 4-3 in Chapter 4 for a discussion of covariance between two variables and the explanation that the population correlation coefficient can be computed using Equation 4-18,

$$\rho = \frac{\sigma_{xy}}{\sigma_x \sigma_y}$$

more the points depart from a straight line, the weaker (closer to 0.0) the correlation is between the two variables.

Excel and Minitab Tutorial

Midwest Distribution Company—Midwest Distribution supplies soft drinks and snack foods to convenience stores in Michigan, Illinois, and Iowa. Although Midwest Distribution has been profitable, the director of marketing has been concerned about the rapid turnover in her sales force. In the course of exit interviews, she discovered a major concern with the compensation structure.

Midwest Distribution has a two-part wage structure: a base salary and a commission computed on monthly sales. Typically, about half of the total wages paid comes from the base salary, which increases with longevity with the company. This portion of the wage structure is not an issue. The concern expressed by departing employees is that new employees tend to be given parts of the sales territory previously covered by existing employees and are assigned prime customers as a recruiting inducement.

At issue, then, is the relationship between sales (on which commissions are paid) and number of years with the company. The data for a random sample of 12 sales representatives are in the file called *Midwest* on your CD-ROM. The first step is to develop a scatter plot of the data. Both Excel and Minitab have procedures for constructing a scatter plot (refer to Chapter 2) and computing the correlation coefficient.

The scatter plot for the Midwest data is shown in Figure 13-3. Based on this plot, total sales and years with the company appear to be linearly related. However, the strength of this relationship is uncertain. That is, how close do the points come to falling on a straight line? To answer this question, we need a quantitative measure of the strength of the linear relationship between the two variables. That measure is the correlation coefficient.

Equation 13-1 is used to determine the correlation between sales and years with the company. Table 13-1 shows the manual calculations necessary to determine the correlation coefficient that equals 0.8325. However, because the calculations are rather tedious and long, we almost always use computer software to perform the computation, as shown in Figure 13-4. The $r = 0.8325$ indicates that there is a fairly strong, positive correlation between these two variables for the sample data.

Significance Test for the Correlation

Although a correlation coefficient of 0.8325 seems quite high (relative to 0), you should remember that this value is based on a sample of 12 data points and is subject to sampling error. To illustrate

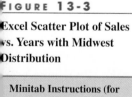

FIGURE 13-3

Excel Scatter Plot of Sales vs. Years with Midwest Distribution

Minitab Instructions (for similar results):
1. Open file: Midwest.MTW.
2. Choose **Graph > Scatterplot.**
3. Under **Scatterplot,** choose **Simple. OK.**
4. Under **Y variable,** enter y column.
5. In **X variable,** enter x column.
6. Click **OK.**

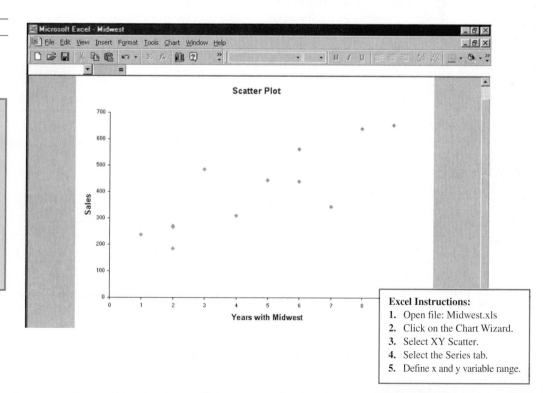

Excel Instructions:
1. Open file: Midwest.xls
2. Click on the Chart Wizard.
3. Select XY Scatter.
4. Select the Series tab.
5. Define x and y variable range.

TABLE 13-1

Correlation Coefficient Calculations for the Midwest Distribution Example

Sales	Years			
y	x	xy	y^2	x^2
487	3	1,461	237,169	9
445	5	2,225	198,025	25
272	2	544	73,984	4
641	8	5,128	410,881	64
187	2	374	34,969	4
440	6	2,640	193,600	36
346	7	2,422	119,716	49
238	1	238	56,644	1
312	4	1,248	97,344	16
269	2	538	72,361	4
655	9	5,895	429,025	81
563	6	3,378	316,969	36
$\Sigma = 4{,}855$	$\Sigma = 55$	$\Sigma = 26{,}091$	$\Sigma = 2{,}240{,}687$	$\Sigma = 329$

$$r = \frac{n \sum xy - \sum x \sum y}{\sqrt{[n(\sum x^2) - (\sum x)^2][n(\sum y^2) - (\sum y)^2]}}$$

$$r = \frac{12(26{,}091) - 55(4{,}855)}{\sqrt{[12(329) - (55)^2][12(2{,}240{,}687) - (4{,}855)^2]}}$$

$$= 0.8325$$

what can happen, consider the scatter plot for the hypothetical situation shown in Figure 13-5. The scatter plot for the population of values indicates there is no linear relationship between the two variables. The population correlation coefficient for these data is 0. We use the Greek symbol ρ (rho), to represent the population correlation coefficient. Now, suppose a random sample of values is selected from the population (see circled values in Figure 13-5.) These sample values appear to have a fairly strong linear relationship. In fact, the correlation coefficient, r, is 0.952 based on these sample data. In this case, the sample correlation coefficient is very high, yet the two variables for the population as a whole are not correlated. This could happen if the sample data exhibit extreme sampling error. Therefore, a formal hypothesis-testing procedure is needed to determine whether the linear relationship between sales and years with the company is significant.

The null and alternative hypotheses to be tested are

$$H_0: \rho = 0 \quad \text{(no correlation)}$$
$$H_A: \rho \neq 0 \quad \text{(correlation exists)}$$

We must test whether the sample data support or refute the null hypothesis. The test procedure utilizes the t test statistic in Equation 13-3.

FIGURE 13-4

Excel Correlation Output for Midwest Distribution

Excel Instructions:
1. Open file: Midwest.xls
2. Select **Tools**.
3. Click on **Data Analysis**.
4. Select **Correlation**.
5. Define Data Range.

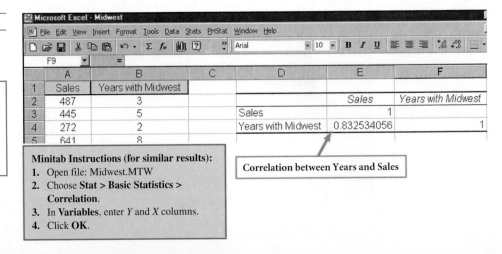

Minitab Instructions (for similar results):
1. Open file: Midwest.MTW
2. Choose **Stat > Basic Statistics > Correlation**.
3. In **Variables**, enter Y and X columns.
4. Click **OK**.

Correlation between Years and Sales

FIGURE 13-5

Scatter Plot—Hypothetical
Data

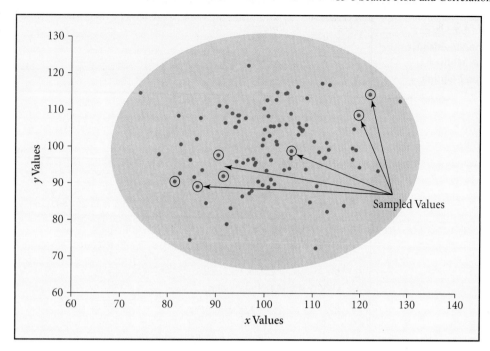

Sampled Values

Test Statistic for Correlation

$$t = \frac{r}{\sqrt{\dfrac{1 - r^2}{n - 2}}} \qquad df = n - 2$$

13-3

where:

t = Number of standard deviations r is from 0
r = Simple correlation coefficient
n = Sample size

The degrees of freedom for this test are $n - 2$, because we lose one degree of freedom for each of the two sample means that are used to estimate the population means for the two variables.

Figure 13-6 shows the hypothesis test for the Midwest Distribution example using an alpha level of 0.05. Recall that the sample correlation coefficient was $r = 0.8325$. Based on these sample data, we should conclude there is a significant, positive linear relationship in the population between years of experience and total sales for Midwest Distribution sales representatives. The implication is that the more years an employee has been with the company, the more sales that representative generates. This runs counter to the claims made by some of the departing employees. The manager will probably want to look further into the situation to see whether a problem might exist in certain regions.

The t test for determining whether the population correlation is significantly different from 0.0 requires the following assumptions.

SSUMPTIONS
1. The data are interval- or ratio-level.
2. The two variables (y and x) are distributed as a *bivariate normal* distribution.

Although the formal mathematical representation is beyond the scope of this text, *two variables are bivariate normal if their joint distribution is normally distributed*. Although the t test assumes a bivariate normal distribution, it is robust—that is, correct inferences can be reached even with slight departures from the normal-distribution assumption. (See Neter et al., *Applied Linear Statistical Models* for further discussion of bivariate normal distributions.)

FIGURE 13-6

Correlation Significance Test for the Midwest Distribution Example

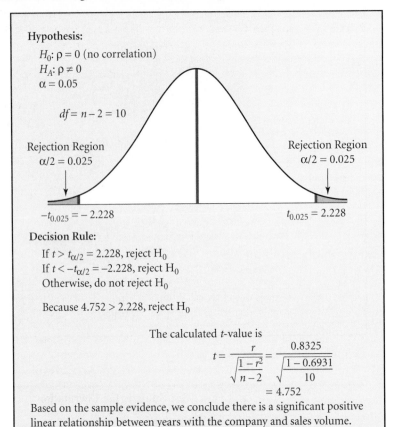

Hypothesis:

$H_0: \rho = 0$ (no correlation)
$H_A: \rho \neq 0$
$\alpha = 0.05$

$df = n - 2 = 10$

Rejection Region
$\alpha/2 = 0.025$

Rejection Region
$\alpha/2 = 0.025$

$-t_{0.025} = -2.228$ $t_{0.025} = 2.228$

Decision Rule:

If $t > t_{\alpha/2} = 2.228$, reject H_0
If $t < -t_{\alpha/2} = -2.228$, reject H_0
Otherwise, do not reject H_0

Because $4.752 > 2.228$, reject H_0

The calculated t-value is

$$t = \frac{r}{\sqrt{\dfrac{1-r^2}{n-2}}} = \frac{0.8325}{\sqrt{\dfrac{1-0.6931}{10}}}$$
$$= 4.752$$

Based on the sample evidence, we conclude there is a significant positive linear relationship between years with the company and sales volume.

*E*XAMPLE 13-1: CORRELATION ANALYSIS

Yellow Page Advertising   Recently a publisher of a regional telephone book surveyed a simple random sample of 10 of its commercial yellow-page advertising customers in an attempt to determine whether the size of their advertisements, in square inches (x), were positively correlated with the proportion of calls to the businesses that were generated by the ads (y). For a one-month period, each commercial customer asked each caller to their business if they had learned about the business through the yellow pages. To determine whether there is a statistically significant correlation between the two variables, the following steps can be employed.

Step 1:   **Specify the population value of interest.**
The publisher wishes to determine whether the size of an ad is positively correlated with the proportion of calls to the business that were generated by the ad. The parameter of interest is, therefore, the population correlation, ρ.

Step 2:   **Formulate the appropriate null and alternative hypotheses.**
Because the regional phone company is interested in establishing a positive relationship between ad size and proportion of calls generated from the ad, the test will be one-tailed, as follows:

$$H_0: \rho \leq 0$$
$$H_A: \rho > 0$$

Step 3:   **Specify the level of significance.**
A significance level of 0.05 is chosen.

Step 4:   **Construct the rejection region.**
For an alpha level equal to 0.05, the one-tailed, upper-tail, critical value for $n - 2 = 10 - 2 = 8$ degrees of freedom is $t = 1.8595$. The decision rule is

If $t > 1.8595$, reject the null hypothesis;
Otherwise, do not reject the null hypothesis.

Step 5: **Compute the correlation coefficient and the test statistic.**
Compute the sample correlation coefficient using Equation 13-1 or 13-2, or by using software such as Excel or Minitab.
The following sample data were obtained:

Square Inches	Proportion of Calls Generated by Ad
9	0.13
16	0.16
25	0.21
16	0.18
20	0.18
16	0.19
20	0.15
20	0.17
16	0.13
9	0.11

Using Equation 13-1, we get:

$$r = \frac{\sum(x - \bar{x})(y - \bar{y})}{\sqrt{[\sum(x - \bar{x})^2][\sum(y - \bar{y})^2]}} = 0.7796$$

Compute the t test statistic using Equation 13-3.

$$t = \frac{r}{\sqrt{\frac{1 - r^2}{n - 2}}} = \frac{0.7796}{\sqrt{\frac{1 - 0.7796^2}{10 - 2}}} = 3.52$$

Step 6: **Reach a decision.**
Because

$$t = 3.52 > 1.8595, \text{ reject the null hypothesis.}$$

Step 7: **Draw a conclusion.**
Because the null hypothesis is rejected, the sample data do support the contention that there is a positive linear relationship between ad size and the proportion of calls that were generated by the ad.

Cause-and-Effect Interpretations

Care must be used when interpreting the correlation results. For example, even though we found a significant linear relationship between years of experience and sales for the Midwest Distribution sales force, the correlation does not imply cause and effect. Although an increase in experience may, in fact, cause sales to change, simply because the two variables are correlated does not guarantee a cause-and-effect situation. Two seemingly unconnected variables will often be highly correlated. For example, over a period of time, teachers' salaries in North Dakota might be highly correlated with the price of grapes in Spain. Yet, we doubt that a change in grape prices will *cause* a corresponding change in salaries for teachers in North Dakota, or vice versa. When a correlation exists between two seemingly unrelated variables, the correlation is said to be a **spurious correlation**. You should take great care to avoid basing conclusions on spurious correlations.

The Midwest Distribution marketing director has a logical reason to believe that years of experience with the company and total sales are related. That is, sales theory and customer feedback hold that product knowledge is a major component in successfully marketing a product. However, a statistically significant correlation alone does not prove that this cause-and-effect relationship exists. When two seemingly unrelated variables are correlated, they may both be responding to changes in some third variable. For example, the observed correlation could be the effect of a company policy of giving better sales territories to more senior salespeople.

13-1: EXERCISES

Skill Development

13.1   Develop a scatter plot for the following data.

y	x
100	88
200	120
150	200
75	100
140	100
160	90
230	125

Based on the scatter plot, describe what, if any, relationship exists between these two variables.

13.2   Develop individual scatter plots for the variable y against variables x_1 and x_2.

y	x_1	x_2
25	4	7
29	3	9
40	1	13
20	6	6
24	5	8
18	7	5
30	3	11
25	3	5

Describe what, if any, relationship is present in each of the scatter plots.

13.3   If two variables have a negative linear relationship, what will the value of y tend to do when the corresponding value of x increases substantially? Show with an example.

13.4   If the scatter plot of two variables shows a weak positive linear relationship, what will be the general change in y associated with a downward change in x? Show with an example.

13.5   If a scatter plot shows that two variables have a curvilinear relationship showing y increasing at a decreasing rate as x increases, what might the scatter plot look like? Describe two variables that might exhibit such a relationship? Explain your reasoning.

13.6   You are given the following data for variables x and y:

x	y
3.0	1.5
2.0	0.5
2.5	1.0
3.0	1.8
2.5	1.2
4.0	2.2
1.5	0.4
1.0	0.3
2.0	1.3
2.5	1.0

a. Plot these variables in scatter-plot format. Based on this plot, what type of relationship appears to exist between the two variables?

b. Compute the correlation coefficient for these sample data. Indicate what the correlation coefficient measures.

c. Test to determine whether the population correlation coefficient is positive. Use the $\alpha = 0.01$ level to conduct the test. Be sure to state the null and alternative hypotheses, and show the test statistic and decision rule clearly.

13.7   You are given the following data for variables x and y:

x	y
20	16
18	12
24	18
20	17
22	21
14	10
18	10

a. Plot these variables in scatter-plot format. Based on this plot, what type of relationship appears to exist between the two variables?

b. Compute the correlation coefficient for these sample data. Indicate what the correlation coefficient measures.

c. Test to determine whether the population correlation coefficient is zero. Use the $\alpha = 0.05$ level to conduct the test. Be sure to state the null and alternative hypotheses, and show the test statistic and decision rule clearly.

d. Refer to part c. Describe the type of hypothesis test error that could have been made.

13.8   You are given the following data for variables x and y:

x	y
100	80
110	90
90	75
100	90
110	80
80	60
90	90
90	70

a. (1) Compute the correlation coefficient for these sample data. Indicate what the correlation coefficient measures. (2) Divide the x variable by 10 and the y by 5. Recalculate the correlation coefficient. What is the mathematical relationship between the two correlation coefficients?

b. Test to determine whether the population correlation coefficient is negative. Use the $\alpha = 0.05$ level to con duct the test. Be sure to state the null and alternative hypotheses, and show the test statistic and decision rule clearly.

Business Applications

13.9 A sample of 32 people was randomly selected, and height and weight measurements were made for each person. The correlation coefficient for the two variables was 0.80.

a. Discuss in your own words what $r = 0.80$ means with respect to the variables height and weight. Determine whether each of the variables is a fixed or a randomly selected value. Explain your answer.

b. Using an $\alpha = 0.10$ level, test to determine if a correlation exists between height and weight in the population. Be sure to state the null and alternative hypotheses.

13.10 A random sample of 50 bank accounts was selected from a local branch bank. Account balance and number of deposits and withdrawals during the past month were the two variables recorded. The correlation coefficient for the two variables was -0.23.

a. Discuss what $r = -0.23$ measures. Make sure to frame your discussion in terms of the two variables discussed here.

b. Using an $\alpha = 0.10$ level, test to determine whether there is a significant linear relationship between account balance and the number of transactions to an account during the past month. State the null and alternative hypotheses and show the decision rule.

c. Consider the decision you reached in part b. Describe the type of error you could have made in the context of this problem.

13.11 Consider these two scenarios:

a. The number of new workers hired per week in your county has a high positive correlation with the average weekly temperature. Can you conclude that an increase in temperature causes an increase in the number of new hires? Discuss.

b. Suppose the stock price and the common dividends declared for a certain company have a high positive correlation. Are you safe in concluding on the basis of the correlation coefficient that an increase in the common dividends declared causes an increase in the stock price? Present other reasons than the correlation coefficient that might lead you to conclude that an increase in common dividends declared causes an increase in the stock price.

Advanced Applications

13.12 💿 The following information taken from the 1998 annual report of Baldor Electric Company shows Net Sales and Working Capital (in thousands of dollars) for 1988 to 1998. The data are also contained in the CD-ROM file *Baldor*.

Year	Net Sales	Working Capital
1988	$234,463	67,168
1989	281,462	69,788
1990	294,030	75,306
1991	286,495	84,740
1992	318,930	97,343
1993	356,595	108,601
1994	418,152	118,550
1995	473,103	145,069
1996	502,875	146,975
1997	557,940	141,268
1998	589,406	176,126

a. Plot the variables Net Sales (y) and Working Capital (x) in scatter-plot format. What type of relationship appears to exist between Working Capital and Net Sales? Indicate whether a regression model or a correlation model would be more appropriate. Give statistical reasons for your answer.

b. Compute the correlation coefficient between Working Capital and Net Sales. What does the correlation coefficient measure?

c. Test to determine if when Net Sales declines, Working Capital will also decline. (Hint: Think what this indicates for the value of the population correlation coefficient.) Clearly state your null and alternative hypotheses. Conduct your test at a significance level of 0.05. Be sure to state a conclusion for your test.

13.13 💿 The following basic earnings per share (EPS) and common dividends declared for 1989 to 1998 were taken from the 1998 annual report of McCormick & Company. The data are also contained in the CD-ROM file *McCormick*.

Year	Basic EPS	Common Dividends Declared
1989	$1.59	$0.19
1990	0.86	0.24
1991	1.01	0.31
1992	1.19	0.40
1993	0.90	0.45
1994	0.75	0.49
1995	1.20	0.53
1996	0.52	0.57
1997	1.30	0.61
1998	1.42	0.65

a. Plot the variables EPS and dividends in scatter-plot format. What, if any, kind of relationship appears to exist between them? Would a regression model or a correlation model be more appropriate for this data? Explain your answer.

b. Compute the correlation coefficient between EPS and dividends. Provide an interpretation of this coefficient.

c. Does it appear that as EPS increases, dividends decrease? Conduct a hypothesis test of the relevant parameter to answer this question. Conduct your test at a significance level of 0.025. Conduct this hypothesis test using the p-value approach.

13-2 SIMPLE LINEAR REGRESSION ANALYSIS

In the Midwest Distribution example, we determined that the relationship between years of experience and total sales is linear and statistically significant, based on the correlation analysis performed in the previous section. Because hiring and training costs have been increasing, we would like to use this relationship to help formulate a more-acceptable wage package for the sales force.

The statistical method we will use to analyze the relationship between years of experience and total sales is *regression analysis*. When we have only two variables—a dependent variable, such as sales, and an independent variable, such as years with the company—the technique is referred to as *simple regression analysis*. When the relationship between the dependent variable and the independent variable is linear, the technique is **simple linear regression**.

THE REGRESSION MODEL AND ASSUMPTIONS

The objective of simple linear regression (which we shall call *regression analysis*) is to represent the relationship between values of x and y with a model of the form shown in Equation 13-4.

Simple Linear Regression Model (Population Model)

$$y = \beta_0 + \beta_1 x + \varepsilon \qquad \qquad \textbf{13-4}$$

where:

y = Value of the dependent variable
x = Value of the independent variable
β_0 = Population's y-intercept
β_1 = Slope of the population regression line
ε = Error term, or residual (i.e., the difference between the actual y value and the value of y predicted by the population model)

The simple linear regression population model described in Equation 13-4 has four assumptions:

SSUMPTIONS

1. Individual values of the error terms, ε, are statistically independent of one another, and these values represent a random sample from the population of possible values at each level of x.
2. For a given value of x, there can exist many values of y and therefore many values of ε. Further, the distribution of possible ε values for any x value is normal.
3. The distributions of possible ε values have equal variances for all values of x.
4. The means of the dependent variable, y, for all specified values of the independent variable, $(\mu_{y|x})$, can be connected by a straight line called the population regression model.

Figure 13-7 illustrates assumptions 2, 3, and 4. The regression model (straight line) connects the average of the y values for each level of the independent variable, x. The actual y values for each level of x are normally distributed around the mean of y. Finally, observe that the spread of possible y values is the same regardless of the level of x. The population regression line is determined by two values, β_0 and β_1. These values are known as the population *regression coefficients*. Value β_0 identifies the y-intercept and β_1 the slope of the regression line. Under the regression assumptions, the coefficients define the true population model. For each observation, the actual value of the dependent variable, y, for any x, is the sum of two components:

$$y = \underset{\text{Linear Component}}{\beta_0 + \beta_1 x} + \underset{\text{Random Error Component}}{\varepsilon}$$

The random error component, ε, may be positive, zero, or negative, depending on whether a single value of y for a given x falls above, on, or below the population regression line.

FIGURE 13-7

**Graphical Display of
Linear Regression
Assumptions**

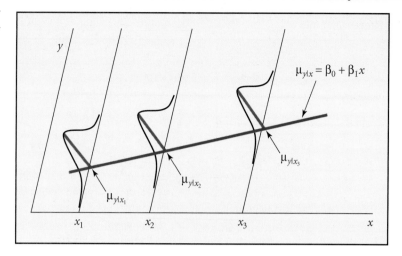

MEANING OF THE REGRESSION COEFFICIENTS

Coefficient β_1, the **regression slope coefficient** of the population regression line, measures the average change in the value of the dependent variable, y, for each unit change in x. The population slope can be either positive, zero, or negative, depending on the relationship between x and y. For example, a positive population slope of 12 ($\beta_1 = 12$) means that for a 1-unit increase in x, we can expect an average 12-unit increase in y. Correspondingly, if the population slope is negative 12 ($\beta_1 = -12$), we can expect an average decrease of 12 units in y for a 1-unit increase in x.

Regression Slope Coefficient

The average change in the dependent variable for a unit increase in the independent variable. The slope coefficient may be positive or negative, depending on the relationship between the two variables.

The population's y-intercept, β_0, indicates the mean value of y when x is 0. However, this interpretation holds only if the population could have x values equal to 0. When this cannot occur, β_0 does not have a meaningful interpretation in the regression model.

Midwest Distribution (continued)—The Midwest Distribution marketing manager has data for a sample of 12 sales representatives. In Section 13-1, she has established that a significant linear relationship exists between years of experience and total sales using correlation analysis. (Recall that the correlation between the two variables was $r = 0.8325$.) Now she would like to estimate the regression equation that defines the *true* linear relationship (that is, the population's linear relationship) between years of experience and sales. Figure 13-3 shows the scatter plot for two variables: years with the company and sales. We need to use the sample data to estimate β_0 and β_1, the true intercept and slope of the line representing the relationship between two variables. The *regression line* through the sample data is the best estimate of the population regression line. However, there are an infinite number of possible regression lines for a set of points. For example, Figure 13-8 shows three of the possible different lines that pass through Midwest Distribution data. Which line should be used to estimate the true regression model?

We must establish a criterion for selecting the best line. The criterion used is the **least squares criterion**.[3]

Least Squares Criterion

The criterion for determining a regression line that minimizes the sum of squared residuals.

To understand the least squares criterion, you need to know about prediction error, or **residual**, the distance between the y-coordinate of an (x,y) point and the estimate of that y-coordinate produced by the regression line. Figure 13-9 shows how the prediction error is calculated for the employee

---

[3]The reason that we are using the sum of the squared residuals is that the sum of the residuals will be zero for the best regression line (the positive values will balance the negative values).

FIGURE 13-8   Possible Regression Lines

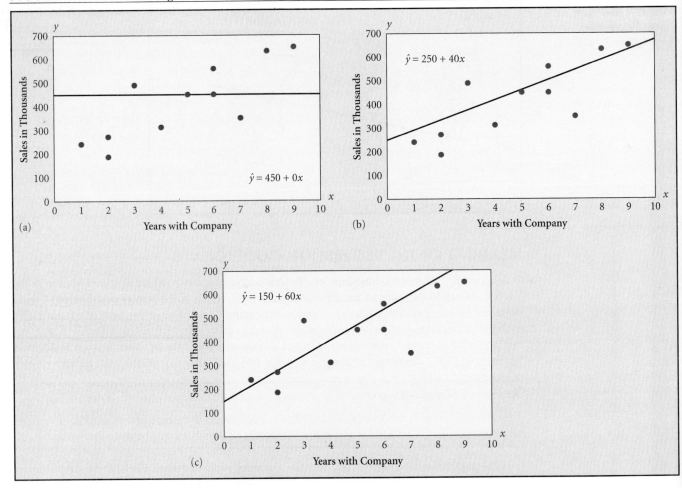

who was with Midwest for 4 years ($x = 4$) using one possible regression line: $\hat{y} = 150 + 60x$ (where $\hat{y}$ is the estimated sales value). The predicted sales value is

$$\hat{y} = 150 + 60(4) = 390$$

However, the actual sales (y) for this employee were 312. Thus, when $x = 4$, the difference between the observed, $y = 312$, and the regression line value, $\hat{y} = 390$, is $312 - 390 = -78$. The residual (or prediction error) for this case when $x = 4$ is -78. Table 13-2 shows the calculated errors

FIGURE 13-9

Computation of Regression Error for the Midwest Distribution Example

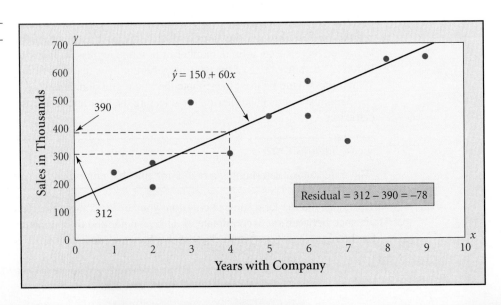

TABLE 13-2

Sum of Squared Errors for Three Linear Equations for Midwest Distribution

From Figure 13-8(a):

$\hat{y} = 450 + 0x$

			RESIDUAL	
x	$\hat{y}$	y	$y - \hat{y}$	$(y - \hat{y})^2$
3	450	487	37	1,369
5	450	445	−5	25
2	450	272	−178	31,684
8	450	641	191	36,481
2	450	187	−263	69,169
6	450	440	−10	100
7	450	346	−104	10,816
1	450	238	−212	44,944
4	450	312	−138	19,044
2	450	269	−181	32,761
9	450	655	205	42,025
6	450	563	113	12,769
				$\Sigma = 301{,}187$

From Figure 13-8(b):

$\hat{y} = 250 + 40x$

			RESIDUAL	
x	$\hat{y}$	y	$y - \hat{y}$	$(y - \hat{y})^2$
3	370	487	117	13,689
5	450	445	−5	25
2	330	272	−58	3,364
8	570	641	71	5,041
2	330	187	−143	20,449
6	490	440	−50	2,500
7	530	346	−184	33,856
1	290	238	−52	2,704
4	410	312	−98	9,604
2	330	269	−61	3,721
9	610	655	45	2,025
6	490	563	73	5,329
				$\Sigma = 102{,}307$

From Figure 13-8(c):

$\hat{y} = 150 + 60x$

			RESIDUAL	
x	$\hat{y}$	y	$y - \hat{y}$	$(y - \hat{y})^2$
3	330	487	157	24,649
5	450	445	−5	25
2	270	272	2	4
8	630	641	11	121
2	270	187	−83	6,889
6	510	440	−70	4,900
7	570	346	−224	50,176
1	210	238	28	784
4	390	312	−78	6,084
2	270	269	−1	1
9	690	655	−35	1,225
6	510	563	53	2,809
				$\Sigma = 97{,}667$

and sum of squared errors for each of the three regression lines shown in Figure 13-8. Of these three potential regression models, the line with the equation $\hat{y} = 150 + 60x$ has the smallest sum of squared errors. However, is this line the best of all possible lines? That is, would $\sum_{i=1}^{n}(y_i - \hat{y}_i)^2$ be smaller than for any other line? One way to determine this is to calculate the sum of squared errors for all other regression lines. However, because there are an infinite number of these lines, this approach is not feasible. Fortunately, through the use of calculus, equations can be derived to directly determine the slope and intercept estimates such that $\sum_{i=1}^{n}(y_i - \hat{y}_i)^2$ is minimized.[4] This is accomplished by letting the estimated regression model be of the form shown in Equation 13-5.

Estimated Regression Model (Sample Model)

$$\hat{y} = b_0 + b_1 x \qquad \textbf{13-5}$$

where:

$\hat{y}$ = Estimated, or predicted, y value
b_0 = Unbiased estimate of the regression intercept, found using Equation 13-8
b_1 = Unbiased estimate of the regression slope, found using Equation 13-6 or 13-7
x = Value of the independent variable

Equations 13-6 and 13-8 are referred to as the *least squares equations* because they provide the slope and intercept that minimize the sum of squared errors. Equation 13-7 is the algbraic equivalent of Equation 13-6 and is easier to use when the computation is performed using a calculator.

Least Squares Equations (Sample Values)

$$b_1 = \frac{\Sigma(x - \bar{x})(y - \bar{y})}{\Sigma(x - \bar{x})^2} \qquad \textbf{13-6}$$

algebraic equivalent:

$$b_1 = \frac{\Sigma xy - \dfrac{\Sigma x \Sigma y}{n}}{\Sigma x^2 - \dfrac{(\Sigma x)^2}{n}} \qquad \textbf{13-7}$$

and

$$b_0 = \bar{y} - b_1 \bar{x} \qquad \textbf{13-8}$$

Table 13-3 shows the manual calculations, which are subject to rounding, for the least square estimates for the Midwest Distribution example. However, you will almost always use a software package such as Excel or Minitab to perform these computations. Figures 13-10a and 13-10b show the regression output. In this case, the "best" regression line, given the least squares criterion, is $\hat{y} = 175.8288 + 49.9101(x)$. Figure 13-11 shows the predicted sales values and the residuals and squared residuals associated with this best simple linear regression line. Keep in mind that the residuals are also referred to as *errors* or *prediction errors*. From Figure 13-11, the sum of the squared errors is 84,834.29. This is the smallest sum of squared residuals possible for this set of sample data. No other simple linear regression line through these 12 (x,y) points will produce a smaller sum of squared residuals. Equation 13-9 presents a formula that can be used to calculate the sum of squared errors manually.

[4]The calculus derivation of the least squares equations is contained on the CD-ROM that accompanies this text under the Chapter 13 folder.

TABLE 13-3

Manual Calculations for Least Squares Regression Coefficients for the Midwest Distribution Example

y	x	xy	x^2	y^2
487	3	1,461	9	237,169
445	5	2,225	25	198,025
272	2	544	4	73,984
641	8	5,128	64	410,881
187	2	374	4	34,969
440	6	2,640	36	193,600
346	7	2,422	49	119,716
238	1	238	1	56,644
312	4	1,248	16	97,344
269	2	538	4	72,361
655	9	5,895	81	429,025
563	6	3,378	36	316,969
$\Sigma\,y = 4{,}855$	$\Sigma\,x = 55$	$\Sigma\,xy = 26{,}091$	$\Sigma\,x^2 = 329$	$\Sigma\,y^2 = 2{,}240{,}687$

$$\bar{y} = \frac{\Sigma y}{n} = \frac{4{,}855}{12} = 404.58 \qquad \bar{x} = \frac{\Sigma x}{n} = \frac{55}{12} = 4.58$$

$$b_1 = \frac{\Sigma xy - \dfrac{\Sigma x \Sigma y}{n}}{\Sigma x^2 - \dfrac{(\Sigma x)^2}{n}} = \frac{26{,}091 - \dfrac{55(4{,}855)}{12}}{329 - \dfrac{(55)^2}{12}}$$

$$= 49.91$$

Then,

$$b_0 = \bar{y} - b_1\bar{x} = 404.58 - 49.91(4.58) = 175.83$$

The least squares regression line is, therefore,

$$\hat{y} = 175.83 + 49.91(x)$$

FIGURE 13-10A

Excel Midwest Distribution Regression Results

Excel Instructions:
1. Open file Midwest.xls
2. Select **Tools**.
3. Click on **Data Analysis**.
4. Select **Regression Analysis**.
5. Define x and y variable data range.
6. Select output location.
7. Click **Residuals**.

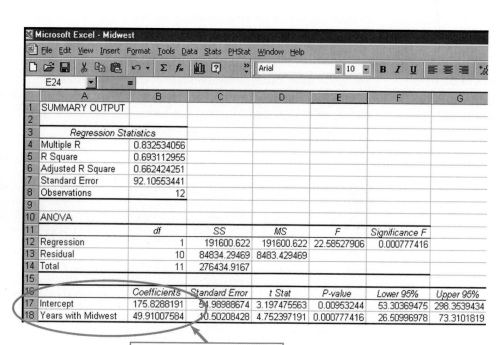

Estimated regression equation is
$\hat{y} = 175.8288 = 49.9101(x)$

FIGURE 13-10B

Minitab Midwest Distribution Regression Results

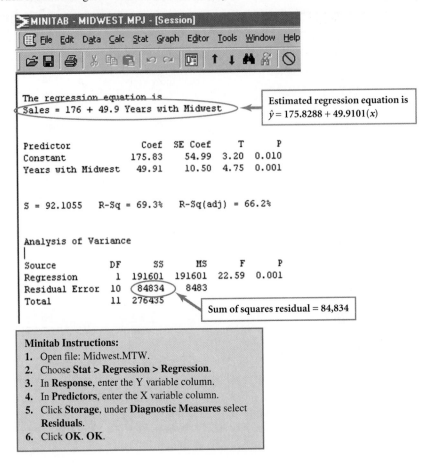

Minitab Instructions:
1. Open file: Midwest.MTW.
2. Choose **Stat > Regression > Regression**.
3. In **Response**, enter the Y variable column.
4. In **Predictors**, enter the X variable column.
5. Click **Storage**, under **Diagnostic Measures** select **Residuals**.
6. Click **OK. OK.**

Sum of Squared Errors

$$SSE = \Sigma\, y^2 - b_0\, \Sigma\, y - b_1\, \Sigma\, xy$$

13-9

Figure 13-12 shows the scatter plot of sales and years experience and the least squares regression line for Midwest Distribution. This line is the *best fit* for these sample data. Note that the regression line passes through the point corresponding to $(\bar{x}, \bar{y})$.

FIGURE 13-11

Residuals and Squared Residuals for the Midwest Distribution Example

Excel Instructions:
1. Create Squared Residuals using Excel formula.

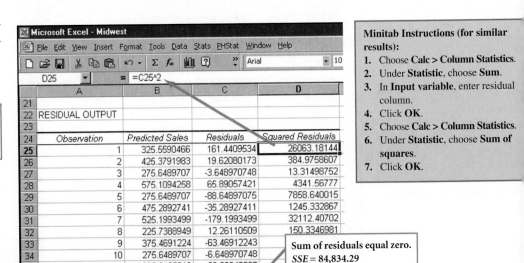

Minitab Instructions (for similar results):
1. Choose **Calc > Column Statistics**.
2. Under **Statistic**, choose **Sum**.
3. In **Input variable**, enter residual column.
4. Click **OK.**
5. Choose **Calc > Column Statistics**.
6. Under **Statistic**, choose **Sum of squares**.
7. Click **OK.**

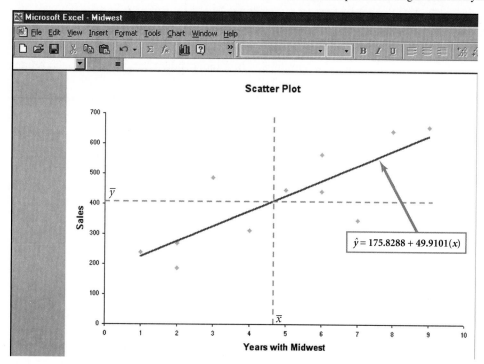

LEAST SQUARES REGRESSION PROPERTIES

Figure 13-11 illustrates several important properties of least squares regression.

1. The sum of the residuals from the least squares regression line is 0 (Equation 13-10). The total underprediction by the regression model is exactly offset by the total overprediction.

Sum of Residuals

$$\sum_{i=1}^{n}(y_i - \hat{y}_i) = 0 \qquad \textbf{13-10}$$

2. The sum of the squared residuals is a minimum (Equation 13-11).

Sum of Squared Residuals (Errors)

$$SSE = \sum_{i=1}^{n}(y_i - \hat{y}_i)^2 \qquad \textbf{13-11}$$

This property provided the basis for developing the equations for b_0 and b_1.

3. The simple regression line always passes through the mean of the y variable, $\bar{y}$, and the mean of the x variable, $\bar{x}$. This is illustrated in Figure 13-12. So, to manually draw any simple linear regression line, all you need to do is to draw a line connecting the least squares y-intercept with the $(\bar{x}, \bar{y})$ point.

4. The least squares coefficients are unbiased estimates of β_0 and β_1. Thus, the expected values of b_0 and b_1 equal β_0 and β_1, respectively.

EXAMPLE 13-2: SIMPLE LINEAR REGRESSION AND CORRELATION

Fitzpatrick & Associates   The investment firm Fitzpatrick & Associates wants to manage the pension fund of a major Chicago retailer. For their presentation to the retailer, the Fitzpatrick analysts want to use simple linear regression to model the relationship between profits and numbers of employees for 50 Fortune 500 companies in the firm's portfolio. The data for the analysis is contained in the CD-ROM file *Fortune 50*. This analysis can be done using the following steps.

Step 1: **Specify the independent and dependent variables.**

The object in this example is to model the linear relationship between number of employees (the independent variable) and each company's profits (the dependent variable).

Excel and Minitab Tutorial

Step 2: **Develop a scatter plot to graphically display the relationship between the independent and dependent variables.**

Figure 13-13 shows the scatter plot, where the dependent variable, y, is company profits and the independent variable, x, is number of employees. There appears to be slight positive linear relationship between the two variables.

Step 3: **Calculate the correlation coefficient and the linear regression equation.**

Do either manually using Equations 13-1, 13-6, and 13-8, respectively, or by using Excel or Minitab software. Figure 13-14 shows the regression results. The sample correlation coefficient (called multiple R in Excel) is

$$r = 0.3638$$

The regression equation is

$$\hat{y} = 2556.88 + 0.0048x$$

The regression slope is estimated to be 0.0048, which means that for each additional employee, the mean increase in company profit is 0.0048 million dollars, or $4,800. The intercept can only be interpreted when a value equal to zero for the x variable (employees) is plausible. Clearly no company has zero employees, so the intercept in this case has no meaning other than it locates the height of the regression line for $x = 0$.

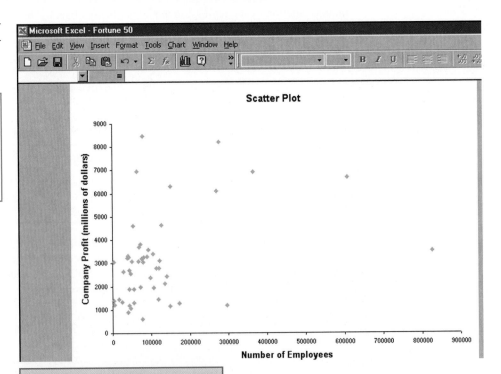

FIGURE 13-14

Excel Regression Results for Fitzpatrick & Associates

Excel Instructions:
1. Open file: Fortune 50.xls
2. Click on **Tools** tab.
3. Select **Regression**.
4. Define *x* and *y* variable data range.

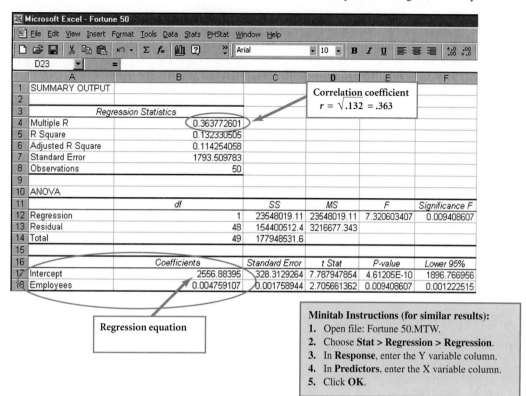

SIGNIFICANCE TESTS IN REGRESSION ANALYSIS

In Section 13-1, we pointed out that the correlation coefficient computed from sample data is a point estimate of the population correlation coefficient and is subject to sampling error. We also introduced a test of significance for the correlation coefficient. Likewise, the regression coefficients developed from a sample of data are also point estimates of the true regression coefficients for the population. The regression coefficients are subject to sampling error. For example, due to sampling error the estimated slope coefficient may be positive or negative while the population slope is really zero. Therefore, we need a test procedure to determine whether the regression slope coefficient is statistically significant. As you will see in this section, the test for the simple linear regression slope coefficient is equivalent to the test for the correlation coefficient. That is, if the correlation between two variables is found to be significant, then the regression slope coefficient will also be significant.

The Coefficient of Determination, R^2

Midwest Distribution (continued)—Recall that the Midwest Distribution marketing manager was analyzing the relationship between the number of years an employee had been with the company (independent variable) and the sales generated by the employee (dependent variable). We note when looking at the sample data for 12 employees (see Table 13-3) that sales vary between employees. Regression analysis aims to determine the extent to which an independent variable can explain this variation. In this case, does number of years with the company help explain the variation in sales from employee to employee?

The *SST* (total sum of squares) can be used in measuring the variation in the dependent variable. *SST* is computed using Equation 13-12. For Midwest Distribution, the total sum of squares for sales is provided in the output generated by Excel or Minitab as shown in Figure 13-15a and Figure 13-15b. As you can see, the total sum of squares in sales that needs to be explained is 276,434.9. Note that the *SST* value is in squared units and has no particular meaning.

Total Sum of Squares

$$SST = \sum_{i=1}^{n} (y_i - \bar{y})^2$$

13-12

where:

$$
\begin{aligned}
SST &= \text{Total sum of squares} \\
n &= \text{Sample size} \\
y_i &= i\text{th value of the dependent variable} \\
\bar{y} &= \text{Average value of the dependent variable}
\end{aligned}
$$

The *SST* is the sum of two other sum of squares, the sum of squares error (*SSE*) and the sum of squares regression (*SSR*). Thus,

$$SST = SSE + SSR$$

The least squares regression line is computed so that the sum of squared residuals is minimized (recall the discussion of the least squares equations). The sum of squares residuals is also called the *sum of squares error* (*SSE*) and is defined by Equation 13-13.

Sum of Squares Error

$$SSE = \sum_{i=1}^{n} (y_i - \hat{y}_i)^2$$

13-13

where:

$$
\begin{aligned}
n &= \text{Sample size} \\
y_i &= i\text{th value of the dependent variable} \\
\hat{y}_i &= i\text{th predicted value of } y \text{ given the } i\text{th value of } x
\end{aligned}
$$

SSE represents the amount of the total sum of squares in the dependent variable that *is not explained* by the least squares regression line. Excel refers to *SSE* as *sum of squares residual*. This value is contained in the regression output shown in Figure 13-15a and Figure 13-15b.

$$SSE = \Sigma(y - \hat{y})^2 = 84,834.29$$

FIGURE 13-15A

Excel Regression Results for Midwest Distribution

Excel Instructions:
1. Open file: Midwest.xls
2. Click on **Tools** tab.
3. Select **Regression**.
4. Define *x* and *y* variable data range.

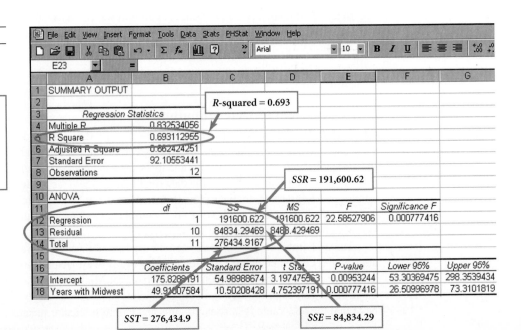

FIGURE 13-15B

Minitab Regression Results
for Midwest Distribution

FIGURE 13-15B

Minitab Regression Results
for Midwest Distribution

Minitab Instructions:
1. Open file:
   Midwest.MTW.
2. Choose **Stat >
   Regression >
   Regression**.
3. In **Response**, enter the y
   variable column.
4. In **Predictors**, enter the x
   variable column.
5. Click **OK**.

```
MINITAB - MIDWEST.MPJ - [Session]
File  Edit  Data  Calc  Stat  Graph  Editor  Tools  Window  Help

Regression Analysis: Sales versus Years with Midwest

The regression equation is
Sales = 176 + 49.9 Years with Midwest


Predictor                Coef   SE Coef      T      P
Constant               175.83     54.99   3.20  0.010
Years with Midwest      49.91     10.50   4.75  0.001


S = 92.1055   R-Sq = 69.3%   R-Sq(adj) = 66.2%


Analysis of Variance

Source           DF       SS      MS      F      P
Regression        1   191601  191601  22.59  0.001
Residual Error   10    84834    8483
Total            11   276435
```

R-squared = 0.693

SSR = 191,601

SSE = 84,834

SST = 276,435

Thus, of the total sum of squares ($SST = 276,434.9$), the regression model leaves $SSE = 84,834.29$ unexplained. Then, the portion of the total sum of squares that *is explained* by the regression line is called the *sum of squares regression* (*SSR*) and is calculated by Equation 13-14.

Sum of Squares Regression

$$SSR = \sum_{i=1}^{n} (\hat{y}_i - \bar{y})^2$$ **13-14**

where:

$\hat{y}_i$ = Estimated value of y for each value of x
$\bar{y}$ = Average value of the y variable

The sum of squares regression ($SSR = 191,600.62$) is also provided in the regression output shown in Figure 13-15a.

We can use these calculations to compute an important measure in regression analysis called the **coefficient of determination**.

Coefficient of Determination

The portion of the total variation in the dependent variable that is explained by its relationship with the independent variable. The coefficient of determination is also called *R*-squared and is denoted as R^2.

The coefficient of determination is calculated using Equation 13-15.

Coefficient of Determination, R^2

$$R^2 = \frac{SSR}{SST}$$ **13-15**

Then, for the Midwest Distribution example, the fraction of variation in sales that can be explained by the years of sales force experience is

$$R^2 = \frac{SSR}{SST} = \frac{191,600.62}{276,434.90} = 0.6931$$

This means that 69.31% of the variation in the sales data for this sample can be explained by the linear relationship between sales and years of experience. Notice that R-squared is part of the regression output in Figures 13-15a and 13-15b.

R^2 can be a value between 0 and 1.0. If there is a perfect linear relationship between two variables, then the coefficient of determination, R^2, will be 1.0. This would correspond to a situation in which the least squares regression line would pass through each of the points in the scatter plot.

R^2 is the measure used by many decision makers to indicate how well the linear regression line fits the (x,y) data points. The better the fit, the closer R^2 will be to 1.0. R^2 will be close to 0 when there is a weak linear relationship.

Finally, when you are employing *simple linear regression* (a linear relationship between the independent and dependent variables in the model), there is an alternative way of computing R^2, as shown in Equation 13-16.

Coefficient of Determination, Single Independent Variable Case

$$R^2 = r^2 \qquad \qquad \textbf{13-16}$$

where:

R^2 = Coefficient of determination
r = Simple correlation coefficient

Therefore, by squaring the correlation coefficient, we can get R^2 for the simple regression model. Figure 13-15a shows the correlation, $r = 0.8325$, which is referred to as Multiple R in Excel. Then using Equation 13-16, we get R^2.

$$\begin{aligned} R^2 &= r^2 \\ &= 0.8325^2 \\ &= 0.6931 \end{aligned}$$

Significance of the Slope Coefficient

Before we use the regression model to analyze the relationship between sales and years of experience, we need to determine if the overall model is statistically significant. For a simple linear regression model (one independent variable), there are two equivalent methods.

1. Test for significance of the correlation between x and y.
2. Test for significance of the regression slope coefficient.

In Section 13-1, we discussed the first method, in which a t test is used to determine whether the population correlation coefficient is equal to 0.0. In simple regression, if the null hypothesis of zero correlation is rejected, we conclude that the two variables have a significant linear relationship. If that is the case, then the resulting regression model will also be statistically significant. However, you can directly test for the significance of the regression model with the null and alternative hypotheses as

$$H_0: \beta_1 = 0$$
$$H_A: \beta_1 \neq 0$$

To test the significance of the simple linear regression model, we test to determine whether the population regression slope coefficient is 0. A slope of 0 would imply that a linear relationship between x and y variables is of no use in explaining the variation in y. If the linear relationship is useful, then we should reject the hypothesis that the regression slope is 0. However, because the estimated regression slope coefficient, b_1, is calculated from sample data, it is subject to sampling error. Therefore, even though b_1 is not 0, we must determine whether its difference from 0 is greater than would generally be attributed to sampling error.

If we selected several samples from the same population and for each sample determined the least squares regression line, we would likely get regression lines with different slopes and different y-intercepts. This is analogous to getting different sample means from different samples. Just as the distribution of possible sample means has a standard deviation, the possible regression slopes have a standard deviation, which is given in Equation 13-17.

Standard Deviation of the Regression Slope Coefficient (Population)

$$\sigma_{b_1} = \frac{\sigma_\varepsilon}{\sqrt{\Sigma(x - \bar{x})^2}}$$ **13-17**

where:

σ_{b_1} = Standard deviation of the regression slope
(called the *standard error of the slope*)
σ_ε = Population standard error of the estimate

Equation 13-17 requires that we know the **standard error of the estimate**. It measures the dispersion of the dependent variable about its mean value at each value of the dependent variable in the original units of the dependent variable. However, because we are sampling from the population, we can estimate σ_ε as shown in Equation 13-18.

Estimator for the Standard Error of the Estimate

$$s_\varepsilon = \sqrt{\frac{SSE}{n - k - 1}}$$ **13-18**

where:

SSE = Sum of squares error
n = Sample size
k = Number of independent variables in the model

Equation 13-17, the standard deviation of the regression slope, applies when we are dealing with a population. However, in most cases, such as the Midwest Distribution example, we are dealing with a sample from the population. Thus, we need to estimate the regression slope's standard deviation using Equation 13-19.

Estimator for the Standard Deviation of the Regression Slope

$$s_{b_1} = \frac{s_\varepsilon}{\sqrt{\Sigma(x - \bar{x})^2}} = \frac{s_\varepsilon}{\sqrt{\Sigma x^2 - \frac{(\Sigma x)^2}{n}}}$$ **13-19**

where:

s_{b_1} = Estimate of the standard error of the least squares slope

$s_\varepsilon = \sqrt{\dfrac{SSE}{n - 2}}$ = Sample standard error of the estimate (the measure of deviation of the actual y values around the regression line)

FIGURE 13-16A

Excel Regression Results for Midwest Distribution

Excel Instructions:
1. Open file: Midwest.xls
2. Click on **Tools** tab.
3. Select **Regression**.
4. Define x and y variable data range.

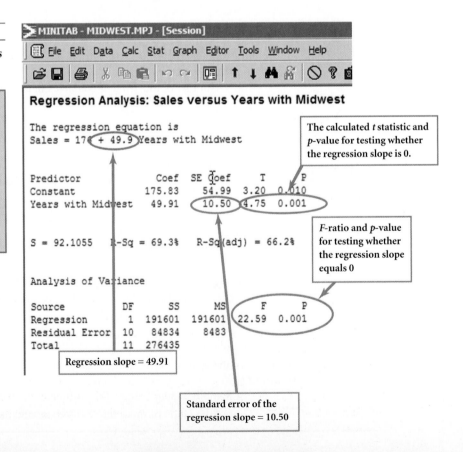

Midwest Distribution (continued)—For Midwest Distribution, the regression outputs in Figure 13-16a and Figure 13-16b show $b_1 = 49.91$. The question is whether this value is different enough from zero to have not been caused by sampling error. We find the answer by looking at the value of the estimate of the standard error of the slope, calculated using Equation 13-19, which is also shown in Figure 13-16a. The standard error of the slope coefficient is 10.50.

If the standard error of the slope is large, then the value of b_1 will be quite variable from sample to sample. Conversely, if σ_{b_1} is small, the slope values will be less variable. However, regardless of the standard error of the slope, the average value of b_1 will equal β_1, the true

FIGURE 13-16B

Minitab Regression Results for Midwest Distribution

Minitab Instructions:
1. Open file: Midwest.MTW.
2. Choose **Stat > Regression > Regression**.
3. In **Response**, enter the y variable column.
4. In **Predictors**, enter the x variable column.
5. Click **OK**.

FIGURE 13-17   Standard Error of the Slope

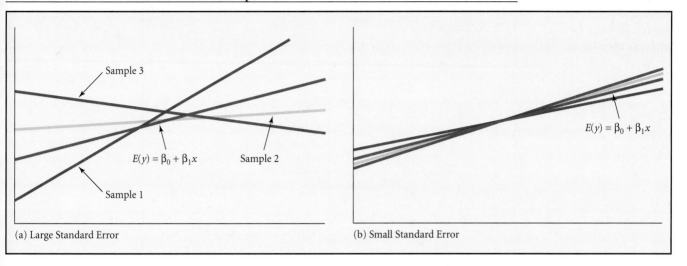

(a) Large Standard Error

(b) Small Standard Error

regression slope, if the assumptions of the regression analysis are satisfied. Figure 13-17 illustrates what this means. Notice that when the standard error of the slope is large, the sample slope can take on values *much* different from the true population slope. As Figure 13-17a shows, a sample slope and the true population slope can even have different signs. However, when σ_{b_1} is small, the sample regression lines will cluster closely around the true population line (Figure 13-17b).

Because the sample regression slope will most likely not equal the true population slope, we must test to determine whether the true slope could possibly be 0. A slope of 0 in the linear model means that the independent variable will not explain any variation in the dependent variable, nor will it be useful in predicting the dependent variable. The null and alternative hypotheses to be tested at the 0.05 level of significance are

$$H_0: \beta_1 = 0$$
$$H_A: \beta_1 \neq 0$$

To test the significance of a slope coefficient, we use the *t* test value in Equation 13-20.

Test Statistic for Test of the Significance of the Regression Slope, Simple Linear Regression

$$t = \frac{b_1 - \beta_1}{s_{b_1}} \qquad df = n - 2 \qquad\qquad \textbf{13-20}$$

where:

$$b_1 = \text{Sample regression slope coefficient}$$
$$\beta_1 = \text{Hypothesized slope}$$
$$s_{b_1} = \text{Estimator of the standard error of the slope}$$

Figure 13-18 illustrates this test for the Midwest Distribution example. The calculated *t*-value of 4.753 exceeds the critical value from the *t*-distribution with 10 degrees of freedom and $\alpha/2 = 0.025$. This indicates that we should reject the hypothesis that the true regression slope is 0. Thus, years of experience can be used to help explain the variation in an individual representative's sales. (Note that the calculated *t* is the same value that we found in Figure 13-6 for the test of the correlation coefficient.)

The output shown in Figures 13-16a and 13-16b also contain the calculated *t* statistic. The *p*-value for the calculated *t* statistic is also provided. As with other situations involving two-tailed hypothesis tests, if the *p*-value is less than α, the null hypothesis is rejected. In this case, because *p*-value = 0.0008 < 0.05, we reject the null hypothesis.

FIGURE 13-18

Significance Test of the Regression Slope for Midwest Distribution

Hypotheses:

H_0: $\beta_1 = 0$
H_A: $\beta_1 \neq 0$
$\alpha = 0.05$

$df = 12 - 2 = 10$

Rejection Region
$\alpha/2 = 0.025$

Rejection Region
$\alpha/2 = 0.025$

$-t_{0.025} = -2.228$ 0 $t_{0.025} = 2.228$

The calculated t is:

$$t = \frac{b_1 - \beta_1}{s_{b_1}} = \frac{49.91 - 0}{10.50} = 4.753$$

Decision Rule:

If $t > t_{\alpha/2} = 2.228$, reject H_0
If $t < -t_{\alpha/2} = -2.228$, reject H_0
Otherwise, do not reject H_0
Because 4.753 > 2.228, we should reject the null hypothesis and conclude that the true slope is not zero. Thus, the simple linear relationship that utilizes the independent variable, years with the company, is useful in explaining the variation in the dependent variable, sales volume.

𝒮UMMARY: SIMPLE LINEAR REGRESSION ANALYSIS

The following steps outline the process that can be used in developing a simple linear regression model and the various hypotheses tests used to determine the significance of a simple linear regression model.

1. Define the independent (x) and dependent (y) variables and select a simple random sample of pairs of x,y values.

2. Develop a scatter plot of y and x. You are looking for a linear relationship between the two variables.

3. Compute the correlation coefficient for the sample data.

4. Calculate the least squares regression line for the sample data and the simple coefficient of determination, R^2. The coefficient of determination measures the proportion of variation in the dependent variable explained by the independent variable.

5. Conduct either of the following tests for determining whether the regression model is statistically significant.

a. Test to determine whether the true regression slope is 0. The test statistic with $df = n - 2$ is

$$t = \frac{b_1 - \beta_1}{s_{b_1}} = \frac{b_1 - 0}{s_{b_1}}$$

b. Test to see whether ρ is significantly different from 0. The test statistic is

$$t = \frac{r}{\sqrt{\dfrac{1 - r^2}{n - 2}}}$$

6. Reach a decision.

7. Draw a conclusion.

Excel and Minitab Tutorial

EXAMPLE 13-3: SIMPLE LINEAR REGRESSION ANALYSIS

Vantage Electronic Systems   Consider the example involving Vantage Electronic Systems in Deerfield, Michigan, which started out supplying electronic equipment for the automobile industry, but in recent years has ventured into other areas. One area is visibility sensors that are used by airports to provide takeoff and landing information and by transportation departments to detect low visibility on roadways during fog and snow. The recognized leader in the visibility sensor business is the SCR Company, which makes a sensor called the Scorpion. The R&D department at Vantage has recently performed a test on its new unit by locating a Vanguard sensor and a Scorpion sensor side-by-side. Various data, including visibility measurements, were collected at randomly selected points in time over a two-week period. These data are contained in a CD-ROM file called *Vantage*.

Step 1: **Define the independent (*x*) and dependent (*y*) variables.**

The analysis included a simple linear regression using the Scorpion visibility measurement as the dependent variable, *y*, and the Vanguard visibility measurement as the independent variable, *x*.

Step 2: **Develop a scatter plot of *y* and *x*.**

The scatter plot is shown in Figure 13-19. There does not appear to be a strong linear relationship.

Step 3: **Compute the correlation coefficient for the sample data.**

Equation 13-1 or 13-2 can be used for manual computation, or we can use Excel or Minitab. The correlation coefficient is

$$r = 0.5778$$

Step 4: **Calculate the least squares regression line for the sample data and the simple coefficient of determination, R^2.**

Equations 13-7 and 13-8 can be used to manually compute the regression slope coefficient and intercept, respectively, and Equation 13-15 or 13-16 can be used to manually compute R^2. Excel and Minitab can also be used to eliminate the computational burden. The coefficient of determination is

$$R^2 = r^2 = 0.5778^2 = 0.3339$$

Thus, approximately 33% of the variation in the Scorpion visibility measures is explained by knowing the corresponding Vanguard system visibility measure. The least squares regression equation is

$$\hat{y} = 0.586 + 3.017x$$

FIGURE 13-19

Scatter Plot—Example 13-3

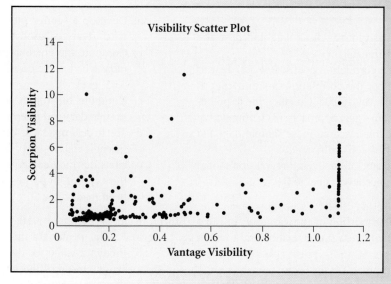

Step 5:   **Conduct a test to determine whether the regression model is statistically significant (or whether the population correlation is equal to zero).**
The null and alternative hypotheses to test the correlation coefficient are

$$H_0: \rho = 0$$
$$H_A: \rho \neq 0$$

The t test statistic is

$$t = \frac{r}{\sqrt{\dfrac{1 - r^2}{n - 2}}} = \frac{0.5778}{\sqrt{\dfrac{1 - 0.5778^2}{280 - 2}}} = 11.81$$

The $t = 11.81$ exceeds the critical t (or the normal approximation to it) for any reasonable level of α for 278 degrees of freedom, so the null hypothesis is rejected and we conclude that there is a statistically significant linear relationship between visibility measures for the two visibility sensors.

Alternatively, the null and alternative hypotheses to test the regression slope coefficient are

$$H_0: \beta_1 = 0$$
$$H_A: \beta_1 \neq 0$$

The t test statistic is

$$t = \frac{b_1 - \beta_1}{s_{b_1}} = \frac{3.017 - 0}{0.256} = 11.81$$

Step 6:   **Reach a decision.**
The t test statistic of 11.81 exceeds the t-critical (or normal approximation to it) for any reasonable level of α for 278 degrees of freedom.

Step 7:   **Draw a conclusion.**
The regression slope coefficient is not equal to zero.

13-2: EXERCISES

Skill Development

13.14 You are given the following sample data for variables y and x:

y	140.1	120.3	80.8	100.7	130.2	90.6	110.5	120.2	130.4	130.3	100.1
x	5	3	2	4	5	4	4	5	6	5	4

a. Develop a scatter plot for these data and describe what, if any, relationship exists.
b. (1) Compute the correlation coefficient. (2) Test to determine whether the correlation is significant at the significance level of 0.05. Conduct this hypothesis test using the p-value approach. (3) Compute the regression equation based on these sample data and interpret the regression coefficients.
c. Test the significance of the overall regression model using a significance level equal to 0.05.

13.15 Refer to Exercise 13.14.
a. Determine the proportion of the variation in the y variable explained by its linear relationship to the x variable.
b. (1) Provide an estimate for the y variable when $x = 0$. (2) There is a name associated with this particular y value. Provide this name.

13.16 You are given the following sample data for variables y and x:

y	12.5	9.0	13.0	7.5	9.0	6.2	3.5	14	15
x	100	120	100	90	110	160	200	95	80

a. Develop a scatter plot for these data and describe what, if any, relationship exists.
b. Compute the correlation coefficient. Test to determine whether the correlation is significant at the $\alpha = 0.05$ level.
c. Compute the regression equation based on these sample data and interpret the regression coefficients.
d. Test to determine whether the true regression slope coefficient is equal to zero. Use a significance level of 0.02.
e. Consider the decision you made in part d. Describe the type of hypothesis test error that could have been made.

13.17 Refer to Exercise 13.16.
a. Predict a value for the y variable when x equals 10.
b. Predict a value for the y variable when x equals the sample mean of the x values. Which of the two predictions produced in part a and in part b, respectively, would have the largest margin of error.

13.18 You are given the following results from computations pertaining to a simple linear regression application:

$$\hat{y} = 23.0 + 1.45x$$
$$SSE = 45,000$$
$$n = 25$$
$$\Sigma(x - \bar{x})^2 = 4,000$$

a. Based on the statistics supplied, can you conclude that there is a significant linear relationship between x and y? Test at the $\alpha = 0.05$ level.

b. Interpret the slope coefficient.

Business Applications

13.19 At State University, a study was done to establish whether a relationship existed between a student's GPA when graduating and SAT score when entering the university. The sample data are reported as follows:

GPA	2.5	3.2	3.5	2.8	3.0	2.4	3.4	2.9	2.7	3.8
SAT	640	700	550	540	620	490	710	600	505	710

a. Develop a scatter plot for these data and describe what, if any, relationship exists between the two variables, GPA and SAT score.

b. (1) Compute the correlation coefficient.
(2) Does it appear that the success of students at State University is related to the SAT scores of those students? Conduct a statistical procedure to answer this question. Use a significance level of 0.01.

c. (1) Compute the regression equation based on these sample data if you wish to predict the university GPA using the students' SAT scores.
(2) Interpret the regression coefficients.

13.20 ⊙ One of the editors of a major automobile publication has collected data on 30 of the best-selling cars in the United States. The data are in a CD-ROM file called *Automobiles*. The editor is particularly interested in the relationship between highway mileage and curb weight of the vehicles.

a. Develop a scatter plot for these data. Discuss what the plot implies about the relationship between two variables. Assume that you wish to predict highway mileage by using vehicle curb weight.

b. Compute the correlation coefficient for the two variables and test to determine whether there is a linear relationship between the curb weight and the highway mileage of automobiles.

c. (1) Compute the linear regression equation based on the sample data. (2) Cadillac's 1999 Sedan DeVille weighs approximately 4,012 pounds. Provide an estimate of the average highway mileage you would expect to obtain from this model.

13.21 An accountant who is performing an audit of the parts inventory for a machinery company has collected the following data. The dependent variable, y, is the actual level of inventory (in hundreds of dollars) determined by the accountant. The independent vari-

able, x, is the inventory level on the computer inventory record.

y	233.23	10.56	24.45	56.87	78.10	102.23	90.94	200.23	344.41	120.53	18.62
x	245.51	12.43	22.52	56.84	90.31	103.85	85.56	190.86	320.74	120.25	23.88

Of course, the accountant wishes to know whether these sample data show a high level of agreement between the measure of inventory level determined during the audit and the levels indicated on the company records. Calculate a value that would give the accountant an indication of the level of agreement between these two measures. Is this measure, based on sample information, statistically significant? Be careful to consider the type and direction of the appropriate measurement.

13.22 The Skeleton Manufacturing Company recently did a study of its customers. A random sample of 50 customer accounts was pulled from the computer records. Two variables were observed:

y = Total dollar volume of business this year
x = Miles customer is from corporate headquarters

The following statistics were computed:

$$\hat{y} = 2,140.23 - 10.12x$$
$$s_{b_1} = 3.12$$

a. Interpret the regression slope coefficient.

b. Using a significance level of 0.01, test to determine whether it is true that the farther a business is from the corporate headquarters the smaller is the total dollar volume of business.

13.23 ⊙ The data shown here and in the CD-ROM file *McCormick* contain information (measured in millions of dollars) from the 1998 McCormick Company annual report.

Year	Net Sales	Capital Expenditures	Current Debt	Long-Term Debt	Shareholders' Equity
1988	$1,099.10	$50.40	$49.50	$229.40	$294.30
1989	1,110.20	53.40	20.30	210.50	346.20
1990	1,166.20	58.40	30.40	311.50	364.40
1991	1,276.30	73.00	78.20	207.60	389.20
1992	1,323.90	79.30	122.60	201.00	437.90
1993	1,400.90	76.10	84.70	346.40	466.80
1994	1,529.40	87.70	214.00	374.30	490.00
1995	1,691.10	82.10	297.30	349.10	519.30
1996	1,732.50	74.70	108.90	291.20	450.00
1997	1,801.00	43.90	121.30	276.50	393.10

a. Compute the linear regression model based on the sample data if net sales are to be predicted using capital expenditures.

b. Conduct a test to determine whether the relationship between McCormick's net sales and capital expenditures is significant. Interpret the meaning of this measure.

c. Refer to part b. Describe the type of hypothesis test error that could have been made in the context of this problem.

d. Provide a brief financial explanation of the regression slope coefficient.

13.24 The data in the CD-ROM file *Baldor* are from that company's 1998 annual report.

a. Compute the linear regression model based on the sample data using net sales as the independent variable and working capital as the dependent variable.

b. Conduct a test to determine whether net sales can be used to predict working capital for Baldor Electric. Conduct this hypothesis test using the *p*-value approach.

c. Compute the *R*-squared value and discuss how well you believe Baldor will be able to predict its working capital using its net sales.

Advanced Applications

13.25 Referring again to the automobile magazine editor discussed in Exercise 13.20, the editor now wants to examine the relationship between price of the vehicle and the horsepower of the engine.

a. (1) Develop a scatter plot for these data. (2) Discuss what the plot implies about the relationship between the two variables. Use price as the dependent (*y*) variable.

b. Compute the correlation coefficient for the two variables.

c. Compute the linear regression equation based on the sample data.

d. Toyota's 1999 Camry four-cylinder model generates 133 horsepower. Provide an estimate of the price of the 1999 Camry. Toyota's suggested retail price for the Camry LE 4A model was $20,278. Calculate the appropriate residual for this model of Camry.

e. (1) Compute the *R*-squared value and discuss what this value means. (2) At a significance level of 0.01, can you conclude that engine horsepower is a good predictor of the price of an automobile?

13.26 A 1998 article in Fortune magazine titled *The 100 Best Companies to Work For in America* (January 12, 1998) contained selected characteristics on the 100

companies. These data are included in the CD-ROM file *Best-Companies*. Two variables of interest are the revenues of each company and the number of hours of training per year per employee. (Note: You will need to omit companies with data marked N.A. before completing the analysis.)

a. Develop a scatter plot for these data. Discuss what the plot implies about the relationship between the two variables.

b. Provide a measurement that will provide an indication of the strength of the linear relationship between revenues and the number of hours of training for employees.

c. Compute the linear regression equation based on the sample data if you wish to use the revenue of a company to predict the number of hours of training per year per employee. Interpret the slope and intercept coefficients.

d. Using a significance level of 0.01, test to determine whether the true regression slope is zero. Do your test results suggest that if companies stop training their employees that their revenues will not suffer? Does the result of your test indicate that there is no relationship whatsoever between revenues and the number of hours of training for employees? Discuss these two related questions.

e. Refer to part d. Describe the type of hypothesis test error that could have been made in the context of this problem.

13.27 A study has been conducted for a sample of cities in the United States. Among the data collected for each city were the 1995 population and the 1998 unemployment rate. The data are contained in the CD-ROM file *Cities*.

a. Develop a scatter plot for these data. Discuss what the plot implies about the relationship between the two variables. Assume you wish to predict the unemployment rate using the population of the city.

b. Compute the correlation coefficient for the two variables.

c. (1) Compute the linear regression equation based on the sample data. (2) Conduct a statistical procedure to determine if cities with larger populations in 1995 had higher employment rates in 1998.

13-3 USES FOR REGRESSION ANALYSIS

Regression analysis is a statistical tool that is used for two main purposes: description and prediction. This section discusses these two applications.

Excel and Minitab Tutorial

REGRESSION ANALYSIS FOR DESCRIPTION

Car Mileage—In the spring of 2000, gasoline prices soared to record levels in the United States, heightening customers' concern for fuel economy. Analysts at a major automobile company collected data on a variety of variables for a sample of 30 different cars and small trucks. Included among those data were the EPA highway mileage rating and the horsepower of each vehicle. What is the relationship between horsepower (x) and highway mileage (y)? The data are contained in the file *Automobiles* on the CD-ROM.

A simple linear regression model can be developed using Excel or Minitab, as shown in Figure 13-20. For these sample data, the coefficient of determination, $R^2 = 0.3016$ indicates that knowing the horsepower of the vehicle explains 30.16% of the variation in the highway mileage. The estimated regression equation is

$$\hat{y} = 31.1658 - 0.0286x$$

Before the analysts attempt to describe the relationship between horsepower and highway mileage, they first need to test whether there is a statistically significant linear relationship between the two variables. To do this, they can apply the t test described in Section 13-2 to test the following null and alternative hypotheses:

$$H_0: \beta_1 = 0$$
$$H_A: \beta_1 \neq 0$$

at the significance level

$$\alpha = 0.05$$

The calculated t statistic and the corresponding p-value are shown in Figure 13-20. Because the
$$p\text{-value} = 0.0017 < 0.05$$
the null hypothesis

$$H_0 \text{ is rejected,}$$

and the analysts can conclude that the population regression slope is not equal to zero.

The sample slope, b_1, equals -0.0286. This means that for each one-unit increase in horsepower, the highway mileage decreases by an average of 0.0286 miles per gallon. However, b_1 is subject to sampling error and is considered a *point estimate* for the true regression slope coefficient. From earlier discussions about point estimates in Chapters 7 and 9, we expect that $b_1 \neq \beta_1$. Therefore, to fully describe the relationship between the independent variable, horsepower, and the dependent variable, highway miles per gallon, we need to develop a *confidence interval estimate* for β_1. Equation 13-21 is used to do this.

FIGURE 13-20

Excel Regression Results for the Automobile Mileage Study

Excel Instructions:
1. Open file: Automobiles.xls
2. Select **Tools**.
3. Click on **Regression**.
4. Define y variable range.
5. Define x variable range.

Minitab Instructions (for similar results):
1. Open file: Automobiles.MTW.
2. Choose **Stat > Regression > Regression**.
3. In **Response**, enter the y variable column.
4. In **Predictors**, enter the x variable column.
5. Click **OK**.

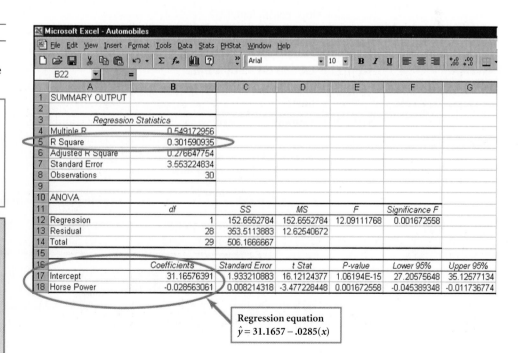

Confidence Interval Estimate for the Regression Slope, Simple Linear Regression

$$b_1 \pm t_{\alpha/2} s_{b_1}$$

13-21

or equivalently,

$$b_1 \pm t_{\alpha/2} \frac{s_\varepsilon}{\sqrt{\Sigma(x - \bar{x})^2}} \qquad df = n - 2$$

where:

s_{b_1} = Standard error of the regression slope coefficient

s_ε = Standard error of the estimate

The regression output shown in Figure 13-20 contains the 95% confidence interval estimate for the slope coefficient, which is

−0.045 - - - - - - - - - - - - - - - - - −0.012

Thus, at the 95% confidence level, based on the sample data, the analysts for the car company can conclude that a one-unit increase in horsepower will result in an average drop in mileage by an average amount between 0.012 and 0.045 miles per gallon.

There are many other situations in which the prime purpose of regression analysis is description. Economists use regression analysis for descriptive purposes as they search for a way of explaining the economy. Market researchers also use regression analysis, among other techniques, in an effort to describe the factors that influence the demand for products.

EXAMPLE 13-4: DEVELOPING A CONFIDENCE INTERVAL ESTIMATE FOR THE REGRESSION SLOPE

Home Prices   Home values are determined by a variety of factors. One factor is the size of the house (square feet). Recently a study was conducted by First City Real Estate aimed at estimating the average value of each additional square foot of space in a house. A simple random sample of 319 homes that were sold within the past year was collected. The data are in a file called *First-City* on the CD-ROM. Here are the steps required to compute a confidence interval estimate for the regression slope coefficient.

Step 1: **Define the y (dependent) and x (independent) variables.**
The dependent variable is sales price, and the independent variable is square feet.

Step 2: **Obtain the sample data.**
The study consists of sales prices and corresponding square feet for a sample of 319 homes.

Step 3: **Compute the regression equation and the standard error of the slope coefficient.**
These computations can be performed manually using Equations 13-7 and 13-8 for the regression model and Equation 13-19 for the standard error of the slope. Alternatively, we can use Excel or Minitab to obtain these values.

	Coefficients	Standard Error
Intercept (b_0)	39838.48333	7304.951587
Square Feet (b_1)	75.69512354	3.775610524

The point estimate for the regression slope coefficient is $75.70. Thus, for a one-square-foot increase in the size of a house, house prices increase by an average of $75.70. This is a point estimate and is subject to sampling error.

Step 4: **Construct and interpret the confidence interval estimate for the regression slope using Equation 13-21.**
The confidence interval estimate is

$$b_1 \pm t_{\alpha/2} s_{b_1}$$

where the degrees of freedom for the critical t is $319 - 2 = 317$. The critical t for a 95% confidence interval estimate is approximately 1.96, and the interval estimate is

$$\$75.70 \pm 1.96(\$3.78)$$
$$\$75.70 \pm \$7.41$$
$$\$68.29 ------------------- \$83.11$$

So, for a one-square-foot increase in house size, at the 95% confidence level, homes increase in price by an average of between \$68.29 and \$83.11.

REGRESSION ANALYSIS FOR PREDICTION

Freedom Hospital—One of the main uses of regression analysis is *prediction.* You may need to predict the value of the dependent variable based on the value of the independent variable. Consider the administrator for Freedom Hospital, who has been asked by the hospital's board of directors to develop a model to predict the total charges for a geriatric patient. The CD-ROM file *Patients* contains the data that the administrator has collected.

Although the Regression tool in Excel works well for generating the simple linear regression equation and other useful information, it does not provide predicted values for the dependent variable. However, both Minitab and the PHStat add-ins do provide predictions. We will illustrate the Minitab output, which is formatted somewhat differently than the Excel output but contains the same basic information.

The administrator is attempting to construct a simple linear regression model, with total charges as the dependent (y) variable and length of stay as the independent (x) variable. Figure 13-21 shows the Minitab regression output. The least squares regression equation is

$$\hat{y} = 528 + 1,353x$$

As shown in the figure, the regression slope coefficient is significantly different from zero ($t = 14.17$; p-value = 0.000). The model explains 59.6% of the variation in the total charges (R-squared = 59.6%). Notice in Figure 13-21 that Minitab has rounded the regression coefficient. The more-precise values are provided in the column headed "Coef" and are

$$\hat{y} = 527.6 + 1,352.80x$$

FIGURE 13-21

Minitab Regression Output for Freedom Hospital

Minitab Instructions:
1. Open file: Patients.MTW.
2. Choose **Stat > Regression > Regression.**
3. In **Response**, enter the y variable column.
4. In **Predictors**, enter the x variable column.
5. Click **OK.**

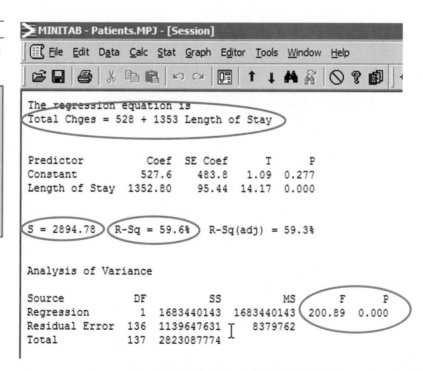

The administrator could use this equation to predict total charges by substituting the length of stay into the regression equation for x. For example, suppose a patient has a five-day stay. The predicted total charges are

$$\hat{y} = 527.6 + 1,352.80(5)$$
$$\hat{y} = \$7,291.60$$

Note that this predicted value is a *point estimate* of the actual charges for this patient. The true charges will be either higher or lower than this amount. The administrator can develop a prediction interval, which is similar to the confidence interval estimates developed in Chapter 7.

Excel and Minitab Tutorial

Confidence Interval for the Average y, Given x

The marketing manager might like a 95% confidence interval for *average* charges for all patients who stay in the hospital five days. The confidence interval for the expected value of a dependent variable, given a specific level of the independent variable, is determined by Equation 13-22. Observe that the specific value of x used to provide the prediction is denoted as x_p.

Confidence Interval for $E(y)|x_p$

$$\hat{y} \pm t_{\alpha/2} s_\varepsilon \sqrt{\frac{1}{n} + \frac{(x_p - \bar{x})^2}{\Sigma(x - \bar{x})^2}}$$

13-22

where:

$\hat{y}$ = Point estimate of the dependent variable
t = Critical value with $n - 2$ df
n = Sample size
x_p = Specific value of the independent variable
$\bar{x}$ = Mean of the independent variable observations in the sample
s_ε = Estimate of the standard error of the estimate

Although the confidence interval estimate can be manually computed using Equation 13-22, using your computer is much easier. For instance, both PHStat and Minitab have built-in options to generate the confidence interval estimate for the dependent variable for a given value of the x variable. Figure 13-22 shows the Minitab results when length of stay, x, equals five days. Given this length of stay, the point estimate for the mean total charges is rounded by Minitab to $7,292, and at the 95% confidence level, the administrators believe the mean total charges will be in the interval $6,790 to $7,794.

FIGURE 13-22

Minitab Output: Freedom Hospital Confidence Interval Estimate

Minitab Instructions:
1. Use instructions in Figure 13-21 to get regression results.
2. Before clicking **OK**, select **Options**.
3. In **Prediction Interval for New Observations**, enter value(s) of x variable.
4. In **Confidence level**, enter $(1 - \alpha)100$.
5. Click **OK. OK.**

Prediction Interval for a Particular *y*, Given *x*

The confidence interval shown in Figure 13-22 is for the average value of *y* given x_p. The administrator might also be interested in predicting the total charges for a *particular* patient with a five-day stay, rather than the average of the charges for all patients staying five days. Developing this 95% prediction interval requires only a slight modification to Equation 13-22. This prediction interval is given by Equation 13-23.

Prediction Interval for $y | x_p$

$$\hat{y} \pm t_{\alpha/2} s_\varepsilon \sqrt{1 + \frac{1}{n} + \frac{(x_p - \bar{x})^2}{\Sigma(x - \bar{x})^2}}$$

13-23

As was the case with the confidence interval application discussed previously, the manual computations required to use Equation 13-23 can be onerous. We recommend using your computer and software such as Minitab or PHStat to find the prediction interval. Figure 13-23 shows the PHStat results. Note that the same PHStat process generates both the prediction and confidence interval estimates.

Based on this regression model, at the 95% confidence level, the hospital administrators can predict total charges for any patient with length of stay of five days to be between $1,545 and $13,038.

As you can see, this prediction has extremely poor precision. We doubt any hospital administrator will use a prediction interval that is so wide. Although the regression model explains a significant proportion of variation in the dependent variable, it is relatively imprecise for predictive purposes. To improve the precision, we might decrease the confidence requirements or increase the sample size and redevelop the model.

The prediction interval for a specific value of the dependent variable is wider (less precise) than the confidence interval for predicting the average value of the dependent variable. This will always be the case, as seen in Equations 13-22 and 13-23. From an intuitive viewpoint, we should expect to come closer to predicting an average value than a single value.

Note, the term $(x_p - \bar{x})^2$ has a particular effect on the confidence interval determined by both Equations 13-22 and 13-23. The farther x_p (the value of the independent variable used to predict *y*), is from $\bar{x}$, the greater $(x_p - \bar{x})^2$ becomes. Figure 13-24 shows two regression lines developed from two samples with the same set of *x* values. We have made both lines pass through the same $(\bar{x}, \bar{y})$

FIGURE 13-23

Excel (PHStat) Prediction Interval for Freedom Hospital

Excel (PHStat) Instructions:
1. Open file: Patients.xls
2. Select **PHStat**.
3. Click on **Regression**.
4. Select **Simple Linear Regression**.
5. Specify *y* and *x* data ranges.
6. Define x_p.
7. Specify confidence level for intervals.

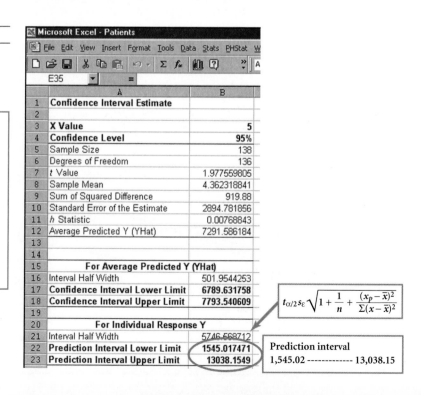

FIGURE **13-24**

Regression Lines Illustrating the Increase in Potential Variation in y as x_p Moves Farther from $\bar{x}$

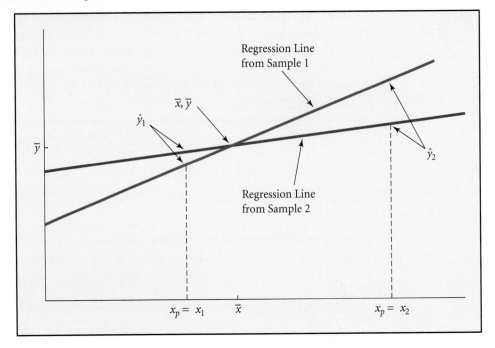

point; however, they have different slopes and intercepts. At $x_p = x_1$, the two regression lines give predictions of y that are close to each other. However, for $x_p = x_2$, the predictions of y are quite different. Thus, when x_p is close to $\bar{x}$, the problems caused by variations in regression slopes are not as great as when x_p is far from $\bar{x}$. Figure 13-25 shows the prediction intervals over the range of possible x_p values. The band around the estimated regression line bends away from the regression line as x_p moves in either direction from $\bar{x}$.

RESIDUAL ANALYSIS

Recall two important assumptions associated with linear regression analysis.

SSUMPTIONS

1. The model errors are normally distributed.
2. The model errors have a constant variance at all levels of the independent variable.

FIGURE **13-25**

Confidence Intervals for $y|x_p$ and $E(y)|x_p$

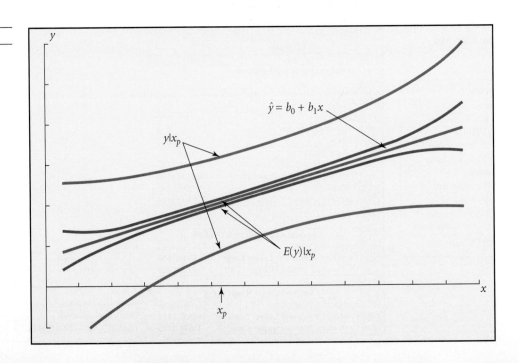

Before using a regression model for description or prediction, you should check to see if these assumptions are satisfied. One way to do this is by examining graphs called *residual plots*. Both Excel and Minitab can be used to generate residual plots.

Excel and Minitab Tutorial

Freedom Hospital (continued)—Previously we showed the regression model constructed by the administrator at Freedom Hospital. He wanted to predict the total patient charges by knowing the patient length of stay. The resulting model was statistically significant. However, before the hospital actually uses this model, the administrator might develop two different residual plots. The first is a *residual frequency histogram*, which is shown in Figure 13-26. As you can see, the histogram closely resembles a normal distribution, which is one indication that the normality assumption is satisfied.

The second residual plot charts the residuals against the *x* variable, as shown in Figure 13-27. Chapter 14 discusses this type of plot more fully. For now, you will be looking for a result in which the residuals have approximately the same spread at all levels of *x*. In Figure 13-27, the plot illustrates that for short lengths of stay, the spread in the residuals is less than when stays are longer. This implies that the assumption of equal variances in the residuals is violated. We will discuss this in more detail in Chapter 14 and suggest possible steps for improving the regression model.

COMMON PROBLEMS USING REGRESSION ANALYSIS

Regression is perhaps the most widely used statistical tool other than descriptive statistical techniques. Because it is so widely used, you need to be aware of the common problems found when the technique is employed.

One potential problem occurs when decision makers apply regression analysis for predictive purposes. The conclusions and inferences made from a regression line are statistically valid only over the range of the data contained in the sample used to develop the regression line. For instance, in the Midwest Distribution example, we analyzed the performance of sales representatives with one to nine years of experience. Therefore, predicting sales levels for employees with one to nine years of experience would be justified. However, if we were to try to predict the sales performance of someone with more than nine years of experience, the relationship between sales and experience might be different. Because no observations were taken for experience levels beyond the one- to nine-year range, we have no information about what might happen outside that range. Figure

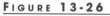

FIGURE 13-26

Minitab Residual Histogram for Freedom Hospital

Minitab Instructions:
1. Open file: Patients.MTW.
2. Choose **Stat > Regression > Regression**.
3. In **Response**, enter the y variable column.
4. In **Predictors**, enter the x variable column.
5. Click **Storage**, under **Diagnostic Measures** select **Residuals**.
6. Click **OK**.
7. Choose **Graphs > Histogram of Residuals**.
8. Click **OK**. **OK**.

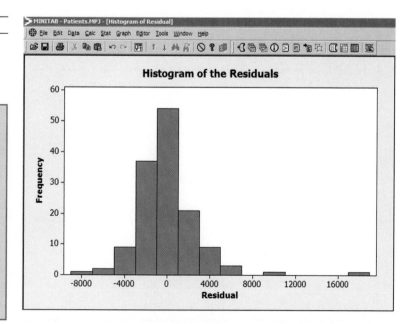

FIGURE 13-27

Minitab Residual Plot for Freedom Hospital Example

Minitab Instructions:
1. Open file: Patients.MTW.
2. Choose **Stat > Regression > Regression**.
3. In **Response**, enter the y variable column.
4. In **Predictors**, enter the x variable column.
5. Select **Graphs**.
6. In **Residuals versus the variables**: enter the x variable column.
7. Click **OK. OK.**

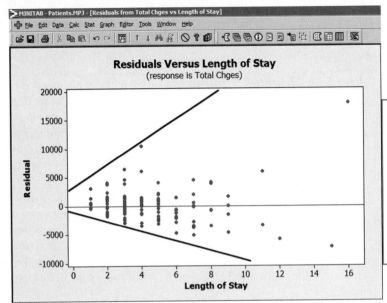

Excel Instructions (for similar results):
1. Open file: Patients.xls
2. Choose **Tools > Data Analysis > Regression**.
3. Select data range for x variable.
4. Select data range for x variable.
5. Check boxes for residuals and residual plots.

13-28 shows a case in which the true relationship between sales and experience reaches a peak value at about 20 years and then starts to decline. If a linear regression equation were used to predict sales based on experience levels beyond the relevant range of data, large prediction errors could occur.

A second important consideration, one that was discussed earlier, involves correlation and causation. The fact that a significant linear relationship exists between two variables does not imply that one variable causes the other. Although there may be a cause-and-effect relationship, you should not infer that such a relationship is present based only on regression and/or correlation analysis. You should also recognize that a cause-and-effect relationship between two variables is not necessary for regression analysis to be an effective tool. What matters is that the regression model accurately reflects the relationship between the two variables and that the relationship remains stable.

Finally, many users of regression analysis mistakenly believe that a high coefficient of determination (R^2) guarantees that the regression model will be a good predictor. You should remember that R^2 is a measure of the variation in the dependent variable explained by the independent variable. Although the least squares criterion assures us that R^2 will be maximized (because the sum of

FIGURE 13-28

Graph for a Sales Peak at 20 Years

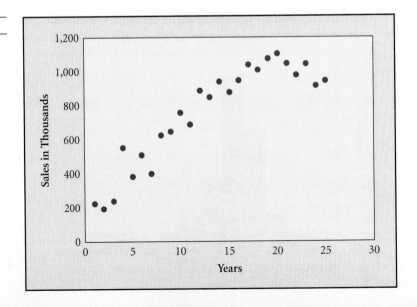

squares error is a minimum) for the given set of sample data, the value applies only to those data used to develop the model. Thus, R^2 measures the fit of the regression line to the sample data. There is no guarantee that there will be an equally good fit with new data. The only true test of a regression model's predictive ability is how well the model actually predicts.

Finally, we should mention that you might find a large R^2 with a large sum of squares error. This can happen if total sum of squares is large in comparison to the SSE. Then, even though R^2 is relatively large, so too is the estimate of the model's standard error. Thus, confidence and prediction errors may be simply too wide for the model to be used in many situations.

13-3: EXERCISES

Skill Development

13.28 You are given the following results from computations pertaining to a simple linear regression application:

$$\hat{y} = 5{,}723.0 + 145x$$
$$n = 25$$
$$s_{b_1} = 10.80$$

a. Based on the statistics supplied, can you conclude that there is a significant linear relationship between x and y? Test at a significance level of 0.05.
b. Interpret the slope coefficient.
c. Develop a 95% confidence interval estimate for the true regression slope and interpret the estimate.

13.29 The following data have been collected by an accountant who is performing an audit of paper products at a large office supply company. The dependent variable, y, is the time taken (in minutes) by the accountant to count the units. The independent variable, x, is the number of units on the computer inventory record.

y	23.1	100.5	242.9	56.4	178.7	10.5	94.2	200.4	44.2	128.7	180.5
x	24	120	228	56	190	13	85	190	32	120	230

a. Develop a scatter plot for these data.
b. Determine the regression equation representing this data. Is the model significant? Test using a significance level of 0.10 and the p-value approach.
c. Develop a 90% confidence interval estimate for the true regression slope and interpret this interval estimate. Based on this interval, could you conclude the accountant takes an additional minute to count each additional unit?

13.30 You are given the following summary statistics from a regression analysis:

$$\hat{y} = 200 + 150x$$
$$SSE = 25.25$$
$$SSX = \text{Sum of squares } x = \Sigma x^2 - \frac{(\Sigma x)^2}{n} = 99{,}645$$
$$n = 18$$
$$x = 52.0$$

a. Determine the point estimate for y if $x_p = 48$ is used.
b. Provide a 95% confidence interval estimate for the average y, given $x_p = 48$.
c. Provide a 95% prediction interval estimate for a particular y, given $x_p = 48$.

d. Discuss the difference between the estimates provided in parts b and c.

13.31 The following summary statistics were obtained from a regression analysis:

$$\hat{y} = 9{,}784 - 345.50x$$
$$SSE = 800.25$$
$$SSX = \text{Sum of squares } x = \Sigma x^2 - \frac{(\Sigma x)^2}{n} = 145{,}789$$
$$\bar{x} = 67.20$$
$$n = 20$$

a. Provide a 90% confidence interval estimate for the average y, given $x_p = 80$.
b. An estimate of a particular y is required for a given $x_p = 80$. Determine the largest error $y_i - \hat{y}_i$ you would expect from estimating the independent variable with a 90% confidence interval.

13.32 You are given the following summary statistics from a regression analysis:

$$\hat{y} = 1{,}200 + 0.878x$$
$$SSE = 145.40$$
$$SSX = \text{Sum of squares } x = 134{,}679$$
$$\bar{x} = 40{,}000$$
$$n = 8$$

a. Provide a 95% prediction interval estimate for the average y, given $x_p = 40{,}000$.
b. Provide a 95% prediction interval estimate for a particular y, given $x_p = 40{,}000$.
c. (1) What would happen to the precision of the estimate if the value of x_p were increased to 43,000? Discuss. (2) What value of x_p would produce the greatest precision?

Business Applications

13.33 The Shelton Manufacturing Company recently did a study of its customers. A random sample of 50 customer accounts was pulled from the computer records. Two variables were observed:

y = Total dollar volume of business this year
x = Miles customer is from corporate headquarters

The following quantities were computed:

$$\hat{y} = 2{,}140.23 - 10.12x$$
$$s_{b_1} = 3.12$$

a. Interpret the regression slope coefficient in the context of this problem.

b. Develop a 95% confidence interval estimate of the change in the amount of total dollar volume you would expect to see if a company relocated to a site that was an additional 100 miles from Shelton's corporate headquarters.

c. Construct a 90% prediction interval for the change in total dollar volume if the firm in part b relocated an additional 50 miles from Shelton's corporate headquarters.

13.34 The state Department of Transportation has conducted a study of 100 randomly selected vehicles in which the speed of each vehicle and the age of the driver were measured. The data were collected from a stretch of highway that produces an unusually high accident rate. A regression model was developed with vehicle speed being predicted, using age as the independent variable. The results obtained were

$$\hat{y} = 56.78 + 0.124x$$
$$s_{b_1} = 2.88$$

a. Develop a 95% interval estimate for the true regression slope and interpret.

b. Based on your response to part a, can you conclude that age and speed are linearly related? Explain your answer.

13.35 The following data have been collected by an accountant who is performing an audit of account balances for a major retail company. The population from which the data were collected represented those accounts for which the customer had indicated the balance was incorrect. The dependent variable, y, is the actual account balance as verified by the accountant. The independent variable, x, is the computer account balance.

| y | 233 | 10 | 24 | 56 | 78 | 102 | 90 | 200 | 344 | 120 | 18 |
| x | 245 | 12 | 22 | 56 | 90 | 103 | 85 | 190 | 320 | 120 | 33 |

a. Compute the least squares regression equation.

b. If a computer account balance were 100, what would you expect to be the actual account balance as verified by the accountant?

c. The computer balance for Timothy Jones is listed as 100 in the computer account record. Provide a 90% interval estimate for Mr. Jones's actual account balance.

d. Provide a 90% interval estimate for the average of all customers' actual account balances in which a computer account balance is the same as that of Mr. Jones. Interpret.

Advanced Applications

13.36 One of the editors of a major automobile publication has collected data on 30 of the best-selling cars in the United States. The data are in the CD-ROM file *Automobiles*. The editor is particularly interested in the relationship between highway mileage and curb weight of the vehicles.

a. Develop a linear regression model in which highway mileage is to be predicted by using curb weight.

b. The editor just purchased a Cadillac Sedan DeVille, which weighs 4,012 lbs. His previous car was a Toyota Camry, which weighed 3,241 lbs. He wonders how much of a decrease in gas mileage he should expect. Give the editor an idea of the maximum and minimum decreases in gas mileage he should expect. You should use a procedure that will allow you to be 90% confident of your answer.

c. Provide an estimate of the gasoline mileage the editor should expect from his newly purchased car. Suppose the estimate you just provided is the true average mpg for cars that weigh the same as the Cadillac. Cadillac advertises that the Sedan DeVille has a mileage rating of 26 mpg. Determine the percentile for the DeVille's mileage rating.

d. The individual from whom the editor purchased the Cadillac said this car got the exceptional gas mileage of 29 mpg. Construct an appropriate 95% interval estimate that would indicate whether the seller of the Cadillac was stretching the truth. Comment on the seller's veracity.

13.37 Refer to Exercise 13.36, in which a major automobile publication has collected data on 30 of the best-selling cars in the United States. The data are in the CD-ROM file *Automobiles*. The editor is particularly interested in the relationship between highway mileage and curb weight of the vehicles.

a. The editor often takes his entire family to visit relatives in a nearby state. The combined weight of his family is 570 lbs. Combining the weight of the editor's new Cadillac and that of his family, provide an estimate for the gas mileage the editor should expect to get on a trip to visit these relatives.

b. Calculate a 95% prediction interval for the average highway mileage for a car with a curb weight equal to the weight of the Cadillac when the editor's family is inside.

c. Compute a 95% prediction interval for the actual highway mileage of this particular Cadillac carrying the editor's family.

d. Compare the prediction intervals computed in this problem to that computed in part d of Exercise 13.36. Discuss why the intervals are different width even though the same confidence level is used.

e. Suppose an editor for the publication wishes to predict the highway mileage of vehicles with a curb weight of 6,000 pounds. What cautions should be made before using this regression model to make that prediction? Discuss.

f. Finally, Toyota considered increasing the horsepower in its Camry motor by 10% (recall that the horsepower for the 1999 Camry was 133). Give advice on how much the cost of the automobile should increase based solely on the increase in horsepower. Provide minimum and maximum amounts of increase you would expect with a 90% probability.

13.38 A 1998 article in *Fortune* magazine titled *The 100 Best Companies to Work For in America* (January 12, 1998) contained data on the 100 companies. These data are included in the CD-ROM file *Best-Companies*. Three variables of interest are the revenues of each company, the number of hours of training per year per employee and the number of employees. (Note: You will need to omit companies with data marked N.A. before completing the analysis.)

a. Compute the linear regression equation based on the sample data if the revenue of each company is to be used to predict the number of hours of training per year per employee.

b. Would you feel comfortable using the revenue of one of the 100 companies to determine the number of hours of training per year per employee with a sim-

ple linear regression model? Conduct a statistical procedure to answer this question.

c. Synovus Financial has 8,827 employees. Predict the number of hours of training per year per employee for Synovus.

d. Referring to part c, develop and interpret a 90% prediction interval for the average training hours per employee for companies with 8,827 employees.

e. Referring to part d, what is the 90% confidence interval for average training hours per employee for companies with 40,000 employees? Compare this interval with the one computed in part d and discuss why the widths of the two are different.

f. Referring to parts d and e, at what number of employees would the width of a 90% prediction interval for average training hours be minimized?

g. Referring to parts d and e, develop and interpret a 90% prediction interval for the actual training hours per employee for Synovus.

Summary and Conclusions

Correlation and regression analysis are two of the most frequently used statistical techniques for business decision makers. This chapter has introduced the basics of these two topics. The discussion of regression analysis has been limited to situations in which you have one dependent variable and one independent variable. In these cases, the technique for modeling the linear relationship between the two variables is referred to as simple linear regression analysis.

If two variables are correlated, then they are said to be linearly related. When that's the case, the resulting simple linear regression model will be statistically significant, which means that the fraction of variation in the dependent variable that is explained by the independent variable (R-squared) is significant and the predictions for the y variable based on values of x will be superior to using the mean of y as the predictor.

This chapter introduced the methods used to test whether a correlation is zero and whether a regression slope coefficient is zero. We also introduced you to the uses of regression for descriptive and predictive purposes and showed how to construct confidence interval estimates for the true regression slope coefficient and prediction intervals.

Chapter 14 will extend the discussion of regression analysis by showing how two or more independent variables are included in the analysis. The focus of that chapter will be on building a model for explaining the variation in the dependent variable. However, the basic concepts presented in this chapter will be carried forward.

or the algebraic equivalent:

$$r = \frac{n \sum xy - \sum x \sum y}{\sqrt{[n(\sum x^2) - (\sum x)^2][n(\sum y^2) - (\sum y)^2]}} \quad \text{13-2}$$

Test Statistic for Correlation

$$t = \frac{r}{\sqrt{\frac{1 - r^2}{n - 2}}} \qquad df = n - 2 \qquad \text{13-3}$$

Simple Linear Regression Model (Population Model)

$$y = \beta_0 + \beta_1 x + \varepsilon \quad \text{13-4}$$

Estimated Regression Model (Sample Model)

$$\hat{y} = b_0 + b_1 x \quad \text{13-5}$$

Least Squares Equations (Sample Values)

$$b_1 = \frac{\sum(x - \bar{x})(y - \bar{y})}{\sum(x - \bar{x})^2} \quad \text{13-6}$$

algebraic equivalent:

$$b_1 = \frac{\sum xy - \frac{\sum x \sum y}{n}}{\sum x^2 - \frac{(\sum x)^2}{n}} \quad \text{13-7}$$

and

$$b_0 = \bar{y} - b_1 \bar{x} \quad \text{13-8}$$

EQUATIONS

Sample Correlation Coefficient

$$r = \frac{\sum(x - \bar{x})(y - \bar{y})}{\sqrt{[\sum(x - \bar{x})^2][\sum(y - \bar{y})^2]}} \quad \text{13-1}$$

Sum of Squared Errors

$$SSE = \sum y^2 - b_0 \sum y - b_1 \sum xy \quad \text{13-9}$$

Sum of Residuals

$$\sum_{i=1}^{n} (y_i - \hat{y}_i) = 0 \qquad \textbf{13-10}$$

Sum of Squared Residuals

$$SSE = \sum_{i=1}^{n} (y_i - \hat{y}_i)^2 \qquad \textbf{13-11}$$

Total Sum of Squares

$$SST = \sum_{i=1}^{n} (y_i - \bar{y})^2 \qquad \textbf{13-12}$$

Sum of Squares Error

$$SSE = \sum_{i=1}^{n} (y_i - \hat{y}_i)^2 \qquad \textbf{13-13}$$

Sum of Squares Regression

$$SSR = \sum_{i=1}^{n} (\hat{y}_i - \bar{y})^2 \qquad \textbf{13-14}$$

Coefficient of Determination, R^2

$$R^2 = \frac{SSR}{SST} \qquad \textbf{13-15}$$

Coefficient of Determination, Single Independent Variable Case

$$R^2 = r^2 \qquad \textbf{13-16}$$

Standard Deviation of the Regression Slope Coefficient (Population)

$$\sigma_{b_1} = \frac{\sigma_\varepsilon}{\sqrt{\sum(x - \bar{x})^2}} \qquad \textbf{13-17}$$

Estimator for the Standard Error of the Estimate

$$s_\varepsilon = \sqrt{\frac{SSE}{n - k - 1}} \qquad \textbf{13-18}$$

Estimator for the Standard Deviation of the Regression Slope

$$s_{b_1} = \frac{s_\varepsilon}{\sqrt{\sum(x - \bar{x})^2}} = \frac{s_\varepsilon}{\sqrt{\sum x^2 - \frac{(\sum x)^2}{n}}} \qquad \textbf{13-19}$$

Test Statistic for Test of the Significance of the Regression Slope

$$t = \frac{b_1 - \beta_1}{s_{b_1}} \qquad df = n - 2 \qquad \textbf{13-20}$$

Confidence Interval Estimate for the Regression Slope, Simple Linear Regression

$$b_1 \pm t_{\alpha/2} s_{b_1} \qquad \textbf{13-21}$$

or equivalently,

$$b_1 \pm t_{\alpha/2} \frac{s_\varepsilon}{\sqrt{\sum(x - \bar{x})^2}} \qquad \text{with } df = n - 2$$

Confidence Interval for $E(y)|x_p$

$$\hat{y} \pm t_{\alpha/2} s_\varepsilon \sqrt{\frac{1}{n} + \frac{(x_p - \bar{x})^2}{\sum(x - \bar{x})^2}} \qquad \textbf{13-22}$$

Prediction Interval for $y|x_p$

$$\hat{y} \pm t_{\alpha/2} s_\varepsilon \sqrt{1 + \frac{1}{n} + \frac{(x_p - \bar{x})^2}{\sum(x - \bar{x})^2}} \qquad \textbf{13-23}$$

Key Terms

CHAPTER EXERCISES

Conceptual Questions

13.39 Think of two variables that you believe would be negatively related in a linear manner. Describe what is meant by a negative linear relationship.

13.40 A statistics student was recently working on a class project that required him to compute a correlation coefficient for two variables. After careful work, he arrived at a correlation coefficient of 0.45. Interpret this correlation coefficient for the student who did the calculations.

13.41 Referring to Exercise 13.40, another student in the same class computed a regression equation relating the two variables. The slope of the equation was found to be −0.735.

After trying several times and always coming up with the same result, she felt that she must have been doing something wrong because the value was negative and she knew that this could not be right. Comment on this student's conclusion.

13.42 If we select a random sample of data for two variables and, after computing the correlation coefficient, conclude that the two variables may have zero correlation, can we say that there is no relationship between the two variables? Discuss.

13.43 Discuss why prediction intervals that attempt to predict a particular y value are less precise than confidence intervals for predicting an average y.

Business Applications

13.44 The Farmington City Council recently commissioned a study of park users in their community. Data were collected on the age of each person surveyed and the amount of hours he or she had spent in the park in the past month. The data collected were as follows:

Time in Park	Age
7.2	16
3.5	15
6.6	28
5.4	16
1.5	29
2.3	38
4.4	48
8.8	18
4.9	24
5.1	33
1.0	56

a. Draw a scatter plot for these data and discuss what, if any, relationship appears to be present between the two variables.
b. Compute the correlation coefficient between age and the amount of time spent in the park. Provide an explanation to the Farmington City Council explaining what the correlation measures.
c. Test to determine whether the amount of time spent in the park increases with the ages of the park users. Use a significance level of 0.10. Use a p-value approach to conduct this hypothesis test.

13.45 A marketing research study performed by the marketing division of the Klondike Company surveyed the income levels and expenditures on recreation for a sample of 20 people. Measurements recorded the expenditures on recreation during the previous year, y, and the total annual family income, x.

y	x	y	x
$1,425	$21,300	$900	$17,600
1,675	30,200	1,000	16,890
1,356	31,500	2,450	28,000
4,530	45,900	650	14,300
3,200	34,600	300	9,800
1,060	17,800	1,500	24,700
4,090	53,600	890	20,500
1,200	17,400	2,300	31,700
1,800	26,800	3,100	47,800
700	15,700	100	8,400

a. Draw a scatter plot for these data and discuss what, if any, relationship appears to exist between the variables, based on the scatter plot.
b. Compute the correlation coefficient for the two variables, income and dollars spent on recreation.
c. Test to determine whether the amount spent on recreation increases as the annual family income increases. Use a significance level of 0.025.

13.46 The Savemore Brokerage Firm of Spokane, Washington, recently studied a random sample of companies whose stocks are sold on the New York Stock Exchange. Among other things, it collected data on stock price, y, and the previous year's profits, x. The following data were collected. (The x variable is measured in thousands of dollars.)

y	x	y	x
$18.70	$40,000	$12.60	$12,500
34.50	24,900	43.60	9,000
25.70	102,000	33.50	23,900
8.90	44,000	71.80	15,000
25.90	123,700	15.00	45,000
11.11	36,900	6.78	99,500
21.00	3,700	21.70	45,300
3.50	145,900	44.70	23,600

Draw a scatter plot for these data and discuss what, if any, relationship appears to exist between the two variables. Also comment on what other factors might be important to consider when studying stock price and earnings of a company.

13.47 A company that makes a cattle feed supplement has studied 335 cattle and found the correlation between the amount of supplement feed and the daily weight gain to be 0.104 ($r = 0.104$). Based on these results, can you conclude that increasing the amount of supplemental feed is associated with an increase in the daily weight gain? Test using an alpha level of 0.01. Comment on the results.

13.48 The Smithfield Tobacco Company recently studied a random sample of 30 of its distributors and found the correlation between sales and advertising dollars to be 0.67.
a. Can it conclude that there is a significant linear relationship between sales and advertising? If so, is it fair to conclude that advertising causes sales to increase?
b. If a regression model were developed using sales as the dependent variable and advertising as the independent variable, determine the proportion of the variation in sales that would be explained by its relationship to advertising. Discuss what this says about the usefulness of using advertising to predict sales.

13.49 The American Airline Company recently performed a customer survey in which it asked a random sample of 100 passengers to indicate their incomes and the total cost of the airfares they purchased for pleasure trips in the past year. A regression model was developed to determine whether income could be used as a variable to explain the variation in number of times individuals fly on airlines in a year. The following regression results were obtained.

$$\hat{y} = 0.25 + 0.0150x$$
$$s_\varepsilon = 721.44$$
$$R^2 = 0.65$$
$$s_{b_1} = 0.000122$$

a. Produce an estimate of the maximum and minimum amounts of difference in the amounts allocated to purchase airline tickets by two families who have a difference of $20,000 in family income. Assume that you wish to use a 90% confidence level.
b. Can the intercept of the regression equation be interpreted in this case, assuming that no one who was surveyed had an income of 0 dollars? Explain.
c. Use the information provided to perform a test of the significance of regression model. Discuss your results, assuming the test is performed at the significance level of 0.05.

13.50 A manager for a major manufacturing company recently delivered a speech to other managers from around the United States. During the course of the speech, he was explaining a study his company had done with respect to sales and price of a particular product. He said that it had developed a simple regression model and had found the regression slope coefficient to be $-3,456.98$. He then said that this meant that increasing price by 1 dollar would cause sales to drop by 3,456.98 units. Comment on this statement, indicating with what, if anything, about the statement you agree or disagree.

13.51 Briggs Bank and Trust recently performed a study of its checking account customers. One objective of the study was to determine whether it is possible to explain a variation in average checking account balance by knowing the number of checks written per month per account. The sample data selected are contained in the CD-ROM file *Briggs Bank*.
a. Draw a scatter plot for these data.
b. Develop the least squares regression equation for these data.
c. Develop the 90% interval estimate for the change in the average checking account balance when a person who formerly wrote 25 checks a month increased to 50 checks a month.
d. Test to determine if an increase in the number of checks written by an individual can be used to predict the checking account balance of that individual. Use $\alpha = 0.05$. Comment on this result and the result of part c.

13.52 An economist for the state of Mississippi recently collected the data contained in the CD-ROM file *Mississippi* on the percentage of people unemployed in the state at randomly selected times over the past 25 years and the interest rate of treasury bills offered by the federal government at those times.
a. (1) Develop a plot showing the relationship between the two variables. (2) Describe the relationship as being either linear or curvilinear.
b. (1) Develop a simple linear regression model with unemployment rate as the dependent variable. (2) Write a short report describing the model and indicating the important measures.

13.53 The Cooley Service Center polishes and cleans automobiles. It has major accounts such as the Bayview Taxi Service and Bayview Police Department. It also does work for the general public by appointment. Recently, the manager decided to survey customers to determine how satisfied they were with the work performed by Cooley. He devised a rating scale between 0 and 100, with 0 being poor and 100 being excellent service. He selected a random sample of 14 customers and asked the customers when they picked up their cars to rate the service. He also recorded the amount of time spent on each customer's car. These data are in the CD-ROM file *Cooley*.
a. (1) Draw a scatter plot showing these two variables, with the y variable on the vertical axis and the x variable on the horizontal axis. (2) Describe the relationship between these two variables.
b. (1) Develop a linear regression model to explain the variation in the service rating. (2) Write a short report describing the model and showing the results of pertinent hypothesis tests, using a significance level of 0.10.

Advanced Applications

Exercises 13.54 through 13.57 refer to the Harris Corporation, which has recently done a study of homes that have sold in the Detroit area within the past 18 months. Data were recorded for the asking price (x) and the number of weeks (y) each home was on the market before it sold. The data collected are in the CD-ROM file *Harris*.

13.54 Produce a graphical representation of this data to determine if a simple linear relationship exists between variables. Specify the relationship indicated by the graph you produced.

13.55 For the Harris data:
a. Compute the correlation coefficient for the number of weeks each house has been on the market and the asking price of the house.
b. Test at a significance level of 0.10 to determine whether it is true that the more expensive a house is, the longer it will take to sell. Discuss your results.

13.56 For the Harris data:
a. Develop a regression model using asking price of a home as the independent variable and weeks on the market as the dependent variable.
b. Provide an interpretation for the regression slope coefficient.
c. Use the t test statistic to determine whether the more expensive a house is, the longer it will take to sell. Use a significance level of 0.01.
d. Use a p-value approach to conduct the test relating expense to time to sell. Comment on the relationship between this hypothesis test and the one conducted in part c.

13.57 For the regression model developed showing the relationship between time to sell and expense, develop a 95% interval estimate to determine how much longer it will take to sell a house if its price is increased by $10,000. (Hint: Be very careful that you determine the parameter you are estimating and its interpretation. This parameter measures the change in the y variable for an increase in a certain number of units of the x variable. Ask yourself how many units that is.)

13.58 Grinfield Service Company's marketing director is interested in analyzing the relationship between her company's sales and the advertising dollars spent. In the course of her analysis, she selected a random sample of 20 weeks and recorded the sales for each week and the amount spent on advertising. These data are contained in the CD-ROM file *Grinfield*.
a. Identify the independent and dependent variables.
b. Draw a scatter plot with the dependent variable on the vertical axis and the independent variable on the horizontal axis.
c. The marketing director wishes to know if increasing the amount spent on advertising increases sales. As a first attempt, use a statistical test that will provide the required information. Use a significance level of 0.025. Upon careful consideration, the marketing manager realizes that it takes a certain amount of time for the effect of advertising to register in terms of increased sales. She, therefore, asks you to calculate a correlation coefficient for sales of the current week against amount of advertising spent in the previous week and conduct a hypothesis test to determine if, under this model, increasing the amount spent on advertising increases sales. Again, use a significance of 0.025.

13.59 Refer to the Grinfield Service Company discussed in Exercise 13.58.

  a. Develop the least squares regression equation for these variables. Plot the regression line on the scatter plot.

  b. Develop a 95% confidence interval estimate for the increase in sales resulting from increasing the advertising budget by $50. Interpret the interval.

  c. Discuss whether it is appropriate to interpret the intercept value of this model. Under what conditions is it appropriate? Discuss.

  d. Develop a 90% confidence interval for the mean sales amount achieved during all weeks in which advertising is $200 for the week.

  e. Suppose you are asked to use this regression model to predict the weekly sales when advertising will be $100. What would you reply to the request? Discuss.

13.60 The Rio-River Railroad, headquartered in Santa Fe, New Mexico, is trying to devise a method for allocating fuel costs to individual railroad cars on a particular route between Denver and Santa Fe. The railroad thinks that fuel consumption will increase as more cars are added to the train, but it is uncertain about how much cost should be assigned to each additional car. In an effort to deal with this problem, the cost-accounting department has randomly sampled 10 trips between the two cities and has recorded the data in the CD-ROM file *Rio-River*.

  a. Draw a scatter plot for these two variables and comment on the apparent relationship between fuel consumption and the number of rail cars on the train.

  b. (1) Compute the correlation coefficient between fuel consumption and the number of rail cars. (2) Test Rio-River's preconception of the relation between fuel consumption and the number of rail cars, using a significance level of 0.025. (3) Comment on the results of this test. Do these results necessarily indicate that adding more cars will increase the fuel usage?

  c. Develop the least square regression model to help explain the variation in fuel consumption.

  d. Write a report that interprets the regression results. In the report, address the issue of, on average, how much the addition of another rail car will increase fuel consumption. Also, calculate the average fuel consumption, average number of cars per train, and average fuel consumption per car for the data given. Does this average equal the average increase in fuel consumption from adding an additional car using the regression model? Explain any difference.

13.61 Sanders Company's production manager, Bill Hendley, is performing a productivity study of the employees at the Black Hills plant. As part of this study, he selected a random sample of 20 employees who have worked for the company for four years or longer. For each employee, he measured the number of hours of special training the employee had taken and the employee's production rate in pieces produced per day. The following summary data are available:

$$y = \text{Pieces produced per day}$$
$$x = \text{Hours of special training}$$
$$\bar{x} = 13.50$$
$$s_\varepsilon = 11.0$$
$$\bar{y} = 125.0$$
$$\hat{y} = 88.5 + 1.5x$$
$$\Sigma(x - \bar{x})^2 = 1,245.0$$

  a. Bill has been having trouble with one of the employees at Black Hills: Jim Svede. Jim often takes naps during working hours. When questioned about this behavior, Jim asserts that these naps make him more alert and productive than other employees. Develop a 95% confidence interval for the average daily production for people, such as Jim, who have taken 15 hours of training. Jim has an average daily production rate of 118 pieces a day. Does his assertion carry any weight?

  b. Develop a 95% prediction interval for a particular individual who has taken 15 hours of special training courses. Does this interval shed any more light on Jim Svede's assertion? Which of the two interval estimates is more appropriate to address Jim's assertion? Discuss.

13.62 A company is considering recruiting new employees from a particular college and plans to place a great deal of emphasis on each student's college grade point average. However, the company is aware that not all schools have the same grading standards, so it is possible that a student at this school might have a lower (or higher) grade point average than a student from another school, yet really be on par with the other student. To make this comparison between schools, the company has devised a test that it has administered utilizing a sample size of 400. With the results of the test, it has developed a regression model that it uses to predict student grade point average. The following equation represents the model:

$$\hat{y} = 1.0 + 0.028x$$

The R^2 for this model is 0.88, and the standard error of the estimate is 0.20, based on the sample data used to develop the model. Note that the dependent variable is the grade point average, and the independent variable is the test score, where this score can range from 0 to 100. For the sample data used to develop the model, the following values are known.

$$\bar{y} = 2.76$$
$$\bar{x} = 68$$
$$\Sigma(x - \bar{x})^2 = 148,885.73$$

  a. Based on the information contained in this problem, can you conclude that as a test score increases, the GPA will also increase, using a significance level of 0.05?

  b. Suppose a student interviews with this company, takes the company test, and scores 80% correct. What is the 90% prediction interval estimate for this student's grade point average? Interpret the interval.

  c. Suppose the student in part b actually has a 2.90 grade point average at this school. Based on this evidence, what might be concluded about this person's actual grade point average compared with other students at other schools with the same grade point average? Discuss the limitations you might place on this conclusion.

  d. Suppose a second student with a 2.45 grade point average took the test and scored 65% correct. What is the 90% prediction interval for this student's "real" grade point average? Interpret.

13.63 Suppose the company that developed the test discussed in Exercise 13.62 is interested in developing a 95% confidence interval estimate for the average grade point average for students who score 88% correct on this test. Calculate this interval and interpret it.

CASE 13-A:

Alamar Industries

While driving home in northern Kentucky at 8:00 P.M., Juan Alamar wondered whether his father had done him any favor by retiring early and letting him take control of the family machine-tool-restoration business. When his father started the business of overhauling machine tools (both for resale and on a contract basis), American companies dominated the tool manufacturing market. During the past 30 years, however, the original equipment industry had been devastated, first by competition from Germany and then from Japan. Although foreign competition had not yet invaded the overhaul segment of the business, Juan had heard about foreign companies establishing operations on the West Coast.

The foreign competitors were apparently stressing the high-quality service and operations that had been responsible for their great inroads into the original equipment market. Last week Juan had attended a daylong conference on total quality management that had discussed the advantages of competing for the Baldrige Award, the national quality award established in 1987. Presenters from past Baldrige winners, including Xerox, Federal Express, Cadillac, and Motorola, stressed the positive effects on their companies of winning and said similar effects would be possible for any company. This assertion of only positive effects was what Juan questioned. He was certain that the effect on his remaining free time would not be positive.

The Baldrige Award considers seven corporate dimensions of quality. Although the award is not based on a numerical score, an overall score is calculated. The maximum score is 1,000, with most

recent winners scoring about 800. Juan did not doubt the award was good for the winners, but he wondered about the nonwinners. In particular, he wondered about any relationship between attempting to improve quality according to the Baldrige dimensions and company profitability. Individual company scores are not released, but Juan was able to talk to one of the conference presenters who shared some anonymous data, such as companies' scores in the year they applied, their returns on investment in the year applied, and returns on investment in the year after application. Juan decided to commit the company to a total quality management process if the data provided evidence that the process would lead to increased profitability.

BALDRIGE SCORE	ROI APPLICATION YEAR	ROI NEXT YEAR
470	11%	13%
520	10	11
660	14	15
540	12	12
600	15	16
710	16	16
580	11	12
600	12	13
740	16	16
610	11	14
570	12	13
660	17	19

CASE 13-B:

Continental Trucking

Norm Painter is the newly hired cost analyst for Continental Trucking. Continental is a nationwide trucking firm, and, until recently, most of its routes were driven under regulated rates. These rates were set to allow small trucking firms to earn an adequate profit, leaving little incentive to work to reduce costs by efficient management techniques. In fact, the greatest effort was made to try to influence regulatory agencies to grant rate increases.

A recent rash of deregulation moves has made the long-distance trucking industry more competitive. Norm has been hired to analyze Continental's whole expense structure. As part of this study, Norm is looking at truck repair costs. Because the trucks are involved in long hauls, they inevitably break down. In the past, little preventive maintenance was done, and if a truck broke down in the middle of a haul, either a replacement tractor was sent or an independent contractor finished the haul. The truck was then repaired at the nearest local shop. Norm is sure this procedure has led to more expense than if major repairs had been made before the trucks failed.

Norm thinks that some method should be found for determining when preventive maintenance is needed. He believes that fuel consumption is a good indicator of possible breakdowns, and as the trucks begin running badly, they will consume more fuel. Unfortunately, the major determinants of fuel consumption are the weight of a truck and head winds. Norm picks a sample of a single

truck model and gathers data relating fuel consumption to truck weight. All trucks in the sample are in good condition. He separates the data by direction of the haul, realizing that winds tend to blow predominantly out of the west.

EAST–WEST HAUL		WEST–EAST HAUL	
Miles/Gallon	Haul Weight	Miles/Gallon	Haul Weight
4.1	41,000 lbs.	4.3	40,000 lbs.
4.7	36,000	4.5	37,000
3.9	37,000	4.8	36,000
4.3	38,000	5.2	38,000
4.8	32,000	5.0	35,000
5.1	37,000	4.7	42,000
4.3	46,000	4.9	37,000
4.6	35,000	4.5	36,000
5.0	37,000	5.2	42,000
		4.8	41,000

Although he can rapidly gather future data on fuel consumption and haul weight, now that Norm has these data, he is not quite sure what to do with them.

General References

1. Berenson, Mark L., and David M. Levine *Basic Business Statistics: Concepts and Applications*, 7th ed. (Upper Saddle River, NJ: Prentice-Hall, 1999).

2. Cryer, Jonathan D., and Robert B. Miller, *Statistics for Business: Data Analysis and Modeling*, 2nd ed. (Belmont, CA: Duxbury Press, 1994).

3. Draper, Norman R., and Harry Smith, *Applied Regression Analysis*, 3rd ed. (New York: John Wiley and Sons, 1998).

4. Frees, Edward W., *Data Analysis Using Regression Models: The Business Perspective* (Englewood Cliffs, NJ: Prentice-Hall, 1996).

5. Kleinbaum, David G., Lawrence L. Kupper, Keith E. Muller, and Azhar Nizam, *Applied Regression Analysis and Other Multivariable Methods*, 3rd ed. (Belmont, CA: Duxbury Press, 1998).

6. *Microsoft Excel 2000* (Redmond, WA: Microsoft Corp., 1999).

7. *Minitab for Windows Version 13* (State College, PA: Minitab, 2000).

8. Neter, John, Michael H. Kutner, Christopher J. Nachtsheim, and William Wasserman, *Applied Linear Statistical Models*, 4th ed. (Homewood, IL: Richard D. Irwin, 1996).

CHAPTER 14

Multiple Regression Analysis and Model Building

CHAPTER OUTCOMES

After studying the material in Chapter 14, you should be able to:

- Understand the general concepts behind model building using multiple regression analysis.
- Use variable transformations to model nonlinear relationships in a regression model.
- Apply multiple regression analysis to business decision-making situations.
- Analyze the computer output for a multiple regression model and interpret the regression results.
- Test hypotheses about the significance of a multiple regression model and test the significance of the independent variables in the model.
- Recognize potential problems when using multiple regression analysis and take steps to correct the problems.
- Incorporate qualitative variables into a regression model by using dummy variables.

WHY YOU NEED TO KNOW

Chapter 13 pointed out that decision-makers often need to consider the relationship between two variables when analyzing a problem. Simple linear regression and correlation analyses provide a basis for analyzing the relationship between two variables. If the two variables are correlated, there is a linear relationship between them, and linear regression analysis can be used to model that relationship.

As you might expect, business problems are not limited to linear relationships involving only two variables. Many practical situations involve analyzing the relationships among three or more variables, and these relationships may be nonlinear. For example, a vice president of planning for an automobile manufacturer would be interested in the relationship between her company's automobile sales and the variables that influence those sales. Included in her analysis might be such independent or explanatory variables as automobile price, competitors' sales, and advertising, as well as such economic variables as disposable personal income, the inflation rate, and the unemployment rate.

When multiple independent variables are to be included in an analysis simultaneously, the technique introduced in this chapter—multiple linear regression—is very useful. When a relationship between variables is nonlinear, we may be able to apply variable transformations that allow us to use multiple linear regression analysis to construct a model. This chapter examines the general topic of model building by extending the concepts of simple linear regression analysis. The background information provided in Chapter 13 will be very helpful in understanding and applying multiple regression analysis to business decision-making situations.

14-1 INTRODUCTION TO MULTIPLE REGRESSION ANALYSIS

Chapter 13 introduced the concept of simple linear regression analysis involving a dependent variable and a single independent, or explanatory, variable. In those situations, we attempt to model the relationship in a population between two variables as shown in Equation 14-1.

Simple Linear Regression Model (Population Model)

$$y = \beta_0 + \beta_1 x + \varepsilon$$

14-1

where:

y = Value of the dependent variable in the population
x = Value of the independent variable in the population
β_0 = The population regression coefficient representing the y intercept
β_1 = The population regression slope coefficient
ε = Error term, or residual

When we have a random sample of data, the regression model represented by Equation 14-1 is estimated in the form shown as Equation 14-2.

Estimated Simple Linear Regression Model

$$\hat{y} = b_0 + b_1 x$$

14-2

where:

$\hat{y}$ = Estimated, or predicted value of y
b_0 = Estimated y intercept
b_1 = Estimated slope coefficient
x = Value of the independent variable

The simple regression model is characterized by two variables: y, the *dependent variable*, and x, the *independent*, or *explanatory*, *variable*. The single independent variable explains some variation in the dependent variable, but unless x and y are perfectly correlated, the proportion explained will be less than 100%. This also means that the predicted (or fitted) y values will often not equal the actual

y values. This means that prediction error, e, will be present. Another word for prediction error is **residual**.

Residual (Prediction Error)

The difference between the actual value of y and the predicted value of y, which is given by:

$$e = y - \hat{y}$$

Chapter 13 indicated that the model's random error (ε) is assumed to have a mean of 0 and a standard deviation called the *standard error of the estimate*. If this standard error of the estimate is too large, the regression model may not be very useful for prediction.

In multiple regression analysis, additional independent variables are added to the regression model to explain some of the yet-unexplained variation in the dependent variable. Adding appropriate independent variables should reduce the sum of squares of error for the regression equation.

You will note as we proceed that multiple regression is merely an extension of simple regression analysis. However, as we expand the model for the population from one independent variable to two or more, there are some new considerations.

The general format of a **multiple regression model for the population** is given by Equation 14-3.

Multiple Regression Model (Population Model)

$$y = \beta_0 + \beta_1 x_1 + \beta_2 x_2 + \ldots + \beta_k x_k + \varepsilon \qquad \textbf{14-3}$$

where:

β_0 = Population's regression constant

β_j = Population's regression coefficient for variable x; $j = 1, 2, \ldots k$

k = Number of independent variables

ε = Model error

There are four general assumptions of the linear multiple regression model.

 SSUMPTIONS

1. The regression model errors are normally distributed.
2. The mean of the model error terms is 0.
3. The model error terms have a constant variance, σ_ε^2, for all combinations of values of the independent variables.
4. The model error terms are independent.

Equation 14-3 represents the multiple regression model for the population. However, in most instances, you will be working with a random sample from the population. Given the above assumptions, the estimated multiple regression model, based on the sample data, is of the form shown in Equation 14-4.

Estimated Multiple Regression Model

$$\hat{y} = b_0 + b_1 x_1 + b_2 x_2 + \ldots + b_k x_k \qquad \textbf{14-4}$$

This estimated model is an extension of the estimated simple regression model shown in Equation 14-2. The principal difference is that, whereas the estimated simple regression model is the equation for a straight line in a two-dimensional space, the estimated multiple regression model forms a hyperplane (or response surface) through multidimensional space. Each regression coefficient represents a different slope. Therefore, for a decision maker, using Equation 14-2 means a value of the dependent variable can be estimated using a value of one independent variable, but a multiple regression model requires values of two or more (k) independent variables to be known. The **regression hyperplane** represents the relationship between the dependent variable and the many independent variables.

(A) ONE INDEPENDENT VARIABLE		(B) TWO INDEPENDENT VARIABLES		
y	x_1	y	x_1	x_2
564.99	50	564.99	50	10
601.06	60	601.06	60	13
560.11	40	560.11	40	14
616.41	50	616.41	50	12
674.96	60	674.96	60	15
630.58	45	630.58	45	16
554.66	53	554.66	53	14

Regression Hyperplane

The multiple regression equivalent of the simple regression line. The plane has a different slope for each independent variable.

For example, Table 14-1a shows sample data for a dependent variable, y, and one independent variable, x_1. Figure 14-1 shows a scatter plot and the regression line for the simple regression analysis for y and x_1. The points are plotted in two-dimensional space, and the regression model is represented by a line through the points such that the sum of squares of error $[SSE = \Sigma(y - \hat{y})^2]$ is minimized.

If we add variable x_2 to the model, as shown in Table 14-1b, the resulting multiple regression equation becomes

$$\hat{y} = 307.71 + 2.85x_1 + 10.94x_2$$

For the time being don't worry about how this equation was computed. That will be discussed shortly. Note, however, that the (y, x_1, x_2) points are plotted in three-dimensional space, as shown in Figure 14-2. The regression equation forms a slice (hyperplane) through the data such that $\Sigma(y - \hat{y})^2$ is minimized. This is the same *least squares criterion* that is used with simple linear regression.

The mathematics for developing the least squares regression equation for simple linear regression involves differential calculus. The same is true for the multiple regression equation. Because the least squares regression coefficients are determined using matrix algebra, the mathematical derivation is beyond the scope of this test.[1]

Multiple regression analysis is virtually always performed with the aid of a computer and appropriate software. Both Minitab and Excel contain procedures for performing multiple regres-

FIGURE 14-1

Simple Regression Line

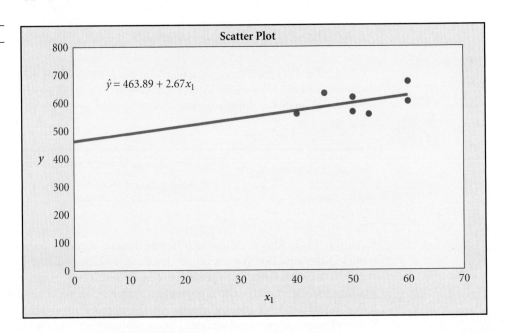

[1]For a complete treatment of the matrix algebra approach for estimating multiple regression coefficients, consult *Applied Linear Statistical Models* by Neter et al.

FIGURE 14-2

Multiple Regression
Hyperplane for Population

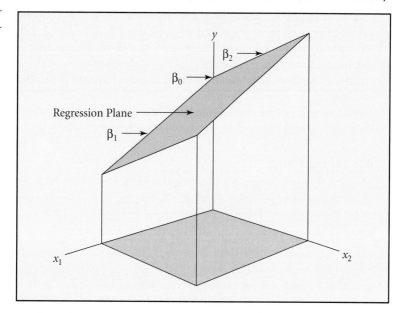

FIGURE 14-2

Multiple Regression
Hyperplane for Population

sion. Minitab has a far-more-complete regression procedure. However, the PHStat Excel add-ins expand Excel's capabilities. Each software package presents the results in a slightly different format; however, the same basic information will appear in all regression output.

BASIC MODEL-BUILDING CONCEPTS

An important activity in business decision making is referred to as **model** building.

Model

A representation of an actual system using either a physical or a mathematical portrayal.

Models are often used to test changes in a system without actually having to change the real system. Models are also used to help describe a system or to predict the output of a system based on certain specified inputs. You are probably quite aware of physical models. Airlines use flight simulators to train pilots. Wind tunnels are used to determine the aerodynamics of automobile designs. Golf ball makers use a physical model of a golfer called "Iron Mike" that can be set to swing golf clubs in a very controlled manner to determine how far a golf ball will fly. Although physical models are very useful in business decision making, our emphasis in this chapter is on mathematical models. In particular, we are interested in statistical models that are developed using multiple regression analysis.

People involved in model building frequently conclude that it is both an art and a science. Determining an appropriate model is a challenging task, but it can be made manageable by employing a model-building process consisting of the following three components: model specification, model fitting, and model diagnosis.

Model Specification

Model specification, or model identification, is the process of determining the dependent variable and deciding which independent variables should be included in the model.

SUMMARY: MODEL SPECIFICATION

In the context of the statistical models discussed in this chapter, this component involves the following three steps:

1. Decide what question you want to ask. The question being asked usually indicates the dependent variable. In the previous chapter we discussed how simple linear regression analysis could be used to describe the relationship between a dependent and an independent variable.

2. List the potential independent variables for your model. Here, your knowledge of the situation you are modeling guides you in identifying potential independent variables.

3. Gather the sample data (observations) for all variables.

As with any statistical tool, the larger the sample size the better, because the potential for extreme sampling error is reduced when the sample size is large. However, at a minimum, the sample size required to compute a regression model must be at least one greater than the number of independent variables.[2] If we are thinking of developing a regression model with five independent variables, the absolute minimum number of cases required is six. Otherwise, the computer software will indicate an error has been made or will print out meaningless values. As a practical matter, the sample size should be at least four times the number of independent variables. Thus, if we had five independent variables ($k = 5$), we would want at least 20 cases to develop the regression model.

Model Building

Model building is the process of actually constructing a mathematical equation in which some or all of the independent variables are used in an attempt to explain the variation in the dependent variable.

Model Diagnosis

Model diagnosis is the process of analyzing the quality of the model you have constructed by determining how well a specified model fits the data you just gathered. You will examine such output values as R-squared and the estimate of the standard deviation of the model error. At this stage, you will also assess the extent to which the model's assumptions appear to be satisfied. (Section 14-5 is devoted to examining whether a model meets the regression analysis assumptions.) If the model is unacceptable in any of these areas, you will be forced to revert to the model-specification step and begin again. However, you will be the final judge of whether the model provides acceptable results, and you will always be constrained by time and cost considerations.

An important consideration in practical situations is to use the simplest available model that will meet your needs. The objective of model building is to help you make better decisions. You do not need to feel that a sophisticated model is better if a simpler one will provide acceptable results.

SUMMARY: DEVELOPING A MULTIPLE REGRESSION MODEL

The following steps are employed in developing a multiple regression model.

1. Specify the model by determining the dependent variable and potential independent variables.

2. Formulate the model. This is done by computing the correlation coefficients for the dependent variable and each independent variable and for each independent variable with all other independent variables. The multiple regression equation is also computed. The computations are performed using computer software such as Excel or Minitab.

3. Perform diagnostic checks on the model to determine how well the specified model fits the data and how well the model appears to meet the multiple regression assumptions.

EXAMPLE 14-1: DEVELOPING A MULTIPLE REGRESSION MODEL

Excel and Minitab Tutorial

First City Real Estate   First City Real Estate executives recently decided to make the firm more responsive to inquiries from people thinking about selling their houses. They wish to build a model to predict sales prices for residential property. This can be done using the following steps.

Step 1: Specify the model.

The question being asked is how can the real estate firm determine what the selling price for a house should be? Thus, the dependent variable is the sales price. This is what the managers want to be able to predict. The managers met in a brainstorming session to derive a list of possible independent (explanatory) variables. Some variables, such as "condition of the house" were eliminated because of lack of data. Others such as "curb appeal" (the appeal of the house to people as they drive by) were eliminated because the values for these variables would be too subjective and difficult to

---

[2]There are mathematical reasons for this sample-size requirement that are beyond the scope of this text. In essence, Equation 14-4 can't be computed if the sample size is not at least one larger than the number of independent variables.

quantify. From a wide list of possibilities, the managers selected the following variables as good candidates:

$$x_1 = \text{Home size (in square feet)}$$
$$x_2 = \text{Age of house}$$
$$x_3 = \text{Number of bedrooms}$$
$$x_4 = \text{Number of bathrooms}$$
$$x_5 = \text{Garage size (number of cars)}$$

Data were obtained for a sample of 319 residential properties that had sold within the previous two months in an area served by two of First City's offices. For each house in the sample, the sales price and values for each potential independent variable were collected. The data are in the CD-ROM file *First City*.

Step 2:   **Formulate the model.**

The regression model is developed by including independent variables from among those for which you have complete data. There is no way to determine whether an independent variable will be a good predictor variable by analyzing the individual variable's descriptive statistics, such as the mean and standard deviation. Instead, we need to look at the correlation between the independent variables and the dependent variable, which is measured by the **correlation coefficient**.

Correlation Coefficient

A quantitative measure of the strength of the linear relationship between two variables. The correlation coefficient, r, ranges from -1.0 to $+1.0$.

When we have multiple independent variables and one dependent variable, we can look at the correlation between all pairs of variables by developing a **correlation matrix**. Each correlation is computed using one of the equations in Equation 14-5. The appropriate formula is determined by whether the correlation is being calculated for an independent variable and the dependent variable or for two independent variables, respectively.

Correlation Matrix

A table showing the pairwise correlations between all variables (dependent and independent).

Correlation Coefficient

$$r = \frac{\sum(x - \bar{x})(y - \bar{y})}{\sqrt{\sum(x - \bar{x})^2 \, \sum(y - \bar{y})^2}} \quad \text{or} \quad r = \frac{\sum(x_1 - \bar{x}_1)(x_2 - \bar{x}_2)}{\sqrt{\sum(x_1 - \bar{x}_1)^2 \, \sum(x_2 - \bar{x}_2)^2}} \qquad \textbf{14-5}$$

One x variable with y $\qquad\qquad$ One x variable with another x

---

The actual calculations are done using Excel's correlation tool or Minitab's correlation command, and the results are shown in Figure 14-3a and Figure 14-3b. The output provides the correlation between y and each x variable and between each pair of independent variables.[3] Recall that in Chapter 13, a t-test (see Equation 13-3) was used to test whether the correlation coefficient is statistically significant.

$$H_0: \rho = 0$$
$$H_A: \rho \neq 0$$

---

[3]Minitab, in addition to providing the correlation matrix, provides the p-values for each correlation. If the p-value is less than the desired alpha, the correlation is statistically significant.

FIGURE 14-3A

Excel Results Showing First City Real Estate Correlation Matrix

Excel Instructions:
1. Open file: First City.xls
2. Click on **Tools**.
3. Select **Correlation**.
4. Define data range and output location.

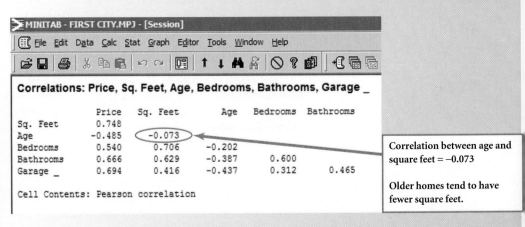

Correlation between age and square feet = −0.07288

Older homes tend to have fewer square feet.

	Price	Sq. Feet	Age	Bedrooms	Bathrooms	Garage #
Price	1					
Sq. Feet	0.747711972	1				
Age	-0.485221836	-0.072883413	1			
Bedrooms	0.540087962	0.705860253	-0.202401652	1		
Bathroom	0.665504255	0.629289554	-0.387104876	0.599640313	1	
Garage #	0.693538499	0.416261286	-0.437379482	0.312034317	0.464601539	1

We will conduct the test with a significance level of

$$\alpha = 0.05$$

Given degrees of freedom equal to

$$n - 2 = 319 - 2 = 317$$

the critical t (see Appendix E) for a two-tailed test is approximately

$$t_{\alpha/2} = 1.96^4$$

Any correlation coefficient generating a t-value > 1.96 or less than -1.96 is determined to be significant.

For now, we will focus on the correlations in the first column in Figures 14-3a and 14-3b, which measure the strength of the linear relationship between each independent variable and the dependent variable, sales price. For example, the t statistic for price and square feet is

$$t = \frac{r}{\sqrt{\frac{1 - r^2}{n - 2}}} = \frac{0.7477}{\sqrt{\frac{1 - 0.7477^2}{319 - 2}}} = 20.048$$

Because

$$t = 20.048 > 1.96$$

the correlation between sales price and square feet is statistically significant. We reject H_0.

Similar calculations for the other independent variables with price show that all variables are statistically correlated with price. This indicates that a significant linear relationship exists between each independent variable and sales price. Variable x_1, square feet, has the highest correlation at 0.748. Variable x_2, age of the house, has the lowest correlation at −0.485. The negative correlation implies that older homes tend to have lower sales prices.

FIGURE 14-3B

Minitab Results Showing First City Real Estate Correlation Matrix

Minitab Instructions:
1. Open file: First City.MTW.
2. Choose **Stat > Basic Statistics > Correlation**.
3. In **Variables**, enter variable columns.
4. Click **OK**.

MINITAB - FIRST CITY.MPJ - [Session]

File Edit Data Calc Stat Graph Editor Tools Window Help

Correlations: Price, Sq. Feet, Age, Bedrooms, Bathrooms, Garage _

	Price	Sq. Feet	Age	Bedrooms	Bathrooms
Sq. Feet	0.748				
Age	-0.485	-0.073			
Bedrooms	0.540	0.706	-0.202		
Bathrooms	0.666	0.629	-0.387	0.600	
Garage _	0.694	0.416	-0.437	0.312	0.465

Cell Contents: Pearson correlation

Correlation between age and square feet = −0.073

Older homes tend to have fewer square feet.

[4]You can use the Excel TINV function to get the precise t-value, which is 1.967.

As we discussed in Chapter 13, it is always a good idea to develop scatter plots to visually see the relationship between two variables. Figure 14-4 shows the scatter plots for each independent variable and the dependent variable, sales price. In each case, the plots indicate a linear relationship between the independent variable and the dependent variable. Note that several of the independent variables (bedrooms, bathrooms, garage size) are quantitative but discrete. The scatter plots for these variables show points at each level of the independent variable rather than over a continuum of values.

Computing the Regression Equation

First City's goal is to develop a regression model to predict the appropriate selling price for a home, using certain measurable characteristics. The first attempt at developing the model will be to run a multiple regression computer program using all available independent variables. The regression outputs from Excel and Minitab are shown in Figure 14-5a and Figure 14-5b.

The estimate of the multiple regression model given in Figure 14-5a is

$$\hat{y} = 31,127.6 + 63.1(\text{sq. feet}) - 1,144.4(\text{age}) - 8,410.4(\text{bedrooms})$$
$$+ 3,522.0(\text{bathrooms}) + 28,203.5(\text{garage})$$

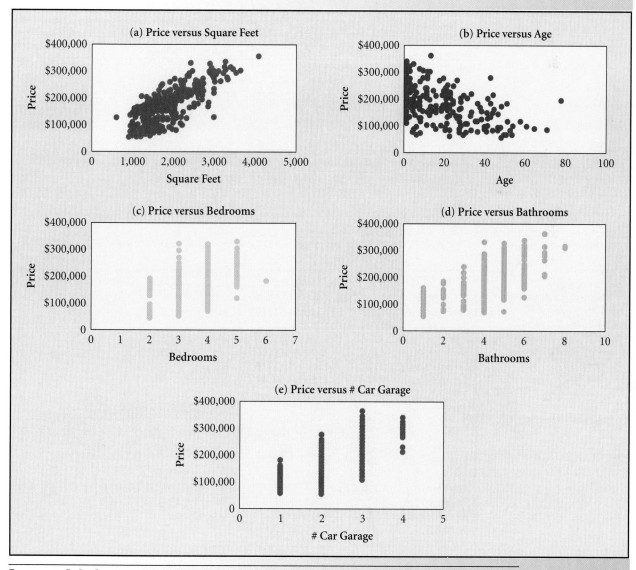

FIGURE 14-4   First City Real Estate Scatter Plots

FIGURE 14-5A

Excel Multiple Regression Model Results for First City Real Estate

Excel Instructions:
1. Open file: First City.xls
2. Click on **Tools**.
3. Select **Regression**.
4. Define dependent and independent variable range.
5. Determine output location.
6. Click **OK**.

FIGURE 14-5B

Minitab Multiple Regression Model Results for First City Real Estate

Minitab Instructions:
1. Open file: First City.MTW.
2. Choose **Stat > Regression > Regression**.
3. In **Response**, enter dependent (Y) variable.
4. In **Predictors**, enter independent (X) variables.
5. Click **OK**.

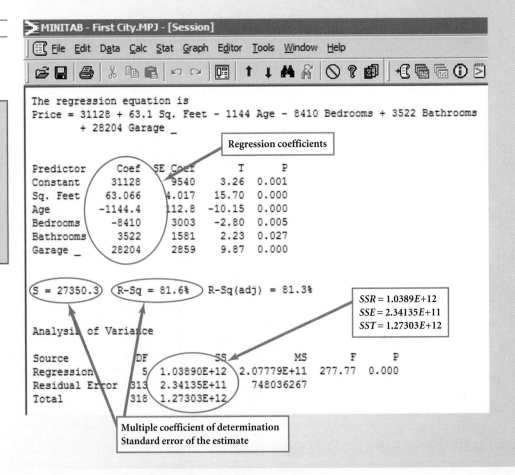

The coefficients for each independent variable represent an estimate of the average change in the dependent variable for a one-unit change in the independent variable, all other independent variables remaining constant. For example, for houses of the same age, with the same number of bedrooms, baths, and garages, a one-square-foot increase in the size of the house is estimated to increase its price by an average of $63.10. Likewise, for houses with the same size, bedrooms, bathrooms, and garages, a one-year increase in the age of the house is estimated to result in an average drop in sales price of $1,144.40. The other coefficients are interpreted in the same way. Note, in each case, we are interpreting the regression coefficient for one independent variable while holding the other variables constant.

To estimate the value of a residential property, First Real Estate brokers would substitute values for the independent variables into the regression equation. For example, suppose a house with the following characteristics is considered.

$$x_1 = \text{Square feet} = 2{,}100$$
$$x_2 = \text{Age} = 15$$
$$x_3 = \text{Number of bedrooms} = 4$$
$$x_4 = \text{Number of baths} = 3$$
$$x_5 = \text{Size of garage} = 2$$

The point estimate for the sales price is

$$\hat{y} = 31{,}127.6 + 63.1(\text{sq. feet}) - 1{,}144.4(\text{age}) - 8{,}410.4(\text{bedrooms}) + 3{,}522.0(\text{baths}) + 28{,}203.5(\text{garages})$$
$$\hat{y} = 31{,}127.6 + 63.1(2{,}100) - 1{,}144.4(15) - 8{,}410.4(4) + 3{,}522.0(3) + 28{,}203.5(2)$$
$$\hat{y} = \$179{,}802.70$$

The Coefficient of Determination

You learned in Chapter 13 that the *coefficient of determination*, R^2, measures the fraction of variation in the dependent variable that can be explained by the dependent variable's relationship to a single independent variable. When there are multiple independent variables in a model, R^2 is also used to determine the proportion of variation in the dependent variable that is explained by the dependent variable's relationship to all the independent variables in the model. However, R^2 is now called the **multiple coefficient of determination**. Equation 14-6 is used to compute R^2 for a multiple regression model.

Multiple Coefficient of Determination (R^2)

$$R^2 = \frac{\text{Sum of squares regression}}{\text{Total sum of squares}} = \frac{SSR}{SST}$$

14-6

As shown in Figure 14-5a, $R^2 = 0.816$. Both SSR and SST are also included in the output. Therefore, you can use Equation 14-6 to get R^2, as follows:

$$\frac{SSR}{SST} = \frac{1.0389E{+}12}{1.27303E{+}12} = 0.816$$

More than 81% of the variation in sales price can be explained by the linear relationship of the five independent variables in the regression model to the dependent variable. However, as we shall shortly see, not all independent variables are equally important to the model's ability to explain this variation.

Step 3: Diagnose the model.

Before First City actually uses this regression model to estimate the sales price of a house, there are several questions that should be answered.

1. Is the overall model significant?
2. Are the individual variables significant?
3. Is the standard deviation of the model error too large to provide meaningful results?
4. Is multicollinearity a problem?
5. Have the regression analysis assumptions been satisfied?

We shall answer the first four questions in order. We will have to wait until Section 14-5 before we have the tools to answer the fifth important question.

Is the Model Significant?

You should keep in mind that the regression model we constructed is based on a sample of data from the population and is subject to sampling error. Therefore, we need to test the statistical significance of the overall regression model. We have previously discussed the multiple coefficient of determination, R^2, which is a measure of how much of the variation in the dependent variable can be explained by the regression model. Because R^2 is a sample statistic, it can be used to make inferences about whether the overall model is statistically significant in explaining the variation in the dependent variable. The specific null and alternative hypotheses tested for First City Real Estate are

$$H_0: \beta_1 = \beta_2 = \beta_3 = \beta_4 = \beta_5 = 0$$
$$H_A: \text{At least one } \beta_i \text{ does not equal zero.}$$

If the null hypothesis is true and all the slope coefficients are simultaneously equal to zero, the overall regression model is not useful for predictive or descriptive purposes.

The analysis of variance F-test is a method for testing whether the regression model explains a significant proportion of the variation in the dependent variable (and whether the overall model is significant). The F test statistic for a multiple regression model is shown in Equation 14-7.

F Test Statistic

$$F = \frac{\dfrac{SSR}{k}}{\dfrac{SSE}{n-k-1}} \qquad \textbf{14-7}$$

where:

$$SSR = \text{Sum of squares regression} = \Sigma(\hat{y} - \bar{y})^2$$
$$SSE = \text{Sum of squares error} = \Sigma(y - \hat{y})^2$$
$$n = \text{Number of data points}$$
$$k = \text{Number of independent variables}$$
$$\text{Degrees of freedom} = D_1 = k \text{ and } D_2 = (n - k - 1)$$

The ANOVA portion of the output shown in Figure 14-5a contains values for SSR, SSE, and the F value. The general format of the ANOVA table in a regression analysis is shown as follows:

ANOVA

	df	SS	MS	F	Significance F
Regression	k	SSR	$MSR = SSR/k$	MSR/MSE	computed p-value
Residual	$n - k - 1$	SSE	$MSE = SSE/(n - k - 1)$		
Total	$n - 1$	SST			

The ANOVA portion of the output from Figure 14-5a is shown as follows:

ANOVA

	df	SS	MS	F	Significance F
Regression	5	$1.0389E+12$	$2.07779E+11$	277.7665571	$9.0374E-113$
Residual	313	$2.34135E+11$	748036266.8		
Total	318	$1.27303E+12$			

We can test the model's significance.

$$H_0: \beta_1 = \beta_2 = \beta_3 = \beta_4 = \beta_5 = 0$$
$$H_A: \text{At least one } \beta_i \neq \text{ zero.}$$

by either comparing the calculated F-value, 277.77, with a table value for a given alpha level

$$\alpha = 0.01$$

and $k = 5$ and $n - k - 1 = 313$ degrees of freedom ($F = 3.079$), or compare the p-value in the output with a specified alpha level. Because

$$F = 277.77 > 3.079, \text{ reject } H_0$$

or because

$$p\text{-value} \approx 0.0 < 0.01, \text{ reject } H_0$$

Therefore, we should conclude that the regression model *does* explain a significant proportion of the variation is sales price. Thus, the overall model is statistically significant. This indicates that for estimating house sales prices, this multiple regression model is superior to using the mean house price as the estimate.

Excel and Minitab also provide a measure called the R-sq(adj), which is the **adjusted R-squared** value (see Figure 14-5a and 14-5b). It is calculated by Equation 14-8.

Adjusted R-Squared

A measure of the percentage of explained variation in the dependent variable that takes into account the relationship between the sample size and the number of independent variables in the regression model.

$$R\text{-sq(adj)} = R_A^2 = 1 - (1 - R^2)\left(\frac{n - 1}{n - k - 1}\right) \qquad \textbf{14-8}$$

where:

$$n = \text{Sample size}$$
$$k = \text{Number of independent variables}$$

Adding independent variables to the regression model will always increase R^2, even if these variables have no relationship to the dependent variable. Therefore, as the number of independent variables is increased (regardless of the quality of the variables), R^2 will increase. However, each additional variable results in the loss of one degree of freedom. This is viewed as part of the cost of adding the specified variable. The addition to R^2 may not justify the reduction in degrees of freedom. The R_A^2 value takes into account this cost and adjusts the R_A^2 value accordingly. R_A^2 will always be less than R^2. When a variable is added that does not contribute its fair share to the explanation of the dependent variable, the R_A^2 will actually decline, even though R^2 will increase. The adjusted R-squared is a particularly important measure when the number of independent variables is large relative to the sample size. It takes into account the relationship between sample size and number of variables. R^2 may appear artificially high if the number of variables is large compared with the sample size.

In this example, in which the sample size is quite large relative to the number of independent variables, the adjusted R-squared is 81.3%, only slightly less than $R^2 = 81.6\%$.

Are the Individual Variables Significant?

We have concluded that the overall model is significant. This means that *at least* one independent variable explains a significant proportion of the variation in sales price. This does not mean that *all* the variables are significant, however. To determine which variables are significant, we test the following hypotheses.

$$H_0:\beta_j = 0$$
$$H_A:\beta_j \neq 0 \qquad \text{for all } j$$

We can test the significance of each independent variable using significance level

$$\alpha = 0.05$$

and a *t*-test, as discussed in Chapter 13. The calculated *t*-values should be compared to the critical *t*-value with

$$n - k - 1 = 319 - 5 - 1 = 313$$

degrees of freedom, which is approximately

$$t_{\alpha/2} \approx 1.96$$

for $\alpha = 0.05$. The calculated *t*-value for each variable is provided on the computer printout in Figures 14-5a and 14-5b. Recall that the *t* statistic is determined by dividing the regression coefficient by the estimator of the standard deviation of the regression coefficient, as shown in Equation 14-9.

---

t-**Test for Significance of Each Regression Coefficient**

$$t = \frac{b_j - 0}{s_{b_j}} \qquad df = n - k - 1 \qquad\qquad \textbf{14-9}$$

where:

b_j = Sample slope coefficient for the *j*th independent variable

s_{b_j} = Estimate of the standard error for the *j*th sample slope coefficient

---

For example, the *t*-value for square feet shown in Figure 14-5a is 15.699. This was computed using Equation 14-9, as follows:

$$t = \frac{b_j - 0}{s_{b_j}} = \frac{63.06564 - 0}{4.01703} = 15.699$$

Because

$$t = 15.699 > 1.96, \text{ we reject } H_0,$$

the hypothesis that the regression slope for square feet is zero.

We can also look at the Excel or Minitab output and compare the *p*-value for each regression slope coefficient with alpha. If the *p*-value is less than alpha, we reject the null hypothesis and conclude that the independent variable is statistically significant in the model. Both the *t*-test and the *p*-value techniques will give the same results.

You should consider that these *t*-tests are *conditional* tests. This means the null hypothesis is that *the value of each slope coefficient is 0, given that the other independent variables are already in the model.*[5] Figure 14-6 shows the hypothesis tests for each independent variable using a 0.05 significance level. We conclude that all five independent variables in the model are significant. When a regression model is to be used for prediction, the model should contain no insignificant variables. If insignificant variables are present, they should be dropped and a new regression equation obtained before the model is used for prediction purposes. We will have more to say about this later.

Is the Standard Deviation of the Regression Model Too Large?

The purpose of developing the First City regression model is to be able to determine values of the dependent variable when corresponding values of the independent variables are known. An indication of how good the regression model is can be found by looking at the relationship between the measured values of the dependent variable and those values that would be predicted by the regression model. The standard deviation of the regression model (also called the **standard error of the estimate**), measures the dispersion of observed home sale values, *y*, around values predicted by the regression model. The estimate for this standard deviation of the model error, shown in Figure 14-5a, can be computed using Equation 14-10.

---

[5]Note that the *t*-tests may be affected if the independent variables in the model are themselves correlated. A procedure known as the *sum of squares drop F test*, discussed by Neter et. al. in *Applied Linear Statistical Models*, should be used in this situation. Each *t*-test considers only the marginal contribution of the independent variables and may indicate that none of the variables in the model are significant, even though the ANOVA procedure indicates otherwise.

FIGURE 14-6

Significance Tests for Each Independent Variable in the First City Real Estate Example

Note: The degrees of freedom for the *t*-distribution is $(n - k - 1)$, where k is the total number of independent variables in the model.

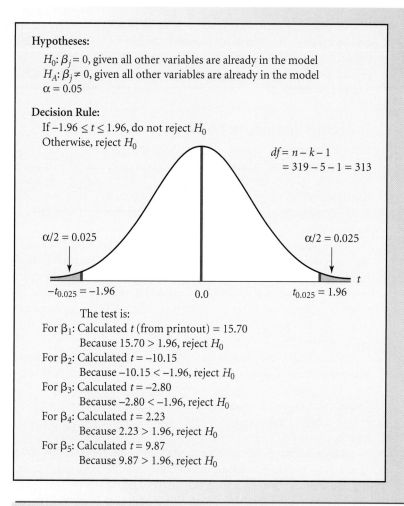

Hypotheses:

$H_0: \beta_j = 0$, given all other variables are already in the model
$H_A: \beta_j \neq 0$, given all other variables are already in the model
$\alpha = 0.05$

Decision Rule:
If $-1.96 \leq t \leq 1.96$, do not reject H_0
Otherwise, reject H_0

$df = n - k - 1$
$= 319 - 5 - 1 = 313$

$\alpha/2 = 0.025$ $\alpha/2 = 0.025$

$-t_{0.025} = -1.96$ 0.0 $t_{0.025} = 1.96$ t

The test is:
For β_1: Calculated t (from printout) = 15.70
    Because $15.70 > 1.96$, reject H_0
For β_2: Calculated $t = -10.15$
    Because $-10.15 < -1.96$, reject H_0
For β_3: Calculated $t = -2.80$
    Because $-2.80 < -1.96$, reject H_0
For β_4: Calculated $t = 2.23$
    Because $2.23 > 1.96$, reject H_0
For β_5: Calculated $t = 9.87$
    Because $9.87 > 1.96$, reject H_0

Estimate for the Standard Deviation of the Model

$$s_\varepsilon = \sqrt{\frac{SSE}{n - k - 1}} = \sqrt{MSE}$$

14-10

where:

SSE = Sum of squares error (residual)
n = Sample size
k = Number of independent variables

Examining Equation 14-10 closely, we see that this standard deviation is the square root of the mean square error of the residuals found in the analysis of variance table.

Sometimes, even though a model has a high R^2, the estimate of the standard deviation of the model error will be too large to provide adequate precision for confidence and prediction intervals. A rule of thumb that we have found useful is to examine the range $\pm 2s_\varepsilon$.[6] If this range is acceptable from a practical viewpoint, the estimate of the standard deviation of the model error might be considered acceptable.

In this First City Real Estate Company example, the model error's estimated standard deviation, shown in Figure 14-5a, is $27,350. Thus, the rough prediction range for the price of an individual home is

$$\pm 2(\$27,350)$$
$$\pm \$54,700$$

[6]The actual confidence interval for prediction of a new observation requires the use of matrix algebra. However, when the sample size is large and dependent variable values near the means of the dependent variables are used, the rule of thumb given here is a close approximation. Refer to *Applied Linear Statistical Models* by Neter et al. for further discussion.

From a practical viewpoint, a potential error of $54,700 above or below the true value is probably not acceptable. Not many homeowners would be willing to have their appraisal value set by a model with a possible error this large. The company needs to take steps to reduce the standard deviation of the model error. Subsequent sections of this chapter discuss some ways we can attempt to reduce it.

Is Multicollinearity a Problem?

Even if the overall regression model is significant and each independent variable is significant, decision makers should still examine the regression model to determine whether it appears reasonable. This is referred to as checking for *face validity*. Specifically, you should check to see that signs on the regression coefficients are consistent with the signs on the correlation coefficient between the independent variable and the dependent variable. Does any regression coefficient have an unexpected sign?

Before answering this question for the First City Real Estate example, we should review what the regression coefficients mean. First, the constant term, b_0, is the estimate of the model's y-intercept. If the data used to develop the regression model contain values of x_1, x_2, x_3, x_4, and x_5 that are simultaneously 0 (such as would be the case for vacant land), the constant is the mean value of y, given that x_1, x_2, x_3, x_4, and x_5 all equal 0. Under these conditions b_0 would estimate the average value of a vacant lot. However, in the First City example, no vacant land was in the sample, so the constant has no particular meaning.

The coefficient for square feet, b_1, estimates the average change in sales price corresponding to a change in house size of 1 square foot, holding the other independent variables constant. The value shown in Figure 14-5a for b_1 is 63.1. The coefficient is positive, indicating that an increase in square footage is associated with an increase in sales price. This relationship is expected. All other things being equal, bigger houses should sell for more money.

Likewise, the coefficient for x_5, the size of the garage, is positive, indicating that an increase in size is also associated with an increase in price. This is expected. The coefficient for x_2, the age of the house is negative, indicating that an older house is worth less than a similar younger house. This also seems reasonable. However, the coefficient for variable x_3, the number of bedrooms, is $-\$8,410.4$ meaning that, if we hold the other variables constant but increase the number of bedrooms by one, the average price will *drop* by $8,410.40. This would appear to run counter to conventional thinking about the housing market. Finally, variable x_4 for bathrooms has the expected positive sign.

Referring to the correlation matrix that was shown earlier in Figure 14-3, the correlation between variable x_3, bedrooms, and y, the sales price, is +0.540. This indicates that, without considering the other independent variables, the linear relationship between number of bedrooms and sales price is positive. But why does the regression coefficient turn out negative in the model? The answer lies in what is called **multicollinearity**.

Multicollinearity

A high correlation between two independent variables such that the two variables contribute redundant information to the model. When highly correlated independent variables are included in the regression model, they can adversely affect the regression results.

Multicollinearity occurs when independent variables overlap with respect to the information they provide in explaining the variation in the dependent variable. For example, x_3 and the other independent variables have the following correlations.

$$r_{x_3,x_1} = 0.706$$
$$r_{x_3,x_2} = -0.202$$
$$r_{x_3,x_4} = 0.600$$
$$r_{x_3,x_5} = 0.312$$

All four correlations have *t*-values indicating a significant linear relationship. Refer to the correlation matrix in Figure 14-3 to see that other independent variables are also correlated with each other.

The problems caused by multicollinearity, and how to deal with them, continue to be of prime concern to statisticians. From a decision maker's viewpoint, you should be aware that multicollinearity can (and usually does) exist and recognize the basic problems it can cause. Some of the most obvious problems and indications of severe multicollinearity are the following:

1. Incorrect signs on the coefficients.
2. A sizable change in the values of the previous coefficients when a new variable is added to the model.
3. A variable that was previously significant in the regression model becomes insignificant when a new independent variable is added.
4. The estimate of the standard deviation of the model error increases when a variable is added to the model.

Mathematical approaches exist for dealing with multicollinearity and reducing its impact. Although these procedures are beyond the scope of this text, one suggestion is to eliminate the variables that are the chief cause of the multicollinearity problems.

If the independent variables in a regression model are correlated and multicollinearity is present, another potential problem is that the *t*-tests for the significance of the individual independent variables may be misleading. That is, a *t*-test may indicate that the variable is not statistically significant when in fact it is.

One method of measuring multicollinearity is known as the **variance inflation factor (VIF)**.

Variance Inflation Factor

A measure of how much the variance of an estimated regression coefficient increases if the independent variables are correlated. A VIF equal to 1.0 for a given independent variable indicates that this independent variable is not correlated with the remaining independent variables in the model. The greater the multicollinearity, the larger the VIF.

Equation 14-11 is used to compute the VIF for each independent variable.

Variance Inflation Factor

$$VIF = \frac{1}{(1 - R_j^2)}$$

14-11

where:

R_j^2 = Coefficient of determination when the *j*th independent variable is regressed against the remaining $k - 1$ independent variables.

Both the PHStat add-ins to Excel and Minitab contain options that provide VIF values.[7]

Figure 14-7 shows the Excel (PHStat) output of the variance inflation factors for the First City Real Estate example. The effect of multicollinearity is to decrease the test statistic, thus reducing the probability that the variable will be declared significant. A related impact is to increase the width of the confidence interval estimate of the slope coefficient in the regression model. Generally, if the VIF < 5 for a particular independent variable, multicollinearity is not considered a problem for that variable. VIF values ≥ 5 imply that the correlation between the independent variables is too extreme and should be dealt with by dropping variables from the model. As Figure 14-7 illustrates, the VIF values for each independent variable are less than 5, so based on variance inflation factors, even though the sign on the variable, bedrooms, is incorrect, the other multicollinearity issues do not exist among these independent variables.

---

[7]Excel's Regression procedure in the Data Analysis Tools area does not provide VIF values directly. Without PHStat, you would need to compute each regression analysis individually and record the *R*-squared value to compute the VIF.

FIGURE 14-7

Excel (PHStat) Multiple Regression Model Results for First City Real Estate with Variance Inflation Factors

Excel Instructions:
1. Open file: First City.xls
2. Select **PHStat**.
3. Select **Regression**.
4. Define *y* variable range.
5. Define *x* variable range.
6. Check Variance Inflation Factor.

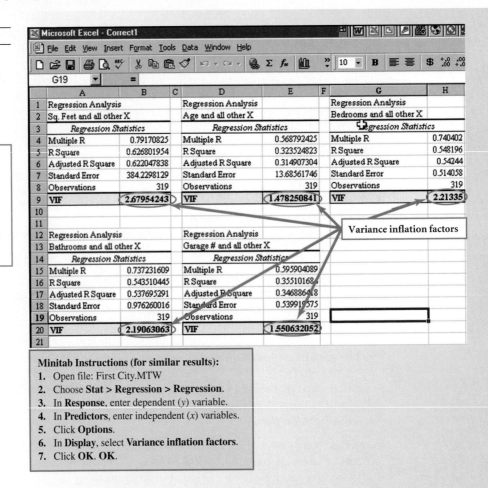

Minitab Instructions (for similar results):
1. Open file: First City.MTW
2. Choose **Stat > Regression > Regression**.
3. In **Response**, enter dependent (*y*) variable.
4. In **Predictors**, enter independent (*x*) variables.
5. Click **Options**.
6. In **Display**, select **Variance inflation factors**.
7. Click **OK. OK**.

Confidence Interval Estimation for Regression Coefficients

Previously we showed how to determine whether the regression coefficients are statistically significant. This was necessary because the estimates of the regression coefficients are developed from sample data and are subject to sampling error. The issue of sampling error also comes into play when interpreting the slope coefficients.

Consider the regression models for First City Real Estate shown in Figures 14-8a and 14-8b. The regression coefficients shown are *point estimates* for the true regression coefficients. For example, the coefficient for the variable, square feet, is $b_1 = 63.07$. We interpret this to mean that, holding the other variables constant, for each increase in the size of a home by one square foot, the price of a house is estimated to increase by $63.07. But like all point estimates, this is subject to sampling error. In Chapter 13 you were introduced to the concept of confidence interval estimates for the regression coefficients. That same concept applies in multiple regression models. Equation 14-12 is used to develop the confidence interval estimate for the regression coefficients.

Confidence Interval Estimate for the Regression Slope

$$b_j \pm t_{\alpha/2} s_{b_j}$$

14-12

where:

b_j = Point estimate for the regression coefficient for x_j

$t_{\alpha/2}$ = Critical *t*-value for a $1 - \alpha$ confidence interval

s_{b_j} = The standard error of the *j*th regression coefficient

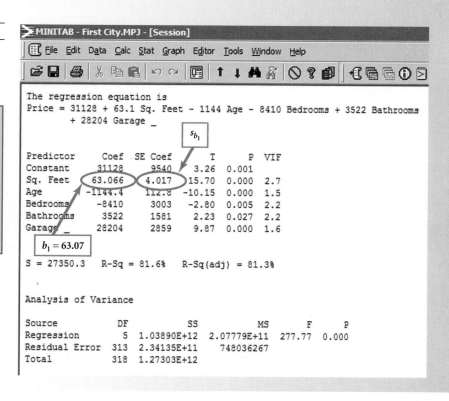

FIGURE 14-8A

Excel Multiple Regression Model—First City Real Estate

Excel Instructions:
1. Open file: First City.xls
2. Select **Tools**.
3. Select **Data Analysis**.
4. Select **Regression**.
5. Define y variable range.
6. Define x variable range.

The Excel output in Figure 14-8a provides the confidence interval estimates for each regression coefficient. For example, the 95% interval estimate for square feet is

$$\$55.16 \text{ ——— } \$70.97$$

Minitab does not have a command to generate confidence intervals for the individual regression parameters. However, statistical quantities are provided on the Minitab output in Figure 14-8b to allow the manual calculation of these confidence intervals. As an example, the

FIGURE 14-8B

Minitab Multiple Regression Model—First City Real Estate

Minitab Instructions:
1. Open file: First City.MTW.
2. Choose **Stat > Regression > Regression**.
3. In **Response**, enter dependent (y) variable.
4. In **Predictors**, enter independent (x) variables.
5. Click **OK**.

confidence interval for the coefficient associated with the square feet variable can be computed using Equation 14-12 as:

$$b_1 \pm t_{\alpha/2}s_{b_1}$$
$$63.07 \pm 1.96\,(4.017)$$
$$63.07 \pm 7.90$$
$$\$55.17 \text{ --------------- } \$70.97^8$$

We interpret this interval as follows: Holding the other variables constant, using a 95% confidence level, a change in square feet by one foot is estimated to generate an average change in home price of between $55.17 and $70.97. Each of the other regression coefficients can be interpreted in the same manner.

14-1: EXERCISES

Skill Development

14.1 You are given the following estimated regression equation involving a dependent and two independent variables.

$$\hat{y} = 12.67 + 4.14x_1 + 8.72x_2$$

a. Interpret the values of the slope coefficients in this equation.
b. Estimate the value of the dependent variable when $x_1 = 4$ and $x_2 = 9$.

14.2 In working for a local retail store, you have developed the following estimated regression equation:

$$\hat{y} = 22,167 - 412x_1 + 818x_2 - 93x_3 - 71x_4$$

where:

y = Weekly sales
x_1 = Local unemployment rate
x_2 = Weekly average high temperature
x_3 = Number of activities in the local community
x_4 = Average gasoline price

a. Interpret the values of b_1, b_2, b_3, and b_4 in this estimated regression equation.
b. What are the estimated sales if the unemployment rate is 5.7%, the average high temperature is 61°, there were 14 activities, and the average gasoline price was $1.39?

14.3 Given the following data for a dependent and two independent variables:

y	x_1	x_2
22	9	14
17	6	15
28	12	17
35	14	18
25	15	15
30	16	17

a. Estimate the regression equation relating the dependent variable to the first independent variable.
b. Estimate the regression equation relating the dependent variable to the second independent variable.
c. Estimate the regression relating the dependent variable to both independent variables.

14.4 The following output is associated with a multiple regression model with three independent variables.

	df	SS	MS	F	Significance F
Regression	3	16646.09124	5548.697	5.327561	0.006890815
Residual	21	21871.66876	1041.508		
Total	24	38517.76			

	Coefficients	Standard Error	t Stat	p-value
Intercept	87.789729	25.46767899	3.447104	0.002415
x_1	−0.9704675	0.586041665	−1.65597	0.112596
x_2	0.0023343	0.000745097	3.132828	0.005028
x_3	−8.7233223	7.495492501	−1.16381	0.257554

	Lower 95%	Upper 95%	Lower 90.0%	Upper 90.0%
Intercept	34.82678246	140.75268	43.96638607	131.613073
x_1	−2.189208073	0.2482731	−1.97889489	0.03795989
x_2	0.000784747	0.0038838	0.001052141	0.00361638
x_3	−24.31105497	6.8644104	−21.6211424	4.1744978

a. What is the regression model associated with this data?
b. Is the model statistically significant?
c. How much of the variation in the dependent variable can be explained by the model?
d. Are all of the independent variables in the model significant? If not, which are not and how can you tell?
e. How much of a change in the dependent variable will be associated with a one-unit change in x_2? In x_3?
f. Do any of the 95% confidence interval estimates of the slope coefficients contain zero? If so, what does this indicate?

14.5 The following correlation matrix is associated with the same data used to build the regression model in Exercise 14-4.

	y	x_1	x_2	x_3
y	1			
x_1	−0.405743076	1		
x_2	0.459099549	0.051276	1	
x_3	−0.244495858	0.503749	0.271800482	1

Does this output indicate any potential multicollinearity problems with the analysis?

Business Applications

14.6 Commercial Federal Savings and Loan has been trying to gain a foothold in the southern United States. Initial plans are to open several branches throughout that region in the next five years. In deciding whether to go ahead with the expansion, the board of directors is trying to determine whether the expanding number of S&L offices nationwide has lead to an increase or decrease in overall profitability. One of the board members has recently come across the article "Entry and Probability in Rate-Free Savings and Loan Market" (*Quarterly Review of Economics and Business* (1978) pp. 87–95). The article relates the overall profit margin of savings and loan companies (y) to their net revenues in that year (x_1, in million dollars) and the number of branch offices (x_2). The data that were presented in the article are in the CD-ROM file *Profit*.

a. Produce scatter plots of each independent variable versus the dependent variable in this data set. On the basis of these plots, determine the relationship between each independent variable and the dependent variable.

b. Determine whether the board can use a multiple regression model containing both net revenue and number of branch offices to predict the profit margins of savings and loans companies. Use a hypothesis test with a significance level of 0.10.

c. Which, if any, of the independent variables is statistically significant? Use a significance level of $\alpha = 0.10$ and the *p*-value approach to conduct these tests.

d. Use a rule of thumb to determine if the standard deviation of the model error is too large for this model. Explain your reasoning in the context of this exercise.

14.7 The Western States Tourist Association gives out pamphlets, maps, and other tourist-related information to people who call a toll-free number and request the information. The association orders the packets of information from a document-printing company and likes to have enough available to meet immediate needs without having too many sitting around taking up space. The marketing manager decided to develop a multiple regression model to be used in predicting the number of calls that will be received in the coming week. A ran-

dom sample of 12 weeks is selected, with the following variables:

y = Number of calls
x_1 = Number of advertisements placed the previous week
x_2 = Number of calls received the previous week
x_3 = Number of airline tour bookings into western cities for the current week

The data that were collected are in the CD-ROM file *Western States*.

a. Produce the correlation matrix and scatter plots for each independent variable versus the dependent variable.

b. Based on the scatter plots and the correlation matrix, specify the relationship that exists between each independent variable and the dependent variable, then comment on whether you think a multiple regression model will be effectively developed from these data.

c. Specify three simple linear regression equations, one for each of the respective independent variables, and then determine the estimate of each model obtained from the sample data.

d. Indicate which of the models in part c is preferred. Provide statistical analysis and reasoning to support your answer.

14.8 Refer to the Western States Tourist Association situation described in Exercise 14-7.

a. Specify and then use the data to estimate a multiple regression model that contains all three independent variables.

b. What percentage of the total variation in the dependent variable is explained by the model containing the three independent variables?

c. Test to determine whether the overall model is statistically significant. Use $\alpha = 0.05$ and the *p*-value approach to conduct this test.

d. Which, if any, of the independent variables is statistically significant? Test using a significance level of 0.05.

e. Determine the adjusted *R*-squared and comment on what it means.

f. Determine an estimate of the standard error of the estimate and discuss whether this regression model is acceptable as a means of predicting the number of calls that will come to Western Tourist in a given week.

g. Indicate what, if any, evidence there is of multicollinearity problems with this multiple regression model. Discuss problems multicollinearity could cause in this example.

h. Determine the *VIF* for each variable and determine whether this measure results in different conclusions regarding the significance of the independent variables. Do the *VIF* calculations imply that a multicollinearity problem exists? Discuss.

Advanced Application

14.9 The athletic director of State University is interested in developing a multiple regression model that might be used to explain the variation in attendance at football games at his school. A sample of 16 games was selected from home games played during the past 10 seasons. Data for the following factors were determined.

y = Game attendance
x_1 = Team win/loss percentage to date
x_2 = Opponent win/loss percentage to date
x_3 = Games played this season
x_4 = Temperature at game time

The data that were collected are in the CD-ROM file *Football*.

a. Produce the scatter plots for each independent variable versus the dependent variable. Based on the scatter plots, produce a model that you believe represents the relationship between the dependent variable and the group of predictor variables represented in the scatter plots.

b. Based on the correlation matrix developed from this data, comment on whether you think a multiple regression model will be effectively developed from these data.

c. Use the sample data to estimate a multiple regression model that contains all four independent variables.

d. What percentage of the total variation in the dependent variable is explained by the four independent variables in the model?

e. Test to determine whether the overall model is statistically significant. Use $\alpha = 0.05$.

f. Which, if any, of the independent variables is statistically significant? Use a significance level of $\alpha = 0.08$ and the *p*-value approach to conduct these tests.

g. Estimate the standard deviation of the model error and discuss whether this regression model is acceptable as a means of predicting the football attendance at State University at any given game.

h. Define the term *multicollinearity* and indicate the potential problems that multicollinearity can cause for this model. Indicate what, if any, evidence there is of multicollinearity problems with this regression model. Use the variance inflation factor to assist you in this analysis.

i. Develop a 95% confidence interval estimate for each of the regression coefficients and interpret each estimate. Comment on whether the interpretation of the intercept is relevant in this situation.

14-2 USING QUALITATIVE INDEPENDENT VARIABLES

In Example 14-1 involving the First City Real Estate Company, the independent variables were quantitative and ratio level. However, you will encounter many situations in which you may wish to use a qualitative, lower-level, variable as an explanatory variable.

If a variable is nominal, and numerical codes are assigned to the categories, you already know not to perform mathematical calculations using those data. The results would be meaningless. Yet, we may wish to use marital status, gender, or geographical location as an independent variable in a regression model. If the variable of interest is coded as an ordinal variable, such as education level or job performance ranking, computing means and variances is also inappropriate. Then how are these variables incorporated into a multiple regression analysis? The answer lies in using what are called **dummy** (or indicator) **variables**.

Dummy Variables

A variable that is assigned a value equal to either zero or one, depending on whether the observation possesses a given characteristic.

For instance, consider the variable gender, which can take on two possible values:

male or female

Gender can be converted to a dummy variable as follows:

x_1 = 1 if female
x_1 = 0 if male

Thus, a data set consisting of males and females will have corresponding values for x_1 equal to 0s and 1s, respectively. Note that it makes no difference which gender is coded 1 and which is coded 0. If a categorical variable has more than two mutually exclusive outcome possibilities, multiple dummy variables must be created. Consider the variable, marital status, with the following possible outcomes:

never married   married   divorced   widowed

In this case, marital status has four values. To account for all the possibilities, you would create three dummy variables, one less than the number of possible outcomes for the original variable. They could be coded as follows.

$$x_1 = 1 \text{ if never married, } 0 \text{ if not}$$
$$x_2 = 1 \text{ if married, } 0 \text{ if not}$$
$$x_3 = 1 \text{ if divorced, } 0 \text{ if not}$$

Note that we don't need the fourth variable because we would know that a person is widowed if $x_1 = 0$, $x_2 = 0$, and $x_3 = 0$. If the person isn't single, married, or divorced, he or she must be widowed. *Always use one fewer dummy variables than categories.* The mathematical reason that the number of dummy variables must be one less than the number of possible responses is called the *dummy variable trap.* Perfect multicollinearity is introduced, and the least squares regression estimates cannot be obtained, if the number of dummy variables equals the number of possible categories.

$\mathcal{E}$XAMPLE 14-2: INCORPORATING DUMMY VARIABLES

Business Executive Salaries   To illustrate the effect of incorporating dummy variables into a regression model, consider the sample data displayed in the scatter plot in Figure 14-9. The population from which the sample was selected consists of executives between the ages of 24 and 60 who are working in U.S. manufacturing businesses. Data for annual salary (y) and age (x_1) are available. The objective is to determine whether a model can be generated to explain the variation in annual salary for business executives. Even though age and annual salary are significantly correlated ($r = 0.686$) at the $\alpha = 0.05$ level, the coefficient of determination is only 47%. Therefore, we would likely search for other independent variables that could help us to further explain the variation in annual salary.

Suppose we can determine which of the 16 people in the sample had an MBA degree. Figure 14-10 shows the scatter plot for these same data, with the MBA data represented by triangles. To incorporate a qualitative variable into the analysis, use the following steps.

Step 1:   **Code the qualitative variable as a dummy variable.**
Create a new variable, x_2, which is a dummy variable coded as

$$x_2 = 1 \text{ if MBA, } 0 \text{ if not}$$

The data with the new variable are shown in Table 14-2.

Step 2:   **Develop a multiple regression model with the dummy variables incorporated as independent variables.**
The two-variable population multiple regression model has the following form:

$$y = \beta_0 + \beta_1 x_1 + \beta_2 x_2 + \varepsilon$$

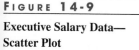

FIGURE 14-9

Executive Salary Data— Scatter Plot

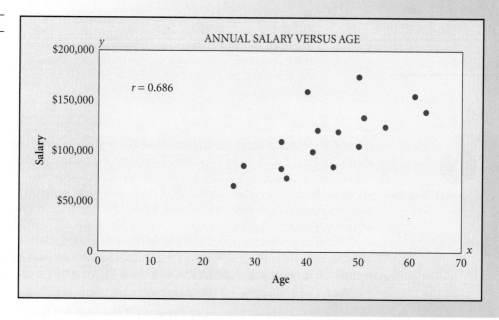

FIGURE 14-10

Impact of a Dummy Variable

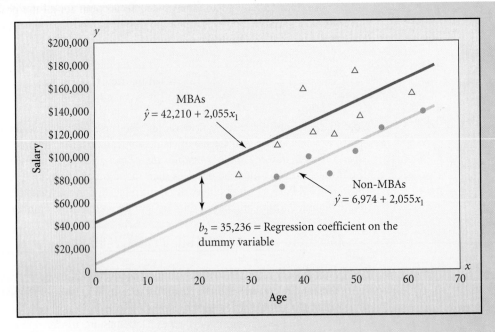

TABLE 14-2

Executive Salary Data Including MBA Variable

SALARY	AGE	MBA
$ 65,000	26	0
85,000	28	1
74,000	36	0
83,000	35	0
110,000	35	1
160,000	40	1
100,000	41	0
122,000	42	1
85,000	45	0
120,000	46	1
105,000	50	0
135,000	51	1
125,000	55	0
175,000	50	1
156,000	61	1
140,000	63	0

Using either Excel or Minitab, we get the following regression equation as an estimate of the population model.

$$\hat{y} = 6{,}974 + 2{,}055x_1 + 35{,}236x_2$$

Because the dummy variable, x_2, has been coded 0 or 1 depending on degree status, incorporating it into the regression model is like having two simple linear regression lines with the same slopes, but different intercepts. For instance, when $x_2 = 0$, the regression equation is

$$\hat{y} = 6{,}974 + 2{,}055x_1 + 35{,}236(0)$$
$$= 6{,}974 + 2{,}055x_1$$

This line is shown in Figure 14-10.

However, when $x_2 = 1$ (the executive has an MBA), the regression equation is

$$\hat{y} = 6{,}974 + 2{,}055x_1 + 35{,}236(1)$$
$$= 42{,}210 + 2{,}055x_1$$

This regression line is also shown in Figure 14-10. As you can see, incorporating the dummy variable affects the regression intercept. In this case, the intercept for executives with an MBA degree is $35,236 higher than for those without an MBA. We interpret the regression coefficient on this dummy variable as follows: Based on these data, and holding age (x_1) constant, we estimate that executives with an MBA degree make an average of $35,236 per year more in salary than their non-MBA counterparts.

Excel and Minitab Tutorial

First City Real Estate (continued)—The regression model developed in Example 14-l for First City Real Estate showed potential because the overall model was statistically significant. Looking back at Figure 14-8, we see that the model explained nearly 82% of the variation in sales prices for the homes in the sample. All of the independent variables were significant, given that the other independent variables were in the model. However, the estimate of the standard error was quite large.

The managers have decided to try to improve the model. First, they have decided to add a new variable: area. However, at this point, the only area variable they can get is whether the house is in the foothills. Because this is a categorical variable with two possible outcomes (foothills or flatland), a dummy variable can be created as follows:

$$x_6 \text{ (area)} = 1 \text{ if foothills, } 0 \text{ if not}$$

FIGURE 14-11

Minitab Output—First City Real Estate Revised Regression Model

Minitab Instructions:
1. Open file: First City.MTW.
2. Choose **Stat > Regression > Regression**.
3. In **Response**, enter dependent (y) variable.
4. In **Predictors**, enter independent (x) variables.
5. Click **Options**.
6. In **Display**, select **Variance inflation Factors**.
7. Click **OK. OK.**

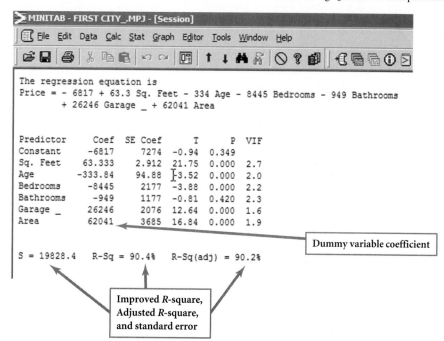

MINITAB - FIRST CITY_.MPJ - [Session]

File Edit Data Calc Stat Graph Editor Tools Window Help

The regression equation is
Price = - 6817 + 63.3 Sq. Feet - 334 Age - 8445 Bedrooms - 949 Bathrooms
        + 26246 Garage _ + 62041 Area

Predictor	Coef	SE Coef	T	P	VIF
Constant	-6817	7274	-0.94	0.349	
Sq. Feet	63.333	2.912	21.75	0.000	2.7
Age	-333.84	94.88	-3.52	0.000	2.0
Bedrooms	-8445	2177	-3.88	0.000	2.2
Bathrooms	-949	1177	-0.81	0.420	2.3
Garage _	26246	2076	12.64	0.000	1.6
Area	62041	3685	16.84	0.000	1.9

S = 19828.4   R-Sq = 90.4%   R-Sq(adj) = 90.2%

Dummy variable coefficient

Improved R-square, Adjusted R-square, and standard error

Of the 319 homes in the sample, 249 were homes in the foothills and 70 were in the flatland. Figure 14-11 shows the revised Minitab multiple regression with the variable, area, added. This model is better than the original model because the adjusted R-squared has increased from 0.813 to 0.904, and the estimate of the standard error of the estimate has decreased from $27,350 to $19,828. The conditional t-tests show that all of the regression model's slope coefficients, except that for the variable bathrooms, differ significantly from 0. Because the variance inflation factors are all less than 5.0, we don't need to be too concerned about the t-tests understating the significance of the regression coefficients. (See the Excel Tutorial on the CD-ROM for this example to get the full *VIF* output from PHStat.)

The resulting regression model is

$$\hat{y} = -6{,}817 + 63.333(\text{sq. feet}) - 333.84(\text{age}) - 8{,}445(\text{bedrooms}) - 949(\text{bathrooms})$$
$$+ 26{,}246(\text{garages}) + 62{,}041(\text{area})$$

Because the variable, bathrooms, is not significant in the presence of the other variables, we can remove the variable and rerun the multiple regression. The resulting model is

$$\text{Price} = -7{,}050 + 62.5(\text{sq. feet}) - 322(\text{age}) - 8{,}830(\text{bedrooms}) + 26{,}054(\text{garage})$$
$$+ 61{,}370(\text{area})$$

Based on the sample data and this regression model, we estimate that a house with the same characteristics (square feet, age, bedrooms, and garages) is worth an average of $61,370 more if it is located in the foothills (based on how the dummy variable was coded).

There are still signals of multicollinearity problems. The coefficient on the independent variable, bedrooms, is negative, when we would expect homes with more bedrooms to sell for more. Also, the estimate of the standard error of the estimate is still too large ($19,817) to provide the precision the managers need to set prices for homes. More work needs to be done before the model is complete.

Possible Improvements to the First City Appraisal Model

Because the standard error of the estimate is still too high, we look to improve the model. We could start by identifying possible problems:

1. Useful independent variables may have been omitted.
2. Independent variables may have been included that should not have been included.

There is no sure way of determining the correct model specification. However, a recommended approach is for the decision maker to try adding variables or removing variables from the model.

We begin by removing the bedrooms variable, which has the incorrect sign on the regression slope coefficient. (Note: If the regression model's sole purpose is for prediction, independent variables with unexpected signs do not automatically pose a problem and do not necessarily need to be

FIGURE 14-12A

Excel Output for the First City Real Estate Revised Model

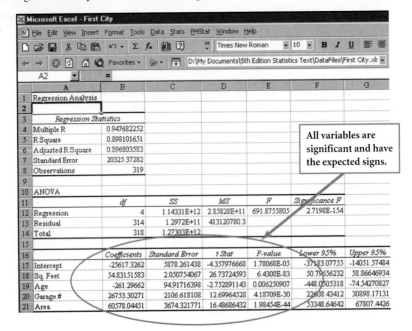

deleted. However, insignificant variables should be deleted.) The resulting model is shown in Figures 14-12a and 14-12b. Now all the variables in the model have the expected signs. However, the estimate of the model's standard error has increased slightly.

Adding other explanatory variables might help. For instance, consider whether the house has central air conditioning, which might affect sales. If we can identify whether a house has air conditioning, we could add a dummy variable coded as follows:

$$\text{If air conditioning, } x_7 = 1$$
$$\text{If no air conditioning, } x_7 = 0$$

Other potential independent variables might include a more-detailed location variable, a measure of the physical condition, or whether the house has one or two stories. Can you think of others?

The First City example illustrates that even though a regression model may pass the statistical tests of significance, it may not be functional. Good appraisal models can be developed using multi-

FIGURE 14-12B

Minitab Output for the First City Real Estate Revised Model

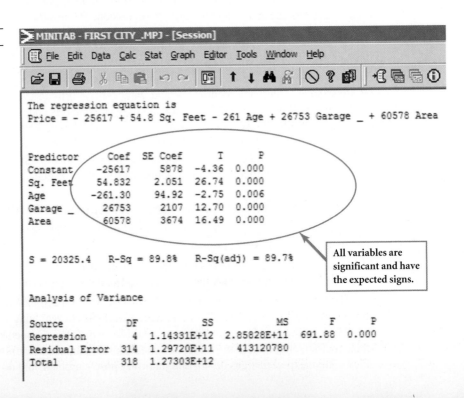

ple regression analysis, provided more detail is available about such characteristics as finish quality, landscaping, location, neighborhood characteristics, and so forth. The cost and effort required to obtain these data can be relatively high.

Developing a multiple regression model is more of an art than a science. The real decisions revolve around how to select the best set of independent variables for the model.

14-2: EXERCISES

Skill Development

14.10 You are considering developing a regression equation relating a dependent variable to two independent variables. One of the variables can be measured on a ratio scale, but the other is a categorical variable with two possible levels.
  a. Write a multiple regression model relating the dependent variable to the independent variables.
  b. Interpret the meaning of the coefficients in the regression model.

14.11 You are considering developing a regression model relating a dependent variable to two independent variables. One of the variables can be measured on a ratio scale, but the other is a categorical variable with four possible levels.
  a. How many dummy variables are needed to represent the categorical variable?
  b. Write a multiple regression model relating the dependent variable to the independent variables.
  c. Interpret the meaning of the coefficients in the regression model.

14.12 A manager is considering incorporating a new variable into her regression model. This variable measures educational level of the respondent. The variable has been measured on four levels, as follows:
  1. No high school degree
  2. High school degree
  3. Some college courses
  4. College degree
  a. She is considering this variable and plans to use the codes 1, 2, 3, and 4 to determine which educational level the respondent has achieved. Comment on this.
  b. How many dummy variables would you set up to handle this situation? Specify the values each dummy variable could assume and what each value would represent.

Business Applications

14.13 The Polk Utility Corporation is developing a multiple regression model that it plans to use to predict customers' utility usage. The analyst currently has three quantitative variables (x_1, x_2, and x_3) in the model, but she is dissatisfied with the R-squared and the estimate of the standard deviation of the model's error. Two variables that she thinks might be useful are whether a house has a gas or an electric water heater and whether a house was constructed before or after the 1974 energy crisis.

Provide the model she should use to predict customers' utility usage. Specify the dummy variables to be used, the values these variables can assume, and what each value will represent.

14.14 A study was recently performed by the American Automobile Association in which it attempted to develop a regression model to explain variation in EPA mileage ratings of new cars. At one stage of the analysis, the estimate of the model took the following form:

$$\hat{y} = 34.20 - 0.003x_1 + 4.56x_2$$

where:

$$x_1 = \text{Vehicle weight}$$
$$x_2 = 1 \text{ if standard transmission}$$
$$= 0 \text{ if automatic transmission}$$

  a. Interpret the regression coefficient for variable x_1.
  b. Interpret the regression coefficient for variable x_2.
  c. Present an estimate of a model that would predict the average EPA mileage rating for an automobile with standard transmission as a function of the vehicle's weight.
  d. Cadillac's 1999 Sedan Deville with automatic transmission weighs approximately 4,012 pounds. Provide an estimate of the average highway mileage you would expect to obtain from this model.
  e. Discuss the effect of a dummy variable being incorporated into a regression equation like this one. Use a graph if it is helpful.

14.15 A recent study by the U.S. Department of Agriculture attempted to develop a multiple regression model to explain variation in farm income. At one stage of development, the estimate of the model took the following form:

$$\hat{y} = -23,200 + 4.2x_1 + 2,345x_2 + 4,670x_3$$

where:

$$x_1 = \text{Number of acres farmed}$$
$$x_2 = 1 \text{ if land is row-irrigated}$$
$$= 0 \text{ if not}$$
$$x_3 = 1 \text{ if land is sprinkler-irrigated}$$
$$= 0 \text{ if not}$$

  a. Interpret the regression coefficient for variable x_1.
  b. Interpret the regression coefficient for variable x_2.
  c. Interpret the regression coefficient for variable x_3.
  d. Present a model that would predict the average farm income for a 1,000-acre farm that irrigated using sprinklers.

Advanced Applications

14.16 💿 Gilmore Accounting collected the data here in an effort to explain variation in client profitability. The data also are in the CD-ROM file *Gilmore*.

y	x_1	x_2
2,345	45	1
4,200	56	2
278	26	3
1,211	56	2
1,406	24	2
500	23	3
−700	34	3
3,457	45	1
2,478	47	1
1,975	24	2
206	32	3

where:

y = Net profit earned from the client
x_1 = Number of hours spent working with the client
x_2 = Type of client:
    1 if manufacturing
    2 if service
    3 if governmental

a. Develop a scatter plot of each independent variable against the client-income variable. Comment on what, if any, relationship appears to exist in each case.
b. Run a simple linear regression analysis using only variable x_1 as the independent variable. Describe the resulting estimate fully.
c. Test to determine if the number of hours spent working with a client is useful in predicting the net profit earned by that client.

14.17 💿 Use the data from Gilmore Accounting found in the CD-ROM file *Gilmore*. (See Exercise 14.16.)
a. Incorporate the client type into the regression analysis using dummy variables. Describe the resulting multiple regression estimate.
b. Test to determine if this model is useful in predicting the net profit earned by a client.
c. Test to determine if the number of hours spent working with a client is useful in this model in predicting the net profit earned by that client.
d. Considering the tests you have performed, construct a model and its estimate for predicting the net profit earned by a client.
e. Predict the average difference in profit if a client is governmental versus manufacturing. Also state this in terms of a 95% confidence interval estimate. (Refer to Chapter 13 if needed.)

14.18 💿 One of the editors of a major automobile publication has collected data on 30 of the best-selling cars in the United States. The data are in the CD-ROM file *Automobiles*. The editor is particularly interested in the relationship between price of a vehicle and the horsepower of the engine. She thinks another variable that might have an impact on price would be the type of vehicle.
a. Specify a model that characterizes the relationship between vehicle price, horsepower, and vehicle type. Specify the dummy variables to be used, the values these variables can assume, and what each value will represent. Note that there are three types of vehicles.
b. Produce an estimate of the model presented in part a.
c. Which of the independent variables from part b are significant? Is the overall model significant?

14-3 WORKING WITH NONLINEAR RELATIONSHIPS

Section 13-1 in Chapter 13 showed there are a variety of ways in which two variables can be related. Correlation and regression analysis techniques are tools for measuring and modeling linear relationships between variables. Many situations in business have a linear relationship between two variables, and regression equations that model that relationship will be appropriate to use in these situations. However, there are also many instances in which the relationship between two variables will be curvilinear, rather than linear. For instance, demand for electricity has grown at an almost exponential rate relative to the population growth in some areas. Advertisers believe that a diminishing returns relationship will occur between sales and advertising if advertising is allowed to grow too large. These two situations are shown in Figures 14-13 and 14-14, respectively. They represent just two of the great many possible curvilinear relationships that could exist between two variables.

As you will soon see, models with nonlinear relationships become more complicated than models showing only linear relationships. Although complicated models are sometimes necessary, decision makers should use them with caution for several reasons. First, management researchers and authors have written that people use decision aids they understand and don't use those they don't understand. So, the more complicated a model is, the less likely it is to be used. Second, the scientific principle of parsimony suggests using the simplest model possible that provides a reasonable fit of the data, because complex models typically do not reflect the underlying phenomena that produce the data in the first place.

FIGURE 14-13

Exponential Relationship of Increased Demand for Electricity versus Population Growth

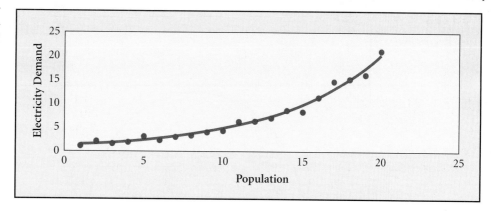

This section provides a brief introduction into how linear regression analysis can be used in dealing with curvilinear relationships. In order to model such curvilinear relationships, we must incorporate terms into the multiple regression model that will create "curves" in the model we are building. Including terms whose independent variable has an exponent larger than one generates these curves. When a model possesses such terms we refer to it as a **polynomial model**. The general equation for a polynomial with one independent variable is given in Equation 14-13.

Polynomial Population Regression Model

$$y = \beta_0 + \beta_1 x + \beta_2 x^2 + \ldots + \beta_p x^p + \varepsilon \qquad \text{14-13}$$

where:

β_0 = Population's regression constant

β_j = Population's regression coefficient for variable x^j; $j = 1, 2, \ldots p$

p = Order (or degree) of the polynomial

ε = Model error

The order, or degree, of the model is determined by the largest exponent of the independent variable in the model. For instance, the model

$$y = \beta_0 + \beta_1 x + \beta_2 x^2 + \varepsilon$$

is a second-order polynomial because the largest exponent in any term of the polynomial is two. You will note that this model contains terms of all orders less than or equal to two. A polynomial with this property is said to be a *complete* polynomial. Therefore, the previous model would be referred to as a complete *second-order regression model*.

A second-order model produces a parabola. The parabola either opens upward ($\beta_2 > 0$) or downward ($\beta_2 < 0$), shown in Figure 14-15. You will notice that the models in Figures 14-13 and 14-14 both possess a single curve.

As more curves appear in the data, the order of the polynomial must be increased. A general (complete) third-order polynomial is given by the equation

$$y = \beta_0 + \beta_1 x + \beta_2 x^2 + \beta_3 x^3 + \varepsilon$$

FIGURE 14-14

Diminishing Returns Relationship of Advertising versus Sales

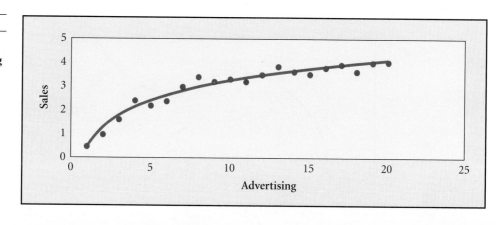

FIGURE 14-15

Second-Order Regression Models

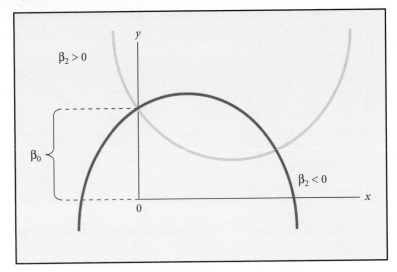

This model produces a curvilinear model that reverses the direction of the initial curve to produce a second curve, as shown in Figure 14-16. Note that there are two curves in the third-order model. In general a pth-order polynomial will exhibit $p - 1$ curves.

Our discussion of polynomials has, thus far, concerned only models with one independent variable raised to a power. When more than one independent variable is involved, the same terminology is used. However, we must use the sum of the exponents of the independent variables in any one term to determine the order of that term. As an example, a term of the form $\beta_i x_1^2 x_2^3$ would be a fifth-order term, because the sum of the independent variables' exponents $(2 + 3)$ equals 5. Using similar logic, the term *complete pth-order polynomial* implies that the polynomial contains all those terms of order p and all orders smaller than p as well. Therefore, the model

$$y = \beta_0 + \beta_1 x_1 + \beta_2 x_2 + \beta_3 x_1^2 + \beta_4 x_2^2 + \beta_5 x_1 x_2 + \varepsilon$$

is a complete second-order model involving the independent variables x_1 and x_2. The model

$$y = \beta_0 + \beta_1 x_1 + \beta_2 x_2 + \beta_3 x_1^2 + \beta_4 x_2^2 + \varepsilon$$

is a second-order model. However, it is not a complete second-order model because it does not contain the term $\beta_5 x_1 x_2$, whose exponents of the independent variables sum to two.

Although polynomials of all orders exist in the business sector, perhaps second-order polynomials are the most common. Sharp reversals in the curvature of a relationship between variables in the business environment usually point to some unexpected or, perhaps, severe changes that were not foreseen. The vast majority of organizations try to avoid such reverses. For this reason, and the fact that this is an introductory business statistics course, we will direct most of our attention to second-order polynomials.

FIGURE 14-16

Third-Order Regression Models

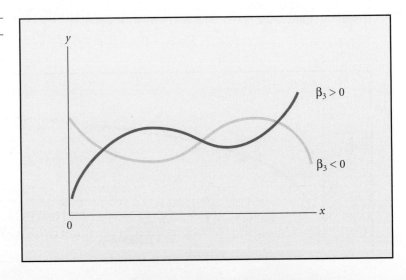

The following examples illustrate two of the most common instances in which curvilinear relationships can be used in decision making. They should give you an idea of how to approach similar situations.

EXAMPLE 14-3: MODELING CURVILINEAR RELATIONSHIPS

Excel and Minitab Tutorial

Ashley Investment Services   Ashley Investment Services has been severely shaken by a recent downturn in the stock market. To maintain profitability and save as many jobs as possible, everyone has been busy analyzing new investment opportunities. The director of personnel has noticed an increased number of people suffering from "burnout," in which physical and emotional fatigue hurt job performance. Although he cannot change the job's pressures, he has read that the more time a person spends socializing with coworkers away from the job, the more likely a higher degree of burnout. With the help of the human resources lab at the local university, the personnel director has administered a questionnaire to company employees. A burnout index has been computed from the responses to the survey. Likewise, the survey responses are used to determine quantitative measures of socialization. Sample data from questionnaires are contained in the file *Ashley* on the CD-ROM. The following steps can be used to model the relationship between the socialization index and the burnout index for Ashley employees:

Step 1: **Specify the model by determining the dependent and potential independent variables.**
The dependent variable is the burnout index. The company wishes to explain the variation in burnout level. One potential independent variable is the socialization index.

Step 2: **Formulate the model.**
We begin by proposing that a linear relationship exists between the two variables. Figures 14-17a and 14-17b show the linear regression analysis results using Excel and Minitab. The correlation between the two variables is $r = 0.818$, which is statistically different from zero at any reasonable significance level. The estimate of the population linear regression model shown in Figure 14-17a is

$$\hat{y} = -66.164 + 9.5889x$$

Step 3: **Perform diagnostic checks on the model.**
The sample data and the regression line are plotted in Figure 14-18. The line appears to fit the data. However, a closer inspection reveals instances where several consecutive points lie above or below the line. The points are not randomly dispersed around the regression line, as we would expect given the regression analysis assumptions. (In Chapter 13 we briefly discussed the concept of residual analysis. Section 14-5 expands the residual analysis discussion.)

FIGURE 14-17A

Excel Output of a Simple Linear Regression for Ashley Investment Services

Excel Instructions:
1. Open file: Ashley.xls
2. Select **Tools**.
3. Click on **Data Analysis**.
4. Select **Regression**.
5. Define *y* and *x* variable range.
6. Specify output location.
7. Click **OK**.

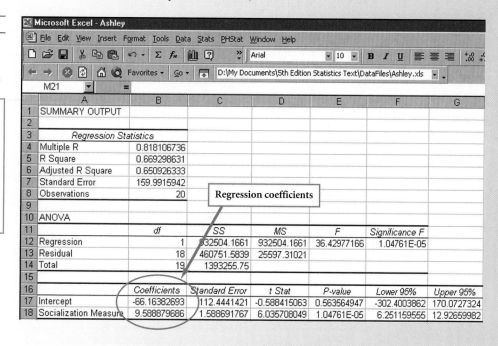

FIGURE 14-17B

Minitab Output of a Simple Linear Regression for Ashley Investment Services

Minitab Instructions:
1. Open file: Ashley.MTW.
2. Choose **Stat > Regression > Regression**.
3. In **Response**, enter the y variable column.
4. In **Predictors**, enter the x variable column.
5. Click **OK**.

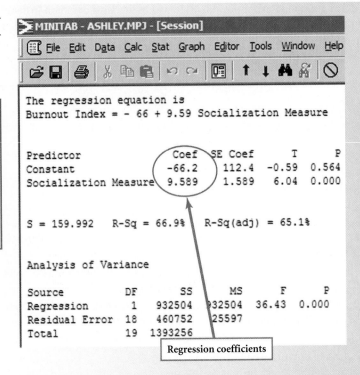

As you will recall from earlier discussions, we can use analysis of variance to test whether a regression line explains a significant amount of variation in the dependent variable.

$$H_0: \beta_1 = 0$$
$$H_A: \beta_1 \neq 0$$

From the output in Figure 14-17a,

$$F = 36.43$$

which has a p-value < 0.0001.

Thus, we conclude that the simple linear model is statistically significant. However, we should also examine the data to determine if any curvilinear relationships may be present.

Step 4: Model the curvilinear relationship.
Finding instances of nonrandom patterns in the residuals for a regression model indicates the possibility of using a curvilinear relationship rather than a linear one. One possible approach to modeling the curvilinear nature of the data in the Ashley

FIGURE 14-18

Plot of Regression Line for the Ashley Investment Services Example

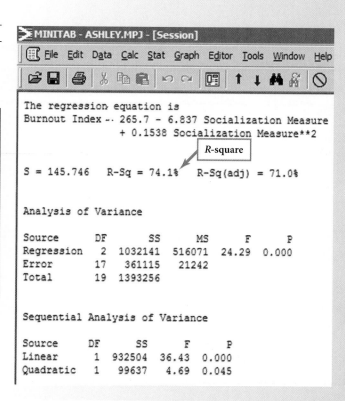

FIGURE 14-19A

Excel Output of a Second-Order Polynomial Fit for Ashley Investment

Excel Instructions:
1. Open file: Ashley.xls
2. Click on **Tools**.
3. Select **Data Analysis**.
4. Select **Regression**.
5. Define y and x variable ranges.
6. Click **OK**.

Investments example is with the use of polynomials. From Figure 14-18, we can see that there is one curve in the data. This suggests fitting the second-order polynomial

$$y = \beta_0 + \beta_1 x + \beta_2 x^2 + \varepsilon$$

Before fitting the estimate for this population model, you will need to create the new independent variable by squaring the socialization measure variable. In Excel, use the formula option, or in Minitab, use the **Calc > Calculator** command to create the new variable. Figures 14-19a and 14-19b show the output after fitting this second-order polynomial model.

Step 5:   Perform diagnostics on the revised curvilinear model.
Notice the second-order polynomial provides a model whose estimated regression equation has an R^2 of 0.741. This is higher than the R^2 of 0.6693 for the linear model. Figure

FIGURE 14-19B

Minitab Output of a Second-Order Polynomial Fit for Ashley Investment

Minitab Instructions:
1. Open file: Ashley.MTW.
2. Choose **Stat > Regression > Fitted Line Plot**.
3. In **Response**, enter y variable.
4. In **Predictor**, enter x variable.
5. Under **Type of Regression Model**, choose **Quadratic**.
6. Click **OK**.

14-20 shows the plot of the second-order polynomial model. Comparing Figure 14-20 with Figure 14-18, we can see that the polynomial model does appear to fit the sample data better than the linear model.

FIGURE 14-20

Plot of Second-Order Polynomial Model—Ashley Investment Example

ANALYZING INTERACTION EFFECTS

Excel and Minitab Tutorial

Ashley Investment Services (continued)—Referring again to Example 14-3 involving Ashley Investment Services, the director of personnel wondered if the effects of burnout differ among male and female workers. He therefore identified the gender of the previously surveyed employees (see the CD-ROM file *Ashley-2*). A multiple scatter plot of the data appears as Figure 14-21.

The personnel director tried to visualize the relationship between the burnout index and socialization measure for men and women. The sketches of the result are presented in Figure 14-21. Note that both relationships appear to be curvilinear with a similarly shaped curve. As we showed earlier, curvilinear shapes often can be modeled by the second-order polynomial

$$\hat{y} = b_0 + b_1 x_1 + b_2 x_1^2$$

FIGURE 14-21

Excel Multiple Scatter Plot for Ashley Investment Services

Excel Instructions:
1. Open file: Ashley-2.mtw
2. Click on **Chart Wizard**.
3. Select **Scatter Plot**.
4. Use **Series** Tab.
5. Identify the *y* Variable Range for males.
6. Identify the *x* Variable Range for males.
7. Repeat steps 5 and 6 for females.
8. Right click on each series and select **Add Trend Lines**, exponential option.

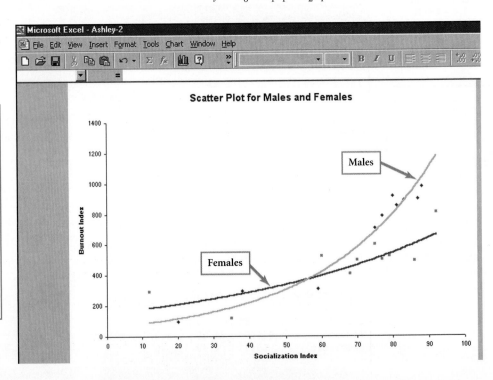

However, the regression equations that estimate this second-order polynomial for men and women are not the same. The two equations seem to have different locations and different rates of curvature. Whether an employee is a man or woman seems to change the basic relationship between burnout index (y) and socialization measure (x_1). In order to represent this difference, the equation's coefficients b_0, b_1, and b_2 must be different for men and women employees. Thus, we could use two models, one for each gender. Alternatively, we could use one model for both males and females by incorporating a dummy independent variable with two levels, which is shown as:

$$x_2 = 1 \text{ if a male, } 0 \text{ if a female}$$

As x_2 changes values from 0 to 1, it affects the values of the coefficients b_0, b_1, and b_2. When the director fitted the second-order model for the female employees only, he obtained the following regression equation:

$$\hat{y} = 291.70 - 4.62x_1 + 0.102x_1^2$$

The equation for the male employees only was

$$\hat{y} = 149.59 - 4.40x_1 + 0.160x_1^2$$

To explain how a change in gender can cause this kind of change, we must introduce the concept of **interaction**.

Interaction

The case in which one independent variable (such as x_2) affects the relationship between another independent variable (x_1) and a dependent variable (y).

Therefore, in our example, gender (x_2) interacts with the relationship between socialization measure (x_1) and burnout index (y). The question is how do we obtain the interaction terms to model such a relationship? To answer this question, we first obtain the model for the basic relationship between the x_1 and the y variables. The population model is

$$y = \beta_0 + \beta_1 x_1 + \beta_2 x_1^2 + \varepsilon$$

To obtain the interaction terms, multiply the terms on the right-hand side of this equation by the variable that is interacting with this relationship between y and x_1. In this case, that interacting variable is x_2. Then the interaction terms would be

$$\beta_3 x_2 + \beta_4 x_1 x_2 + \beta_5 x_1^2 x_2$$

Notice that we have changed the coefficient subscripts so we do not duplicate those in the original model. Then the interaction terms are added to the original model to produce the **composite model**.

$$y = \beta_0 + \beta_1 x_1 + \beta_2 x_1^2 + \beta_3 x_2 + \beta_4 x_1 x_2 + \beta_5 x_1^2 x_2 + \varepsilon$$

Composite Model

The model that contains both the basic terms and the interaction terms.

Note, the model for women is obtained by substituting $x_2 = 0$ into the composite model. This gives:

$$y = \beta_0 + \beta_1 x_1 + \beta_2 x_1^2 + \beta_3(0) + \beta_4 x_1(0) + \beta_5 x_1^2(0) + \varepsilon$$
$$= \beta_0 + \beta_1 x_1 + \beta_2 x_1^2 + \varepsilon$$

Similarly, for men we substitute the value of $x_2 = 1$. The model then becomes

$$y = \beta_0 + \beta_1 x_1 + \beta_2 x_1^2 + \beta_3(1) + \beta_4 x_1(1) + \beta_5 x_1^2(1) + \varepsilon$$
$$= (\beta_0 + \beta_3) + (\beta_1 + \beta_4)x_1 + (\beta_2 + \beta_5)x_1^2 + \varepsilon$$

This illustrates how the coefficients are changed for different values of x_2, and, therefore, how x_2 is interacting with the relationship between x_1 and y. Once we know β_3, β_4, and β_5, we know the effect of the interaction of gender on the original relationship between the burnout index (y) and the socialization measure (x_1). In order to estimate the composite model, we need to create the required variables, as shown in Figure 14-22. Figures 14-23a and 14-23b show the regression for the composite model. The estimate for the composite model is

$$\hat{y} = 291.706 - 4.615x_1 + 0.102x_1^2 - 142.113x_2 + 0.215x_1 x_2 + 0.058x_1^2 x_2$$

We obtain the model for females by substituting $x_2 = 0$, giving

$$\hat{y} = 291.706 - 4.615x_1 + 0.102x_1^2 - 142.113(0) + 0.215x_1(0) + 0.058x_1^2(0)$$
$$\hat{y} = 291.706 - 4.615x_1 + 0.102x_1^2$$

For males, we substitute $x_2 = 1$, giving

$$\hat{y} = 291.706 - 4.615x_1 + 0.102x_1^2 - 142.113(1) + 0.215x_1(1) + 0.058x_1^2(1)$$
$$\hat{y} = 149.593 - 4.40x_1 + 0.160x_1^2$$

Note that these equations for males and females are the same as what we found earlier when we generated two separate regression models, one for each gender.

In this example we have looked at a case in which a dummy variable interacts with the relationship between another independent variable and the dependent variable. However, the interacting variable need not be a dummy variable. It can be any independent variable. Also, strictly speaking, interaction is not said to exist if the only effect of the interaction variable is to change the

---

FIGURE 14-22

Data Preparation for Estimating Interactive Effects for Second-Order Model for Ashley Investment

Excel Instructions:
1. Open file: Ashley-2.xls
2. Use Excel formulas to create new variables.

Minitab Instructions (for similar results):
1. Open file: Ashley-2.MTW.
2. Use Minitab **Calc** menu to create new variables.

	A	B	C	D	E	F
	Burnout Index	Socialization Measure	Socialization Squared	Gender		
1	y	x_1	x_1^2	x_2	$x_1 x_2$	$x_1^2 x_2$
2	100	20	400	1	20	400
3	980	88	7744	1	88	7744
4	310	59	3481	1	59	3481
5	900	87	7569	1	87	7569
6	920	80	6400	1	80	6400
7	892	83	6889	1	83	6889
8	855	81	6561	1	81	6561
9	709	75	5625	1	75	5625
10	791	77	5929	1	77	5929
11	300	38	1444	1	38	1444
12	810	92	8464	0	0	0
13	120	35	1225	0	0	0
14	525	60	3600	0	0	0
15	410	68	4624	0	0	0
16	296	12	144	0	0	0
17	501	70	4900	0	0	0
18	506	77	5929	0	0	0
19	493	86	7396	0	0	0
20	527	79	6241	0	0	0
21	600	75	5625	0	0	0

The spreadsheet window shows: Microsoft Excel - Ashley-2. File Edit View Insert Format Tools Data Stats PHStat Window Help. Arial, 10. Cell G22.

FIGURE 14-23A

Excel Composite Model for Ashley Investment Services

Excel Instructions:
1. Continue from previous figure.
2. Click on **Tools**.
3. Select **Data Analysis**.
4. Select **Regression**.
5. Define y and x variable ranges.
6. Click **OK**.

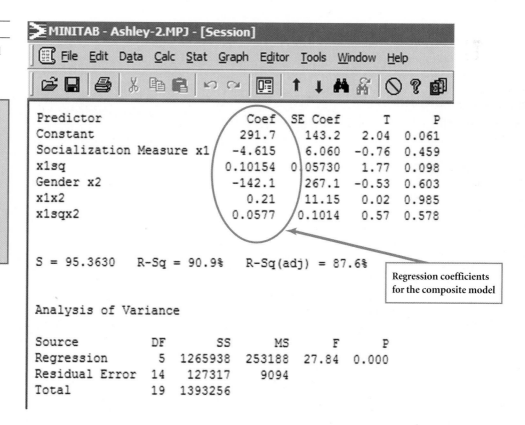

Microsoft Excel - Ashley-2

	A	B	C	D	E	F
1	SUMMARY OUTPUT					
2						
3	Regression Statistics					
4	Multiple R	0.953214973				
5	R Square	0.908618786				
6	Adjusted R Square	0.875982638				
7	Standard Error	95.36299162				
8	Observations	20				
9						
10	ANOVA					
11		df	SS	MS	F	Significance F
12	Regression	5	1265938.348	253187.6695	27.84087098	8.36133E-07
13	Residual	14	127317.4024	9094.10017		
14	Total	19	1393255.75			
15						
16		Coefficients	Standard Error	t Stat	P-value	Lower 95%
17	Intercept	291.706482	143.2066877	2.036961309	0.061022133	-15.44158861
18	Socialization Measure x1	-4.614860035	6.059800777	-0.761553095	0.458964051	-17.61185163
19	Socialization Squared x1²	0.101542196	0.057298798	1.77215229	0.098121813	-0.021351612
20	Gender x2	-142.1126468	267.1118714	-0.532034185	0.603043605	-715.0111424
21	x1x2	0.21461137	11.15341632	0.019241761	0.984919788	-23.70710875
22	x1²x2	0.057722105	0.101359601	0.569478412	0.578055103	-0.159672812

Regression coefficients for the composite model

y-intercept of the equation relating another independent variable to the dependent variable. Therefore, when you search a scatter plot to detect interaction, you are trying to determine if the relationships produced, when the interaction variable changes values, are parallel or not. If the relationships are parallel, that indicates that only the y-intercept is being affected by the change of the interacting variable and that interaction does not exist. Figure 14-24 demonstrates this concept graphically.

FIGURE 14-23B

Minitab Composite Model for Ashley Investment Services

Minitab Instructions:
1. Continue from previous figure.
2. Choose **Stat > Regression > Regression**.
3. In **Response**, enter dependent (y) variable.
4. In **Predictors**, enter independent (x) variables.
5. Click **OK**.

MINITAB - Ashley-2.MPJ - [Session]

```
Predictor                   Coef  SE Coef      T      P
Constant                   291.7    143.2   2.04  0.061
Socialization Measure x1  -4.615    6.060  -0.76  0.459
x1sq                      0.10154  0.05730   1.77  0.098
Gender x2                 -142.1    267.1  -0.53  0.603
x1x2                        0.21    11.15   0.02  0.985
x1sqx2                    0.0577   0.1014   0.57  0.578

S = 95.3630   R-Sq = 90.9%   R-Sq(adj) = 87.6%
```

Regression coefficients for the composite model

```
Analysis of Variance

Source          DF       SS      MS      F      P
Regression       5  1265938  253188  27.84  0.000
Residual Error  14   127317    9094
Total           19  1393256
```

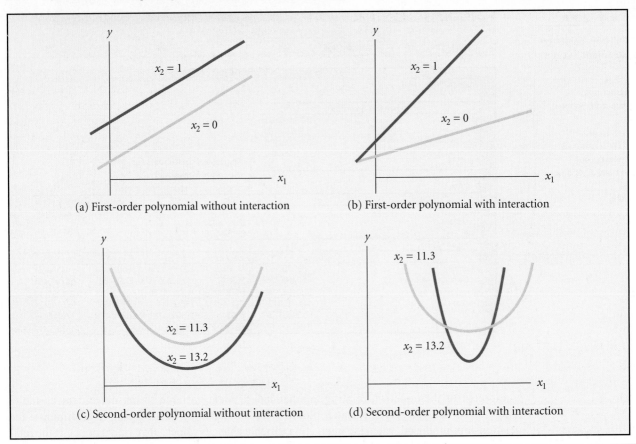

(a) First-order polynomial without interaction

(b) First-order polynomial with interaction

(c) Second-order polynomial without interaction

(d) Second-order polynomial with interaction

FIGURE 14-24 **Graphical Evidence of Interaction**

14-3: EXERCISES

Skill Development

14.19 Consider the following values for dependent and independent variables:

y	x
8	4
14	8
20	10
18	16
16	18

a. Develop a scatter plot of the data. Does the plot suggest a linear or nonlinear relationship between the dependent and independent variables?

b. Develop an estimated linear regression equation for these data. Is the relationship significant? Test at an $\alpha = 0.05$ level.

c. Develop a regression equation of the form $b_1x + b_2x^2$. Does this equation provide a better fit to the data than that found in part b?

14.20 Consider the following values for dependent and independent variables:

x	y
5	10
15	15
40	25
50	44
60	79
80	112

a. Develop a scatter plot of the data. Does the plot suggest a linear or nonlinear relationship between the dependent and independent variables?

b. Develop an estimated linear regression equation for these data. Is the relationship significant? Test at an $\alpha = 0.05$ level.

c. Develop a regression equation of the form $\hat{y} = b_0 + b_1x + b_2x^2$. Does this equation provide a better fit to the data than that found in part b?

14.21 Consider the following values for dependent and independent variables:

x	y
6	5
9	20
14	28
18	30
22	33
27	35

a. Develop a scatter plot of the data. Does the plot suggest a linear or nonlinear relationship between the dependent and independent variables?
b. Develop an estimated linear regression equation for these data. Is the relationship significant? Test at an $\alpha = 0.05$ level.
c. Develop a regression equation of the form $\hat{y} = b_0 + b_1 \ln(x)$. Does this equation provide a better fit to the data than that found in part b?

Business Applications

14.22 Gilmore Accounting collected the following in an effort to explain variation in client profitability. The data are also in the CD-ROM file *Gilmore*.

y	x_1	x_2
2,345	45	1
4,200	56	2
278	26	3
1,211	56	2
1,406	24	2
500	23	3
−700	34	3
3,457	45	1
2,478	47	1
1,975	24	2
206	32	3

where:

y = Net profit earned from the client
x_1 = Number of hours spent working with the client
x_2 = Type of client:
    1 if manufacturing
    2 if service
    3 if governmental

Gilmore has asked if it needs the client type in addition to the number of hours spent working with the client to predict the net profit earned from the client. You are asked to provide this information.

a. Fit a model to the data that incorporates the number of hours spent working with the client and the type of client as independent variables. (Hint: Client type has three levels.)
b. Fit a second-order model to the data, again using dummy variables for client type. Does this model

provide a better fit than that found in part a? Which model would you recommend be used?

14.23 McCullom's International Grains is constantly searching out areas in which to expand its market. Such markets present different challenges because tastes in the international market are different than domestic tastes. India is one country on which McCullom's has recently focused. Paddy is a grain used widely in India, but its characteristics are unknown to McCullom's. Charles Walters has been assigned to take charge of the handling of this grain. He has researched its characteristics. During his research, he came across the article "Determination of Biological Maturity and Effect of Harvesting and Drying Conditions on Milling Quality of Paddy" [*Journal of Agricultural Engineering Research* (1975), pp. 353–361]. The article examines the relationship between y, the yield (kg/ha) of paddy, as a function of x, the number of days after flowering at which harvesting took place. The accompanying data appeared in the article and are in the CD-ROM file *Paddy*.

y	x	y	x
2,508	16	3,823	32
2,518	18	3,646	34
3,304	20	3,708	36
3,423	22	3,333	38
3,057	24	3,517	40
3,190	26	3,241	42
3,500	28	3,103	44
3,883	30	2,776	46

a. Construct a scatter plot of the yield (kg/ha) of paddy as a function of the number of days after flowering at which harvesting took place. Display at least two models that would explain the relationship you see in the scatter plot.
b. Conduct tests of hypotheses to determine if the models you selected are useful in predicting the yield of paddy.
c. Consider a model that includes the second-order term x_2. Would a simple linear regression model be preferable to the model containing the second-order term? Conduct a hypothesis test using the p-value approach to arrive at your answer.
d. Which model should Charles use to predict the yield of paddy? Explain your answer.

14.24 Badeaux Brothers Louisiana Treats ships packages of Louisiana coffee, cakes, and Cajun spices to individual customers around the United States. The cost to ship these products depends primarily on the weight of the package being shipped. Badeaux charges customers for shipping and then ships the product itself. As a part of a study of whether it is economically feasible to continue to ship products, Badeaux sampled 20 recent shipments to determine what, if any, relationship exists between shipping costs and package weight. These data are in the CD-ROM file *Badeaux*.

a. Develop a scatter plot of the data with the dependent variable, cost, on the vertical axis and the independent variable, weight, on the horizontal axis. Does there appear to be a relationship between the two variables? Is the relationship linear?

b. Compute the sample correlation coefficient between the two variables. Conduct a test, using a significance level of 0.05, to determine whether the population correlation coefficient is significantly different from zero.

c. Badeaux Brothers has been using a simple linear regression equation to predict the cost of shipping various items. Would you recommend they use a second-order polynomial model instead? Is the second-order polynomial model a significant improvement over the simple linear regression equation?

d. Badeaux Brothers has made a decision to stop shipping products if the shipping charges exceed $100. They have asked you to determine the maximum weight for future shipments. Do this for both the first- and second-order models you have developed.

14.25   ● The State Tax Commission must download information files each morning. The time to download the files primarily depends on the size of the file. The Tax Commission has asked your computer consulting firm to determine what, if any, relationship exists between download time and size of files. The Tax Commission randomly selected a sample of 20 days and provided the information to your firm in the CD-ROM file *Tax Commission*.

a. Develop a scatter plot of the data with the dependent variable, download time, on the vertical axis and the independent variable, size, on the horizontal axis. Specify the relationship between the two variables by supplying a model that describes this relationship.

b. Compute the sample correlation coefficient between the two variables. Conduct a test, using a significance level of 0.025, to determine whether the population correlation coefficient is significantly different from zero. Use a p-value approach to conduct this test.

c. Estimate the simple linear regression model for this data. Plot the simple linear regression model together with the data. Would a nonlinear model better fit the sample data? Explain the reasons for your answer.

d. Estimate a nonlinear model and plot the model against the data. Does the nonlinear model provide a better fit than the linear model developed in part c? Describe the criterion you used to reach your conclusion.

14.26   ● First City Real Estate is an established, family-owned firm located in the Midwest. First City management wishes to build a model that can be used to predict sales price for residential property. From a wide list of possibilities, the managers selected the following as good candidates: x_1 = home size in square feet, x_2 = age of house, x_3 = number of bedrooms, x_4 = number of bathrooms, and x_5 = garage size (number of cars).

Data were obtained for a sample of 319 residential properties that had sold within the previous two months in an area served by two of First City's offices. For each house in the sample, the sales price and values for all potential independent variables were collected. The data are in the CD-ROM file *First City*.

a. Construct a model that would use home size to predict a home's selling price.

b. Use a statistical technique to determine if the number of bathrooms in a home affects the relationship between the selling price of the home and its size (Hint: What type of terms measure such an effect?)

14.27   ● Refer to Exercise 14-26. Recently managers have begun to suspect that the age of a house has an unusual relationship to its price. They conjecture that the price decreases at a decreasing rate as a function of age until the house is almost 50 years old. Then the price begins to increase at an increasing rate.

a. From the description given above, construct a model that would describe the relationship between the price and the age of a home. Produce an estimate of such a model.

b. Construct a scatter plot of the price versus the age of a home.

c. The manager indicates that the scatter plot seems to say that there is only a linear relationship between the price and age of a home. Produce an estimate of such a model.

14-4 STEPWISE REGRESSION

One option in regression analysis is to bring all possible independent variables into the model in one step. This is what we have done in the previous sections. We use the term *full regression* to describe this approach. Another method for developing a regression model is called *stepwise regression*. Stepwise regression, as the name implies, develops the least squares regression equation in steps, either through *forward selection*, *backward elimination*, or *standard stepwise* regression.

FORWARD SELECTION

The forward selection procedure begins by selecting a single independent variable from all those available. The independent variable selected at step 1 is the variable that is most highly correlated with the dependent variable. An F-test is used to determine if this variable explains a significant amount of the variation in the dependent variable. The F-value that defines the beginning of the rejection region here is known as the *F-to-enter*. If the variable does explain a significant amount of the dependent variable's variation, it is selected to be part of the final model used to predict the dependent variable. If it does not, the process is terminated. If no variables are found to be significant, the researcher will have to search for different independent variables than the ones already tested.

At step 2, a second independent variable is selected based on its ability to explain the remaining unexplained variation in the dependent variable. The independent variable selected in the second, and each subsequent, step is the variable with the highest **coefficient of partial determination**.

Coefficient of Partial Determination

The measure of the marginal contribution of each independent variable, given that other independent variables are in the model.

Recall that the coefficient of determination (R^2) measures the proportion of variation explained by all of the independent variables in the model. Thus, after the first variable (say, x_1) is selected, R^2 will indicate the percentage of variation explained by this variable. The forward selection routine will then compute all possible two-variable regression models, with x_1 included, and determine the R^2 for each model. The coefficient of partial determination at step 2 is the proportion of unexplained variation (after x_1 is in the model) that is explained by the additional variable. The independent variable that adds the most to R^2, given the variable(s) already in the model, is the one selected. Then an F-test is conducted to determine if the proportion of unexplained variation that is explained by the additional variable is significant. This process continues until either all independent variables have been entered or the remaining independent variables do not add appreciably to R^2.

Backward elimination is just the reverse of the forward selection procedure. In the backward elimination procedure, all variables are forced into the model to begin the process. Variables are removed one at a time until no more insignificant variables are found. Once a variable has been removed from the model, it cannot be reentered. For the forward selection procedure, the model begins with no variables. Variables are entered one at a time, and after a variable is entered, it cannot be removed.

$\mathcal{E}$XAMPLE 14-4: APPLYING FORWARD SELECTION STEPWISE REGRESSION ANALYSIS

B. T. Longmont Company   The B. T. Longmont Company operates a large retail department store in Macon, Georgia. Like other department stores, Longmont has incurred heavy losses due to shoplifting and employee pilferage. The store's security manager wants to develop a regression model to explain the monthly dollar loss. The following steps can be used when developing a multiple regression model using stepwise regression.

Step 1:   **Specify the model by determining the dependent variable and potential independent variables.**

The dependent variable (y) is the monthly dollar losses due to shoplifting and pilferage. The security manager has identified the following potential independent variables:

x_1 = Average monthly temperature (degrees Fahrenheit)
x_2 = Number of sales transactions
x_3 = Dummy variable for holiday month (1 if holiday during month, 0 if not)
x_4 = Number of persons on the store's monthly payroll

The data are contained in a CD-ROM file called *Longmont*.

Step 2:   **Formulate step 1 of the regression model.**

The correlation matrix for the data is presented in Figure 14-25. The forward selection procedure will select the independent variable most highly correlated with the dependent variable. By examining the bottom row in the correlation matrix in Figure 14-25, you can see the variable x_2, number of sales transactions, is most highly correlated ($r = 0.6307$) with dollars lost. Once this variable is entered into the model, the remaining

FIGURE 14-25

Excel Correlation Matrix Output for Longmont

Excel Instructions:
1. Open file: Longmont.xls
2. Click on Tools.
3. Select Data Analysis.
4. Select Correlation.
5. Define data range.

	Month	Average Temperature	Number of Sales Transactions	Holiday	Employees	Shoplifting Loss
Month	1					
Average Temperature	-0.068525647	1				
Number of Sales Transactions	0.815085742	-0.024107419	1			
Holiday	0.144337567	-0.143178951	0.062559195	1		
Employees	0.816495224	-0.082057775	0.918479738	-0.19655	1	
Shoplifting Loss	0.476151389	0.285757558	0.63074948	0.136069	0.41324611	1

Minitab Instructions (for similar results):
1. Open file: Longmont.MTW.
2. Choose **Stat > Basic Statistics > Correlation**.
3. In **Variables**, enter variable columns.
4. Click **OK**.

independent variables will be entered based on their ability to explain the remaining variation in the dependent variable.

Figure 14-26a shows the PHStat stepwise regression output, and Figure 14-26b has the Minitab output. At step 1, variable x_2, number of monthly sales transactions, enters the model.

Step 3:   Perform diagnostic checks on the model.

Although PHStat does not provide R^2 or the estimate of the standard error of the estimate directly, they can be computed from the output in the ANOVA section of the printout. Recall from Chapter 13 that R^2 is computed as

$$R^2 = \frac{SSR}{SST} = \frac{1,270,172.193}{3,192,631.529} = 0.398$$

This one independent variable explains 39.8% ($R^2 = 0.398$) of the variation in the dependent variable. The estimate of the standard error of the estimate is the square root of the mean square residual.

$$s_\varepsilon = \sqrt{MSE} = \sqrt{MS\ \text{Residual}} = \sqrt{128,163.96} = 358$$

Now at step 1, we test the following:

$$H_0: \beta_2 = 0 \ (\text{Slope for variable } x_2 = 0)$$
$$H_A: \beta_2 \neq 0$$
$$\alpha = 0.05$$

FIGURE 14-26A

Excel (PHStat) Forward Selection Results for Longmont Co.—Step 1

Excel (PHStat) Instructions:
1. Open file: Longmont.xls
2. Select the **PHStat** tab.
3. Define the *y* variable data range.
4. Define the *x* variables data range.
5. Select **Forward Stepwise** option.
6. Select *p*-value (or *t*-value) criteria.
7. Set *p*-value or *t*-value to enter.

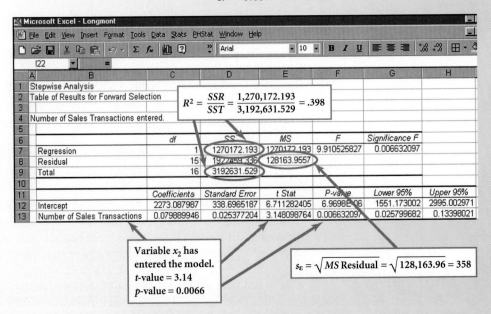

FIGURE 14-26B

Minitab Forward Selection Results for Longmont Co.—Step 1

Minitab Instructions:
1. Open file: Longmont.MTW.
2. Choose **Stat > Regression > Stepwise**.
3. In **Response**, enter dependent variable (y).
4. In **Predictors**, enter independent variables (x).
5. Select **Methods**.
6. Select **Forward selection**, enter α in **Alpha to enter** and F in **F to enter**.
7. Click **OK**.

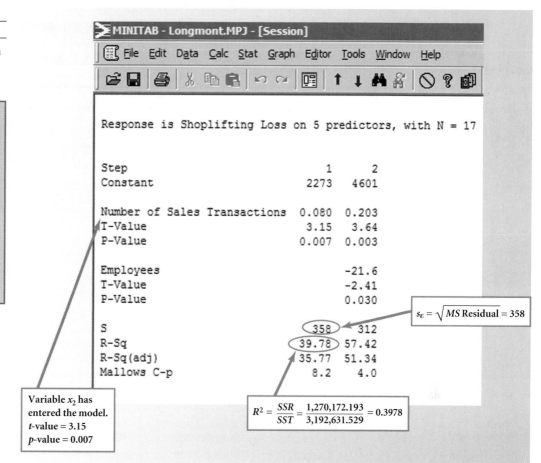

Response is Shoplifting Loss on 5 predictors, with N = 17

Step	1	2
Constant	2273	4601
Number of Sales Transactions	0.080	0.203
T-Value	3.15	3.64
P-Value	0.007	0.003
Employees		-21.6
T-Value		-2.41
P-Value		0.030
S	358	312
R-Sq	39.78	57.42
R-Sq(adj)	35.77	51.34
Mallows C-p	8.2	4.0

$s_\varepsilon = \sqrt{MS\ \text{Residual}} = 358$

Variable x_2 has entered the model.
t-value = 3.15
p-value = 0.007

$$R^2 = \frac{SSR}{SST} = \frac{1{,}270{,}172.193}{3{,}192{,}631.529} = 0.3978$$

As shown in Figures 14-26a and 14-26b, the calculated t-value is 3.15. We compare this to the critical value from the t-distribution for $\frac{\alpha}{2} = \frac{0.05}{2} = 0.025$ and degrees of freedom equal to

$$n - k - 1 = 17 - 1 - 1 = 15$$

This critical value is

$$t_{\alpha/2} = 2.131$$

Because

$$t = 3.15 > 2.131$$

we

reject the null hypothesis

and conclude that the regression slope coefficient for the variable, number of sales transactions, is not zero. Note also, because the

$$p\text{-value} = 0.0066 < \alpha = 0.05$$

we would reject the null hypothesis.

Step 4: **Continue to formulate and diagnose the model by adding other independent variables.**

The next variable to be selected will be the one that can do the most to increase R^2. If you were doing this manually, you would try each variable to see which one yields the highest R^2, given that the transactions variable is already in the model. Both the PHStat add-in software and Minitab do this automatically. As shown in Figure 14-27, the variable selected in step 2 is x_4, number of employees. Using the ANOVA section, we can determine R^2 and s_ε as before.

$$R^2 = \frac{SSR}{SST} = \frac{1{,}833{,}270.524}{3{,}192{,}631.529} = 0.5742 \quad \text{and}$$

$$s_\varepsilon = \sqrt{MS\ \text{Residual}} = \sqrt{97{,}097.22} = 311.6$$

FIGURE 14-27

PHStat Forward Selection Results for Longmont Co.—Step 2

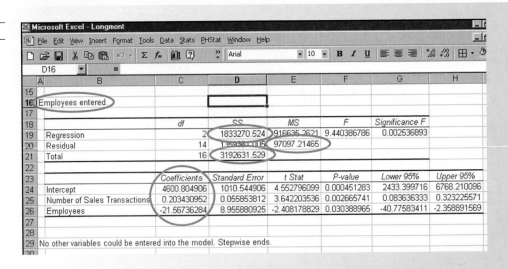

The model now explains 57.42% of the variation in the dependent variable. The t-values for both slope coefficients exceed $t = 2.145$ (the critical value from the t-distribution table with a one-tailed area equal to 0.025 and $17 - 2 - 1 = 14$ degrees of freedom), so we conclude that both variables are significant in explaining the variation in the dependent variable, shoplifting loss.

The forward selection routine continues to enter variables as long as each additional variable explains a significant amount of the remaining variation in the dependent variable. Note that PHStat allows you to set the significance level in terms of a p-value or in terms of the t statistic. Then as long as the calculated p-value for an incoming variable is less than your limit, the variable is allowed to enter the model. Likewise, if the calculated statistic exceeds your t limit, the variable is allowed to enter.

In this example, with the p-value limit set at 0.05, neither of the two remaining independent variables would explain a significant amount of the remaining variation in the dependent variable.

The procedure is, therefore, terminated. The resulting regression equation provided by forward selection is

$$\hat{y} = 4600.8 + 0.203x_2 - 21.57x_4$$

Note that the dummy variables for holiday and temperature did not enter the model. This implies that, given the other variables, knowing whether the month in question has a holiday or knowing its average temperature does not add significantly to the model's ability to explain the variation in the dependent variable.

The Longmont Company can now use this regression model to explain variation in shoplifting losses based on knowing the number of sales transactions and the number of employees.

STANDARD STEPWISE REGRESSION

The standard stepwise procedure (sometimes referred to as forward stepwise regression—not to be confused with forward selection) combines attributes of both backward elimination and forward selection. The forward stepwise method serves one more important function. If two or more variables overlap, a variable selected in an early step may become insignificant when other variables are added at later steps. The forward stepwise procedure will drop this insignificant variable from the model. Forward stepwise regression also offers a means of observing multicollinearity problems, because we can see how the regression model changes as each new variable is added to it.

The forward stepwise procedure is widely used in decision-making applications and is generally recognized as a useful regression method. However, care should be exercised when using this procedure because it is easy to rely too heavily on the automatic selection process. Remember, the order of variable selection is conditional, based on the variables already in the model. There is no guarantee that stepwise regression will lead you to the best set of independent variables from those available. Decision makers still must use common sense in applying regression analysis to make sure they have usable regression models.

BEST SUBSETS REGRESSION

Another method for developing multiple regression models is called the *best subsets* method. As the name implies, the best subsets method works by trying possible subsets from the list of possible independent variables. The user can then select the "best" model based on such measures as R-squared or the estimate of the standard deviation of the model error. Both Minitab and PHStat contain procedures for performing best subsets regression.

 OPTIONAL CD-ROM TOPICS BACKWARD ELIMINATION, STEPWISE REGRESSION

You can also perform stepwise regression analysis by starting out with all the independent variables in the model and then removing the variables one at a time. For more information, go to the CD-ROM.

14-4: EXERCISES

Skill Development

14.28 You are given the following set of data:

y	x_1	x_2	x_3
33	9	192	40
44	11	397	47
34	10	235	37
60	13	345	61
20	11	245	23
30	7	235	35
45	12	296	52
25	9	235	27
53	10	295	57
45	13	335	50
37	11	243	41
44	13	413	51

a. Determine the appropriate correlation matrix and use it to predict which variable will enter in the first step of a stepwise regression model.
b. Use forward stepwise regression to construct a regression equation, entering all significant variables.
c. Construct an estimate of the full regression model. What are the differences between the estimate of this model and the equation in part b? Which equation explains the most variation in the dependent variable?

14.29 You are given the following set of data:

y	x_1	x_2	x_3
45	40	41	39
41	31	41	35
43	45	49	39
38	43	41	41
50	42	42	51
39	48	40	42
50	44	44	41
45	42	39	37
43	37	52	41
34	40	47	40
49	35	44	44
45	39	40	45
40	43	30	42
43	53	34	34

a. Determine the appropriate correlation matrix and use it to predict which variable will enter in the first step of a stepwise regression model.
b. Use forward stepwise regression to construct a regression equation. Initiate the procedure using all three independent variables.
c. Construct an estimate of the full regression model. What are the differences between the estimate of this model and the equation in part b? Which equation

explains the most variation in the dependent variable?

14.30 Suppose you have four potential independent variables, x_1, x_2, x_3, and x_4, from which you want to develop an estimate of a multiple regression model. Using stepwise regression, x_2 and x_4 enter the regression equation.
a. Why did only two variables enter the equation? Discuss.
b. Suppose a regression equation with only variables x_2 and x_4 had been constructed. Would the resulting equation be different from the stepwise equation that included only these two variables? Discuss.
c. Now suppose an estimate of a full regression model was developed, with all four independent variables in the equation. Which would have the higher R^2 value, the estimate of the full regression model or the stepwise regression equation? Discuss.

Business Applications

14.31 💿 The Western States Tourist Association gives out pamphlets, maps, and other tourist-related information to people who call a toll-free number and request the information. The association orders the packets of information from a document-printing company and likes to have enough available to meet its immediate needs without having too many sitting around taking up space. The marketing manager decided to develop a multiple regression model to be used in predicting the number of calls that will be received in the coming week. A random sample of 12 weeks is selected, with the following variables:

> y = Number of calls
> x_1 = Number of advertisements placed the previous week
> x_2 = Number of calls received the previous week
> x_3 = Number of airline tour bookings into western cities for the current week

These data are in the CD-ROM file *Western States*.
a. Develop an estimate of the multiple regression model for predicting the number of calls received, using backward elimination stepwise regression. (Review the CD-ROM topic.)
b. At the final step of the analysis, how many variables are in the equation?
c. Discuss why the variables were removed from the equation in the order shown by the stepwise regression.

14.32 💿 Refer to Exercise 14-31.
a. Develop the correlation matrix that includes all independent variables and the dependent variable. Predict the order that the variables will be selected into the regression equation if forward selection stepwise regression is used.
b. Use forward selection stepwise regression to develop an estimate of a model for predicting the number of calls that the company will receive. Write a report that describes what has taken place at each step of the regression process.

c. Compare the results of the forward selection stepwise regression results in part b and the backward elimination results determined in Exercise 14-31. Which regression equation would you choose? Explain your answer.

14.33 💿 The athletic director at State University is interested in developing a multiple regression model for explaining the variation in home-game football attendance. Use forward stepwise regression to develop a regression equation to estimate the model. (The data are in the CD-ROM file *Football*.)
a. Which variable entered the regression equation at step 1? Discuss why this variable entered.
b. Indicate the order of variables entering the stepwise regression equation. What happens to R^2 and the estimate of the standard error of the estimate for each variable entering?
c. Discuss the regression equation at the final step. Also discuss why the procedure stopped at this step.
d. Test the overall significance of the regression model at the final step. Also test whether each regression coefficient is statistically significant. Use an $\alpha = 0.05$ level.

Advanced Application

14.34 💿 Lands' End is a leading direct merchant of traditionally styled casual clothing for men, women, and children, as well as soft luggage and products for the home. *Catalog Age* ranked Lands' End as the 12th largest mail-order company and the second largest for apparel only. Its R&D department is constantly looking for ways to improve its products. Jeremy Walters, one of its consulting scientists, recently read an article titled "Applying Stepwise Multiple Regression Analysis to the Reaction of Formaldehyde with Cotton Cellulose" (*Textile Research Journal*, 1984, pp. 157–165). This article attempted to establish a relationship between the durable-press rating of cotton and the formaldehyde concentration (HCHO, x_1), the catalyst ratio (x_2), the curing temperature (x_3), and the curing time (x_4) to which the cotton was subjected. The data are in the CD-ROM file *Cotton*.
a. Construct scatter plots of each of the independent variables versus the durable-press rating. Specify the model that would describe the relationship of each of these variables to the dependent variable.
b. Whether or not your scatter plots indicated such a relationship, develop a model using stepwise regression that could include all the dependent variables ($x_1 \ldots x_4$), their squares ($x_1^2 \ldots x_4^2$), and all possible (second-order) interaction terms ($x_1 x_2 \ldots x_3 x_4$).
c. Perform backward elimination on the data used for the stepwise regression procedure in part b. Which of the resulting equations would you suggest in order to predict the durable-press rating? Explain and give statistical reasons for your answer. (This exercise can only be done using Minitab. Excel cannot handle the number of independent variables required.)

14-5 DETERMINING THE APTNESS OF THE MODEL

In Section 14-1 we discussed the basic steps involved in building a multiple regression model. These are

1. Specify the model.
2. Formulate the model.
3. Perform diagnostic checks on the model.

The final step is the diagnostic step in which you examine the model to determine how well it performs. In Section 14-2, we discussed several statistics that you need to consider when performing the diagnostic step, including analyzing R^2, adjusted R^2, and the estimate of the standard error of the estimate. In addition, we discussed the concept of multicollinearity and the impacts that can occur when multicollinearity is present. Section 14-3 introduced another diagnostic step that involves looking for potential curvilinear relationships between the independent variables and the dependent variable. We presented some basic data transformation techniques for dealing with curvilinear situations. However, a major part of the diagnostic process involves an analysis of how well the model fits the regression analysis assumptions.

The basic assumptions of multiple regression include the following.

SSUMPTIONS

1. The relationship between the dependent and independent variables is linear.
2. The variance of the model errors is constant over the range of the values of the independent variables.
3. The model errors are independent from observation to observation.
4. The model errors are normally distributed.

The degree to which a regression model satisfies these assumptions is called **aptness**.

ANALYSIS OF RESIDUALS

The **residual**, the difference between the actual value of the dependent variables and the value predicted by the regression model, is defined by Equation 14-14:

Residual

$$e_i = y_i - \hat{y}_i$$

14-14

A residual value can be computed for each observation in the data set. A great deal can be learned about the aptness of the regression model by analyzing the residuals. The principal means of residual analysis is a study of residual plots. The following problems can be inferred through graphical analysis of residuals.

1. The regression function is not linear.
2. The model errors do not have a constant variance.
3. The model errors are not independent.
4. The model error terms are not normally distributed.

We will address each of these in order. The regression options in both Minitab and Excel provide extensive residual analysis. In Excel, the residual options are shown on the Regression drop-down box. In Minitab, they are accessed in the Regression window by clicking on either the Graphs or Results buttons.

Checking for Linearity

A plot of the residuals (on the vertical axis) against the independent variable (on the horizontal axis) is useful for detecting whether a linear function is the appropriate regression function. Figure 14-28 illustrates two different residual plots. Figure 14-28a shows residuals that systematically depart from 0. When x is small, the residuals are negative. When x is in the midrange, the residuals are positive; and for large x values, the residuals are negative again. This type of plot suggests that the relationship between y and x is nonlinear. Figure 14-28b shows a plot in which residuals do not show a systematic variation from 0, implying that the relationship between x and y is linear.

If a linear model is appropriate, we expect the residuals to band around 0 with no systematic pattern displayed. If the residual plot shows a systematic pattern, it may be possible to transform the

FIGURE 14-28

**Residual Plots Showing
Linear and Nonlinear
Patterns**

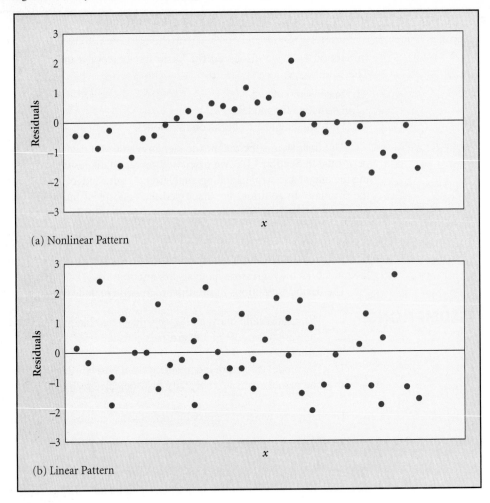

(a) Nonlinear Pattern

(b) Linear Pattern

independent variable (refer to Section 14-3) so that the revised model will produce residual plots that will not systematically vary from 0.

Excel and Minitab Tutorial

First City Real Estate (continued)—We have been using First City Real Estate to introduce multiple regression tools throughout this chapter. Remember, the managers wish to develop a multiple regression model for predicting the sales prices of homes in their market. Suppose that the most current model incorporates a transformation of the lot size variable as log of lot size. The output for this model is shown in Figure 14-29. Notice the model now has a R^2 value of 96.9%.

There are currently four independent variables in the model: square feet, bedrooms, garages, and the log of lot size. Both Minitab and Excel provide procedures for automatically producing residual plots. Figure 14-30 shows the plots of the residuals against each of the independent variables. The transformed variable, log lot size, has a residual pattern that shows a systematic pattern. The residuals are positive for small values of log lot size, negative for intermediate values of log lot size, and positive again for large values of log lot size. This pattern suggests that the curvature of the relationship between sales prices of homes and lot size is even more pronounced than the logarithm implies. Potentially, a second- or third-degree polynomial in the lot size should be pursued.

Do the Residuals Have a Constant Variance?

Residual plots also can be used to determine whether the residuals have a constant variance. Consider Figure 14-31, in which the residuals are plotted against an independent variable. The plot in Figure 14-31a shows an example in which, as x increases, the residuals become less variable. Figure 14-31b shows the opposite situation. When x is small, the residuals are tightly packed around 0, but as x increases, the residuals become more variable. Figure 14-31c shows an example in which the residuals exhibit a constant variance around the zero mean.

When a multiple regression model has been employed, we can analyze the constant variance assumption by plotting the residuals against the fitted ($\hat{y}$) values. When the residual plot is cone-

FIGURE 14-29

Minitab Output of First City Real Estate Appraisal Model

Minitab Instructions:
1. Open file: First City-3.MTW.
2. Choose **Stat > Regression > Regression**.
3. In **Response**, enter dependent (y) variable.
4. In **Predictors**, enter independent (x) variables.
5. Click **OK**.

Regression Analysis: Price versus Sq. Feet, Bedrooms, ...

The regression equation is
Price = - 521920 + 17.9 Sq. Feet - 2319 Bedrooms + 6013 Garage _
        + 159050 log Lot Size

Predictor	Coef	SE Coef	T	P
Constant	-521920	10798	-48.34	0.000
Sq. Feet	17.858	1.682	10.62	0.000
Bedrooms	-2319	1174	-1.98	0.049
Garage _	6013	1299	4.63	0.000
log Lot Size	159050	3286	48.40	0.000

S = 11249.9   R-Sq = 96.9%   R-Sq(adj) = 96.8%

Analysis of Variance

Source	DF	SS	MS	F	P
Regression	4	1.23329E+12	3.08323E+11	2436.16	0.000
Residual Error	314	39740194153	126561128		
Total	318	1.27303E+12			

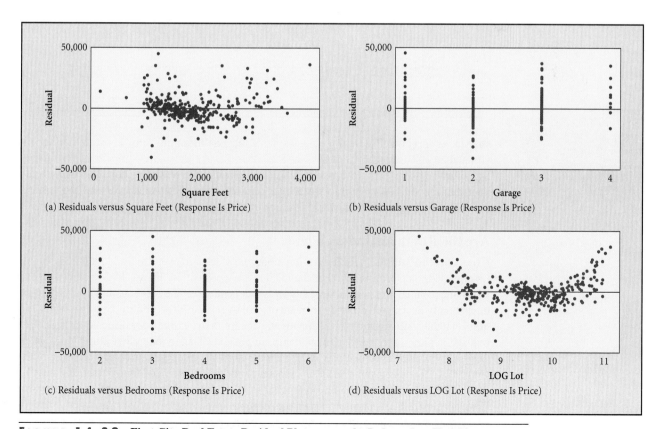

(a) Residuals versus Square Feet (Response Is Price)

(b) Residuals versus Garage (Response Is Price)

(c) Residuals versus Bedrooms (Response Is Price)

(d) Residuals versus LOG Lot (Response Is Price)

FIGURE 14-30   **First City Real Estate Residual Plots versus the Independent Variables**

FIGURE 14-31

**Residual Plots Showing
Constant and Nonconstant
Variances**

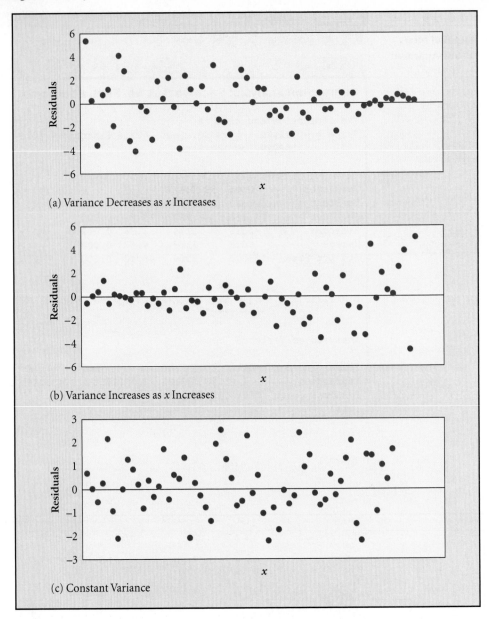

(a) Variance Decreases as x Increases

(b) Variance Increases as x Increases

(c) Constant Variance

shaped, as in either Figure 14-32 it suggests that the assumption of constant variance has been violated.

Figure 14-33 shows the residuals plotted against the $\hat{y}$ values for First City Real Estate's appraisal model. We have drawn a band around the residuals that shows that the variance of the residuals stays quite constant over the range of the fitted values.

Are the Residuals Independent?

If the data used to develop the regression model are measured over time, a plot of the residuals against time is used to determine whether the residuals are correlated. Figure 14-34a shows an example in which the residual plot against time suggests independence. The residuals in Figure 14-34a appear to be randomly distributed around the mean of zero over time. However, in Figure 14-34b, the plot suggests that the residuals are not independent, because in the early time periods the residuals are negative and in later time periods the residuals are positive. This, or any other nonrandom pattern in the residuals over time, indicates that the assumption of independent residuals has been violated. Generally, this means some variable associated with the passage of time has been omitted from the model. Often, time is used as a surrogate for other time-related variables in a regression model. Chapter 15 will discuss time series data analysis and forecasting techniques in more detail and will address the issue of incorporating the time variable into the model. In Chapter 15, we introduce a procedure called the Durbin-Watson test to determine whether residuals are correlated over time.

FIGURE 14-32

Residual Plots Against the Fitted ($\hat{y}$) Values

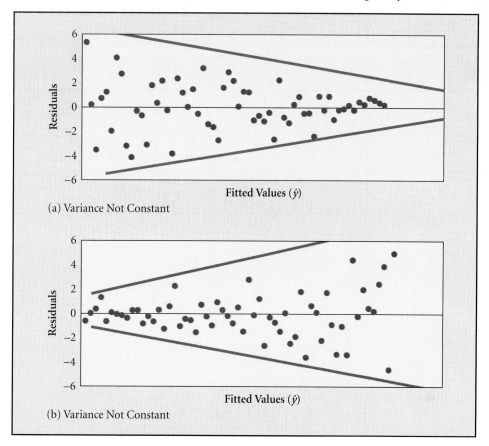

(a) Variance Not Constant

(b) Variance Not Constant

Checking for Normally Distributed Error Terms

The need for normally distributed model errors occurs when we want to test a hypothesis about the regression model. Small departures from normality do not cause serious problems. However, if the model errors depart dramatically from a normal distribution, there is cause for concern. Examining the sample residuals will allow us to detect such dramatic departures. One method for graphically

FIGURE 14-33

Minitab Plot of Residuals versus Fitted Values for First City Real Estate

Minitab Instructions:
1. Open file: First City-3.MTW.
2. Choose **Stat > Regression > Regression**.
3. In **Response**, enter dependent (y) variable.
4. In **Predictors**, enter independent (x) variables.
5. Choose **Graphs**.
6. Under **Residual Plots**, select **Residuals versus fits**.
7. Click **OK. OK**.

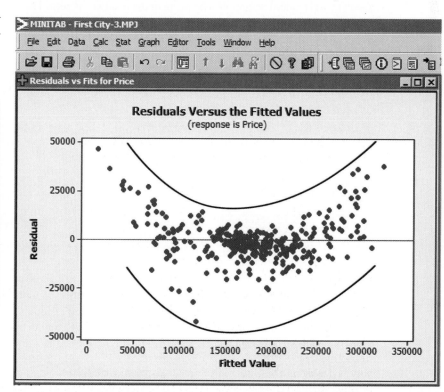

FIGURE 14-34

Plot of Residuals Against Time

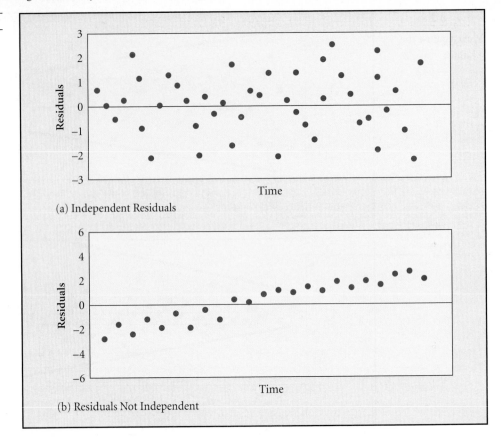

(a) Independent Residuals

(b) Residuals Not Independent

analyzing the residuals is to form a frequency histogram of the residuals to determine whether the general shape is normal. The chi-square goodness-of-fit test presented in Chapter 12 can be used to test whether the residuals fit a normal distribution.

Another method for determining normality is to calculate and plot the **standardized residuals**. In Chapter 3 you learned that a random variable is standardized by subtracting its mean and dividing the result by its standard deviation. The mean of the residuals is zero. Therefore, dividing each residual by an estimate of its standard deviation gives the standardized residual.[9] Although the proof is beyond the scope of this text, it can be shown that the standardized residual for any particular observation for a simple linear regression model is found using Equation 14-15.

Standardized Residual—Simple Linear Regression

$$s_{e_i} = \frac{e_i}{s_\varepsilon \sqrt{1 + \dfrac{1}{n} + \dfrac{(x_i - \bar{x})^2}{\sum x^2 - \dfrac{(\sum x)^2}{n}}}}$$

14-15

where:

$e_i = i$th residual value

$s_\varepsilon =$ Estimate of the standard error of the estimate

$x_i =$ Value of x used to generate the predicted y value for the ith observation

---

Computing the standardized residual for an observation in a multiple regression model is too complicated to be done by hand. However, the standardized residuals are generated from most statistical software, including Minitab and Excel. The Excel and Minitab tutorials on your CD-ROM illustrate the methods required to generate the standardized residuals and residual plots. Because other

[9]The standardized residual is also referred to as the studentized residual.

FIGURE 14-35

Minitab Histogram of Residuals for First City Real Estate

Minitab Instructions:
1. Open file: First City-3.MTW.
2. Choose **Stat > Regression > Regression**.
3. In **Response**, enter dependent (y) variable.
4. In **Predictors**, enter independent (x) variables.
5. Choose **Graphs**.
6. Under **Residual Plots**, select **Histogram of residuals**.
7. Click **OK. OK**.

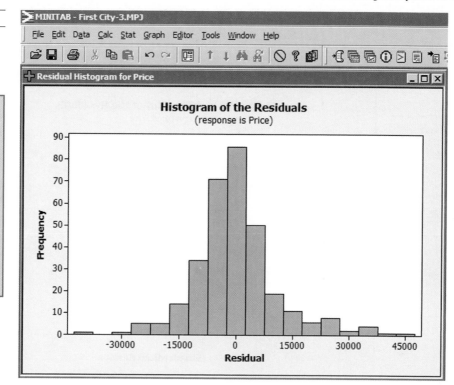

problems such as nonconstant variance and nonindependent residuals can result in residuals that seem to be abnormal, you should check these other factors before addressing the normality assumption.

Recall that for a normal distribution, approximately 68% of the values will fall within one standard deviation of the mean, 95% within two standard deviations of the mean, and virtually all values will fall within three standard deviations of the mean.

Figure 14-35 illustrates the histogram of the residuals for the First City Real Estate example. The distribution of residuals looks to be close to a normal distribution. Figure 14-36 shows the his-

FIGURE 14-36

Minitab Histogram of Standardized Residuals for First City Real Estate

Minitab Instructions:
1. Open file: First City-3.MTW.
2. Choose **Stat > Regression > Regression**.
3. In **Response**, enter dependent (y) variable.
4. In **Predictors**, enter independent (x) variables.
5. Choose **Graphs**.
6. Under **Residual for Plots**, select **Standardized**.
7. Under **Residual Plots**, select **Histogram of residuals**.
8. Click **OK. OK**.

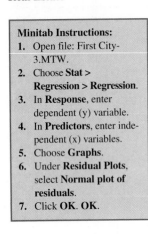

FIGURE 14-37

Minitab Normal
Probability Plot of
Residuals for First City
Real Estate

Minitab Instructions:
1. Open file: First City-3.MTW.
2. Choose **Stat > Regression > Regression**.
3. In **Response**, enter dependent (y) variable.
4. In **Predictors**, enter independent (x) variables.
5. Choose **Graphs**.
6. Under **Residual Plots**, select **Normal plot of residuals**.
7. Click **OK. OK.**

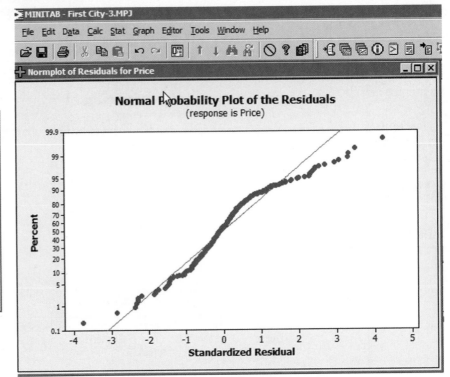

togram for the standardized residuals, which will have the same basic shape as the residual distribution in Figure 14-35.

Another approach for checking for normality of the residuals is to form a *probability plot*. We start by arranging the residuals in numerical order from smallest to largest. The standardized residuals are plotted on the horizontal axis, and the corresponding expected value for the standardized residual is plotted on the vertical axis. Although we won't delve into how the expected value is computed, you can examine the normal probability plot to see whether the plot forms a straight line. The closer the line is to linear, the closer the residuals are to being normally distributed. Figure 14-37 shows the normal probability plot for the First City Real Estate Company example.

You should be aware that Minitab and Excel format their residual plots slightly differently. However, the same general information is conveyed, and you can look for the same signs of problems with the regression model.

CORRECTIVE ACTIONS

If, based on analyzing the residuals, you decide the model constructed is not appropriate, but you still want a regression-based model, some corrective action may be warranted. There are three approaches that may work: transform some of the existing independent variables; remove some variables from the model; or start over in the development of the regression model.

Earlier in this chapter, we discussed a basic approach involved in variable transformation. In general, the transformations of the independent variables (such as raising x to a power, taking the square root of x, or taking the log of x) are used to make the data better conform to a linear relationship. If the model suffers from non-linearity and if the residuals have a non-constant variance, you may want to transform both the independent and dependent variables. In cases in which the normality assumption is not satisfied, transforming the dependent variable is often useful. In many instances, a log transformation works. In some instances a transformation involving the product of two independent variables will help. A more detailed discussion is beyond the scope of this text. However, you can read more about this subject in the Neter et al. reference listed at the end of the chapter.

The alternative of using a different regression model means that we respecify the model to include new independent variables or remove existing variables from the model. In most modeling situations, we are in a continual state of model respecification. We are always seeking to improve the regression model by finding new independent variables.

14-5: EXERCISES

Skill Development

14.35 Consider the following values for dependent and independent variables:

x	y
6	5
9	20
14	28
18	30
22	33
27	35
33	45

a. Determine the estimated linear regression equation relating the dependent and independent variables.
b. Is the regression equation you found significant? Test at the $\alpha = 0.05$ level.
c. Determine both the residuals and standardized residuals. Is there anything about the residuals that would lead you to question whether the assumptions necessary to use regression analysis are satisfied?

14.36 Consider the following values for dependent and independent variables:

x	y
6	5
9	20
14	28
18	15
22	27
27	31
33	32
50	60
61	132
75	160

a. Determine the estimated linear regression equation relating the dependent and independent variables.
b. Is the regression equation you found significant? Test at the $\alpha = 0.05$ level.
c. Determine both the residuals and standardized residuals. Is there anything about the residuals that would lead you to question whether the assumptions necessary to use regression analysis are satisfied?

14.37 Consider the following values for dependent and independent variables:

x	y
16	15
19	20
24	28
28	15
32	35
37	20
43	55
60	25
71	32
75	40

a. Determine the estimated linear regression equation relating the dependent and independent variables.
b. Is the regression equation you found significant? Test at the $\alpha = 0.10$ level.
c. Determine both the residuals and standardized residuals. Plot the residuals. Is there anything about the residuals that would lead you to question whether the assumptions necessary to use regression analysis are satisfied?

14.38 Under what conditions is it desirable to plot the residuals against the predicted y values? Discuss.

14.39 In a multiple regression model, if we wish to determine whether the residuals have a constant variance, is it appropriate to plot the residuals against each x variable individually? If not, what should be done?

Business Applications

14.40 The Western States Tourist Association gives out pamphlets, maps, and other tourist-related information to people who call a toll-free number and request the information. The association orders the packets of information from a document-printing company and likes to have enough available to meet immediate needs without having too many sitting around taking up space. The marketing manager decided to develop a multiple regression model to be used in predicting the number of calls that will be received in the coming week. A random sample of 12 weeks is selected, with the following variables:

y = Number of calls
x_1 = Number of advertisements placed the previous week
x_2 = Number of calls received the previous week
x_3 = Number of airline tour bookings into western cities for the current week

The data are in the CD-ROM file *Western States*.

a. Construct a multiple regression model using all three independent variables. Write a short report discussing the model.

b. Based on the appropriate residual plots, what can you conclude about the constant variance assumption? Discuss.

c. Based on the appropriate residual analysis, does it appear that the residuals are independent? Discuss.

d. Use an appropriate analysis of the residuals to determine whether the regression model meets the assumption of normally distributed error terms. Discuss.

14.41 The athletic director of State University is interested in developing a multiple regression model that might be used to explain variations in attendance at football games at his school. A sample of 16 games was selected from home games played during the past 10 seasons. Data for the following factors were determined.

$$y = \text{Game attendance}$$
$$x_1 = \text{Team win/loss percentage to date}$$
$$x_2 = \text{Opponent win/loss percentage to date}$$
$$x_3 = \text{Games played this season}$$
$$x_4 = \text{Temperature at game time}$$

The sample data are in the CD-ROM file *Football*.

a. Build an estimate of a multiple regression model using all four independent variables. Write a short report that outlines the characteristics of this model.

b. Develop a table of residuals for this model. What is the average residual value? Why do you suppose it came out to this value? Discuss.

c. Based on the appropriate residual plot, what can you conclude about the constant variance assumption? Discuss.

d. Based on the appropriate residual analysis, does it appear that the model errors are independent? Discuss.

e. Can you conclude, based on the appropriate method of analysis, that the model error terms are approximately normally distributed?

Advanced Applications

14.42 Charles Walters has been assigned to take charge of the handling of paddy, an Indian grain. He has researched the various characteristics of the grain. During his research he came across the article "Determination of

Biological Maturity and Effect of Harvesting and Drying Conditions on Milling Quality of Paddy" [*Journal of Agricultural Engineering Research* (1975) pp. 353–361]. The article examines the relationship between y, the yield (kg/ha) of paddy, as a function of x, the number of days after flowering at which harvesting took place. The data are in the CD-ROM file *Paddy* and are shown as follows:

y	x	y	x
2,508	16	3,823	32
2,518	18	3,646	34
3,304	20	3,708	36
3,423	22	3,333	38
3,057	24	3,517	40
3,190	26	3,241	42
3,500	28	3,103	44
3,883	30	2,776	46

a. Fit a simple linear regression model to this data. Calculate the residuals associated with the resulting regression equation.

b. Plot the residuals against the independent variable. On the basis of this plot, determine if a linear function is the appropriate regression function to use for this data, and if the residuals demonstrate a constant variance. Be sure to explain your answers using statistical concepts as support.

c. Whether you determined that a linear model is appropriate or had to select another model to fit the data, conduct a hypothesis test to determine if that model is significant.

14.43 Refer to Exercise 14-42. Use a curvilinear model to fit the data.

a. Construct a scatter plot of the residuals versus the independent variable. Determine if the residuals possess a constant variance for each value of the independent variables. Explain your answer using statistical reasoning.

b. Produce a histogram of the residuals. Based on this histogram, do the residuals seem to possess a normal distribution? Explain your answer.

c. Determine the percentages of the residuals that are one standard deviation, two standard deviations, or three standard deviations from their mean. On this basis, do the residuals seem to possess a normal distribution? Explain your answer.

Summary and Conclusions

Multiple regression is an extension of simple regression analysis. In multiple regression, two or more independent variables are used to explain the variation in the dependent variable. Just as a manager searches for the best combination of employees to perform a job, the decision maker using multiple regression analysis

searches for the best combination of independent variables to explain variation in the dependent variable.

The presentation of multiple regression analysis has largely been an analysis of computer printouts. As a decision maker, you will almost assuredly not be required to manually develop the regression model, but you will have to judge its applicability based on a computer printout. The Excel and Minitab software we have used in Chapters 13 and 14 are representative of the many software packages that are available. You no doubt will encounter printouts that look somewhat different from those shown in this text and some of the terms used may differ slightly. However, the basic information will be the same, as will be the inferences you can make from the model.

This chapter has discussed the difference between R^2 and adjusted R^2, as well as the difference between statistical significance and practical significance. As a decision maker, you must recognize that a regression model can be statistically significant yet have no practical use because the standard error of the estimate is too large or multicollinearity impacts too heavily.

As you continue your study of business, you will find that multiple regression is one of the most widely used statistical tools. You will find it applied particularly to the areas of production, finance, accounting, and economics.

EQUATIONS

Simple Linear Regression Model
$$y = \beta_0 + \beta_1 x + \varepsilon \qquad \textbf{14-1}$$

Estimated Simple Linear Regression Model
$$\hat{y} = b_0 + b_1 x \qquad \textbf{14-2}$$

Population Multiple Regression Model
$$y = \beta_0 + \beta_1 x_1 + \beta_2 x_2 + \ldots + \beta_k x_k + \varepsilon \qquad \textbf{14-3}$$

Estimated Multiple Regression Model
$$\hat{y} = b_0 + b_1 x_1 + b_2 x_2 + \ldots + b_k x_k \qquad \textbf{14-4}$$

Correlation Coefficient
$$r = \frac{\sum(x - \bar{x})(y - \bar{y})}{\sqrt{\sum(x - \bar{x})^2 \sum(y - \bar{y})^2}}$$
$$\text{or} \quad r = \frac{\sum(x_1 - \bar{x}_1)(x_2 - \bar{x}_2)}{\sqrt{\sum(x_1 - \bar{x}_1)^2 \sum(x_2 - \bar{x}_2)^2}} \qquad \textbf{14-5}$$

Multiple Coefficient of Determination (R^2)
$$R^2 = \frac{\text{Sum of squares regression}}{\text{Total sum of squares}} = \frac{SSR}{SST} \qquad \textbf{14-6}$$

F Test Statistic
$$F = \frac{\dfrac{SSR}{k}}{\dfrac{SSE}{n - k - 1}} \qquad \textbf{14-7}$$

Adjusted R-Squared
$$R\text{-sq(adj)} = R_A^2 = 1 - (1 - R^2)\left(\frac{n - 1}{n - k - 1}\right) \qquad \textbf{14-8}$$

t-Test for Significance of Each Regression Coefficient
$$t = \frac{b - 0}{s_b} \qquad df = n - k - 1 \qquad \textbf{14-9}$$

Estimate for the Standard Deviation of the Model (Standard Error of the Estimate)
$$s_\varepsilon = \sqrt{\frac{SSE}{n - k - 1}} = \sqrt{MSE} \qquad \textbf{14-10}$$

Variance Inflation Factor
$$VIF = \frac{1}{(1 - R_j^2)} \qquad \textbf{14-11}$$

Confidence Interval Estimate for the Regression Slope
$$b \pm t_{\alpha/2} s_b \qquad \textbf{14-12}$$

Polynomial Regression Model
$$y = \beta_0 + \beta_1 x + \beta_2 x^2 + \ldots + \beta_p x^p + \varepsilon \qquad \textbf{14-13}$$

Residual
$$e_i = y_i - \hat{y}_i \qquad \textbf{14-14}$$

Standardized Residual
$$s_{e_i} = \frac{e_i}{s_\varepsilon \sqrt{1 + \dfrac{1}{n} + \dfrac{(x_i - \bar{x})^2}{\sum x^2 - \dfrac{(\sum x)^2}{n}}}} \qquad \textbf{14-15}$$

Key Terms

CHAPTER EXERCISES

Conceptual Questions

14.44 Discuss in your own terms the similarities and differences between simple linear regression analysis and multiple regression analysis.

14.45 Discuss what is meant by the least squares criterion as it pertains to multiple regression analysis. Is the least squares criterion any different for simple regression analysis? Discuss.

14.46 List the basic assumptions of regression analysis and discuss in your own terms what each means.

14.47 What does it mean if we have developed a multiple regression model and have concluded that the model is apt?

14.48 Go to the library, or use the Internet, to locate three articles using a regression model with more than one independent variable. For each article, write a short summary covering the following points:
   a. purpose for using the model
   b. how the variables in the model were selected
   c. how the data in the model were selected
   d. any possible violations of the needed assumptions
   e. the conclusions drawn from using the model

14.49 Select a company in your area that you think might use a regression model and interview a decision maker in that company. If the company uses a regression model, outline its use. If the company does not use a regression model, discuss the alternate tools used.

14.50 A financial analyst for a Wall Street firm recently collected a random sample of 24 companies and recorded their year-end stock prices. He hopes to be able to develop a regression model that can be used to explain the variation in stock prices for these 24 firms. He plans to use financial ratios such as the debt/equity ratio as independent variables. What would you suggest to him as the maximum number of independent variables to use in the model? Discuss.

Business Applications

14.51 The managerial development director of a major corporation is trying to determine what personal abilities are necessary for a manager to move from middle- to upper-level management. Although she has been relatively successful predicting who will move rapidly from lower- to middle-management levels, she has had difficulty determining the characteristics necessary to move to the next major level. For a long time, the director has heard that the most glaring deficiency in college graduates entering the company is in communication skills, so she decides to measure whether these skills may be a determining factor.

   The director decides to try to develop a multiple regression relationship between job ratings and communication ability. She picks a random sample of middle-level managers who have been in their present positions fewer than five years but more than one year. These managers are given a series of cases to analyze and are asked to present both written and oral recommendations. They are rated by a group of top-level managers on their analyses and on their written and oral presentations. These ratings are then compared with the latest employee ratings. The data are listed in the CD-ROM file *Job Rating*.

   Determine the multiple regression equation for these data. Write a report that summarizes the characteristics of the model.

14.52 Refer to the situation described in Exercise 14-51. One of the assumptions of multiple regression is that the independent variables are not correlated with each other. Is this assumption satisfied for these data? What do you check to see if multicollinearity is a problem? Use a significance level of 0.05.

14.53 Refer to the situation described in Exercise 14-51.
   a. Does the multiple regression model you have estimated show a significant relationship between job ratings and each of the three independent variables measured? How did you measure this significance? Test with a significance level of 0.05.
   b. If a middle manager were to ask you which of the three variables is most important for his chances of getting promoted, what would you respond?

14.54 Referring to Exercise 14-51, if you were a middle-level manager, would you be willing to have your job rating determined only on the basis of your performance on these three independent variables? Explain in statistical terms why or why not.

14.55 Referring to the regression model you developed in Exercise 14-53, respond to each of the following:
   a. Discuss how much of the variation in job rating is explained by the three independent variables. How do you measure this factor?
   b. As a test, the development director gives the same case to a group of middle-level managers without knowing their job ratings. One of the managers received the following scores:

Case analysis	9.1
Written presentations	9.4
Verbal presentations	9.3

   Based on these data, what is the best estimate of the job rating this manager received?
   c. One manager who participated in this study is concerned with his job rating and would like to know how much his job rating should change if his written presentation score increased by a full point. You are to develop a 95% confidence interval for the regression coefficient for the independent variable, written presentation. Be sure to interpret this interval.

The following information applies to Exercises 14-56, 14-57, and 14-58.

A publishing company in New York is attempting to develop a model that it can use to help predict textbook sales for books it is considering for future publication. The marketing department has collected data on several variables from a random sample of 15 books. These data are given in the CD-ROM file *Textbook*.

14.56 Develop the correlation matrix showing the correlation between all possible pairs of variables. Test statistically to determine which independent variables are significantly correlated with the dependent variable, book sales. Use a significance level of 0.05.

14.57 ⊙ Develop a multiple regression model containing all four independent variables. Show clearly the regression coefficients. Write a short report discussing the model. In your report make sure you cover the following issues:
a. How much of the total variation in book sales can be explained by these four independent variables? Would you conclude that the model is significant at the 0.05 level?
b. Develop a 95% confidence interval for each regression coefficient and interpret these confidence intervals.
c. Which of the independent variables can be concluded to be significant in explaining the variation in book sales? Test using an alpha level of 0.05.
d. How much, if any, does adding one more page to the book impact the sales volume of the book? Develop and interpret a 95% confidence interval estimate to answer this question.
e. Perform the appropriate analysis to determine the aptness of this regression model. Discuss your results and conclusions.

14.58 ⊙ The publishing company recently came up with some additional data for the 15 books in the original sample. Two new variables, production expenditures (x_5) and number of prepublication reviewers (x_6), have been added. These additional data are as follows:

Book	x_5	x_6	Book	x_5	x_6
1	$38,000	5	9	$51,000	4
2	86,000	8	10	34,000	6
3	59,000	3	11	20,000	2
4	80,000	9	12	80,000	5
5	29,500	3	13	60,000	5
6	31,000	3	14	87,000	8
7	40,000	5	15	29,000	3
8	69,000	4			

Incorporating this additional data, calculate the correlation between each of these additional variables and the dependent variable, book sales. Then respond to each of the following questions in the form of a report to the chief editor.
a. Test the significance of the correlation coefficients, using an alpha level of 0.05. Comment on your results.
b. Develop a multiple regression model that includes all six independent variables. Which, if any, variables would you recommend be retained if this model is going to be used to predict book sales for the publishing company? For any statistical tests you might perform, use a significance level of 0.05. Discuss your results.
c. Use the ANOVA approach to test the null hypothesis that all slope coefficients are 0. Test with a significance level of 0.05. What do these results mean? Discuss.
d. Do multicollinearity problems appear to be present in the model? Discuss the potential consequences of multicollinearity with respect to the regression model.

e. Discuss whether the standard error of the estimate is small enough to make this model useful for predicting the sales of textbooks.
f. Plot the residuals against the predicted value of y, and comment on what this plot means relative to the aptness of the model.
g. Compute the standardized residuals and form these into a frequency histogram. What does this indicate about the normality assumption?
h. Comment on the overall aptness of this model and indicate what might be done to improve the model.

The following information applies to Exercises 14-59 through 14-68.

The J. J. McCracken Company has authorized its marketing research department to make a study of customers who have been issued a McCracken charge card. The marketing research department hopes to be able to identify the significant variables that explain the variations in purchases. Once these variables are determined, the department intends to try to attract new customers who would be predicted to have a high volume of purchases.

Twenty-five customers were selected at random, and values for the following variables were recorded in the CD-ROM file *McCracken*.

y = Average monthly purchases (in dollars) at McCracken
x_1 = Customer age
x_2 = Customer family income
x_3 = Family size

14.59 A first step in regression analysis often involves developing a scatter plot of the data. Develop the scatter plots of all the possible pairs of variables, and with a brief statement indicate what each plot says about the relationship between the two variables.

14.60 Compute the correlation matrix for these data. Develop the decision rule for testing the significance of each coefficient. Which, if any, correlations are not significant? Use an alpha level of 0.05.

14.61 Use forward selection stepwise regression to develop the multiple regression model. The variable x_2, family income, was brought into the model. Discuss why this happened.

14.62 Test the significance of the regression model at step 1 of the computer printout. Justify the significance level you have selected.

14.63 Develop a 95% confidence level for the slope coefficient for the family income variable at step 1 of the model. Be sure to interpret this confidence interval.

14.64 Describe the regression model at step 2 of the analysis. In your discussion, be sure to discuss the effect of adding a new variable on the standard error of the estimate and on R^2.

14.65 Referring to Exercise 14-64, suppose the manager of McCracken's marketing department questions the appropriateness of adding a second variable. How would you respond to her question?

14.66 Looking carefully at the stepwise regression model, you can see that the value of the slope coefficient for variable x_2, family income, changes each time a new variable is added to the regression model. Discuss why this change takes place.

14.67 Analyze the regression model at step 3 and the intermediate results at steps 1 and 2. Write a report to the marketing manager pointing out the strengths and weaknesses of the model. Be sure to comment on the department's goal of being able to use the model to predict customers who will purchase high volumes from McCracken.

14.68 Plot the residuals against the predicted value of y, and comment on what this plot means relative to the aptness of the model.
   a. Compute the standardized residuals and form these in a frequency histogram. What does this indicate about the normality assumption?
   b. Comment on the overall aptness of this model, and indicate what might be done to improve the model.

Advanced Applications

14.69 Refer to the State Department of Transportation file on the CD-ROM, *Liabins*. The department was interested in determining the rate of compliance with the state's mandatory liability insurance law, as well as other things. *Assume the data were collected using a simple random sampling process.* Develop the best possible estimated linear regression model using driving citations as the dependent variable and any or all of the other variables as potential independent variables. Assume that your objective is to develop a predictive model. Write a report that discusses the steps you took to develop the estimate of the final model. Include a correlation matrix and all appropriate statistical tests. Use an $\alpha = 0.05$. If you are using a nominal or ordinal variable, remember that you must make sure it is in the form of one or more dummy variables.

14.70 Refer to the Department of Transportation CD-ROM file described in the previous exercise. Develop the best possible estimated linear regression model using number of years of formal education as the dependent variable and any or all of the other variables as potential independent variables. Assume that your objective is to develop a predictive model. Write a report that discusses the steps you took to develop the estimate of the final model. Include a correlation matrix and all appropriate statistical tests. Use an $\alpha = 0.05$. If you are using a nominal or ordinal variable, remember that you must make sure it is in the form of one or more dummy variables.

14.71 Refer to the CD-ROM file *Cities*, in which an economist from a major East Coast bank has collected data on major cities in the United States. You are to develop an estimate of a multiple regression model that would allow you to predict the labor market stress index, x_8, based on the other variables in the database. (Note: Be careful about the SAT/ACT variables.)
   a. Develop a correlation matrix for all relevant variables and write a short report that discusses the correlation results. Be sure to indicate which potential independent variables appear to have the most promise in the model.
   b. Bring all the relevant independent variables into the model at one time. Show an estimate of the model,

including the intercept and regression coefficients. Look at the signs on the coefficients and indicate which, if any, seem to have inappropriate signs. Discuss.
   c. Is the overall model significant? State clearly the null and alternative hypotheses and show your test procedure. Test at the $\alpha = 0.05$ level. Discuss.
   d. What is the coefficient of determination? Does the model explain a significant proportion of the variation in the dependent variable? Test at an $\alpha = 0.05$ level.
   e. Test each of the regression slope coefficients individually to determine which variables are significant in the model. Test at an $\alpha = 0.05$ level. Write a short report describing your results.

14.72 Referring to the data collected by the economist discussed in Exercise 14-71, use forward stepwise regression to develop the regression model using appropriate independent variables. Write a complete report describing step-by-step what took place as the variables were entered into the model. In your analysis, perform any appropriate tests of significance. Would you recommend that this model be used to predict a city's labor stress market index? Explain.

14.73 The objective set forth in a recent staff meeting at D. L. Green & Associates is to develop a regression model for predicting company stock price. The CD-ROM file *FAST100* contains data on several potential independent variables. Construct a correlation matrix that shows the correlation between the independent variables and the dependent variable and between all possible pairs of independent variables. Write a report that discusses the correlation matrix. Which variables appear to have most promise as predictors of stock price? Discuss.

14.74 Referring to the D. L. Green data discussed in the previous exercise, develop an estimate of a multiple regression model with stock price as the dependent variable. Bring in all appropriate independent variables.
   a. Identify the regression equation, including the intercept and slope coefficients. Comment on whether these coefficients look reasonable given the correlations in the previous exercise. Discuss.
   b. Is the overall model significant? State clearly the null and alternative hypotheses and show your test procedure. Test at the $\alpha = 0.10$ level. Discuss.
   c. What is the coefficient of determination? Does the model explain a significant proportion of the variation in the dependent variable? Test at an $\alpha = 0.10$ level.
   d. Test each of the regression slope coefficients individually to determine which variables are significant in the model. Test at an $\alpha = 0.10$ level. Write a short report describing your results.

14.75 Referring to the D. L. Green data discussed in the previous exercise, use forward stepwise regression to develop the estimated regression model using appropriate independent variables. Write a complete report describing step-by-step what took place as the variables were entered into the model's estimate. Be sure to indicate what, if any, evidence of multicollinearity is present in the model. In your analysis, perform any appropriate tests of significance. Would you recommend that this model be used as a predictive tool? Explain. (This problem can only be done using Minitab.)

CASE 14-A:

Dynamic Scales, Inc.

In 1985, Stanley Ahlon and three financial partners formed Dynamic Scales, Inc. The company was based on an idea Stanley had for developing a scale to weigh trucks in motion and thus eliminate the need for every truck to stop at weigh stations along highways. This dynamic scale would be placed in the highway approximately one-quarter mile from the regular weigh station. The scale would have a minicomputer that would automatically record truck speed, axle weights, and climate variables, including temperature, wind, and moisture. Stanley Ahlon and his partners believed that state transportation departments in the United States would be the primary market for such a scale.

Like many technological advances, developing the dynamic scale has been difficult. When the scale finally proved accurate for trucks traveling 40 miles per hour, it would not perform for trucks traveling at higher speeds. However, eight months ago, Stanley announced that the dynamic scale was ready to be field-tested by the Nebraska State Department of Transportation under a grant from the federal government. Stanley explained to his financial partners, and to Nebraska transportation officials, that the dynamic weight would not exactly equal the static weight (truck weight on a static scale). However he was sure a statistical relationship between dynamic weight and static weight could be determined, which would make the dynamic scale useful.

Nebraska officials, along with people from Dynamic Scales, installed a dynamic scale on a major highway in Nebraska. Each month for six months, data were collected for a random sample of trucks weighed on both the dynamic scale and a static scale. Table 14-3 presents these data.

Once the data were collected, the next step was to determine whether, based on this test, the dynamic scale measurements could be used to predict static weights. A complete report will be submitted to the U.S. government and to Dynamic Scales.

TABLE 14-3

Test Data for the Dynamic Scales Example

MONTH	FRONT-AXLE STATIC WEIGHT	FRONT-AXLE DYNAMIC WEIGHT	TRUCK SPEED	TEMPERATURE	MOISTURE
January	1,800 lbs.	1,625 lbs.	52 mph	21°F	0.00%
	1,311	1,904	71	17	0.15
	1,504	1,390	48	13	0.40
	1,388	1,402	50	19	0.10
	1,250	1,100	61	24	0.00
February	2,102	1,950	55	26	0.10
	1,410	1,475	58	32	0.20
	1,000	1,103	59	38	0.15
	1,430	1,387	43	24	0.00
	1,073	948	59	18	0.40
March	1,502	1,493	62	34	0.00
	1,721	1,902	67	36	0.00
	1,113	1,415	48	42	0.21
	978	983	59	29	0.32
	1,254	1,149	60	48	0.00
April	994	1,052	58	37	0.00
	1,127	999	52	34	0.21
	1,406	1,404	59	40	0.40
	875	900	47	48	0.00
	1,350	1,275	68	51	0.00
May	1,102	1,120	55	52	0.00
	1,240	1,253	57	57	0.00
	1,087	1,040	62	63	0.00
	993	1,102	59	62	0.10
	1,408	1,400	67	68	0.00
June	1,420	1,404	58	70	0.00
	1,808	1,790	54	71	0.00
	1,401	1,396	49	83	0.00
	933	1,004	62	88	0.40
	1,150	1,127	64	81	0.00

General References

1. Berenson, Mark L., and David M. Levine, *Basic Business Statistics: Concepts and Applications*, 7th ed. (Upper Saddle River, NJ: Prentice-Hall, 1999).

2. Bowerman, Bruce L., and Richard T. O'Connell, *Linear Statistical Models: An Applied Approach*, 2d ed. (Belmont, CA: Duxbury Press, 1990).

3. Cryer, Jonathan D., and Robert B. Miller, *Statistics for Business: Data Analysis and Modeling*, 2d ed. (Belmont, CA: Duxbury Press, 1994).

4. Demmert, Henry, and Marshall Medoff, "Game-Specific Factors and Major League Baseball Attendance: An Econometric Study," *Santa Clara Business Review* (1977) pp. 49–56.

5. Draper, Norman R., and Harry Smith, *Applied Regression Analysis*, 3rd ed. (New York: John Wiley and Sons, 1998).

6. Frees, Edward W., *Data Analysis Using Regression Models: The Business Perspective* (Englewood Cliffs, NJ: Prentice-Hall, 1996).

7. Gloudemans, Robert J., and Dennis Miller, "Multiple Regression Analysis Applied to Residential Properties." *Decision Sciences 7* (April 1976) pp. 294–304.

8. Kleinbaum, David G., Lawrence L. Kupper, Keith E. Muller, and Azhar Nizam, *Applied Regression Analysis and Other Multivariable Methods*, 3rd ed. (Belmont, CA: Duxbury Press, 1998).

9. *Microsoft Excel 2000* (Redmond, WA: Microsoft Corp. 1999).

10. *Minitab for Windows Version 13* (State College, PA: Minitab, 2000).

11. Neter, John, Michael H. Kutner, Christopher J. Nachtsheim, and William Wasserman, *Applied Linear Statistical Models*, 4th ed. (Homewood, IL: Richard D. Irwin, 1996).

CHAPTER 15

Analyzing and Forecasting Time-Series Data

CHAPTER OUTCOMES

After studying the material in Chapter 15, you should be able to:

- Apply the fundamental steps in developing and implementing forecasting models.
- Identify the components present in a time series.
- Understand and compute basic index numbers.
- Use smoothing-based forecasting models, including single and double exponential smoothing.
- Apply trend-based forecasting models, including linear trend, nonlinear trend, and seasonally adjusted trend.

WHY YOU NEED TO KNOW

No organization, large or small, can function effectively without a forecast for the goods or services it provides. A retail clothing store must forecast the demand for the shirts it sells by shirt size. The concessionaire at Dodger Stadium in Los Angeles must forecast each game's attendance to determine how many soft drinks and hot dogs to have on hand. Your state's elected officials must forecast tax revenues in order to establish a budget each year. These are only a few of the instances in which forecasting is required. For many organizations, the success of the forecasting effort will play a major role in determining the general success of the organization.

When you graduate and join an organization in the public or private sectors, you will almost certainly be required to prepare forecasts or to use forecasts provided by someone else in the organization. You won't have access to a crystal ball on which to rely for an accurate prediction of the future. Fortunately, if you have learned the material presented in this chapter, you will have a basic understanding of forecasting and of how and when to apply various forecasting techniques. We urge you to focus on the material and take with you the tools that will give you a competitive advantage over those who are not familiar with forecasting techniques.

15-1 INTRODUCTION TO FORECASTING, TIME-SERIES DATA, AND INDEX NUMBERS

Decision makers often confuse forecasting and planning. Planning is the process of determining how to deal with the future. On the other hand, *forecasting* is the process of predicting what the future will be like. Forecasts are used as inputs for the planning process.

Experts agree that good planning is essential for an organization to be effective. Because forecasts are an important part of the planning process, you need to be familiar with forecasting methods. There are two broad categories of forecasting techniques: qualitative and quantitative. *Qualitative forecasting* techniques are based on expert opinion and judgment. *Quantitative forecasting* techniques are based on statistical methods for analyzing quantitative historical data. This chapter focuses on quantitative forecasting techniques.

In general, quantitative forecasting techniques are used whenever the following conditions are true: historical data relating to the variable to be forecast exist; the historical data can be quantified; and one can assume that the historical pattern will continue into the future.

GENERAL FORECASTING ISSUES

Decision makers who are actively involved in forecasting frequently say that forecasting is both an art and a science. Operationally, the forecaster is engaged in the process of modeling a real-world system. Determining the appropriate forecasting model is a challenging task, but it can be made manageable by employing the same model-building process discussed in Chapter 14, consisting of: **model specification**, **model fitting**, and **model diagnosis**.

Model Specification

The process of selecting the forecasting technique to be used in a particular situation.

As we will point out in later sections, guidelines exist for determining which techniques may be more appropriate than others in certain situations. However, you may have to specify (and try) several model forms for a given situation before deciding on one that is acceptable.

Model Fitting

The process of determining how well a specified model fits past data.

The idea is that if the future tends to look like the past, a model must adequately fit the past data to have a reasonable chance of forecasting the future. As a forecaster, you will spend much time selecting a model's specification and estimating its parameters to reach an acceptable fit of the past data.

Model Diagnosis

The process of determining how well a model fits past data and how well the model's assumptions appear to be satisfied.

You will need to determine how well a model fits past data, how well it performs in mock forecasting trials, and how well its assumptions appear to be satisfied. If the model is unacceptable in any of these areas, you will be forced to revert to the model specification step and begin again.

An important consideration when you are developing a forecasting model is to use the simplest available model that will meet your forecasting needs. The objective of forecasting is to provide good forecasts. You do not need to feel that a sophisticated approach is better if a simpler one will provide acceptable forecasts. As in football, in which some players specialize in defense and others in offense, forecasting techniques have been developed for special situations, which are generally dependent on the **forecasting horizon**.

Forecasting Horizon

The number of future periods covered by a forecast. It is sometimes referred to as *forecast lead time*.

For the purpose of categorizing forecasting techniques in most business situations, the forecast horizon, or lead time, is typically divided into four categories:

1. Immediate term—less than one month
2. Short term—one to three months
3. Medium term—three months to two years
4. Long term—two years or more

As we introduce various forecasting techniques, we will indicate the forecasting horizon(s) for which each is typically best suited.

In addition to determining the desired forecasting horizon, the forecaster must determine the **forecasting period**.

Forecasting Period

The unit of time for which forecasts are to be made.

For instance, the forecasting period might be a day, a week, a month, a quarter, or a year. Thus, the forecasting horizon consists of one or more forecasting periods. If quantitative forecasting techniques are to be employed, historical quantitative data must be available for a similar period. If we want weekly forecasts, weekly historical data must be available.

Forecasting Interval

The frequency with which new forecasts are prepared.

The **forecasting interval** is generally the same length as the forecast period. That is, if the forecast period is one week, then we will provide a new forecast each week.

COMPONENTS OF A TIME SERIES

Most quantitative forecasting models have one factor in common: they use past measurements of the variable of interest to generate a forecast of the future. The past data, measured over time, are called *time-series data*. The decision maker who plans to develop a quantitative forecasting model must analyze the relevant time-series data.

TABLE 15-1

Time-Series Data For Consultant's Billings (Thousands of Dollars)

	BILLING TOTAL			
Month	**1999**	**2000**	**2001**	**2002**
January	170	390	500	750
February	200	350	470	700
March	190	300	510	680
April	220	320	480	710
May	180	310	530	710
June	230	350	500	660
July	220	380	540	630
August	260	420	580	670
September	300	460	630	700
October	330	500	690	720
November	370	540	770	850
December	390	560	760	880

Software Consulting Revenues—For the past four years, a software consulting company has been helping firms to implement enterprise-wide support systems such as SAP and PeopleSoft. In forecasting this company's revenue for next year, managers should consider the historical pattern over the prior four years. They want to know whether demand for consulting services has tended to increase or decrease and whether there have been particular times during the year when demand was typically higher than at other times. The forecasters can perform a time-series analysis of the historical billings.

Table 15-1 presents the time-series data for the revenue generated by the firm's billings for the four-year period. An effective means for analyzing these data is to develop a *time-series plot*, as shown in Figure 15-1. By graphing the data, much can be observed about the firm's revenue over the past four years. In fact, the time-series plot is an important tool in identifying the time-series components. All time-series data exhibit one or more of the following:

1. Trend component
2. Seasonal component
3. Cyclical component
4. Random component

FIGURE 15-1   Time-Series Plot for Consultant Billing Data

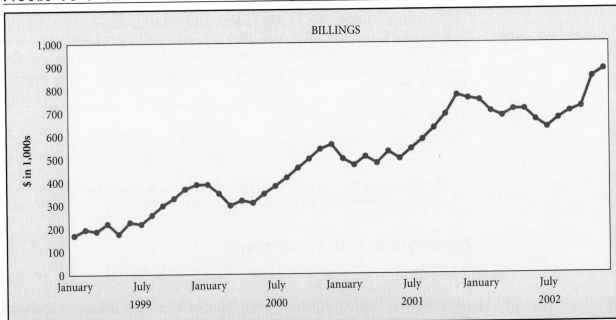

FIGURE 15-2

Albertson's, Inc.—Linear
Trend Example

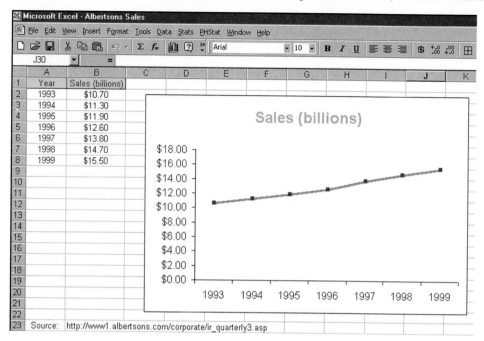

Trend Component

A *trend* is the long-term increase or decrease in a variable being measured over time. Figure 15-1 shows that the software-consulting company's demand exhibited an upward trend over the four-year period. In other situations, the time series may exhibit a downward trend.

Trends can be classified as linear or nonlinear.

Linear Trend

A long-term increase or decrease in a time series in which the rate of change is relatively constant.

Figure 15-1 is a good example showing a positive **linear trend**. Figure 15-2 shows the time-series plot of total sales for 1993 to 1999 for Albertson's, Inc., the nation's second-largest grocery chain. The sales data, taken from the *Albertson's 1999 Annual Report*, exhibit a positive linear trend, because sales have tended to increase at a fairly constant rate. In a *nonlinear trend*, the rate of change is not constant. The sales data in Figure 15-3 show that Microsoft's sales, taken from

FIGURE 15-3

Microsoft Corporation—a
Nonlinear Trend

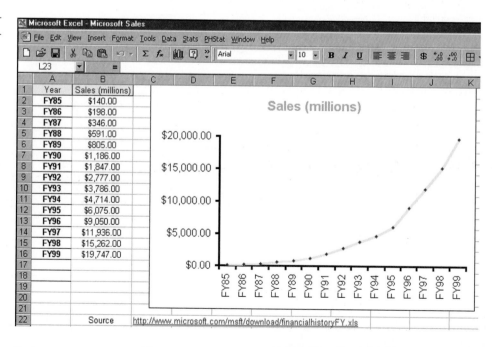

Microsoft 1999 Annual Report, between 1985 and 1999 have exhibited a nonlinear trend. Although sales have increased over time, the rate of increase has been much higher in recent years.

A trend can be observed when a time-series is measured in any time increment, such as years, quarters, months, or days. However, not all of the components of a time series are evident over all time increments. For instance, you will see shortly that a seasonal component is not evident if a time series is measured in years.

Seasonal Component

Another time-series component that may be present is called the **seasonal component**. Many time series show a repeating pattern over time. For instance, Figure 15-1 showed a time series that exhibits a wave-like pattern. This pattern repeats itself throughout the time series. The consultant billings reach a local maximum around January and then decline to a local minimum around April. This pattern repeats itself every 12 months, and the entire pattern is not repeated more often than once in 12 months. The shortest period of repetition for a pattern is known as its *recurrence period*. A seasonal component's recurrence period is at most one year. If the time series exhibits a repetitious pattern with a recurrence period longer than a year, the time series is said to exhibit a cyclical effect—a term to be explored shortly.

Seasonal Component

A wave-like pattern that is repeated throughout a time series and has a recurrence period of at most one year.

In analyzing past sales data for a retail toy store, we would expect to see that sales increase in the months leading into Christmas and then substantially decrease after Christmas. Automobile gasoline sales might show a seasonal increase during the summer months, when people drive more, and a decrease during the cold winter months. These predictable highs and lows at specific times during the year indicate seasonality in data.

In order to view seasonality in a time series, the data must be measured quarterly, monthly, weekly, or daily. Annual data will not show seasonal patterns of highs and lows. Figure 15-4 shows quarterly sales data for 1992 through 1997 for the Marriott Corporation, the hotel and food-service company.

FIGURE 15-4   Marriott Sales by Quarter

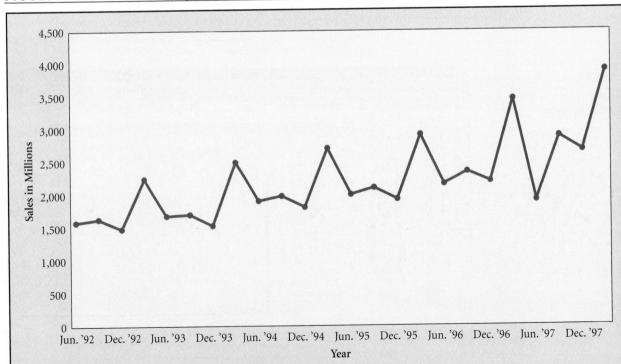

Notice that the data exhibits a definite seasonal pattern. The local maximums occur in March (spring). The recurrence period of the component in the time series is, therefore, one year. The December (winter) quarter tends to be low, whereas the following quarter (spring) is the high quarter each year.

Seasonality can be observed in time-series data measured over time periods shorter than a year. For example, the number of checks processed daily by a bank may show predictable highs and lows at certain times during a month. The pattern of customers arriving at the bank during any hour may be "seasonal" within a day, with more customers arriving near opening time, around the lunch hour, and near closing time.

Cyclical Component

If you observe time-series data over a long enough time span, you may see sustained periods of high values followed by periods of lower values. If the recurrence period of these fluctuations is larger than a year, the data are said to contain a **cyclical component**.

Cyclical Component

A wave-like pattern within the time series that repeats itself throughout the time series and has a recurrence period of more than one year.

National economic measures such as the unemployment rate, gross national product, stock market indexes, and personal saving rates tend to cycle. The cycles vary in length and magnitude. That is, some cyclical time series may have longer runs of high and low values than others. Also, some time series may exhibit deeper troughs and higher crests than others. Figure 15-5 shows quarterly housing starts in the United States between 1973 and 1997. Note the definite cyclical pattern, with low periods in 1974, 1982, and 1991. Although the pattern resembles the shape of a seasonal component, the length of the recurrence period identifies this pattern as being the result of a cyclical component.

Random Component

Although not all time series possess a trend, seasonal, or cyclical component, virtually all time series will have a **random component**.

Random Component

Changes in time-series data that are unpredictable and cannot be associated with a trend, seasonal, or cyclical component.

FIGURE 15-5 **U.S. Housing Starts, Showing a Cyclical Component**

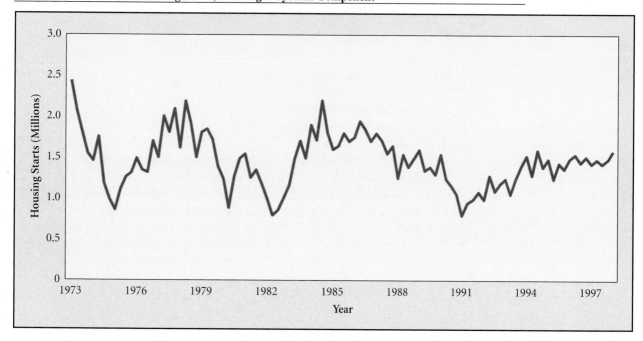

The random component is often referred to as "noise" in the data. A time series with no identifiable pattern is completely random and contains only noise. In addition to other components, each of the time series in Figures 15-1 through 15-5 contains random fluctuations.

In the following sections of this chapter, you will see how various forecasting techniques deal with the time-series components. An important first step in forecasting is to identify which components are present in the time series to be analyzed. As we have shown, constructing a time-series plot is a good first step in this process.

INTRODUCTION TO INDEX NUMBERS

When analyzing time-series data, decision makers must often compare one value measured at one point in time with other values measured at different points in time. For example, a real estate broker may wish to compare house prices in 2002 with house prices in previous years. A common procedure for making relative comparisons is to begin by determining a **base period index** to which all other data values can be fairly compared.

Base Period Index

The time-series value to which all other values in the time series are compared. The index number for the base period is defined as 100.

Equation 15-1 is used to make relative comparison for data found in different periods by calculating a *simple index number*.

Simple Index Number

$$I_t = \frac{y_t}{y_0} 100$$

15-1

where:

I_t = Index number at time period t

y_t = Value of the time series at time t

y_0 = Value of the time series at the index base period

$\mathcal{E}$XAMPLE 15-1: COMPUTING SIMPLE INDEX NUMBERS

Armstrong Corporation   The Armstrong Corporation is considering purchasing a small textile mill in Georgia. The present mill owners are stressing as a positive attribute the mill's rapid sales growth over the past 10 years. Armstrong executives wish to convert the sales data to index numbers. The following steps can be used to do this.

Step 1: **Obtain the time-series data.**
The company has sales data for each of the 10 years since 1993.

Step 2: **Select a base period.**
Armstrong managers have selected 1993 as the index base period. Sales in 1993 were $14.0 million.

Step 3: **Compute the simple index numbers for each year using Equation 15-1.**
For instance, sales in 1994 were $15.2 million. Using Equation 15-1, the index for 1994 is

$$I_t = \frac{y_t}{y_0} 100$$

$$I_{1994} = \frac{15.2}{14.0} 100 = 108.6$$

For the 10 years, we get:

Year	Sales (millions)	Index
1993	14.0	100.0
1994	15.2	108.6
1995	17.8	127.1
1996	21.4	152.9
1997	24.6	175.7
1998	30.5	217.9
1999	29.8	212.9
2000	32.4	231.4
2001	37.2	265.7
2002	39.1	279.3

Referring to Example 15-1, we can use the index numbers to determine the percentage change any year is from the base year. For instance, sales in 2000 have an index of 231.4. This means that sales in 2000 are 131.4% above sales in the base year of 1993. Sales in 2002 are 179.3% higher than they were in 1993.

Note that although you can use the index number to compare values between any one time period and the base period, and express the difference in percentage-change terms, you cannot compare period-to-period changes by subtracting the index numbers. For instance, in Example 15-1, when comparing sales for 2001 and 2002, we cannot say that the growth has been

$$279.3 - 265.7 = 13.6\%$$

To determine the actual percentage growth, we do the following:

$$\frac{279.3 - 265.7}{265.7} 100 = 5.1\%$$

Thus, the sales growth rate over the past two years has been 5.1%, not 13.6%.

AGGREGATE PRICE INDEXES

"The dollar's not worth what it once was" is a saying that everyone has heard. The problem is that nothing is worth what it used to be; sometimes it is worth more, and other times it is worth less. The simple index shown in Equation 15-1 works well for comparing prices when we wish to analyze the price of a single item over time. For instance, we could use the simple index to analyze how apartment rents have changed over time or how college tuition has increased over time. However, if we wish to compare prices of a group of items, we might construct an **aggregate price index**.

Aggregate Price Index

An index that is used to measure the rate of change from a base period for a group of two or more items.

Equation 15-2 is used to compute an unweighted aggregate price index.

Unweighted Aggregate Price Index

$$I_t = \frac{\sum p_t}{\sum p_0} (100)$$

15-2

where:

I_t = Unweighted aggregate index at time period t

$\sum p_t$ = Sum of the prices for the group of items at time period t

$\sum p_0$ = Sum of the prices for the group of items at base time period

---

EXAMPLE 15-2: COMPUTING AN UNWEIGHTED AGGREGATE PRICE INDEX

College Costs   There have been many news stories recently discussing the rate of growth of college and university costs. One university is interested in analyzing the growth in the total costs for students over the past five years. The university wishes to consider three main costs: tuition and fees, board and room, and books and supplies. Rather than analyzing these factors individually using three simple indexes, an unweighted aggregate price index can be developed using the following steps.

Step 1: **Define the variables to be included in the index and gather the time-series data.**
The university has identified three main categories of costs: tuition fees, board and room, and books and supplies. Data for the past five years have been collected. Full-time tuition and fees for two semesters are used. The full dorm-and-meal package offered by the university is priced for the board-and-room variable, and the books-and-supplies cost for a "typical" student are used for that component of the total costs.

Step 2: **Select a base period.**
The base period for this study will be the 1997–1998 academic year.

Step 3: **Use Equation 15-2 to compute the unweighted aggregate price index.**
The equation is

$$I_t = \frac{\sum p_t}{\sum p_0}(100)$$

The sum of the prices for the three components during the base academic year of 1997–1998 is $13,814. The sum of the prices in the 2001–2002 academic year is $19,492. Applying Equation 15-2, the unweighted aggregate price index is

$$I_{2001-2002} = \frac{\$19,492}{\$13,814}(100) = 141.1$$

This means, as a group, the components making up the cost of attending this university has increased by 41.1% since the 1997–1998 academic year. The indexes for the other years are shown as follows:

Academic Year	Tuition & Fees	Board & Room	Books & Supplies	$\sum p_t$	Index
1997–98	$7,300	$5,650	$864	$13,814	100.0
1998–99	7,720	5,980	945	14,645	106.0
1999–00	8,560	6,350	1,067	15,977	115.7
2000–01	9,430	6,590	1,234	17,254	124.9
2001–02	10,780	7,245	1,467	19,492	141.1

WEIGHTED AGGREGATE PRICE INDEXES

Example 15-2 utilized an unweighted aggregate price index to determine the change in university costs. This was appropriate because each student would incur the same set of three costs. However, in some situations, the items composing a total cost are not equally weighted. For instance, in a consumer price study of a "market basket" of 10 food items, a typical household will not use the same number (or volume) of each item. During a week, a typical household might use the three gallons of milk, but only two loaves of bread. In these types of situations, we need to compute a weighted aggregate price index to account for the different levels of use. Two common weighted indexes are the Paasche Index and the Laspeyres Index.

The Paasche Index

Equation 15-3 is used to compute a Paasche Index. Note that the weighting percentage in Equation 15-3 for the Paasche Index is always the percentage for the time period for which the index is being computed. The idea is that the prices in the base period should be weighted relative to their current use, not to what that use level was in other periods.

Paasche Index

$$I_t = \frac{\sum q_t p_t}{\sum q_t p_0}(100)$$

15-3

where:

q_t = Weighting percentage at time t
p_t = Price in time period t
p_0 = Price in the base period

EXAMPLE 15-3: COMPUTING THE PAASCHE INDEX

Wage Rates   Before a company makes a decision to locate a new manufacturing plant in a community, the managers will be interested in knowing how the wage rates have changed. Two categories of wages are to be analyzed as a package: production hourly wages and administrative/clerical hourly wages. Annual data showing the average hourly wage rates since 1993 are available. Each year, the makeup of the labor market differs in terms of the percentage of employees in the two categories. To compute a Paasche Index, use the following steps.

Step 1:   **Define the variables to be included in the index and gather the time-series data.**
The variables are the mean hourly price for production workers and the mean average price for administrative/clerical workers. Data are collected for the 10-year period through 2002.

Step 2:   **Select the base period.**
Because similar data for another community is only available back to 1996, the company will use 1996 as the base period to make comparisons between the two communities easier.

Step 3:   **Use Equation 15-3 to compute the Paasche Index.**
The equation is

$$I_t = \frac{\sum q_t p_t}{\sum q_t p_0}(100)$$

The hourly wage rate for production workers in the base year 1996 was $10.80, whereas average hourly administrative/clerical rate was $10.25.

In 2002, the production hourly rate had increased to $15.45, and the administrative/clerical rate was $13.45. Last year (2002), 60% of the employees in the community were designated as in production and 40% were administrative/clerical. Equation 15-3 is used to compute the Paasche Index for 2002, as follows:

$$I_{2002} = \frac{(0.60)(\$15.45) + (0.40)(\$13.45)}{(0.60)(\$10.80) + (0.40)(\$10.25)}(100) = 138.5$$

This means that, overall, the wage rates in this community have increased by 38.5% since the base year of 1996. The following table shows the Paasche Indexes for all years.

Year	Production Wage Rate	Percent Production	Administrative/Clerical Wage Rate	Percent Admin/Clerical	Paasche Index
1993	8.50	0.78	9.10	0.22	80.8
1994	9.10	0.73	9.45	0.27	86.3
1995	10.00	0.69	9.80	0.31	93.5
1996	10.80	0.71	10.25	0.29	100.0
1997	11.55	0.68	10.60	0.32	105.9
1998	12.15	0.67	10.95	0.33	110.7
1999	12.85	0.65	11.45	0.35	116.5
2000	13.70	0.65	11.90	0.35	123.2
2001	14.75	0.62	12.55	0.38	131.4
2002	15.45	0.60	13.45	0.40	138.5

The Laspeyres Index

The Paasche Index is computed using the logic that the index for the current period should be compared to a base period with the same weightings. An alternate index, called the Laspeyres Index, uses the base-period weighting in its computation, as shown in Equation 15-4.

Laspeyres Index

$$I_t = \frac{\sum q_0 p_t}{\sum q_0 p_0} (100)$$

15-4

where:

q_0 = Weighting percentage at base period
p_t = Price in time period t
p_0 = Price in base period

EXAMPLE 15-4: COMPUTING THE LASPEYRES INDEX

Wage Rates   Refer to Example 15-3, in which the managers of a company are interested in knowing how the wage rates have changed in the community in which they are considering building a plant. Two categories of wages are to be analyzed as a package: production hourly wages and administrative/clerical hourly wages. Annual data showing the average hourly wage rate since 1993 are available. Each year, the makeup of the labor market differs in terms of the percentage of employees in the two categories. To compute a Laspeyres Index, use the following steps.

Step 1:   Define the variables to be included in the index and gather the time-series data.
The variables are the mean hourly price for production workers and the mean average price for administrative/clerical workers. Data are collected for the 10-year period through 2002.

Step 2:   Select the base period.
Because similar data for another community is only available back to 1996, the company will use 1996 as the base period to make comparisons between the two communities easier.

Step 3:   Use Equation 15-4 to compute the Laspeyres Index.
The equation is

$$I_t = \frac{\sum q_0 p_t}{\sum q_0 p_0} (100)$$

The hourly wage rate for production workers in the base year of 1996 was $10.80, whereas the average hourly administrative/clerical rate was $10.25. In that year, 71% of the workers were classified as production. In 2002, the production hourly rate had increased to $15.45, and the administrative/clerical rate was at $13.45. Equation 15-4 is used to compute the Laspeyres Index for 2002, as follows:

$$I_{2002} = \frac{(0.71)(\$15.45) + (0.29)(\$13.45)}{(0.71)(\$10.80) + (0.29)(\$10.25)} (100) = 139.7$$

This means that, overall, the wage rates in this community have increased by 39.7% since the base year of 1996. The following table shows the Laspeyres Indexes for all years.

Year	Production Wage Rate	Percent Production	Administrative/Clerical Wage Rate	Percent Admin/Clerical	Laspeyres Index
1993	8.50	0.78	9.10	0.22	81.5
1994	9.10	0.73	9.45	0.27	86.5
1995	10.00	0.69	9.80	0.31	93.4
1996	10.80	0.71	10.25	0.29	100.0
1997	11.55	0.68	10.60	0.32	106.0
1998	12.15	0.67	10.95	0.33	110.9
1999	12.85	0.65	11.45	0.35	116.9
2000	13.70	0.65	11.90	0.35	123.8
2001	14.75	0.62	12.55	0.38	132.6
2002	15.45	0.60	13.45	0.40	139.7

COMMONLY USED INDEX NUMBERS

In addition to converting time-series data to index numbers, you will encounter a variety of indexes in your professional and personal life.

Consumer Price Index

To most of us, inflation has come to mean increased prices and less purchasing power for our dollar. The Consumer Price Index (CPI) attempts to measure the overall changes in retail prices for goods and services. The CPI, originally published in 1913 by the U.S. Department of Labor, uses a "market basket" of goods and services used by a typical wage earner living in a city. The CPI, a weighted aggregate index similar to a Laspeyres Index, is based on items grouped into seven categories, including food, housing, clothing, transportation, medical care, entertainment, and miscellaneous items. The items in the "market basket" have changed over time to keep pace with the buying habits of our society and as new products and services have become available.

Since 1945, the base period used to construct the CPI has been updated. Currently, the base period, 1982 to 1984, has an index of 100. Table 15-2 shows the CPI index values for 1992 to 2001. For instance, the index for 2001 is 173.2, which means that the price of the "market basket" of goods increased 73.2% between 1984 and 2001. Remember also that you cannot determine the inflation rate by subtracting index values for successive years. Instead, you must divide the difference by the earlier year's index. For instance, the rate of inflation between 2000 and 2001 was

$$\text{Inflation Rate} = \frac{173.2 - 167.6}{167.6}(100) = 3.34\%$$

Thus, in general terms, if your income did not increase by at least 3.34% between 2000 and 2001, you failed to keep pace with inflation and your purchasing power was reduced.

Producer Price Index

The U.S. Bureau of Labor Statistics publishes the *Producer Price Index* (PPI) on a monthly basis to measure the rate of change in nonretail prices. Like the CPI, the Producer Price Index is a Laspeyres weighted aggregate index. This index is used as a leading indicator of upcoming changes in the CPI. Table 15-3 shows the PPI between 1992 and 2001.

TABLE 15-2	**Year**	1992	1993	1994	1995	1996	1997	1998	1999	2000	2001
CPI Index (1992 to 2001)	**CPI**	137.1	141.3	144.5	148.9	153.1	157.0	159.0	162.0	167.6	173.2

Base = 1982 to 1984 (Index = 100)

Source: Bureau of Labor Statistics: **http://www.bls.gov/cpi/home.htm#data**

TABLE 15-3	**Year**	1992	1993	1994	1995	1996	1997	1998	1999	2000	2001
PPI Index (1992 to 2001)	**PPI**	117.9	119.1	120.7	124.2	127.1	127.5	126.2	128.3	133.5	134.6

Base = 1984 (Index = 100)
Source: Bureau of Labor Statistics: **http://www.bls.gov/ppi/home.htm#data**

STOCK MARKET INDEXES

Every night on the national and local TV news, reporters tell us what happened on the stock market that day by reporting on the *Dow Jones Industrial Average* (DJIA). The Dow, as this index is commonly referred to, is not the same type of index as the CPI or PPI, in that it is not a percentage of a base year. Rather, the DJIA is the sum of the stock prices for 30 large industrial companies whose stocks trade on the New York Stock Exchange divided by a factor that is adjusted for stock splits. Many analysts use the DJIA, which is computed daily, as a measure of the health of the stock market. Other analysts prefer other indexes, such as the *Standard and Poor's 500*. The S&P 500 includes stock prices for 500 companies and is thought by some to be more representative of the broader market.

The *NASDAQ* is an index made up of stocks on the NASDAQ exchange and is heavily influenced by technology-based companies that are traded on this exchange. Publications such as *The Wall Street Journal* and *Barrons* publish all these indexes and more every day for investors to use in their investing decisions.

USING INDEX NUMBERS TO DEFLATE A TIME SERIES

A common use of index numbers is to convert values measured at different times into more directly comparable values. For instance, if your wages increase, but at a rate less than inflation, you will in fact be earning less in "real terms." A company experiencing increasing sales at a rate of increase less than inflation is actually not increasing in "real terms."

Wyman-Gorman Company—The Wyman-Gorman Company, located in Massachusetts, designs and produces forgings, primarily for internal combustion engines. The company has recently been experiencing some financial difficulty and has discontinued its agricultural and earthmoving divisions. Table 15-4 shows sales in millions of dollars for the company since 1992. Also shown is the PPI for the same years. Finally, sales, adjusted to 1984 dollars, is also shown.

Equation 15-5 is used to determine the adjusted time-series values.

Deflation Formula

$$y_{adj_t} = \frac{y_t}{I_t}(100)$$

15-5

where:

y_{adj_t} = Deflated time series value at time t
y_t = Actual value of the time series at time t
I_t = Index (such as CPI or PPI) at time t

TABLE 15-4	YEAR	SALES (MILLIONS)	PPI (BASE = 1984)	SALES (ADJUSTED TO 1984 DOLLARS)
Deflated Sales Data—	1992	$610.3	117.9	$517.6
Using Producer Price	1993	473.1	119.1	397.2
Index	1994	383.5	120.7	317.7
	1995	425.5	124.2	342.6
	1996	384.1	127.1	302.2
	1997	341.0	127.5	267.5
	1998	310.3	126.2	245.9
	1999	271.6	128.3	211.7
	2000	371.6	133.5	278.4
	2001	390.0	134.6	289.7

For instance, in 1992 sales were $610.3 million. The producer price index for that year was 117.9. The sales, adjusted to 1984 dollars is

$$y_{adj_{1992}} = \frac{610.3}{117.9}(100) = \$517.6$$

15-1: EXERCISES

Skill Development

15.1 What is the difference between planning and forecasting? Give an example of planning, and describe how forecasting would be used in the planning process.

15.2 What are the differences between quantitative and qualitative forecasting techniques? Under what conditions is it appropriate to use a quantitative technique?

15.3 Provide an example of a business decision that requires
  1. a short-term forecast
  2. a medium-term forecast
  3. a long-term forecast

15.4 What is meant by time-series data? Give an example.

15.5 Explain the difference between time-series data and data that occur in regression models. Are these two types of data sets mutually exclusive? What do they have in common? How do they differ?

15.6 What is meant by trend component of a time series? How is a linear trend different from a nonlinear trend?

15.7 Must a seasonal component be associated with the seasons (fall, spring, summer, winter) of the year? Provide an example of a seasonal effect that is not associated with the seasons of the year.

15.8 Consider the following revenue data for the past 13 years:

Year	Revenue (in Millions)
1	$19.4
2	22.6
3	23.7
4	25.5
5	27.8
6	28.1
7	30.0
8	32.2
9	33.8
10	35.3
11	36.1
12	38.9
13	40.7

Use year 1 as a base year to construct a relative index showing how revenues have increased.

15.9 The following values represent advertising rates paid by a regional catalog retailer that advertises either on radio or in newspapers.

Year	Radio Advertisement	% on Radio	Newspaper Ad
1	$300	30	$400
2	310	35	420
3	330	35	460
4	346	38	520
5	362	40	580
6	380	42	640
7	496	45	660

a. Determine a relative index for each type of advertisement using year 1 as the base year.
b. Determine an unweighted aggregate index for the two types of advertisements.
c. In year 1, the retailer spent 30% of the advertisement budget on radio advertising. Construct a Laspeyres Index for the above data using year 1 as the base.
d. Using year 1 as the base, construct a Paasche Index for the same data.

Business Applications

15.10 The following are the research and development (R&D) expenditures for the most recent 12 years for the Wilson Manufacturing Company.

Year	R&D Expenditures
1	$1,549,800
2	1,547,870
3	1,550,860
4	1,548,770
5	1,553,830
6	1,548,590
7	1,553,390
8	1,546,660
9	1,554,270
10	1,550,810
11	1,554,210
12	1,551,880

a. Graph the time series for R&D expenditures.
b. What time-series components are present? Identify the recurrence period of the component for seasonal or cyclical components.

15.11 Ice-World is a family-oriented ice skating facility. The sales manager has the following data for the past 11 days. The data reflect the number of admissions to Ice-World each day.

Day	Admissions
1	1,258
2	1,275
3	1,287
4	1,299
5	1,304
6	1,311
7	1,330
8	1,349
9	1,364
10	1,388
11	1,399

Year	Hourly Wages	Average Materials Costs	% Material in Totals
1992	$30.10	$66,500	60
1993	30.50	68,900	58
1994	31.70	70,600	55
1995	32.50	70,900	55
1996	34.00	71,200	56
1997	34.50	71,700	54
1998	35.10	72,500	52
1999	35.05	73,700	50
2000	34.90	73,400	52
2001	33.80	74,100	50
2002	34.20	74,000	47

Develop a time-series graph for these data. Describe the time-series components that are present. Identify the recurrence period of any seasonal or cyclical components.

Exercises 15.12 through 15.15 refer to U.S. Homes, a major developer of housing communities in the New England area. The company had kept a record of the relative cost of labor and materials in its market areas for the past 11 years. These data are as follows:

15.12 Using 1992 as the base year, construct a separate index for each component in the construction of a house.

15.13 Plot both series of data and comment on the trend you see in both plots.

15.14 Construct a Paasche Index using the data. Use 1992 as the base year.

15.15 Construct a Laspeyres Index using the data. Use 1992 as the base year.

15-2 TREND-BASED FORECASTING TECHNIQUES

As we discussed in Section 15-1, some time series exhibit an increasing or decreasing trend. Further, the trend may be linear or nonlinear. A plot of the data usually will be very helpful in identifying which, if any, of these trends exist.

DEVELOPING A TREND-BASED FORECASTING MODEL

In this section, we introduce *trend-based forecasting techniques*. As the name implies, these techniques are used to identify the presence of a trend and to model that trend. Once the trend model has been defined, it is used to provide forecasts for future time periods.

Excel and Minitab Tutorial

The Taft Ice Cream Company—The Taft Ice Cream Company is a family-operated company selling gourmet ice cream to resort areas, primarily on the North Carolina coast. Figures 15-6a and 15-6b display the annual sales data for the past 10 years and show the time-series plots that illustrate that sales have trended up in the 10-year period. Note, the graphs appear different due to different scales used on the y-axis.

Taft's owners are considering expanding their ice cream manufacturing facilities. As part of the bank's financing requirements, the managers are asked to supply a forecast of future sales. Recall from our earlier discussions that the forecasting process has three steps: (1) model specification, (2) model fitting, and (3) model diagnosis.

STEP 1: Model Specification—The time-series plot in Figure 15-6a indicates that the sales have exhibited a linear growth pattern. A possible forecasting tool is a linear trend (straight-line) model.

STEP 2: Model-Fitting—Because we have specified a linear trend model, the process of fitting can be accomplished using least squares regression analysis of a form described by Equation 15-6.

FIGURE 15-6A

Excel Output—Taft Ice Cream Sales Trend Line

Excel Instructions:
1. Open file: Taft.xls
2. Click on **Chart Wizard**.
3. Select **Line Graph**.
4. Select Data.
5. Define x-axis on Series Tab.
6. Label Graph.

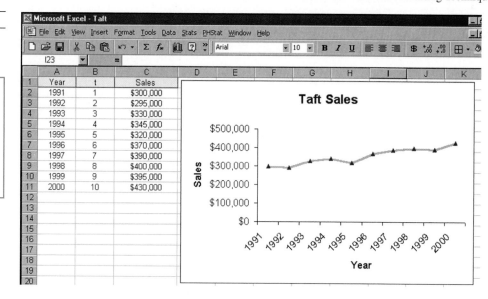

Linear Trend Model

$$y_t = \beta_0 + \beta_1 t + \varepsilon_t$$

15-6

where:

y_t = Value of the trend at time t
β_0 = y intercept of the trend line
β_1 = Slope of the trend line
t = Time ($t = 1, 2, \ldots$)
ε_t = Error term at time t

We let the first period in the time series be $t = 1$, the second period be $t = 2$, and so forth. The values for time form the independent variable, with sales being the dependent variable. Referring to Chapter 13, the least squares regression equations for the slope and intercept are estimated by Equations 15-7 and 15-8. Here the sums are taken over the values of t ($t = 1, 2, \ldots$).

FIGURE 15-6B

Minitab Output—Taft Ice Cream Sales Trend Line

Minitab Instructions:
1. Open file: Taft.MTW.
2. Choose **Graph > Time Series Plot**.
3. Select **Simple**.
4. Under **Series**, enter time series' column.
5. Click **Time/Scale**.
6. Under **Time Scale** select **Calendar** and **Year**.
7. Under **Start Values**, insert the starting year.
8. Click **OK. OK**.

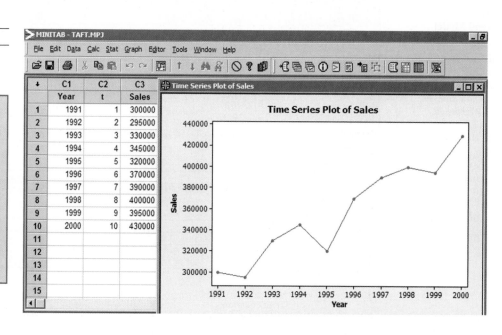

Least Squares Equations Estimates

$$b_1 = \frac{\sum ty_t - \dfrac{\sum t \sum y_t}{n}}{\sum t^2 - \dfrac{(\sum t)^2}{n}}$$

15-7

$$b_0 = \frac{\sum y_t}{n} - b_1 \frac{\sum t}{n}$$

15-8

where:

n = Number of periods in the time series
t = Time period (independent variable)
y_t = Dependent variable at time t

The linear regression procedures in either Excel or Minitab can be used to compute the least squares trend model. Figure 15-7 shows the output for the Taft Ice Cream Company example. The least squares trend model for the Taft Ice Cream Company is

$$\hat{y}_t = b_0 + b_1 t$$
$$\hat{y}_t = 277{,}333.33 + 14{,}575.76(t)$$

For a forecast, we use F_t as the forecast value or predicted value at time period t. Thus,

$$F_t = 277{,}333.33 + 14{,}575.76(t)$$

STEP 3: Model Diagnosis—The linear trend regression output in Figure 15-7 offers some conclusions about the potential capabilities of our model. The R-squared = 0.912 shows that for these 10 years of data, the linear trend model explains more than 91% of the variation in sales. The p-value for the regression slope coefficient is 0.0000168. This means that time (t) explains a significant portion of the variation in sales. Figures 15-8a and 15-8b show the Excel and Minitab plots of the trend line through the data. You can see the trend models fit the historical data quite closely. Although these results are a good sign, the model diagnosis step requires further analysis.

FIGURE 15-7

Excel Output for Taft Ice Cream Trend Model

Excel Instructions:
1. Open file: Taft.xls
2. Click **Tools**.
3. Select **Data Analysis**.
4. Select **Regression Analysis**.
5. Define data range for y variable.
6. Define data range for the time variable (t = 1, 2, 3, 4, . . . 10).
7. Indicate output location.
8. Click **OK**.

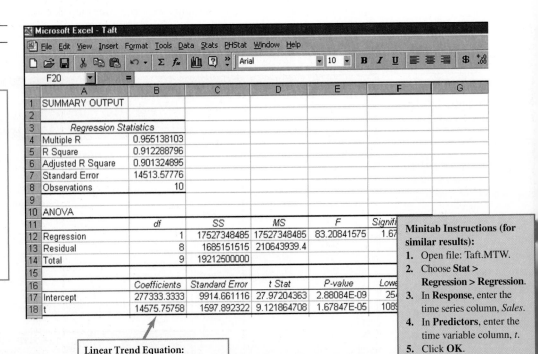

Minitab Instructions (for similar results):
1. Open file: Taft.MTW.
2. Choose **Stat** > **Regression > Regression**.
3. In **Response**, enter the time series column, *Sales*.
4. In **Predictors**, enter the time variable column, *t*.
5. Click **OK**.

Linear Trend Equation:
Sales = 277,333 + 14,5756(t)

FIGURE 15-8A

Excel Output for Taft Ice Cream Trend Line

Excel Instructions:
1. Select Data to be graphed.
2. Click on **Chart Wizard**.
3. Select **Line** option.
4. Define chart format.
5. After Constructing the Line Graph: Click on the data.
6. Right click.
7. Click on the **Options** tab.
8. Select **Add Trend Line**.
9. Select **Show Equation**.

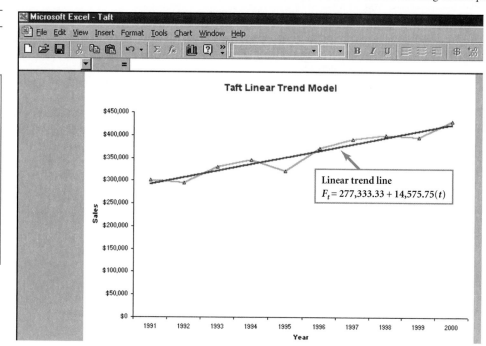

FIGURE 15-8A

Excel Output for Taft Ice Cream Trend Line

Excel Instructions:
1. Select Data to be graphed.
2. Click on **Chart Wizard**.
3. Select **Line** option.
4. Define chart format.
5. After Constructing the Line Graph: Click on the data.
6. Right click.
7. Click on the **Options** tab.
8. Select **Add Trend Line**.
9. Select **Show Equation**.

COMPARING THE FORECAST VALUES TO THE ACTUAL DATA

The slope of the trend line indicates the Taft Ice Cream Company has experienced an average increase in sales of $14,575.76 per year over the 10-year period. The linear trend model's fitted sales values for periods $t = 1$ through $t = 10$ can be found by substituting for t in the following forecast equation.

$$F_t = 277,333.33 + 14,575.76(t)$$

For example, for $t = 1$, we get

$$F_t = 277,333.33 + 14,575.76(1)$$
$$= \$291,909.09$$

FIGURE 15-8B

Minitab Output for Taft Ice Cream Trend Line

Minitab Instructions:
1. Open file: Taft.MTW.
2. Choose **Stat > Times Series > Trend Analysis**.
3. In **Variable**, enter time series column.
4. Under **Model Type**, choose **Linear**.
5. Click **OK**.

Note that the actual sales figure, y_1, for period 1 was $300,000. The difference between the actual sales in time t and the forecast values in time t, found using the trend model, is called the *forecast error* or the *residual*. Figure 15-9 shows the forecasts for periods 1 through 10 and the forecast errors at each period.

Computing the forecast error by comparing the trend-line values with actual past data is an important part of the model diagnosis step. The errors measure how closely the model fits the actual data at each point. A perfect fit would lead to residuals of 0 each time. We would like to see small residuals and an overall good fit. Two commonly used measures of fit are mean squared residual, or *mean squared error* (MSE), and *mean absolute deviation* (MAD). These measures are computed using Equations 15-9 and 15-10, respectively. *MAD* measures the average magnitude of the forecast errors. *MSE* is a measure of the variability in the forecast errors. The construction of *MSE* is similar to that for *MSE* in regression and analysis of variance. The forecast error is the observed value, here y_t, minus the predicted value, here F_t.

Mean Squared Error	**Mean Absolute Deviation**
$$MSE = \frac{\Sigma(y_t - F_t)^2}{n} \qquad \textbf{15-9}$$	$$MAD = \frac{\Sigma |y_t - F_t|}{n} \qquad \textbf{15-10}$$
where:	where:
y_t = Actual value at time t	y_t = Actual value at time t
F_t = Predicted value at time t	F_t = Predicted value at time t
n = Number of time periods	n = Number of time periods

Figure 15-10 shows the *MSE* and *MAD* calculations using Excel for the Taft Ice Cream example. Figure 15-8 shows the results of these calculations using Minitab. For example, the *MAD* value of $11,042 indicates the linear trend model has an average absolute error of $11,042 per period. The *MSE* (in squared units) equals 168,515,152. The square root of the *MSE* is $12,981, and although it is not equal to the *MAD* value, it does provide similar information about the relationship between the forecast values and the actual values of the time series.[1]

These error measures are particularly helpful when comparing two or more forecasting techniques. We can compute the *MSE* and/or the *MAD* for each forecasting technique. The forecasting technique that gives the smallest *MSE* or *MAD* is generally considered to provide the best fit.

Autocorrelation

In addition to examining the fit of the forecasts to the actual time series, the model-diagnosis step also should examine how a model meets the assumptions of the regression model. These key assumptions, which were introduced and discussed in Chapters 13 and 14, are restated here.

FIGURE 15-9

Excel Residual Output for Taft Ice Cream

Excel Instructions:
1. Follow instructions on Figure 15-7.
2. In the **Regression** Tool Template, check **Residuals**.

	File Edit View Insert Format Tools Data Stats PHStat Windo

Residual = forecast error

	Observation	Predicted Sales	Residuals
22	RESIDUAL OUTPUT		
24	*Observation*	*Predicted Sales*	*Residuals*
25	1	291909.0909	8090.909091
26	2	306484.8485	-11484.84848
27	3	321060.6061	8939.393939
28	4	335636.3636	9363.636364
29	5	350212.1212	-30212.12121
30	6	364787.8788	5212.121212
31	7	379363.6364	10636.36364
32	8	393939.3939	6060.606061
33	9	408515.1515	-13515.15152
34	10	423090.9091	6909.090909

[1]Technically this is the square root of the average squared distance between the forecasts and the observed data values. Algebraically, of course, this is not the same as the average forecast error, but it is comparable.

FIGURE 15-10

Excel *MSE* and *MAD* Computations for Taft Ice Cream

Excel Instructions:
1. Go to the Residual output section of the printout.
2. Use Excel formulas to compute squared and absolute value residuals.
3. Use Equations 15-9 and 15-10 to determine *MSE* and *MAD*.

Microsoft Excel - Taft

File Edit View Insert Format Tools Data Stats PHStat Window Help

A42

New

Excel equations:
Squared residual = C25^2
Absolute value = ABS(C25)

	A	B	C	D		
20						
21						
22	MSE and MAD Calculations					
23		F_t	$y_t - F_t$	$(y_i - F_i)^2$		$|y_i - F_i|$
24		*Predicted Sales*	*Residuals*	*Squared Residuals*		*Absolute Value of Residuals*
25	1	291909.0909	8090.909091	65462809.92		8090.909091
26	2	306484.8485	-11484.84848	131901744.7		11484.84848
27	3	321060.6061	8939.393939	79912764		8939.393939
28	4	335636.3636	9363.636364	87677685.95		9363.636364
29	5	350212.1212	-30212.12121	912772268.1		30212.12121
30	6	364787.8788	5212.121212	27166207.53		5212.121212
31	7	379363.6364	10636.36364	113132231.4		10636.36364
32	8	393939.3939	6060.606061	36730945.82		6060.606061
33	9	408515.1515	-13515.15152	182659320.5		13515.15152
34	10	423090.9091	6909.090909	47735537.19		6909.090909
35						
36			Sum =	1,685,151,515.15		110,424.24
37						
38						

$$MSE = \frac{\sum(y_t - F_t)^2}{n} = 168,515,151.52 \qquad MAD = \frac{\sum|y_t - F_t|}{n} = 11,042.42$$

ASSUMPTIONS

1. The regression model errors are normally distributed.
2. The mean of the model error terms is 0.
3. The model error terms have a constant variance, σ_ε^2, for all combinations of values of the independent variables.
4. The model error terms are independent.

We previously discussed approaches for dealing with situations when some of these assumptions are violated. However, when using regression with time-series data, the assumption, of independent error terms, could be violated. That is, the residuals may be correlated over time. We call this *serial correlation*, or **autocorrelation**.

Autocorrelation

Correlation of the error terms (residuals) occurs when the residuals at successive points in time are related.

The error terms are functionally related to the time-series values by Equation 15-6. Therefore, if the error terms exhibit autocorrelation, so do the time-series values. When dealing with a time-series variable, the value of y at time period t is commonly related to the value of y at the previous time periods. If a relationship between y_t and y_{t-1} exists, we conclude that first-order autocorrelation exists. If y_t is related to y_{t-2}, second-order autocorrelation exists, and so forth. If the times-series values are autocorrelated, the assumption that the error terms are independent is violated.

The autocorrelation can be positive or negative. For instance when the values are first-order positively autocorrelated, we expect a positive residual to be followed by a positive residual in the next period, and we expect a negative residual to be followed by another negative residual. With negative first-order autocorrelation, we expect a positive residual to be followed by a negative residual, followed by a positive residual, and so on. The presence of autocorrelation can have adverse consequences on tests of statistical significance in a regression model. Thus, you need to be able to detect the presence of autocorrelation and take action to remove the problem. The *Durbin-Watson statistic*, which is shown in Equation 15-11, is used to test whether residuals are autocorrelated.

Durbin-Watson Statistic

$$d = \frac{\sum\limits_{t=2}^{n}(e_t - e_{t-1})^2}{\sum\limits_{t=1}^{n}e_t^2} \qquad \text{15-11}$$

where:

$$d = \text{Durbin-Watson test statistic}$$
$$e_t = (y_t - \hat{y}_t) = \text{Residual at time } t$$
$$n = \text{Number of time periods in the time series}$$

Figure 15-11 shows the Minitab output providing the Durbin-Watson statistic of

$$d = \frac{\sum\limits_{t=2}^{n}(e_t - e_{t-1})^2}{\sum\limits_{t=1}^{n}e_t^2} = 2.65$$

Examining Equation 15-11, we see that if successive values of the residual are close in value, the Durbin-Watson d statistic will be small. This situation would describe one in which residuals are positively correlated. On the other hand, if there is a big difference between successive residuals, the d value will be large, implying negative autocorrelation.

The Durbin-Watson statistic can have a value ranging from 0 to 4. A value of 2 indicates no autocorrelation. However, like any other statistic computed from a sample, the Durbin-Watson d is subject to sampling error. We need to test formally to determine whether autocorrelation exists. In most business situations, if autocorrelation exists it will be positive. The following null and alternative hypotheses are established:

$$H_0: \rho = 0$$
$$H_A: \rho > 0$$

FIGURE 15-11

Minitab Output—Durbin-Watson Statistic: Taft Ice Cream Company Example

Minitab Instructions:
1. Open file: Taft.MTW.
2. Choose **Stat > Regression > Regression**.
3. In **Response**, enter the time series column, *Sales*.
4. In **Predictors**, enter the time variable column, *t*.
5. Select **Options**.
6. Under **Display**, select **Durbin-Watson statistic**.
7. Click **OK. OK**.

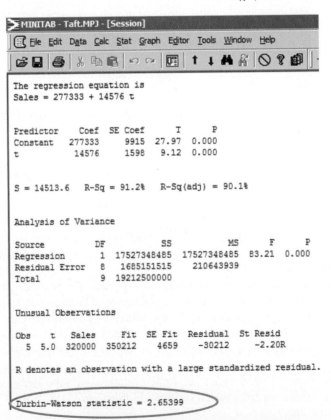

MINITAB - Taft.MPJ - [Session]

File Edit Data Calc Stat Graph Editor Tools Window Help

```
The regression equation is
Sales = 277333 + 14576 t


Predictor    Coef  SE Coef      T       P
Constant   277333     9915   27.97   0.000
t           14576     1598    9.12   0.000


S = 14513.6   R-Sq = 91.2%   R-Sq(adj) = 90.1%


Analysis of Variance

Source           DF          SS           MS       F       P
Regression        1   17527348485   17527348485   83.21   0.000
Residual Error    8    1685151515     210643939
Total             9   19212500000


Unusual Observations

Obs    t    Sales     Fit   SE Fit   Residual   St Resid
  5  5.0   320000  350212    4659     -30212      -2.20R

R denotes an observation with a large standardized residual.


Durbin-Watson statistic = 2.65399
```

If the d statistic is too small, we will reject the null hypothesis and conclude that positive auto-correlation exists. If the d statistic is too large, we will reject and conclude that negative autocorre-lation exists. Appendix O contains a table of one-tailed Durbin-Watson critical values for $\alpha = 0.05$ and $\alpha = 0.01$ levels. (Note: The critical values in Appendix O are for one-tailed tests with $\alpha = 0.05$ or 0.01. For a two-tailed test, the alpha is doubled.) The Durbin-Watson table provides two critical values: d_L and d_U. In this test for positive autocorrelation, the decision rule is

> If $d < d_L$, reject H_0 and conclude that positive autocorrelation exists.
> If $d > d_U$, conclude that positive autocorrelation does not exist.
> If $d_L < d < d_U$, the test is inconclusive.

The Durbin-Watson test is not reliable for sample sizes smaller than 15. Therefore, for the Taft Ice Cream Company application, we are unable to conduct the hypothesis test for autocorrelation. However, Example 15-5 shows a Durbin-Watson test carried out.

EXAMPLE 15-5: TESTING FOR AUTOCORRELATION

Grey Harbor Shipping   Grey Harbor Shipping is a family-owned freight company located near Providence, Rhode Island. The company has been in business since 1985. During this time, revenues have grown steadily. Figure 15-12 displays the data in line-chart form. The data are in a CD-ROM file called *Grey Harbor*.

Recently the managers of the company developed a linear trend regression model that they hope to use to forecast revenue for the next two years to determine whether they can support adding another ship to their fleet. They are now interested in determining whether the linear model is subject to positive autocorrelation. To test for this, the following steps can be used.

Step 1:   Specify the model.
Based on a study of the line chart, the forecasting model is to be a simple linear trend regression model, with revenue as the dependent variable and time (t) as the independent variable.

FIGURE 15-12   Line Chart of Grey Harbor Revenue Data

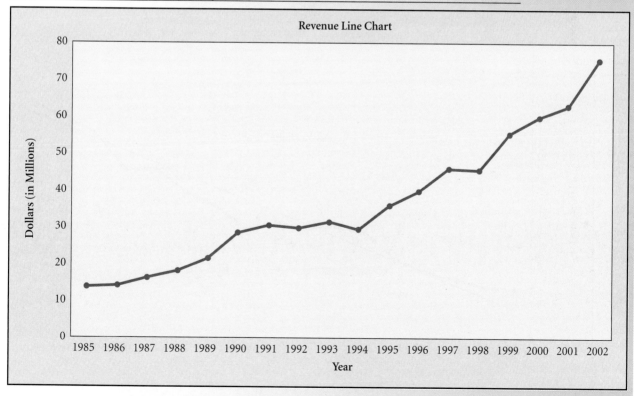

Step 2: **Fit the model.**

Because we have specified a linear trend model, the process of fitting can be accomplished using least squares regression analysis and Equations 15-7 and 15-8 to estimate the slope and intercept for the model. Fitting the 18 data points with a least squares line, we find the following:

$$F_t = 5.0175 + 3.3014(t)$$

Step 3: **Diagnose the model.**

The following values have been computed:

$$R^2 = 0.935$$
$$F\text{-statistic} = 230.756$$
$$\text{standard error} = 4.78$$

The model explains a significant amount of variation in revenue per share over time. However, looking at a plot of the trend line shown in Figure 15-13, we see a pattern of actual values first above, and then below, the trend line. This pattern indicates possible autocorrelation among the residuals. We will test for autocorrelation by calculating the Durbin-Watson d statistic. Both Minitab and the PHStat add-ins for Excel have the option to generate the Durbin-Watson test statistic. The output is shown in Figure 15-14.

Figure 15-14 shows the Durbin-Watson d statistic as:

$$d = 0.661$$

The null and alternative hypotheses for testing for positive autocorrelation are

$$H_0 : \rho = 0$$
$$H_A : \rho > 0$$

We next go to the Durbin-Watson table (Appendix O) for $\alpha = 0.05$, sample size 18, and number of independent variables, $k = 1$. The values from the table for d_L and d_U are

$$d_L = 1.16 \quad \text{and} \quad d_U = 1.39$$

FIGURE 15-13 **Grey Harbor Trend Line**

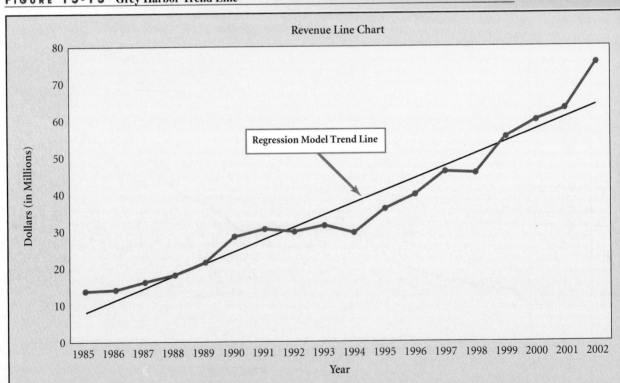

FIGURE 15-14

**Excel (PHStat) Output—
Durbin-Watson Statistic
for Grey Harbor**

Excel PHStat Instructions:
1. Open File Grey Harbor.xls
2. Select **PHStat**.
3. Select **Regression**.
4. Select **Simple Linear Regression**.
5. Define y and x variable ranges.
6. Click on **Durbin-Watson Statistic**.
7. Click **OK**.

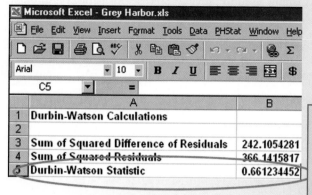

Minitab Instructions (for similar results):
1. Open file: Grey Harbor.MTW.
2. Choose **Stat > Regression > Regression**.
3. In **Response**, enter the time series column, *Revenue*.
4. In **Predictors**, enter the time variable column, *t*.
5. Select **Options**.
6. Under **Display**, select **Durbin-Watson statistic**.
7. Click **OK. OK**.

The decision rule for testing whether we have positive autocorrelation is

If $d < 1.16$, reject H_0 and conclude that positive autocorrelation exists.
If $d > 1.39$, conclude that positive autocorrelation does not exist.
If $1.16 < d < 1.39$, the test is inconclusive.

Because $d = 0.661 < d_L = 1.16$, we must reject the null hypothesis and conclude that significant positive autocorrelation exists in the regression model. This means that the assumption of uncorrelated residuals has been violated in this case. Thus, the linear trend model is not the appropriate model to provide the annual revenue forecasts for the next three years.

There are several techniques for dealing with the problem of autocorrelation. Some of these are beyond the scope of this text. (Refer to books by Nelson and Wonnacott and Wonnacott.) However, one option is to attempt to fit a nonlinear trend to the data, which is discussed in the next section.

True Forecasts

Although a decision maker is interested in how well a forecasting technique can fit historical data, the real test comes with how well it forecasts future values. In the Taft example, we had 10 years of historical data. If we wish to forecast ice cream sales for year 11 using the linear trend model, we substitute $t = 11$ into the forecast equation to produce a forecast as follows.

$$F_{11} = 277,333.33 + 14,575.76(11) = \$437,666.69$$

This method of forecasting is called *trend projection*. To determine how well our trend model actually forecasts, we would have to wait until the actual sales amount for period 11 is known.

As we just indicated, a model's true forecasting ability is determined by how well it forecasts future values, not by how well it fits historical values. However, having to wait until after the forecast period to know how effective a forecast is doesn't help us assess a model's effectiveness ahead of time. This problem can be partially overcome by using *split samples*, which involves dividing a time series into two groups. You put the first (n_1) periods of historical data in the first group. These (n_1) periods will be used to develop the forecasting model. The second group contains the remaining (n_2) periods of historical data, which will be used to test the model's forecasting ability. These data are called the *holdout data*. Usually, three to five periods are held out, depending on the total number of periods in the time series.

In the Taft Ice Cream example, we have only 10 years of historical data, so we will hold out the last three periods and use the first seven periods to develop the linear trend model. The computations are performed as before, using Excel or Minitab and Equations 15-7 and 15-8. Because we are using a different data set to develop the linear equation, we get a slightly different trend line than when all 10 periods were used. The new trend line is

$$F_t = 277,142.85 + 14,642.85(t)$$

This model is now used to provide forecasts for periods 8 through 10 by using trend projection. These forecasts are

Year	Actual	Forecast	Error
t	y_t	F_t	$(y_t - F_t)$
8	400,000	394,285.65	5,714.35
9	395,000	408,928.50	-13,928.50
10	430,000	423,561.35	6,428.65

Then we can compute the *MSE* and the *MAD* values for periods 8 through 10.

$$MSE = [(5,714.35)^2 + (-13,928.50)^2 + (6,428.65)^2]/3 = 89,328,149.67$$

and

$$MAD = (|5,714.35| + |-13,928.50| + |6,428.65|)/3 = 8,690.50$$

These values could be compared with those produced using other forecasting techniques or evaluated against the forecaster's own standards. Smaller values are preferred. Other factors should also be considered. For instance, in some cases, the forecast values might tend to be higher (or lower) than the actual values. This may imply the linear trend model isn't the best model to use. Forecasting models that tend to over- or underforecast are said to contain *forecast bias*. Equation 15-12 is used as an estimator of the bias.

Forecast Bias

$$\text{Forecast Bias} = \frac{\Sigma(y_t - F_t)}{n}$$

15-12

or:

$$\text{Forecast Bias} = \frac{\Sigma(\text{error})}{n}$$

The forecast bias can be either positive or negative. A positive value indicates a tendency to underforecast. A negative value indicates a tendency to overforecast. The estimated bias taken from the forecasts for periods 8 through 10 in our example is

$$\text{Forecast Bias} = [(5,714.35) + (-13,928.50) + (6,428.65)]/3 = -595.17$$

This means that, on average, the model overforecast sales by an average of $595.17.

Suppose that we judge on the basis of our bias estimate that the linear trend model does an acceptable job in forecasting. Then all available data (periods 1 through 10) would be used to develop a linear trend model (see Figure 15-7), and a trend projection would be used to forecast for future time periods by substituting appropriate values for t into the trend model.

$$F_t = 277,333.33 + 14,575.76(t)$$

However, if the linear model is judged to be unacceptable, the forecaster will need to try a different technique. For the purpose of the bank loan application, the Taft Ice Cream Company needs to forecast sales for the next three years (periods 11 through 13.) Assuming the linear trend model is acceptable, these forecasts are

$$F_{11} = 277,333.33 + 14,575.76(11) = \$437,666.69$$
$$F_{11} = 277,333.33 + 14,575.76(12) = \$452,242.45$$
$$F_{11} = 277,333.33 + 14,575.76(13) = \$466,818.21$$

NONLINEAR TREND FORECASTING

As we indicated earlier, you may encounter a time series that exhibits a nonlinear trend. Figure 15-3 showed an example of a nonlinear trend. When the historical data show a nonlinear trend, you should consider using a nonlinear trend forecasting model. A common method for dealing with nonlinear trends is to use an extension of the linear trend method. This extension calls for making a data transformation before applying the least squares regression analysis.

Harrison Equipment Company—Consider Harrison Equipment Company, which leases large construction equipment to contractors in the Southwest. The lease arrangements call for Harrison to perform all repairs and maintenance on this equipment. Figure 15-15 shows a line chart for the repair costs for a crawler tractor leased to a contractor in Phoenix for the past 20 quarters. The data are contained in the CD-ROM file *Harrison*.

STEP 1: Model Specification—Harrison Equipment is interested in forecasting future repair costs for the crawler tractor. Recall that the first step in forecasting is model specification. Even though the plot in Figure 15-15 indicates a sharp upward nonlinear trend, the forecaster may start by specifying a linear trend model.

STEP 2: Model Fitting—As a part of the model-fitting step, she could use Excel's or Minitab's regression procedure to obtain the linear forecasting model as shown in Figure 15-16.

As shown in Figure 15-16, the linear trend model is

$$F_t = -3,357.54 + 958.408(t)$$

STEP 3: Model Diagnosis—The fit is pretty good with an R-squared = 0.7719 and a standard error of 3,166.9. But we need to look closer. Figure 15-16 shows a plot of the trend line compared with the actual data. A close inspection indicates the linear trend model may not be best for this case. Notice that the linear model underforecasts, then overforecasts, then underforecasts again. From this we might suspect positive autocorrelation.

We can establish the following null and alternative hypotheses:

$$H_0: \rho = 0$$
$$H_A: \rho > 0$$

Equation 15-11 could be used to manually compute the Durbin-Watson d statistic, or more likely, we would use either PHStat or Minitab. The calculated Durbin-Watson is

$$d = 0.505$$

The d_L critical value from the Durbin-Watson table in Appendix O for $\alpha = 0.05$ and a sample size of $n = 20$ and $k = 1$ independent variable is 1.20.

Because $d = 0.505 < d_L = 1.20$, we reject the null hypothesis.

FIGURE 15-15

Minitab Time-Series Plot for Harrison Equipment Repair Costs

Excel Instructions (for similar results):
1. Open file Harrison.xls
2. Select Repair Cost data.
3. Click on **Chart Wizard**.
4. Select **Line Graph**.
5. Under series Tab, define *x*-axis labels as columns A-C.
6. Complete labeling.

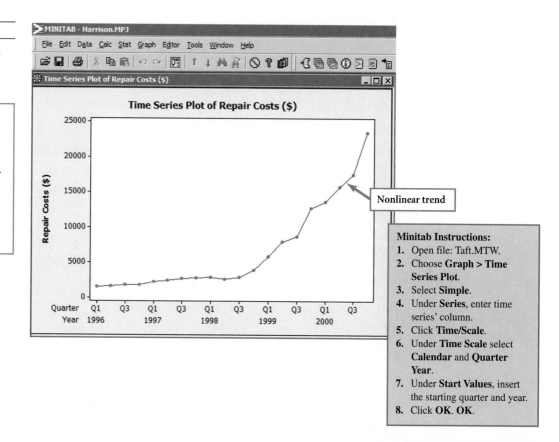

FIGURE 15-16

Excel Output for the Harrison Equipment Company Linear Trend Model

Excel Instructions:
1. Open file: Harrison.xls
2. Click on **Tools** tab.
3. Select **Regression**.
4. Define dependent variable.
5. Define the independent variable ($t - 1, 2, 3 \ldots 20$).
6. Check **Residuals**.
7. Copy graph onto sheet (see Figure 15-15).

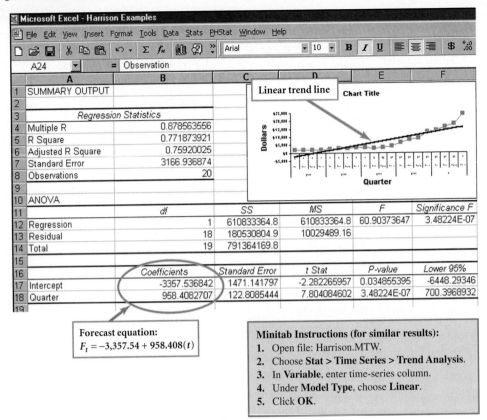

Forecast equation:
$F_t = -3{,}357.54 + 958.408(t)$

Minitab Instructions (for similar results):
1. Open file: Harrison.MTW.
2. Choose **Stat > Time Series > Trend Analysis**.
3. In **Variable**, enter time-series column.
4. Under **Model Type**, choose **Linear**.
5. Click **OK**.

Thus, we do conclude that the residuals are significantly autocorrelated. The model-building process needs to be repeated.

STEP 1: Model Specification—After examining Figure 15-16 and determining the results of the test for positive autocorrelation, a nonlinear trend will likely provide a better fit for these data. To account for the nonlinear growth trend, which starts out slowly and then builds rapidly, the forecaster might consider transforming the time variable by squaring t to form a model of the form:

$$y = \beta_0 + \beta_1 t^2 + \varepsilon$$

This transformation is suggested because the growth in costs appears to be increasing at an increasing rate. Other nonlinear trends may require different types of transformations, such as taking a square root or natural log. Each situation must be analyzed separately. (See the text by Neter et al., which is listed in the General References section, for further discussion of transformations. Also refer to the discussion on polynomial transformations in Chapter 14 of this text.)

STEP 2: Model Fitting—Figures 15-17a and 15-17b show the Excel and Minitab regression results, and Figure 15-18 shows the revised time-series plot using the t^2 transformation. The resulting nonlinear trend regression model is

$$F_t = -245.256 + 48.439 t^2$$

STEP 3: Model Diagnosis—Visually, the transformed model now looks more appropriate. The fit is much better as the R-squared value is increased to 0.921 and the standard error is reduced to 1,856.99. The null and alternative hypotheses for testing whether positive autocorrelation exists are

$$H_0: \rho = 0$$
$$H_A: \rho > 0$$

Using either PHStat or Minitab, we get a calculated Durbin-Watson test statistic equal to

$$d = 1.201$$

The d_L and d_U critical values from the Durbin-Watson table in Appendix O for $\alpha = 0.05$ and a sample size of $n = 20$ and $k = 1$ independent variable are 1.20 and 1.41, respectively.

Because $1.20 < d < 1.41$, the Durbin-Watson test is inconclusive.

FIGURE 15-17A

Excel Transformed Regression Model for Harrison Equipment

Excel Instructions:
1. Open Harrison.xls
2. Create a new column using Excel Formula to create t^2 values.
3. Select **Tools**.
4. Select **Data Analysis-Regression**.
5. Define dependent variable (repair costs).
6. Define independent variable (t-squared).
7. Check **Residuals**.
8. Click **OK**.

	A	B	C	D	E	F	G
1	SUMMARY OUTPUT						
2							
3		*Regression Statistics*					
4	Multiple R	0.959981211					
5	R Square	0.921563926					
6	Adjusted R Square	0.917206367					
7	Standard Error	1856.99127					
8	Observations	20					
9							
10	ANOVA						
11		*df*	*SS*	*MS*	*F*	*Significance F*	
12	Regression	1	729292671.4	729292671.4	211.4862445	2.16184E-11	
13	Residual	18	62071498.38	3448416.577			
14	Total	19	791364169.8				
15							
16		*Coefficients*	*Standard Error*	*t Stat*	*P-value*	*Lower 95%*	*Upper 95%*
17	Intercept	-245.255771	633.1527519	-0.387356401	0.70303438	-1575.461372	1084.94983
18	t -squared	48.43906461	3.330847009	14.54256664	2.16184E-11	41.4412093	55.43691992

Forecast equation:
$F_t = -245.256 + 48.439t^2$

Thus, there is no statistical evidence to say that positive autocorrelation exists, but at the same time, the evidence does not show that it does not exist either. Given this result and the improvements to R^2 and the standard error of the estimate, the nonlinear model is judged superior to the original linear model.

Forecasts for periods 21 and 22, using this latest model, are obtained using the trend projection method.

For period $t = 21$:

$$F_{21} = -245.256 + 48.439(21^2) = \$21,116.34$$

For period $t = 22$:

$$F_{22} = -245.256 + 48.439(22^2) = \$23,199.22$$

FIGURE 15-17B

Minitab Transformed Regression Model for Harrison Equipment

Minitab Instructions:
1. Open file. Harrison.MTW
2. Choose **Calc > Calculator**
3. In **Store result in variable**, enter destination column, Qtr^2
4. With cursor in **Expressions**, enter *Quarter* column then **2
5. Click **OK**
6. Choose **Stat > Regression > Regression**
7. In **Response**, enter *Repair Costs*. In **Predictors**, enter Qtr^2
8. Click **Storage**,
9. Under **Diagnostic Measures**, select **Residuals**. Under **Characteristics of Estimated Equation**, select **Fits**
10. Click **OK. OK.**

MINITAB - Harrison.MPJ - [Session]

File Edit Data Calc Stat Graph Editor Tools Window Help

Repair Costs ($) = - 245 + 48.4 Qtr2

```
Predictor    Coef    SE Coef      T      P
Constant    -245.3     633.2   -0.39  0.703
Qtr2        48.439     3.331   14.54  0.000


S = 1856.99    R-Sq = 92.2%    R-Sq(adj) = 91.7%


Analysis of Variance

Source           DF        SS          MS        F      P
Regression        1   729292671   729292671   211.49  0.000
Residual Error   18    62071498     3448417
Total            19   791364170
```

Forecast equation:
$F_t = -245 + 48.4t^2$

FIGURE 15-18

Transformed Model for Harrison Equipment Company

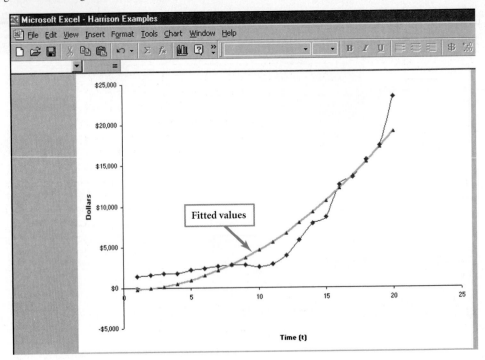

Using transformations often provides a very effective way of improving the fit of a time series. However, a forecaster should be careful not to get caught up in an exercise of "curve-fitting." One suggestion is that only explainable terms—terms that can be justified—be used for transforming data. For instance, in our example, we might well expect repair costs to increase at a faster rate as a tractor gets older and begins wearing out. Thus, the t^2 transformation seems to make sense.

Some Words of Caution

The trend projection method relies on the future behaving in a manner similar to the past. In the previous example, if equipment repair costs continue to follow the pattern displayed over the past 20 quarters, these forecasts may prove acceptable. However, if the future pattern changes, there is no reason to believe these forecasts will be close to actual costs.

ADJUSTING FOR SEASONALITY

In Section 15-1, we discussed seasonality in a time series. The seasonal component represents those changes (highs and lows) in the time series that occur at approximately the same time every year. If the forecasting model that you are using does not already explicitly account for seasonality, you should adjust your forecast to take into account the seasonal component. The linear and nonlinear trend models discussed thus far do not automatically incorporate the seasonal component. Forecasts using these models should be adjusted as illustrated in the following example.

Excel and Minitab Tutorial

Big Mountain Ski Resort—Most businesses in the tourist industry know that sales are seasonal. For example, at the Big Mountain Ski Resort, business peaks at two times during the year: winter for skiing and summer for golf and tennis. These peaks can be identified in a time series if the sales data are measured on at least a quarterly basis. Figure 15-19 shows the quarterly sales data for the past four years in spreadsheet form. The line chart for these data is also shown. The data are in the CD-ROM file *Big Mountain*. The time-series plot clearly shows that the summer and winter quarters are the busy times. There has also been a slightly increasing linear trend in sales over the four years.

Big Mountain Resort wants to forecast sales for each quarter of the coming year, and it hopes to use a linear trend model. When the historical data show a trend and seasonality, the trend-based forecasting model needs to be adjusted to incorporate the seasonality. This can be done by computing **seasonal indexes**.

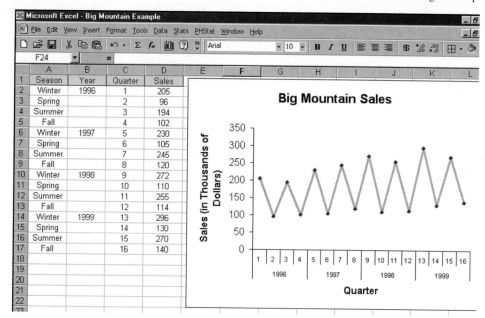

FIGURE 15-19

Big Mountain Resort Quarterly Sales Data

Excel Instructions:
1. Open file: Big Mountain.xls
2. Select Sales column.
3. Click on **Chart Wizard**.
4. Select **Line Chart**.
5. Select **Series** tab.
6. Define X axis as columns B and C.

Seasonal Index

A number used to quantify the effect of seasonality in time-series data.

For instance, when we have quarterly data, we can develop four seasonal indexes, one each for winter, spring, summer and fall. A seasonal index below 1.00 indicates that the quarter has values that are typically below the average value for the year. On the other hand, an index greater than 1.00 indicates that the quarter's value is higher than average.

Computing Seasonal Indexes

Although there are several methods for computing the seasonal indexes, the procedure introduced here is the *ratio-to-moving-average method*. This method assumes that the actual time-series data can be represented as a product of the four time-series components—trend, seasonal, cyclical, and random—which produces the multiplicative model shown in Equation 15-13.

Multiplicative Time-Series Model

$$y_t = T_t \times S_t \times C_t \times I_t$$

15-13

where:

y_t = Value of the time series at time t
T_t = Trend value at time t
S_t = Seasonal value at time t
C_t = Cyclical value at time t
I_t = Irregular or random value at time t

The ratio-to-moving-average method begins by removing the seasonal and irregular components, S_t and I_t, from the data, leaving the combined trend and cyclical components, T_t and C_t. This is done by first computing successive four-period moving averages for the time series. A moving average is the average of n consecutive values of a time series. Using the Big Mountain sales data in Figure 15-19, we find that the **moving average** using the first four quarters is

$$\frac{205 + 96 + 194 + 102}{4} = 149.25$$

Moving Averages

The successive averages of n consecutive values in a time series.

This moving average is associated with the middle time period of the data values in the moving average. The middle period of the first four quarters is 2.5 (between quarter 2 and quarter 3).

The second moving average is found by dropping the value from period 1 and adding the value from period 5, as follows.

$$\frac{96 + 194 + 102 + 230}{4} = 155.50$$

This moving average is associated with time period 3.5, the middle period between quarters 3 and 4.

Figure 15-20 shows the moving averages for the Big Mountain sales data in Excel spreadsheet form.[2] We selected four data values for the moving average because we have quarterly data; with monthly data, 12 data values would have been used.

The next step is to compute the *centered moving averages* by averaging each successive pair of moving averages. Centering the moving averages is necessary so that the resulting moving average will be associated with one of the data set's original time periods. In this example, Big Mountain is interested in quarterly sales data—that is, time periods 1, 2, 3, etc. Therefore, the moving averages we have representing time periods 2.5, 3.5, and so forth are not of interest to Big Mountain. Centering these latter time series, however, produces moving averages for the (quarterly) time periods of interest. For example, the first two moving averages are averaged to produce the first centered moving average. We get

$$\frac{149.25 + 155.5}{2} = 152.38$$

This centered moving average is associated with quarter 3. The centered moving averages are shown in Figure 15-21.[3] These values estimate the $T_t \times C_t$ value.

If the number of data values used for a moving average is odd, the moving average will be associated with the time period of the middle observation. In such cases, we would not have to center the moving average, as we did in Figure 15-21, because the moving averages would already be associated with one of the original time periods from the original time series.

Next, we estimate the $S_t \times I_t$ value. Dividing the actual sales value for each quarter by the corresponding centered moving average, as in Equation 15-14, does this. As an example, we examine the third time period: summer of the first year. The sales value of 194 is divided by the centered moving average of 152.38, to produce 1.273.

This value is called the *ratio-to-moving-average*. Figure 15-22 shows these values for the Big Mountain data.

FIGURE 15-20

Seasonal Index—Step 1:
Moving Average Values for
Big Mountain Resort

Excel Instructions:
1. Open file: Big Mountain
2. Compute the moving average using the AVERAGE function.

	A	B	C	D	E
	Season	Year	Quarter	Sales	4 Period Moving Average
2	Winter	1996	1	205	
3	Spring		2	96	149.25
4	Summer		3	194	155.5
5	Fall		4	102	157.75
6	Winter	1997	5	230	170.5
7	Spring		6	105	175
8	Summer		7	245	185.5
9	Fall		8	120	186.75
10	Winter	1998	9	272	189.25
11	Spring		10	110	187.75
12	Summer		11	255	193.75
13	Fall				
14	Winter	1			
15	Spring				
16	Summer				
17	Fall				

Each moving average corresponds to the midpoint between its cell and the following cell.

E3 = =AVERAGE(D2:D5)

[2]The Excel process illustrated by Figures 15-20 through 15-24 is also accomplished using Minitab's **Time Series > Decomposition** command, which is illustrated in Figure 15-26.

[3]Excel's tabular format does not allow the uncentered moving averages to be displayed with their "inter-quarter" time periods. That is, 149.25 is associated with time period 2.5, 155.50 with time period 3.5, and so forth.

FIGURE 15-21

Seasonal Index—Step 2:
Big Mountain Resort
Centered Moving Averages

Excel Instructions:
1. Open file: Big Mountain
2. Compute the centered
   moving average using
   the **AVERAGE** function.

	Season	Year	Quarter	Sales	4 Period Moving Average	Centered Moving Average
2	Winter	1996	1	205		
3	Spring		2	96	149.25	
4	Summer		3	194	155.5	152.38
5	Fall		4	102	157.75	156.63
6	Winter	1997	5	230	170.5	164.13
7	Spring		6	105	175	172.75
8	Summer		7	245	185.5	180.25
9	Fall		8	120	186.75	186.13
10	Winter	1998	9	272	189.25	188.00
11	Spring		10	110	187.75	188.50
12	Summer		11	255	193.75	190.75
13	Fall		12	114	198.75	196.25
14	Winter	1999	13	296	202.5	200.63
15	Spring		14	130	209	205.75
16	Summer		15	270		
17	Fall		16	140		

F4 = =AVERAGE(E3:E4)

Ratio-to-Moving-Average

$$S_t \times I_t = \frac{y_t}{T_t \times C_t}$$

15-14

The final step in determining the seasonal indexes is to compute the mean ratio-to-moving-average value for each season. Each quarter's ratio-to-moving-average is averaged over the years to produce the *seasonal index* for that quarter. Figure 15-23 shows the seasonal indexes. The seasonal index for the winter quarter is 1.441. This indicates that sales for Big Mountain during the winter are 44.1% above the average for the year. Also, sales in the spring quarter are only 60.8% of the average for the year.

One important point about the seasonal indexes is that the sum of the indexes is equal to the number of seasonal indexes. That is, the average seasonal index equals 1.0. In the Big Mountain Resort example, we find:

Summer		Fall		Winter		Spring		
1.323	+	0.626	+	1.441	+	0.608	=	3.998 (difference from 4 due to rounding)

Likewise, in an example with monthly data instead of quarterly data, we would generate 12 seasonal indexes, one for each month. The sum of these indexes would be 12.

FIGURE 15-22

Seasonal Index—Step 3:
Big Mountain Resort:
Ratio-to-Moving Averages

Excel Instructions:
1. Using Excel formula to
   compute ratio.

	Season	Year	Quarter	Sales	4 Period Moving Average	Centered Moving Average	Ratio to MA
2	Winter	1996	1	205			
3	Spring		2	96	149.25		
4	Summer		3	194	155.5	152.375	1.273
5	Fall		4	102	157.75	156.625	0.651
6	Winter	1997	5	230	170.5	164.125	1.401
7	Spring		6	105	175	172.75	0.608
8	Summer		7	245	185.5	180.25	1.359
9	Fall		8	120	186.75	186.125	0.645
10	Winter	1998	9	272	189.25	188	1.447
11	Spring		10	110	187.75	188.5	0.584
12	Summer		11	255	193.75	190.75	1.337
13	Fall		12	114	198.75	196.25	0.581
14	Winter	1999	13	296	202.5	200.625	1.475
15	Spring		14	130	209	205.75	0.632
16	Summer		15	270			
17	Fall		16	140			

G4 = =+D4/F4

FIGURE 15-23

**Seasonal Index—Step 4:
Big Mountain Resort:
Mean Ratios**

Excel Instructions:
1. Use PHStat Unstack
   Option under Data
   Preparation.
2. Compute Total and
   Average using Excel
   Formulas.

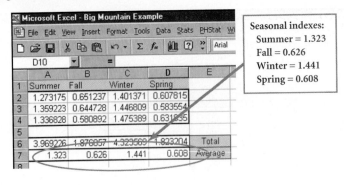

The Need to Normalize the Indexes

If the sum of the seasonal indexes does not equal the number of time periods in the recurrence period of the time series, an adjustment is necessary. In the Big Mountain Resort example, the sum of the four seasonal indexes may have been something other than 4 (the recurrence period). In such cases, we must adjust the seasonal indexes by multiplying each by the number of time periods in the recurrence period over the sum of the unadjusted seasonal indexes. For quarterly data such as the Big Mountain Resort example, we would multiply each seasonal index by 4/(sum of the unadjusted seasonal indexes). Performing this multiplication will *normalize* the seasonal indexes. This adjustment is necessary if the seasonal adjustments are going to even out over the recurrence period.

Deseasonalizing

A strong seasonal component may partially mask a trend in the time-series data. Consequently, to identify the trend you should first remove the effect of the seasonal component. This is called *deseasonalizing* the time series.

Again, assume that the multiplicative model shown previously in Equation 15-13 is appropriate:

$$y_t = T_t \times S_t \times C_t \times I_t$$

Deseasonalizing is accomplished by dividing y_t by the appropriate seasonal index, S_t, as shown in Equation 15-15.

Deseasonalization	
$$T_t \times C_t \times I_t = \frac{y_t}{S_t}$$	15-15

For time period 1, which is the winter quarter, the seasonal index is 1.441. The deseasonalized value for y_1 is

$$205/1.441 = 142.26$$

Figure 15-24 presents the deseasonalized values and the graph of these deseasonalized sales data for the Big Mountain example. This shows that there has been a gentle upward trend over the four years. Once the data have been deseasonalized, the next step is to determine the trend. As in the previous examples of trend estimation, you can use either Excel or Minitab to develop the linear model for the deseasonalized data. The results are shown in Figure 15-25. The linear regression trend-line equation is

$$F_t = 142.096 + 4.683(t)$$

You can use this trend line and the trend-projection method to forecast sales for period $t = 17$:

$$F_{17} = 142.096 + 4.683(17) = 221.707 = \$221,707$$

FIGURE 15-24

Deseasonalized Time Series for Big Mountain Sales Data

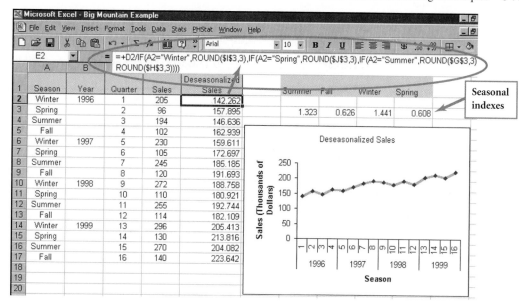

Excel Instructions:
1. Using Excel formula to compute Deseasonalized Sales.
2. Select **Chart Wizard** line chart option.
3. Specify X axis label as columns B and C.

This is a **seasonally unadjusted forecast**, because the time-series data used in developing the trend line were deseasonalized.

Seasonally Unadjusted Forecast

A forecast made for seasonal data that does not include an adjustment for the seasonal component in the time series.

Now we need to adjust the forecast for period 17 to reflect the quarterly fluctuations. We do this by multiplying the unadjusted forecast values by the appropriate seasonal index. In this case, period 17 corresponds to the winter quarter. The winter quarter has a seasonal index of 1.441, indicating a high sales period. The adjusted forecast is

$$F_{17} = (221.707)(1.441) = 319.48, \text{ or } \$319,480$$

FIGURE 15-25

Regression Trend Line of Big Mountain Deseasonalized Data

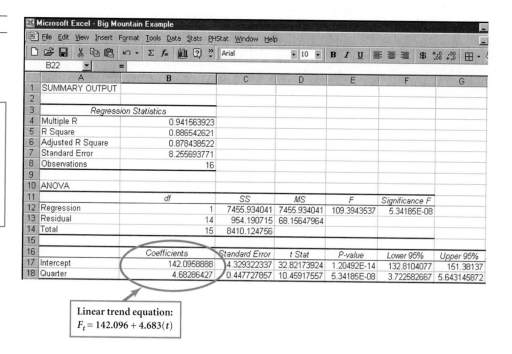

Excel Instructions:
1. Select **Tools**.
2. Click on **Regression**.
3. Define Y variable as Deseasonalized data.
4. Define X variable as quarter number ($t = 1, 2, 3 \ldots 16$).

Linear trend equation:
$F_t = 142.096 + 4.683(t)$

The seasonally adjusted forecasts for each quarter in year 5 are

QUARTER (YEAR 5)	t	UNADJUSTED FORECAST	INDEX	ADJUSTED FORECAST
Winter	17	221.707	1.441	319.480 = $319,480
Spring	18	226.390	0.608	137.645 = $137,645
Summer	19	231.073	1.323	305.710 = $305,710
Fall	20	235.756	0.626	147.583 = $147,583

$\mathcal{S}$UMMARY: THE SEASONAL ADJUSTMENT PROCESS

We can summarize the steps for performing a seasonal adjustment to a trend-based forecast as follows:

1. Compute each moving average from the k appropriate consecutive data values, where k is the number of values in one period of the time series.

2. Compute the centered moving averages.

3. Isolate the seasonal component by computing the ratio-to-moving-average values.

4. Compute the seasonal indexes by averaging the ratio-to-moving-averages for comparable periods.

5. Normalize the seasonal indexes (if necessary).

6. Deseasonalize the time series by dividing the actual data by the appropriate seasonal index.

7. Use least squares regression to develop the trend line using the deseasonalized data.

8. Develop the unadjusted forecasts using trend projection.

9. Seasonally adjust the forecasts by multiplying the unadjusted forecasts by the appropriate seasonal index.

You can use the seasonally adjusted trend model when a time series exhibits both a trend and seasonality. This process allows for a better identification of the trend and produces forecasts that are more sensitive to seasonality in the data.

Minitab contains a procedure for generating seasonal indexes and seasonally adjusted forecasts. Figure 15-26 shows the Minitab results for the Big Mountain Ski Resort example. Notice that the forecast option in Minitab gives different forecasts than we showed earlier. This is because

FIGURE 15-26

Minitab Output Showing Big Mountain Seasonal Indexes

Minitab Instructions:
1. Open file: Big Mountain.mtw
2. Select Stat > Time Series > Decomposition
3. In Variable, enter time series column
4. In Seasonal length, enter number of time periods in season
5. Under Model Type, choose Multiplicative
6. Under Model Components, choose Trend plus seasonal
7. Select Generate forecasts, for Number of forecasts insert 4; for Starting with origin insert the last time series' time period: *16*
8. Click OK.

Minitab generates the linear trend model using original sales data rather than deseasonalized data. Our suggestion is to use Minitab to generate the seasonal indexes, but then follow our outline to generate seasonally adjusted forecasts.[4]

OPTIONAL CD-ROM TOPIC REGRESSION-BASED FORECASTING MODELS

Regression models of various forms can be used to develop both short- and long-term forecasts. For more about this, go to the CD-ROM.

15-2: EXERCISES

Skill Development

Exercises 15.16 to 15.20 refer to Tran's Furniture Store, which has maintained monthly sales records for the past 48 months, with the following results.

Month	Sales	Month	Sales
1 (Jan.)	$23,500	25 (Jan.)	31,000
2	21,700	26	30,400
3	18,750	27	29,800
4	22,000	28	32,500
5	23,000	29	34,500
6	26,200	30	33,800
7	27,300	31	34,200
8	29,300	32	36,700
9	31,200	33	39,700
10	34,200	34	42,400
11	39,500	35	43,600
12	43,400	36	47,400
13 (Jan.)	23,500	37 (Jan.)	32,400
14	23,400	38	35,600
15	21,400	39	31,200
16	24,200	40	34,600
17	26,900	41	36,800
18	29,700	42	35,700
19	31,100	43	37,500
20	32,400	44	40,000
21	34,500	45	43,200
22	35,700	46	46,700
23	42,000	47	50,100
24	42,600	48	52,100

15.16 Do you see any evidence of autocorrelation in this data?

15.17 Using the multiplicative model, estimate the $T \times C$ portion by computing a 12-month moving average and then the centered 12-month moving average.

15.18 Estimate the $S \times I$ portion of the multiplicative model by finding the ratios-to-moving-averages for the time-series data. Determine whether these ratios-to-moving-averages are stable from year to year.

15.19 Extract the irregular component by taking the normalized average of the ratios-to-moving-averages. Make a table that shows the normalized seasonal indexes. Interpret what the index for January means relative to the index for July.

15.20 Based on your work in the previous three exercises,
a. Determine a seasonally adjusted linear-trend forecasting model. Compare this model with an unadjusted linear-trend model. Use both models to forecast Tran's sales for period 49.
b. Which of the two models developed has the lower *MAD* and lower *MSE*?

15.21 Lobo Theater Company operates a chain of movie theaters in the Midwest. The company recently purchased a theater in Rapid City, South Dakota. The new manager obtained ticket-sales records for the previous 36 months. She hoped to analyze these data and use them in her planning for the next 12 months. The data are as follows:

Month	Tickets Sold	Month	Tickets Sold	Month	Tickets Sold	Month	Tickets Sold
1 (Jan.)	1,580	10	980	19	1,580	28	1,750
2	1,608	11	1,260	20	1,680	29	1,690
3	1,370	12	1,680	21	1,560	30	1,730
4	1,260	13 (Jan.)	1,630	22	1,520	31	1,690
5	1,125	14	1,700	23	1,670	32	1,780
6	1,306	15	1,610	24	1,920	33	1,670
7	1,240	16	1,590	25 (Jan.)	1,960	34	1,560
8	1,340	17	1,498	26	1,880	35	1,760
9	1,090	18	1,540	27	1,820	36	2,040

Plot these data as a time series. In a short report, describe what ticket sales have been like for this theater in the past three years. Do you see any evidence of auto-correlation in these data?

15.22 Referring to Exercise 15.21, develop seasonal indexes for ticket sales at Rapid City theater, based on the 36 months of data.

[4]Neither Excel nor PHStat offers a procedure for automatically generating seasonal indexes. However, as shown in the Big Mountain example, you can use the spreadsheet formulas to do this. See the Excel Tutorial on your CD-ROM.

15.23 Referring to the Lobo Theater data (Exercises 15.21 and 15.22), develop two linear-trend forecasting models: one seasonally unadjusted and the other seasonally adjusted. Analyze each model and indicate which one you think is more accurate.

15.24 How does model specification differ from model fitting?

15.25 Consider the following set of sales data given in millions of dollars.

1997		1999	
1st quarter	152	1st quarter	217
2nd quarter	162	2nd quarter	209
3rd quarter	157	3rd quarter	202
4th quarter	167	4th quarter	221

1998		2000	
1st quarter	182	1st quarter	236
2nd quarter	192	2nd quarter	242
3rd quarter	191	3rd quarter	231
4th quarter	197	4th quarter	224

a. Plot these data. Based on your visual observations, what time-series components are present in the data?
b. Determine the seasonal index for each quarter.
c. Fit a linear trend model to the deseasonalized data for 1997 through 2000 and determine the *MAD* and *MSE* values. Comment on the adequacy of the linear trend model based on these measures of forecast error.
d. Provide a seasonally unadjusted forecast using the linear trend model for each quarter of 2001.
e. Use the seasonal index values computed in part b to provide seasonal adjusted forecasts for each quarter of 2001.

15.26 Consider the following set of inventory data given in hundreds of thousands of dollars.

1997		1999	
1st quarter	109	1st quarter	118
2nd quarter	95	2nd quarter	103
3rd quarter	115	3rd quarter	126
4th quarter	108	4th quarter	120

1998		2000	
1st quarter	115	1st quarter	130
2nd quarter	110	2nd quarter	127
3rd quarter	120	3rd quarter	138
4th quarter	116	4th quarter	135

a. Plot these data. Based on your visual observations, what time-series components are present in the data?
b. Determine the seasonal index for each quarter, and convert the data to deseasonalized data.

c. Fit a linear trend model to the deseasonalized data for 1997 through 1999, and determine the *MAD* and *MSE* values for 2000. Comment on the adequacy of the linear trend model based on these measures of forecast error.
d. Provide a seasonally unadjusted forecast using the linear trend model for each quarter of 2001.
e. Use the seasonal index values computed in part b to provide seasonal adjusted forecasts for each quarter of 2001. Compare the results of the forecasts made in parts c and d.

Business Applications

15.27 Manuel Gutierrez correctly predicted the increasing need for home health care services due to the country's aging population. Five years ago, he started a company offering meal delivery, physical therapy, and minor housekeeping services in the New Orleans area. Since that time, he has opened offices in seven additional Gulf State cities. Manuel is currently analyzing the revenue data from his first location for the first five years of operation.

	Revenue ($10,000s)				
	1997	*1998*	*1999*	*2000*	*2001*
January	23	67	72	76	81
February	34	63	64	75	72
March	45	65	64	77	71
April	48	71	77	81	83
May	46	75	79	86	85
June	49	70	72	75	77
July	60	72	71	80	79
August	65	75	77	82	84
September	67	80	79	86	91
October	60	78	78	87	86
November	71	89	87	91	94
December	76	94	92	96	99

a. Plot these data. Based on your visual observations, what time-series components are present in the data?
b. Determine the seasonal index for each month
c. (1) Fit a linear trend model to the deseasonalized data for 1997 through 2000 and determine the *MAD* and *MSE* forecasts for each of the months in 2001. (2) Conduct a test of hypothesis to determine if the linear trend model fits the existing data. (3) Comment on the adequacy of the linear trend model based on the measures of forecast error and the hypothesis test you conducted.
d. Manuel had hoped to reach $2,000,000 in revenues by the time he had been in business for 10 years. Based on the results in part c, is this a feasible goal based on the historical data provided? Consider and comment on the size of the standard error for this prediction. What makes this value so large? How does it affect your conclusion?

e. Use the seasonal index values computed in part b to provide seasonal adjusted forecasts for each month of 2002.

15.28 The Grogan Company operates an egg farm in Wisconsin. The following data represents the number of cases of eggs (times 100,000) the company has sold in each month from 1999 through 2001. The company is considering expanding facilities and needs to provide the lending institution with a monthly sales forecast for 2002.

	1999	2000	2001
January	5.4	5.8	7.0
February	10.4	12.8	14.6
March	18.6	20.1	22.6
April	4.8	8.2	7.6
May	12.2	15.6	16.2
June	14.6	14.8	15.9
July	13.0	11.0	13.0
August	19.4	19.2	17.8
September	26.8	27.0	28.6
October	21.2	21.4	23.0
November	10.2	9.9	13.1
December	6.7	5.6	7.9

a. Plot these data. Based on your visual observations, what time-series components are present in the data?

b. Determine the seasonal index for each month.

c. Fit a linear trend model to the deseasonalized data for 1999 through 2001 and determine the MAD and MSE values. Comment on the adequacy of the linear trend model based on these measures of forecast error.

d. Provide a seasonally unadjusted forecast using the linear trend model for each month of 2002.

e. Use the seasonal index values computed in part b to provide seasonal adjusted forecasts for each month of 2002.

15.29 A major brokerage company has an office in Miami, Florida. The manager of the office is evaluated based on the number of new clients generated each quarter. The following data reflect the number of new customers added during each quarter between 1998 and 2001.

1998		1999	
1st quarter	218	1st quarter	250
2nd quarter	190	2nd quarter	220
3rd quarter	236	3rd quarter	265
4th quarter	218	4th quarter	241

2000		2001	
1st quarter	244	1st quarter	229
2nd quarter	228	2nd quarter	221
3rd quarter	263	3rd quarter	248
4th quarter	240	4th quarter	231

a. Plot the time series and discuss components that are present in the data.

b. Referring to part a, fit the linear trend model to the data for 1998 through 2000. Then use the resulting model to forecast the number of new brokerage customers for each quarter in 2001. Compute the MAD and MSE for these forecasts and discuss the results.

c. Using the data for 1998 through 2000, determine the seasonal indexes for each quarter.

d. Develop a seasonally unadjusted forecast for the four quarters of 2001.

e. Using the seasonal indexes computed in part d, determine the seasonally adjusted forecast for each quarter of 2001. Compute the MAD and MSE for these forecasts.

f. Examine the values for the MAD and MSE in parts b and e. Which of the two forecasting techniques would you recommend the manager use to forecast the number of new clients generated each quarter? Support your choice by giving your rationale.

Advanced Applications

15.30 ⊙ Harsin-Williams & Company is a construction company headquartered in Baton Rouge, Louisiana. A very important issue for construction companies is cash management, because they tend to be paid in lump sums when projects are completed or hit milestones. However, their expenses, such as payroll, must be paid regularly. The CD-ROM file *Harsin-Williams* contains month-end cash balances for the past 16 months.

a. Plot the data as a time-series graph. Discuss what the graph implies concerning the relationship between cash balance and the time variable, month.

b. Fit a linear trend model to the data. Compute the coefficient of determination for this model and show the trend line on the time-series graph. Discuss the appropriateness of the linear trend model. What are the strengths and weaknesses of the model?

c. Referring to part b, compute the MAD and MSE for the 16 data points.

d. Use the t^2 transformation approach and recompute the linear model using the transformed time variable. Plot the new trend line against the transformed data. Discuss whether this model appears to provide a better fit than the model without the transformation. Compare the coefficients of determination for the two models. Which model seems to be superior, using the coefficient of determination as the criterion?

e. Refer to part d. Compute the MAD and MSE for the 16 data values. Discuss how these compare to those that were computed in part c, prior to transformation. Do the measures of fit (R^2, MSE, and MAD) agree on the best model to use for forecasting purposes?

15.31 ⊙ Refer to Exercise 15.30.

a. Use the linear trend model (without transformation) for the first 15 months and provide a cash balance forecast for month 16. Then make the t^2 transformation and develop a new linear-trend forecasting model based on months 1 through 15. Forecast the cash balance for month 16. Now compare the accuracy of the forecasts with and without the transformation. Which of the two forecast models would you prefer? Explain your answer.

b. Provide a 95% prediction interval for the cash-balance forecast for month 16 using the linear trend model both with and without the transformation. Which interval has the widest width? On this basis, which procedure would you choose?

15.32 Volker Sales and Service sells and installs home security systems in the Detroit area. In order to plan for parts inventory, the company needs an accurate forecast of the number of installations it will do each month. The company's sales manager has collected data for the past 12 months. These data are in a CD-ROM file called *Volker*.

a. Plot the data as a time-series graph. Discuss what the graph implies.

b. Fit a linear trend model to the data. Compute the *R*-squared value and show the trend line on the time-series graph.

c. Transform the time variable by taking the square root of the month number, and recompute the linear model using the transformed time variable. Discuss whether this model appears to provide a better fit than the model without the transformation. Compare *R*-squared values.

d. Compute the *MAD* and *MSE* for the 12 data values for the two models in parts b and c. Discuss which model is the best model to use for forecasting purposes. What are the strengths and weaknesses of the two models?

e. Provide forecasts for the number of installations of home security systems for the next four months.

f. The personnel director has been told that when 200 installations a month is reached, additional service personnel will be required. Provide an estimate of which month this will occur.

g. Use the linear trend model (without transformation) for the first 11 months and provide a forecast of the number of installations for month 12. Then make the $\sqrt{t}$ transformation and develop a new linear-trend forecasting model based on months 1 through 11. Forecast the cash balance for month 12. Now compare the accuracy of the forecasts with and without the transformation. Discuss.

15-3 FORECASTING USING SMOOTHING METHODS

The trend-based forecasting technique introduced in the previous section is widely used and can be very effective in some situations. However, it has a disadvantage in that it gives as much weight to the earliest data in the time series as it does to the data that are close to the period for which the forecast is required. Also, this trend approach does not provide an opportunity for the model to "learn" or "adjust" to changes in the time series.

A class of forecasting techniques called *smoothing models* is widely used to overcome these problems and to provide forecasts in situations in which there is no pronounced trend in the data. These models attempt to "smooth out" the random or irregular component in the time series by an averaging process. In this section we introduce two frequently used smoothing-based forecasting techniques: single exponential smoothing and double exponential smoothing. Double exponential smoothing offers a modification to the single exponential smoothing model that specifically deals with trends.

EXPONENTIAL SMOOTHING

The trend-based forecasting methods discussed in Section 15-2 are used in many forecasting situations. As we showed, the least squares trend line is computed using all available historical data. Each observation is given equal input in establishing the trend line, thus allowing the trend line to reflect all the past data. If the future pattern looks like the past, the forecast should be reasonably accurate.

However, in many situations involving time-series data, the more recent the observation, the more indicative it is of possible future values. For example, this month's sales are probably a better indicator of next month's sales than would be sales from 20 months ago. However, the regression analysis approach to trend-based forecasting does not take this fact into account. The data from 20 periods ago will be given the same weight as data from the most current period in developing a forecasting model. This equal valuation can be a drawback to the trend-based forecasting approach.

With **exponential smoothing**, current observations can be weighted more heavily than older observations in determining the forecast.

Exponential Smoothing

A time-series and forecasting technique that produces an exponentially weighted moving average in which each smoothing calculation or forecast is dependent on all previous observed values.

Therefore, if in recent periods the time-series values are much higher (or lower) than those in earlier periods, the forecast can be made to reflect this difference. The extent to which the forecast reflects the current data depends on the weights assigned by the decision maker.

We will introduce two classes of exponential smoothing models: single exponential smoothing and double exponential smoothing. Double smoothing is used when a time series exhibits a linear trend. Single smoothing is used when no linear trend is present in the time series. Both single and double exponential smoothing are appropriate for short-term forecasting of one or two periods into the future and for time series that are not seasonal.

Single Exponential Smoothing

Just as its name implies, single exponential smoothing uses one smoothing constant. Equations 15-16 and 15-17 represent two equivalent methods for forecasting using single exponential smoothing.

Exponential Smoothing Model

$$F_{t+1} = F_t + \alpha(y_t - F_t) \qquad \textbf{15-16}$$

or:

$$F_{t+1} = \alpha y_t + (1 - \alpha)F_t \qquad \textbf{15-17}$$

where:

$$F_{t+1} = \text{Forecast value for period } t + 1$$
$$y_t = \text{Actual value for period } t$$
$$F_t = \text{Forecast value for period } t$$
$$\alpha = \text{Alpha (smoothing constant } 0 \leq \alpha \leq 1)$$

The logic of the exponential smoothing model is that the forecast made for the next period will equal the forecast made for the current period, plus or minus some adjustment factor. The adjustment factor is determined by how far this period's forecast is from the actual value $(y_t - F_t)$, times the smoothing constant, α. The idea is that if we forecast low, we will adjust next period's forecast upward, but not by the entire amount of the error.

EXAMPLE 15-6: DEVELOPING A SINGLE EXPONENTIAL SMOOTHING MODEL

Excel and Minitab Tutorial

Humbolt Electronics Company Consider the past 10 weeks of sales figures for printed circuits at the Humbolt Electronics Company in Austin, Texas. These data and their line graph are shown in Figure 15-27. The data are in the CD-ROM file *Humbolt*. Suppose the current time period is the end of week 10 and we wish to forecast sales for week 11 using a single exponential smoothing model. The following steps can be used.

Step 1: **Specify the model.**
Because the data do not exhibit a pronounced trend and because we are interested in a short-term forecast (one period ahead), the single exponential smoothing model with a single smoothing constant can be used.

Step 2: **Fit the model.**
We start by selecting a value for α, the smoothing constant, between 0.0 and 1.0. The closer α is to 0.0, the less influence the current observations have in determining the forecast. Small α values will result in greater smoothing of the time series. Likewise, when α is near 1.0, the current observations have greater impact in determining the forecast and less smoothing will occur. There is no firm rule for selecting the value for the smoothing constant. However, in general, if the time series is quite stable, a small α should be used to lessen the impact of random or irregular fluctuations. Because the time series shown in Figure 15-27 appears to be relatively stable, we will use $\alpha = 0.20$ in this example.

FIGURE 15-27

Printed-Circuit Sales Data and Line Graph for Humbolt Electronics

Excel Instructions:
1. Open file: Humbolt.xls
2. Select Chart Wizard Line Chart.
3. Define variables and *x*-axis variable.

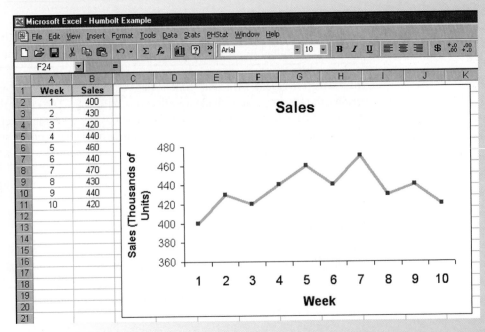

The forecast value for period $t = 11$ is found using Equation 15-17, as follows.

$$F_{11} = 0.20y_{10} + (1 - 0.20)F_{10}$$

This demonstrates that the forecast for period 11 is a weighted average of the actual sales in period 10 and the forecast for period 10. Although we know the sales for period 10, we don't know the forecast for period 10. However, we can determine it by

$$F_{10} = 0.20y_9 + (1 - 0.20)F_9$$

Again, this forecast is a weighted average of the actual sales in period 9 and the forecast sales for period 9. We would continue in this manner until we get to

$$F_2 = 0.20y_1 + (1 - 0.20)F_1$$

This requires a forecast for period 1. Because we have no sales data before period 1 from which to develop a forecast, a rule often used is to assume that $F_1 = y_1$.[5]

Forecast for period 1 = actual value in period 1

This assumption is used to set the starting forecast value for period 1. Because setting the starting value is somewhat arbitrary, you should obtain as much historical data as possible to "warm" the model and dampen out the effect of the starting value. In our example, we have 10 periods of data to warm the model before the forecast for period 11 is made. Note that when using an exponential smoothing model, the effect of the initial forecast is reduced by $(1 - \alpha)$ in the forecast for period 2, then reduced again for period 3, and so on. After sufficient periods, any error due to the arbitrary initial forecast should be very small.

Figure 15-28. shows the results of using the single exponential smoothing equation and Excel or Minitab for weeks 1 through 10. For week 1, $F_1 = y_1 = 400$. Then, for week 2, we get

$$F_2 = 0.20y_1 + (1 - 0.20)F_1$$
$$F_2 = (0.20)400 + (1 - 0.20)400 = 400$$

For week 3,

$$F_3 = 0.20y_2 + (1 - 0.20)F_2$$
$$F_3 = (0.20)430 + (1 - 0.20)400 = 406$$

At the end of week 2, after seeing what actually happened to sales in week 2, our forecasts for week 3 is 406 units. This is a 6-unit increase over the forecast for week 2 of

---

[5]Another approach for establishing the starting value, F_1, is to use the mean value for some portion of the available data. Regardless of the method used, the quantity of available data should be large enough to dampen out the impact of the starting value.

FIGURE 15-28

Humbolt Electronics Single
Exponential Smoothing—
Excel Spreadsheet

Excel Instructions
1. Open file: Humbolt.xls
2. Use Excel formulas to
   generate F_t and F_{t+1}
   using equations 16-11

	Microsoft Excel - Humbolt Example

File Edit View Insert Format Tools Data Stats PHStat

D12 = =+B14*B12+(1-B14)*C12

	A	B	C	D
1	Week	Sales	Forecast for Period t	Forecast for Next Period
2	t	y	F_t	F_{t+1}
3	1	400	400.00	400.00
4	2	430	400.00	406.00
5	3	420	406.00	408.80
6	4	440	408.80	415.04
7	5	460	415.04	424.03
8	6	440	424.03	427.23
9	7	470	427.23	435.78
10	8	430	435.78	434.62
11	9	440	434.62	435.70
12	10	420	435.70	432.56
13				
14	Alpha =	0.2		

Forecast for
period 11 = 432.56

400 units. The actual amount of sales in week 2 was 430, rather than 400. The amount of sales for week 2 was 30 units higher than the forecast for that time period. Because the actual amount of sales was larger than the forecast, an adjustment must be made. The 6-unit adjustment is calculated by multiplying the smoothing constant by this forecast error [0.20(30) = 6], as specified in Equation 15-16. The adjustment compensates for the forecast error in week 2.

Continuing for week 4,

$$F_4 = 0.20y_3 + (1 - 0.20)F_3$$
$$F_4 = (0.20)420 + (1 - 0.20)406 = 408.80$$

Recall that our forecast for week 3 was 406. However, actual sales were higher than forecast at 420 units, and we underforecast by 14 units. The adjustment for week 4 is then 0.20(14) = 2.80, and the forecast for week 4 is 406 + 2.80 = 408.80.

This process continues through the data until we are ready to forecast week 11, as shown in Figure 15-28.

$$F_{11} = 0.20y_{10} + (1 - 0.20)F_{10}$$
$$F_{11} = (0.20)420 + (1 - 0.20)435.70 = 432.56$$

Humbolt managers would forecast sales for week 11 of 432,560 units. If we wished to forecast week 12 sales, we would either use the week 11 forecast or wait until the actual week 11 sales are known and then update the smoothing equations to get a new forecast for week 12.

Step 3: Diagnose the model.

However, before we actually use the exponential smoothing forecast for decision-making purposes, we need to determine how successfully the model fits the historical data. Unlike the trend-based forecast, which uses least squares regression, there is no need to use split samples to test the forecasting ability of an exponential smoothing model, because the forecasts are "true forecasts." The forecast for a given period is made before considering the actual value for that period.

Figure 15-29 shows the *MAD* computation for the forecast model with α = 0.20 and a plot of the forecast values versus the actual sales values. This plot shows the smoothing that has occurred.

Our next step would be to try different smoothing constants and find the *MAD* for each new α. The forecast for period 11 would be made using the smoothing constant that generates the smallest *MAD*.

In this Humbolt example, we have used Excel formulas and Minitab commands to perform the single exponential smoothing. Both Excel and Minitab have single exponential smoothing procedures, although Minitab's procedure is much more

FIGURE 15-29

Humbolt Electronics *MAD* Computation for Single Exponential Smoothing, $\alpha = 0.20$

Excel Instructions:
1. Use Excel formulas to find forecast error, absolute forecast error, and *MAD*.
2. Use **Chart Wizard**, line graph option for columns B and C, with Column A as *x*-axis label.

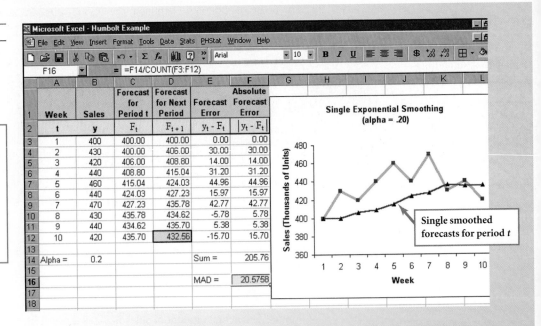

extensive. Refer to the Excel and Minitab tutorials on the CD-ROM for instructions on each. Minitab provides optional methods for determining the initial forecast value for period 1 and a variety of useful graphs. Minitab also has an option for determining the optimal smoothing constant value.[6] Figure 15-30 shows the output generated using Minitab. This shows that the best forecast is found using an $\alpha = 0.524$. Note, *MAD* is decreased from 20.576 (when $\alpha = 0.20$) to 17.321 when the optimal smoothing constant is used. The forecast for period 11 is also changed from 432.56 to 430.17 when a smoothing constant of 0.524 is used rather than 0.20. Note, Minitab automatically uses as the default the average of the first six periods as the initial forecast for period 1.

FIGURE 15-30

Minitab Output for Humbolt Electronics Single Exponential Smoothing Model

Minitab Instructions:
1. Open file: Humboldt.MTW.
2. Choose **Stat > Time Series > Single Exp Smoothing**.
3. In **Variable**, enter the time series column.
4. Under **Weight to Use in Smoothing**, select **Optimal ARIMA**.
5. Click **OK**.

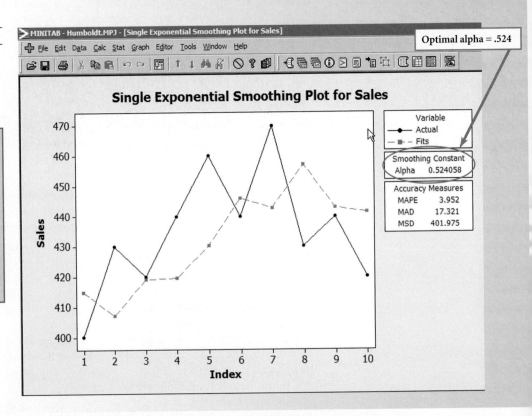

[6]The solver in Excel can be used to determine the optimal alpha level to minimize the *MAD*.

A major advantage of the single exponential smoothing model is that it is easy to update. In Example 15-6, the forecast for week 12, using this model, is found by simply plugging the actual sales in week 11, once they are known, into the smoothing formula.

$$F_{12} = \alpha y_{11} + (1 - \alpha)F_{11}$$

We do not need to go back and recompute the entire model, as would have been necessary with a trend-based regression model.

Double Exponential Smoothing

When the time series has an increasing or decreasing linear trend, a modification to the single exponential smoothing model is used to explicitly account for the trend. The resulting technique is called *double exponential smoothing*. The double exponential smoothing model is often referred to as *exponential smoothing with trend*. In double exponential smoothing, a second smoothing constant, beta (β), is included to account for the trend. Equations 15-18, 15-19, and 15-20 are needed to provide the forecasts.

Double Exponential Smoothing Model

$$C_t = \alpha y_t + (1 - \alpha)(C_{t-1} + T_{t-1}) \qquad \textbf{15-18}$$

$$T_t = \beta (C_t - C_{t-1}) + (1 - \beta)T_{t-1} \qquad \textbf{15-19}$$

$$F_{t+1} = C_t + T_t \qquad \textbf{15-20}$$

where:

$$y_t = \text{Actual value in time } t$$
$$\alpha = \text{Constant-process smoothing constant}$$
$$\beta = \text{Trend-smoothing constant}$$
$$C_t = \text{Smoothed constant-process value for period } t$$
$$T_t = \text{Smoothed trend value for period } t$$
$$F_{t+1} = \text{Forecast value for period } t + 1$$
$$t = \text{Current time period}$$

Equation 15-18 is used to smooth the time-series data. Equation 15-19 is used to smooth the trend, and Equation 15-20 combines the two smoothed values to form the forecast for period $t + 1$.

EXAMPLE 15-7: DOUBLE EXPONENTIAL SMOOTHING

Excel and Minitab Tutorial

Billingsley Insurance Company   The Billingsley Insurance Company has maintained data on the number of automobile claims filed at its Denver office over the past 12 months. These data, which are in the CD-ROM file *Billingsley*, are listed and graphed in Figure 15-31. The claims manager wants to forecast claims for month 13. A double exponential smoothing model can be developed using the following steps.

Step 1: **Specify the model.**

The time series contains a strong upward trend, so a double exponential smoothing model might be selected.

As was the case with single exponential smoothing, we must select starting values. In the case of the double exponential smoothing model, we must select initial values for C_0, T_0, and the smoothing constants α and β. The choice of smoothing constant values (α and β) depends on the same issues as those discussed earlier for single exponential smoothing. That is, use larger smoothing constants when less smoothing is desired and values closer to 0.0 when more smoothing is desired. The larger the smoothing constant value, the more impact that current data will have on the forecast. Suppose we use $\alpha = 0.20$ and $\beta = 0.30$ in this example. There are several approaches for selecting starting values for C_0 and T_0. The method we use here is to fit the least squares trend to the historical data,

$$\hat{y}_t = b_0 + b_1 t$$

FIGURE 15-31

Excel Billingsley Insurance
Company Data and Time-
Series Plot

Excel Instructions:
1. Open file: Billingsley.xls
2. Use **Chart Wizard—
   Line Chart** option.

where the y intercept, b_0, is used as the starting value, C_0, and the slope, b_1, is used as the starting value for the trend, T_0. We can use the regression procedure in Excel or Minitab to perform these calculations, giving

$$\hat{y}_t = 34.273 + 4.1119(t)$$

So,

$$C_0 = 34.273 \text{ and } T_0 = 4.1119$$

Keep in mind that these are arbitrary starting values and, as with single exponential smoothing, their effect will be dampened out as you proceed through the sample data to the current period. The more historical data you have, the less impact the starting values will have in the forecast.

Step 2:   Fit the model.
The forecast for period 1 made at the beginning of period 1 is

$$F_1 = C_0 + T_0$$
$$F_1 = 34.273 + 4.1119 = 38.385$$

At the close of period 1, in which actual claims were 38, the smoothing equations are updated as follows.

$$C_1 = 0.20(38) + (1 - 0.20)(34.273 + 4.1119) = 38.308$$
$$T_1 = 0.30(38.308 - 34.273) + (1 - 0.30)(4.1119) = 4.089$$

Next, the forecast for period 2 is

$$F_2 = 38.308 + 4.089 = 42.397$$

We then repeat the process through period 12 to find the forecast for period 13.

Step 3:   Diagnose the model.
Figures 15-32a and 15-32b show the results of the computations and the *MAD* value. The forecast for period 13 is

$$F_{13} = C_{12} + T_{12}$$
$$F_{13} = 83.867 + 3.908 = 87.776$$

Based on this double exponential smoothing model, the number of claims for period 13 is forecast to be about 88. However, before settling on this forecast, we should try different smoothing constants to determine whether a smaller *MAD* can be found.

FIGURE 15-32A

Excel Double Exponential Smoothing Spreadsheet for Billingsley Insurance

Excel Instructions:
1. Open file: Billingsley.xls
2. Apply Equations 15-18, 15-19, and 15-20 using Excel formulas.
3. Compute forecast errors and absolute forecast errors.
4. Compute *MAD*.

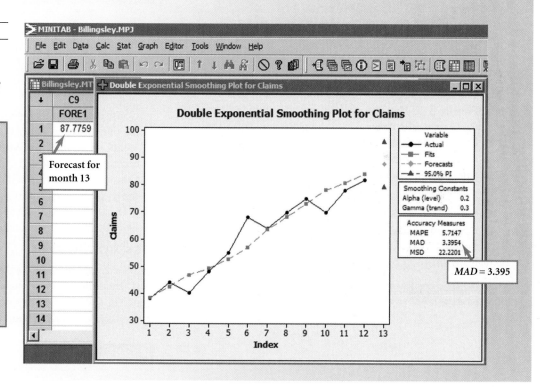

FIGURE 15-32B

Minitab Double Exponential Smoothing Spreadsheet for Billingsley Insurance

Minitab Instructions:
1. Open file: Billingsley:MTW.
2. Choose **Stat > Time Series > Double Exp Smoothing**.
3. In **Variable**, enter time series column.
4. Check **Generate forecasts** and enter 1 in **Number of forecasts** and 12 in **Starting from origin**.
5. Click **OK**.

As you can see, the computations required for double exponential smoothing are somewhat tedious and are ideally suited for your computer. Although Excel does not have a double exponential smoothing procedure, in Figure 15-32a we have used Excel formulas to develop our model in conjunction with the regression tool for determining the starting values. Minitab does have a double exponential smoothing routine, as illustrated in Figure 15-32b.

The *MAPE* on the Minitab output is the *Mean Absolute Percent Error*, which is computed using Equation 15-21. The *MAPE* = 5.7147, indicating that on average, the double exponential smoothing model produced a forecast that differed from the actual claims by 5.7%.

Mean Absolute Percent Error

$$MAPE = \frac{\sum \frac{|y_t - F_t|}{y_t}(100)}{n}$$

15-21

where:

y_t = Actual value of time series in time t
F_t = Forecast value for time period t
n = Number of periods of available data

15-3: EXERCISES

Skill Development

15.33 The following table includes two years of data:

Year 1		Year 2	
1st quarter	242	1st quarter	272
2nd quarter	252	2nd quarter	267

Year 1		Year 2	
3rd quarter	257	3rd quarter	276
4th quarter	267	4th quarter	281

a. Prepare a single exponential smoothing forecast for the first quarter of year 3 using an alpha value of 0.10. Use 250 as the forecast for the first quarter of year 1.
b. Prepare a single exponential smoothing forecast for the first quarter of year 3 using an alpha value of 0.25.
c. Calculate the *MAD* value for the forecasts you generated in parts a and b. Which alpha value provides the smaller *MAD* value at the end of the 4th quarter in year 2?

15.34 The following data represents enrollment in a major at your university for the past 6 semesters (Note: Semester 1 is the oldest data; semester 6 is the most recent data).

Semester	Enrollment
1	87
2	110
3	123
4	127
5	145
6	160

a. Prepare a graph of enrollment for the six semesters.
b. Based on the graph you prepared in part a, does it appear that a trend is present in the enrollment figures?
c. Prepare a double exponential smoothing forecast for semester 7 using an alpha value of 0.35. Assume that the initial forecast for semester 1 is $y_1 = 87$.
d. Prepare a double exponential smoothing forecast for semester 7 using an alpha value of 0.20 and a beta value of 0.25.

e. Calculate the *MAD* value for the simple exponential smoothing model at the end of semester 6 and the *MAD* value for the double exponential smoothing model at the end of semester 6. Which model appears to be doing the better job of forecasting course enrollment?

15.35 The following data represent permits issued by a city over the past 10 years:

Year	Permits	Year	Permits
1	1,500	6	1,350
2	1,470	7	1,180
3	2,100	8	1,550
4	2,380	9	2,000
5	2,050	10	2,040

a. Construct single exponential smoothing models for the data, using α values of 0.2, 0.5, and 0.8.
b. Which of the three forecasting models would you recommend? Why? What is your forecast for year 11?
c. Construct double exponential smoothing models using the α values given in part a and corresponding β values of 0.2, 0.4, and 0.6, respectively. Indicate which one you would prefer to use to forecast permits for year 11.

Business Applications

15.36 The sales manager of Carl's Discount TV and Stereo Shop must decide how many 27-inch GB Super TVs to order for May. The following sales report shows the sales of the 27-inch GB Super for the months of January through April:

Month	Sales
January	845
February	825
March	820
April	851

a. Use an alpha value of 0.3 to prepare a single exponential smoothing forecast for May.
b. What is the *MAD* value?

15.37 The fleet manager for a regional sales office is trying to estimate the dollar expenditure for gasoline for next period. The past six months of gasoline expenditures are shown here.

Month	Gasoline Expenditures
April	$23,586.41
May	23,539.22
June	23,442.06
July	23,988.71
August	23,727.13
September	23,799.69

Using the past history, prepare a simple moving exponential forecast for October using an α value of 0.25.

15.38 The human resources manager for a medium-sized business is interested in predicting the dollar value of medical expenditures filed by employees of her company for 2001. From her company's database, she has collected the following information showing the dollar value of medical expenditures made by employees for the previous seven years.

Year	Medical Claims
1994	$405,642.43
1995	407,180.60
1996	408,203.30
1997	410,088.03
1998	411,085.64
1999	412,200.39
2000	414,043.90

a. Prepare a graph of medical expenditures for 1994 to 2000. Which forecasting technique do you think is most appropriate for this time series, single exponential smoothing or double exponential smoothing? Why?

b. Use an α value of 0.25 and a β value of 0.15 to produce a double exponential forecast for the medical claims data. Be sure to update your constant process value and your trend value each year.

c. Compute the *MAD* value for your model for 1994 to 2000. Also produce a graph of your forecast values.

Advanced Applications

15.39 Boondocks in Phoenix, Arizona, is one of the biggest water-amusement parks in the country. The park has numerous water slides and a variety of other water-related play areas for children and adults. While people are at the park, they buy food and drinks. In order for the catering manager at Boondocks to determine how much food to have on hand, she needs an accurate forecast of the number of people who will be at the park each week. Attendance data for the past 16 weeks are contained in the CD-ROM file *Boondocks*.

a. Develop a times-series plot for the weekly attendance at Boondocks. Comment on the components that are visible in this time series.

b. Use the single exponential smoothing model with $\alpha = 0.25$ to develop a forecast for period 17. Also compute the *MAD* value for the past 16 weeks using this forecasting model.

c. Referring to part b, change the α smoothing constant to 0.40 and repeat the forecasting and *MAD* computation processes.

d. Referring to parts b and c, write a short report to the catering manager indicating which forecasting model you would recommend and why.

15.40 Referring to Exercise 15-39, use single exponential smoothing with a variety of alpha levels (say, 0.10, 0.30, 0.50, 0.70, and 0.90) to determine the "best" value for the smoothing constant based on minimizing the *MAD*. (Hint: If you are using Minitab, you can use the smoothing constant optimization option to directly find the "best" alpha value. If you use Excel, you can employ its Data Table Feature to simultaneously calculate the *MAD* values for the alternative alpha values.) Discuss your results.

15.41 The sales manager at Grossmieller Importers in New York City needs to determine a monthly forecast for the number of men's golf sweaters that will be sold so he can order an appropriate amount of packing boxes. Grossmieller ships sweaters to retail stores throughout the United States and Canada. Shirts are packed six to a box. Data for the past 12 months are contained in the CD-ROM file *Grossmieller*.

a. Plot the sales data using a time-series plot. Based on the graph, what time-series components are present? Discuss.

b. (1) Use a single exponential smoothing model with $\alpha = 0.30$ to forecast sales for month 17. (2) Compute the *MAD* for this model. (3) Graph the smoothing model fitted values on the time-series plot.

c. (1) Referring to part b, try different alpha levels to determine which smoothing constant value you would recommend. (2) Indicate why you have selected this value and then develop the forecast for month 17. (3) Compare this to the forecast you got using $\alpha = 0.30$ in part b(1).

15.42 Refer to Exercise 15.41, in which the sales manager for Grossmieller Imports of New York City needs to forecast monthly sales.

a. Discuss why a double exponential smoothing model might be preferred over a single exponential smoothing model.

b. (1) Develop a double exponential smoothing model using $\alpha = 0.20$ and $\beta = 0.30$ as smoothing constants. To obtain the starting values, use the regression trend line approach discussed in this section. (2) Determine the forecast for month 17. (3) Also compute the *MAD* for this model. (4) Graph the fitted values on the time-series graph.

c. Compare the results for this double exponential smoothing model with the "best" single exponential smoothing model developed in part c of Exercise 15.41. Discuss which model is preferred.

d. Referring to part b, try different alpha and beta values in an attempt to determine an improved forecast model for monthly sales. For each model, show the forecast for period 17 and the *MAD*. Write a short report that compares the different models.

e. Referring to parts c and d for Exercise 15.41, write a report to the Grossmieller sales manager that indicates your choice for the forecasting model, with your justification for the selection.

15.43 The sales manager has reviewed your analysis from Exercise 15.42. You have convinced him that a double exponential forecast model is a model that will provide adequate forecasts because there is an upward trend in the number of men's golf sweaters sold. He, however, has asked how confident you are in the forecast for month 17. If you cannot provide an answer to this enquiry, select a method that will provide a prediction interval with a 99% confidence level. Use this method to produce the required prediction interval.

Summary and Conclusions

In this chapter, we have introduced the basics of time series analysis and forecasting. Although we have included a variety of forecasting techniques, the discussion here does not cover the entire topic of forecasting. The subject of forecasting and time-series analysis could easily require one or more semester-long courses. Our objective has been to provide insight into some of the more frequently used techniques and to acquaint you with the basic terminology of forecasting and time-series analysis.

Quantitative forecasting techniques require historical data for the variable to be forecasted. The success of a quantitative model is determined by two factors:

1. How well the model fits the historical time-series data
2. How closely the future resembles the past

Ultimately, the best forecasting method is the one that provides the most accurate forecasts.

You will find that the techniques introduced in this chapter are used frequently as an initial basis for a forecast. However, in most cases, the decision maker will modify the forecast based on his or her own judgment and other qualitative inputs that are not considered by the quantitative model. Thus, forecasting is as much an art as it is a science. The more experience you have in a given situation, the more effective you likely will be at identifying and applying the appropriate foreacasting tool.

EQUATIONS

Simple Index Number

$$I_t = \frac{y_t}{y_0} 100 \qquad \textbf{15-1}$$

Unweighted Aggregate Price Index

$$I_t = \frac{\sum p_t}{\sum p_0} (100) \qquad \textbf{15-2}$$

The Paasche Index

$$I_t = \frac{\sum q_t p_t}{\sum q_t p_0} (100) \qquad \textbf{15-3}$$

Laspeyres Index

$$I_t = \frac{\sum q_0 p_t}{\sum q_0 p_0} (100) \qquad \textbf{15-4}$$

Deflation Formula

$$y_{adj_t} = \frac{y_t}{I_t} (100) \qquad \textbf{15-5}$$

Linear Trend Model

$$y_t = \beta_0 + \beta_1 t + \varepsilon_t \qquad \textbf{15-6}$$

Least Squares Equations Estimates

$$b_1 = \frac{\sum t y_t - \dfrac{\sum t \sum y_t}{n}}{\sum t^2 - \dfrac{(\sum t)^2}{n}} \qquad \textbf{15-7}$$

$$b_0 = \frac{\sum y_t}{n} - b_1 \frac{\sum t}{n} \qquad \textbf{15-8}$$

Mean Squared Error

$$MSE = \frac{\sum (y_t - F_t)^2}{n} \qquad \textbf{15-9}$$

Mean Absolute Deviation

$$MAD = \frac{\sum |y_t - F_t|}{n} \qquad \textbf{15-10}$$

Durbin-Watson Statistic

$$d = \frac{\sum_{t=2}^{n} (e_t - e_{t-1})^2}{\sum_{t=1}^{n} e_t^2} \qquad \textbf{15-11}$$

Forecast Bias

$$\text{Forecast Bias} = \frac{\sum (y_t - F_t)}{n} \qquad \textbf{15-12}$$

$$\text{Forecast Bias} = \frac{\sum (\text{error})}{n}$$

Mulitplicative Time-Series Model

$$y_t = T_t \times S_t \times C_t \times I_t \qquad \textbf{15-13}$$

Ratio-to-Moving-Average

$$S_t \times I_t = \frac{y_t}{T_t \times C_t} \qquad \textbf{15-14}$$

Deseasonalization

$$T_t \times C_t \times I_t = \frac{y_t}{S_t} \qquad \textbf{15-15}$$

Exponential Smoothing Model

$$F_{t+1} = F_t + \alpha(y_t - F_t) \qquad \textbf{15-16}$$

or:

$$F_{t+1} = \alpha y_t + (1 - \alpha)F_t \qquad \textbf{15-17}$$

Double Exponential Smoothing Model

$$C_t = \alpha y_t + (1 - \alpha)(C_{t-1} + T_{t-1}) \qquad \textbf{15-18}$$

$$T_t = \beta (C_t - C_{t-1}) + (1 - \beta)T_{t-1} \qquad \textbf{15-19}$$

$$F_{t+1} = C_t + T_t \qquad \textbf{15-20}$$

Mean Absolute Percent Error

$$MAPE = \frac{\sum \frac{|y_t - F_t|}{y_t}(100)}{n} \qquad \textbf{15-21}$$

Key Terms

CHAPTER EXERCISES

Conceptual Questions

15.44 Identify three businesses in your community that might be expected to have sales that exhibit a seasonal component. Discuss.

15.45 Suppose that enrollments at a particular university have steadily declined over the past 10 years. Which time-series component would be illustrated if enrollments were graphed for this period of time? Discuss.

15.46 Discuss the difference between cyclical component and a seasonal component. Which component is more predictable, seasonal or cyclical? Discuss and illustrate with examples.

15.47 Go to the library or use the Internet to find data showing your state's population for the past 20 years. Plot these data and indicate which of the time-series components are present.

15.48 Contact the university registrar's office for enrollment data by quarter (or semester), including summer term, for the past six years. Graph the data and indicate which of the time-series components are present.

Business Applications

Exercises 15.49 to 15.52 refer to Malcar Autoparts Company, which has started producing replacement control microcomputers for automobiles. This has been a growth industry since the first control units were introduced in 1985. Sales data since the control unit was introduced are as follows:

Year	Sales
1985	$240,000
1986	218,000
1987	405,000
1988	587,000
1989	795,000
1990	762,000
1991	998,000
1992	1,217,000
1993	1,570,000
1994	1,947,000
1995	2,711,000
1996	3,104,000
1997	2,918,000
1998	4,606,000
1999	5,216,000
2000	5,010,000

15.49 As a start in analyzing this data,
a. Graph these data and indicate whether they appear to have a linear trend.
b. Develop a simple linear regression model with time as the independent variable. Using this regression model, describe the trend and the strength of the linear trend over the 16 years. Is the trend line statistically significant? Plot the trend line against the actual data.
c. Compute the *MAD* value for this model.
d. Provide the Malcar Autoparts Company an estimate of its expected sales for the next five years.

e. Provide the maximum and minimum sales Malcar can expect with 90% confidence for 2005.

15.50 Develop a single exponential smoothing model using $\alpha = 0.20$. Use as a starting value the average of the first six years' data. Determine the forecasted value for 2001.
a. Compute the *MAD* for this model.
b. Plot the forecast values against the actual data.
c. Use the same starting value, but try different smoothing constants (say, 0.05, 0.10, 0.25, and 0.30) in an effort to reduce the *MAD* value.
d. Is it possible to answer part d of Exercise 15.49 for this forecasting technique? Explain your answer.

15.51 Develop a double exponential smoothing model using smoothing constants $\alpha = 0.20$ and $\beta = 0.40$. As starting values, use the least squares trend line slope and intercept values.
a. Compute the *MAD* for this model.
b. Plot the forecast values against the actual data.
c. Use the same starting values but try different smoothing constants [say, $(\alpha, \beta) = (0.10, 0.50), (0.30, 0.30)$, and $(0.40, 0.20)$] in an effort to reduce the *MAD* value.

15.52 Using whatever diagnostic tools you are familiar with, determine which of the three forecasting methods utilized to forecast sales for Malcar Autoparts Company in the previous three exercises provide superior forecasts. Explain the reasons for your choice.

15.53 💿 The Chesterfield Company in Omaha, Nebraska, manufactures airplane parts. Sales data for the past 22 years are as follows and are also provided in the CD-ROM file *Chesterfield*.

Year	Sales	Year	Sales
1	$ 133,000	12	$ 1,335,000
2	128,000	13	1,567,000
3	202,000	14	1,234,000
4	278,000	15	1,897,000
5	388,000	16	2,300,000
6	376,000	17	2,124,000
7	504,000	18	2,579,000
8	613,000	19	3,200,000
9	745,000	20	3,106,000
10	975,000	21	3,678,000
11	1,233,900	22	3,789,000

a. Develop a simple linear regression model with time as the independent variable.
b. Plot the trend line against the actual data. Discuss any relationships you see between the plotted trend line and the actual data.
c. Compute the *MAD* for this model.
d. Use simple linear regression to obtain a prediction interval for sales in year 23.

15.54 💿 Refer to Exercise 15.53.
a. Develop a double exponential smoothing model to forecast year 23 sales. Use as starting values the intercept and slope coefficient from the linear trend model. Use smoothing constants with alpha = 0.25 and beta = 0.30.
b. Compute the *MAD* for this model and compare the double smoothing model with the linear trend model developed in Exercise 15.53. Which of these two models would you select to provide forecasts for this data? Provide the reasons for your selection.

Advanced Applications

15.55 Sunrise Sports has experienced rapidly expanding retail sales. Here are its sales levels (in millions) for the past 12 years.

Year	Sales
1989	$ 1.9
1990	3.1
1991	2.8
1992	4.5
1993	5.7
1994	5.8
1995	8.6
1996	9.3
1997	11.0
1998	13.9
1999	16.6
2000	19.4

As part of the company's financial-planning effort, the managers need an accurate forecast of annual sales.
a. Graph this series and describe the trend in the data.
b. Estimate a least squares regression line to fit the data. How good a job does this line do in explaining the variation in past sales data? Comment on any patterns you see in the relationship between the actual sales values and those values predicted by the regression analysis.
c. Determine the forecast value for 2000.
d. Conduct a test of hypothesis to determine if a long-term trend is evident in the sales data for Sunrise Sports.
e. Graph the residuals for the chosen least squares regression line against the year. Does this graph suggest a different regression model to use for forecasting purposes? Develop the regression model that you would use to forecast sales. Provide your rationale, of course.

15.56 Referring to the Sunrise Sports data discussed in Exercise 15.55, develop a single exponential smoothing model using alpha = 0.30. Use as a starting value the average of the first six years' data. Determine the forecasted value for 2001.
a. Compute the *MAD* for this model.
b. Plot the forecast values against the actual data.
c. Use the same starting value, but try a different smoothing constant (say, 0.10, 0.20, 0.40, and 0.50) in an effort to reduce the *MAD* value.

15.57 Referring again to the Sunrise Sports data of the previous exercises (15.55 and 15.56), develop a double exponential smoothing model using smoothing constants $\alpha = 0.30$ and $\beta = 0.30$. As starting values, use the least squares trend line slope and intercept values.
a. Compute the *MAD* for this model.
b. Plot the forecast values against the actual data.
c. Use the same starting values, but try a different smoothing constants [say, $(\alpha, \beta) = (0.10, 0.50), (0.20, 0.40)$, and $(0.40, 0.20)$] in an effort to reduce the *MAD* value. Prepare a short report that summarizes your efforts.

15.58 💿 DataNet is an Internet service where clients can find information and purchase various items such as airline tickets, stereo equipment, and listed stocks. DataNet has been in operation for four years. Data on monthly calls for service for the time that the company has been in business are contained in the CD-ROM file *DataNet*.

a. Plot these data in a time-series graph. Based on the graph, what time-series components are present in the data?

b. Develop the seasonal indexes for each month. Describe what the seasonal index for August means.

c. Fit a linear trend model to the deseasonalized data for months 1 through 48, and determine the *MAD* value. Comment on the adequacy of the linear trend model based on these measures of forecast error.

d. Provide a seasonally unadjusted forecast using the linear trend model for each month of the year.

e. Use the seasonal index values computed in part b to provide seasonal adjusted forecasts for months 49 through 52.

15.59 DataNet managers (discussed in Exercise 15.58) need to know how rapidly the monthly calls for service are increasing.

a. Provide them with an estimate (of which they can be very confident, say 99%) of the average increase in monthly calls for service.

b. The current telephone system can handle 60,000 calls a month. Provide the managers an estimate of the month in which they will have to replace their phone system.

15.60 Referring to Exercises 15.58 and 15.59, the managers of DataNet, the Internet company where users can purchase products such as airline tickets, need to forecast monthly call volumes in order to have sufficient capacity. Develop a single exponential smoothing model using $\alpha = 0.30$. Use as a starting value the average of the first six months' data.

a. Compare the *MAD* for this model.

b. Plot the forecast values against the actual data.

c. Use the same starting value, but try different smoothing constants (say, 0.10, 0.20, 0.40, and 0.50) in an effort to reduce the *MAD* value.

d. Reflect on the type of time series for which the single exponential smoothing model is designed to provide forecasts. Does it surprise you that the *MAD* for this method is relatively large for this data? Explain your reasoning.

15.61 Continuing with the DataNet forecasting exercises, develop a double exponential smoothing model using smoothing constants $\alpha = 0.20$ and $\beta = 0.20$. As starting values, use the least squares trend line slope and intercept values.

a. Compute the *MAD* for this model.

b. Plot the forecast values against the actual data.

c. Compare this with a linear trend model. Which forecast method would you use? Explain your rationale.

d. Use the same starting values, but try different smoothing constants [say, $(\alpha, \beta) = (0.10, 0.30)$, $(0.15, 0.25)$, and $(0.30, 0.10)$] in an effort to reduce the *MAD* value. Prepare a short report that summarizes your efforts.

15.62 Anna Chen is the personnel manager for Datatron Corporation, which is located in the Silicon Valley in California. She has been asked to assist the production managers in developing a staffing plan for the coming year. One factor that influences staffing is the amount of sick time taken by employees each month. The data

located in the CD-ROM file *Datatron* represent the number of sick days, by month, for the past three years.

a. Plot these data in a time-series graph. Based on the graph, what time-series components are present in the data.

b. Develop the seasonal indexes for each month.

c. Fit a linear trend model to the deseasonalized data for months 1 through 36 and determine the *MAD* value. Comment on the adequacy of the linear trend model based on these measures of forecast error. Provide a 95% confidence interval estimate for the number of sick days for the next January.

d. Provide a seasonally adjusted forecast using the linear trend model for each month of next year.

e. Use the seasonal index values computed in part b to provide seasonal adjusted forecasts for months 37 through 40. Compare the utility of this forecast to that made in part c.

15.63 Refer to Exercise 15.62, in which Anna Chen was interested in forecasting the number of sick days taken by employees at Datatron each month.

a. Develop a single exponential smoothing model using alpha = 0.20. Use as a starting value the average of the first six months' data. Determine the forecasted value for month 37.

b. Compute the *MAD* for this model.

c. Plot the forecast values against the actual data.

d. Use the same starting value, but try different smoothing constants (say, 0.10, 0.20, 0.40, and 0.50) in an effort to reduce the *MAD* value. Prepare a short report that summarizes your efforts.

15.64 Referring to Exercises 15.62 and 15.63, develop a double exponential smoothing model using smoothing constants alpha = 0.30 and beta = 0.20. As starting values, use the least squares trend line slope and intercept values.

a. Compute the *MAD* for this model.

b. Plot the forecast values against the actual data.

c. Using a linear trend model, provide a prediction for number of absent days for December of the third year. Compare this with the forecast obtained using the double exponential smoothing method. Discuss the two estimates' relative merits.

d. Use the same starting values, but try different smoothing constants [say, $(\alpha, \beta) = (0.10, 0.30)$, $(0.15, 0.25)$, and $(0.30, 0.10)$] in an effort to reduce the *MAD* value. Prepare a short report that summarizes your efforts.

15.65 Elliel's Quality Discount Store has applied for a line of credit with the First National Bank. This line of credit is to be used primarily for financing inventory purchases. As part of the financial application, Elliel's has been asked to provide monthly inventory levels for the past five years. These inventory levels (in millions of dollars) are located in the CD-ROM file *Elliels*.

a. Determine the seasonal index number for each month.

b. First National Bank has also asked Elliel's to provide a monthly forecast for months 61 through 72. Compute the least squares trend model and determine the seasonally unadjusted forecast for months 37 through 48. Prepare a report discussing the forecasts for the bank loan officer.

c. Referring to part b, prepare a seasonally adjusted forecast for months 37 through 48. Write a report that compares these forecasts with the unadjusted forecasts determined in part b.

d. Discuss the advantage and reasons for incorporating the seasonal indexes into the forecasts.

CASE 15-A:

Park Falls Chamber of Commerce

Masao Sugiyama is the recently elected president of the Chamber of Commerce in Park Falls, Wisconsin. He is the long-time owner of the only full-service hardware store in this small farming town. Being president of the Chamber of Commerce has been considered largely a ceremonial post because business conditions have not changed in Park Falls for as long as anyone can remember. However, Masao has just read an article in *The Wall Street Journal* that has made him think he needs to take a more-active interest in the business conditions of his town.

The article concerned Wal-Mart, the largest retailer in the United States. Wal-Mart has expanded primarily by locating in small towns and avoiding large suburban areas. Although the Park Falls merchants have not had to deal with either Kmart or Sears because these companies have located primarily in large urban centers, Wal-Mart has recently entered Wisconsin. In addition, a supplier has recently told Masao that both Sears and Kmart are considering locating stores in smaller towns to prevent future expansion by Wal-Mart. Sugiyama knows that Wal-Mart has moved into the outskirts of metropolitan areas and now is considering smaller stores for smaller, untapped markets. He also has heard that Kmart and Sears have recently had difficulty, and only Sears seems to have rebounded.

Masao decided he needs to know more about all three retailers. He asked the son of a friend to locate the following sales data using the Compustat Database:

Kmart	SALES VALUES (Million)	Sears	SALES VALUES (Million)	Wal-Mart	SALES VALUES (Million)
1988	$25,822	1988	$48,439	1988	$ 15,959
1989	27,496	1989	50,251	1989	20,649
1990	29,736	1990	53,793	1990	25,810
1991	32,281	1991	55,971	1991	32,601
1992	34,792	1992	57,242	1992	43,886
1993	37,942	1993	52,344	1993	55,483
1994	34,353	1994	50,837	1994	67,344

Kmart	SALES VALUES (Million)	Sears	SALES VALUES (Million)	Wal-Mart	SALES VALUES (Million)
1995	34,313	1995	54,559	1995	82,494
1996	34,654	1996	34,925	1996	93,627
1997	31,437	1997	38,925	1997	104,859
1998	32,183	1998	41,296	1998	117,958

QUARTERLY SALES VALUES IN MILLIONS OF DOLLARS

Quarter	Kmart	Sears	Wal-Mart
1	$ 8,015	$ 7,810	$17,686
2	7,845	7,926	20,417
3	9,967	10,194	24,447
4	7,501	7,463	20,440
5	8,503	8,226	22,723
6	8,041	8,440	22,914
7	10,609	10,796	27,550
8	6,975	7,995	22,772
9	7,566	9,133	25,587
10	7,212	9,067	24,644
11	9,684	12,042	25,409
12	7,263	8,732	25,409
13	7,846	9,731	28,386
14	7,315	9,752	28,777
15	9,759	13,081	35,386
16	7,515	9,163	29,819

Masao is interested in what all these data tell him. How much faster has Wal-Mart grown than the other two firms? Is there any evidence Wal-Mart's growth has leveled off? Does Sears seem to be rebounding, based on sales? Are seasonal fluctuations an issue in these sales figures? Is there any evidence that one firm is more affected by the cyclical component than the others? He needs some help in analyzing these data.

CASE 15-B:

The St. Louis Companies 💿

An irritated Roger Hatton finds himself sitting in the St. Louis airport after hearing that his flight to Chicago had been delayed—and, if the storm in Chicago continues, possibly cancelled. Because he must get to Chicago if at all possible, Roger is stuck at

the airport. He decides he might as well try to get some work done so he opens his laptop computer and calls up the CLAIMNUM file

Roger was recently assigned as an analyst in the worker's compensation section of the St. Louis Companies, one of the biggest issuers of worker's compensation insurance in the country

Until this year, the revenues and claim costs for all parts of the company were grouped together to determine any yearly profit or loss. Therefore, no one really knew if an individual department was profitable. Now, however, the new president is looking at each part of the company as a profit center. The clear implication is that money-losing departments may not have a future unless they develop a clear plan to become profitable.

When Roger asked the accounting department for a listing, by client, of all policy payments and claims filed and paid, he was told that the information is available but he may have to wait two or three months to get it. He was able to determine, however, that the department has been keeping track of the clients who file frequent (at least one a month) claims and the total number of firms that purchase worker's compensation insurance. Using the data from this report, Roger divides the number of clients filing frequent claims by the corresponding number of clients. These ratios, kept on the CD-ROM file *CLAIMNUM*, are as follows:

YEAR	RATIO (%)	YEAR	RATIO (%)
1	3.8	12	6.1
2	3.6	13	7.8
3	3.5	14	7.1
4	4.9	15	7.6
5	5.9	16	9.7
6	5.6	17	9.6
7	4.9	18	7.5
8	5.6	19	7.9
9	8.5	20	8.3
10	7.7	21	8.4
11	7.1		

Staring at these figures, Roger feels there should be some way to use them to project what the next several years may hold if the company doesn't change its underwriting policies.

CASE 15-C:

Wagner Machine Works

Mary Lindsey has recently agreed to leave her upper-level management job at a major paper manufacturing firm and return to her hometown to take over the family machine-products business. The U.S. machine-products industry had a strong position of world dominance until recently, when it was devastated by foreign competition, particularly from Germany and Japan. Among the many problems facing the American industry is that it is made up of many small firms that must compete with foreign industrial giants.

Wagner Machine Works, the company Mary is taking over, is one of the few survivors in its part of the state, but it, too, faces increasing competitive pressure. Mary's father let the business slide as he approached retirement, and Mary sees the need for an immediate modernization of their plant. She has arranged for a loan from the local bank, but now she must forecast sales for the next 3 years to ensure that the company has enough cash flow to repay the debt. Surprisingly, Mary finds that her father has no forecasting system in place, and she cannot afford the time, or money, to install a system like that used at her previous company.

Wagner Machine Works' quarterly sales (in millions of dollars) for the past 15 years are as follows:

	QUARTER			
Year	1	2	3	4
1986	$10,490	$11,130	$10,005	$11,058
1987	11,424	12,550	10,900	12,335
1988	12,835	13,100	11,660	13,767
1989	13,877	14,100	12,780	14,738
1990	14,798	15,210	13,785	16,218
1991	16,720	17,167	14,785	17,725
1992	18,348	18,951	16,554	19,889
1993	20,317	21,395	19,445	22,816
1994	23,335	24,179	22,548	25,029
1995	25,729	27,778	23,391	27,360
1996	28,886	30,125	26,049	30,300
1997	30,212	33,702	27,907	31,096
1998	31,715	35,720	28,554	34,326
1999	35,533	39,447	30,046	37,587
2000	39,093	44,650	30,046	37,587

While looking at these data, Mary wonders whether they can be used to forecast sales for the next three years. She wonders how much, if any, confidence she can have in a forecast made with these data. She also wonders if the recent increase in sales is due to growing business or just to inflationary price increases in the national economy.

General References

1. Armstrong, J. Scott, "Forecasting by Extrapolation: Conclusions from 25 years of Research." *Interfaces*, 14, no. 6 (1984).
2. The Ombudsman: Research on Forecasting—A Quarter-Century Review, 1960–1984." *Interfaces*, 16, no. 1 (1986).
3. Bails, Dale G., and Larry C. Peppers, *Business Fluctuations: Forecasting Techniques and Applications* (Englewood Cliffs, NJ: Prentice-Hall, 1982).
4. Berenson, Mark L., and David M. Levine, *Basic Business Statistics: Concepts and Applications*, 7th ed. (Upper Saddle River, NJ: Prentice-Hall 1999).
5. Bowerman, Bruce L., and Richard T. O'Connell, *Forecasting and Time Series: An Applied Approach*, 3rd ed. (North Scituate, MA: Duxbury Press, 1993).

6. Brandon, Charles, R. Fritz, and J. Xander, "Econometric Forecasts: Evaluation and Revision." *Applied Economics*, 15, no. 2 (1983).

7. Cryer, Jonathan D., *Time Series Analysis* (Boston: Duxbury Press, 1986).

8. Frees, Edward W., *Data Analysis Using Regression Models: The Business Perspective* (Englewood Cliffs, NJ: Prentice-Hall, 1996).

9. Granger, C. W. G., *Forecasting in Business and Economics*, 2d ed. (New York: Academic Press, 1989).

10. Makridakis, Spyros, Steven C. Wheelwright, and Rob J. Hyndman, *Forecasting: Methods and Applications*, 3rd ed. (New York: John Wiley & Sons, 1997).

11. McLaughlin, Robert L., "Forecasting Models: Sophisticated or Naive?" *Journal of Forecasting*, 2, no. 3 (1983).

12. *Microsoft Excel 2000* (Redmond, WA: Microsoft Corp., 1999).

13. *Minitab for Windows Version 13* (State College, PA: Minitab, 2000).

14. Montgomery, Douglas C., and Lynwood A. Johnson, *Forecasting and Time Series Analysis*, 2d ed. (New York: McGraw-Hill, 1990).

15. Nelson, C. R., *Applied Time Series Analysis for Managerial Forecasting* (San Francisco, CA: Holdon-Day, 1983).

16. Neter, John., Michael H. Kutner, Christopher J. Nachtsheim, and William Wassermen, *Applied Linear Statistical Models*, 4th ed. (Homewood, IL: Richard D. Irwin, 1996).

17. Willis, R. E., *A Guide to Forecasting for Planners* (Englewood Cliffs, NJ: Prentice-Hall, 1987).

18. Wonnacott, T. H., and R. J. Wonnacott, *Econometrics* (New York: John Wiley & Sons, 1979).

CHAPTER 16

Introduction to Nonparametric Statistics

CHAPTER OUTCOMES

After studying the material in Chapter 16, you should be able to:

- Recognize when and how to use the Wilcoxon signed rank test for a population median.
- Recognize the situations for which the Mann–Whitney U test for the difference between two population medians applies and be able to use it in a decision-making context.
- Know when to apply the Wilcoxon matched pairs signed rank test for related samples.
- Perform nonparametric analysis of variance using the Kruskal-Wallis one-way ANOVA.

WHY YOU NEED TO KNOW

A major electronics firm is considering building a new assembly plant in the southeastern United States. Housing prices are particularly important in picking the plant's location because the company would like affordable housing to be available for employees who transfer to the new location. The company has taken a sample of real estate listings from the four cities in contention for the new plant and would like to make a statistically valid comparison of home prices based on this sample information. This comparison then would be used to help determine where the new assembly plant should be located. The same company is also considering what type of employee evaluation system to use in the new plant. It has been experimenting with a group-based, rather than an individual-based, employee evaluation system in one of its plants. As a part of this experiment, the firm has gathered questionnaire data from employees who were asked to rate their experience with the evaluation system as being one with which they were *very satisfied*, *satisfied*, *no opinion*, *dissatisfied*, or *very dissatisfied*.

In previous chapters, you were introduced to a wide variety of statistical techniques that would seem to be useful statistical analysis tools for this company. However, many of the techniques discussed earlier are not appropriate for this situation.

For instance, hypothesis tests involving small samples and an unknown population standard deviation utilize the *t*-distribution. However, using the *t*-distribution in that situation assumes the population from which the sample is selected is normally distributed. If a small-sample situation involves testing the difference between two population means, the *t*-distribution is used under the assumption that both populations are normally distributed. The analysis of variance (ANOVA) *F*-test introduced in Chapter 11 is based on the assumptions that all populations are normally distributed and the population variances are equal. In addition, each of these techniques requires the variables of interest to be either interval or ratio level.

Although in many instances these underlying conditions are satisfied, you will encounter other situations in which either the level of data measurement is too low or the distribution assumptions are clearly violated. This is the case for both of the issues facing the electronics company here. Housing prices are generally not normally distributed because most locations have a few very expensive houses, and the employee questionnaire answers were measured on an ordinal, not on an interval or ratio scale. To handle such cases as these, a class of statistical tools called nonparametric statistics has been developed.

16-1 THE WILCOXON SIGNED RANK TEST FOR ONE POPULATION CENTER

Up to this point, the text has presented a wide array of statistical tools for describing data and for drawing inferences about a population based on sample information from that population. These tools are widely used in decision-making situations. However, you will also encounter decision situations in which major departures from the required assumptions exist. For example, many populations, such as family income levels and house prices, are highly skewed. In other instances, the level of data measurement will be too low (ordinal or nominal) to warrant use of the techniques presented earlier. In such cases, the alternative is to employ a *nonparametric statistical procedure* that has been developed to meet specific inferential needs. Such procedures have fewer restrictive assumptions concerning data level and underlying probability distributions. There are a great many nonparametric procedures that cover a wide range of applications. The purpose of this chapter is to introduce you to the concept of nonparametric statistics and illustrate some of the more frequently used methods.

THE WILCOXON SIGNED RANK TEST—SINGLE POPULATION

In Chapter 8, you were introduced to examples that involved testing hypotheses about a single population mean. Recall that if the data were interval or ratio level and the population was normally distributed, a *t*-test was used to test whether a population mean had a specified value. However, in cases in which the data level is ordinal or when populations are not believed to be approximately normally distributed, the *t*-test is not appropriate. In these instances, a nonparametric statistical technique known as the *Wilcoxon signed rank test* can be used. This test makes no highly restrictive assumption about the shape of the population distribution. (Section 16-2 introduces another Wilcoxon signed rank test for the difference between two population centers.)

The Wilcoxon test is used to test hypotheses about a population median rather than a population mean. The basic logic of the Wilcoxon test is quite straightforward. Because the median is the midpoint in a population, allowing for sampling error, we would expect approximately half the data values in a random sample to lie below the population median and about half to lie above it. The hypothesized median will be rejected if the actual data distribution shows too large a departure from this expectation.

University Undergraduate Starting Salaries—The university placement office is interested in testing to determine whether the median starting salary distribution for undergraduates exceeds $35,000. People in the office believe the salary distribution is highly skewed to the right, so the *t*-test from Chapter 8 cannot be properly used. In this case, the center of the distribution should be measured by the median. A simple random sample of $n = 10$ graduates is selected. The Wilcoxon signed rank test can be used to test whether the population median exceeds $35,000.

As with all tests, we start by stating the appropriate null and alternative hypotheses. The null and alternative hypotheses for the one-tailed test are

$$H_0: \tilde{\mu} \le \$35,000$$
$$H_A: \tilde{\mu} > \$35,000$$

The test will be conducted using

$$\alpha = 0.05$$

For small samples, the hypothesis is tested using a W test statistic determined by the following steps.

STEP 1: Collect the sample data.

STEP 2: Compute d_i the deviation between each value and the hypothesized median.

STEP 3: Convert the d_i values to absolute differences.

STEP 4: Determine the ranks for each d_i value, eliminating any zero d_i values. The lowest d_i value receives a rank of 1. If observations are tied, assign the average rank of the tied observations to each of the tied values.

STEP 5: For any data value greater than the hypothesized median, place the rank in an R+ column. For data values less the hypothesized median, place the rank in an R− column.

STEP 6: The test statistic W is the sum of the ranks in the R+ column.

Table 16-1 shows the results for a random sample of 10 starting salaries. The hypothesis is tested comparing the calculated W-value with the critical values for the Wilcoxon signed rank test that are shown in Appendix P. Both upper and lower critical values are shown corresponding to $n = 6$ to $n = 25$ for various levels of alpha. Note that n equals the number of nonzero d_i values. In this example, we have $n = 9$ nonzero d_i values. The lower critical value for $n = 9$ and a one-tailed $\alpha = 0.05$ is 8. The corresponding upper-tailed critical value is 37.

Because this is an upper-tail test, we are interested only in the upper critical value W_α. Therefore, the decision rule is

If $W > 37$, reject H_0.

Because

$$W = 29.5 < 37$$
we do not reject the null hypothesis

and are unable to conclude that the median starting salary for university graduates exceeds $35,000.

TABLE 16-1

Wilcoxon Ranking Table for Starting Salaries Example

SALARY = x_i	$d_i = x_i - \$35,000$	$|d_i|$	RANK	R+	R−
$36,400	1,400	1,400	2	2	
38,500	3,500	3,500	3	3	
27,000	−8,000	8,000	8		8
35,000	0	0			
29,000	−6,000	6,000	6.5		6.5
40,000	5,000	5,000	5	5	
52,000	17,000	17,000	9	9	
34,000	−1,000	1,000	1		1
38,900	3,900	3,900	4	4	
41,000	6,000	6,000	6.5	6.5	
				Total = W = 29.5	15.5

FIGURE 16-1

Minitab Output—Wilcoxon
Ranked Sum Test for
Starting Salaries

Minitab Instructions:
1. Enter data in column.
2. Choose **Stat > Nonparametrics > 1-Sample Wilcoxon**.
3. In **Variable**, enter the data column.
4. Choose **Test median** and enter median value tested.
5. From **Alternative**, select appropriate hypothesis.
6. Click **OK**.

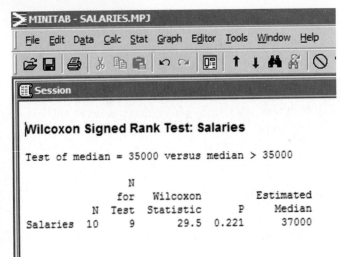

```
MINITAB - SALARIES.MPJ

File  Edit  Data  Calc  Stat  Graph  Editor  Tools  Window  Help
```

Session

Wilcoxon Signed Rank Test: Salaries

Test of median = 35000 versus median > 35000

```
                     N
                    for    Wilcoxon                Estimated
              N    Test   Statistic      P          Median
Salaries     10     9         29.5    0.221          37000
```

Although neither Excel nor PHStat has a Wilcoxon signed rank test, Minitab does. Figure 16-1 illustrates the Minitab output for this example. Note that the p-value = 0.221 > α = 0.05, which reinforces the conclusion that the null hypothesis should not be rejected.

The starting salary example illustrated how the Wilcoxon signed rank test is used when the sample sizes are small. The W test statistic approaches a normal distribution as n increases. Therefore, for sample sizes > 20, the Wilcoxon test can be approximated using the normal distribution where the test statistic is a z-value, as shown in Equation 16-1.

Large-Sample Wilcoxon Signed Rank Test Statistic

$$z = \frac{W - \dfrac{n(n+1)}{4}}{\sqrt{\dfrac{n(n+1)(2n+1)}{24}}}$$

16-1

where:

$$W = \text{Sum of the } R+ \text{ ranks}$$
$$n = \text{Number of nonzero } d_i \text{ values}$$

EXAMPLE 16-1: WILCOXON SIGNED RANK TEST, ONE SAMPLE, n > 20

Home Prices   A recent article in the business section of a regional newspaper indicated that the median price of houses in the region was less than $176,200. A legislative intern was assigned to test this statement. A random sample of 25 homes was selected. The large-sample Wilcoxon signed rank test can be conducted using the following steps.

Step 1:   **Specify the null and alternative hypotheses.**
In this case, the null and alternative hypotheses are

$$H_0: \tilde{\mu} \geq \$176,200$$
$$H_A: \tilde{\mu} < \$176,200$$

Step 2:   **Determine the significance level for the test.**
The test will be conducted using
$$\alpha = 0.01$$

Step 3:   **Collect the sample data and compute the W test statistic.**
Using the steps outlined in the previous example, we manually compute the W test statistic as shown in Table 16-2.

	PRICE = x_i	d_i	$|d_i|$	RANK	$R+$	$R-$
TABLE 16-2	$173,000	−3,200	3,200	1		1
Wilcoxon Ranking Table	169,900	−6,300	6,300	2		2
for Home Prices	163,500	−12,700	12,700	3		3
Example	160,600	−15,600	15,600	4		4
	159,200	−17,000	17,000	5		5
	157,200	−19,000	19,000	6		6
	156,500	−19,700	19,700	7		7
	155,400	−20,800	20,800	8		8
	155,200	−21,000	21,000	9		9
	197,750	21,550	21,550	10	10	
	154,200	−22,000	22,000	11		11
	200,750	24,550	24,550	12	12	
	149,500	−26,700	26,700	13		13
	203,000	26,800	26,800	14	14	
	204,900	28,700	28,700	15	15	
	145,900	−30,300	30,300	16		16
	143,500	−32,700	32,700	17		17
	137,650	−38,550	38,550	18		18
	216,250	40,050	40,050	19	19	
	134,500	−41,700	41,700	20		20
	128,900	−47,300	47,300	21		21
	117,000	−59,200	59,200	22		22
	112,400	−63,800	63,800	23		23
	104,500	−71,700	71,700	24		24
	102,600	−73,600	73,600	25		25
					70	255

Step 4:   Compute the z-test statistic.
The z-test statistic using the sum of the positive range is:

$$z = \frac{W - \dfrac{n(n+1)}{4}}{\sqrt{\dfrac{n(n+1)(2n+1)}{24}}} = \frac{70 - \dfrac{25(25+1)}{4}}{\sqrt{\dfrac{25(25+1)(2(25)+1)}{24}}} = -2.49$$

Step 5:   Reach a decision.
The critical value for a one-tailed test for alpha = 0.01 from the standard normal distribution is −2.33.
    Because $z = -2.49 < -2.33$, we reject the null hypothesis.

Step 6:   Draw a conclusion.
Thus, based on the sample data, the intern should conclude that the median is less than $176,200.

16-1: EXERCISES

Skill Development

16.1   Consider the following set of observations.

10.21	13.65	12.30	9.51	11.32	12.77	6.16	8.55	11.78	12.32

You should not assume these data come from a normal distribution. Test the hypothesis that these data come from a distribution with a median less than or equal to 10.

16.2   Consider the following set of observations.

3.1	4.8	2.3	5.6	2.8	2.9	4.4

You should not assume these data come from a normal distribution. Test the hypothesis that these data come from a distribution with a median equal to 4.

16.3   Consider the following set of observations.

9.0	15.6	21.1	11.1	13.5	9.2	13.6	15.8	12.5	18.7	18.9

You should not assume these data come from a normal distribution. Test the hypothesis that the median of these data is greater than or equal to 14.

Business Applications

16.4 A telemarketing company located in Los Angeles has established a guideline that states that the median time for each completed call should not exceed 4 minutes. Recently the operations manager was concerned that calls were taking too long. The operations manager did not wish to make that assertion if the sample data did not strongly indicate it. A sample of 12 calls was selected, and the following times (in seconds) were recorded.

194	278	302	140	245	234	268	208	102	190	220	255

a. Construct the appropriate null and alternative hypotheses.
b. Based on the sample data, what should the operations manager conclude? Test at the 0.10 significance level.

16.5 Bowman Electronics sells electronic components for car stereos. The owners claim that the median life of a component exceeds 4,000 hours. To test this claim, they have selected a random sample of $n = 12$ components and have traced their lifespans between installation and failure. The following data were obtained.

1,973	4,838	3,805	4,494	4,738	5,249
4,459	4,098	4,722	5,894	3,322	4,800

a. State the appropriate null and alternative hypothesis.
b. Assuming that the test is to be conducted using a 0.05 level of significance, what conclusion should be reached based on these sample data? Be sure to examine the required normality assumption.

16.6 A recent trade newsletter reported that during the initial six-month period of employment, new sales personnel in an insurance company spent a median of 119 hours per month in the field. A random sample of 20 new salespersons was selected. The numbers of hours spent in the field by members in a randomly chosen month are listed here.

163	103	112	96	134
147	102	95	134	126
189	126	135	114	129
142	111	103	89	115

Do the data support the trade newsletter's claim? Conduct the appropriate hypothesis test with a significance level of 0.05.

16.7 The quality control department of a sunblock manufacturer requires the mean weight of its containers to be 11 ounces. The quality control department has answered complaints that the company underfills their containers by using a statistical study that concluded that the average weight of the sunblock containers is indeed 11 ounces. However, a consumer organization while acknowledging these findings believes that more than 50% of the containers have less than 11 ounces. A sample of 20 sunblock containers was selected. The data obtained follow.

10.9	11.7	10.5	11.8	10.2
11.5	10.8	11.2	11.8	10.7
10.6	10.9	11.6	11.2	11.0
10.7	10.8	10.5	11.3	10.1

Test the consumer organization's claim at a significance level of 0.05.

16.8 Sylvania's quality control division is constantly monitoring various parameters related to its products. One investigation addressed the life of incandescent light bulbs (in hours). Initially, they were satisfied with examining the average length of life. However, a recent sample taken from the production floor gave them pause for thought. The data follow.

1,100	1,140	1,550	1,210	1,280	840	1,620	1,500
1,460	1,940	2,080	1,350	1,150	730	2,410	1,060
1,150	1,260	1,760	1,250	1,500	1,560	1,210	1,440
1,770	1,270	1,210	1,230	1,230	2,100	1,630	500

Their initial efforts indicated that the average length of life of the light bulbs was 1,440 hours.
a. Construct a box and whisker plot of this data. On this basis, draw a conclusion concerning the distribution of the population from which this sample was drawn.
b. Conduct a hypothesis test to determine if the median length of life of the light bulbs is longer than the average length of life.

16.9 Mobile Oil Company wished to verify the viscosity of its premium 30-weight oil. A simple random sample of specimens taken from automobiles running at normal temperatures was obtained. The viscosities observed were as follows.

25	24	21	35	25
25	35	38	32	36
35	29	30	27	28
27	31	32	30	30

Determine if the median viscosity at normal running temperatures is equal to 30 as advertised for Mobile's premium 30-weight oil.

Advanced Applications

16.10 The Cell Tone Company sells cellular phones and airtime in several northwestern states. At a recent meeting, the marketing manager stated that the median age of its customers is less than 40. This came up in conjunction with a proposed advertising plan that is to be directed toward a young audience. Before actually completing the advertising plan, Cell Tone decided to randomly sample customers. Among the questions asked in a survey of 50 customers in the Jacksonville, Florida, area was the customers' ages. The data are in the CD-ROM file *Cell Phone Survey*.

a. Examine the sample data. Is the variable being measured a discrete or a continuous variable? Does it seem feasible that this data could have come from a normal distribution?

b. The marketing manager must support his statement concerning customer age in an upcoming board meeting. Using a significance level of 0.10, provide this support for the marketing manager.

16.11 The Wilson Company uses a great deal of water in the process of making industrial milling equipment. To comply with federal clean-water laws, it has a water purification system that all wastewater goes through before being discharged into a settling pond on the company's property. To determine whether the company is complying with federal requirements, sample measures are taken every so often. One requirement is that the median pH level must be less than 7.4. A sample of 95 pH measures has been taken. The data for these measures are shown in the CD-ROM file *Wilson Water*.

a. Carefully examine the data. Use an appropriate procedure to determine if the data could have been sampled from a normal distribution.

b. Based on the sample data of pH level, what should the company conclude about its current status on meeting federal requirements? Test the hypothesis at the 0.05 level.

16-2 NONPARAMETRIC TESTS FOR TWO POPULATION CENTERS

Chapters 8, 9, 10, and 11 introduced a variety of hypothesis-testing tools and techniques. Included were tests involving two or more population means. These tests carried with them several assumptions and requirements. For some situations in which you are testing about the difference between two population means, the student t-distribution is employed. The assumption for the t-distribution is that the two populations are normally distributed. The data are also restricted to being interval or ratio level. Although in many situations this assumption and the data requirements will be satisfied, you will often encounter situations in which that is not the case.

In this section we introduce two nonparametric techniques that do not require such stringent assumptions and data requirements: the *Mann–Whitney U test*[1] and the *Wilcoxon matched-pairs signed rank test*. Both tests can be used with ordinal (ranked) data, and neither requires that the populations be normally distributed. The Mann–Whitney U test is used when the samples are independent, whereas the Wilcoxon matched-pairs signed rank test is used when the design has paired samples.

THE MANN–WHITNEY *U* TEST

Blaine County Highway District—The workforce of the Blaine County Highway District (BCHD) is made up of the rural and urban divisions. A few months ago, several rural division supervisors began claiming that the urban division employees waste gravel from the county gravel pit. The supervisors claimed the urban division uses more gravel per mile of road maintenance than the rural division. In response to these claims, the BCHD materials manager performed a test. He selected a random sample from the district's job-cost records of jobs performed by the urban (U) division and jobs performed by the rural (R) division. The yards of gravel per mile for each job are recorded.

Even though the data are of a ratio-level measurement, the manager is not willing to make the normality assumptions necessary to employ the two-sample t-test (discussed in Chapter 9). However, the Mann–Whitney U test will allow him to compare the gravel use of the two divisions.

The Mann–Whitney U test is one of the most commonly used nonparametric tests that can be used to compare samples from two populations in those cases when the following assumptions are satisfied.

ASSUMPTIONS

1. The two samples are independent and random.
2. The value measured is a continuous variable.
3. The measurement scale used is at least ordinal.
4. If they differ, the distributions of the two populations will differ only with respect to central location.

---

[1]An equivalent test to the Mann–Whitney U test is the Wilcoxon rank-sum test.

The fourth point is instrumental in setting your null and alternative hypotheses. We are interested in determining whether two populations have the same or different centers, where the center is defined as the median. The test can be performed using the following steps.

STEP 1: State the appropriate null and alternative hypotheses. In this situation, the variable of interest is cubic yards of gravel used. This is a ratio-level variable, so the material manager has decided to test the following hypotheses, stated in terms of the population medians:

H_0: $\tilde{\mu}_U \leq \tilde{\mu}_R$ (Median urban gravel use is less than or equal to median rural use.)
H_A: $\tilde{\mu}_U > \tilde{\mu}_R$ (Urban median exceeds rural median.)

STEP 2: Specify the desired level of significance. The decision makers have determined that the test will be conducted using

$$\alpha = 0.05$$

STEP 3: Select the sample data and compute the appropriate test statistic. Computing the test statistic manually requires several steps.

1. Combine the raw data from the two samples into one set of numbers, keeping track of from which sample each value came.
2. Rank the numbers in this combined set from low to high. Note that we expect no ties to occur because the values are considered to have come from continuous distributions. However, in actual situations ties will sometimes occur. When they do, we give tied observations the average of the rank positions for which they are tied. For instance, if the lowest four data points were each 460, each of the four 460s would receive a rank of $(1 + 2 + 3 + 4)/4 = 10/4 = 2.5$.[2]
3. Separate the two samples, listing each observation with the rank it has been assigned. This leads to the rankings shown in Table 16-3.

   The logic of the Mann–Whitney U test centers on the idea that if the sum of the rankings of one sample differs greatly from the sum of the rankings of the second sample, we should conclude that there is a difference in the population medians.

4. Calculate a U-value for each sample, as shown in Equations 16-2 and 16-3.

U Statistics

$$U_1 = n_1 n_2 + \frac{n_1(n_1 + 1)}{2} - \Sigma R_1 \qquad \textbf{16-2}$$

$$U_2 = n_1 n_2 + \frac{n_2(n_2 + 1)}{2} - \Sigma R_2 \qquad \textbf{16-3}$$

where:

n_1 and n_2 are the two sample sizes
ΣR_1 and ΣR_2 = sum of ranks for samples 1 and 2

For our example using the ranks in Table 16-3,

$$U_1 = 12(12) + \frac{12(13)}{2} - 142$$
$$= 80$$
$$U_2 = 12(12) + \frac{12(13)}{2} - 158$$
$$= 64$$

Note that $U_1 + U_2 = n_1 n_2$. This is always the case, and it provides a good check on the correctness of the rankings in Table 16-3. Although not intuitively obvious, the higher the population median, the lower the value of U we would expect. Thus, if population 1 has the larger median, we would expect U_1 to be smaller.

5. Select the U-value to be the test statistic.

   The Mann–Whitney U tables in Appendices L and M give the lower tail of the U-distribution. For one-tailed tests such as our Blaine County example, you need to look at the alterna-

[2]Noether provides an adjustment when ties occur. He, however, points out that using the ties has little effect unless a large proportion of the observations are tied or there are ties of considerable extent. See the General References at the end of this chapter.

TABLE 16-3

Ranking of Yards of Gravel per Mile for the Blaine County Highway District Example

URBAN ($n_1 = 12$)		RURAL ($n_2 = 12$)	
Yards of Gravel	**Rank**	**Yards of Gravel**	**Rank**
460	2	600	6
830	16	652	9
720	12	603	7
930	20	594	5
500	4	1,402	23
620	8	1,111	21
703	11	902	18
407	1	700	10
1,521	24	827	15
900	17	490	3
750	13	904	19
800	14	1,400	22
	$\Sigma R_1 = 142$		$\Sigma R_2 = 158$

tive hypothesis to determine whether U_1 or U_2 should be selected as the test statistic. Recall that

$$H_A: \tilde{\mu}_U > \tilde{\mu}_R$$

If the alternative hypothesis indicates that population 1 has a higher median, as in this case, then U_1 is selected as the test statistic. If population 2 is expected to have a higher median, then U_2 should be selected as the test statistic. The reason is that the population with the largest median should have the largest sum of ranked values, thus producing the smallest U-value. It is very important to note that this logic must be made in terms of the alternative hypothesis and not on the basis of the U-values obtained from the samples.

Now, we select the U-value that the alternative hypothesis indicates should be the smallest and call this U. Because population 1 (urban) should have the smallest U-value (larger median) if the alternative hypothesis is true, the sample data give a

$$U = 80$$

This is actually higher than the U-value for the rural population, but we still use it as the test statistic because the alternative hypothesis indicates that $\tilde{\mu}_U > \tilde{\mu}_R$.[3]

STEP 4: Determine the critical value for the Mann–Whitney U test. For sample sizes less than 9, use the Mann–Whitney U table in Appendix L for the appropriate sample size. For sample sizes from 9 to 20, as in this example, the null hypothesis can be tested by comparing U with the appropriate critical value given in the Mann–Whitney U table in Appendix M. We begin by locating the part of the table associated with the desired significance level. In this case, we have a one-tailed test with

$$\alpha = 0.05$$

Go across the top of the Mann–Whitney U table to locate the value corresponding to the sample size from population 2 (Rural) and down the left side of the table to the sample size from population 1 (Urban).

In the Blaine County example, both sample sizes are 12, so we will use the Mann–Whitney table in Appendix M for $\alpha = 0.05$. Go across the top of the table to

$$n_2 = 12$$

and down the left-hand side to

$$n_1 = 12$$

The intersection of these column and row values gives a critical value of

$$U_\alpha = 42$$

We can now form the decision rule as follows.

If $U \le 42$, reject H_0;
Otherwise, do not reject H_0.

[3]For a two-tailed test, you should select the smaller U-value as your test statistic. This will force you toward the lower tail. If the U-value is smaller than the critical value in the Mann–Whitney U table, you will reject the null hypothesis.

STEP 5: Reach a decision. Now because

$$U = 80 > 42$$

we do not reject the null hypothesis.

STEP 6: Draw a conclusion. Therefore, based upon the sample data, there is not sufficient evidence to conclude that the median yards of gravel per mile used by the urban division is greater than that for the rural division.

Neither Excel nor the PHStat add-ins contain a Mann–Whitney U test, although you could program a spreadsheet to perform the appropriate calculations. Minitab does have this test procedure. Figure 16-2 shows the output for the Blaine County application. Note, Minitab actually uses the *Wilcoxon rank sum test*, which is equivalent to the Mann–Whitney test. The Wilcoxon test uses, as its test statistic, the sum of the ranks from the population that is supposed to have the largest median. Referring earlier to Table 16-3, Urban is supposed to have the largest median, and the sum of the ranks is 142. As shown in Figure 16-2, the two methods yield the same conclusions.

MANN–WHITNEY *U* TEST—LARGE SAMPLES

When you encounter a situation with sample sizes in excess of 20, the previous approaches to the Mann–Whitney U test cannot be used because of table limitations. However, the U statistic approaches a normal distribution as the sample sizes increase, and the Mann–Whitney U test can be conducted using a normal approximation approach, where the mean and standard deviation for the U statistic are as given in Equations 16-4 and 16-5, respectively.

Mean and Standard Deviation for *U* Statistic

$$\mu = \frac{n_1 n_2}{2} \qquad \textbf{16-4}$$

$$\sigma = \sqrt{\frac{(n_1)(n_2)(n_1 + n_2 + 1)}{12}} \qquad \textbf{16-5}$$

where:

n_1 and n_2 = Sample sizes from populations 1 and 2

Equations 16-4 and 16-5 are used to form the U test statistic in Equation 16-6.

Mann–Whitney *U* Test Statistic

$$z = \frac{U - \dfrac{n_1 n_2}{2}}{\sqrt{\dfrac{(n_1)(n_2)(n_1 + n_2 + 1)}{12}}} \qquad \textbf{16-6}$$

FIGURE 16-2

Minitab Output— Mann–Whitney *U* Test for the Blaine County Example

Minitab Instructions:
1. Enter data in columns.
2. Choose **Stat > Nonparametrics > Mann-Whitney**.
3. In **First Sample**, enter one data column.
4. In **Second Sample**, enter the other data column.
5. In **Alternative**, select *greater than*.
6. Click **OK**.

```
MINITAB - Blaine County.MPJ - [Session]
File  Edit  Data  Calc  Stat  Graph  Editor  Tools  Window  Help
```

Mann-Whitney Test and CI: Urban, Rural

```
         N   Median
Urban   12   735.0
Rural   12   763.5


Point estimate for ETA1-ETA2 is -78.5
95.4 Percent CI for ETA1-ETA2 is (-327.1,147.1)
W = 142.0
Test of ETA1 = ETA2 vs ETA1 > ETA2


Cannot reject since W is < 150.0
```

Excel and Minitab Tutorial

Future Vision—Consider an example involving the managers for a local network-television affiliate who were preparing for a national television advertising conference. The theme of the presentation was to center around the advantage for businesses to advertise on network TV rather than on cable. The managers believe that median household income for cable subscribers is less than the median for those who do not subscribe. Therefore, by advertising on network stations, businesses could reach a higher-income audience.

The managers are concerned with the median (as opposed to the mean) income because, as you discovered in Chapter 3, data such as household income are notorious for having large outliers. In such cases, the median is a preferable measure of the center of the data. The large outliers are also an indication that the data do not have a symmetric (such as the normal) distribution—a reason to use a nonparametric procedure such as the Mann–Whitney test.

The managers can use the Mann–Whitney U test and the following steps to conduct a test about the median incomes for cable subscribers versus nonsubscribers.

STEP 1: Specify the null and alternative hypotheses. Given that the managers believe that median household income for cable subscribers is less than the median for those who do not subscribe, the null and alternative hypotheses to be tested are

$$H_0: \tilde{\mu}_C \geq \tilde{\mu}_{NC}$$
$$H_A: \tilde{\mu}_C < \tilde{\mu}_{NC}$$

STEP 2: Specify the desired level of significance. The test is to be conducted using

$$\alpha = 0.05$$

STEP 3: Select the random sample and compute the test statistic. In the spirit of friendly cooperation, the network managers joined forces with the local cable provider, Future-Vision, to survey a total of 548 households (144 nonsubscribers and 404 cable subscribers) in the market area. The results of the survey are contained in the CD-ROM file *Future-Vision*. Given the size sample, we can use the large-sample approach to the Mann–Whitney U test. To compute the test statistic shown in Equation 16-6, use the following steps.

1. The income data must be converted to ranks. The sample data and ranks are in a CD-ROM file called *Future-Vision-Ranks*. Note that when data are tied in value, they share the same rank. For example if four values are tied for the fifth position, each one is assigned the average of rankings 5, 6, 7, and 8, or $(5 + 6 + 7 + 8)/4 = 6.5$.
2. Next, we use the file data to compute the U-value. The sum of the ranks for non–cable subscribers is

$$\Sigma R_1 = 41{,}204$$

and the sum of the ranks for cable subscribers is

$$\Sigma R_2 = 109{,}222$$

3. Based on sample sizes of

$$n_1 = 144$$

non-cable subscribers and

$$n_2 = 404$$

cable subscribers, we compute the U-values using Equations 16-2 and 16-3.

$$U_1 = 144(404) + \frac{144(145)}{2} - 41{,}204 = 27{,}412$$
$$U_2 = 144(404) + \frac{404(405)}{2} - 109{,}222 = 30{,}764$$

Because the alternative hypothesis predicts that non–cable subscribers will have a higher median, U_1 is selected to be U. Thus,

$$U = 27{,}412$$

4. We now substitute appropriate values into Equations 16-4 and 16-5.

$$\mu = \frac{n_1 n_2}{2} = \frac{(144)(404)}{2} = 29{,}088$$

and

$$\sigma = \sqrt{\frac{(n_1)(n_2)(n_1 + n_2 + 1)}{12}} = \sqrt{\frac{(144)(404)(144 + 404 + 1)}{12}} = 1{,}631.43$$

5. The test statistic is computed using Equation 16-6.

$$z = \frac{U - \dfrac{n_1 n_2}{2}}{\sqrt{\dfrac{(n_1)(n_2)(n_1 + n_2 + 1)}{12}}} = \frac{27{,}412 - 29{,}088}{\sqrt{\dfrac{(144)(404)(144 + 404 + 1)}{12}}} = \frac{-1{,}676}{1{,}631.43} = -1.027$$

STEP 4: Determine the critical value for the test. Based on a one-tailed test with $\alpha = 0.05$, the critical value from the standard normal distribution table is

$$-z_\alpha = -1.645$$

STEP 5: Reach a decision. Since $z = -1.027 > -1.645$ the null hypothesis cannot be rejected.

STEP 6: Draw a conclusion. This means that the claim that non–cable families have higher median incomes than cable families is not supported by the sample data.

Both Excel (using the PHStat add-in) and Minitab can be used to perform the Mann–Whitney U test. (See the CD-ROM tutorials.)

THE WILCOXON MATCHED-PAIRS SIGNED RANK TEST

The Mann–Whitney U test is a very useful nonparametric technique. However, as discussed in the Blaine County Highway District example, its use is limited to those situations in which the samples from the two populations are independent. As we discussed in Chapter 9, you will encounter decision situations in which the samples will be paired and, therefore, are not independent.

A nonparametric test called the *Wilcoxon matched-pairs signed rank test* has been developed for situations in which you have related samples and are unwilling or unable (due to data-level limitations) to use the paired-sample *t*-test. It is useful when the two related samples have a measurement scale that allows us to determine not only whether the pairs of observations differ, but also the magnitude of any difference. The Wilcoxon matched-pairs test can be used in those cases in which the following assumptions are satisfied.

SSUMPTIONS

1. The differences are measured on a continuous variable.
2. The measurement scale used is at least interval.
3. The distribution of the population differences is symmetric about their median.

*E*XAMPLE 16-2: SMALL-SAMPLE WILCOXON TEST

The Quick-Calc Company   Consider the Quick-Calc Financial Corporation, which develops and markets software add-ons for common personal-computer spreadsheet packages. To differentiate its products from the other packages on the market, Quick-Calc has built many macros into its software. According to Quick-Calc, once a user learns the macro keystrokes, complicated financial computations become much easier to perform.

As part of its product-development testing program, software engineers at Quick-Calc have selected a focus group of seven people who frequently use spreadsheet packages. Each person is given complicated financial and accounting data and is asked to prepare a detailed analysis. A systems program determines the amount of time each person takes to complete the task. Once the analysis is complete, these same seven individuals are given a training course in Quick-Calc add-ons. After the training course, they are given a similar set of data and are asked to do the same analysis. Again the systems software determines the time needed to complete the analysis.

You should recognize that the samples in this application are not independent because the same subjects are used in both cases. If the software engineers performing the analysis are unwilling to make the normal distribution assumption required of the paired-sample *t*-test, they can use the Wilcoxon matched-pairs signed rank test. This test can be conducted using the following steps.

Step 1: **Specify the appropriate null and alternative hypotheses.**
The null and alternative hypotheses being tested are

$$H_0: \tilde{\mu}_b \leq \tilde{\mu}_a$$
$$H_A: \tilde{\mu}_b > \tilde{\mu}_a \quad \text{(Median time will be smaller \textit{after} the Quick-Calc training.)}$$

Step 2: **Specify the desired level of significance.**
The test will be conducted using

$$\alpha = 0.025$$

Step 3: **Collect the sample data and compute the test statistic.**
The data are shown in Table 16-4.

First, we convert the data in Table 16-4 to differences. The column of differences, d, gives the "before minus after" differences. The next column is the rank of the d-values from low to high. Note that the ranks are determined without considering the sign on the d-value. However, once the rank is determined, the original sign on the d-value is attached to the rank. For example, $d = 13$ is given a rank of 7, whereas $d = -4$ has a rank of -3.

The final column is titled "Ranks with Smallest Expected Sum." To determine the values in this column, we take the absolute values of either the positive or the negative ranks, depending on which group has the smallest expected sum of absolute valued ranks. We look to the alternative hypothesis, which is

$$H_A: \tilde{\mu}_b > \tilde{\mu}_a$$

Because the before median is predicted to exceed the after median, we would expect the positive differences to exceed the negative differences. Therefore, the negative ranks should have the smaller sum, and therefore, should be used in the final column, as shown in Table 16-4. The critical value, T, is equal to the sum of absolute values of these negative ranks. Thus, $T = 5$.

Step 4: **Determine the critical value.**
To determine whether T is sufficiently small to reject the null hypothesis, we consult the Wilcoxon table of critical T-values in Appendix N. If the calculated T is less than or equal to the critical T from the table, the null hypothesis is rejected. For instance, with $\alpha = 0.025$ for our one-tailed test and $n = 7$ we get a critical value of

$$T_\alpha = 2$$

Step 5: **Reach a decision.**
Because

$$T = 5 > 2, \text{ do not reject } H_0$$

Step 6: **Draw a conclusion.**
Based on these sample data, the Quick-Calc Company has no basis for stating that its product will reduce the median time required to perform complicated financial analyses.

TABLE 16-4

Quick-Calc Financial Corporation Ranked Data

SUBJECT	BEFORE TRAINING	AFTER TRAINING	d	RANK OF d	RANKS WITH SMALLEST EXPECTED SUM
1	24	11	13	7	
2	20	18	2	1	
3	19	23	−4	−3	3
4	20	15	5	4	
5	13	16	−3	−2	2
6	28	22	6	5	
7	15	8	7	6	
					$T = 5$

Ties in the Data

If the two measurements of an observed data pair have the same values and, therefore, a d-value of 0, that case is dropped from the analysis and the sample size is reduced accordingly. You should note that this procedure favors rejecting the null hypothesis because we are eliminating cases in which the two sample points have exactly the same values.

If two or more d-values have the same absolute values, we assign the same rank to each one using the same approach as with the Mann–Whitney U test. For example, if we have two d-values that tie for ranks 4 and 5, we average them as $(4 + 5)/2 = 4.5$ and assign both a rank of 4.5. Studies have shown that this method of assigning ranks to ties has little effect on the Wilcoxon test results. For a more complete discussion of the effect of ties on the Wilcoxon matched-pairs signed rank test, please see the text by Marascuilo and McSweeney referenced at the end of this chapter.

Large-Sample Wilcoxon Test

If the sample size (number of matched pairs) exceeds 25, the Wilcoxon table of critical T-values in Appendix N cannot be used. However, it can be shown that for large samples, the distribution of T-values is approximately normal, with a mean and standard deviation given by Equations 16-7 and 16-8, respectively.

Wilcoxon Mean and Standard Deviation

$$\mu = \frac{n(n + 1)}{4} \qquad \text{16-7}$$

$$\sigma = \sqrt{\frac{n(n + 1)(2n + 1)}{24}} \qquad \text{16-8}$$

where:

$$n = \text{Number of paired values}$$

The *Wilcoxon test statistic* is given by Equation 16-9.

Wilcoxon Test Statistic

$$z = \frac{T - \dfrac{n(n + 1)}{4}}{\sqrt{\dfrac{n(n + 1)(2n + 1)}{24}}} \qquad \text{16-9}$$

Then, the z-value is compared to the critical value from the standard normal table in the usual manner.

16-2: EXERCISES

Skill Development

16.12 The following sample data have been collected from two independent samples from two populations. The claim is that the second population median will exceed the median of the first population.

Sample 1		Sample 2	
12	11	9	20
21	14	18	7
15	12	16	12
10	8	17	19

a. State the appropriate null and alternative hypotheses.
b. If you are unwilling to assume that the two populations are normally distributed, based on the sample data, what should you conclude about the null hypothesis? Test using $\alpha = 0.05$.

16.13 For each of the following tests, determine which of the two U statistics (U_1 or U_2) you would choose, the appropriate test statistic, and the rejection region for the Mann–Whitney test:

a. H_A: $\tilde{\mu}_1 < \tilde{\mu}_2$, $\alpha = 0.05$, $n_1 = 5$, and $n_2 = 10$
b. H_A: $\tilde{\mu}_1 > \tilde{\mu}_2$, $\alpha = 0.05$, $n_1 = 15$, and $n_2 = 12$

c. H_A: $\tilde{\mu}_1 \neq \tilde{\mu}_2$, $\alpha = 0.10$, $n_1 = 12$, and $n_2 = 17$

d. H_A: $\tilde{\mu}_1 < \tilde{\mu}_2$, $\alpha = 0.05$, $n_1 = 22$, and $n_2 = 25$

e. H_A: $\tilde{\mu}_1 \neq \tilde{\mu}_2$, $\alpha = 0.10$, $n_1 = 44$, and $n_2 = 15$

16.14 The following sample data have been collected from two independent random samples from two populations. The claim is that the first population median will exceed the median of the second population.

Sample 1		Sample 2	
50	43	38	31
47	46	44	38
44	72	38	39
48	40	37	54
40	55	43	41
36	38	44	40

a. State the appropriate null and alternative hypotheses.

b. Using the Mann–Whitney U test, based on the sample data, what should you conclude about the null hypothesis? Test using a significance level of 0.01.

16.15 The following sample data have been collected from independent samples from two populations. The claim is that the first population median will be at least as large as the median of the second population.

Sample 1		Sample 2	
4.4	2.6	3.7	4.2
2.7	2.4	3.5	5.2
1.0	2.0	4.0	4.4
3.5	2.8	4.9	4.3
2.8		3.1	

a. State the appropriate null and alternative hypotheses.

b. Using the Mann–Whitney U test, based on the sample data, what should you conclude about the null hypothesis? Test using $\alpha = 0.05$.

16.16 Determine the rejection region for the Mann–Whitney U test in each of the following cases:

a. H_A: $\tilde{\mu}_1 < \tilde{\mu}_2$, $\alpha = 0.05$, $n_1 = 3$, and $n_2 = 15$

b. H_A: $\tilde{\mu}_1 \neq \tilde{\mu}_2$, $\alpha = 0.10$, $n_1 = 5$, and $n_2 = 20$

c. H_A: $\tilde{\mu}_1 < \tilde{\mu}_2$, $\alpha = 0.025$, $n_1 = 9$, and $n_2 = 12$

d. H_A: $\tilde{\mu}_1 \neq \tilde{\mu}_2$, $\alpha = 0.10$, $n_1 = 124$, and $n_2 = 25$

16.17 The following sample data have been collected from independent samples from two populations. Do the populations have different medians? Test at a significance level of 0.05.

Sample 1		Sample 2	
550	489	594	538
483	480	542	505
379	433	447	486
438	436	466	425
398	540	560	497
582	415	447	511
528	532	526	576
502	412	446	558
352	572	573	500
488	579	542	467
400	556	473	556
451	383	418	383
571	515	511	515
382	501	510	501
588	353	577	353
465	369	585	
492	475	436	
384	470	461	
563	595	545	
506	361	441	

16.18 For each of the following tests, determine which of the two sums of absolute ranks (negative or positive) you would choose, the appropriate test statistic, and the rejection region for the Wilcoxon matched pairs signed rank test:

a. H_A: $\tilde{\mu}_1 < \tilde{\mu}_2$, $\alpha = 0.025$, $n = 15$

b. H_A: $\tilde{\mu}_1 > \tilde{\mu}_2$, $\alpha = 0.01$, $n = 12$

c. H_A: $\tilde{\mu}_1 \neq \tilde{\mu}_2$, $\alpha = 0.05$, $n = 9$

d. H_A: $\tilde{\mu}_1 < \tilde{\mu}_2$, $\alpha = 0.05$, $n = 26$

e. H_A: $\tilde{\mu}_1 \neq \tilde{\mu}_2$, $\alpha = 0.10$, $n = 44$

16.19 Given two paired samples with the following information:

Item	Sample 1	Sample 2
1	19.6	21.3
2	22.1	17.4
3	19.5	19.0
4	20.0	21.2
5	21.5	20.1
6	20.2	23.5
7	17.9	18.9
8	23.0	22.4
9	12.5	14.3
10	19.0	17.8

Based on these paired samples, test at the $\alpha = 0.05$ level whether the true median paired difference is 0.

16.20 Given two paired samples with the following information:

Item	Sample 1	Sample 2
1	3.4	2.8
2	2.5	3.0
3	7.0	5.5
4	5.9	6.7
5	4.0	3.5
6	5.0	5.0
7	6.2	7.5
8	5.3	4.2

a. Based on these paired samples, test at the $\alpha = 0.05$ level whether the true median paired difference is 0.

b. Suppose the data given here were sampled from normal distributions with equal variances. Answer part a.

16.21 Given two paired samples with the following information:

Item	Sample 1	Sample 2
1	1,004	1,045
2	1,245	1,145
3	1,360	1,400
4	1,150	1,000
5	1,300	1,350
6	1,450	1,350
7	900	1,140

Based on these paired samples, test at the $\alpha = 0.05$ level whether the true median paired difference is 0.

16.22 From a recent study we have collected the following data from two independent random samples:

Sample 1	Sample 2
405	300
450	340
290	400
370	250
345	270
460	410
425	435
275	390
380	225
330	210
500	395
215	315

Suppose we do not wish to assume normal distributions. Use the appropriate nonparametric test to determine whether the populations have equal medians. Test at the $\alpha = 0.05$.

16.23 Given two paired samples with the following information:

Item	Sample 1	Sample 2
1	234	245
2	221	224
3	196	194
4	245	267
5	234	230
6	204	198

Based on these paired samples, test at the $\alpha = 0.05$ level whether the true median paired difference is 0.

16.24 Consider the following data for two paired samples.

Case #	Sample 1	Sample 2
1	258	304
2	197	190
3	400	500
4	350	340
5	237	250
6	400	358
7	370	390
8	130	100

a. Test the following null and alternative hypotheses at an $\alpha = 0.05$ level:

H_0: There is no difference between the two population distributions.
H_A: There is a difference between the two populations.

b. Answer part a as if the samples were independent samples from normal distributions with equal variances.

Business Applications

16.25 The makers of the Plus 20 Hardcard, a plug-in hard disk unit on a PC board, have recently done a marketing research study in which they asked two independently selected groups to rate the Hardcard on a scale of 1 to 100, with 100 being perfect satisfaction. The first group consisted of professional computer programmers. The second group consisted of home computer users. The company hoped to be able to say that the product would receive the same median ranking from each group. The following summary data were recorded.

Professionals	Home Users
$n = 10$	$n = 8$
Sum of ranks = 92	Sum of ranks = 79

Based on these data, what should the company conclude? Test at the $\alpha = 0.02$ level.

16.26 The Acme Speed Reading Company claims that graduates of its program have a higher median reading speed per minute than people who do not take the course. An independent agency conducted a study to determine whether this claim was justified. Researchers from the agency selected a random sample of people who had taken the speed reading course and another random sample of people who had not taken the course. The agency was unwilling to make the assumption that the populations were normally distributed. Therefore, a nonparametric test was needed. The following summary data were observed:

With Course	Without Course
$n = 7$	$n = 5$
Sum of ranks = 42	Sum of ranks = 36

Assuming that higher ranks imply more words per minute being read, what should the testing agency conclude based on the sample data? Test at an $\alpha = 0.05$ level.

16.27 The Tax Commission for a midwestern state recently conducted a study to determine whether there is a difference in median deductions taken for charitable contributions depending on whether a tax return is filed as a single or a joint return. A random sample from each category was selected, with the following results:

Single	Joint
$n = 6$	$n = 8$
Sum of ranks = 43	Sum of ranks = 62

Based on these data, what should the tax commission conclude? Use an $\alpha = 0.05$ level.

16.28 Property taxes are based on assessed values of property. In most states, the law requires that assessed values be "at or near" market value of the property. In one Washington county, a tax protest group has claimed that assessed values are higher than market values. To address this claim, the county tax assessor, together with representatives from the protest group, has selected 15 properties at random that have sold within the past six months. Both parties agree that the sales price was the market value at the time of the sale.

The assessor then listed the assessed values and the sales values side-by-side, as shown.

House	Assessed Value	Market Value
1	$102,000	$ 98,000
2	76,000	82,400
3	49,000	54,300
4	98,500	98,500
5	114,000	118,000
6	135,000	130,000
7	205,000	198,900
8	87,500	90,000
9	50,000	49,800
10	123,000	122,000
11	78,500	80,000
12	145,000	150,900
13	67,000	65,200
14	119,000	120,700
15	234,000	220,000

a. Assuming that the population of assessed values and the population of market values have the same shape distribution and that they may differ only with respect to medians, state the appropriate null and alternative hypotheses.
b. Test the hypotheses using an $\alpha = 0.01$ level.
c. Discuss why one would not assume that the samples were obtained from normal distributions for this problem. What characteristic about the market values of houses would lead you to conclude that these data were not normally distributed?

16.29 A cattle feedlot operator has collected data for 40 matched pairs of cattle showing weight gain on two different feed supplements. His purpose in collecting the data is to determine whether there is a difference in the median weight gain for the two supplements. He has no preconceived idea about which supplement might produce higher weight gain. He wishes to test using an $\alpha = 0.05$ level.

Assuming that the T-value for these data is 480, what should be concluded concerning which supplement might produce higher weight gain? Use the large-sample Wilcoxon matched-pairs signed rank test normal approximation. Conduct the test using a p-value approach.

16.30 Radio advertisements have been stressing the virtues of an audiotape program to help children learn to read. To test whether this tape program can cause a quick improvement in reading ability, 10 children were given a nationally recognized reading test that measures reading ability. The same 10 children were then given the tapes to listen to for four hours spaced over a two-day period. The children then were tested again. The test scores were as follows:

Child	Before	After
1	60	63
2	40	38
3	78	77
4	53	50
5	67	74
6	88	96
7	77	80
8	60	70
9	64	65
10	75	75

Use the Wilcoxon matched-pairs signed rank test to test whether this tape program produces quick improvement in reading ability. Use an $\alpha = 0.025$.

Advanced Applications

16.31 For at least the past 20 years, there has been a debate over whether children who are placed in child care facilities while their parents work suffer as a result. A recent study discussed in the March 1999 issue of *Developmental Psychology*, of 6,000 children found "no permanent negative effects caused by their mothers' absence." In fact, the study indicated that there might be some positive benefits from the day care experience. To investigate this premise, a nonprofit organization called Child Care Connections conducted a small study in which children were observed playing in neutral settings (not at home or at a day care center). Over a period of 20 hours of observation, 15 children who did not go to day care and 21 children who had spent much time in day care were observed. The variable of interest was the total minutes of play in which each child was actively interacting with other students. Child Care Connections leaders hoped to show that the children who had been in day care would have a higher median time in interactive situations than the stay-at-home children. The CD-ROM file *Children* contains the results of the study.

a. Conduct a hypothesis test to determine if the hopes of the Child Care Connections leaders can be substantiated. Use a significance level of 0.05, and write a short statement that describes the results of the test.

b. Based on the outcome of the hypothesis test, which statistical error might have been committed?

16.32 🌐 The California State Highway Patrol recently conducted a study on a stretch of interstate highway south of San Francisco to determine whether the mean speed for California vehicles exceeded the mean speed for out-of-state vehicles. A total of 140 California cars were included in the study, whereas 75 out-of-state cars were included. Radar was used to measure the speed. The CD-ROM file *Speed-Test* contains the data collected by the California Highway Patrol.

a. Past studies have indicated that the speeds at which both out-of-state and California drivers drive have normal distributions. However, the out-of-state drivers have a much larger variance in the speeds they drive. Using a significance level equal to 0.10, obtain the results desired by the California Highway Patrol. Use a *p*-value approach to conduct the relevant hypothesis test. Discuss the results of this test in a short written statement.

b. Describe in the context of this problem what a Type I error would be.

16.33 💿 The Sunbeam Corporation makes a wide variety of appliances for the home. One product is a digital blood pressure gauge. For obvious reasons, the blood pressure readings made by the monitor need to be accurate. When a new model is being designed, one of the steps is to test it. To do this, a sample of people is selected. Each person has his/her systolic blood pressure taken by a highly respected physician. They then immediately have their systolic blood pressure taken using the Sunbeam monitor. If the mean blood pressure is the same for the monitor as it is as determined by the physician, the monitor is determined to pass the test.

In a recent test, 15 people were randomly selected to be in the sample. The blood pressure readings for these people using both methods are contained in the CD-ROM file *Sunbeam*.

a. Based on the sample data and a significance level equal to 0.05, what conclusion should the Sunbeam engineers reach regarding the latest blood pressure monitor? Discuss your answer in a short written statement.

b. Conduct the test as a paired *t*-test.

c. Discuss which of the two procedures in parts a and b is more appropriate to analyze the data presented in this problem.

16.34 🌐 The Hersh Corporation is considering two word-processing systems for its computers. One factor that will influence its decision is the ease of use in preparing a business report. Consequently, nine typists were selected from the clerical pool and asked to type a typical report using both word-processing systems. The typists then rated the systems on a scale of 0 to 100. The resulting ratings are in the CD-ROM file *Hersh*.

a. Which measurement level describes the data collected for this analysis?

b. (1) Could a normal distribution describe the population distribution from which these data were sampled? (2) Which measure of central tendency would be appropriate to describe the center of the populations from which these data were sampled?

c. Choose the appropriate hypothesis procedure to determine if there is a difference in the measures of central tendency you selected in part b between these two word-processing systems. Use a significance level of 0.01.

d. Which word-processing system would you recommend the Hersh Corporation adopt? Support your answer with statistical reasoning.

16.35 The Montgomery Athletic Shoe Company has developed a new shoe sole material it thinks provides superior wear compared with the old material the company has been using for its running shoes. The company selected 10 cross-country runners and supplied each runner with a pair of shoes. Each pair had one sole made of the old material and the other made of the new material. The shoes were monitored until the soles were worn out. The following lifetimes (in hours) were recorded for each material

Runner	Old Material	New Material
1	45.5	47.0
2	50.0	51.0
3	43.0	42.0
4	45.5	46.0
5	58.5	58.0
6	49.0	50.5
7	29.5	39.0
8	52.0	53.0
9	48.0	48.0
10	57.5	61.0

a. If the populations from which these samples were taken could be considered to have normal distributions, determine if the soles made of the new material have a longer mean lifetime than those made from the old material. Use a significance level of 0.025.

b. Suppose you were not willing to consider that the populations have normal distributions. Make the determination requested in part a.

c. Given only the information in this problem, which of the two procedures indicated in parts a and b would you choose to use? Give reasons for your answer.

16-3 KRUSKAL-WALLIS ONE-WAY ANALYSIS OF VARIANCE

Section 16-2 showed that the Mann–Whitney U test is a useful nonparametric procedure for determining whether two independent samples are from populations with the same median. However, as discussed in Chapter 11, many decisions involve comparing more than two populations. Chapter 11 introduced one-way analysis of variance and showed how, if the assumptions of normally distributed populations with equal variances are satisfied, the F-distribution can be used to test the hypothesis of equal population means. However, what if decision makers are not willing to assume normally distributed populations? In that case, they can turn to a nonparametric procedure to compare the populations. *Kruskal-Wallis One-Way Analysis of Variance* is the nonparametric counterpart to the one-way ANOVA procedure presented in Chapter 11. It is applicable any time the variables in question satisfy the following conditions:

SSUMPTIONS

1. They have a continuous distribution.
2. The data are at least ordinal.
3. The samples are independent.
4. The samples come from populations whose only possible difference is that at least one may have a different central location than the others.

The East Hope Medical Center—The East Hope Medical Center is considering acquiring a distributed client-server computer system to handle its online data-processing activities, including patient scheduling, facility assignment, and general accounting and billing. On the basis of cost and performance standards, the medical center's information systems manager has reduced the possible suppliers to three. One critical factor in the decision is downtime (the time when the system is not operational). When the system goes down, the online applications stop and normal hospital activities are interrupted. The information systems manager received from each supplier a list of firms using its system. From these lists, the manager selected random samples of nine users of each computer system. In a telephone interview, she found the number of hours of downtime in the previous month for each system. At issue is whether the centers of the three populations are different. If the manager is unwilling to make the assumptions of normality and equal variances required for the one-way ANOVA technique introduced in Chapter 11, she can implement the Kruskal-Wallis nonparametric test using the following steps.

STEP 1: Specify the appropriate null and alternative hypotheses to be tested. In this application we are interested in determining whether a difference exists between median downtime for the three systems. Thus, the null and alternative hypotheses are

$$H_0: \tilde{\mu}_1 = \tilde{\mu}_2 = \tilde{\mu}_3$$
$$H_A: \text{Not all population medians are equal.}$$

STEP 2: Specify the desired level of significance for the test. The test will be conducted using a significance level equal to

$$\alpha = 0.10$$

STEP 3: Collect the sample data and compute the test statistic. The data represent a random sample of downtimes from each system. The samples are independent. To use the Kruskal-Wallis ANOVA, first replace each downtime measurement by its *relative ranking* within all groups combined. The smallest downtime is given a rank of 1, the next smallest a rank of 2, and so forth, until all downtimes for the three systems have been replaced by their relative rankings. Table 16-5 shows the sample data and the rankings for the 27 observations. Notice that the rankings are summed for each computer system. The Kruskal-Wallis test will determine whether these sums are so different that it is not likely that they came from populations with equal medians.

If the samples actually do come from populations with equal medians (that is, the three systems have the same per-month median downtime), then the H-statistic, calculated by Equation 16-10, will be approximately distributed as a chi-square variable with $k - 1$ degrees of freedom, where k equals the number of samples under study.

	SYSTEM A		SYSTEM B		SYSTEM C	
Data	**Ranking**	**Data**	**Ranking**	**Data**	**Ranking**
4.0	11	6.9	19	0.5	1
3.7	10	11.3	23	1.4	4
5.1	15	21.7	27	1.0	2
2.0	6	9.2	20	1.7	5
4.6	12	6.5	17	3.6	9
9.3	21	4.9	14	5.2	16
2.7	8	12.2	25	1.3	3
2.5	7	11.7	24	6.8	18
4.8	13	10.5	22	14.1	26
Sum of ranks = 103		Sum of ranks = 191		Sum of ranks = 84	

TABLE 16-5

Sample Data and Rankings of System Downtimes for the East Hope Medical Center Example

---

H Statistic

$$H = \frac{12}{N(N+1)} \sum_{i=1}^{k} \frac{R_i^2}{n_i} - 3(N+1) \qquad \textbf{16-10}$$

where:

N = Sum of the sample sizes in all samples
k = Number of samples
R_i = Sum of ranks in the ith sample
n_i = Size of the ith sample

Using Equation 16-10, the H statistic is

$$H = \frac{12}{N(N+1)} \sum_{i=1}^{k} \frac{R_i^2}{n_i} - 3(N+1)$$

$$= \frac{12}{27(27+1)} \left[\frac{103^2}{9} + \frac{191^2}{9} + \frac{84^2}{9} \right] - 3(27+1) = 11.50$$

STEP 4: Determine the critical value from the chi-square distribution. If H is larger than χ^2 from the chi-square distribution with $k - 1$ degrees of freedom in Appendix G, the hypothesis of equal medians should be rejected. The critical value for $\alpha = 0.10$ and

$$k - 1 = 3 - 1 = 2$$

degrees of freedom is

$$\chi_\alpha^2 = 4.605$$

STEP 5: Reach a decision. Since $H = 11.50 > 4.605$ reject the null hypothesis based on these sample data.

STEP 6: Draw a conclusion. Thus, the Kruskal-Wallis one-way ANOVA shows the information systems manager should conclude, based on the sample data, that the three computer systems *do not* have equal median downtimes. From this analysis, the supplier of system B would most likely be eliminated from consideration unless other factors such as price or service offset the apparent longer downtimes.

EXAMPLE 16-3: USING KRUSKAL-WALLIS ONE-WAY ANOVA

Amalgamated Sugar   Amalgamated Sugar has recently begun a new effort called total productive maintenance (TPM). The TPM concept is to increase the overall operating effectiveness of the company's equipment. One component of the TPM process attempts to reduce unplanned

Excel and Minitab Tutorial

machine downtime. The first step is to gain an understanding of the current downtime situation. To do this, a sample of 20 days has been collected for each of the three shifts (day, swing, and graveyard). The variable of interest is the minutes of unplanned downtime per shift per day. The minutes are tabulated by summing the downtime minutes for all equipment in the plant. The Kruskal-Wallis test can be performed using the following steps.

Step 1:   **State the appropriate null and alternative hypotheses.**
The Kruskal-Wallis one-way ANOVA procedure can test whether the medians are equal, as follows:

$$H_0: \tilde{\mu}_1 = \tilde{\mu}_2 = \tilde{\mu}_3$$
$$H_A: \text{Not all population medians are the same.}$$

Step 2:   **Specify the desired significance level for the test.**
The test will be conducted using an

$$\alpha = 0.05$$

Step 3:   **Collect the sample data and compute the test statistic.**
The sample data are in the *Amalgamated* file on your CD-ROM.
Both Minitab and Excel (using the PHStat add-ins) can be used to perform Kruskal-Wallis nonparametric ANOVA tests.* Figures 16-3a and 16-3b illustrate the Excel and Minitab outputs for these sample data. The calculated H statistic is

$$H = 0.185902$$

Step 4:   **Determine the critical value from the chi-square distribution.**
The critical value for $\alpha = 0.05$ and $k - 1 = 2$ degrees of freedom is

$$\chi_\alpha^2 = 5.9915$$

Step 5:   **Reach a decision.**
Because

$$H = 0.185902 < 5.9915$$
we do not reject the null hypothesis.

FIGURE 16-3A

Excel (PHStat) Kruskal-Wallis ANOVA Output for Amalgamated Sugar

Excel Instructions:
1. Open file: Amalgamated.xls
2. Click on the **PHStat** tab.
3. Select *c*-**Sample** Tests.
4. Select **Kruskal-Wallis Rank Test** option.
5. Define the data range.

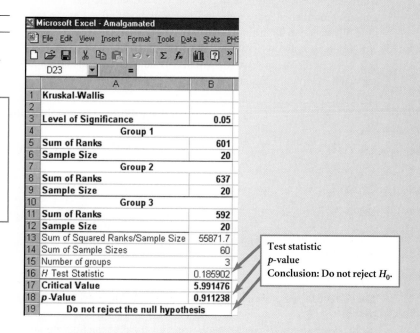

*In Minitab, the variable of interest must be in one column. A second column contains the population identifier. In Excel, the data are placed in separate columns by population. The column headings identify the population.

FIGURE 16-3B

FIGURE **16-3B**

Minitab Kruskal-Wallis
ANOVA Output for
Amalgamated Sugar

Minitab Instructions:
1. Open file: Amalgamated.MTW.
2. Choose **Data > Stack > Columns**.
3. In **Stack the following columns**, enter data columns.
4. In **Store the stacked data in**, select **Column of current worksheet**, and enter column name: *Downtime*.
5. In **Store subscripts in**, enter column name: *Shifts*. Click **OK**.
6. Choose **Stat > Nonparametrics > Kruskal-Wallace**.
7. In **Response**, enter data column: *Downtime*.
8. In **Factor**, enter factor levels column: *Shifts*.
9. Click **OK**.

Also, the PHStat output provides the *p*-value associated with the H statistic. The *p*-value of 0.911238 far exceeds an alpha of 0.05.

Step 6:   Draw a conclusion.
Thus, based on the sample data, the three shifts do not appear to differ with respect to median equipment downtime. The company can now begin to work on steps that will reduce the downtime across the three shifts.

LIMITATIONS AND OTHER CONSIDERATIONS

The Kruskal-Wallis one-way ANOVA does *not* require the assumption of normality and is, therefore, often used instead of the ANOVA technique discussed in Chapter 11. However, the Kruskal-Wallis test as discussed here applies only if the sample size from each population is at least 5, the samples are independently selected, and each population has the same distribution except for a possible difference in central location.

When ranking observations, you will sometimes encounter ties. When ties occur, each observation is given the mean rank for which it is tied. The H statistic is influenced by ties and should be corrected by dividing Equation 16-10 by Equation 16-11.

Correction for Tied Rankings—Kruskal-Wallis Test

$$1 - \frac{\sum_{i=1}^{g}(t_i^3 - t_i)}{N^3 - N}$$

16-11

where:

g = Number of different groups of ties
t_i = Number of tied observations in the ith tied group of scores
N = Total number of observations

The correct formula for calculating the Kruskal-Wallis H statistic when ties are present is Equation 16-12.

Correcting for ties increases H and thus makes rejecting the null hypothesis more likely than if the correction is not used. A rule of thumb is that if no more than 25% of the observations are involved in ties, the correction factor is not required. Note that if you use Minitab to perform the Kruskal-Wallis test, the adjusted H statistic is provided. The PHStat add-in to Excel for performing the Kruskal-Wallis test does not provide the adjusted H statistic. However, the adjustment is only necessary when the null hypothesis is not rejected and the H statistic is "close" to the rejection region. In that case, making the proper adjustment could lead to rejecting the null hypothesis.

H Statistic Corrected for Tied Rankings

$$H = \frac{\dfrac{12}{N(N + 1)} \sum_{i=1}^{k} \dfrac{R_i^2}{n_i} - 3(N + 1)}{1 - \dfrac{\sum_{i=1}^{g} (t_i^3 - t_i)}{N^3 - N}}$$

16-12

16-3: EXERCISES

Skill Development

16.36 Given the following sample data:

Item	Group 1	Group 2	Group 3
1	10	8	13
2	9	6	12
3	11	8	12
4	12	9	11
5	13	10	13
6	12	10	15

a. State the appropriate null and alternative hypotheses for determining whether a difference exists in the median value for the three populations.

b. Based on the sample data, use the Kruskal-Wallis ANOVA procedure to test the null hypothesis using $\alpha = 0.05$. What conclusion should be reached?

16.37 Given the following sample data:

Group 1	Group 2	Group 3
21	17	29
25	15	38
36	34	28
35	22	27
33	16	14
23	19	26
31	30	39
32	20	36

a. State the appropriate null and alternative hypotheses to test whether there is a difference in the medians of the three populations.

b. Based on the sample data and a significance level of 0.05, what conclusion should be reached about the medians of the three populations if you are not willing to make the assumption that the populations are normally distributed?

c. Test the hypothesis stated in part a, assuming that the populations are normally distributed with equal variances.

d. Given the information given in the heading to this exercise, which of the procedures described in parts b and c would you select to analyze the data? Explain your reasoning.

16.38 Given the following data:

Item	Group 1	Group 2	Group 3	Group 4
1	20	28	17	21
2	27	26	15	23
3	26	21	18	19
4	22	29	20	17
5	25	30	14	20
6	30	25		
7	23			

a. State the appropriate null and alternative hypotheses for determining whether a difference exists in the median value for the four populations.

b. Based on the sample data, use the Kruskal-Wallis one-way ANOVA procedure to test the null hypothesis. What conclusion should be reached using a significance level of 0.10? Discuss.

c. Determine the H-value adjusted for ties.

d. Given the results in part b, is it necessary to use the H-value adjusted for ties? If it is, conduct the hypothesis test using this adjusted value of H. If not, explain why not.

16.39 A study was conducted in which samples were selected independently from four populations. The sample size from each population was 20. The data were converted to ranks. The sum of the ranks for the data from each sample is

	Sample 1	Sample 2	Sample 3	Sample 4
Sum of Ranks	640	780	460	1,360

a. State the appropriate null and alternative hypotheses if we wish to determine whether the populations have equal medians.

b. Use the information in this exercise to perform a Kruskal-Wallis one-way ANOVA.

Business Applications

16.40 A study was conducted by the sports department of a national-network television station in which the objective was to determine whether a difference exists between median annual salaries of NBA basketball players, NFL football players, and MLB baseball players. The analyst in charge of the study believes that the normal distribution assumption is violated in this study. Thus, she thinks that a nonparametric test is in order.

The following summary data have been collected.

NBA	NFL	MLB
$n = 20$	$n = 30$	$n = 40$
$\Sigma R_i = 1{,}655$	$\Sigma R_i = 1{,}100$	$\Sigma R_i = 1{,}340$

a. Why would the sports department address the median as the parameter of interest in this analysis, as opposed to the mean? Explain your answer.
b. What characteristics of the salaries of professional athletes suggest that such data are not normally distributed? Explain.
c. Based on these data, what can be concluded about the median salaries for the three sports? Test at an $\alpha = 0.05$. Assume no ties.

16.41 Referring to Exercise 16-40, suppose that there were 40 ties at eight different salary levels. The following shows how many scores were ties at each salary level:

Level	t
1	2
2	3
3	2
4	4
5	8
6	10
7	6
7	5

a. Given the results in the previous exercise, is it necessary to use the H-value adjusted for ties?
b. If your answer to part a is yes, conduct the test of hypothesis using this adjusted value of H. If it is not, explain why not.

16.42 The American Beef Growers Association is trying to promote the consumption of beef products. The organization performs numerous studies, the results of which are often used in advertising campaigns. One such study involved a quality perception test. Three grades of beef were involved: choice, standard, and economy. A random sample of people was provided pieces of choice-grade beefsteak and was asked to rate its quality on a scale of 1 to 100. A second sample of people was given pieces of standard-grade beefsteak, and a third sample was given pieces of economy-grade

beefsteak, with instructions to rate the beef on the 100-point scale. The following data were obtained.

Choice	Standard	Economy
78	67	65
87	80	62
90	78	70
87	80	66
89	67	70
90	70	73

a. What measurement level do these data possess? Would it be appropriate to assume that such data could be obtained from a normal distribution? Explain your answers.
b. Based on the sample data, what conclusions should be reached concerning the median quality perception scores for the three grades of beef? Test using an alpha = 0.01.

16.43 As purchasing agent for the Horner-Williams Company, you have primary responsibility for securing high-quality raw materials at the best possible prices. One particular material the Horner-Williams Company uses a great deal is aluminum. After careful study, you have been able to reduce the prospective vendors to three. It is unclear whether these three vendors produce aluminum that is equally durable.

To compare durability, the recommended procedure is to put pressure on aluminum until it cracks. The vendor whose aluminum requires the highest mean pressure will be judged to be the one that provides the most durable product. To carry out this test, 14 pieces from each vendor have been selected. These data are in the CD-ROM file *Horner-Williams*. (The data are pounds per square inch pressure.) Using $\alpha = 0.05$, what should the company conclude about whether there is a difference in the mean strength of the three vendors' aluminum?

16.44 Suppose as part of your job you are responsible for installing emergency lighting in a series of state office buildings. Bids have been received from four manufacturers of battery-operated emergency lights. The costs are about equal, so the decision will be based on the length of time the lights last before failing. A sample of four lights from each manufacturer has been tested, with the following values (time in hours) recorded for each manufacturer.

Type A	Type B	Type C	Type D
1,024	1,270	1,121	923
1,121	1,325	1,201	983
1,250	1,426	1,190	1,087
1,022	1,322	1,122	1,121

Using $\alpha = 0.01$, what conclusion should you reach about the median length of time the lights last before failing for the four manufacturers? Explain.

Advanced Applications

16.45 A large metropolitan police force is considering changing from full-size to mid-size cars. The police force sampled cars from each of three manufacturers. The number sampled represents the number that the manufacturer was able to provide for the test. Each car was driven for 5,000 miles, and the operating cost per mile was computed. The operating costs, in cents per mile, for the 21 cars are provided in the CD-ROM file *Police*. Perform the appropriate ANOVA test on these data. Assume a significance level of 0.05. State the appropriate null and alternative hypotheses. Do the experimental data provide evidence that the median operating costs per mile for the three types of police cars are different?

16.46 A nationwide moving company is considering five different types of nylon tie-down straps. The purchasing department randomly selected straps from each company and determined their breaking strengths in pounds. The sample data are contained in the CD-ROM file *Nylon*. Based on your analysis, with a Type I error rate of 0.05, can you conclude that a difference exists among the median breaking strengths of the types of nylon ropes?

OPTIONAL CD-ROM TOPIC SPEARMAN RANK CORRELATION

The correlation coefficient introduced in Chapter 11 assumed that the data for the two variables are at least interval scaled and the joint distribution of the variables is bivariate normal. However, a nonparametric correlation coefficient called the Spearman Rank Correlation does not have these data restrictions. For more about this, go to the CD-ROM.

Summary and Conclusions

Many people make the mistake of learning one or two statistical techniques and then using these techniques in all situations. Surprisingly, some people even get emotional about being able to analyze a particular problem using their favorite technique. As a future manager and decision maker, you cannot afford the luxury of defining a problem situation so you can apply your favorite technique. Statistics should be an aid to decision making, not an end in itself.

Many powerful statistical tools discussed in this book rest on the assumptions that the data being analyzed can be measured by at least an interval scale and that the underlying populations being analyzed are normal. If these assumptions come close to being satisfied, many of the tools discussed before this chapter apply and are useful. However, in many practical situations these assumptions just do not apply. In such cases the tools discussed in this chapter may be appropriate. In any case, nonparametric statistical tests should be part of every decision maker's tools. There are many other nonparametric statistical techniques that have been developed for specific applications. Many are aimed at situations involving small samples. Figure 16-4 may help you determine which nonparametric test to use in different situations. You should

FIGURE 16-4

Nonparametric Tests Introduced in Chapter 16

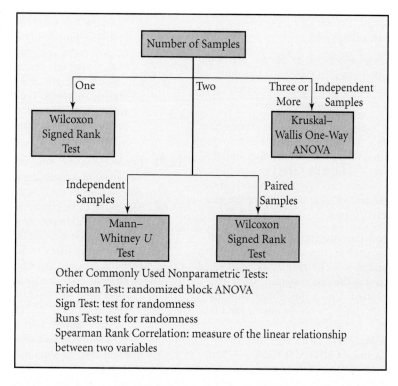

Other Commonly Used Nonparametric Tests:
Friedman Test: randomized block ANOVA
Sign Test: test for randomness
Runs Test: test for randomness
Spearman Rank Correlation: measure of the linear relationship between two variables

consult the references at the end of the chapter for further reading and discussion.

EQUATIONS

Large-Sample Wilcoxon Test Statistic

$$z = \frac{W - \dfrac{n(n + 1)}{4}}{\sqrt{\dfrac{n(n + 1)(2n + 1)}{24}}} \qquad \textbf{16-1}$$

U Statistics

$$U_1 = n_1 n_2 + \frac{n_1(n_1 + 1)}{2} - \sum R_1 \qquad \textbf{16-2}$$

$$U_2 = n_1 n_2 + \frac{n_2(n_2 + 1)}{2} - \sum R_2 \qquad \textbf{16-3}$$

Mean and Standard Deviation for U Statistic

$$\mu = \frac{n_1 n_2}{2} \qquad \textbf{16-4}$$

$$\sigma = \sqrt{\frac{(n_1)(n_2)(n_1 + n_2 + 1)}{12}} \qquad \textbf{16-5}$$

Mann–Whitney U Test Statistic

$$z = \frac{U - \dfrac{n_1 n_2}{2}}{\sqrt{\dfrac{(n_1)(n_2)(n_1 + n_2 + 1)}{12}}} \qquad \textbf{16-6}$$

Wilcoxon Mean and Standard Deviation

$$\mu = \frac{n(n + 1)}{4} \qquad \textbf{16-7}$$

$$\sigma = \sqrt{\frac{n(n + 1)(2n + 1)}{24}} \qquad \textbf{16-8}$$

Wilcoxon Test Statistic

$$z = \frac{T - \dfrac{n(n + 1)}{4}}{\sqrt{\dfrac{n(n + 1)(2n + 1)}{24}}} \qquad \textbf{16-9}$$

H Statistic

$$H = \frac{12}{N(N + 1)} \sum_{i=1}^{k} \frac{R_i^2}{n_i} - 3(N + 1) \qquad \textbf{16-10}$$

Correction for Tied Rankings—Kruskal-Wallis Test

$$1 - \frac{\displaystyle\sum_{i=1}^{g} (t_i^3 - t_i)}{N^3 - N} \qquad \textbf{16-11}$$

H Statistic Corrected for Tied Rankings

$$H = \frac{\dfrac{12}{N(N + 1)} \displaystyle\sum_{i=1}^{k} \dfrac{R_i^2}{n_i} - 3(N + 1)}{1 - \dfrac{\displaystyle\sum_{i=1}^{g} (t_i^3 - t_i)}{N^3 - N}} \qquad \textbf{16-12}$$

CHAPTER EXERCISES

Conceptual Questions

16.47 Discuss the data conditions that would lead you to use the Kruskal-Wallis test as opposed to the ANOVA procedure introduced in Chapter 10. Present an example illustrating these conditions.

16.48 In the library, locate two journal articles that use one of the nonparametric tests discussed in this chapter. Prepare a brief outline of the articles, paying particular attention to the reasons given for using the particular test.

16.49 Find an organization that you think would be interested in data that would violate the measurement scale or known distribution assumptions necessary to use the statistical tools found in Chapters 9–11 (retail stores are a good candidate). Determine to what extent this organization considers these problems and whether it uses any of the techniques discussed in this chapter.

16.50 As an example of how the sampling distribution for the Mann–Whitney Test is derived, consider two samples with sample sizes $n_1 = 2$ and $n_2 = 3$. The distribution is obtained under the assumption that the two variables, say x and y, are identically distributed. Under this assumption, each measurement is equally likely to obtain one of the ranks between 1 and $n_1 + n_2$.
  a. List all the possible sets of two ranks that could be obtained from five ranks. Calculate the Mann–Whitney U-value for each of these sets of two ranks.
  b. The number of ways in which we may choose n_1 ranks from $n_1 + n_2$ is given by $\dbinom{n_1 + n_2}{n_1}$.
  Calculate this value for the n_1 and n_2 given in this problem. The probability that each of the Mann–Whitney Us will occur is obtained by computing the reciprocal of this. Find this probability.
  c. List all the possible Mann–Whitney U-values you obtained in part a. Then using part b, calculate the probability that each of these U-values occurs, thereby producing the sampling distribution for the Mann–Whitney U statistic when $n_1 = 2$ and $n_2 = 3$.

16.51 Let us examine how the sampling distribution of the Wilcoxon test statistic is obtained. Consider the sampling distributions of the positive ranks from a sample size of 4. The ranks to be considered are, therefore, 1, 2, 3, and 4. Under the null hypothesis, the differences to be ranked are distributed symmetrically about zero. Thus, each difference is just as likely to be positively as negatively ranked.
  a. For a sample size of four, there are $2^4 = 16$ possible sets of signs associated with the four ranks. List the 16 possible sets of ranks that could be positive—that is, (none), (1), (2) . . . (1, 2, 3, 4). Each of these sets of positive ranks (under the null hypothesis) has the same probability of occurring.
  b. Calculate the sum of the ranks of each set specified in part a.

c. Using parts a and b, produce the sampling distribution for the Wilcoxon test statistic when $n = 4$.

Business Applications

16.52 The H. F. Houston Company is the parent franchiser for a nationwide fast-food chain, with corporate headquarters in Austin, Minnesota. For the past few months, the company has undertaken a new advertising study. Initially, company executives selected 22 of its retail outlets that were similar with respect to sales volume, profitability, location, climate, economic status of customers, and experience of store management. Each of the outlets was randomly assigned one of two advertising plans promoting a new sandwich product. The accompanying data represent the number of new sandwiches sold during the specific test period at each retail outlet.

Houston executives want you to determine which of the two advertising plans leads to the largest average sales levels for the new product. They are not willing to make the assumptions necessary for you to use the t-test. They do not wish to have an error rate of more than 0.05.

Advertising Plan 1	Advertising Plan 2
1,711	2,100
1,915	2,210
1,905	1,950
2,153	3,004
1,504	2,725
1,195	2,619
2,103	2,483
1,601	2,520
1,580	1,904
1,475	1,875
1,588	1,943

16.53 Two small regional life insurance companies are being studied by the Triangle Life Insurance Company as candidates for a possible merger. Triangle can merge with only one of these regional companies at this time and, as part of its study, wishes to determine whether there is a difference in the average annual premiums received by the two companies. The following data represent sample policy premiums for each company.

Company 1	Company 2
$246	$300
211	305
235	308
270	325
411	340
310	295
450	320
502	330
311	240
200	360

a. Do these data indicate a difference in mean annual premiums for the two companies? Apply the Mann–Whitney U test with a significance level of 0.10.
b. Apply the t-test to determine whether the data indicate a difference between annual premiums for the two regional companies. Use a significance level of 0.10. Indicate what assumptions must be made to apply the t-test.

16.54 The Style-Rite Company of Atlanta makes windbreaker jackets for people who play golf and who are active outdoors during the spring and fall months. The company recently developed a new material and is in the process of test-marketing jackets made from the material. As part of this test-marketing effort, 10 people were each supplied with a jacket made from the original material and were asked to wear it for two months, washing it at least twice during that time. A second group of 10 people were each given a jacket made from the new material and asked to wear it for two months with the same washing requirements.

Following the two-month trial period, the individuals were asked to rate the jackets on a scale of 0 to 100, with 0 being the worst performance rating and 100 being the best. The ratings for each material are shown as follows.

Original Material	New Material
76	55
34	90
70	72
23	17
45	56
80	69
10	91
46	95
67	86
75	74

The company expects that, on the average, the performance ratings will be superior for the new material.
a. Do the sample data support this belief at a significance level of 0.05? Discuss.
b. Examine the data given. What characteristics of these data sets would lead you to reject the assumption that the data came from populations that had normal distributions and equal variances?

16.55 A study was recently conducted by the Bonneville Power Association to determine attitudes regarding the association's policies in western U.S. states. One part of the study asked respondents to rate the performance of the BPA on its responsiveness to environmental issues. The following responses were obtained for a sample of 12 urban residents and 10 rural residents. The ratings are on a 1 to 100 scale, with 100 being perfect.

Urban	Rural
76	55
90	80
86	94
60	40
43	85
96	92
50	77
20	68
30	35
82	59
75	
84	

a. Based on the sample data, should the BPA conclude that there is no difference between the urban and rural residents with respect to median environmental rating? Test using a significance level of 0.02.

b. Perform the appropriate parametric statistical test and indicate the assumptions necessary to use this test that were not required by the Mann–Whitney tests. Use a significance level of 0.02. (Refer to Chapter 9, if needed.)

16.56 The Miltmore Corporation performs consulting services for companies that think they have image problems. Recently, the Bluedot Beer Company approached Miltmore. Bluedot executives were concerned that the company's image, relative to its two closest competitors, had diminished. Miltmore conducted an image study in which a random sample of 8 people was asked to rate Bluedot's image. Five people were asked to rate competitor A's image, and 10 people were asked to rate competitor B's image. The image ratings were made on a 100-point scale, with 100 being the best possible rating. Here are the results of the sampling.

Bluedot	Competitor A	Competitor B
40	95	50
60	53	80
70	55	82
40	92	87
55	90	93
90		51
20		63
20		72
		96
		88

a. Based on these sample results, should Bluedot conclude there is an image difference among the three companies? Use a significance level equal to 0.05.

b. Should Bluedot infer that its image has been damaged by last year's federal government recall of its product? Discuss why or why not.

c. Why might the decision maker wish to use parametric ANOVA rather than the corresponding nonparametric test? Discuss.

16.57 💿 A major car manufacturer is experimenting with three new methods of pollution control. The testing lab must determine whether the three methods produce equal pollution reductions. Readings from a calibrated carbon monoxide meter are taken from groups of engines randomly equipped with one of the three control units. The data are in the CD-ROM file *Pollution*. Determine whether the three pollution-control methods will produce equal results.

16.58 During the production of a textbook, there are many steps between when the author begins preparing the manuscript and when the book is finally printed and bound. Tremendous effort is made to minimize the number of errors of any type in the text. One type of error that is especially difficult to eliminate is the typographical error that can creep in when the book is typeset. The Prolythic Type Company does contract work for many publishers. As part of its quality control efforts, it charts the number of corrected errors per page in its manuscripts. In one particu-

larly difficult book to typeset, the following data were observed for a sample of 15 pages (in sequence).

Page	1	2	3	4	5	6	7	8	9	10	11	12	13	14	15
Errors	2	4	1	0	6	7	4	2	9	4	3	6	2	4	2

Is there sufficient evidence to conclude the median number of errors per page is greater than 6?

16.59 A Vermont company is monitoring a process that fills maple syrup bottles. When the process is filling correctly, the median average fill in an 8-ounce bottle of syrup is 8.03 ounces. The last 15 bottles sampled revealed the following levels of fill.

7.95 8.02 8.07 8.06 8.05 8.04 7.97 8.01 8.04 8.05 8.08 8.11 7.99 8.00 8.02

a. Formulate the null and alternative hypotheses needed in this situation.

b. Do the sample values support the null or alternative hypothesis?

16.60 The manager of credit card operations for a small regional bank has determined that last year's median credit card balance was $1,989.32. A sample of 18 customer balances this year revealed the following figures, in dollars.

Sample 1	Sample 2	Sample 3	Sample 4	Sample 5	Sample 6
1,827.85	1,992.75	2,012.35	1,955.64	2,023.19	1,998.52
Sample 7	Sample 8	Sample 9	Sample 10	Sample 11	Sample 12
2,003.75	1,752.55	1,865.32	2,013.13	2,225.35	2,100.35
Sample 13	Sample 14	Sample 15	Sample 16	Sample 17	Sample 18
2,002.02	1,850.37	1,995.35	2,001.18	2,252.54	2,035.75

Based on the 18 customer balances sampled, is there enough evidence to allow you to conclude the median balance has changed? Test at the 0.05 level of significance.

Advanced Applications

16.61 💿 A business statistics instructor at State University has been experimenting with her testing procedure. This term, she has taken the approach of giving two tests over each section of material. The first test is a problem-oriented exam, in which students have to set up and solve an applications problem. The exam is worth 50 points. The second test, given a day later, is a multiple-choice test, covering the concepts introduced in the section of the text covered by the exam. This exam is also worth 50 points.

In one class of 15 students, the observed test scores over the first section of material in the course are contained in the CD-ROM file *State University*.

a. If the instructor is unwilling to make the assumptions for the paired-sample *t*-test, what should she conclude based on these data about the distribution of scores for the two tests if she tests at a significance level of 0.05?

b. In the context of this problem, define a Type II error.

16.62 💿 Two brands of tires are being tested for tread wear. To control for vehicle and driver variation, one tire of each brand is put on the front wheels of 10 cars. The cars are driven under normal driving conditions a total of 15,000 miles. The tread wear is then measured using a very sophisticated instrument. The data that were observed are in the CD-ROM file *Tread Wear*. (Note that the larger the number, the less wear in the tread.)

a. What would be the possible objection in this case for employing the paired-sample *t*-test? Discuss.

b. Assuming that the decision makers in this situation are not willing to make the assumptions required to perform the paired-sample *t*-test, what decision should be reached using the appropriate nonparametric test if a significance level of 0.05 is used? Discuss.

16.63 High Fuel Company markets a gasoline additive for automobiles that it claims will increase a car's miles per gallon (MPG) performance. In an effort to determine whether High Fuel's claim is valid, a consumer testing agency randomly selected eight makes of automobiles. Each car's tank was filled with gasoline and driven around a track until empty. Then the car's tank was refilled with gasoline and the additive, and the car was driven until the gas tank was empty again. The miles per gallon were measured for each car with and without the additive. The results are reported in the CD-ROM file *High Fuel*.

The testing agency is unwilling to accept the assumption that the underlying probability distribution is normally distributed, but it would still like to perform a statistical test to determine the validity of High Fuel's claim.

a. What statistical test would you recommend the testing agency use in this case? Why?

b. Conduct the test that you believe to be appropriate. Use a significance level of 0.025.

c. State your conclusions based on the test you have just conducted. Is High Fuel's claim supported by the test's findings?

16.64 A company assembles remote controls for television sets. The company's design engineers have developed a revised design that they think will make it faster to assemble the controls. To test whether the new design leads to faster assembly, 14 assembly workers were randomly selected and each worker was asked to assemble a control using the current design and then asked to assemble a control using the revised design. The times in seconds to assemble the controls are shown in the CD-ROM file *Remote Control*. The company's engineers are unable to assume that the assembly times are normally distributed, but they would like to test whether assembly times are less using the revised design.

a. What statistical test do you recommend the company use? Why?

b. State the null an alternative hypotheses of interest to the company.

c. At the 0.025 level of significance, is there any evidence to support the engineers' belief that the revised design reduces assembly time?

d. How might the results of the statistical test be used by the company's management?

CASE 16-A:

Bentford Electronics, Part 2

On Saturday morning, Jennifer Bentford received a call at her home from the production supervisor at Bentford Electronics Plant 1. The supervisor indicated that she and the supervisors from Plants 2, 3, and 4 had agreed that something must be done to improve company morale and, thereby, increase the production output of their plants. Jennifer Bentford, president of Bentford Electronics, agreed to set up a Monday morning meeting with the supervisors to see if they could arrive at a plan for accomplishing these objectives.

By Monday each supervisor had compiled a list of several ideas, including a four-day work week and interplant competition of various kinds.

After listening to the discussion for some time, Jennifer Bentford asked if anyone knew if there was a difference in average daily output for the four plants. When she heard no positive response, she told the supervisors to select a random sample of daily production reports from each plant and test whether there was a difference. They were to meet again on Wednesday afternoon with test results.

By Wednesday morning, the supervisors had collected the following data on units produced:

PLANT 1	PLANT 2	PLANT 3	PLANT 4
4,306	1,853	2,700	1,704
2,852	1,948	2,705	2,320
1,900	2,702	2,721	4,150
4,711	4,110	2,900	3,300
2,933	3,950	2,650	3,200
3,627	2,300	2,480	2,975

The supervisors had little trouble collecting the data, but they were at a loss about how to determine whether there was a difference in the output of the four plants. Jerry Gibson, the company's research analyst, told the supervisors that there were statistical procedures that could be used to test hypotheses regarding multiple samples if the daily output was distributed in a bell shape (normal distribution) at each plant. The supervisors expressed dismay because no one thought his or her output was normal. Jerry Gibson indicated that there were techniques that did not require the normality assumption, but he did not know what they were.

The meeting with Jennifer Bentford was scheduled to begin in three hours, so she needed some statistical-analysis help immediately.

General References

1. Berenson, Mark L., and David M. Levine, *Basic Business Statistics: Concepts and Applications*, 7th ed. (Upper Saddle River, NJ: Prentice Hall, 1999).

2. Conover, W. J., *Practical Nonparametric Statistics*, 3rd ed. (New York: John Wiley and Sons, 1999).

3. Dunn, O. J., "Multiple Comparisons Using Rank Sums," *Technometrics* 6 (1964), pp. 241–252.

4. Marascuilo, Leonard A., and Maryellen McSweeney, *Nonparametric and Distribution-Free Methods for Social Sciences*, (Pacific Grove, CA: Brooks/Cole, 1977).

5. *Microsoft Excel 2000* (Redmond, WA: Microsoft Corp., 1999).

6. *Minitab for Windows Version 13* (State College, PA: Minitab, 2000).

7. Noether, G. E., *Elements of Nonparametric Statistics* (New York: John Wiley & Sons, 1967).

CHAPTER 17

Introduction to Quality and Statistical Process Control

CHAPTER OUTCOMES

After studying the material in Chapter 17, you should be able to:

- Use the seven basic tools of quality.
- Construct and interpret $\bar{x}$-charts and R-charts.
- Construct and interpret p-charts.
- Construct and interpret c-charts.

WHY YOU NEED TO KNOW

Organizations across the United States and around the world have turned to quality management in an effort to meet the competitive challenges of the international marketplace. Although there is no set approach for implementing quality management, a commonality among most organizations is for employees at all levels to be brought into the effort as members of process improvement teams.

Successful organizations, such as General Electric and Hewlett-Packard, realize that thrusting people together in teams and then expecting process improvement to occur will generally lead to disappointment. They know that their employees need to understand how to work together as a team. In many instances, teams are formed to improve a process so that product or service quality is enhanced. However, teamwork and team building must be combined with training and education in the proper tools if employees are to be successful at making lasting process improvements. Over the past several decades, a number of techniques and methods for process improvement have been developed and used by organizations. As a group, these are referred to as the *Tools of Quality*. Many of these tools are based on statistical procedures and data analysis.

One set of quality tools known as *statistical process control charts* is so prevalent in business today, and is so closely linked to the material in Chapters 6 through 9, that its coverage merits a separate chapter. Today, successful managers must have an appreciation of, and familiarity with, the role of quality in process improvement activities. This chapter is designed to introduce you to the fundamental tools and techniques of quality management and to show you how to construct and interpret statistical process control charts.

17-1 QUALITY MANAGEMENT AND TOOLS FOR PROCESS IMPROVEMENT

From the end of World War II through about the mid-1970s, industry in the United States was kept busy meeting a pent-up demand for its products both at home and abroad. The emphasis in most companies was on getting the "product out the door." The U.S. effort to produce large quantities of goods and services led to less emphasis on quality. During this same time, Dr. W. Edwards Deming and Dr. Joseph Juran were consulting with Japanese business leaders to help them rebuild their economic base after World War II. Deming, a statistician, and Juran, an engineer, emphasized that quality was the key to being competitive and that quality could be best achieved by improving the processes that produced the products and delivered the services.

Employing the process improvement approach was a slow, but effective, method for improving quality, and by the early 1970s Japanese products began to exceed those of the United States in terms of quality. The impact was felt by entire industries, such as automobiles and electronics. Whereas Juran focused on quality planning and helping businesses drive costs down by eliminating waste in processes, Deming preached a new management philosophy, which has become known as **Total Quality Management**, or TQM. There are about as many definitions of TQM as there are companies who have attempted to implement it. Here is a representative definition and one that has been used by Hewlett-Packard since the early 1980s.

> *Total Quality Management*
>
> A journey to excellence in which everyone in the organization is focused on continuous process improvement directed toward increased customer satisfaction.

In the early 1980s, U.S. business leaders began to realize the competitive importance of providing high-quality products and services and a *quality revolution* was under way in the United States. Deming's 14 points (see Table 17-1) reflected a new philosophy of management that emphasized the importance of leadership. The numbers attached to each point do not indicate an order of importance, rather the 14 points collectively are seen as necessary steps to becoming a world-class company.

Juran's role in the quality movement is virtually on a par with Deming's. Juran is noted for many contributions to TQM, including his 10 steps to quality improvement, which are outlined in Table 17-2. Note that Juran and Deming differed with respect to the use of goals and targets. Juran is also credited with applying the **Pareto Principle** to quality.

TABLE 17-1	1. Create a constancy of purpose toward the improvement of products and services in order to become competitive, stay in business, and provide jobs.
Deming's 14 Points	2. Adopt the new philosophy. Management must learn that it is in a new economic age and awaken to the challenge, learn their responsibilities, and take on leadership for change.
	3. Stop depending on inspection to achieve quality. Build in quality from the start.
	4. Stop awarding contracts on the basis of low bids.
	5. Improve continuously and forever the system of production and service to improve quality and productivity, and thus constantly reduce costs.
	6. Institute training on the job.
	7. Institute leadership. The purpose of leadership should be to help people and technology work better.
	8. Drive out fear so that everyone may work effectively.
	9. Break down barriers between departments so that people can work as a team.
	10. Eliminate slogans, exhortations, and targets for the workforce. They create adversarial relationships.
	11. Eliminate quotas and management by objectives. Substitute leadership.
	12. Remove barriers that rob employees of their pride of workmanship.
	13. Institute a vigorous program of education and self-improvement.
	14. Make the transformation everyone's job and put everyone to work on it.

Pareto Principle

80% of the trouble comes from 20% of the causes.

Juran urges managers to use the Pareto principle to focus on the *vital few* sources of problems and to separate the vital few from the trivial many. Pareto charts are used to display data in a way that helps managers find the most important problem issues.

There have been numerous other individuals who have played significant roles in the quality movement. Among these are Philip B. Crosby, who is probably best known for his book, *Quality Is Free*, in which he emphasized that in the long run, the costs of improving quality are more than offset by the reductions in waste, rework, returns, and unsatisfied customers. Kauro Ishikawa is credited with developing and popularizing the application of the *Fishbone Diagram* that we will discuss shortly in the section on the Basic 7 Tools of Quality. There is also the work of Masaaki Imai, who popularized the philosophy of *kaizen*, or people-based continuous improvement.

Finally, we must not overlook the contributions of many different managers at companies such as Hewlett-Packard, General Electric, Motorola, and Federal Express. These leaders synthesized and applied many different quality ideas and concepts to their organizations in order to create world-class corporations. By sharing their successes with other firms, they have inspired and motivated others to continually seek opportunities in which the tools of quality can be applied to improve business processes.

THE TOOLS OF QUALITY FOR PROCESS IMPROVEMENT

Once U.S. managers realized that their businesses were engaged in a competitive battle with companies around the world, they reacted in many ways. Some managers ignored the challenge and continued to see their market presence erode. Other managers realized that they needed a system or

TABLE 17-2	1. Build awareness of both the need for improvement and the opportunity for improvement.
Juran's 10 Steps to Quality Improvement	2. Set goals for improvement.
	3. Organize to meet the goals that have been set.
	4. Provide training.
	5. Implement projects aimed at solving problems.
	6. Report progress.
	7. Give recognition.
	8. Communicate the results.
	9. Keep score.
	10. Maintain momentum by building improvement into the company's regular systems.

FIGURE 17-1

The Deming Cycle

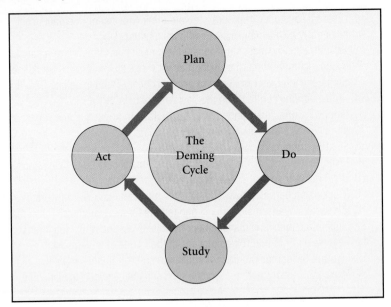

approach for improving their firms' operations and processes. The *Deming Cycle*, which is illustrated in Figure 17-1, has been effectively used by many organizations as a guide to their quality improvement efforts. The approach taken by the Deming Cycle is that problems should be identified and solved based on data.

Over time, a collection of tools and techniques known as the *Basic 7 Tools* have been developed for quality and process improvement. Some of these tools have already been introduced at various points throughout this text. However, we will briefly introduce all Basic 7 Tools in this section. Section 17-2 will explore one of these tools—Statistical Process Control Charts (SPC)—in greater depth.

Process Flowcharts

A flowchart is a diagram that illustrates the steps in a process. Flowcharts provide a visualization of the process and are good beginning points in planning a process improvement effort.

Brainstorming

Brainstorming is a tool that is used to generate ideas from the members of the team. Employees are encouraged to share any idea that comes to mind, and all ideas are listed with no ideas being evaluated until all ideas are posted. Brainstorming can be either structured or unstructured. In structured brainstorming, team members are asked for their ideas, in order, around the table. Members may pass if they have no further ideas. With unstructured brainstorming, members are free to interject ideas at any point.

Fishbone Diagram

Kauro Ishikawa from Japan is credited with developing the Fishbone Diagram, which is also called the cause-and-effect diagram or the Ishikawa Diagram. The Fishbone Diagram can be applied as a simple graphical brainstorming tool in which team members are given a problem and several categories of possible causes. They then brainstorm possible causes in any or all of the cause categories.

Histograms

You were introduced to histograms in Chapter 2 as a method for graphically displaying quantitative data. Recall that histograms are useful for seeing the center, spread, and shape of a distribution of measurements. As a tool of quality, histograms are used to display measurements to determine whether the output of a process is centered on the target value and whether the process is capable of meeting specifications.

Trend Charts

In Chapter 2 we illustrated the use of a line chart to display time-series data. A trend chart is a line chart that is used to track output from a process over time.

Scatter Plots

There are many instances in quality improvement efforts in which you will want to examine the relationship between two quantitative variables. A scatter plot is an excellent tool for doing this. You were first introduced to scatter plots in Section 2-3 in Chapter 2. Scatter plots were also used in developing regression models in Chapters 13 and 14.

Statistical Process Control Charts

One of the most frequently used Basic 7 Tools is the statistical process control (SPC) chart. SPC charts are a special type of trend chart. In addition to the data, the charts display the process average and the upper and lower control limits. These control limits define the range of random variation expected in the output of a process. SPC charts are used to provide early warnings when a process has gone out of control. There are several types of control charts depending on the type of data generated by the process of interest. Section 17-2 presents an introductory discussion of why control charts work and how to develop and interpret some of the most commonly used SPC charts.

Most organizations (public and private) in the United States and the developed countries of the world are involved in some form of quality improvement effort. Those that are not will likely not survive in the competitive global marketplace that exists today. Statistics plays a key role in the efforts of organizations to improve their quality. You will have the opportunity to use the techniques presented in this chapter and throughout this text as you help your organization meet its quality challenges.

17-1: EXERCISES

Skill Development

17.1 Discuss the similarities and differences between Dr. Deming's 14 points and Dr. Juran's 10 steps to quality improvement.

17.2 Deming is opposed to setting quotas or specific targets for workers.
   a. Use the library or the Internet to locate information that explains his reasoning.
   b. Discuss whether you agree or disagree with him.
   c. If possible, cite one or more examples based on your own experience to support your position.

17.3 Philip Crosby wrote the book, *Quality Is Free*. In it he argues that it is possible to have high quality and low price. Do you agree? Provide examples that support your position.

Business Applications

17.4 Develop a process flowchart that describes the registration process at your college or university.

17.5 Generate a process flowchart showing the steps you have to go through to buy a concert ticket at your school.

17.6 Assume that you are a member of a team at your university charged with the task of improving student, faculty, and staff parking. Use brainstorming to generate a list of problems with the current parking plan. After you have generated the list, prioritize the list of problems. (What criteria are you using to prioritize?)

17.7 Refer to Exercise 17.6.
   a. Use brainstorming to generate a list of solutions for the top-rated parking problem.
   b. Order these possible solutions according to each of the following factors: cost to implement, time to implement, and easiest to gain approval.
   c. Did your lists come out in a different order? Why?

Advanced Applications

17.8 Suppose the computer lab manager at your school has been receiving complaints from students about long waits to use a computer. The "effect" is long wait times. The categories of possible causes are people, equipment, methods/rules, and the environment. Develop a fishbone diagram containing your brainstormed ideas for causes of the problem.

17.9 The city bus line is consistently running behind schedule. Develop a fishbone diagram showing the possible causes organized by such cause categories as people, methods, equipment, and the environment. Once you have finished, develop a priority order based on which cause is most likely to be the root cause of the problem.

17-2 INTRODUCTION TO STATISTICAL PROCESS CONTROL CHARTS

As we stated in Section 17-1, one of the most important tools for quality improvement is the *statistical process control* (SPC) chart. In this section we provide an overview of SPC charts. As you will see, SPC is actually an application of hypothesis testing. The concepts that have been introduced beginning in Chapter 2 provide you with the background needed to understand and use SPC.

THE EXISTENCE OF VARIATION

After studying the material in Chapters 1 through 16, you should be well aware of the importance of variation in business decision making. Variation exists naturally in the world around us. In any process or activity, the day-to-day outcomes are generally different; rarely are they exactly the same. As a practical example, think about the time it takes you to travel to the university each morning. You know it's about a 15-minute trip, and even though you travel the same route, your actual time will vary somewhat from day to day. You will notice this variation in many daily occurrences. The next time you renew your car license plates, notice that some people seem to get through faster than others. The same is true at a bank, where the time to cash your payroll check varies each payday.

Even in instances when variation is hard to detect, it is present. For example, when you measure a stack of 4-foot-by-8-foot sheets of plywood using a tape measure, they are all 4 feet wide. However, when the stack is measured using an engineer's scale, you may be able to detect slight variations among sheets, and using a caliper you can detect even more (see Figure 17-2).

Therefore, three concepts to remember about variation are

1. Variation is natural; it is inherent in the world around us.
2. No two products or service experiences are exactly the same.
3. With a fine enough gauge, all things can be seen to differ.

Sources of Variation

What causes variation? Variation in the output of a process comes from variation in the inputs to the process. Let's go back to your travel time to school. Why isn't it always exactly the same? Your travel time depends on many factors, such as what route you take, how much traffic you encounter, whether you are in a hurry, how your car is running, and so on.

The six most common sources of variations are

1. people
2. machines
3. materials
4. methods
5. measurement
6. environment

FIGURE 17-2

Plywood Variation

Types of Variation

Although variation is always present, we can define two major types that occur. The first is called *common cause variation*, which means it is naturally occurring or expected in the system. Other terms people use for common cause variation include normal, random, chance occurrence, inherent, and stable variation.

The other type of variation is called *special cause variation*. This type of variation is abnormal, indicating that something out of the ordinary has happened. This type of variation is also called non-random, unstable, and assignable cause variation.

In our example of travel time to school, there are common causes of variation such as traffic lights, traffic patterns, weather, and departure time. On the days when it takes you significantly more or less time to arrive at work, there are also special causes of variation occurring. These may be factors such as accidents, road construction detours, or needing to stop for gas.

Examples of the two types of variation and some sources are

Sources of Common Cause Variation	Sources of Special Cause Variation
Weather conditions	Equipment not maintained and cleaned
Inconsistent work methods	Poor training
Machine wear	Worker fatigue
Temperature	Procedures not followed
Employee skill levels	Misuse of tools
Computer response times	Incorrect data entry

In any process or system, the total process variation is a combination of common cause and special cause factors. This can be expressed by Equation 17-1.

Variation Components

Total Process Variation = Common Cause Variation + Special Cause Variation   **17-1**

In process improvement efforts, the goal is to first remove the special cause variation and then to reduce the common cause variation in a system. This requires that the source of a variation be identified and its cause eliminated.

The Predictability of Variation: Understanding the Normal Distribution

Dr. W. Edwards Deming said there is no such thing as consistency. However there is such a thing as a *constant-cause system*. A system that contains only common cause variations is very predictable. Though the outputs vary, they exhibit an important feature called stability. This means that some percentage of the output will continue to lie within given limits hour after hour, day after day, so long as the constant-cause system is operating. When a process exhibits stability, it is in control.

The reason that the outputs vary in a predictable manner is because measurable data, when subgrouped and pictured in a histogram, tend to cluster around the average and spread out symmetrically on both sides. This tendency is a function of the central limit theorem that you first encountered in Chapter 6. This means that the frequency distribution of most processes will begin to resemble the shape of the normal distribution as the values are collected and grouped into classes.

The Concept of Stability

We showed in Chapter 5 that the normal distribution can be divided evenly into six sections, the sum of which includes 99.7% of the data values. The width of each of these sections is called the standard deviation. The standard deviation is the primary way the spread (or dispersion) of the distribution is measured. Thus, we expect virtually all (99.7%) of the data in a stable process to fall within three standard deviations of the mean. Generally speaking, as long as the measurements fall within the three-standard-deviation boundary, we consider the process to be stable. This concept provides the basis for *statistical process control charts*.

INTRODUCING STATISTICAL PROCESS CONTROL CHARTS

Most cars are equipped with a temperature gauge that measures engine temperature. We come to rely on the gauge to let us know if "everything is all right." As long as the gauge points to the *normal* range, we conclude that there is no problem. However, if the gauge moves outside the *normal* range toward the *hot* mark, it's a signal that the engine is overheating and something is wrong. If the gauge moves out of the *normal* range toward the *cold* mark, it's also a signal of potential problems.

Under typical driving conditions, engine temperature will fluctuate. The normal range on the car's gauge defines the expected temperature variation when the car is operating properly. Over time, we come to know what to expect. If something changes, the gauge is designed to give us a signal.

The engine temperature gauge is analogous to a process control chart. Like the engine gauge, process control charts are used in business to define the boundaries that represent the amount of variation that can be considered normal.

Figure 17-3 illustrates the general format of a process control chart. The upper and lower *control limits* define the normal operating region for the process. The horizontal axis reflects the passage of time, or order of production. The vertical axis corresponds to the variable of interest.

There are a number of different types of process control charts. In this section, we introduce four of the most commonly used process control charts:

- $\bar{x}$-chart
- R-chart (range chart)
- p-chart
- c-chart

Each of these charts is designed for a special purpose. However, as you will see, the underlying logic is the same for each. The $\bar{x}$-chart and R-chart are almost always used in tandem. The $\bar{x}$-charts are used to monitor a process average. R-charts are used to monitor the variation of individual process values. They require that the variable of interest be quantitative. The next example shows how these two charts are developed and used.

Excel and Minitab Tutorial

$\bar{x}$-Chart and R-Chart

Cattlemen's Bar and Grill—The Cattlemen's Bar and Grill in Kansas City has developed a name for its excellent food and service. To maintain this reputation, the owners have established key measures of product and service quality, and they monitor these regularly. One measure is the amount of time customers wait from the time they are seated until they are served.

FIGURE 17-3   Process Control Chart Format

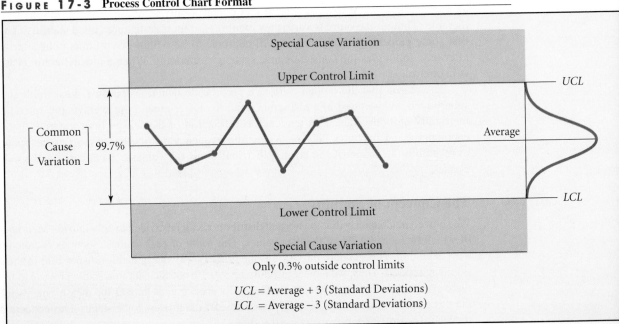

Every day, each hour that the business is open, four tables are randomly selected. The elapsed time from when customers are seated at these tables until their orders arrive is recorded. The owners wish to use these data to construct an $\bar{x}$-chart and an R-chart. These control charts can be developed using the following steps.

STEP 1: Collect the initial sample data from which the control charts will be developed. Four measurements during each hour for 30 hours are contained in a CD-ROM file called *Cattlemen*. The four values recorded each hour make up a *subgroup*. The $\bar{x}$-charts and R-charts are typically generated from small subgroups (three to six observations), and the general recommendation is that data from a minimum of 20 subgroups be gathered before a chart is constructed. Once the subgroup size is determined, all subgroups must be the same size. In this case, each subgroup is a sample of four tables.

STEP 2: Calculate subgroup means and ranges. Figure 17-4 shows the Excel worksheet with a partial listing of the data after the means and ranges have been computed for each subgroup.

STEP 3: Compute the average of the subgroup means and the average range value. The average of the subgroup means and the average range value are computed using Equations 17-2 and 17-3.

Average of Subgroup Means

$$\bar{\bar{x}} = \frac{\sum_{i=1}^{k} \bar{x}_i}{k}$$

17-2

where:

$\bar{x}_i$ = *i*th subgroup average

k = Number of subgroups

Average Subgroup Range

$$\bar{R} = \frac{\sum_{i=1}^{k} R_i}{k}$$

17-3

where:

R_i = *i*th subgroup range

k = Number of subgroups

Using Equations 17-2 and 17-3, we get:

$$\bar{\bar{x}} = \frac{\sum \bar{x}}{k} = \frac{19.5 + 21 + \cdots + 20.75}{30} = 19.24$$

$$\bar{R} = \frac{\sum R}{k} = \frac{7 + 7 + \cdots + 3}{30} = 5.73$$

FIGURE 17-4

Excel Worksheet of Cattlemen's Service Time Data, Including Subgroup Means and Ranges

Excel Instructions:
1. Open file: Cattlemen.xls
2. Use Excel formulas to compute Mean and Range values for each sample.

	A	B	C	D	E	F	G	H
1	Hour	Table 1	Table 2	Table 3	Table 4		Mean	Range
2	1	16	18	21	23		19.5	7
3	2	26	20	19	19		21	7
4	3	20	22	18	18		19.5	4
5	4	24	16	22	20		20.5	8
6	5	17	19	24	17		19.25	7
7	6	17	17	15	18		16.75	3
8	7	22	12	20	22		19	10
9	8	24	19	19	17		19.75	7
10	9	18	18	20	14		17.5	6

Microsoft Excel - Cattlemen.xls
File Edit View Insert Format Tools Data PHStat Window Help
Arial   12
F1   =

Minitab Instructions (for similar results):
1. Open file: Cattlemen.MTW.
2. Choose **Calc > Row Statistics**.
3. Under **Statistic**, choose **Mean**.
4. In **Input variables**, enter data columns.
5. In **Store result in**, enter storage column.
6. Click **OK**.
7. Repeat 3 through 6 choosing **Range** under **Statistic**.

STEP 4: Prepare graphs of the subgroup means and ranges as a line chart. On one graph, plot the $\bar{x}$-values in time order across the graph and draw a line across the graph at the value corresponding to $\bar{\bar{x}}$. This is shown in Figure 17-5. Likewise, graph the R-values and $\bar{R}$ as a line chart, as shown in Figure 17-6.

The $\bar{\bar{x}}$ and $\bar{R}$ values in Figures 17-5 and 17-6 are called the "process control centerlines." The *centerline* is a graph of the mean value of the sample data. We use $\bar{\bar{x}}$ as the notation for centerline, which represents the current process average. For these sample data, the average time people in the subgroups wait between being seated and being served is 19.24 minutes. However, as seen in Figure 17-5, there is variation around the centerline. The next step is to establish the boundaries that define the limits for what is considered *normal* variation in the process.

STEP 5: Compute the upper and lower control limits for the $\bar{x}$ chart. You learned in Chapter 5 that for a normal distribution with mean μ and standard deviation σ, approximately 99.7% of the values will fall within $\mu \pm 3\sigma$. Most process control charts are developed as 3-sigma control charts, meaning that the range of inherent variation is ± 3 standard deviations from the mean.

Because the $\bar{x}$ chart is a graph of subgroup (sample) means, the control limits are established at points ± 3 standard errors from the centerline, $\bar{\bar{x}}$. The control limits are analogous to the critical values we establish in hypothesis testing problems. Using this analogy, the null hypothesis is that the process is in control. We will reject this null hypothesis whenever we obtain a subgroup mean beyond three standard errors from the centerline in either direction. Because the control chart is based on sample data, our conclusions are subject to error. Approximately 3 times in 1,000 (0.003), a subgroup mean should be outside the control limits when, in fact, the process is still in control. If this happens, we will have committed a Type I error. The 0.003 value is the significance level for the test. This small alpha level implies that 3-sigma control charts are very conservative when it comes to saying that a process is out of control. We might also conclude that the process is in control when in fact it isn't. If this happens, we have committed a Type II error.

To construct the control limits, we must determine an estimator for the standard error of the sample means, $\dfrac{\sigma}{\sqrt{n}}$. Based on what you have learned in previous chapters, you might suspect that we would use $\dfrac{s}{\sqrt{n}}$. However, in most applications this is not done. In the 1930s, when process control charts were first introduced, there was no such thing as pocket calculators. In order to make control charts usable by people without calculators and without statistical training, a simpler approach was needed. An unbiased estimator of the standard error of the sample means, $\dfrac{\sigma}{\sqrt{n}}$, that was relatively easy to calculate was developed by Walter Shewhart.[1] The unbiased estimator is

$$\frac{A_2}{3}\bar{R}$$

where:

$\bar{R}$ = the mean of the subgroups' ranges

A_2 = a Shewhart factor that makes $\dfrac{A_2}{3}\bar{R}$ an unbiased estimator of the standard error of the sample means, $\dfrac{\sigma}{\sqrt{n}}$

Thus, 3 standard errors of the sample means can be estimated by

$$3\left(\frac{A_2}{3}\bar{R}\right) = A_2\bar{R}$$

Appendix Q displays the Shewhart factors for various subgroup sizes. Equations 17-4 and 17-5 are used to compute the upper and lower control limits for the $\bar{x}$-chart.[2] (The development of the *Shewhart table* is outside the scope of this text.)

---

[1] The leader of a group at the Bell Telephone Laboratories that did much of the original work in SPC, Shewhart is credited with developing the idea of control charts.

[2] When $A_2/3$ is multiplied by $\bar{R}$, this product becomes an unbiased estimator of the standard error, which is the reason for A_2's use here.

FIGURE 17-5 Line Chart for $\bar{x}$ Values for Cattlemen's Data

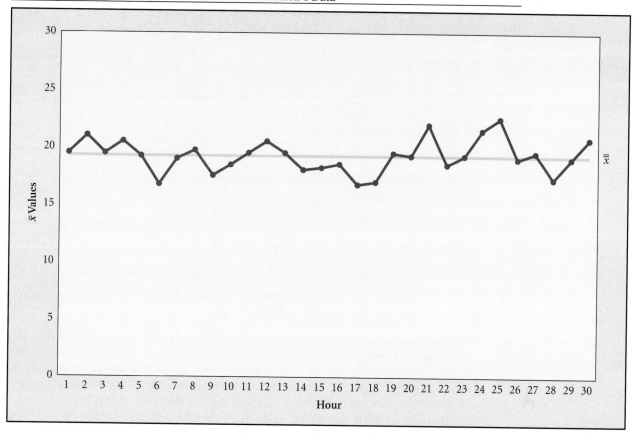

FIGURE 17-6 Line Chart for R-Values for Cattlemen's Data

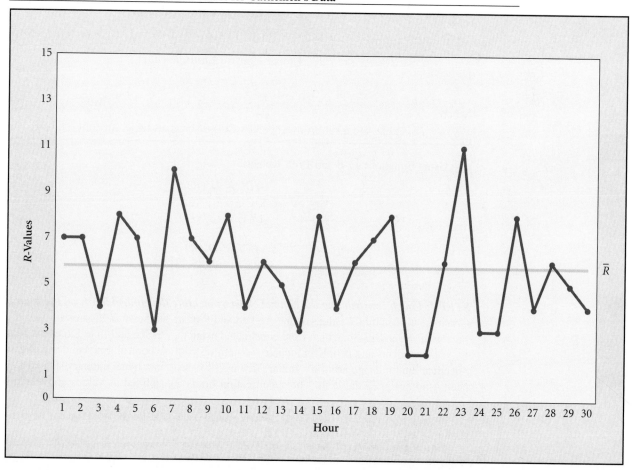

Upper Control Limit, $\bar{x}$-Chart

$$UCL = \bar{\bar{x}} + A_2(\bar{R})$$

17-4

Lower Control Limit, $\bar{x}$-Chart

$$LCL = \bar{\bar{x}} - A_2(\bar{R})$$

17-5

where:

$$A_2 = \text{Shewhart factor for subgroup size} = n$$

For the Cattlemen's Bar and Grill example, the subgroup size is 4. Thus, the A_2 factor from the Shewhart table (Appendix Q) is 0.73. We can compute the upper and lower control limits as follows:

$$UCL = \bar{\bar{x}} + A_2(\bar{R})$$
$$UCL = 19.24 + 0.73(5.73)$$
$$UCL = 23.42$$

$$LCL = \bar{\bar{x}} - A_2(\bar{R})$$
$$LCL = 19.24 - 0.73(5.73)$$
$$LCL = 15.06$$

STEP 6: Compute the upper and lower control limits for the R-chart. The D_3 and D_4 factors in the Shewhart table presented in Appendix Q are used to compute the 3-sigma control limits for the R-chart. The control limits are established at points ±3 standard errors from the centerline, $\bar{R}$. However, unlike the case for the $\bar{x}$-chart, the unbiased estimator of the standard error of the sample ranges is a constant multiplied by $\bar{R}$. The constant for the lower control limit is the D_3 value from the Shewhart table. The D_4 value from the Shewhart table is the constant for the upper control limit.

Equations 17-6 and 17-7 are used to find the UCL and LCL values. Because the subgroup size is 4 in our example, $D_3 = 0.0^3$ and $D_4 = 2.28$.

Upper Control Limit, R-chart

$$UCL = D_4(\bar{R})$$

17-6

Lower Control Limit, R-chart

$$LCL = D_3(\bar{R})$$

17-7

where:

$$D_3 \text{ and } D_4 \text{ are taken from Appendix Q, the Shewhart table, for subgroup size} = n$$

Using Equations 17-6 and 17-7, we get:

$$UCL = D_4(\bar{R})$$
$$UCL = 2.28(5.73)$$
$$UCL = 13.06$$

$$LCL = D_3(\bar{R})$$
$$LCL = 0.0(5.73)$$
$$LCL = 0.0$$

STEP 7: Finish constructing the control chart by locating the control limits on the $\bar{x}$ and R-charts. Graph the UCL and LCL values on the $\bar{x}$-chart and R-chart, as shown in Figures 17-7a and 17-7b, and Figures 17-8a and 17-8b, which were constructed using the PHStat add-in to Excel and Minitab.[4]

Both students and people in industry sometimes confuse control limits and specification limits. Specification limits are arbitrary and are defined by a customer, by an industry standard, or by engineers who designed the item. The specification limits are defined as values above and below the

---

[3]Because a range cannot be negative, the constant is adjusted to indicate that the lower boundary for the range must equal 0.

[4]See the Excel and Minitab Tutorial on the CD-ROM for the specific steps required to obtain the x-bar and R-charts. Minitab provides a much more extensive set of SPC options than PHStat.

FIGURE 17-7A

Excel (PHStat) Cattlemen's $\bar{x}$-Chart Output

Excel Instructions:
1. Open file: Cattlemen's.xls
2. Compute column of $\bar{x}$ and R-values.
3. Select **PHStat**.
4. Click on **Control Charts**.
5. Select **R** and **x-bar Charts**.
6. Enter subgroup size.
7. Define range of R-values.
8. Select **R- and x-bar chart option**.
9. Define range of $\bar{x}$ values.

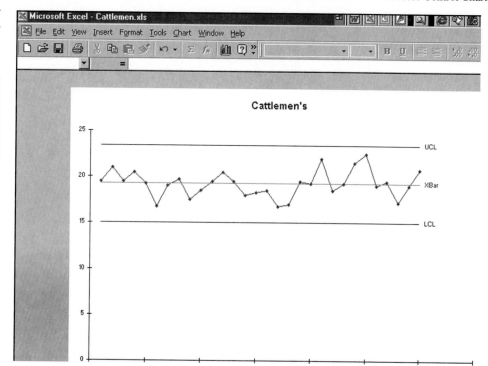

"target" value for the item. The specification limits pertain to individual items—an item either meets specifications, or it does not. Process control limits are computed from actual data from the process. These limits define the range of inherent variation that is actually occurring in the process. The control limits are values above and below the current process average (which may be higher or lower than the "target").

Therefore, a process may be operating in a state of control, but it may be producing individual items that do not meet the specifications. Companies interested in improving quality must first bring the process under control before attempting to make changes in the process to reduce the defect level.

FIGURE 17-7B

Minitab Cattlemen's $\bar{x}$-Chart Output

Minitab Instructions:
1. Open file: Cattlemen.MTW.
2. Choose **Stat > Control Charts > Variables Charts for Subgroups > X-bar**.
3. Select *Observations for a subgroup are in one row of columns:*
4. Enter data columns in box.
5. Because file contains additional data Select **Data Options, Specify which rows to exclude.** Select **Row Numbers** and enter **31 32 33 34 35 36. OK**
6. Click on **Xbar Options** and select **Tests** tab.
7. Select *Perform the following tests for special causes* and select the first four test.
8. Click **OK. OK.**

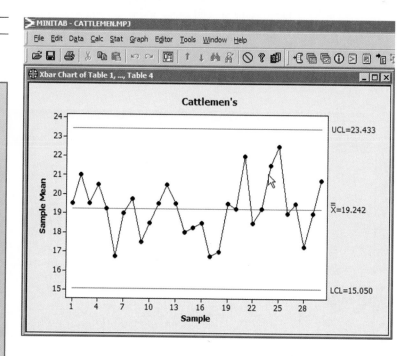

FIGURE **17-8A**

Excel (PHStat) Cattlemen's
R-Chart Output

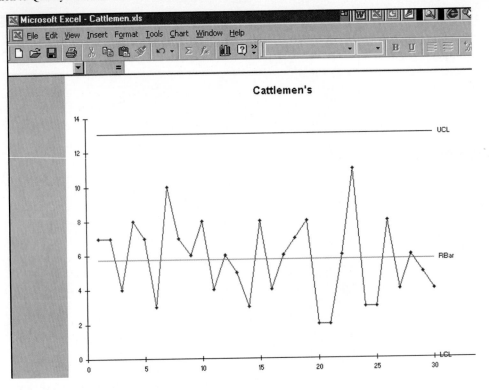

Using the Control Charts

Once control charts for Cattlemen's service time have been developed, they can be used to determine whether the time it takes to serve customers remains *in control*. The concept involved is essentially a hypothesis test in which the null and alternative hypotheses can be stated as:

H_0: The process is in control; the variation around the centerline is
a result of common causes inherent in the process.
H_A: The process is out of control; the variation around the centerline is
due to some special cause and is beyond what is normal for the process.

In the Cattlemen's Bar and Grill example, the hypothesis is tested every hour, when four tables are selected and the service time is recorded for each table. The $\bar{x}$ and R values for the new subgroup are computed and plotted on their respective control charts.

FIGURE **17-8B**

Minitab Cattlemen's
R-Chart Output

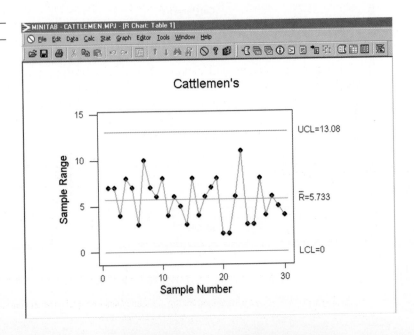

There are three main process changes that can be detected with a process control chart:

1. The process average has shifted up or down from normal.
2. The process average is trending up or down from normal.
3. The process is behaving in such a manner that the existing variation is not random in nature.

If any of these has happened, the null hypothesis is considered false and the process is *out of control*.

The control charts are used to provide signals that something has changed. There are four primary signals that indicate a change and that, if observed, cause us to reject the null hypothesis.[5] These are

1. one or more points outside the upper or lower control limits
2. nine or more points in a row above (or below) the center line
3. six or more consecutive points moving in the same direction (increasing or decreasing)
4. fourteen points in a row, alternating up and down

These signals were derived such that the probability of a Type I error is less than 0.01. Thus, there is a very small chance that we will conclude the process has changed when, in fact, it has not.

If we examine the control charts in Figures 17-7a and 17-7b and 17-8a and 17-8b, we find that none of these signals occur. Thus, the process is deemed in control during the period in which the initial sample data were collected.

Suppose that the Cattlemen's owners monitor the process for the next five hours. Table 17-3 shows these new values, along with the mean and range for each hour. The means are plotted on the $\bar{x}$-chart, and the R values are plotted on the R-chart, as shown in Figures 17-9 and 17-10.

When $\bar{x}$ and R-charts are used, we first look at the R-chart. Figure 17-10 shows the range (R) has been below the centerline $(\bar{R} = 5.7)$ for seven consecutive hours. Although this doesn't quite come up to the nine points of signal 2, the owners should begin to suspect something unusual might be happening to cause a downward shift in the variation in service time between tables. Although the R-chart does not indicate the reason for the shift, the owners should be pleased, because this indicates greater consistency in service times. This change actually represents a quality improvement. If this trend continues, the owners will want to study the situation so they will be able to retain these improvements in service time variability.

The $\bar{x}$-chart in Figure 17-9 indicates that the average service time is out of control because in hour 35 the mean service time exceeded the upper control limit of 23.4 minutes. The mean wait time for the four tables during this hour was 25.5 minutes. The chance of this happening is extremely low unless something has changed in the process. This should be a signal to the owners that a special cause exists. They should immediately investigate possible problems to determine if there has been a system change (e.g., training issue) or if this is truly a one-time event (e.g., fire in the kitchen). They could use a brainstorming technique or a fishbone diagram to identify possible causes of the problem.

An important point is that analysis of each of the control charts should not be done in isolation. A moment's consideration will lead you to see that if the variation of the process has gotten out of control (above the upper control limit), then trying to interpret the $\bar{x}$-chart can be very misleading. Widely fluctuating variation could make it much more probable than an $\bar{x}$-value would exceed the control limits even though the process mean had not changed.

Adding (or subtracting) a given number from all of the numbers in a data set does not change the variance of that data set, so a shift in the mean of a process can occur without that shift affecting the variation of the process. However, a change in the variation almost always affects the $\bar{x}$ control chart. For this reason, the general advice is to control the variation of a process before the mean of the process is subjected to control chart analysis.

HOUR	TABLE 1	TABLE 2	TABLE 3	TABLE 4	MEAN	RANGE
31	20	21	24	22	21.75	4
32	17	22	18	20	19.25	5
33	23	20	22	22	21.75	3
34	24	23	19	20	21.50	5
35	24	25	26	27	25.50	3

[5]There is some minor disagreement on the signals, depending on which process control source you refer. Minitab actually lets the user define the signals under the option Define Tests.

FIGURE 17-9 Cattlemen's $\bar{x}$-Chart

FIGURE 17-10 Cattlemen's R-Chart

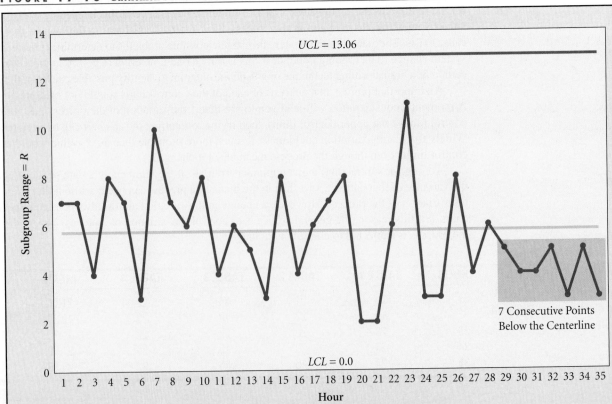

The process control charts signal the user when something in the process has changed. In order for process control charts to be effective, they must be updated immediately after data have been collected, and action must be taken when the charts signal that a change has occurred.

p-Charts

The previous example illustrated how $\bar{x}$-charts and *R*-charts can be developed and applied. They are used in tandem and are applicable when the characteristic being monitored is a variable measured on a continuous scale (e.g., time, weight, length, etc.). However, there are instances when the process issue involves an *attribute* rather than a quantitative variable. An attribute is a quality characteristic that is either present or not present. In many quality control situations, an attribute is whether an item is good (meets specifications) or defective, and in those cases a *p-chart* can be used to monitor the proportion of defects.

Excel and Minitab Tutorial

Hilder's Publishing Company—Hilder's Publishing Company sells books and records through a catalog, processing hundreds of mail and phone orders each day. Each customer order requires numerous data entry steps. Mistakes made in data entry can be costly, resulting in shipping delays, incorrect prices, or the wrong items being shipped. As part of its ongoing efforts to improve quality, Hilder's managers and employees want to reduce errors.

The manager of the order entry department has developed a process control chart to monitor order entry errors. She has gone back for the past 30 days and for each day has selected a random sample of 100 orders. These orders were examined with the attribute being:

- Order entry is correct.

- Order entry is incorrect.

In developing a *p*-chart, the sample size should be large enough such that $np \geq 5$ and $n(1 - p) \geq 5$. Unlike the $\bar{x}$- and *R*-chart cases, the sample size may differ from sample to sample. However, this complicates the development of the *p*-chart.

The *p*-chart can be developed using the following steps.

STEP 1: Collect the sample data. The sample size is 100 orders. This size sample was selected for each of 30 days. The proportion of incorrect orders, called *nonconformances*, are displayed on the CD-ROM file called *Hilders*. The proportions are given the notation, $\bar{p}$.

STEP 2: Plot the subgroup proportions as a line chart. Figure 17-11a and Figure 17-11b show the line chart for the 30 days.

FIGURE 17-11A

Excel (PHStat) *p*-Chart for Hilder's Publishing

Excel (PHStat) Instructions:
1. Open file: Hilders.xls
2. Click on **PHStat**.
3. Select the **Control Chart** option.
4. Select ***p*-Chart**.
5. Define the column with the number of nonconforming values.
6. Indicate the sample size.

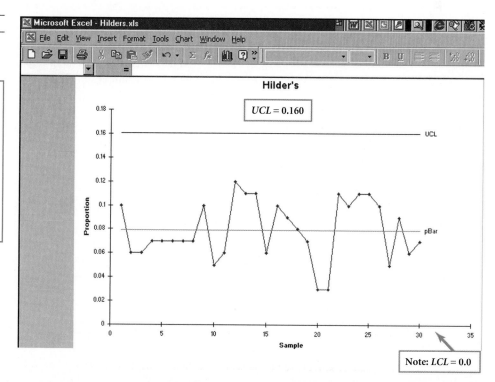

FIGURE 17-11B

Minitab *p*-Chart for
Hilder's Publishing

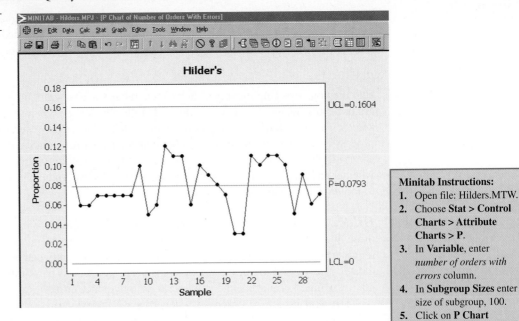

Minitab Instructions:
1. Open file: Hilders.MTW.
2. Choose **Stat > Control Charts > Attribute Charts > P**.
3. In **Variable**, enter *number of orders with errors* column.
4. In **Subgroup Sizes** enter size of subgroup, 100.
5. Click on **P Chart Options** and select **Tests** tab.
6. Select *Perform all tests for special causes*.
7. Click **OK. OK**.

STEP 3: *Compute the mean subgroup proportion for all samples using Equation 17-8 or 17-9, depending on whether the sample sizes are equal.*

Mean Subgroup Proportion

For equal-size samples

$$\bar{\bar{p}} = \frac{\sum_{i=1}^{k} \bar{p}_i}{k} \qquad \text{17-8}$$

where:

$\bar{p}_i$ = Sample proportion for subgroup i
k = Number of samples of size n

For unequal sample sizes:

$$\bar{\bar{p}} = \frac{\sum_{i=1}^{k} n_i \bar{p}_i}{\sum_{i=1}^{k} n_i} \qquad \text{17-9}$$

where:

n_i = The number of items in sample i
$\sum n_i$ = Total number of items sampled in k samples

Because we have equal sample sizes, we use Equation 17-8, as follows.

$$\bar{\bar{p}} = \frac{\sum \bar{p}_i}{k} = \frac{0.10 + 0.06 + 0.06 + 0.07 + \cdots}{30} = \frac{2.38}{30} = 0.079$$

Thus, the average proportion of orders with errors is 0.079.

STEP 4: Compute the estimate of the standard error of $\bar{p}$ using Equation 17-10.

Estimate of the Standard Error for the Subgroup Proportions

For equal sample sizes:

$$s_{\bar{p}} = \sqrt{\frac{(\bar{\bar{p}})(1 - \bar{\bar{p}})}{n}}$$

17-10

where:

$$\bar{\bar{p}} = \text{Mean subgroup proportion}$$
$$n = \text{Common sample size}$$

For unequal sample sizes:

Option 1. Compute $s_{\bar{p}}$ using largest sample size and $s_{\bar{p}}$ using the smallest sample size. Construct control limits using each value.

Option 2. Compute a unique value of $s_{\bar{p}}$ for each different sample size. Consruct control limits for each $s_{\bar{p}}$ value.

We compute $s_{\bar{p}}$ using Equation 17-10, as follows.

$$s_{\bar{p}} = \sqrt{\frac{(\bar{\bar{p}})(1 - \bar{\bar{p}})}{n}} = \sqrt{\frac{(0.079)(1 - 0.079)}{100}} = 0.027$$

STEP 5: Compute the 3-sigma control limits using Equations 17-11 and 17-12.

Control Limits for p-Chart

$$UCL = \bar{\bar{p}} + 3s_{\bar{p}}$$

17-11

$$LCL = \bar{\bar{p}} - 3s_{\bar{p}}$$

17-12

where:

$$\bar{\bar{p}} = \text{Mean subgroup proportion}$$

$$s_{\bar{p}} = \text{Estimated standard error of } \bar{p} = \sqrt{\frac{(\bar{\bar{p}})(1 - \bar{\bar{p}})}{n}}$$

Using Equations 17-11 and 17-12, we get the following control limits.

$$UCL = \bar{\bar{p}} + 3s_{\bar{p}} = 0.079 + 3(0.027) = 0.160$$
$$LCL = \bar{\bar{p}} - 3s_{\bar{p}} = 0.079 - 3(0.027) = -0.002 \rightarrow 0.0$$

Because a proportion of nonconforming items cannot be negative, the lower control limit is set to 0.0.

STEP 6: Plot the centerline and control limits on the control chart. Both upper and lower control limits are plotted on the control charts in Figure 17-11a and Figure 17-11b.

Using the p-Chart

Once the control chart is developed, the same rules are used as for the $\bar{x}$ and R-charts:[6]

1. one or more points outside the upper or lower control limits
2. nine or more points in a row above (or below) the centerline
3. six or more consecutive points moving in the same direction (up or down)
4. fourteen points in a row, alternating up and down

The p-chart shown in Figure 17-11a indicates the process is in control. None of the signals are present in these data. The variation in the nonconformance rates is assumed to be due to the common cause issues.

[6]Minitab allows the user to specify the signals that you want to use. This is done in the Define Tests feature under Stat—Control Charts. See the Excel and Minitab Tutorial on the CD-ROM for specifics in developing a p-chart.

For future days, the managers would select a random sample of 100 orders, count the number with errors, and compute the proportion. This value would be plotted on the p-chart. For each day, the managers would use the control chart to test the hypotheses:

H_0: The process is in control: The variation around the centerline is a result
    of common causes and is inherent in the process.

H_A: The process is out of control: The variation around the centerline is due
    to some special cause and is beyond what is normal for the process.

The signals mentioned previously would be used to test the null hypothesis. Remember, control charts are most useful when the charts are updated as soon as the new sample data become available. When a signal of special cause variation is present, you should take action to determine the source of the problem and remove it as quickly as possible.

c-Charts

The p-chart just discussed is used when you select a sample of items and you determine the number of the sampled items that possess a specific attribute of interest. Each item either has or does not have that attribute. You will encounter other situations that involve attribute data but differ from the p-chart applications. In these situations, you have what is defined as a sampling unit (or experimental unit), which could be a sheet of plywood, a door panel on a car, a textbook page, an hour of service, or any other defined unit of space, volume, time, and so on. Each sampling unit could have one or more of the attributes of interest, and you would be able to count the number of attributes present in each sampling unit. In cases in which the sampling units are the same size, the appropriate control chart is a c-chart.

Excel and Minitab Tutorial

Chandler Tile Company—The Chandler Tile Company makes ceramic tile. In recent years, there has been a big demand for tile products in private residences in kitchens and bathrooms and in commercial establishments for decorative counter and wall covering. Although the demand has increased, so has the competition. The senior management at Chandler knows that three factors are key to winning business from contractors: price, quality, and service.

One quality issue is scratches on a tile. The production managers wish to set up a control chart to monitor the level of scratches per tile to determine whether the production process remains in control.

SPECIAL NOTE

Control charts monitor a process as it currently operates, not necessarily how you would like it to operate. Thus, a process that is in control might still yield a higher number of scratches per tile than the managers would like.

The managers may be able to believe that the numbers of scratches per tile are independent of each other and that the prevailing operating conditions are consistent from tile to tile. In this case, the proper control chart is a c-chart. Here the tiles being sampled are the same size, and the managers will tally the number of scratches per tile. However, if we asked, "How many opportunities were there to scratch each tile?" we probably would not be able to answer the question. There are more opportunities than we could count. For this reason, the c-chart is based on the Poisson probability distribution, which was introduced in Chapter 5. You might recall that the Poisson distribution is defined by the mean number of *successes* per interval, or sampling unit, as shown in Equation 17-13. A success can be regarded as a defective, a nonconformance, or any other characteristic of interest. In the Chandler example, a success is a scratch on a tile.

Mean for c-Chart

$$\bar{c} = \frac{\sum_{i=1}^{k} x_i}{k}$$

17-13

where:

x_i = Number of successes per sampling unit
k = Number of sampling units

Because the Poisson distribution is skewed when the mean of the sampling unit is small, we must define the sampling unit so that it is large enough to provide an average of at least 5 successes per sampling unit ($\bar{c} \geq 5$). This may require that you combine smaller sampling units into a larger unit size.

The mean and the variance of the Poisson distribution are identical. Therefore, the standard deviation of the Poisson distribution is the square root of its mean. For this reason, the estimator of the standard deviation for the Poisson distribution is computed as the square root of the sample mean, as shown in Equation 17-14.

Standard Deviation for *c*-Chart

$$s_c = \sqrt{\bar{c}}$$

17-14

Then Equations 17-15 and 17-16 are used to compute the 3-sigma (3 standard deviation) control limits for the *c*-chart.

---

c-Chart Control Limits

$$UCL = \bar{c} + 3\sqrt{\bar{c}}$$

17-15

and

$$LCL = \bar{c} - 3\sqrt{\bar{c}}$$

17-16

You can use the following steps to construct a *c*-chart.

STEP 1: Collect the sample data. The original plan called for the Chandler Tile Company to select six tiles each hour from the production line and to perform a thorough inspection to count the number of scratches per tile. Like all control charts, at least 20 samples are desired in developing the initial control chart. After sampling 240 tiles (six each for 40 hours), the total number of scratches found was 228. The data set is contained in the CD-ROM file *Chandler*.

STEP 2: Compute the average number of occurrences per sampling unit using Equation 17-13. The mean would be

$$\bar{c} = \frac{\sum x}{k} = \frac{228}{40} = 5.70 \text{ scratches per sampling unit}$$

STEP 3: Construct the 3-sigma control limits, using Equations 17-15 and 17-16. The following steps are used.

1. The mean is

$$\bar{c} = \frac{\sum x}{k} = \frac{228}{40} = 5.70$$

2. The standard deviation is computed using Equation 17-14.

$$s = \sqrt{\bar{c}} = \sqrt{5.70} = 2.387$$

3. The upper and lower 3-sigma control limits are

$$UCL = \bar{c} + 3\sqrt{\bar{c}} = 5.7 + 3(2.387) = 12.86$$
$$LCL = \bar{c} - 3\sqrt{\bar{c}} = 5.7 - 3(2.387) = -1.461 \rightarrow 0.0$$

As with the *p*-chart, the lower control limit can't be negative. We change it to zero, which is the fewest possible scratches on a tile. The completed *c*-chart is shown in Figure 17-12a and Figure 17-12b.

Note in both figures that four samples of six tiles each had a total number of scratches that fell outside the upper control limit of 12.86. The managers need to consult production records and other information to determine what special cause might have generated this level of scratches. If they can determine the cause, these data points should be removed and the control limits should be recomputed from the remaining 36 values. You might also note that the graph changes beginning with about sample 22. The process seems more stable from sample 22 onward. Managers might consider inspecting for another 13 to 15 hours and recomputing the control limits using data from hours 22 and higher.

FIGURE 17-12A

Excel *c*-Chart for Chandler Tile Company

Excel Instructions:
1. Open file: Chandler
2. Use Excel formulas to compute centerline and *UCL*.
3. Create a column of values corresponding to the centerline and *UCL*.
4. Use **Chart Wizard— Line Chart**.

OPTIONAL CD-ROM TOPIC *u*-CHARTS

You will encounter situations in which a *c*-chart is needed but the sampling units differ substantially in size. When this happens, the *c*-chart can't be used. Instead a control chart known as a *u*-Chart is appropriate. For more on this, go to the CD-ROM.

FIGURE 17-12B

Minitab *c*-Chart for Chandler Tile Company

Minitab Instructions:
1. Open file: Chandler.MTW.
2. Choose **Stat > Control Charts > Attributes Charts > C**.
3. In **Variable**, enter number of defectives column.
4. Click on **C Chart Options** and select **Tests** tab.
5. Select *Perform all tests for special causes*.
6. Click **OK. OK.**

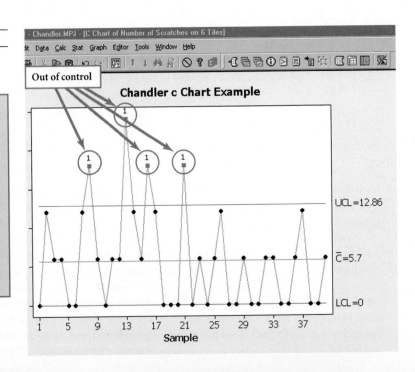

Other Control Charts

Our purpose in this chapter has been to introduce SPC charts. We have illustrated a few of the most frequently used charts. However, there are many other types of control charts that can be used in special situations. You are encouraged to consult several of the references listed at the end of the chapter for information about these other charts. Regardless of the type of statistical quality control chart you are using, the same general steps are used.

SUMMARY: CONSTRUCTING SPC CHARTS

The following steps are employed when constructing statistical quality control charts.

1. Collect the sample data.

2. Compute the centerline value. The centerline on the control chart is the average value for the sample data. This is the current process average.

3. Compute the upper and lower control limits.

4. Plot the appropriate data on the control chart, along with the centerline and control limits.

17-2: EXERCISES

Skill Development

17.10 Data were collected on a quantitative measure with a subgroup size of 5 observations. Thirty subgroups were collected, with the following results:

$$\bar{\bar{x}} = 44.52 \qquad \bar{R} = 5.6$$

a. Determine the Shewhart factors that will be needed if $\bar{x}$- and R-charts are to be developed.
b. Compute the upper and lower control limits for the R-chart.
c. Compute the upper and lower control limits for the $\bar{x}$-chart.

17.11 Data were collected from a process in which the factor of interest was whether the finished item contained a particular attribute. The fraction of items that did not contain the attribute was recorded. A total of 30 samples were selected. The common sample size was 100 items. The total number of nonconforming items was 270. Based on these data, compute the upper and lower control limits for the p-chart.

17.12 Fifty sampling units of equal size were inspected, and the number of nonconforming situations were recorded. The total number of instances was 449.
a. Determine the appropriate control chart to use for this process.
b. Compute the mean value for the control chart.
c. Compute the upper and lower control limits.

17.13 Explain why it is important to update the control charts as soon as new data become available.

Business Applications

17.14 The Haines Lumber Company makes plywood for residential and commercial construction. One of the key quality measures is plywood thickness. Every hour, five pieces of plywood are selected and the thicknesses are measured. The data (in inches) for the first 20 subgroups are in the CD-ROM file *Haines*.
a. Construct an $\bar{x}$-chart based on these data. Make sure you plot the centerline and both 3-sigma upper and lower control limits.
b. Construct an R-chart based on these data.
c. Examine both control charts and determine if there are any special causes of variation that require attention in this process.

17.15 Referring to Exercise 17.14, suppose the process remained in control for the next 40 hours. The thickness measurements for hours 41 through 43 are

Hour 41	0.764	0.737	0.724	0.716	0.752
Hour 42	0.766	0.785	0.777	0.790	0.799
Hour 43	0.812	0.774	0.767	0.799	0.821

a. Based on these data and the two control charts, what should you conclude about the process? Has the process gone out of control? Discuss.
b. Was it necessary to obtain your answer to Exercise 17.14 before part a could be answered? Explain your reasoning.

17.16 Grandfoods, Inc., makes energy supplement bars for use by athletes and others who need an energy boost. One of the critical quality characteristics is the weight of the bars. Too much weight implies that too many liquids have been added to the mix and the bar will be too chewy. If the bars are light, the implication is that the bars are too dry. To monitor the weights, the production manager wishes to use process control charts. Data for 30 subgroups of size 4 bars are contained in the CD-ROM file *Grandfoods*. Note that a subgroup is selected every 15 minutes as bars come off the manufacturing line.

a. Use these data to construct the appropriate process control chart(s).

b. Discuss what each chart is used for. Why do we need both charts?

c. Examine the control charts and indicate which, if any, of the signals are present. Is the process currently in control?

d. Develop a histogram for the energy bar weights. Discuss the shape of the distribution and the implications of this toward the validity of the control chart procedures you have used.

17.17 Referring to the process control charts developed in Exercise 17.16, data for periods 31 to 40 are contained in the CD-ROM file *Grandfoods-Extra*.

a. Based on these data, what would you conclude about the energy bar process?

b. Write a report discussing the results, and show the control charts along with the new data.

17.18 Trinkle & Sons performs subcontract body paint work for one of the "Big Three" automakers. One of its recent contracts called for the company to paint 12,500 door panels. Several quality characteristics are very important to the manufacturer, one of which is blemishes in the paint. The manufacturer has required Trinkle & Sons to have control charts to monitor the number of paint blemishes per door panels. The panels are all for the same model car and are the same size. To initially develop the control chart, data for 88 door panels were collected and are provided in the CD-ROM file *CarPaint*.

a. Determine the appropriate type of process control chart to develop.

b. Develop a 3-sigma control chart.

c. Based on the control chart and the standard signals discussed in this chapter, what conclusions can you reach about whether the paint process is in control? Discuss.

17.19 Wilson, Ryan, and Reed is a large CPA firm in Charleston, South Carolina. They have been monitoring the accuracy of their employees and wish to get the number of errors per account under statistical control. They have sampled 100 accounts for each of the last 30 days and have examined them for errors. The data are presented in the CD-ROM file *Accounts*.

a. Construct the relevant control chart for the account process.

b. What does the chart indicate about the statistical stability of the process? Give reasons for your answers.

c. Suppose that for the next three days, sample sizes of 100 accounts are examined with the following results:

Number of Errors	6	7	9

Plot the appropriate data on the control chart and indicate whether any of the control chart signals are present. Discuss your results.

17.20 Tony Perez is the manager of one of the largest chains of service stores that specialize in oil and lubri-

cation of automobiles, Fastlube, Inc. One of the company's stated goals is to provide a lube and oil change for anyone's automobile in 15 minutes. Tony has thought for some time now that there is a growing disparity among his workers in the time it takes to lube and change the oil of an automobile. To monitor this aspect of Fastlube, Inc., Tony has selected a sample of 20 days and has recorded the time it took five randomly selected employees to service an automobile. The data is located in the CD-ROM file *Fastlube*.

a. Tony glanced through the data and noticed that the longest time it took to service a car was 25.33 minutes. Suppose the distribution of times to service a car was normal, with a mean of 15. Use your knowledge of a normal distribution to let Tony know what the standard deviation is for the time it takes to service a car.

b. Use the *Fastlube* data to construct an $\bar{x}$-and an R-chart.

c. Based on these data, what would you conclude about the service time process?

d. Based on your findings on the R-chart, would it be advisable to draw conclusions based on the $\bar{x}$-chart?

Advanced Applications

17.21 The Kaiser Corporation makes aluminum at various locations around the country. One of the key factors in being profitable is keeping the machinery running. One particularly troublesome machine is a roller that flattens the sheets to the appropriate thickness. This machine tends to break down for various reasons. Consequently, the maintenance manager has decided to develop a process control chart. Over a period of 10 weeks, 20 subgroups consisting of 5 downtime measures (in minutes) were collected (one measurement at the end of each of the two shifts.) The subgroup means and ranges are shown as follows and are contained in a CD-ROM file called *Kaiser*.

Subgroup mean	104.8	85.9	78.6	72.8	102.6	84.8	67.0
Subgroup range	9.6	14.3	8.6	10.6	11.2	13.5	10.8
Subgroup mean	91.1	79.5	71.9	47.6	106.7	80.7	81.0
Subgroup range	5.2	14.2	14.1	14.9	12.7	13.3	15.4
Subgroup mean	57.0	98.9	87.9	64.9	101.6	83.9	
Subgroup range	15.5	13.8	16.6	11.2	9.6	11.5	

a. Explain why the $\bar{x}$- and R-charts would be appropriate in this case.

b. Find the centerline value for the $\bar{x}$-chart.

c. Calculate the centerline value for the R-chart.

d. Compute the upper and lower control limits for the R-chart, and construct the chart with appropriate labels.

e. Compute the upper and lower control limits for the $\bar{x}$-chart, and construct the chart with appropriate labels.

f. Examine the charts constructed in parts d and e and determine whether the process was in control during the period for which the control charts were developed. Explain.

17.22 Referring to Exercise 17.21, if necessary delete any out of control points and determine the appropriate $\bar{x}$ and R-charts. Now, suppose the process stays in control for the next six weeks (subgroups 21 through 32). The subgroup means and ranges for subgroups 33 to 38 are as follows:

Subgroup	33	34	35	36	37	38
Subgroup mean	89.0	88.4	85.2	89.3	97.2	105.3
Subgroup range	11.4	5.4	14.2	11.7	9.5	10.2

a. Plot the ranges on the R-chart. Is there evidence based on the range chart that the process has gone out of control? Discuss.

b. Plot the subgroup means on the $\bar{x}$-chart. Is there evidence to suggest that the process has gone out of control with respect to the process mean? Discuss.

17.23 The Ajax Taxi company in Manhattan, New York, wishes to set up an $\bar{x}$-chart and an R-chart to monitor the number of miles driven per day by their taxi drivers. Each week, the scheduler selects four taxis and (without the drivers' knowledge) monitors the number of miles driven. He has done this for the past 40 weeks. The data are in the CD-ROM file *AJAX*.

a. Construct the R-chart for these 40 subgroups.

b. Construct the $\bar{x}$-chart for these 40 subgroups. Be sure to label the chart correctly.

c. Look at both control charts and determine if any of the control chart signals are present to indicate that the process is not in control. Explain the implications of what you have found for the Ajax Taxi Company.

17.24 Referring to Exercise 17.23, the data for weeks 41 through 45 are in the *AJAX-Extra* CD-ROM file.

a. Using the control limits developed from the first 40 weeks, do these data indicate that the order entry process is now out of control? Explain.

b. If a change has occurred, brainstorm some of the possible reasons.

c. What will be the impact on the control charts when the new data are included?

d. Use the data in the files *AJAX* and *AJAX-Extra* to develop the new control charts.

e. Are any of the typical control chart signals present? Discuss.

17.25 Regis Printing Company performs printing services for individuals and business customers. Many of the jobs require that brochures be folded for mailing. The company has a machine that does the folding. It generally does a good job, but it can have problems that cause it to do improper folds. To monitor this process, the company selects a sample of 50 brochures from every order and counts the number of incorrectly folded items in each sample. Until now, nothing has been done with the 300 samples that have been collected. The data are located in the CD-ROM file *Regis*.

a. What is the appropriate control chart to use to monitor this process?

b. Using the data in this file, construct the appropriate control chart and label it properly.

c. Suppose that for the next three orders, sample sizes of 50 brochures are examined with the following results:

Sample Number	301	302	303
Number of Bad Folds	6	9	7

Plot the appropriate data to the control chart and indicate whether any of the control chart signals are present. Discuss your results.

d. Suppose that the next sample of 50 has 14 improperly folded brochures, what conclusion should be reached based on the control chart? Discuss.

17.26 Recall from Exercise 17.20 that Tony Perez is the manager of one of the largest chains of service stores that specialize in oil and lubrication of automobiles, Fastlube, Inc. One of the company's stated goals is to provide a lube and oil change for anyone's automobile in 15 minutes. Tony has thought for some time now that there is a growing disparity among his workers in the time it takes to lube and change the oil of an automobile. To monitor this aspect of Fastlube, Inc., Tony has selected a sample of 24 days and has recorded the time it took to service 100 automobiles each day. The number of times the service was performed in 15 minutes or less (≤ 15) is given in the CD-ROM file *Lubeoil*.

a. (1) Convert the sample data to proportions and plot the data as a line graph. (2) Compute $\bar{p}$ and plot this value on the line graph. (3) Compute s_p and interpret what it measures.

b. Construct a p-chart and determine if the process of the time required for oil and lube jobs is in control.

c. Specify the signals that are used to indicate an out-of-control situation on a p-chart.

17.27 Susan Booth is the director of operations for National Skyways, a small commuter airline with headquarters in Cedar Rapids, Iowa. She has become increasingly concerned about the amount of carry-on luggage passengers have been carrying on board National Skyways' planes. She collected data concerning the number of pieces of baggage that were taken on board over a one-month period. The data collected are provided in the CD-ROM file *Carryon*.

a. Set up a control chart for the number of carry-on bags per day.

b. Is the process in a state of statistical control? Explain your answer.

c. Suppose that National Skyways' aircraft were full for each of the 30 days. Each Skyways aircraft holds 40 passengers. Describe the control chart you would use. Is it necessary that you use this latter alternative, or is it just a preference? Explain your answer.

17.28 Sid Luka is the service manager for Brakes Unlimited, a franchise corporation that specializes in servicing automobile brakes. He wants to study the length of time required to replace the rear drum brakes of automobiles. A subgroup of 10 automobiles needing their brakes replaced was selected on each day for a period of 20 days. The times required (in hours) for this service were recorded and are presented in the CD-ROM file *Brakes*. (This problem can not be done using Minitab.)

a. Sid has been trying to get the average time required to replace the rear drum brakes of an automobile to be under 1.65 hours. Use the data Sid has collected to determine if he has reached his goal.

b. Set up the appropriate control charts to determine if this process is under control.

c. Determine whether the process is under control. If the process is not under control, brainstorm suggestions that might help Sid bring it under control. What tools of quality might Sid find useful?

Summary and Conclusions

The quality movement throughout the United States and much of the rest of the world has created great expectations among consumers. We now believe that our televisions, computers, stereo systems, automobiles, and even textbooks should be quality products. This movement was slow getting started in the United States because many managers did not believe that there was a need to increase quality when so many units of their products were already being demanded. However, competitive pressures changed that misconception, and corporate America began to buy into the messages that had been communicated by people such as W. Edwards Deming and Joseph Juran for many years. Ideas such as continuous process improvement and customer focus have become a central part of the operations of many of our successful companies.

Statistics has played a key role in this transition. The enemy of quality is variation. Variation exists in everything. Through the use of appropriate statistical tools and the concept of statistical reasoning, managers and employees have developed better understandings of their processes. Although they haven't yet figured out how to eliminate variations, statistics has helped them reduce them and understand how to operate more effectively when they exist.

Statistical process control (SPC) has played a big part in the understanding of variation. SPC is quite likely the most frequently used of the Basic 7 Tools. This chapter has introduced you to the basics of SPC. Hopefully, you realize that these tools are merely extensions of the hypothesis testing and estimation concepts presented in Chapters 7 to 9. You will very likely have the opportunity to use SPC in one form or another after you leave this course and enter the workforce. Figure 17-13 summarizes some of the key SPC charts and the conditions under which each is developed.

EQUATIONS

Variation Components

$$\text{Total Process Variation} = \text{Common Cause Variation} + \text{Special Cause Variation} \quad \textbf{17-1}$$

FIGURE 17-13

Statistical Process Control Chart Options

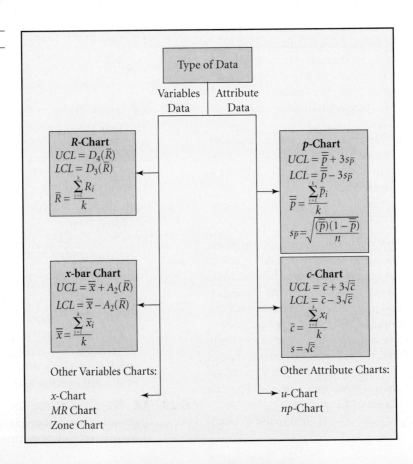

Type of Data

Variables Data | Attribute Data

R-Chart
$UCL = D_4(\bar{R})$
$LCL = D_3(\bar{R})$
$\bar{R} = \dfrac{\sum_{i=1}^{k} R_i}{k}$

p-Chart
$UCL = \bar{\bar{p}} + 3s_{\bar{p}}$
$LCL = \bar{\bar{p}} - 3s_{\bar{p}}$
$\bar{\bar{p}} = \dfrac{\sum_{i=1}^{k} \bar{p}_i}{k}$
$s_{\bar{p}} = \sqrt{\dfrac{(\bar{\bar{p}})(1 - \bar{\bar{p}})}{n}}$

x-bar Chart
$UCL = \bar{\bar{x}} + A_2(\bar{R})$
$LCL = \bar{\bar{x}} - A_2(\bar{R})$
$\bar{\bar{x}} = \dfrac{\sum_{i=1}^{k} \bar{x}_i}{k}$

c-Chart
$UCL = \bar{c} + 3\sqrt{\bar{c}}$
$LCL = \bar{c} - 3\sqrt{\bar{c}}$
$\bar{c} = \dfrac{\sum_{i=1}^{k} x_i}{k}$
$s = \sqrt{\bar{c}}$

Other Variables Charts:

x-Chart
MR Chart
Zone Chart

Other Attribute Charts:

u-Chart
np-Chart

Average of Subgroup Means

$$\bar{\bar{x}} = \frac{\sum\limits_{i=1}^{k} \bar{x}_i}{k} \qquad \textbf{17-2}$$

Average Subgroup Range

$$\bar{R} = \frac{\sum\limits_{i=1}^{k} R_i}{k} \qquad \textbf{17-3}$$

Upper Control Limit, $\bar{x}$-Chart
$$UCL = \bar{\bar{x}} + A_2(\bar{R}) \qquad \textbf{17-4}$$

Lower Control Limit, $\bar{x}$-Chart
$$LCL = \bar{\bar{x}} - A_2(\bar{R}) \qquad \textbf{17-5}$$

Upper Control Limit, R-Chart
$$UCL = D_4(\bar{R}) \qquad \textbf{17-6}$$

Lower Control Limit, R-Chart
$$LCL = D_3(\bar{R}) \qquad \textbf{17-7}$$

Mean Subgroup Proportion
For equal-size samples:

$$\bar{\bar{p}} = \frac{\sum\limits_{i=1}^{k} \bar{p}_i}{k} \qquad \textbf{17-8}$$

For unequal sample sizes:

$$\bar{\bar{p}} = \frac{\sum\limits_{i=1}^{k} n_i \bar{p}_i}{\sum\limits_{i=1}^{k} n_i} \qquad \textbf{17-9}$$

Estimate of the Standard Error for the Subgroup Proportions
For equal sample sizes:

$$s_{\bar{p}} = \sqrt{\frac{(\bar{\bar{p}})(1 - \bar{\bar{p}})}{n}} \qquad \textbf{17-10}$$

Control Limits for p-Chart
$$UCL = \bar{\bar{p}} + 3s_{\bar{p}} \qquad \textbf{17-11}$$

$$LCL = \bar{\bar{p}} - 3s_{\bar{p}} \qquad \textbf{17-12}$$

Mean for c-Chart

$$\bar{c} = \frac{\sum\limits_{i=1}^{k} x_i}{k} \qquad \textbf{17-13}$$

Standard Deviation for c-Chart
$$s_c = \sqrt{\bar{c}} \qquad \textbf{17-14}$$

c-Chart Control Limits
$$UCL = \bar{c} + 3\sqrt{\bar{c}} \qquad \textbf{17-15}$$

$$LCL = \bar{c} - 3\sqrt{\bar{c}} \qquad \textbf{17-16}$$

Key Terms

Pareto Principle, 701

Total Quality Management, 700

CHAPTER EXERCISES

Conceptual Questions

17.29 Data were collected on a quantitative measure with a subgroup size of three observations. Thirty subgroups were collected, with the following results:

$$\bar{\bar{x}} = 2.33 \qquad \bar{R} = 0.80$$

a. Determine the Shewhart factors that will be needed if $\bar{x}$- and R-charts are to be developed.
b. Compute the upper and lower control limits for the R-chart.
c. Compute the upper and lower control limits for the $\bar{x}$-chart.

17.30 Data were collected on a quantitative measure with subgroups of four observations. Twenty-five subgroups were collected, with the following results:

$$\bar{\bar{x}} = 1345.4 \qquad \bar{R} = 209.3$$

a. Determine the Shewhart factors that will be needed if $\bar{x}$- and R-charts are to be developed.
b. Compute the upper and lower control limits for the R-chart.
c. Compute the upper and lower control limits for the $\bar{x}$-chart.

17.31 Data were collected from a process in which the factor of interest was whether a finished item contained a particular attribute. The fraction of items that did not contain the attribute was recorded. A total of 20 samples were selected. The common sample size was 150 items. The total number of nonconforming items was 720. Based on these data, compute the upper and lower control limits for the p-chart.

17.32 Data were collected from a process in which the factor of interest was whether a finished item contained a particular attribute. The fraction of items that did not contain the attribute was recorded. A total of 30 samples were selected. The common sample size was 100 items. The average number of nonconforming items per sample was 14. Based on these data, construct the upper and lower control limits for the p-chart.

Business Applications

17.33 🔘 A & A Enterprises ships integrated circuits to companies that assemble computers. Because computer manufacturing operations run on little inventory, parts must be available when promised. Thus, a critical element of A & A's customer satisfaction is on-time delivery performance. To ensure that their delivery process is performing as intended, a quality improvement team decided to monitor the firm's distribution and delivery process. From the A & A corporate data base, 100 monthly shipping records were randomly selected for the previous 21 months, and the number of on-time shipments was counted. This information is contained in the CD-ROM file *A & A On Time Shipments*. Develop the appropriate 3-sigma control chart(s) for monitoring this process. Does it appear that the delivery process is in control? If not, can you suggest some possible assignable causes?

17.34   Fifi Carpets, Inc., produces carpet for homes and offices. Fifi has recently opened a new production process dedicated to the manufacture of a special type of carpet used by firms who want a floor covering for high-traffic spaces. As a part of their ongoing quality improvement activities, the managers of Fifi regularly monitor their production processes using statistical process control. For their new production process, Fifi managers would like to develop control charts to help them in their monitoring activities. Thirty samples of carpet sections, with each section having an area of 50 square meters, were randomly selected and the numbers of stains, cuts, snags, and tears were counted on each section. The sample data are contained in the CD-ROM file *Fifi Carpets*.

Use the sample data to construct the appropriate three-sigma control chart(s) for monitoring the production process. Does the process appear to be in statistical control?

17.35   CC, Inc., provides billing services for the health care industry. To ensure that its processes are operating as intended, CC selects 100 billing records at random every day and inspects each record to determine if it is free of errors. A billing record is classified as defective whenever there is an error that requires that the bill be reprocessed and mailed again. Such errors can occur for a variety of reasons. For example, a defective bill could have an incorrect mailing address, a wrong insurance identification number, or an improper doctor or hospital reference. The sample data taken from the most recent five weeks of billing records are contained in the CD-ROM file *CC Inc*.

Use the sample information to construct the appropriate 3-sigma control chart. Does CC, Inc.'s billing process appear to be in control? What, if any, comments can you make regarding the performance of their billing process?

17.36   The order entry, order processing, call center for PS Industries is concerned about the amounts of time that customers must wait before their calls are handled. A quality improvement consultant suggests that they monitor their call wait times using control charts. Using call center statistics maintained by the company's database system, the consultant randomly selects four calls every hour for 30 different hours and examines the wait time, in seconds, for each call. This information is contained in the CD-ROM file *PS Industries*.

Use the sample data to construct the appropriate control chart(s). Does the process appear to be in statistical control? What other information concerning the call center's process should the consultant be aware of?

Advanced Application

17.37   Varians Controls manufactures a variety of different electric motors and drives. One step in the manufacturing process involves cutting copper wire from large reels into smaller lengths. For a particular motor, there is a dedicated machine for cutting wire to the required length. As a part of their regular quality-improvement activities, the continuous process improvement team at Varians took a sample size of 5 cuttings every hour for 30 consecutive hours of operation. At the time the samples were taken, Varians had every reason to believe that its process was working as intended. The automatic cutting machine records the length of each cut, and the following results are reported in the CD-ROM file *Varians Controls*.

a. Develop the appropriate 3-sigma control chart(s) for this process. Does the process appear to be working as intended (in control)?

b. A few weeks after the previous data were sampled, a new operator was hired to calibrate the company's cutting machines. The first 5 samples taken from the machine after the calibration adjustments (samples 225 to 229) are shown as follows:

	Cutting 1	Cutting 2	Cutting 3	Cutting 4	Cutting 5
Sample 225	0.7818	0.7760	0.7814	0.7824	0.7702
Sample 226	0.7694	0.7838	0.7675	0.7834	0.7730
Sample 227	0.7875	0.7738	0.7737	0.7594	0.7837
Sample 228	0.7762	0.7711	0.7700	0.7823	0.7673
Sample 229	0.7805	0.7724	0.7748	0.7823	0.7924

Based on these sample values, what can you say about the cutting process? Does it appear to be in control?

CASE 17-A:

Izbar Precision Casters, Inc.

Izbar Precision Casters, Inc., manufactures a variety of structural steel products for the construction trade. Currently, there is a strong demand for their I-beam product produced at a mill outside Memphis. Beams at this facility are shipped throughout the Midwest and mid-South, and demand for the product is high due to the strong economy in the regions served by the plant. Angie Schneider, the mill's manager, wants to ensure that the plant's

operations are in control, and she has selected several characteristics to monitor. Specifically, she collects data on the number of weekly accidents at the plant, the number of orders shipped on time, and the thickness of the steel I beams produced.

For the number of reported accidents, Angie selected 30 days at random from the company's safety records. Angie and all the plant employees are very concerned about workplace safety; and management, labor, and government officials have worked together to help create a safe work environment. As a part of their safety program, the company requires employees to report every accident regardless of how minor it may be. In fact, most accidents are very minor, but Izbar still records them and works to prevent them from reoccurring. Because of their strong reporting requirement, Angie was able to get a count of the number of reported accidents for each of the 30 sampled days. These data are shown in Table 17-4.

To monitor the percentage of on-time shipments, Angie randomly selected 50 records from the firm's shipping and billing system every day for 20 different days over the past six months. These records contained the actual and promised shipping dates for each order. Angie used a spreadsheet to determine the number of shipments that were made after the promised shipment dates. The number of late shipments from the 50 sampled records was then reported. These data are shown in Table 17-5.

Finally, to monitor the thickness of the I beam produced at the plant, Angie randomly selected six I beams every day for 30 days and had each sampled beam measured. The thickness of each beam, in inches, was recorded. All of the data collected by Angie are contained in the CD-ROM file *Izbar*. She wants to use the information she has collected to construct and analyze the appropriate control charts for the plant's production processes. She intends to present this information at the next manager's meeting on Monday morning.

a. Use the data that Angie has collected to develop and analyze the appropriate control charts for this process. Be sure to label each control chart carefully and also to identify the type of control chart used.

b. Do the processes analyzed appear to be in control? Why or why not? What would you suggest that Angie do?

c. Does Angie need to continue to monitor her processes on a regular basis? How should she do this? Also, are there other variables that might be of interest to her in monitoring the plant's performance? If so, what do you think they might be?

TABLE 17-4   Accident Data

DAY	NUMBER OF REPORTED ACCIDENTS	DAY	NUMBER OF REPORTED ACCIDENTS
1	9	16	4
2	11	17	11
3	9	18	7
4	9	19	7
5	11	20	10
6	10	21	11
7	10	22	6
8	10	23	6
9	4	24	7
10	7	25	4
11	7	26	9
12	8	27	11
13	11	28	9
14	10	29	6
15	7	30	5

TABLE 17-5   Late Shipments

DAY	NUMBER OF LATE SHIPMENTS	DAY	NUMBER OF LATE SHIPMENTS
1	5	11	8
2	3	12	2
3	1	13	5
4	6	14	6
5	5	15	2
6	8	16	7
7	5	17	7
8	6	18	3
9	4	19	2
10	4	20	7

General References

1. Crosby, Philip B., *Quality Is Free: The Art of Making Quality Certain* (New York: McGraw-Hill, 1979).
2. Deming, W. Edwards, *Out of the Crisis* (Cambridge, MA: MIT Center for Advanced Engineering Study, 1986).
3. Evans, James R., and William M. Lindsay, *The Management and Control of Quality*, 4th ed. (Cincinnati, OH: South-Western College Publishing, 1999).
4. Gitlow, Howard, Alan Oppenheim, and Rosa Oppenheim, *Quality Management: Tools and Methods for Improvement*, 2d ed. (Burr Ridge, IL: Irwin, 1995).
5. Juran, Joseph M. *Quality Control Handbook*, 5th ed. (New York: McGraw-Hill, 1999).
6. *Microsoft Excel 2000* (Redmond, WA: Microsoft Corp., 1999).
7. *Minitab for Windows Version 13* (State College, PA: Minitab, 2000).
8. Mitra, Amitava, *Fundamentals of Quality Control and Improvement*, 2d ed. (Upper Saddle River, NJ: Prentice Hall, 1998).

LIST OF APPENDIX TABLES

1511	4745	8716	2793	9142	4958	5245	8312	8925
6249	7073	0460	0819	0729	6806	2713	6595	5149
2587	4800	3455	7565	1196	7768	6137	4941	0488
0168	1379	7838	7487	7420	5285	8045	6679	1361
9664	9021	4990	5570	4697	7939	5842	5353	7503
1384	4981	2708	6437	2298	6230	7443	9425	5384
6390	8953	4292	7372	7197	2121	6538	2093	7629
6944	8134	0704	8500	6996	3492	4397	8802	3253
3610	3119	7442	6218	7623	0546	8394	3286	4463
9865	0028	1783	9029	2858	8737	7023	0444	8575
7044	6712	7530	0018	0945	8803	4467	0979	1342
9304	4857	5476	8386	1540	5760	9815	7191	3291
1717	8278	0072	2636	3217	1693	6081	1330	3458
2461	3598	5173	9666	6165	7438	6805	2357	6994
8240	9856	0075	7599	8468	7653	6272	0573	4344
1697	6805	1386	2340	6694	9786	0536	6423	1083
4695	2251	8962	5638	9459	5578	0676	2276	4724
3056	8558	3020	7509	5105	4283	5390	5715	8405
6887	9035	8520	6571	3233	7175	2859	1615	3349
1267	8824	5588	2821	1247	0967	4355	1385	0727
4369	9267	9377	8205	6479	7002	0649	4731	7086
2888	0333	5347	4849	5526	2975	5295	5071	6011
9893	7251	6243	4617	9256	4039	4800	9393	3263
8927	3977	6054	5979	8566	8120	2566	4449	2414
2676	7064	2198	3234	3796	5506	4462	5121	9052
0775	7316	2249	5606	9411	3818	5268	7652	6098
3828	9178	3726	0743	4075	3560	9542	3922	7688
3281	3419	6660	7968	1238	2246	2164	4567	1801
0328	7471	5352	2019	5842	1665	5939	6337	9102
8406	1826	8437	3078	9068	1425	1232	0573	7751
7076	8418	6778	1292	2019	3506	7474	0141	6544
0446	8641	3249	5431	4068	6045	1939	5626	1867
3719	9712	7472	1517	8850	6862	6990	5475	6227
5648	0563	6346	1981	9512	0659	5694	6668	2563
3694	8582	3434	4052	8392	3883	5126	0477	4034
3554	9876	4249	9473	9085	6594	2434	9453	8883
4934	8446	4646	2054	1136	1023	6295	6483	9915
7835	1506	0019	5011	0563	4450	1466	6334	2606
1098	2113	8287	3487	8250	2269	1876	3684	8856
1186	2685	7225	8311	3835	8059	9163	2539	6487
4618	1522	0627	0448	0669	4086	4083	0881	4270
5529	4173	5711	7419	2535	5876	8435	2564	3031
0754	5808	8458	2218	9180	6213	5280	4753	0696
5865	0806	2070	7986	4800	3076	2866	0515	7417
6168	8963	0235	1514	7875	2176	3095	1171	7892
7479	4144	6697	2255	5465	7233	4981	3553	8144
4608	6576	9422	4198	2578	1701	4764	7460	3509
0654	2483	6001	4486	4941	1500	3502	9693	1956
3000	9694	6616	5599	7759	1581	9896	2312	8140
2686	3675	5760	2918	0185	7364	9985	5930	9869
4713	4121	5144	5164	8104	0403	4984	3877	8772
9281	6522	7916	8941	6710	1670	1399	5961	4714
5736	9419	5022	6955	3356	5732	1042	0527	7441
2383	0408	2821	7313	5781	6951	7181	0608	2864
8740	8038	7284	6054	2246	1674	9984	0355	0775

APPENDIX B

Binomial Distribution Table

$$P(x) = \frac{n!}{x!(n-x)!} p^x (1-p)^{n-x}$$

$n = 1$

x	$p = 0.01$	$p = 0.02$	$p = 0.03$	$p = 0.04$	$p = 0.05$	$p = 0.06$	$p = 0.07$	$p = 0.08$	$p = 0.09$	
0	0.9900	0.9800	0.9700	0.9600	0.9500	0.9400	0.9300	0.9200	0.9100	1
1	0.0100	0.0200	0.0300	0.0400	0.0500	0.0600	0.0700	0.0800	0.0900	0
	$p = 0.99$	$p = 0.98$	$p = 0.97$	$p = 0.96$	$p = 0.95$	$p = 0.94$	$p = 0.93$	$p = 0.92$	$p = 0.91$	x

x	$p = 0.10$	$p = 0.15$	$p = 0.20$	$p = 0.25$	$p = 0.30$	$p = 0.35$	$p = 0.40$	$p = 0.45$	$p = 0.50$	
0	0.9000	0.8500	0.8000	0.7500	0.7000	0.6500	0.6000	0.5500	0.5000	1
1	0.1000	0.1500	0.2000	0.2500	0.3000	0.3500	0.4000	0.4500	0.5000	0
	$p = 0.90$	$p = 0.85$	$p = 0.80$	$p = 0.75$	$p = 0.70$	$p = 0.65$	$p = 0.60$	$p = 0.55$	$p = 0.50$	x

$n = 2$

x	$p = 0.01$	$p = 0.02$	$p = 0.03$	$p = 0.04$	$p = 0.05$	$p = 0.06$	$p = 0.07$	$p = 0.08$	$p = 0.09$	
0	0.9801	0.9604	0.9409	0.9216	0.9025	0.8836	0.8649	0.8464	0.8281	2
1	0.0198	0.0392	0.0582	0.0768	0.0950	0.1128	0.1302	0.1472	0.1638	1
2	0.0001	0.0004	0.0009	0.0016	0.0025	0.0036	0.0049	0.0064	0.0081	0
	$p = 0.99$	$p = 0.98$	$p = 0.97$	$p = 0.96$	$p = 0.95$	$p = 0.94$	$p = 0.93$	$p = 0.92$	$p = 0.91$	x

x	$p = 0.10$	$p = 0.15$	$p = 0.20$	$p = 0.25$	$p = 0.30$	$p = 0.35$	$p = 0.40$	$p = 0.45$	$p = 0.50$	
0	0.8100	0.7225	0.6400	0.5625	0.4900	0.4225	0.3600	0.3025	0.2500	2
1	0.1800	0.2550	0.3200	0.3750	0.4200	0.4550	0.4800	0.4950	0.5000	1
2	0.0100	0.0225	0.0400	0.0625	0.0900	0.1225	0.1600	0.2025	0.2500	0
	$p = 0.90$	$p = 0.85$	$p = 0.80$	$p = 0.75$	$p = 0.70$	$p = 0.65$	$p = 0.60$	$p = 0.55$	$p = 0.50$	x

$n = 3$

x	$p = 0.01$	$p = 0.02$	$p = 0.03$	$p = 0.04$	$p = 0.05$	$p = 0.06$	$p = 0.07$	$p = 0.08$	$p = 0.09$	
0	0.9703	0.9412	0.9127	0.8847	0.8574	0.8306	0.8044	0.7787	0.7536	3
1	0.0294	0.0576	0.0847	0.1106	0.1354	0.1590	0.1816	0.2031	0.2236	2
2	0.0003	0.0012	0.0026	0.0046	0.0071	0.0102	0.0137	0.0177	0.0221	1
3	0.0000	0.0000	0.0000	0.0001	0.0001	0.0002	0.0003	0.0005	0.0007	0
	$p = 0.99$	$p = 0.98$	$p = 0.97$	$p = 0.96$	$p = 0.95$	$p = 0.94$	$p = 0.93$	$p = 0.92$	$p = 0.91$	x

x	$p = 0.10$	$p = 0.15$	$p = 0.20$	$p = 0.25$	$p = 0.30$	$p = 0.35$	$p = 0.40$	$p = 0.45$	$p = 0.50$	
0	0.7290	0.6141	0.5120	0.4219	0.3430	0.2746	0.2160	0.1664	0.1250	3
1	0.2430	0.3251	0.3840	0.4219	0.4410	0.4436	0.4320	0.4084	0.3750	2
2	0.0270	0.0574	0.0960	0.1406	0.1890	0.2389	0.2880	0.3341	0.3750	1
3	0.0010	0.0034	0.0080	0.0156	0.0270	0.0429	0.0640	0.0911	0.1250	0
	$p = 0.90$	$p = 0.85$	$p = 0.80$	$p = 0.75$	$p = 0.70$	$p = 0.65$	$p = 0.60$	$p = 0.55$	$p = 0.50$	x

$n = 4$

x	$p = 0.01$	$p = 0.02$	$p = 0.03$	$p = 0.04$	$p = 0.05$	$p = 0.06$	$p = 0.07$	$p = 0.08$	$p = 0.09$	
0	0.9606	0.9224	0.8853	0.8493	0.8145	0.7807	0.7481	0.7164	0.6857	4
1	0.0388	0.0753	0.1095	0.1416	0.1715	0.1993	0.2252	0.2492	0.2713	3
2	0.0006	0.0023	0.0051	0.0088	0.0135	0.0191	0.0254	0.0325	0.0402	2
3	0.0000	0.0000	0.0001	0.0002	0.0005	0.0008	0.0013	0.0019	0.0027	1
4	0.0000	0.0000	0.0000	0.0000	0.0000	0.0000	0.0000	0.0000	0.0001	0
	$p = 0.99$	$p = 0.98$	$p = 0.97$	$p = 0.96$	$p = 0.95$	$p = 0.94$	$p = 0.93$	$p = 0.92$	$p = 0.91$	x

x	$p = 0.10$	$p = 0.15$	$p = 0.20$	$p = 0.25$	$p = 0.30$	$p = 0.35$	$p = 0.40$	$p = 0.45$	$p = 0.50$	
0	0.6561	0.5220	0.4096	0.3164	0.2401	0.1785	0.1296	0.0915	0.0625	4
1	0.2916	0.3685	0.4096	0.4219	0.4116	0.3845	0.3456	0.2995	0.2500	3
2	0.0486	0.0975	0.1536	0.2109	0.2646	0.3105	0.3456	0.3675	0.3750	2
3	0.0036	0.0115	0.0256	0.0469	0.0756	0.1115	0.1536	0.2005	0.2500	1
4	0.0001	0.0005	0.0016	0.0039	0.0081	0.0150	0.0256	0.0410	0.0625	0
	$p = 0.90$	$p = 0.85$	$p = 0.80$	$p = 0.75$	$p = 0.70$	$p = 0.65$	$p = 0.60$	$p = 0.55$	$p = 0.50$	x

n = 5

x	p = 0.01	p = 0.02	p = 0.03	p = 0.04	p = 0.05	p = 0.06	p = 0.07	p = 0.08	p = 0.09	
0	0.9510	0.9039	0.8587	0.8154	0.7738	0.7339	0.6957	0.6591	0.6240	5
1	0.0480	0.0922	0.1328	0.1699	0.2036	0.2342	0.2618	0.2866	0.3086	4
2	0.0010	0.0038	0.0082	0.0142	0.0214	0.0299	0.0394	0.0498	0.0610	3
3	0.0000	0.0001	0.0003	0.0006	0.0011	0.0019	0.0030	0.0043	0.0060	2
4	0.0000	0.0000	0.0000	0.0000	0.0000	0.0001	0.0001	0.0002	0.0003	1
5	0.0000	0.0000	0.0000	0.0000	0.0000	0.0000	0.0000	0.0000	0.0000	0
	p = 0.99	p = 0.98	p = 0.97	p = 0.96	p = 0.95	p = 0.94	p = 0.93	p = 0.92	p = 0.91	x

x	p = 0.10	p = 0.15	p = 0.20	p = 0.25	p = 0.30	p = 0.35	p = 0.40	p = 0.45	p = 0.50	
0	0.5905	0.4437	0.3277	0.2373	0.1681	0.1160	0.0778	0.0503	0.0313	5
1	0.3281	0.3915	0.4096	0.3955	0.3602	0.3124	0.2592	0.2059	0.1563	4
2	0.0729	0.1382	0.2048	0.2637	0.3087	0.3364	0.3456	0.3369	0.3125	3
3	0.0081	0.0244	0.0512	0.0879	0.1323	0.1811	0.2304	0.2757	0.3125	2
4	0.0005	0.0022	0.0064	0.0146	0.0284	0.0488	0.0768	0.1128	0.1563	1
5	0.0000	0.0001	0.0003	0.0010	0.0024	0.0053	0.0102	0.0185	0.0313	0
	p = 0.90	p = 0.85	p = 0.80	p = 0.75	p = 0.70	p = 0.65	p = 0.60	p = 0.55	p = 0.50	x

n = 6

x	p = 0.01	p = 0.02	p = 0.03	p = 0.04	p = 0.05	p = 0.06	p = 0.07	p = 0.08	p = 0.09	
0	0.9415	0.8858	0.8330	0.7828	0.7351	0.6899	0.6470	0.6064	0.5679	6
1	0.0571	0.1085	0.1546	0.1957	0.2321	0.2642	0.2922	0.3164	0.3370	5
2	0.0014	0.0055	0.0120	0.0204	0.0305	0.0422	0.0550	0.0688	0.0833	4
3	0.0000	0.0002	0.0005	0.0011	0.0021	0.0036	0.0055	0.0080	0.0110	3
4	0.0000	0.0000	0.0000	0.0000	0.0001	0.0002	0.0003	0.0005	0.0008	2
5	0.0000	0.0000	0.0000	0.0000	0.0000	0.0000	0.0000	0.0000	0.0000	1
6	0.0000	0.0000	0.0000	0.0000	0.0000	0.0000	0.0000	0.0000	0.0000	0
	p = 0.99	p = 0.98	p = 0.97	p = 0.96	p = 0.95	p = 0.94	p = 0.93	p = 0.92	p = 0.91	x

x	p = 0.10	p = 0.15	p = 0.20	p = 0.25	p = 0.30	p = 0.35	p = 0.40	p = 0.45	p = 0.50	
0	0.5314	0.3771	0.2621	0.1780	0.1176	0.0754	0.0467	0.0277	0.0156	6
1	0.3543	0.3993	0.3932	0.3560	0.3025	0.2437	0.1866	0.1359	0.0938	5
2	0.0984	0.1762	0.2458	0.2966	0.3241	0.3280	0.3110	0.2780	0.2344	4
3	0.0146	0.0415	0.0819	0.1318	0.1852	0.2355	0.2765	0.3032	0.3125	3
4	0.0012	0.0055	0.0154	0.0330	0.0595	0.0951	0.1382	0.1861	0.2344	2
5	0.0001	0.0004	0.0015	0.0044	0.0102	0.0205	0.0369	0.0609	0.0938	1
6	0.0000	0.0000	0.0001	0.0002	0.0007	0.0018	0.0041	0.0083	0.0156	0
	p = 0.90	p = 0.85	p = 0.80	p = 0.75	p = 0.70	p = 0.65	p = 0.60	p = 0.55	p = 0.50	x

n = 7

x	p = 0.01	p = 0.02	p = 0.03	p = 0.04	p = 0.05	p = 0.06	p = 0.07	p = 0.08	p = 0.09	
0	0.9321	0.8681	0.8080	0.7514	0.6983	0.6485	0.6017	0.5578	0.5168	7
1	0.0659	0.1240	0.1749	0.2192	0.2573	0.2897	0.3170	0.3396	0.3578	6
2	0.0020	0.0076	0.0162	0.0274	0.0406	0.0555	0.0716	0.0886	0.1061	5
3	0.0000	0.0003	0.0008	0.0019	0.0036	0.0059	0.0090	0.0128	0.0175	4
4	0.0000	0.0000	0.0000	0.0001	0.0002	0.0004	0.0007	0.0011	0.0017	3
5	0.0000	0.0000	0.0000	0.0000	0.0000	0.0000	0.0000	0.0001	0.0001	2
6	0.0000	0.0000	0.0000	0.0000	0.0000	0.0000	0.0000	0.0000	0.0000	1
	p = 0.99	p = 0.98	p = 0.97	p = 0.96	p = 0.95	p = 0.94	p = 0.93	p = 0.92	p = 0.91	x

x	p = 0.10	p = 0.15	p = 0.20	p = 0.25	p = 0.30	p = 0.35	p = 0.40	p = 0.45	p = 0.50	
0	0.4783	0.3206	0.2097	0.1335	0.0824	0.0490	0.0280	0.0152	0.0078	7
1	0.3720	0.3960	0.3670	0.3115	0.2471	0.1848	0.1306	0.0872	0.0547	6
2	0.1240	0.2097	0.2753	0.3115	0.3177	0.2985	0.2613	0.2140	0.1641	5
3	0.0230	0.0617	0.1147	0.1730	0.2269	0.2679	0.2903	0.2918	0.2734	4
4	0.0026	0.0109	0.0287	0.0577	0.0972	0.1442	0.1935	0.2388	0.2734	3
5	0.0002	0.0012	0.0043	0.0115	0.0250	0.0466	0.0774	0.1172	0.1641	2
6	0.0000	0.0001	0.0004	0.0013	0.0036	0.0084	0.0172	0.0320	0.0547	1
7	0.0000	0.0000	0.0000	0.0001	0.0002	0.0006	0.0016	0.0037	0.0078	0
	p = 0.90	p = 0.85	p = 0.80	p = 0.75	p = 0.70	p = 0.65	p = 0.60	p = 0.55	p = 0.50	x

n = 8

x	p = 0.01	p = 0.02	p = 0.03	p = 0.04	p = 0.05	p = 0.06	p = 0.07	p = 0.08	p = 0.09	
0	0.9227	0.8508	0.7837	0.7214	0.6634	0.6096	0.5596	0.5132	0.4703	8
1	0.0746	0.1389	0.1939	0.2405	0.2793	0.3113	0.3370	0.3570	0.3721	7
2	0.0026	0.0099	0.0210	0.0351	0.0515	0.0695	0.0888	0.1087	0.1288	6
3	0.0001	0.0004	0.0013	0.0029	0.0054	0.0089	0.0134	0.0189	0.0255	5
4	0.0000	0.0000	0.0001	0.0002	0.0004	0.0007	0.0013	0.0021	0.0031	4
5	0.0000	0.0000	0.0000	0.0000	0.0000	0.0000	0.0001	0.0001	0.0002	3
6	0.0000	0.0000	0.0000	0.0000	0.0000	0.0000	0.0000	0.0000	0.0000	2
	p = 0.99	p = 0.98	p = 0.97	p = 0.96	p = 0.95	p = 0.94	p = 0.93	p = 0.92	p = 0.91	x

x	p = 0.10	p = 0.15	p = 0.20	p = 0.25	p = 0.30	p = 0.35	p = 0.40	p = 0.45	p = 0.50	
0	0.4305	0.2725	0.1678	0.1001	0.0576	0.0319	0.0168	0.0084	0.0039	8
1	0.3826	0.3847	0.3355	0.2670	0.1977	0.1373	0.0896	0.0548	0.0313	7
2	0.1488	0.2376	0.2936	0.3115	0.2965	0.2587	0.2090	0.1569	0.1094	6
3	0.0331	0.0839	0.1468	0.2076	0.2541	0.2786	0.2787	0.2568	0.2188	5
4	0.0046	0.0185	0.0459	0.0865	0.1361	0.1875	0.2322	0.2627	0.2734	4
5	0.0004	0.0026	0.0092	0.0231	0.0467	0.0808	0.1239	0.1719	0.2188	3
6	0.0000	0.0002	0.0011	0.0038	0.0100	0.0217	0.0413	0.0703	0.1094	2
7	0.0000	0.0000	0.0001	0.0004	0.0012	0.0033	0.0079	0.0164	0.0313	1
8	0.0000	0.0000	0.0000	0.0000	0.0001	0.0002	0.0007	0.0017	0.0039	0
	p = 0.90	p = 0.85	p = 0.80	p = 0.75	p = 0.70	p = 0.65	p = 0.60	p = 0.55	p = 0.50	x

n = 9

x	p = 0.01	p = 0.02	p = 0.03	p = 0.04	p = 0.05	p = 0.06	p = 0.07	p = 0.08	p = 0.09	
0	0.9135	0.8337	0.7602	0.6925	0.6302	0.5730	0.5204	0.4722	0.4279	9
1	0.0830	0.1531	0.2116	0.2597	0.2985	0.3292	0.3525	0.3695	0.3809	8
2	0.0034	0.0125	0.0262	0.0433	0.0629	0.0840	0.1061	0.1285	0.1507	7
3	0.0001	0.0006	0.0019	0.0042	0.0077	0.0125	0.0186	0.0261	0.0348	6
4	0.0000	0.0000	0.0001	0.0003	0.0006	0.0012	0.0021	0.0034	0.0052	5
5	0.0000	0.0000	0.0000	0.0000	0.0000	0.0001	0.0002	0.0003	0.0005	4
6	0.0000	0.0000	0.0000	0.0000	0.0000	0.0000	0.0000	0.0000	0.0000	3
7	0.0000	0.0000	0.0000	0.0000	0.0000	0.0000	0.0000	0.0000	0.0000	2
	p = 0.99	p = 0.98	p = 0.97	p = 0.96	p = 0.95	p = 0.94	p = 0.93	p = 0.92	p = 0.91	x

x	p = 0.10	p = 0.15	p = 0.20	p = 0.25	p = 0.30	p = 0.35	p = 0.40	p = 0.45	p = 0.50	
0	0.3874	0.2316	0.1342	0.0751	0.0404	0.0207	0.0101	0.0046	0.0020	9
1	0.3874	0.3679	0.3020	0.2253	0.1556	0.1004	0.0605	0.0339	0.0176	8
2	0.1722	0.2597	0.3020	0.3003	0.2668	0.2162	0.1612	0.1110	0.0703	7
3	0.0446	0.1069	0.1762	0.2336	0.2668	0.2716	0.2508	0.2119	0.1641	6
4	0.0074	0.0283	0.0661	0.1168	0.1715	0.2194	0.2508	0.2600	0.2461	5
5	0.0008	0.0050	0.0165	0.0389	0.0735	0.1181	0.1672	0.2128	0.2461	4
6	0.0001	0.0006	0.0028	0.0087	0.0210	0.0424	0.0743	0.1160	0.1641	3
7	0.0000	0.0000	0.0003	0.0012	0.0039	0.0098	0.0212	0.0407	0.0703	2
8	0.0000	0.0000	0.0000	0.0001	0.0004	0.0013	0.0035	0.0083	0.0176	1
9	0.0000	0.0000	0.0000	0.0000	0.0000	0.0001	0.0003	0.0008	0.0020	0
	p = 0.90	p = 0.85	p = 0.80	p = 0.75	p = 0.70	p = 0.65	p = 0.60	p = 0.55	p = 0.50	x

n = 10

x	p = 0.01	p = 0.02	p = 0.03	p = 0.04	p = 0.05	p = 0.06	p = 0.07	p = 0.08	p = 0.09	
0	0.9044	0.8171	0.7374	0.6648	0.5987	0.5386	0.4840	0.4344	0.3894	10
1	0.0914	0.1667	0.2281	0.2770	0.3151	0.3438	0.3643	0.3777	0.3851	9
2	0.0042	0.0153	0.0317	0.0519	0.0746	0.0988	0.1234	0.1478	0.1714	8
3	0.0001	0.0008	0.0026	0.0058	0.0105	0.0168	0.0248	0.0343	0.0452	7
4	0.0000	0.0000	0.0001	0.0004	0.0010	0.0019	0.0033	0.0052	0.0078	6
5	0.0000	0.0000	0.0000	0.0000	0.0001	0.0001	0.0003	0.0005	0.0009	5
6	0.0000	0.0000	0.0000	0.0000	0.0000	0.0000	0.0000	0.0000	0.0001	4
7	0.0000	0.0000	0.0000	0.0000	0.0000	0.0000	0.0000	0.0000	0.0000	3
	p = 0.99	p = 0.98	p = 0.97	p = 0.96	p = 0.95	p = 0.94	p = 0.93	p = 0.92	p = 0.91	x

multiply by total number to get (×100)

x	$p = 0.10$	$p = 0.15$	$p = 0.20$	$p = 0.25$	$p = 0.30$	$p = 0.35$	$p = 0.40$	$p = 0.45$	$p = 0.50$	
0	0.3487	0.1969	0.1074	0.0563	0.0282	0.0135	0.0060	0.0025	0.0010	10
1	0.3874	0.3474	0.2684	0.1877	0.1211	0.0725	0.0403	0.0207	0.0098	9
2	0.1937	0.2759	0.3020	0.2816	0.2335	0.1757	0.1209	0.0763	0.0439	8
3	0.0574	0.1298	0.2013	0.2503	0.2668	0.2522	0.2150	0.1665	0.1172	7
4	0.0112	0.0401	0.0881	0.1460	0.2001	0.2377	0.2508	0.2384	0.2051	6
5	0.0015	0.0085	0.0264	0.0584	0.1029	0.1536	0.2007	0.2340	0.2461	5
6	0.0001	0.0012	0.0055	0.0162	0.0368	0.0689	0.1115	0.1596	0.2051	4
7	0.0000	0.0001	0.0008	0.0031	0.0090	0.0212	0.0425	0.0746	0.1172	3
8	0.0000	0.0000	0.0001	0.0004	0.0014	0.0043	0.0106	0.0229	0.0439	2
9	0.0000	0.0000	0.0000	0.0000	0.0001	0.0005	0.0016	0.0042	0.0098	1
10	0.0000	0.0000	0.0000	0.0000	0.0000	0.0000	0.0001	0.0003	0.0010	0
	$p = 0.90$	$p = 0.85$	$p = 0.80$	$p = 0.75$	$p = 0.70$	$p = 0.65$	$p = 0.60$	$p = 0.55$	$p = 0.50$	x

$n = 11$

x	$p = 0.01$	$p = 0.02$	$p = 0.03$	$p = 0.04$	$p = 0.05$	$p = 0.06$	$p = 0.07$	$p = 0.08$	$p = 0.09$	
0	0.8953	0.8007	0.7153	0.6382	0.5688	0.5063	0.4501	0.3996	0.3544	11
1	0.0995	0.1798	0.2433	0.2925	0.3293	0.3555	0.3727	0.3823	0.3855	10
2	0.0050	0.0183	0.0376	0.0609	0.0867	0.1135	0.1403	0.1662	0.1906	9
3	0.0002	0.0011	0.0035	0.0076	0.0137	0.0217	0.0317	0.0434	0.0566	8
4	0.0000	0.0000	0.0002	0.0006	0.0014	0.0028	0.0048	0.0075	0.0112	7
5	0.0000	0.0000	0.0000	0.0000	0.0001	0.0002	0.0005	0.0009	0.0015	6
6	0.0000	0.0000	0.0000	0.0000	0.0000	0.0000	0.0000	0.0001	0.0002	5
7	0.0000	0.0000	0.0000	0.0000	0.0000	0.0000	0.0000	0.0000	0.0000	4
	$p = 0.99$	$p = 0.98$	$p = 0.97$	$p = 0.96$	$p = 0.95$	$p = 0.94$	$p = 0.93$	$p = 0.92$	$p = 0.91$	x

x	$p = 0.10$	$p = 0.15$	$p = 0.20$	$p = 0.25$	$p = 0.30$	$p = 0.35$	$p = 0.40$	$p = 0.45$	$p = 0.50$	
0	0.3138	0.1673	0.0859	0.0422	0.0198	0.0088	0.0036	0.0014	0.0005	11
1	0.3835	0.3248	0.2362	0.1549	0.0932	0.0518	0.0266	0.0125	0.0054	10
2	0.2131	0.2866	0.2953	0.2581	0.1998	0.1395	0.0887	0.0513	0.0269	9
3	0.0710	0.1517	0.2215	0.2581	0.2568	0.2254	0.1774	0.1259	0.0806	8
4	0.0158	0.0536	0.1107	0.1721	0.2201	0.2428	0.2365	0.2060	0.1611	7
5	0.0025	0.0132	0.0388	0.0803	0.1321	0.1830	0.2207	0.2360	0.2256	6
6	0.0003	0.0023	0.0097	0.0268	0.0566	0.0985	0.1471	0.1931	0.2256	5
7	0.0000	0.0003	0.0017	0.0064	0.0173	0.0379	0.0701	0.1128	0.1611	4
8	0.0000	0.0000	0.0002	0.0011	0.0037	0.0102	0.0234	0.0462	0.0806	3
9	0.0000	0.0000	0.0000	0.0001	0.0005	0.0018	0.0052	0.0126	0.0269	2
10	0.0000	0.0000	0.0000	0.0000	0.0000	0.0002	0.0007	0.0021	0.0054	1
11	0.0000	0.0000	0.0000	0.0000	0.0000	0.0000	0.0000	0.0002	0.0005	0
	$p = 0.90$	$p = 0.85$	$p = 0.80$	$p = 0.75$	$p = 0.70$	$p = 0.65$	$p = 0.60$	$p = 0.55$	$p = 0.50$	x

$n = 12$

x	$p = 0.01$	$p = 0.02$	$p = 0.03$	$p = 0.04$	$p = 0.05$	$p = 0.06$	$p = 0.07$	$p = 0.08$	$p = 0.09$	
0	0.8864	0.7847	0.6938	0.6127	0.5404	0.4759	0.4186	0.3677	0.3225	12
1	0.1074	0.1922	0.2575	0.3064	0.3413	0.3645	0.3781	0.3837	0.3827	11
2	0.0060	0.0216	0.0438	0.0702	0.0988	0.1280	0.1565	0.1835	0.2082	10
3	0.0002	0.0015	0.0045	0.0098	0.0173	0.0272	0.0393	0.0532	0.0686	9
4	0.0000	0.0001	0.0003	0.0009	0.0021	0.0039	0.0067	0.0104	0.0153	8
5	0.0000	0.0000	0.0000	0.0001	0.0002	0.0004	0.0008	0.0014	0.0024	7
6	0.0000	0.0000	0.0000	0.0000	0.0000	0.0000	0.0001	0.0001	0.0003	6
7	0.0000	0.0000	0.0000	0.0000	0.0000	0.0000	0.0000	0.0000	0.0000	5
	$p = 0.99$	$p = 0.98$	$p = 0.97$	$p = 0.96$	$p = 0.95$	$p = 0.94$	$p = 0.93$	$p = 0.92$	$p = 0.91$	x

x	p = 0.10	p = 0.15	p = 0.20	p = 0.25	p = 0.30	p = 0.35	p = 0.40	p = 0.45	p = 0.50	
0	0.2824	0.1422	0.0687	0.0317	0.0138	0.0057	0.0022	0.0008	0.0002	12
1	0.3766	0.3012	0.2062	0.1267	0.0712	0.0368	0.0174	0.0075	0.0029	11
2	0.2301	0.2924	0.2835	0.2323	0.1678	0.1088	0.0639	0.0339	0.0161	10
3	0.0852	0.1720	0.2362	0.2581	0.2397	0.1954	0.1419	0.0923	0.0537	9
4	0.0213	0.0683	0.1329	0.1936	0.2311	0.2367	0.2128	0.1700	0.1208	8
5	0.0038	0.0193	0.0532	0.1032	0.1585	0.2039	0.2270	0.2225	0.1934	7
6	0.0005	0.0040	0.0155	0.0401	0.0792	0.1281	0.1766	0.2124	0.2256	6
7	0.0000	0.0006	0.0033	0.0115	0.0291	0.0591	0.1009	0.1489	0.1934	5
8	0.0000	0.0001	0.0005	0.0024	0.0078	0.0199	0.0420	0.0762	0.1208	4
9	0.0000	0.0000	0.0001	0.0004	0.0015	0.0048	0.0125	0.0277	0.0537	3
10	0.0000	0.0000	0.0000	0.0000	0.0002	0.0008	0.0025	0.0068	0.0161	2
11	0.0000	0.0000	0.0000	0.0000	0.0000	0.0001	0.0003	0.0010	0.0029	1
12	0.0000	0.0000	0.0000	0.0000	0.0000	0.0000	0.0000	0.0001	0.0002	0
	p = 0.90	p = 0.85	p = 0.80	p = 0.75	p = 0.70	p = 0.65	p = 0.60	p = 0.55	p = 0.50	x

n = 13

x	p = 0.01	p = 0.02	p = 0.03	p = 0.04	p = 0.05	p = 0.06	p = 0.07	p = 0.08	p = 0.09	
0	0.8775	0.7690	0.6730	0.5882	0.5133	0.4474	0.3893	0.3383	0.2935	13
1	0.1152	0.2040	0.2706	0.3186	0.3512	0.3712	0.3809	0.3824	0.3773	12
2	0.0070	0.0250	0.0502	0.0797	0.1109	0.1422	0.1720	0.1995	0.2239	11
3	0.0003	0.0019	0.0057	0.0122	0.0214	0.0333	0.0475	0.0636	0.0812	10
4	0.0000	0.0001	0.0004	0.0013	0.0028	0.0053	0.0089	0.0138	0.0201	9
5	0.0000	0.0000	0.0000	0.0001	0.0003	0.0006	0.0012	0.0022	0.0036	8
6	0.0000	0.0000	0.0000	0.0000	0.0000	0.0001	0.0001	0.0003	0.0005	7
7	0.0000	0.0000	0.0000	0.0000	0.0000	0.0000	0.0000	0.0000	0.0000	6
8	0.0000	0.0000	0.0000	0.0000	0.0000	0.0000	0.0000	0.0000	0.0000	5
	p = 0.99	p = 0.98	p = 0.97	p = 0.96	p = 0.95	p = 0.94	p = 0.93	p = 0.92	p = 0.91	x

x	p = 0.10	p = 0.15	p = 0.20	p = 0.25	p = 0.30	p = 0.35	p = 0.40	p = 0.45	p = 0.50	
0	0.2542	0.1209	0.0550	0.0238	0.0097	0.0037	0.0013	0.0004	0.0001	13
1	0.3672	0.2774	0.1787	0.1029	0.0540	0.0259	0.0113	0.0045	0.0016	12
2	0.2448	0.2937	0.2680	0.2059	0.1388	0.0836	0.0453	0.0220	0.0095	11
3	0.0997	0.1900	0.2457	0.2517	0.2181	0.1651	0.1107	0.0660	0.0349	10
4	0.0277	0.0838	0.1535	0.2097	0.2337	0.2222	0.1845	0.1350	0.0873	9
5	0.0055	0.0266	0.0691	0.1258	0.1803	0.2154	0.2214	0.1989	0.1571	8
6	0.0008	0.0063	0.0230	0.0559	0.1030	0.1546	0.1968	0.2169	0.2095	7
7	0.0001	0.0011	0.0058	0.0186	0.0442	0.0833	0.1312	0.1775	0.2095	6
8	0.0000	0.0001	0.0011	0.0047	0.0142	0.0336	0.0656	0.1089	0.1571	5
9	0.0000	0.0000	0.0001	0.0009	0.0034	0.0101	0.0243	0.0495	0.0873	4
10	0.0000	0.0000	0.0000	0.0001	0.0006	0.0022	0.0065	0.0162	0.0349	3
11	0.0000	0.0000	0.0000	0.0000	0.0001	0.0003	0.0012	0.0036	0.0095	2
12	0.0000	0.0000	0.0000	0.0000	0.0000	0.0000	0.0001	0.0005	0.0016	1
13	0.0000	0.0000	0.0000	0.0000	0.0000	0.0000	0.0000	0.0000	0.0001	0
	p = 0.90	p = 0.85	p = 0.80	p = 0.75	p = 0.70	p = 0.65	p = 0.60	p = 0.55	p = 0.50	x

n = 14

x	p = 0.01	p = 0.02	p = 0.03	p = 0.04	p = 0.05	p = 0.06	p = 0.07	p = 0.08	p = 0.09	
0	0.8687	0.7536	0.6528	0.5647	0.4877	0.4205	0.3620	0.3112	0.2670	14
1	0.1229	0.2153	0.2827	0.3294	0.3593	0.3758	0.3815	0.3788	0.3698	13
2	0.0081	0.0286	0.0568	0.0892	0.1229	0.1559	0.1867	0.2141	0.2377	12
3	0.0003	0.0023	0.0070	0.0149	0.0259	0.0398	0.0562	0.0745	0.0940	11
4	0.0000	0.0001	0.0006	0.0017	0.0037	0.0070	0.0116	0.0178	0.0256	10
5	0.0000	0.0000	0.0000	0.0001	0.0004	0.0009	0.0018	0.0031	0.0051	9
6	0.0000	0.0000	0.0000	0.0000	0.0000	0.0001	0.0002	0.0004	0.0008	8
7	0.0000	0.0000	0.0000	0.0000	0.0000	0.0000	0.0000	0.0000	0.0001	7
8	0.0000	0.0000	0.0000	0.0000	0.0000	0.0000	0.0000	0.0000	0.0000	6
	p = 0.99	p = 0.98	p = 0.97	p = 0.96	p = 0.95	p = 0.94	p = 0.93	p = 0.92	p = 0.91	x

x	p = 0.10	p = 0.15	p = 0.20	p = 0.25	p = 0.30	p = 0.35	p = 0.40	p = 0.45	p = 0.50	
0	0.2288	0.1028	0.0440	0.0178	0.0068	0.0024	0.0008	0.0002	0.0001	14
1	0.3559	0.2539	0.1539	0.0832	0.0407	0.0181	0.0073	0.0027	0.0009	13
2	0.2570	0.2912	0.2501	0.1802	0.1134	0.0634	0.0317	0.0141	0.0056	12
3	0.1142	0.2056	0.2501	0.2402	0.1943	0.1366	0.0845	0.0462	0.0222	11
4	0.0349	0.0998	0.1720	0.2202	0.2290	0.2022	0.1549	0.1040	0.0611	10
5	0.0078	0.0352	0.0860	0.1468	0.1963	0.2178	0.2066	0.1701	0.1222	9
6	0.0013	0.0093	0.0322	0.0734	0.1262	0.1759	0.2066	0.2088	0.1833	8
7	0.0002	0.0019	0.0092	0.0280	0.0618	0.1082	0.1574	0.1952	0.2095	7
8	0.0000	0.0003	0.0020	0.0082	0.0232	0.0510	0.0918	0.1398	0.1833	6
9	0.0000	0.0000	0.0003	0.0018	0.0066	0.0183	0.0408	0.0762	0.1222	5
10	0.0000	0.0000	0.0000	0.0003	0.0014	0.0049	0.0136	0.0312	0.0611	4
11	0.0000	0.0000	0.0000	0.0000	0.0002	0.0010	0.0033	0.0093	0.0222	3
12	0.0000	0.0000	0.0000	0.0000	0.0000	0.0001	0.0005	0.0019	0.0056	2
13	0.0000	0.0000	0.0000	0.0000	0.0000	0.0000	0.0001	0.0002	0.0009	1
14	0.0000	0.0000	0.0000	0.0000	0.0000	0.0000	0.0000	0.0000	0.0001	0
	p = 0.90	p = 0.85	p = 0.80	p = 0.75	p = 0.70	p = 0.65	p = 0.60	p = 0.55	p = 0.50	x

n = 15

x	p = 0.01	p = 0.02	p = 0.03	p = 0.04	p = 0.05	p = 0.06	p = 0.07	p = 0.08	p = 0.09	
0	0.8601	0.7386	0.6333	0.5421	0.4633	0.3953	0.3367	0.2863	0.2430	15
1	0.1303	0.2261	0.2938	0.3388	0.3658	0.3785	0.3801	0.3734	0.3605	14
2	0.0092	0.0323	0.0636	0.0988	0.1348	0.1691	0.2003	0.2273	0.2496	13
3	0.0004	0.0029	0.0085	0.0178	0.0307	0.0468	0.0653	0.0857	0.1070	12
4	0.0000	0.0002	0.0008	0.0022	0.0049	0.0090	0.0148	0.0223	0.0317	11
5	0.0000	0.0000	0.0001	0.0002	0.0006	0.0013	0.0024	0.0043	0.0069	10
6	0.0000	0.0000	0.0000	0.0000	0.0000	0.0001	0.0003	0.0006	0.0011	9
7	0.0000	0.0000	0.0000	0.0000	0.0000	0.0000	0.0000	0.0001	0.0001	8
	p = 0.99	p = 0.98	p = 0.97	p = 0.96	p = 0.95	p = 0.94	p = 0.93	p = 0.92	p = 0.91	x

x	p = 0.10	p = 0.15	p = 0.20	p = 0.25	p = 0.30	p = 0.35	p = 0.40	p = 0.45	p = 0.50	
0	0.2059	0.0874	0.0352	0.0134	0.0047	0.0016	0.0005	0.0001	0.0000	15
1	0.3432	0.2312	0.1319	0.0668	0.0305	0.0126	0.0047	0.0016	0.0005	14
2	0.2669	0.2856	0.2309	0.1559	0.0916	0.0476	0.0219	0.0090	0.0032	13
3	0.1285	0.2184	0.2501	0.2252	0.1700	0.1110	0.0634	0.0318	0.0139	12
4	0.0428	0.1156	0.1876	0.2252	0.2186	0.1792	0.1268	0.0780	0.0417	11
5	0.0105	0.0449	0.1032	0.1651	0.2061	0.2123	0.1859	0.1404	0.0916	10
6	0.0019	0.0132	0.0430	0.0917	0.1472	0.1906	0.2066	0.1914	0.1527	9
7	0.0003	0.0030	0.0138	0.0393	0.0811	0.1319	0.1771	0.2013	0.1964	8
8	0.0000	0.0005	0.0035	0.0131	0.0348	0.0710	0.1181	0.1647	0.1964	7
9	0.0000	0.0001	0.0007	0.0034	0.0116	0.0298	0.0612	0.1048	0.1527	6
10	0.0000	0.0000	0.0001	0.0007	0.0030	0.0096	0.0245	0.0515	0.0916	5
11	0.0000	0.0000	0.0000	0.0001	0.0006	0.0024	0.0074	0.0191	0.0417	4
12	0.0000	0.0000	0.0000	0.0000	0.0001	0.0004	0.0016	0.0052	0.0139	3
13	0.0000	0.0000	0.0000	0.0000	0.0000	0.0001	0.0003	0.0010	0.0032	2
14	0.0000	0.0000	0.0000	0.0000	0.0000	0.0000	0.0000	0.0001	0.0005	1
15	0.0000	0.0000	0.0000	0.0000	0.0000	0.0000	0.0000	0.0000	0.0000	0
	p = 0.90	p = 0.85	p = 0.80	p = 0.75	p = 0.70	p = 0.65	p = 0.60	p = 0.55	p = 0.50	x

n = 20

x	p = 0.01	p = 0.02	p = 0.03	p = 0.04	p = 0.05	p = 0.06	p = 0.07	p = 0.08	p = 0.09	
0	0.8179	0.6676	0.5438	0.4420	0.3585	0.2901	0.2342	0.1887	0.1516	20
1	0.1652	0.2725	0.3364	0.3683	0.3774	0.3703	0.3526	0.3282	0.3000	19
2	0.0159	0.0528	0.0988	0.1458	0.1887	0.2246	0.2521	0.2711	0.2818	18
3	0.0010	0.0065	0.0183	0.0364	0.0596	0.0860	0.1139	0.1414	0.1672	17
4	0.0000	0.0006	0.0024	0.0065	0.0133	0.0233	0.0364	0.0523	0.0703	16
5	0.0000	0.0000	0.0002	0.0009	0.0022	0.0048	0.0088	0.0145	0.0222	15
6	0.0000	0.0000	0.0000	0.0001	0.0003	0.0008	0.0017	0.0032	0.0055	14
7	0.0000	0.0000	0.0000	0.0000	0.0000	0.0001	0.0002	0.0005	0.0011	13
8	0.0000	0.0000	0.0000	0.0000	0.0000	0.0000	0.0000	0.0001	0.0002	12
9	0.0000	0.0000	0.0000	0.0000	0.0000	0.0000	0.0000	0.0000	0.0000	11
	p = 0.99	p = 0.98	p = 0.97	p = 0.96	p = 0.95	p = 0.94	p = 0.93	p = 0.92	p = 0.91	x

x	p = 0.10	p = 0.15	p = 0.20	p = 0.25	p = 0.30	p = 0.35	p = 0.40	p = 0.45	p = 0.50	
0	0.1216	0.0388	0.0115	0.0032	0.0008	0.0002	0.0000	0.0000	0.0000	20
1	0.2702	0.1368	0.0576	0.0211	0.0068	0.0020	0.0005	0.0001	0.0000	19
2	0.2852	0.2293	0.1369	0.0669	0.0278	0.0100	0.0031	0.0008	0.0002	18
3	0.1901	0.2428	0.2054	0.1339	0.0716	0.0323	0.0123	0.0040	0.0011	17
4	0.0898	0.1821	0.2182	0.1897	0.1304	0.0738	0.0350	0.0139	0.0046	16
5	0.0319	0.1028	0.1746	0.2023	0.1789	0.1272	0.0746	0.0365	0.0148	15
6	0.0089	0.0454	0.1091	0.1686	0.1916	0.1712	0.1244	0.0746	0.0370	14
7	0.0020	0.0160	0.0545	0.1124	0.1643	0.1844	0.1659	0.1221	0.0739	13
8	0.0004	0.0046	0.0222	0.0609	0.1144	0.1614	0.1797	0.1623	0.1201	12
9	0.0001	0.0011	0.0074	0.0271	0.0654	0.1158	0.1597	0.1771	0.1602	11
10	0.0000	0.0002	0.0020	0.0099	0.0308	0.0686	0.1171	0.1593	0.1762	10
11	0.0000	0.0000	0.0005	0.0030	0.0120	0.0336	0.0710	0.1185	0.1602	9
12	0.0000	0.0000	0.0001	0.0008	0.0039	0.0136	0.0355	0.0727	0.1201	8
13	0.0000	0.0000	0.0000	0.0002	0.0010	0.0045	0.0146	0.0366	0.0739	7
14	0.0000	0.0000	0.0000	0.0000	0.0002	0.0012	0.0049	0.0150	0.0370	6
15	0.0000	0.0000	0.0000	0.0000	0.0000	0.0003	0.0013	0.0049	0.0148	5
16	0.0000	0.0000	0.0000	0.0000	0.0000	0.0000	0.0003	0.0013	0.0046	4
17	0.0000	0.0000	0.0000	0.0000	0.0000	0.0000	0.0000	0.0002	0.0011	3
18	0.0000	0.0000	0.0000	0.0000	0.0000	0.0000	0.0000	0.0000	0.0002	2
	p = 0.90	p = 0.85	p = 0.80	p = 0.75	p = 0.70	p = 0.65	p = 0.60	p = 0.55	p = 0.50	x

n = 25

x	p = 0.01	p = 0.02	p = 0.03	p = 0.04	p = 0.05	p = 0.06	p = 0.07	p = 0.08	p = 0.09	
0	0.7778	0.6035	0.4670	0.3604	0.2774	0.2129	0.1630	0.1244	0.0946	25
1	0.1964	0.3079	0.3611	0.3754	0.3650	0.3398	0.3066	0.2704	0.2340	24
2	0.0238	0.0754	0.1340	0.1877	0.2305	0.2602	0.2770	0.2821	0.2777	23
3	0.0018	0.0118	0.0318	0.0600	0.0930	0.1273	0.1598	0.1881	0.2106	22
4	0.0001	0.0013	0.0054	0.0137	0.0269	0.0447	0.0662	0.0899	0.1145	21
5	0.0000	0.0001	0.0007	0.0024	0.0060	0.0120	0.0209	0.0329	0.0476	20
6	0.0000	0.0000	0.0001	0.0003	0.0010	0.0026	0.0052	0.0095	0.0157	19
7	0.0000	0.0000	0.0000	0.0000	0.0001	0.0004	0.0011	0.0022	0.0042	18
8	0.0000	0.0000	0.0000	0.0000	0.0000	0.0001	0.0002	0.0004	0.0009	17
9	0.0000	0.0000	0.0000	0.0000	0.0000	0.0000	0.0000	0.0001	0.0002	16
10	0.0000	0.0000	0.0000	0.0000	0.0000	0.0000	0.0000	0.0000	0.0000	15
	p = 0.99	p = 0.98	p = 0.97	p = 0.96	p = 0.95	p = 0.94	p = 0.93	p = 0.92	p = 0.91	x

x	p = 0.10	p = 0.15	p = 0.20	p = 0.25	p = 0.30	p = 0.35	p = 0.40	p = 0.45	p = 0.50	
0	0.0718	0.0172	0.0038	0.0008	0.0001	0.0000	0.0000	0.0000	0.0000	25
1	0.1994	0.0759	0.0236	0.0063	0.0014	0.0003	0.0000	0.0000	0.0000	24
2	0.2659	0.1607	0.0708	0.0251	0.0074	0.0018	0.0004	0.0001	0.0000	23
3	0.2265	0.2174	0.1358	0.0641	0.0243	0.0076	0.0019	0.0004	0.0001	22
4	0.1384	0.2110	0.1867	0.1175	0.0572	0.0224	0.0071	0.0018	0.0004	21
5	0.0646	0.1564	0.1960	0.1645	0.1030	0.0506	0.0199	0.0063	0.0016	20
6	0.0239	0.0920	0.1633	0.1828	0.1472	0.0908	0.0442	0.0172	0.0053	19
7	0.0072	0.0441	0.1108	0.1654	0.1712	0.1327	0.0800	0.0381	0.0143	18
8	0.0018	0.0175	0.0623	0.1241	0.1651	0.1607	0.1200	0.0701	0.0322	17
9	0.0004	0.0058	0.0294	0.0781	0.1336	0.1635	0.1511	0.1084	0.0609	16
10	0.0001	0.0016	0.0118	0.0417	0.0916	0.1409	0.1612	0.1419	0.0974	15
11	0.0000	0.0004	0.0040	0.0189	0.0536	0.1034	0.1465	0.1583	0.1328	14
12	0.0000	0.0001	0.0012	0.0074	0.0268	0.0650	0.1140	0.1511	0.1550	13
13	0.0000	0.0000	0.0003	0.0025	0.0115	0.0350	0.0760	0.1236	0.1550	12
14	0.0000	0.0000	0.0001	0.0007	0.0042	0.0161	0.0434	0.0867	0.1328	11
15	0.0000	0.0000	0.0000	0.0002	0.0013	0.0064	0.0212	0.0520	0.0974	10
16	0.0000	0.0000	0.0000	0.0000	0.0004	0.0021	0.0088	0.0266	0.0609	9
17	0.0000	0.0000	0.0000	0.0000	0.0001	0.0006	0.0031	0.0115	0.0322	8
18	0.0000	0.0000	0.0000	0.0000	0.0000	0.0001	0.0009	0.0042	0.0143	7
19	0.0000	0.0000	0.0000	0.0000	0.0000	0.0000	0.0002	0.0013	0.0053	6
20	0.0000	0.0000	0.0000	0.0000	0.0000	0.0000	0.0000	0.0003	0.0016	5
21	0.0000	0.0000	0.0000	0.0000	0.0000	0.0000	0.0000	0.0001	0.0004	4
22	0.0000	0.0000	0.0000	0.0000	0.0000	0.0000	0.0000	0.0000	0.0001	3
	p = 0.90	p = 0.85	p = 0.80	p = 0.75	p = 0.70	p = 0.65	p = 0.60	p = 0.55	p = 0.50	x

APPENDIX C

Poisson Probability Distribution Table

Values of $P(x) = \dfrac{(\lambda t)^x e^{-\lambda t}}{x!}$

λt

x	0.005	0.01	0.02	0.03	0.04	0.05	0.06	0.07	0.08	0.09
0	0.9950	0.9900	0.9802	0.9704	0.9608	0.9512	0.9418	0.9324	0.9231	0.9139
1	0.0050	0.0099	0.0196	0.0291	0.0384	0.0476	0.0565	0.0653	0.0738	0.0823
2	0.0000	0.0000	0.0002	0.0004	0.0008	0.0012	0.0017	0.0023	0.0030	0.0037
3	0.0000	0.0000	0.0000	0.0000	0.0000	0.0000	0.0000	0.0001	0.0001	0.0001

λt

x	0.10	0.20	0.30	0.40	0.50	0.60	0.70	0.80	0.90	1.00
0	0.9048	0.8187	0.7408	0.6703	0.6065	0.5488	0.4966	0.4493	0.4066	0.3679
1	0.0905	0.1637	0.2222	0.2681	0.3033	0.3293	0.3476	0.3595	0.3659	0.3679
2	0.0045	0.0164	0.0333	0.0536	0.0758	0.0988	0.1217	0.1438	0.1647	0.1839
3	0.0002	0.0011	0.0033	0.0072	0.0126	0.0198	0.0284	0.0383	0.0494	0.0613
4	0.0000	0.0001	0.0003	0.0007	0.0016	0.0030	0.0050	0.0077	0.0111	0.0153
5	0.0000	0.0000	0.0000	0.0001	0.0002	0.0004	0.0007	0.0012	0.0020	0.0031
6	0.0000	0.0000	0.0000	0.0000	0.0000	0.0000	0.0001	0.0002	0.0003	0.0005
7	0.0000	0.0000	0.0000	0.0000	0.0000	0.0000	0.0000	0.0000	0.0000	0.0001

λt

x	1.10	1.20	1.30	1.40	1.50	1.60	1.70	1.80	1.90	2.00
0	0.3329	0.3012	0.2725	0.2466	0.2231	0.2019	0.1827	0.1653	0.1496	0.1353
1	0.3662	0.3614	0.3543	0.3452	0.3347	0.3230	0.3106	0.2975	0.2842	0.2707
2	0.2014	0.2169	0.2303	0.2417	0.2510	0.2584	0.2640	0.2678	0.2700	0.2707
3	0.0738	0.0867	0.0998	0.1128	0.1255	0.1378	0.1496	0.1607	0.1710	0.1804
4	0.0203	0.0260	0.0324	0.0395	0.0471	0.0551	0.0636	0.0723	0.0812	0.0902
5	0.0045	0.0062	0.0084	0.0111	0.0141	0.0176	0.0216	0.0260	0.0309	0.0361
6	0.0008	0.0012	0.0018	0.0026	0.0035	0.0047	0.0061	0.0078	0.0098	0.0120
7	0.0001	0.0002	0.0003	0.0005	0.0008	0.0011	0.0015	0.0020	0.0027	0.0034
8	0.0000	0.0000	0.0001	0.0001	0.0001	0.0002	0.0003	0.0005	0.0006	0.0009
9	0.0000	0.0000	0.0000	0.0000	0.0000	0.0000	0.0001	0.0001	0.0001	0.0002

λt

x	2.10	2.20	2.30	2.40	2.50	2.60	2.70	2.80	2.90	3.00
0	0.1225	0.1108	0.1003	0.0907	0.0821	0.0743	0.0672	0.0608	0.0550	0.0498
1	0.2572	0.2438	0.2306	0.2177	0.2052	0.1931	0.1815	0.1703	0.1596	0.1494
2	0.2700	0.2681	0.2652	0.2613	0.2565	0.2510	0.2450	0.2384	0.2314	0.2240
3	0.1890	0.1966	0.2033	0.2090	0.2138	0.2176	0.2205	0.2225	0.2237	0.2240
4	0.0992	0.1082	0.1169	0.1254	0.1336	0.1414	0.1488	0.1557	0.1622	0.1680
5	0.0417	0.0476	0.0538	0.0602	0.0668	0.0735	0.0804	0.0872	0.0940	0.1008
6	0.0146	0.0174	0.0206	0.0241	0.0278	0.0319	0.0362	0.0407	0.0455	0.0504
7	0.0044	0.0055	0.0068	0.0083	0.0099	0.0118	0.0139	0.0163	0.0188	0.0216
8	0.0011	0.0015	0.0019	0.0025	0.0031	0.0038	0.0047	0.0057	0.0068	0.0081
9	0.0003	0.0004	0.0005	0.0007	0.0009	0.0011	0.0014	0.0018	0.0022	0.0027
10	0.0001	0.0001	0.0001	0.0002	0.0002	0.0003	0.0004	0.0005	0.0006	0.0008
11	0.0000	0.0000	0.0000	0.0000	0.0000	0.0001	0.0001	0.0001	0.0002	0.0002
12	0.0000	0.0000	0.0000	0.0000	0.0000	0.0000	0.0000	0.0000	0.0000	0.0001

λt

x	3.10	3.20	3.30	3.40	3.50	3.60	3.70	3.80	3.90	4.00
0	0.0450	0.0408	0.0369	0.0334	0.0302	0.0273	0.0247	0.0224	0.0202	0.0183
1	0.1397	0.1304	0.1217	0.1135	0.1057	0.0984	0.0915	0.0850	0.0789	0.0733
2	0.2165	0.2087	0.2008	0.1929	0.1850	0.1771	0.1692	0.1615	0.1539	0.1465
3	0.2237	0.2226	0.2209	0.2186	0.2158	0.2125	0.2087	0.2046	0.2001	0.1954
4	0.1733	0.1781	0.1823	0.1858	0.1888	0.1912	0.1931	0.1944	0.1951	0.1954
5	0.1075	0.1140	0.1203	0.1264	0.1322	0.1377	0.1429	0.1477	0.1522	0.1563
6	0.0555	0.0608	0.0662	0.0716	0.0771	0.0826	0.0881	0.0936	0.0989	0.1042
7	0.0246	0.0278	0.0312	0.0348	0.0385	0.0425	0.0466	0.0508	0.0551	0.0595
8	0.0095	0.0111	0.0129	0.0148	0.0169	0.0191	0.0215	0.0241	0.0269	0.0298
9	0.0033	0.0040	0.0047	0.0056	0.0066	0.0076	0.0089	0.0102	0.0116	0.0132
10	0.0010	0.0013	0.0016	0.0019	0.0023	0.0028	0.0033	0.0039	0.0045	0.0053
11	0.0003	0.0004	0.0005	0.0006	0.0007	0.0009	0.0011	0.0013	0.0016	0.0019
12	0.0001	0.0001	0.0001	0.0002	0.0002	0.0003	0.0003	0.0004	0.0005	0.0006
13	0.0000	0.0000	0.0000	0.0000	0.0001	0.0001	0.0001	0.0001	0.0002	0.0002
14	0.0000	0.0000	0.0000	0.0000	0.0000	0.0000	0.0000	0.0000	0.0000	0.0001

λt

x	4.10	4.20	4.30	4.40	4.50	4.60	4.70	4.80	4.90	5.00
0	0.0166	0.0150	0.0136	0.0123	0.0111	0.0101	0.0091	0.0082	0.0074	0.0067
1	0.0679	0.0630	0.0583	0.0540	0.0500	0.0462	0.0427	0.0395	0.0365	0.0337
2	0.1393	0.1323	0.1254	0.1188	0.1125	0.1063	0.1005	0.0948	0.0894	0.0842
3	0.1904	0.1852	0.1798	0.1743	0.1687	0.1631	0.1574	0.1517	0.1460	0.1404
4	0.1951	0.1944	0.1933	0.1917	0.1898	0.1875	0.1849	0.1820	0.1789	0.1755
5	0.1600	0.1633	0.1662	0.1687	0.1708	0.1725	0.1738	0.1747	0.1753	0.1755
6	0.1093	0.1143	0.1191	0.1237	0.1281	0.1323	0.1362	0.1398	0.1432	0.1462
7	0.0640	0.0686	0.0732	0.0778	0.0824	0.0869	0.0914	0.0959	0.1002	0.1044
8	0.0328	0.0360	0.0393	0.0428	0.0463	0.0500	0.0537	0.0575	0.0614	0.0653
9	0.0150	0.0168	0.0188	0.0209	0.0232	0.0255	0.0281	0.0307	0.0334	0.0363
10	0.0061	0.0071	0.0081	0.0092	0.0104	0.0118	0.0132	0.0147	0.0164	0.0181
11	0.0023	0.0027	0.0032	0.0037	0.0043	0.0049	0.0056	0.0064	0.0073	0.0082
12	0.0008	0.0009	0.0011	0.0013	0.0016	0.0019	0.0022	0.0026	0.0030	0.0034
13	0.0002	0.0003	0.0004	0.0005	0.0006	0.0007	0.0008	0.0009	0.0011	0.0013
14	0.0001	0.0001	0.0001	0.0001	0.0002	0.0002	0.0003	0.0003	0.0004	0.0005
15	0.0000	0.0000	0.0000	0.0000	0.0001	0.0001	0.0001	0.0001	0.0001	0.0002

λt

6.5 = 1404 × 305
= mean 3drinks × total

x	5.10	5.20	5.30	5.40	5.50	5.60	5.70	5.80	5.90	6.00
0	0.0061	0.0055	0.0050	0.0045	0.0041	0.0037	0.0033	0.0030	0.0027	0.0025
1	0.0311	0.0287	0.0265	0.0244	0.0225	0.0207	0.0191	0.0176	0.0162	0.0149
2	0.0793	0.0746	0.0701	0.0659	0.0618	0.0580	0.0544	0.0509	0.0477	0.0446
3	0.1348	0.1293	0.1239	0.1185	0.1133	0.1082	0.1033	0.0985	0.0938	0.0892
4	0.1719	0.1681	0.1641	0.1600	0.1558	0.1515	0.1472	0.1428	0.1383	0.1339
5	0.1753	0.1748	0.1740	0.1728	0.1714	0.1697	0.1678	0.1656	0.1632	0.1606
6	0.1490	0.1515	0.1537	0.1555	0.1571	0.1584	0.1594	0.1601	0.1605	0.1606
7	0.1086	0.1125	0.1163	0.1200	0.1234	0.1267	0.1298	0.1326	0.1353	0.1377
8	0.0692	0.0731	0.0771	0.0810	0.0849	0.0887	0.0925	0.0962	0.0998	0.1033
9	0.0392	0.0423	0.0454	0.0486	0.0519	0.0552	0.0586	0.0620	0.0654	0.0688
10	0.0200	0.0220	0.0241	0.0262	0.0285	0.0309	0.0334	0.0359	0.0386	0.0413
11	0.0093	0.0104	0.0116	0.0129	0.0143	0.0157	0.0173	0.0190	0.0207	0.0225
12	0.0039	0.0045	0.0051	0.0058	0.0065	0.0073	0.0082	0.0092	0.0102	0.0113
13	0.0015	0.0018	0.0021	0.0024	0.0028	0.0032	0.0036	0.0041	0.0046	0.0052
14	0.0006	0.0007	0.0008	0.0009	0.0011	0.0013	0.0015	0.0017	0.0019	0.0022
15	0.0002	0.0002	0.0003	0.0003	0.0004	0.0005	0.0006	0.0007	0.0008	0.0009
16	0.0001	0.0001	0.0001	0.0001	0.0001	0.0002	0.0002	0.0002	0.0003	0.0003
17	0.0000	0.0000	0.0000	0.0000	0.0000	0.0001	0.0001	0.0001	0.0001	0.0001

λt

x	6.10	6.20	6.30	6.40	6.50	6.60	6.70	6.80	6.90	7.00
0	0.0022	0.0020	0.0018	0.0017	0.0015	0.0014	0.0012	0.0011	0.0010	0.0009
1	0.0137	0.0126	0.0116	0.0106	0.0098	0.0090	0.0082	0.0076	0.0070	0.0064
2	0.0417	0.0390	0.0364	0.0340	0.0318	0.0296	0.0276	0.0258	0.0240	0.0223
3	0.0848	0.0806	0.0765	0.0726	0.0688	0.0652	0.0617	0.0584	0.0552	0.0521
4	0.1294	0.1249	0.1205	0.1162	0.1118	0.1076	0.1034	0.0992	0.0952	0.0912
5	0.1579	0.1549	0.1519	0.1487	0.1454	0.1420	0.1385	0.1349	0.1314	0.1277
6	0.1605	0.1601	0.1595	0.1586	0.1575	0.1562	0.1546	0.1529	0.1511	0.1490
7	0.1399	0.1418	0.1435	0.1450	0.1462	0.1472	0.1480	0.1486	0.1489	0.1490
8	0.1066	0.1099	0.1130	0.1160	0.1188	0.1215	0.1240	0.1263	0.1284	0.1304
9	0.0723	0.0757	0.0791	0.0825	0.0858	0.0891	0.0923	0.0954	0.0985	0.1014
10	0.0441	0.0469	0.0498	0.0528	0.0558	0.0588	0.0618	0.0649	0.0679	0.0710
11	0.0244	0.0265	0.0285	0.0307	0.0330	0.0353	0.0377	0.0401	0.0426	0.0452
12	0.0124	0.0137	0.0150	0.0164	0.0179	0.0194	0.0210	0.0227	0.0245	0.0263
13	0.0058	0.0065	0.0073	0.0081	0.0089	0.0099	0.0108	0.0119	0.0130	0.0142
14	0.0025	0.0029	0.0033	0.0037	0.0041	0.0046	0.0052	0.0058	0.0064	0.0071
15	0.0010	0.0012	0.0014	0.0016	0.0018	0.0020	0.0023	0.0026	0.0029	0.0033
16	0.0004	0.0005	0.0005	0.0006	0.0007	0.0008	0.0010	0.0011	0.0013	0.0014
17	0.0001	0.0002	0.0002	0.0002	0.0003	0.0003	0.0004	0.0004	0.0005	0.0006
18	0.0000	0.0001	0.0001	0.0001	0.0001	0.0001	0.0001	0.0002	0.0002	0.0002
19	0.0000	0.0000	0.0000	0.0000	0.0000	0.0000	0.0001	0.0001	0.0001	0.0001

λt

x	7.10	7.20	7.30	7.40	7.50	7.60	7.70	7.80	7.90	8.00
0	0.0008	0.0007	0.0007	0.0006	0.0006	0.0005	0.0005	0.0004	0.0004	0.0003
1	0.0059	0.0054	0.0049	0.0045	0.0041	0.0038	0.0035	0.0032	0.0029	0.0027
2	0.0208	0.0194	0.0180	0.0167	0.0156	0.0145	0.0134	0.0125	0.0116	0.0107
3	0.0492	0.0464	0.0438	0.0413	0.0389	0.0366	0.0345	0.0324	0.0305	0.0286
4	0.0874	0.0836	0.0799	0.0764	0.0729	0.0696	0.0663	0.0632	0.0602	0.0573
5	0.1241	0.1204	0.1167	0.1130	0.1094	0.1057	0.1021	0.0986	0.0951	0.0916
6	0.1468	0.1445	0.1420	0.1394	0.1367	0.1339	0.1311	0.1282	0.1252	0.1221
7	0.1489	0.1486	0.1481	0.1474	0.1465	0.1454	0.1442	0.1428	0.1413	0.1396
8	0.1321	0.1337	0.1351	0.1363	0.1373	0.1381	0.1388	0.1392	0.1395	0.1396
9	0.1042	0.1070	0.1096	0.1121	0.1144	0.1167	0.1187	0.1207	0.1224	0.1241
10	0.0740	0.0770	0.0800	0.0829	0.0858	0.0887	0.0914	0.0941	0.0967	0.0993
11	0.0478	0.0504	0.0531	0.0558	0.0585	0.0613	0.0640	0.0667	0.0695	0.0722
12	0.0283	0.0303	0.0323	0.0344	0.0366	0.0388	0.0411	0.0434	0.0457	0.0481
13	0.0154	0.0168	0.0181	0.0196	0.0211	0.0227	0.0243	0.0260	0.0278	0.0296
14	0.0078	0.0086	0.0095	0.0104	0.0113	0.0123	0.0134	0.0145	0.0157	0.0169
15	0.0037	0.0041	0.0046	0.0051	0.0057	0.0062	0.0069	0.0075	0.0083	0.0090
16	0.0016	0.0019	0.0021	0.0024	0.0026	0.0030	0.0033	0.0037	0.0041	0.0045
17	0.0007	0.0008	0.0009	0.0010	0.0012	0.0013	0.0015	0.0017	0.0019	0.0021
18	0.0003	0.0003	0.0004	0.0004	0.0005	0.0006	0.0006	0.0007	0.0008	0.0009
19	0.0001	0.0001	0.0001	0.0002	0.0002	0.0002	0.0003	0.0003	0.0003	0.0004
20	0.0000	0.0000	0.0001	0.0001	0.0001	0.0001	0.0001	0.0001	0.0001	0.0002
21	0.0000	0.0000	0.0000	0.0000	0.0000	0.0000	0.0000	0.0000	0.0001	0.0001

λt

x	8.10	8.20	8.30	8.40	8.50	8.60	8.70	8.80	8.90	9.00
0	0.0003	0.0003	0.0002	0.0002	0.0002	0.0002	0.0002	0.0002	0.0001	0.0001
1	0.0025	0.0023	0.0021	0.0019	0.0017	0.0016	0.0014	0.0013	0.0012	0.0011
2	0.0100	0.0092	0.0086	0.0079	0.0074	0.0068	0.0063	0.0058	0.0054	0.0050
3	0.0269	0.0252	0.0237	0.0222	0.0208	0.0195	0.0183	0.0171	0.0160	0.0150
4	0.0544	0.0517	0.0491	0.0466	0.0443	0.0420	0.0398	0.0377	0.0357	0.0337
5	0.0882	0.0849	0.0816	0.0784	0.0752	0.0722	0.0692	0.0663	0.0635	0.0607
6	0.1191	0.1160	0.1128	0.1097	0.1066	0.1034	0.1003	0.0972	0.0941	0.0911
7	0.1378	0.1358	0.1338	0.1317	0.1294	0.1271	0.1247	0.1222	0.1197	0.1171
8	0.1395	0.1392	0.1388	0.1382	0.1375	0.1366	0.1356	0.1344	0.1332	0.1318
9	0.1256	0.1269	0.1280	0.1290	0.1299	0.1306	0.1311	0.1315	0.1317	0.1318
10	0.1017	0.1040	0.1063	0.1084	0.1104	0.1123	0.1140	0.1157	0.1172	0.1186
11	0.0749	0.0776	0.0802	0.0828	0.0853	0.0878	0.0902	0.0925	0.0948	0.0970
12	0.0505	0.0530	0.0555	0.0579	0.0604	0.0629	0.0654	0.0679	0.0703	0.0728
13	0.0315	0.0334	0.0354	0.0374	0.0395	0.0416	0.0438	0.0459	0.0481	0.0504
14	0.0182	0.0196	0.0210	0.0225	0.0240	0.0256	0.0272	0.0289	0.0306	0.0324
15	0.0098	0.0107	0.0116	0.0126	0.0136	0.0147	0.0158	0.0169	0.0182	0.0194
16	0.0050	0.0055	0.0060	0.0066	0.0072	0.0079	0.0086	0.0093	0.0101	0.0109
17	0.0024	0.0026	0.0029	0.0033	0.0036	0.0040	0.0044	0.0048	0.0053	0.0058
18	0.0011	0.0012	0.0014	0.0015	0.0017	0.0019	0.0021	0.0024	0.0026	0.0029
19	0.0005	0.0005	0.0006	0.0007	0.0008	0.0009	0.0010	0.0011	0.0012	0.0014
20	0.0002	0.0002	0.0002	0.0003	0.0003	0.0004	0.0004	0.0005	0.0005	0.0006
21	0.0001	0.0001	0.0001	0.0001	0.0001	0.0002	0.0002	0.0002	0.0002	0.0003
22	0.0000	0.0000	0.0000	0.0000	0.0001	0.0001	0.0001	0.0001	0.0001	0.0001

λt

x	9.10	9.20	9.30	9.40	9.50	9.60	9.70	9.80	9.90	10.00
0	0.0001	0.0001	0.0001	0.0001	0.0001	0.0001	0.0001	0.0001	0.0001	0.0000
1	0.0010	0.0009	0.0009	0.0008	0.0007	0.0007	0.0006	0.0005	0.0005	0.0005
2	0.0046	0.0043	0.0040	0.0037	0.0034	0.0031	0.0029	0.0027	0.0025	0.0023
3	0.0140	0.0131	0.0123	0.0115	0.0107	0.0100	0.0093	0.0087	0.0081	0.0076
4	0.0319	0.0302	0.0285	0.0269	0.0254	0.0240	0.0226	0.0213	0.0201	0.0189
5	0.0581	0.0555	0.0530	0.0506	0.0483	0.0460	0.0439	0.0418	0.0398	0.0378
6	0.0881	0.0851	0.0822	0.0793	0.0764	0.0736	0.0709	0.0682	0.0656	0.0631
7	0.1145	0.1118	0.1091	0.1064	0.1037	0.1010	0.0982	0.0955	0.0928	0.0901
8	0.1302	0.1286	0.1269	0.1251	0.1232	0.1212	0.1191	0.1170	0.1148	0.1126
9	0.1317	0.1315	0.1311	0.1306	0.1300	0.1293	0.1284	0.1274	0.1263	0.1251
10	0.1198	0.1210	0.1219	0.1228	0.1235	0.1241	0.1245	0.1249	0.1250	0.1251
11	0.0991	0.1012	0.1031	0.1049	0.1067	0.1083	0.1098	0.1112	0.1125	0.1137
12	0.0752	0.0776	0.0799	0.0822	0.0844	0.0866	0.0888	0.0908	0.0928	0.0948
13	0.0526	0.0549	0.0572	0.0594	0.0617	0.0640	0.0662	0.0685	0.0707	0.0729
14	0.0342	0.0361	0.0380	0.0399	0.0419	0.0439	0.0459	0.0479	0.0500	0.0521
15	0.0208	0.0221	0.0235	0.0250	0.0265	0.0281	0.0297	0.0313	0.0330	0.0347
16	0.0118	0.0127	0.0137	0.0147	0.0157	0.0168	0.0180	0.0192	0.0204	0.0217
17	0.0063	0.0069	0.0075	0.0081	0.0088	0.0095	0.0103	0.0111	0.0119	0.0128
18	0.0032	0.0035	0.0039	0.0042	0.0046	0.0051	0.0055	0.0060	0.0065	0.0071
19	0.0015	0.0017	0.0019	0.0021	0.0023	0.0026	0.0028	0.0031	0.0034	0.0037
20	0.0007	0.0008	0.0009	0.0010	0.0011	0.0012	0.0014	0.0015	0.0017	0.0019
21	0.0003	0.0003	0.0004	0.0004	0.0005	0.0006	0.0006	0.0007	0.0008	0.0009
22	0.0001	0.0001	0.0002	0.0002	0.0002	0.0002	0.0003	0.0003	0.0004	0.0004
23	0.0000	0.0001	0.0001	0.0001	0.0001	0.0001	0.0001	0.0001	0.0002	0.0002
24	0.0000	0.0000	0.0000	0.0000	0.0000	0.0000	0.0000	0.0001	0.0001	0.0001

λt

x	11.00	12.00	13.00	14.00	15.00	16.00	17.00	18.00	19.00	20.00
0	0.0000	0.0000	0.0000	0.0000	0.0000	0.0000	0.0000	0.0000	0.0000	0.0000
1	0.0002	0.0001	0.0000	0.0000	0.0000	0.0000	0.0000	0.0000	0.0000	0.0000
2	0.0010	0.0004	0.0002	0.0001	0.0000	0.0000	0.0000	0.0000	0.0000	0.0000
3	0.0037	0.0018	0.0008	0.0004	0.0002	0.0001	0.0000	0.0000	0.0000	0.0000
4	0.0102	0.0053	0.0027	0.0013	0.0006	0.0003	0.0001	0.0001	0.0000	0.0000
5	0.0224	0.0127	0.0070	0.0037	0.0019	0.0010	0.0005	0.0002	0.0001	0.0001
6	0.0411	0.0255	0.0152	0.0087	0.0048	0.0026	0.0014	0.0007	0.0004	0.0002
7	0.0646	0.0437	0.0281	0.0174	0.0104	0.0060	0.0034	0.0019	0.0010	0.0005
8	0.0888	0.0655	0.0457	0.0304	0.0194	0.0120	0.0072	0.0042	0.0024	0.0013
9	0.1085	0.0874	0.0661	0.0473	0.0324	0.0213	0.0135	0.0083	0.0050	0.0029
10	0.1194	0.1048	0.0859	0.0663	0.0486	0.0341	0.0230	0.0150	0.0095	0.0058
11	0.1194	0.1144	0.1015	0.0844	0.0663	0.0496	0.0355	0.0245	0.0164	0.0106
12	0.1094	0.1144	0.1099	0.0984	0.0829	0.0661	0.0504	0.0368	0.0259	0.0176
13	0.0926	0.1056	0.1099	0.1060	0.0956	0.0814	0.0658	0.0509	0.0378	0.0271
14	0.0728	0.0905	0.1021	0.1060	0.1024	0.0930	0.0800	0.0655	0.0514	0.0387
15	0.0534	0.0724	0.0885	0.0989	0.1024	0.0992	0.0906	0.0786	0.0650	0.0516
16	0.0367	0.0543	0.0719	0.0866	0.0960	0.0992	0.0963	0.0884	0.0772	0.0646
17	0.0237	0.0383	0.0550	0.0713	0.0847	0.0934	0.0963	0.0936	0.0863	0.0760
18	0.0145	0.0255	0.0397	0.0554	0.0706	0.0830	0.0909	0.0936	0.0911	0.0844
19	0.0084	0.0161	0.0272	0.0409	0.0557	0.0699	0.0814	0.0887	0.0911	0.0888
20	0.0046	0.0097	0.0177	0.0286	0.0418	0.0559	0.0692	0.0798	0.0866	0.0888
21	0.0024	0.0055	0.0109	0.0191	0.0299	0.0426	0.0560	0.0684	0.0783	0.0846
22	0.0012	0.0030	0.0065	0.0121	0.0204	0.0310	0.0433	0.0560	0.0676	0.0769
23	0.0006	0.0016	0.0037	0.0074	0.0133	0.0216	0.0320	0.0438	0.0559	0.0669
24	0.0003	0.0008	0.0020	0.0043	0.0083	0.0144	0.0226	0.0328	0.0442	0.0557
25	0.0001	0.0004	0.0010	0.0024	0.0050	0.0092	0.0154	0.0237	0.0336	0.0446
26	0.0000	0.0002	0.0005	0.0013	0.0029	0.0057	0.0101	0.0164	0.0246	0.0343
27	0.0000	0.0001	0.0002	0.0007	0.0016	0.0034	0.0063	0.0109	0.0173	0.0254
28	0.0000	0.0000	0.0001	0.0003	0.0009	0.0019	0.0038	0.0070	0.0117	0.0181
29	0.0000	0.0000	0.0001	0.0002	0.0004	0.0011	0.0023	0.0044	0.0077	0.0125
30	0.0000	0.0000	0.0000	0.0001	0.0002	0.0006	0.0013	0.0026	0.0049	0.0083
31	0.0000	0.0000	0.0000	0.0000	0.0001	0.0003	0.0007	0.0015	0.0030	0.0054
32	0.0000	0.0000	0.0000	0.0000	0.0001	0.0001	0.0004	0.0009	0.0018	0.0034
33	0.0000	0.0000	0.0000	0.0000	0.0000	0.0001	0.0002	0.0005	0.0010	0.0020
34	0.0000	0.0000	0.0000	0.0000	0.0000	0.0000	0.0001	0.0002	0.0006	0.0012
35	0.0000	0.0000	0.0000	0.0000	0.0000	0.0000	0.0000	0.0001	0.0003	0.0007
36	0.0000	0.0000	0.0000	0.0000	0.0000	0.0000	0.0000	0.0001	0.0002	0.0004
37	0.0000	0.0000	0.0000	0.0000	0.0000	0.0000	0.0000	0.0000	0.0001	0.0002
38	0.0000	0.0000	0.0000	0.0000	0.0000	0.0000	0.0000	0.0000	0.0000	0.0001
39	0.0000	0.0000	0.0000	0.0000	0.0000	0.0000	0.0000	0.0000	0.0000	0.0001

APPENDIX D

Standard Normal Distribution Table

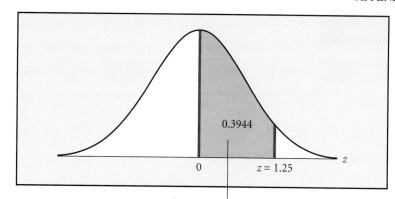

0.3944

$z = 1.25$

z	0	0.01	0.02	0.03	0.04	0.05	0.06	0.07	0.08	0.09
0.0	0.0000	0.0040	0.0080	0.0120	0.0160	0.0199	0.0239	0.0279	0.0319	0.0359
0.1	0.0398	0.0438	0.0478	0.0517	0.0557	0.0596	0.0636	0.0675	0.0714	0.0753
0.2	0.0793	0.0832	0.0871	0.0910	0.0948	0.0987	0.1026	0.1064	0.1103	0.1141
0.3	0.1179	0.1217	0.1255	0.1293	0.1331	0.1368	0.1406	0.1443	0.1480	0.1517
0.4	0.1554	0.1591	0.1628	0.1664	0.1700	0.1736	0.1772	0.1808	0.1844	0.1879
0.5	0.1915	0.1950	0.1985	0.2019	0.2054	0.2088	0.2123	0.2157	0.2190	0.2224
0.6	0.2257	0.2291	0.2324	0.2357	0.2389	0.2422	0.2454	0.2486	0.2517	0.2549
0.7	0.2580	0.2611	0.2642	0.2673	0.2704	0.2734	0.2764	0.2794	0.2823	0.2852
0.8	0.2881	0.2910	0.2939	0.2967	0.2995	0.3023	0.3051	0.3078	0.3106	0.3133
0.9	0.3159	0.3186	0.3212	0.3238	0.3264	0.3289	0.3315	0.3340	0.3365	0.3389
1.0	0.3413	0.3438	0.3461	0.3485	0.3508	0.3531	0.3554	0.3577	0.3599	0.3621
1.1	0.3643	0.3665	0.3686	0.3708	0.3729	0.3749	0.3770	0.3790	0.3810	0.3830
1.2	0.3849	0.3869	0.3888	0.3907	0.3925	0.3944	0.3962	0.3980	0.3997	0.4015
1.3	0.4032	0.4049	0.4066	0.4082	0.4099	0.4115	0.4131	0.4147	0.4162	0.4177
1.4	0.4192	0.4207	0.4222	0.4236	0.4251	0.4265	0.4279	0.4292	0.4306	0.4319
1.5	0.4332	0.4345	0.4357	0.4370	0.4382	0.4394	0.4406	0.4418	0.4429	0.4441
1.6	0.4452	0.4463	0.4474	0.4484	0.4495	0.4505	0.4515	0.4525	0.4535	0.4545
1.7	0.4554	0.4564	0.4573	0.4582	0.4591	0.4599	0.4608	0.4616	0.4625	0.4633
1.8	0.4641	0.4649	0.4656	0.4664	0.4671	0.4678	0.4686	0.4693	0.4699	0.4706
1.9	0.4713	0.4719	0.4726	0.4732	0.4738	0.4744	0.4750	0.4756	0.4761	0.4767
2.0	0.4772	0.4778	0.4783	0.4788	0.4793	0.4798	0.4803	0.4808	0.4812	0.4817
2.1	0.4821	0.4826	0.4830	0.4834	0.4838	0.4842	0.4846	0.4850	0.4854	0.4857
2.2	0.4861	0.4864	0.4868	0.4871	0.4875	0.4878	0.4881	0.4884	0.4887	0.4890
2.3	0.4893	0.4896	0.4898	0.4901	0.4904	0.4906	0.4909	0.4911	0.4913	0.4916
2.4	0.4918	0.4920	0.4922	0.4925	0.4927	0.4929	0.4931	0.4932	0.4934	0.4936
2.5	0.4938	0.4940	0.4941	0.4943	0.4945	0.4946	0.4948	0.4949	0.4951	0.4952
2.6	0.4953	0.4955	0.4956	0.4957	0.4959	0.4960	0.4961	0.4962	0.4963	0.4964
2.7	0.4965	0.4966	0.4967	0.4968	0.4969	0.4970	0.4971	0.4972	0.4973	0.4974
2.8	0.4974	0.4975	0.4976	0.4977	0.4977	0.4978	0.4979	0.4979	0.4980	0.4981
2.9	0.4981	0.4982	0.4982	0.4983	0.4984	0.4984	0.4985	0.4985	0.4986	0.4986
3.0	0.4987	0.4987	0.4987	0.4988	0.4988	0.4989	0.4989	0.4989	0.4990	0.4990

Exponential Distribution Table

Values of $e^{-\lambda a}$

λa	$e^{-\lambda a}$	λa	$e^{-\lambda a}$	λa	$e^{-\lambda a}$	λa	$e^{-\lambda a}$	λa	$e^{-\lambda a}$
0.00	1.0000	2.05	0.1287	4.05	0.0174	6.05	0.0024	8.05	0.0003
0.05	0.9512	2.10	0.1225	4.10	0.0166	6.10	0.0022	8.10	0.0003
0.10	0.9048	2.15	0.1165	4.15	0.0158	6.15	0.0021	8.15	0.0003
0.15	0.8607	2.20	0.1108	4.20	0.0150	6.20	0.0020	8.20	0.0003
0.20	0.8187	2.25	0.1054	4.25	0.0143	6.25	0.0019	8.25	0.0003
0.25	0.7788	2.30	0.1003	4.30	0.0136	6.30	0.0018	8.30	0.0002
0.30	0.7408	2.35	0.0954	4.35	0.0129	6.35	0.0017	8.35	0.0002
0.35	0.7047	2.40	0.0907	4.40	0.0123	6.40	0.0017	8.40	0.0002
0.40	0.6703	2.45	0.0863	4.45	0.0117	6.45	0.0016	8.45	0.0002
0.45	0.6376	2.50	0.0821	4.50	0.0111	6.50	0.0015	8.50	0.0002
0.50	0.6065	2.55	0.0781	4.55	0.0106	6.55	0.0014	8.55	0.0002
0.55	0.5769	2.60	0.0743	4.60	0.0101	6.60	0.0014	8.60	0.0002
0.60	0.5488	2.65	0.0707	4.65	0.0096	6.65	0.0013	8.65	0.0002
0.65	0.5220	2.70	0.0672	4.70	0.0091	6.70	0.0012	8.70	0.0002
0.70	0.4966	2.75	0.0639	4.75	0.0087	6.75	0.0012	8.75	0.0002
0.75	0.4724	2.80	0.0608	4.80	0.0082	6.80	0.0011	8.80	0.0002
0.80	0.4493	2.85	0.0578	4.85	0.0078	6.85	0.0011	8.85	0.0001
0.85	0.4274	2.90	0.0550	4.90	0.0074	6.90	0.0010	8.90	0.0001
0.90	0.4066	2.95	0.0523	4.95	0.0071	6.95	0.0010	8.95	0.0001
0.95	0.3867	3.00	0.0498	5.00	0.0067	7.00	0.0009	9.00	0.0001
1.00	0.3679	3.05	0.0474	5.05	0.0064	7.05	0.0009	9.05	0.0001
1.05	0.3499	3.10	0.0450	5.10	0.0061	7.10	0.0008	9.10	0.0001
1.10	0.3329	3.15	0.0429	5.15	0.0058	7.15	0.0008	9.15	0.0001
1.15	0.3166	3.20	0.0408	5.20	0.0055	7.20	0.0007	9.20	0.0001
1.20	0.3012	3.25	0.0388	5.25	0.0052	7.25	0.0007	9.25	0.0001
1.25	0.2865	3.30	0.0369	5.30	0.0050	7.30	0.0007	9.30	0.0001
1.30	0.2725	3.35	0.0351	5.35	0.0047	7.35	0.0006	9.35	0.0001
1.35	0.2592	3.40	0.0334	5.40	0.0045	7.40	0.0006	9.40	0.0001
1.40	0.2466	3.45	0.0317	5.45	0.0043	7.45	0.0006	9.45	0.0001
1.45	0.2346	3.50	0.0302	5.50	0.0041	7.50	0.0006	9.50	0.0001
1.50	0.2231	3.55	0.0287	5.55	0.0039	7.55	0.0005	9.55	0.0001
1.55	0.2122	3.60	0.0273	5.60	0.0037	7.60	0.0005	9.60	0.0001
1.60	0.2019	3.65	0.0260	5.65	0.0035	7.65	0.0005	9.65	0.0001
1.65	0.1920	3.70	0.0247	5.70	0.0033	7.70	0.0005	9.70	0.0001
1.70	0.1827	3.75	0.0235	5.75	0.0032	7.75	0.0004	9.75	0.0001
1.75	0.1738	3.80	0.0224	5.80	0.0030	7.80	0.0004	9.80	0.0001
1.80	0.1653	3.85	0.0213	5.85	0.0029	7.85	0.0004	9.85	0.0001
1.85	0.1572	3.90	0.0202	5.90	0.0027	7.90	0.0004	9.90	0.0001
1.90	0.1496	3.95	0.0193	5.95	0.0026	7.95	0.0004	9.95	0.0000
1.95	0.1423	4.00	0.0183	6.00	0.0025	8.00	0.0003	10.00	0.0000
2.00	0.1353								

Values of *t* for
Selected Probabilities

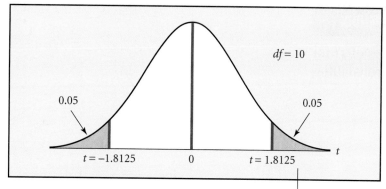

PROBABILITES (OR AREAS UNDER *t*-DISTRIBUTION CURVE)

Conf. Level One Tail Two Tails	0.1 0.45 0.9	0.3 0.35 0.7	0.5 0.25 0.5	0.7 0.15 0.3	0.8 0.1 0.2	0.9 0.05 0.1	0.95 0.025 0.05	0.98 0.01 0.02	0.99 0.005 0.01
df					Values of t				
1	0.1584	0.5095	1.0000	1.9626	3.0777	6.3137	12.7062	31.8210	63.6559
2	0.1421	0.4447	0.8165	1.3862	1.8856	2.9200	4.3027	6.9645	9.9250
3	0.1366	0.4242	0.7649	1.2498	1.6377	2.3534	3.1824	4.5407	5.8408
4	0.1338	0.4142	0.7407	1.1896	1.5332	2.1318	2.7765	3.7469	4.6041
5	0.1322	0.4082	0.7267	1.1558	1.4759	2.0150	2.5706	3.3649	4.0321
6	0.1311	0.4043	0.7176	1.1342	1.4398	1.9432	2.4469	3.1427	3.7074
7	0.1303	0.4015	0.7111	1.1192	1.4149	1.8946	2.3646	2.9979	3.4995
8	0.1297	0.3995	0.7064	1.1081	1.3968	1.8595	2.3060	2.8965	3.3554
9	0.1293	0.3979	0.7027	1.0997	1.3830	1.8331	2.2622	2.8214	3.2498
10	0.1289	0.3966	0.6998	1.0931	1.3722	1.8125	2.2281	2.7638	3.1693
11	0.1286	0.3956	0.6974	1.0877	1.3634	1.7959	2.2010	2.7181	3.1058
12	0.1283	0.3947	0.6955	1.0832	1.3562	1.7823	2.1788	2.6810	3.0545
13	0.1281	0.3940	0.6938	1.0795	1.3502	1.7709	2.1604	2.6503	3.0123
14	0.1280	0.3933	0.6924	1.0763	1.3450	1.7613	2.1448	2.6245	2.9768
15	0.1278	0.3928	0.6912	1.0735	1.3406	1.7531	2.1315	2.6025	2.9467
16	0.1277	0.3923	0.6901	1.0711	1.3368	1.7459	2.1199	2.5835	2.9208
17	0.1276	0.3919	0.6892	1.0690	1.3334	1.7396	2.1098	2.5669	2.8982
18	0.1274	0.3915	0.6884	1.0672	1.3304	1.7341	2.1009	2.5524	2.8784
19	0.1274	0.3912	0.6876	1.0655	1.3277	1.7291	2.0930	2.5395	2.8609
20	0.1273	0.3909	0.6870	1.0640	1.3253	1.7247	2.0860	2.5280	2.8453
21	0.1272	0.3906	0.6864	1.0627	1.3232	1.7207	2.0796	2.5176	2.8314
22	0.1271	0.3904	0.6858	1.0614	1.3212	1.7171	2.0739	2.5083	2.8188
23	0.1271	0.3902	0.6853	1.0603	1.3195	1.7139	2.0687	2.4999	2.8073
24	0.1270	0.3900	0.6848	1.0593	1.3178	1.7109	2.0639	2.4922	2.7970
25	0.1269	0.3898	0.6844	1.0584	1.3163	1.7081	2.0595	2.4851	2.7874
26	0.1269	0.3896	0.6840	1.0575	1.3150	1.7056	2.0555	2.4786	2.7787
27	0.1268	0.3894	0.6837	1.0567	1.3137	1.7033	2.0518	2.4727	2.7707
28	0.1268	0.3893	0.6834	1.0560	1.3125	1.7011	2.0484	2.4671	2.7633
29	0.1268	0.3892	0.6830	1.0553	1.3114	1.6991	2.0452	2.4620	2.7564
30	0.1267	0.3890	0.6828	1.0547	1.3104	1.6973	2.0423	2.4573	2.7500
40	0.1265	0.3881	0.6807	1.0500	1.3031	1.6839	2.0211	2.4233	2.7045
50	0.1263	0.3875	0.6794	1.0473	1.2987	1.6759	2.0086	2.4033	2.6778
60	0.1262	0.3872	0.6786	1.0455	1.2958	1.6706	2.0003	2.3901	2.6603
70	0.1261	0.3869	0.6780	1.0442	1.2938	1.6669	1.9944	2.3808	2.6479
80	0.1261	0.3867	0.6776	1.0432	1.2922	1.6641	1.9901	2.3739	2.6387
90	0.1260	0.3866	0.6772	1.0424	1.2910	1.6620	1.9867	2.3685	2.6316
100	0.1260	0.3864	0.6770	1.0418	1.2901	1.6602	1.9840	2.3642	2.6259
250	0.1258	0.3858	0.6755	1.0386	1.2849	1.6510	1.9695	2.3414	2.5956
500	0.1257	0.3855	0.6750	1.0375	1.2832	1.6479	1.9647	2.3338	2.5857
∞					See Normal Distribution				

Values of χ^2 for Selected Probabilities

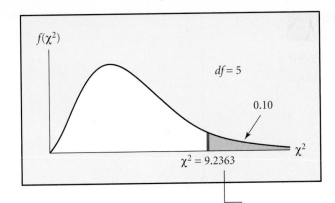

PROBABILITIES (OR AREAS UNDER CHI-SQUARE DISTRIBUTION CURVE ABOVE GIVEN CHI-SQUARE VALUES)

df	0.995	0.99	0.975	0.95	0.90	0.10	0.05	0.025	0.01	0.005
					Values of Chi-Squared					
1	0.0000	0.0002	0.0010	0.0039	0.0158	2.7055	3.8415	5.0239	6.6349	7.8794
2	0.0100	0.0201	0.0506	0.1026	0.2107	4.6052	5.9915	7.3778	9.2104	10.5965
3	0.0717	0.1148	0.2158	0.3518	0.5844	6.2514	7.8147	9.3484	11.3449	12.8381
4	0.2070	0.2971	0.4844	0.7107	1.0636	7.7794	9.4877	11.1433	13.2767	14.8602
5	0.4118	0.5543	0.8312	1.1455	1.6103	9.2363	11.0705	12.8325	15.0863	16.7496
6	0.6757	0.8721	1.2373	1.6354	2.2041	10.6446	12.5916	14.4494	16.8119	18.5475
7	0.9893	1.2390	1.6899	2.1673	2.8331	12.0170	14.0671	16.0128	18.4753	20.2777
8	1.3444	1.6465	2.1797	2.7326	3.4895	13.3616	15.5073	17.5345	20.0902	21.9549
9	1.7349	2.0879	2.7004	3.3251	4.1682	14.6837	16.9190	19.0228	21.6660	23.5893
10	2.1558	2.5582	3.2470	3.9403	4.8652	15.9872	18.3070	20.4832	23.2093	25.1881
11	2.6032	3.0535	3.8157	4.5748	5.5778	17.2750	19.6752	21.9200	24.7250	26.7569
12	3.0738	3.5706	4.4038	5.2260	6.3038	18.5493	21.0261	23.3367	26.2170	28.2997
13	3.5650	4.1069	5.0087	5.8919	7.0415	19.8119	22.3620	24.7356	27.6882	29.8193
14	4.0747	4.6604	5.6287	6.5706	7.7895	21.0641	23.6848	26.1189	29.1412	31.3194
15	4.6009	5.2294	6.2621	7.2609	8.5468	22.3071	24.9958	27.4884	30.5780	32.8015
16	5.1422	5.8122	6.9077	7.9616	9.3122	23.5418	26.2962	28.8453	31.9999	34.2671
17	5.6973	6.4077	7.5642	8.6718	10.0852	24.7690	27.5871	30.1910	33.4087	35.7184
18	6.2648	7.0149	8.2307	9.3904	10.8649	25.9894	28.8693	31.5264	34.8052	37.1564
19	6.8439	7.6327	8.9065	10.1170	11.6509	27.2036	30.1435	32.8523	36.1908	38.5821
20	7.4338	8.2604	9.5908	10.8508	12.4426	28.4120	31.4104	34.1696	37.5663	39.9969
21	8.0336	8.8972	10.2829	11.5913	13.2396	29.6151	32.6706	35.4789	38.9322	41.4009
22	8.6427	9.5425	10.9823	12.3380	14.0415	30.8133	33.9245	36.7807	40.2894	42.7957
23	9.2604	10.1957	11.6885	13.0905	14.8480	32.0069	35.1725	38.0756	41.6383	44.1814
24	9.8862	10.8563	12.4011	13.8484	15.6587	33.1962	36.4150	39.3641	42.9798	45.5584
25	10.5196	11.5240	13.1197	14.6114	16.4734	34.3816	37.6525	40.6465	44.3140	46.9280
26	11.1602	12.1982	13.8439	15.3792	17.2919	35.5632	38.8851	41.9231	45.6416	48.2898
27	11.8077	12.8785	14.5734	16.1514	18.1139	36.7412	40.1133	43.1945	46.9628	49.6450
28	12.4613	13.5647	15.3079	16.9279	18.9392	37.9159	41.3372	44.4608	48.2782	50.9936
29	13.1211	14.2564	16.0471	17.7084	19.7677	39.0875	42.5569	45.7223	49.5878	52.3355
30	13.7867	14.9535	16.7908	18.4927	20.5992	40.2560	43.7730	46.9792	50.8922	53.6719

$(k-1)(r-1)$

APPENDIX H

F-Distribution Table: Upper 5% Probability (or 5% Area) Under F-Distribution Curve

$$df = D_1 = 5$$
$$D_2 = 10$$
$$0.05$$
$$F = 3.326$$

Critical value

F-critical

DENOMINATOR $df = D_2$

NUMERATOR $df = D_1$

	1	2	3	4	5	6	7	8	9	10
1	161.446	199.499	215.707	224.583	230.160	233.988	236.767	238.884	240.543	241.882
2	18.513	19.000	19.164	19.247	19.296	19.329	19.353	19.371	19.385	19.396
3	10.128	9.552	9.277	9.117	9.013	8.941	8.887	8.845	8.812	8.785
4	7.709	6.944	6.591	6.388	6.256	6.163	6.094	6.041	5.999	5.964
5	6.608	5.786	5.409	5.192	5.050	4.950	4.876	4.818	4.772	4.735
6	5.987	5.143	4.757	4.534	4.387	4.284	4.207	4.147	4.099	4.060
7	5.591	4.737	4.347	4.120	3.972	3.866	3.787	3.726	3.677	3.637
8	5.318	4.459	4.066	3.838	3.688	3.581	3.500	3.438	3.388	3.347
9	5.117	4.256	3.863	3.633	3.482	3.374	3.293	3.230	3.179	3.137
10	4.965	4.103	3.708	3.478	3.326	3.217	3.135	3.072	3.020	2.978
11	4.844	3.982	3.587	3.357	3.204	3.095	3.012	2.948	2.896	2.854
12	4.747	3.885	3.490	3.259	3.106	2.996	2.913	2.849	2.796	2.753
13	4.667	3.806	3.411	3.179	3.025	2.915	2.832	2.767	2.714	2.671
14	4.600	3.739	3.344	3.112	2.958	2.848	2.764	2.699	2.646	2.602
15	4.543	3.682	3.287	3.056	2.901	2.790	2.707	2.641	2.588	2.544
16	4.494	3.634	3.239	3.007	2.852	2.741	2.657	2.591	2.538	2.494
17	4.451	3.592	3.197	2.965	2.810	2.699	2.614	2.548	2.494	2.450
18	4.414	3.555	3.160	2.928	2.773	2.661	2.577	2.510	2.456	2.412
19	4.381	3.522	3.127	2.895	2.740	2.628	2.544	2.477	2.423	2.378
20	4.351	3.493	3.098	2.866	2.711	2.599	2.514	2.447	2.393	2.348
24	4.260	3.403	3.009	2.776	2.621	2.508	2.423	2.355	2.300	2.255
30	4.171	3.316	2.922	2.690	2.534	2.421	2.334	2.266	2.211	2.165
40	4.085	3.232	2.839	2.606	2.449	2.336	2.249	2.180	2.124	2.077
50	4.034	3.183	2.790	2.557	2.400	2.286	2.199	2.130	2.073	2.026
100	3.936	3.087	2.696	2.463	2.305	2.191	2.103	2.032	1.975	1.927
200	3.888	3.041	2.650	2.417	2.259	2.144	2.056	1.985	1.927	1.878
300	3.873	3.026	2.635	2.402	2.244	2.129	2.040	1.969	1.911	1.862

DENOMINATOR $df = D_2$

NUMERATOR $df = D_1$

	11	12	13	14	15	16	17	18	19	20
1	242.981	243.905	244.690	245.363	245.949	246.466	246.917	247.324	247.688	248.016
2	19.405	19.412	19.419	19.424	19.429	19.433	19.437	19.440	19.443	19.446
3	8.763	8.745	8.729	8.715	8.703	8.692	8.683	8.675	8.667	8.660
4	5.936	5.912	5.891	5.873	5.858	5.844	5.832	5.821	5.811	5.803
5	4.704	4.678	4.655	4.636	4.619	4.604	4.590	4.579	4.568	4.558
6	4.027	4.000	3.976	3.956	3.938	3.922	3.908	3.896	3.884	3.874
7	3.603	3.575	3.550	3.529	3.511	3.494	3.480	3.467	3.455	3.445
8	3.313	3.284	3.259	3.237	3.218	3.202	3.187	3.173	3.161	3.150
9	3.102	3.073	3.048	3.025	3.006	2.989	2.974	2.960	2.948	2.936
10	2.943	2.913	2.887	2.865	2.845	2.828	2.812	2.798	2.785	2.774
11	2.818	2.788	2.761	2.739	2.719	2.701	2.685	2.671	2.658	2.646
12	2.717	2.687	2.660	2.637	2.617	2.599	2.583	2.568	2.555	2.544
13	2.635	2.604	2.577	2.554	2.533	2.515	2.499	2.484	2.471	2.459
14	2.565	2.534	2.507	2.484	2.463	2.445	2.428	2.413	2.400	2.388
15	2.507	2.475	2.448	2.424	2.403	2.385	2.368	2.353	2.340	2.328
16	2.456	2.425	2.397	2.373	2.352	2.333	2.317	2.302	2.288	2.276

(continued)

DENOMINATOR
$df = D_2$

NUMERATOR $df = D_1$

	11	12	13	14	15	16	17	18	19	20
17	2.413	2.381	2.353	2.329	2.308	2.289	2.272	2.257	2.243	2.230
18	2.374	2.342	2.314	2.290	2.269	2.250	2.233	2.217	2.203	2.191
19	2.340	2.308	2.280	2.256	2.234	2.215	2.198	2.182	2.168	2.155
20	2.310	2.278	2.250	2.225	2.203	2.184	2.167	2.151	2.137	2.124
24	2.216	2.183	2.155	2.130	2.108	2.088	2.070	2.054	2.040	2.027
30	2.126	2.092	2.063	2.037	2.015	1.995	1.976	1.960	1.945	1.932
40	2.038	2.003	1.974	1.948	1.924	1.904	1.885	1.868	1.853	1.839
50	1.986	1.952	1.921	1.895	1.871	1.850	1.831	1.814	1.798	1.784
100	1.886	1.850	1.819	1.792	1.768	1.746	1.726	1.708	1.691	1.676
200	1.837	1.801	1.769	1.742	1.717	1.694	1.674	1.656	1.639	1.623
300	1.821	1.785	1.753	1.725	1.700	1.677	1.657	1.638	1.621	1.606

DENOMINATOR
$df = D_2$

NUMERATOR $df = D_1$

	24	30	40	50	100	200	300
1	249.052	250.096	251.144	251.774	253.043	253.676	253.887
2	19.454	19.463	19.471	19.476	19.486	19.491	19.492
3	8.638	8.617	8.594	8.581	8.554	8.540	8.536
4	5.774	5.746	5.717	5.699	5.664	5.646	5.640
5	4.527	4.496	4.464	4.444	4.405	4.385	4.378
6	3.841	3.808	3.774	3.754	3.712	3.690	3.683
7	3.410	3.376	3.340	3.319	3.275	3.252	3.245
8	3.115	3.079	3.043	3.020	2.975	2.951	2.943
9	2.900	2.864	2.826	2.803	2.756	2.731	2.723
10	2.737	2.700	2.661	2.637	2.588	2.563	2.555
11	2.609	2.570	2.531	2.507	2.457	2.431	2.422
12	2.505	2.466	2.426	2.401	2.350	2.323	2.314
13	2.420	2.380	2.339	2.314	2.261	2.234	2.225
14	2.349	2.308	2.266	2.241	2.187	2.159	2.150
15	2.288	2.247	2.204	2.178	2.123	2.095	2.085
16	2.235	2.194	2.151	2.124	2.068	2.039	2.030
17	2.190	2.148	2.104	2.077	2.020	1.991	1.981
18	2.150	2.107	2.063	2.035	1.978	1.948	1.938
19	2.114	2.071	2.026	1.999	1.940	1.910	1.899
20	2.082	2.039	1.994	1.966	1.907	1.875	1.865
24	1.984	1.939	1.892	1.863	1.800	1.768	1.756
30	1.887	1.841	1.792	1.761	1.695	1.660	1.647
40	1.793	1.744	1.693	1.660	1.589	1.551	1.537
50	1.737	1.687	1.634	1.599	1.525	1.484	1.469
100	1.627	1.573	1.515	1.477	1.392	1.342	1.323
200	1.572	1.516	1.455	1.415	1.321	1.263	1.240
300	1.554	1.497	1.435	1.393	1.296	1.234	1.210

(continued)

F-Distribution Table: Upper 2.5% Probability (or 2.5% Area) Under F-Distribution Curve

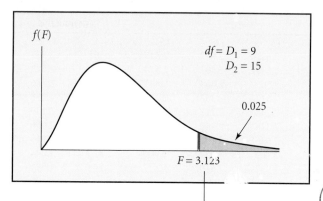

$f(F)$

$df = D_1 = 9$
$D_2 = 15$

0.025

$F = 3.123$

$(F critical)$

DENOMINATOR
$df = D_2$

NUMERATOR $df = D_1$

	1	2	3	4	5	6	7		9	10	11
1	647.793	799.482	864.151	899.599	921.835	937.114	948.203	9.	963.279	968.634	973.028
2	38.506	39.000	39.166	39.248	39.298	39.331	39.356	3⟩ 3	39.387	39.398	39.407
3	17.443	16.044	15.439	15.101	14.885	14.735	14.624	1⟩ ⟩	14.473	14.419	14.374
4	12.218	10.649	9.979	9.604	9.364	9.197	9.074		8.905	8.844	8.794
5	10.007	8.434	7.764	7.388	7.146	6.978	6.853		6.681	6.619	6.568
6	8.813	7.260	6.599	6.227	5.988	5.820	5.695		5.523	5.461	5.410
7	8.073	6.542	5.890	5.523	5.285	5.119	4.995		4.823	4.761	4.70⟩
8	7.571	6.059	5.416	5.053	4.817	4.652	4.529	⟩	4.357	4.295	4.243
9	7.209	5.715	5.078	4.718	4.484	4.320	4.197	4 ⟩02	4.026	3.964	3.912
10	6.937	5.456	4.826	4.468	4.236	4.072	3.950	3.855	3.779	3.717	3.665
11	6.724	5.256	4.630	4.275	4.044	3.881	3.759	3.664	3.588	3.526	3.474
12	6.554	5.096	4.474	4.121	3.891	3.728	3.607	3.⟩12	3.436	3.374	3.321
13	6.414	4.965	4.347	3.996	3.767	3.604	3.483	3.388	3.312	3.250	3.197
14	6.298	4.857	4.242	3.892	3.663	3.501	3.380	3.285	3.209	3.147	3.095
15	6.200	4.765	4.153	3.804	3.576	3.415	3.293	3.199	3.123	3.060	3.008
16	6.115	4.687	4.077	3.729	3.502	3.341	3.219	3.125	3.049	2.986	2.934
17	6.042	4.619	4.011	3.665	3.438	3.277	3.156	3.061	2.985	2.922	2.870
18	5.978	4.560	3.954	3.608	3.382	3.221	3.100	3.005	2.929	2.866	2.814
19	5.922	4.508	3.903	3.559	3.333	3.172	3.051	2.956	2.880	2.817	2.765
20	5.871	4.461	3.859	3.515	3.289	3.128	3.007	2.913	2.837	2.774	2.721
24	5.717	4.319	3.721	3.379	3.155	2.995	2.874	2.779	2.703	2.640	2.586
30	5.568	4.182	3.589	3.250	3.026	2.867	2.746	2.651	2.575	2.511	2.458
40	5.424	4.051	3.463	3.126	2.904	2.744	2.624	2.529	2.452	2.388	2.334
50	5.340	3.975	3.390	3.054	2.833	2.674	2.553	2.458	2.381	2.317	2.263
100	5.179	3.828	3.250	2.917	2.696	2.537	2.417	2.321	2.244	2.179	2.124
200	5.100	3.758	3.182	2.850	2.630	2.472	2.351	2.256	2.178	2.113	2.058
300	5.075	3.735	3.160	2.829	2.609	2.451	2.330	2.234	2.156	2.091	2.036

DENOMINATOR
$df = D_2$

NUMERATOR $df = D_1$

	12	13	14	15	16	17	18	19	20	24	30
1	976.725	979.839	982.545	984.874	986.911	988.715	990.345	991.800	993.081	997.272	1001.405
2	39.415	39.421	39.427	39.431	39.436	39.439	39.442	39.446	39.448	39.457	39.465
3	14.337	14.305	14.277	14.253	14.232	14.213	14.196	14.181	14.167	14.124	14.081
4	8.751	8.715	8.684	8.657	8.633	8.611	8.592	8.575	8.560	8.511	8.461
5	6.525	6.488	6.456	6.428	6.403	6.381	6.362	6.344	6.329	6.278	6.227
6	5.366	5.329	5.297	5.269	5.244	5.222	5.202	5.184	5.168	5.117	5.065
7	4.666	4.628	4.596	4.568	4.543	4.521	4.501	4.483	4.467	4.415	4.362
8	4.200	4.162	4.130	4.101	4.076	4.054	4.034	4.016	3.999	3.947	3.894
9	3.868	3.831	3.798	3.769	3.744	3.722	3.701	3.683	3.667	3.614	3.560
10	3.621	3.583	3.550	3.522	3.496	3.474	3.453	3.435	3.419	3.365	3.311
11	3.430	3.392	3.359	3.330	3.304	3.282	3.261	3.243	3.226	3.173	3.118
12	3.277	3.239	3.206	3.177	3.152	3.129	3.108	3.090	3.073	3.019	2.963
13	3.153	3.115	3.082	3.053	3.027	3.004	2.983	2.965	2.948	2.893	2.837
14	3.050	3.012	2.979	2.949	2.923	2.900	2.879	2.861	2.844	2.789	2.732
15	2.963	2.925	2.891	2.862	2.836	2.813	2.792	2.773	2.756	2.701	2.644
16	2.889	2.851	2.817	2.788	2.761	2.738	2.717	2.698	2.681	2.625	2.568
17	2.825	2.786	2.753	2.723	2.697	2.673	2.652	2.633	2.616	2.560	2.502
18	2.769	2.730	2.696	2.667	2.640	2.617	2.596	2.576	2.559	2.503	2.445

(continued)

DENOMINATOR
$df = D_2$

NUMERATOR $df = D_1$

	12	13	14	15	16	17	18	19	20	24	30
19	2.720	2.681	2.647	2.617	2.591	2.567	2.546	2.526	2.509	2.452	2.394
20	2.676	2.637	2.603	2.573	2.547	2.523	2.501	2.482	2.464	2.408	2.349
24	2.541	2.502	2.468	2.437	2.411	2.386	2.365	2.345	2.327	2.269	2.209
30	2.412	2.372	2.338	2.307	2.280	2.255	2.233	2.213	2.195	2.136	2.074
40	2.288	2.248	2.213	2.182	2.154	2.129	2.107	2.086	2.068	2.007	1.943
50	2.216	2.176	2.140	2.109	2.081	2.056	2.033	2.012	1.993	1.931	1.866
100	2.077	2.036	2.000	1.968	1.939	1.913	1.890	1.868	1.849	1.784	1.715
200	2.010	1.969	1.932	1.900	1.870	1.844	1.820	1.798	1.778	1.712	1.640
300	1.988	1.947	1.910	1.877	1.848	1.821	1.797	1.775	1.755	1.688	1.616

DENOMINATOR
$df = D_2$

NUMERATOR $df = D_1$

	40	50	100	200	300
1	1005.596	1008.098	1013.163	1015.724	1016.539
2	39.473	39.478	39.488	39.493	39.495
3	14.036	14.010	13.956	13.929	13.920
4	8.411	8.381	8.319	8.288	8.278
5	6.175	6.144	6.080	6.048	6.037
6	5.012	4.980	4.915	4.882	4.871
7	4.309	4.276	4.210	4.176	4.165
8	3.840	3.807	3.739	3.705	3.693
9	3.505	3.472	3.403	3.368	3.357
10	3.255	3.221	3.152	3.116	3.104
11	3.061	3.027	2.956	2.920	2.908
12	2.906	2.871	2.800	2.763	2.750
13	2.780	2.744	2.671	2.634	2.621
14	2.674	2.638	2.565	2.526	2.513
15	2.585	2.549	2.474	2.435	2.422
16	2.509	2.472	2.396	2.357	2.343
17	2.442	2.405	2.329	2.289	2.275
18	2.384	2.347	2.269	2.229	2.215
19	2.333	2.295	2.217	2.176	2.162
20	2.287	2.249	2.170	2.128	2.114
24	2.146	2.107	2.024	1.981	1.966
30	2.009	1.968	1.882	1.835	1.819
40	1.875	1.832	1.741	1.691	1.673
50	1.796	1.752	1.656	1.603	1.584
100	1.640	1.592	1.483	1.420	1.397
200	1.562	1.511	1.393	1.320	1.293
300	1.536	1.484	1.361	1.285	1.255

(continued)

F-Distribution Table: Upper 1% Probability (or 1% Area) Under *F*-Distribution Curve

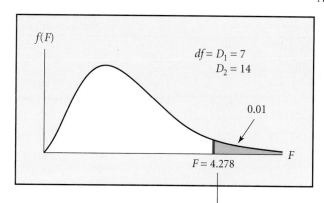

$$f(F)$$
$$df = D_1 = 7$$
$$D_2 = 14$$
$$0.01$$
$$F = 4.278$$

DENOMINATOR
$df = D_2$

NUMERATOR $df = D_1$

D_2	1	2	3	4	5	6	7	8	9	10	11
1	4052.185	4999.340	5403.534	5624.257	5763.955	5858.950	5928.334	5980.954	6022.397	6055.925	6083.399
2	98.502	99.000	99.164	99.251	99.302	99.331	99.357	99.375	99.390	99.397	99.408
3	34.116	30.816	29.457	28.710	28.237	27.911	27.671	27.489	27.345	27.228	27.132
4	21.198	18.000	16.694	15.977	15.522	15.207	14.976	14.799	14.659	14.546	14.452
5	16.258	13.274	12.060	11.392	10.967	10.672	10.456	10.289	10.158	10.051	9.963
6	13.745	10.925	9.780	9.148	8.746	8.466	8.260	8.102	7.976	7.874	7.790
7	12.246	9.547	8.451	7.847	7.460	7.191	6.993	6.840	6.719	6.620	6.538
8	11.259	8.649	7.591	7.006	6.632	6.371	6.178	6.029	5.911	5.814	5.734
9	10.562	8.022	6.992	6.422	6.057	5.802	5.613	5.467	5.351	5.257	5.178
10	10.044	7.559	6.552	5.994	5.636	5.386	5.200	5.057	4.942	4.849	4.772
11	9.646	7.206	6.217	5.668	5.316	5.069	4.886	4.744	4.632	4.539	4.462
12	9.330	6.927	5.953	5.412	5.064	4.821	4.640	4.499	4.388	4.296	4.220
13	9.074	6.701	5.739	5.205	4.862	4.620	4.441	4.302	4.191	4.100	4.025
14	8.862	6.515	5.564	5.035	4.695	4.456	4.278	4.140	4.030	3.939	3.864
15	8.683	6.359	5.417	4.893	4.556	4.318	4.142	4.004	3.895	3.805	3.730
16	8.531	6.226	5.292	4.773	4.437	4.202	4.026	3.890	3.780	3.691	3.616
17	8.400	6.112	5.185	4.669	4.336	4.101	3.927	3.791	3.682	3.593	3.518
18	8.285	6.013	5.092	4.579	4.248	4.015	3.841	3.705	3.597	3.508	3.434
19	8.185	5.926	5.010	4.500	4.171	3.939	3.765	3.631	3.523	3.434	3.360
20	8.096	5.849	4.938	4.431	4.103	3.871	3.699	3.564	3.457	3.368	3.294
24	7.823	5.614	4.718	4.218	3.895	3.667	3.496	3.363	3.256	3.168	3.094
30	7.562	5.390	4.510	4.018	3.699	3.473	3.305	3.173	3.067	2.979	2.906
40	7.314	5.178	4.313	3.828	3.514	3.291	3.124	2.993	2.888	2.801	2.727
50	7.171	5.057	4.199	3.720	3.408	3.186	3.020	2.890	2.785	2.698	2.625
100	6.895	4.824	3.984	3.513	3.206	2.988	2.823	2.694	2.590	2.503	2.430
200	6.763	4.713	3.881	3.414	3.110	2.893	2.730	2.601	2.497	2.411	2.338
300	6.720	4.677	3.848	3.382	3.079	2.862	2.699	2.571	2.467	2.380	2.307

DENOMINATOR
$df = D_2$

NUMERATOR $df = D_1$

D_2	12	13	14	15	16	17	18	19	20	24	30
1	6106.682	6125.774	6143.004	6156.974	6170.012	6181.188	6191.432	6200.746	6208.662	6234.273	6260.350
2	99.419	99.422	99.426	99.433	99.437	99.441	99.444	99.448	99.448	99.455	99.466
3	27.052	26.983	26.924	26.872	26.826	26.786	26.751	26.719	26.690	26.597	26.504
4	14.374	14.306	14.249	14.198	14.154	14.114	14.079	14.048	14.019	13.929	13.838
5	9.888	9.825	9.770	9.722	9.680	9.643	9.609	9.580	9.553	9.466	9.379
6	7.718	7.657	7.605	7.559	7.519	7.483	7.451	7.422	7.396	7.313	7.229
7	6.469	6.410	6.359	6.314	6.275	6.240	6.209	6.181	6.155	6.074	5.992
8	5.667	5.609	5.559	5.515	5.477	5.442	5.412	5.384	5.359	5.279	5.198
9	5.111	5.055	5.005	4.962	4.924	4.890	4.860	4.833	4.808	4.729	4.649
10	4.706	4.650	4.601	4.558	4.520	4.487	4.457	4.430	4.405	4.327	4.247
11	4.397	4.342	4.293	4.251	4.213	4.180	4.150	4.123	4.099	4.021	3.941
12	4.155	4.100	4.052	4.010	3.972	3.939	3.910	3.883	3.858	3.780	3.701
13	3.960	3.905	3.857	3.815	3.778	3.745	3.716	3.689	3.665	3.587	3.507
14	3.800	3.745	3.698	3.656	3.619	3.586	3.556	3.529	3.505	3.427	3.348
15	3.666	3.612	3.564	3.522	3.485	3.452	3.423	3.396	3.372	3.294	3.214
16	3.553	3.498	3.451	3.409	3.372	3.339	3.310	3.283	3.259	3.181	3.101
17	3.455	3.401	3.353	3.312	3.275	3.242	3.212	3.186	3.162	3.083	3.003
18	3.371	3.316	3.269	3.227	3.190	3.158	3.128	3.101	3.077	2.999	2.919

(continued)

DENOMINATOR
$df = D_2$

NUMERATOR $df = D_1$

	12	13	14	15	16	17	18	19	20	24	30
19	3.297	3.242	3.195	3.153	3.116	3.084	3.054	3.027	3.003	2.925	2.844
20	3.231	3.177	3.130	3.088	3.051	3.018	2.989	2.962	2.938	2.859	2.778
24	3.032	2.977	2.930	2.889	2.852	2.819	2.789	2.762	2.738	2.659	2.577
30	2.843	2.789	2.742	2.700	2.663	2.630	2.600	2.573	2.549	2.469	2.386
40	2.665	2.611	2.563	2.522	2.484	2.451	2.421	2.394	2.369	2.288	2.203
50	2.563	2.508	2.461	2.419	2.382	2.348	2.318	2.290	2.265	2.183	2.098
100	2.368	2.313	2.265	2.223	2.185	2.151	2.120	2.092	2.067	1.983	1.893
200	2.275	2.220	2.172	2.129	2.091	2.057	2.026	1.997	1.971	1.886	1.794
300	2.244	2.190	2.142	2.099	2.061	2.026	1.995	1.966	1.940	1.854	1.761

DENOMINATOR
$df = D_2$

NUMERATOR $df = D_1$

	40	50	100	200	300
1	6286.427	6302.260	6333.925	6349.757	6355.345
2	99.477	99.477	99.491	99.491	99.499
3	26.411	26.354	26.241	26.183	26.163
4	13.745	13.690	13.577	13.520	13.501
5	9.291	9.238	9.130	9.075	9.057
6	7.143	7.091	6.987	6.934	6.916
7	5.908	5.858	5.755	5.702	5.685
8	5.116	5.065	4.963	4.911	4.894
9	4.567	4.517	4.415	4.363	4.346
10	4.165	4.115	4.014	3.962	3.944
11	3.860	3.810	3.708	3.656	3.638
12	3.619	3.569	3.467	3.414	3.397
13	3.425	3.375	3.272	3.219	3.202
14	3.266	3.215	3.112	3.059	3.040
15	3.132	3.081	2.977	2.923	2.905
16	3.018	2.967	2.863	2.808	2.790
17	2.920	2.869	2.764	2.709	2.691
18	2.835	2.784	2.678	2.623	2.604
19	2.761	2.709	2.602	2.547	2.528
20	2.695	2.643	2.535	2.479	2.460
24	2.492	2.440	2.329	2.271	2.251
30	2.299	2.245	2.131	2.070	2.049
40	2.114	2.058	1.938	1.874	1.851
50	2.007	1.949	1.825	1.757	1.733
100	1.797	1.735	1.598	1.518	1.490
200	1.694	1.629	1.481	1.391	1.357
300	1.660	1.594	1.441	1.346	1.309

Critical Values of Hartley's F_{max} Test

$$F_{max} = \frac{S^2_{largest}}{S^2_{smallest}} \sim F_{max_{1-a(c,v)}}$$

UPPER 5% POINTS ($\alpha = 0.05$)

$\frac{c}{v}$	2	3	4	5	6	7	8	9	10	11	12
2	39.0	87.5	142	202	266	333	403	475	550	626	704
3	15.4	27.8	39.2	50.7	62.0	72.9	83.5	93.9	104	114	124
4	9.60	15.5	20.6	25.2	29.5	33.6	37.5	41.1	44.6	48.0	51.4
5	7.15	10.8	13.7	16.3	18.7	20.8	22.9	24.7	26.5	28.2	29.9
6	5.82	8.38	10.4	12.1	13.7	15.0	16.3	17.5	18.6	19.7	20.7
7	4.99	6.94	8.44	9.70	10.8	11.8	12.7	13.5	14.3	15.1	15.8
8	4.43	6.00	7.18	8.12	9.03	9.78	10.5	11.1	11.7	12.2	12.7
9	4.03	5.34	6.31	7.11	7.80	8.41	8.95	9.45	9.91	10.3	10.7
10	3.72	4.85	5.67	6.34	6.92	7.42	7.87	8.28	8.66	9.01	9.34
12	3.28	4.16	4.79	5.30	5.72	6.09	6.42	6.72	7.00	7.25	7.48
15	2.86	3.54	4.01	4.37	4.68	4.95	5.19	5.40	5.59	5.77	5.93
20	2.46	2.95	3.29	3.54	3.76	3.94	4.10	4.24	4.37	4.49	4.59
30	2.07	2.40	2.61	2.78	2.91	3.02	3.12	3.21	3.29	3.36	3.39
60	1.67	1.85	1.96	2.04	2.11	2.17	2.22	2.26	2.30	2.33	2.36
∞	1.00	1.00	1.00	1.00	1.00	1.00	1.00	1.00	1.00	1.00	1.00

UPPER 1% POINTS ($\alpha = 0.01$)

$\frac{c}{v}$	2	3	4	5	6	7	8	9	10	11	12
2	199	448	729	1036	1362	1705	2063	2432	2813	3204	3605
3	47.5	85	120	151	184	21(6)	24(9)	28(1)	31(0)	33(7)	36(1)
4	23.2	37	49	59	69	79	89	97	106	113	120
5	14.9	22	28	33	38	42	46	50	54	57	60
6	11.1	15.5	19.1	22	25	27	30	32	34	36	37
7	8.89	12.1	14.5	16.5	18.4	20	22	23	24	26	27
8	7.50	9.9	11.7	13.2	14.5	15.8	16.9	17.9	18.9	19.8	21
9	6.54	8.5	9.9	11.1	12.1	13.1	13.9	14.7	15.3	16.0	16.6
10	5.85	7.4	8.6	9.6	10.4	11.1	11.8	12.4	12.9	13.4	13.9
12	4.91	6.1	6.9	7.6	8.2	8.7	9.1	9.5	9.9	10.2	10.6
15	4.07	4.9	5.5	6.0	6.4	6.7	7.1	7.3	7.5	7.8	8.0
20	3.32	3.8	4.3	4.6	4.9	5.1	5.3	5.5	5.6	5.8	5.9
30	2.63	3.0	3.3	3.4	3.6	3.7	3.8	3.9	4.0	4.1	4.2
60	1.96	2.2	2.3	2.4	2.4	2.5	2.5	2.6	2.6	2.7	2.7
∞	1.00	1.0	1.0	1.0	1.0	1.0	1.0	1.0	1.0	1.00	1.0

Note: $S^2_{largest}$ is the largest and $s^2_{smallest}$ the smallest in a set of c independent mean squares, each based on v degrees of freedom.

Source: Reprinted from E. S. Pearson and H. O. Hartley, eds., *Biometrika Tables for Statisticians*, 3d ed., 1966, by permission of the Biometrika Trustees.

Distribution of the Studentized Range (*q*-values)

p = 0.95

D_2 \ D_1	2	3	4	5	6	7	8	9	10
1	17.97	26.98	32.82	37.08	40.41	43.12	45.40	47.36	49.07
2	6.08	8.33	9.80	10.88	11.74	12.44	13.03	13.54	13.99
3	4.50	5.91	6.82	7.50	8.04	8.48	8.85	9.18	9.46
4	3.93	5.04	5.76	6.29	6.71	7.05	7.35	7.60	7.83
5	3.64	4.60	5.22	5.67	6.03	6.33	6.58	6.80	6.99
6	3.46	4.34	4.90	5.30	5.63	5.90	6.12	6.32	6.49
7	3.34	4.16	4.68	5.06	5.36	5.61	5.82	6.00	6.16
8	3.26	4.04	4.53	4.89	5.17	5.40	5.60	5.77	5.92
9	3.20	3.95	4.41	4.76	5.02	5.24	5.43	5.59	5.74
10	3.15	3.88	4.33	4.65	4.91	5.12	5.30	5.46	5.60
11	3.11	3.82	4.26	4.57	4.82	5.03	5.20	5.35	5.49
12	3.08	3.77	4.20	4.51	4.75	4.95	5.12	5.27	5.39
13	3.06	3.73	4.15	4.45	4.69	4.88	5.05	5.19	5.32
14	3.03	3.70	4.11	4.41	4.64	4.83	4.99	5.13	5.25
15	3.01	3.67	4.08	4.37	4.59	4.78	4.94	5.08	5.20
16	3.00	3.65	4.05	4.33	4.56	4.74	4.90	5.03	5.15
17	2.98	3.63	4.02	4.30	4.52	4.70	4.86	4.99	5.11
18	2.97	3.61	4.00	4.28	4.49	4.67	4.82	4.96	5.07
19	2.96	3.59	3.98	4.25	4.47	4.65	4.79	4.92	5.04
20	2.95	3.58	3.96	4.23	4.45	4.62	4.77	4.90	5.01
24	2.92	3.53	3.90	4.17	4.37	4.54	4.68	4.81	4.92
30	2.89	3.49	3.85	4.10	4.30	4.46	4.60	4.72	4.82
40	2.86	3.44	3.79	4.04	4.23	4.39	4.52	4.63	4.73
60	2.83	3.40	3.74	3.98	4.16	4.31	4.44	4.55	4.65
120	2.80	3.36	3.68	3.92	4.10	4.24	4.36	4.47	4.56
∞	2.77	3.31	3.63	3.86	4.03	4.17	4.29	4.39	4.47

D_2 \ D_1	11	12	13	14	15	16	17	18	19	20
1	50.59	51.96	53.20	54.33	55.36	56.32	57.22	58.04	58.83	59.56
2	14.39	14.75	15.08	15.38	15.65	15.91	16.14	16.37	16.57	16.77
3	9.72	9.95	10.15	10.35	10.52	10.69	10.84	10.98	11.11	11.24
4	8.03	8.21	8.37	8.52	8.66	8.79	8.91	9.03	9.13	9.23
5	7.17	7.32	7.47	7.60	7.72	7.83	7.93	8.03	8.12	8.21
6	6.65	6.79	6.92	7.03	7.14	7.24	7.34	7.43	7.51	7.59
7	6.30	6.43	6.55	6.66	6.76	6.85	6.94	7.02	7.10	7.17
8	6.05	6.18	6.29	6.39	6.48	6.57	6.65	6.73	6.80	6.87
9	5.87	5.98	6.09	6.19	6.28	6.36	6.44	6.51	6.58	6.64
10	5.72	5.83	5.93	6.03	6.11	6.19	6.27	6.34	6.40	6.47
11	5.61	5.71	5.81	5.90	5.98	6.06	6.13	6.20	6.27	6.33
12	5.51	5.61	5.71	5.80	5.88	5.95	6.02	6.09	6.15	6.21
13	5.43	5.53	5.63	5.71	5.79	5.86	5.93	5.99	6.05	6.11
14	5.36	5.46	5.55	5.64	5.71	5.79	5.85	5.91	5.97	6.03
15	5.31	5.40	5.49	5.57	5.65	5.72	5.78	5.85	5.90	5.96
16	5.26	5.35	5.44	5.52	5.59	5.66	5.73	5.79	5.84	5.90
17	5.21	5.31	5.39	5.47	5.54	5.61	5.67	5.73	5.79	5.84
18	5.17	5.27	5.35	5.43	5.50	5.57	5.63	5.69	5.74	5.79
19	5.14	5.23	5.31	5.39	5.46	5.53	5.59	5.65	5.70	5.75
20	5.11	5.20	5.28	5.36	5.43	5.49	5.55	5.61	5.66	5.71
24	5.01	5.10	5.18	5.25	5.32	5.38	5.44	5.49	5.55	5.59
30	4.92	5.00	5.08	5.15	5.21	5.27	5.33	5.38	5.43	5.47
40	4.82	4.90	4.98	5.04	5.11	5.16	5.22	5.27	5.31	5.36
60	4.73	4.81	4.88	4.94	5.00	5.06	5.11	5.15	5.20	5.24
120	4.64	4.71	4.78	4.84	4.90	4.95	5.00	5.04	5.09	5.13
∞	4.55	4.62	4.68	4.74	4.80	4.85	4.89	4.93	4.97	5.01

Note: $D_1 = K$ populations and $D_2 = N - K$.

$p = 0.99$

D_2 \ D_1	2	3	4	5	6	7	8	9	10
1	90.03	135.0	164.3	185.6	202.2	215.8	227.2	237.0	245.6
2	14.04	19.02	22.29	24.72	26.63	28.20	29.53	30.68	31.69
3	8.26	10.62	12.17	13.33	14.24	15.00	15.64	16.20	16.69
4	6.51	8.12	9.17	9.96	10.58	11.10	11.55	11.93	12.27
5	5.70	6.98	7.80	8.42	8.91	9.32	9.67	9.97	10.24
6	5.24	6.33	7.03	7.56	7.97	8.32	8.61	8.87	9.10
7	4.95	5.92	6.54	7.01	7.37	7.68	7.94	8.17	8.37
8	4.75	5.64	6.20	6.62	6.96	7.24	7.47	7.68	7.86
9	4.60	5.43	5.96	6.35	6.66	6.91	7.13	7.33	7.49
10	4.48	5.27	5.77	6.14	6.43	6.67	6.87	7.05	7.21
11	4.39	5.15	5.62	5.97	6.25	6.48	6.67	6.84	6.99
12	4.32	5.05	5.50	5.84	6.10	6.32	6.51	6.67	6.81
13	4.26	4.96	5.40	5.73	5.98	6.19	6.37	6.53	6.67
14	4.21	4.89	5.32	5.63	5.88	6.08	6.26	6.41	6.54
15	4.17	4.84	5.25	5.56	5.80	5.99	6.16	6.31	6.44
16	4.13	4.79	5.19	5.49	5.72	5.92	6.08	6.22	6.35
17	4.10	4.74	5.14	5.43	5.66	5.85	6.01	6.15	6.27
18	4.07	4.70	5.09	5.38	5.60	5.79	5.94	6.08	6.20
19	4.05	4.67	5.05	5.33	5.55	5.73	5.89	6.02	6.14
20	4.02	4.64	5.02	5.29	5.51	5.69	5.84	5.97	6.09
24	3.96	4.55	4.91	5.17	5.37	5.54	5.69	5.81	5.92
30	3.89	4.45	4.80	5.05	5.24	5.40	5.54	5.65	5.76
40	3.82	4.37	4.70	4.93	5.11	5.26	5.39	5.50	5.60
60	3.76	4.28	4.59	4.82	4.99	5.13	5.25	5.36	5.45
120	3.70	4.20	4.50	4.71	4.87	5.01	5.12	5.21	5.30
∞	3.64	4.12	4.40	4.60	4.76	4.88	4.99	5.08	5.16

D_2 \ D_1	11	12	13	14	15	16	17	18	19	20
1	253.2	260.0	266.2	271.8	277.0	281.8	286.3	290.4	294.3	298.0
2	32.59	33.40	34.13	34.81	35.43	36.00	36.53	37.03	37.50	37.95
3	17.13	17.53	17.89	18.22	18.52	18.81	19.07	19.32	19.55	19.77
4	12.57	12.84	13.09	13.32	13.53	13.73	13.91	14.08	14.24	14.40
5	10.48	10.70	10.89	11.08	11.24	11.40	11.55	11.68	11.81	11.93
6	9.30	9.48	9.65	9.81	9.95	10.08	10.21	10.32	10.43	10.54
7	8.55	8.71	8.86	9.00	9.12	9.24	9.35	9.46	9.55	9.65
8	8.03	8.18	8.31	8.44	8.55	8.66	8.76	8.85	8.94	9.03
9	7.65	7.78	7.91	8.03	8.13	8.23	8.33	8.41	8.49	8.57
10	7.36	7.49	7.60	7.71	7.81	7.91	7.99	8.08	8.15	8.23
11	7.13	7.25	7.36	7.46	7.56	7.65	7.73	7.81	7.88	7.95
12	6.94	7.06	7.17	7.26	7.36	7.44	7.52	7.59	7.66	7.73
13	6.79	6.90	7.01	7.10	7.19	7.27	7.35	7.42	7.48	7.55
14	6.66	6.77	6.87	6.96	7.05	7.13	7.20	7.27	7.33	7.39
15	6.55	6.66	6.76	6.84	6.93	7.00	7.07	7.14	7.20	7.26
16	6.46	6.56	6.66	6.74	6.82	6.90	6.97	7.03	7.09	7.15
17	6.38	6.48	6.57	6.66	6.73	6.81	6.87	6.94	7.00	7.05
18	6.31	6.41	6.50	6.58	6.65	6.73	6.79	6.85	6.91	6.97
19	6.25	6.34	6.43	6.51	6.58	6.65	6.72	6.78	6.84	6.89
20	6.19	6.28	6.37	6.45	6.52	6.59	6.65	6.71	6.77	6.82
24	6.02	6.11	6.19	6.26	6.33	6.39	6.45	6.51	6.56	6.61
30	5.85	5.93	6.01	6.08	6.14	6.20	6.26	6.31	6.36	6.41
40	5.69	5.76	5.83	5.90	5.96	6.02	6.07	6.12	6.16	6.21
60	5.53	5.60	5.67	5.73	5.78	5.84	5.89	5.93	5.97	6.01
120	5.37	5.44	5.50	5.56	5.61	5.66	5.71	5.75	5.79	5.83
∞	5.23	5.29	5.35	5.40	5.45	5.49	5.54	5.57	5.61	5.65

Source: Reprinted with permission from E. S. Pearson and H. O. Hartley, *Biometrika Tables for Statisticians* (New York: Cambridge University Press, 1954).

APPENDIX K

Critical Values of r in the Runs Test

a. Lower Tail: Too Few Runs

$n_1 \backslash n_2$	2	3	4	5	6	7	8	9	10	11	12	13	14	15	16	17	18	19	20
2											2	2	2	2	2	2	2	2	2
3					2	2	2	2	2	2	2	2	2	3	3	3	3	3	3
4				2	2	2	3	3	3	3	3	3	3	3	4	4	4	4	4
5			2	2	3	3	3	3	3	4	4	4	4	4	4	4	5	5	5
6		2	2	3	3	3	3	4	4	4	4	5	5	5	5	5	5	6	6
7		2	2	3	3	3	4	4	5	5	5	5	5	6	6	6	6	6	6
8		2	3	3	3	4	4	5	5	5	6	6	6	6	6	7	7	7	7
9		2	3	3	4	4	5	5	5	6	6	6	7	7	7	7	8	8	8
10		2	3	3	4	5	5	5	6	6	7	7	7	7	8	8	8	8	9
11		2	3	4	4	5	5	6	6	7	7	7	8	8	8	9	9	9	9
12	2	2	3	4	4	5	6	6	7	7	7	8	8	8	9	9	9	10	10
13	2	2	3	4	5	5	6	6	7	7	8	8	9	9	9	10	10	10	10
14	2	2	3	4	5	5	6	7	7	8	8	9	9	9	10	10	10	11	11
15	2	3	3	4	5	6	6	7	7	8	8	9	9	10	10	11	11	11	12
16	2	3	4	4	5	6	6	7	8	8	9	9	10	10	11	11	11	12	12
17	2	3	4	4	5	6	7	7	8	9	9	10	10	11	11	11	12	12	13
18	2	3	4	5	5	6	7	8	8	9	9	10	10	11	11	12	12	13	13
19	2	3	4	5	6	6	7	8	8	9	10	10	11	11	12	12	13	13	13
20	2	3	4	5	6	6	7	8	9	9	10	10	11	12	12	13	13	13	14

b. Upper Tail: Too Many Runs

$n_1 \backslash n_2$	2	3	4	5	6	7	8	9	10	11	12	13	14	15	16	17	18	19	20
2																			
3																			
4				9	9														
5			9	10	10	11	11												
6			9	10	11	12	12	13	13	13	13								
7				11	12	13	13	14	14	14	14	15	15	15					
8				11	12	13	14	14	15	15	16	16	16	16	17	17	17	17	17
9					13	14	14	15	16	16	16	17	17	18	18	18	18	18	18
10					13	14	15	16	16	17	17	18	19	19	19	20	20	20	21
11					13	14	15	16	17	17	18	19	19	20	20	21	21	21	22
12					13	14	16	16	17	18	19	19	20	20	21	21	22	22	23
13						15	16	17	18	19	19	20	20	21	22	22	23	23	24
14						15	16	17	18	19	20	20	21	22	22	23	23	24	25
15						15	16	18	18	19	20	21	22	22	23	23	24	24	25
16							17	18	19	20	21	21	22	23	23	24	25	25	26
17							17	18	19	20	21	22	23	23	24	25	25	26	27
18							17	18	19	20	21	22	23	24	25	25	26	26	27
19							17	18	20	21	22	23	23	24	25	26	26	27	28
20							17	18	20	21	22	23	24	25	25	26	27	27	28

Source: Adapted from Frieda S. Swed and C. Eisenhart, "Tables for testing randomness of grouping in a sequence of alternatives," *Ann. Math. Statist.* 14 (1943): 83–86, with the permission of the publisher.

APPENDIX L

Mann-Whitney U Test Probabilities ($n < 9$)

$n_2 = 3$

U \ n_1	1	2	3
0	.250	.100	.050
1	.500	.200	.100
2	.750	.400	.200
3		.600	.350
4			.500
5			.650

$n_2 = 4$

U \ n_1	1	2	3	4
0	.200	.067	.028	.014
1	.400	.133	.057	.029
2	.600	.267	.114	.057
3		.400	.200	.100
4		.600	.314	.171
5			.429	.243
6			.571	.343
7				.443
8				.557

$n_2 = 5$

U \ n_1	1	2	3	4	5
0	.167	.047	.018	.008	.004
1	.333	.095	.036	.016	.008
2	.500	.190	.071	.032	.016
3	.667	.286	.125	.056	.028
4		.429	.196	.095	.048
5		.571	.286	.143	.075
6			.393	.206	.111
7			.500	.278	.155
8			.607	.365	.210
9				.452	.274
10				.548	.345
11					.421
12					.500
13					.579

$n_2 = 6$

U \ n_1	1	2	3	4	5	6
0	.143	.036	.012	.005	.002	.001
1	.286	.071	.024	.010	.004	.002
2	.428	.143	.048	.019	.009	.004
3	.571	.214	.083	.033	.015	.008
4		.321	.131	.057	.026	.013
5		.429	.190	.086	.041	.021
6		.571	.274	.129	.063	.032
7			.357	.176	.089	.047
8			.452	.238	.123	.066
9			.548	.305	.165	.090
10				.381	.214	.120
11				.457	.268	.155
12				.545	.331	.197
13					.396	.242
14					.465	.294
15					.535	.350
16						.409
17						.469
18						.531

$n_2 = 7$

U \ n_1	1	2	3	4	5	6	7
0	.125	.028	.008	.003	.001	.001	.000
1	.250	.056	.017	.006	.003	.001	.001
2	.375	.111	.033	.012	.005	.002	.001
3	.500	.167	.058	.021	.009	.004	.002
4	.625	.250	.092	.036	.015	.007	.003
5		.333	.133	.055	.024	.011	.006
6		.444	.192	.082	.037	.017	.009
7		.556	.258	.115	.053	.026	.013
8			.333	.158	.074	.037	.019
9			.417	.206	.101	.051	.027
10			.500	.264	.134	.069	.036
11			.583	.324	.172	.090	.049
12				.394	.216	.117	.064
13				.464	.265	.147	.082
14				.538	.319	.183	.104
15					.378	.223	.130
16					.438	.267	.159
17					.500	.314	.191
18					.562	.365	.228
19						.418	.267
20						.473	.310
21						.527	.355
22							.402
23							.451
24							.500
25							.549

$n_2 = 8$

U \ n_1	1	2	3	4	5	6	7	8	t	Normal
0	.111	.022	.006	.002	.001	.000	.000	.000	3.308	.001
1	.222	.044	.012	.004	.002	.001	.000	.000	3.203	.001
2	.333	.089	.024	.008	.003	.001	.001	.000	3.098	.001
3	.444	.133	.042	.014	.005	.002	.001	.001	2.993	.001
4	.556	.200	.067	.024	.009	.004	.002	.001	2.888	.002
5		.267	.097	.036	.015	.006	.003	.001	2.783	.003
6		.356	.139	.055	.023	.010	.005	.002	2.678	.004
7		.444	.188	.077	.033	.015	.007	.003	2.573	.005
8		.556	.248	.107	.047	.021	.010	.005	2.468	.007
9			.315	.141	.064	.030	.014	.007	2.363	.009
10			.387	.184	.085	.041	.020	.010	2.258	.012
11			.461	.230	.111	.054	.027	.014	2.153	.016
12			.539	.285	.142	.071	.036	.019	2.048	.020
13				.341	.177	.091	.047	.025	1.943	.026
14				.404	.217	.114	.060	.032	1.838	.033
15				.467	.262	.141	.076	.041	1.733	.041
16				.533	.311	.172	.095	.052	1.628	.052
17					.362	.207	.116	.065	1.523	.064
18					.416	.245	.140	.080	1.418	.078
19					.472	.286	.168	.097	1.313	.094
20					.528	.331	.198	.117	1.208	.113
21						.377	.232	.139	1.102	.135
22						.426	.268	.164	.998	.159
23						.475	.306	.191	.893	.185
24						.525	.347	.221	.788	.215
25							.389	.253	.683	.247
26							.433	.287	.578	.282
27							.478	.323	.473	.318
28							.522	.360	.368	.356
29								.399	.263	.396
30								.439	.158	.437
31								.480	.052	.481
32								.520		

Source: Reproduced from H. B. Mann and D. R. Whitney, "On a test of whether one of two random variables is stochastically larger than the other," *Ann. Math Statist*, 18 (1947): 52–54, with the permission of the publisher.

APPENDIX M

Mann-Whitney U Test Critical Values ($9 \leq n \leq 20$)

Critical Values of U for a One-Tailed Test at $\alpha = 0.001$ or for a Two-Tailed Test at $\alpha = 0.002$

n_1 \ n_2	9	10	11	12	13	14	15	16	17	18	19	20
1												
2												
3									0	0	0	0
4		0	0	0	1	1	1	2	2	3	3	3
5	1	1	2	2	3	3	4	5	5	6	7	7
6	2	3	4	4	5	6	7	8	9	10	11	12
7	3	5	6	7	8	9	10	11	13	14	15	16
8	5	6	8	9	11	12	14	15	17	18	20	21
9	7	8	10	12	14	15	17	19	21	23	25	26
10	8	10	12	14	17	19	21	23	25	27	29	32
11	10	12	15	17	20	22	24	27	29	32	34	37
12	12	14	17	20	23	25	28	31	34	37	40	42
13	14	17	20	23	26	29	32	35	38	42	45	48
14	15	19	22	25	29	32	36	39	43	46	50	54
15	17	21	24	28	32	36	40	43	47	51	55	59
16	19	23	27	31	35	39	43	48	52	56	60	65
17	21	25	29	34	38	43	47	52	57	61	66	70
18	23	27	32	37	42	46	51	56	61	66	71	76
19	25	29	34	40	45	50	55	60	66	71	77	82
20	26	32	37	42	48	54	59	65	70	76	82	88

Critical Values of U for a One-Tailed Test at $\alpha = 0.01$ or for a Two-Tailed Test at $\alpha = 0.02$

n_1 \ n_2	9	10	11	12	13	14	15	16	17	18	19	20
1												
2					0	0	0	0	0	0	1	1
3	1	1	1	2	2	2	3	3	4	4	4	5
4	3	3	4	5	5	6	7	7	8	9	9	10
5	5	6	7	8	9	10	11	12	13	14	15	16
6	7	8	9	11	12	13	15	16	18	19	20	22
7	9	11	12	14	16	17	19	21	23	24	26	28
8	11	13	15	17	20	22	24	26	28	30	32	34
9	14	16	18	21	23	26	28	31	33	36	38	40
10	16	19	22	24	27	30	33	36	38	41	44	47
11	18	22	25	28	31	34	37	41	44	47	50	53
12	21	24	28	31	35	38	42	46	49	53	56	60
13	23	27	31	35	39	43	47	51	55	59	63	67
14	26	30	34	38	43	47	51	56	60	65	69	73
15	28	33	37	42	47	51	56	61	66	70	75	80
16	31	36	41	46	51	56	61	66	71	76	82	87
17	33	38	44	49	55	60	66	71	77	82	88	93
18	36	41	47	53	59	65	70	76	82	88	94	100
19	38	44	50	56	63	69	75	82	88	94	101	107
20	40	47	53	60	67	73	80	87	93	100	107	114

Critical Values of U for a One-Tailed Test at $\alpha = 0.025$ or for a Two-Tailed Test at $\alpha = 0.05$

n_1 \ n_2	9	10	11	12	13	14	15	16	17	18	19	20
1												
2	0	0	0	1	1	1	1	1	2	2	2	2
3	2	3	3	4	4	5	5	6	6	7	7	8
4	4	5	6	7	8	9	10	11	11	12	13	13
5	7	8	9	11	12	13	14	15	17	18	19	20
6	10	11	13	14	16	17	19	21	22	24	25	27
7	12	14	16	18	20	22	24	26	28	30	32	34
8	15	17	19	22	24	26	29	31	34	36	38	41
9	17	20	23	26	28	31	34	37	39	42	45	48
10	20	23	26	29	33	36	39	42	45	48	52	55
11	23	26	30	33	37	40	44	47	51	55	58	62
12	26	29	33	37	41	45	49	53	57	61	65	69
13	28	33	37	41	45	50	54	59	63	67	72	76
14	31	36	40	45	50	55	59	64	67	74	78	83
15	34	39	44	49	54	59	64	70	75	80	85	90
16	37	42	47	53	59	64	70	75	81	86	92	98
17	39	45	51	57	63	67	75	81	87	93	99	105
18	42	48	55	61	67	74	80	86	93	99	106	112
19	45	52	58	65	72	78	85	92	99	106	113	119
20	48	55	62	69	76	83	90	98	105	112	119	127

Critical Values of U for a One-Tailed Test at $\alpha = 0.05$ or for a Two-Tailed Test at $\alpha = 0.10$

n_1 \ n_2	9	10	11	12	13	14	15	16	17	18	19	20
1											0	0
2	1	1	1	2	2	2	3	3	3	4	4	4
3	3	4	5	5	6	7	7	8	9	9	10	11
4	6	7	8	9	10	11	12	14	15	16	17	18
5	9	11	12	13	15	16	18	19	20	22	23	25
6	12	14	16	17	19	21	23	25	26	28	30	32
7	15	17	19	21	24	26	28	30	33	35	37	39
8	18	20	23	26	28	31	33	36	39	41	44	47
9	21	24	27	30	33	36	39	42	45	48	51	54
10	24	27	31	34	37	41	44	48	51	55	58	62
11	27	31	34	38	42	46	50	54	57	61	65	69
12	30	34	38	42	47	51	55	60	64	68	72	77
13	33	37	42	47	51	56	61	65	70	75	80	84
14	36	41	46	51	56	61	66	71	77	82	87	92
15	39	44	50	55	61	66	72	77	83	88	94	100
16	42	48	54	60	65	71	77	83	89	95	101	107
17	45	51	57	64	70	77	83	89	96	102	109	115
18	48	55	61	68	75	82	88	95	102	109	116	123
19	51	58	65	72	80	87	94	101	109	116	123	130
20	54	62	69	77	84	92	100	107	115	123	130	138

Source: Adapted and abridged from Tables 1, 3, 5, and 7 of D. Auble, "Extended tables for the Mann-Whitney statistic," *Bulletin of the Institute of Educational Research at Indiana University* 1, No. 2 (1953) with the permission of the publisher.

Critical Values of T in the Wilcoxon Matched-Pairs Signed-Ranks Test ($n \leq 25$)

n	LEVEL OF SIGNIFICANCE FOR ONE-TAILED TEST		
	0.025	0.01	0.005
	LEVEL OF SIGNIFICANCE FOR TWO-TAILED TEST		
	0.05	0.02	0.01
6	0	—	—
7	2	0	—
8	4	2	0
9	6	3	2
10	8	5	3
11	11	7	5
12	14	10	7
13	17	13	10
14	21	16	13
15	25	20	16
16	30	24	20
17	35	28	23
18	40	33	28
19	46	38	32
20	52	43	38
21	59	49	43
22	66	56	49
23	73	62	55
24	81	69	61
25	89	77	68

Source: Adapted from Table 1 of F. Wilcoxon, *Some Rapid Approximate Statistical Procedures* (New York: American Cyanamid Company, 1949), 13, with the permission of the publisher.

Critical Values d_L and d_U of the Durbin-Watson Statistic D (Critical Values Are One-Sided)

$\alpha = .05$

n	P = 1 d_L	d_U	P = 2 d_L	d_U	P = 3 d_L	d_U	P = 4 d_L	d_U	P = 5 d_L	d_U
15	1.08	1.36	.95	1.54	.82	1.75	.69	1.97	.56	2.21
16	1.10	1.37	.98	1.54	.86	1.73	.74	1.93	.62	2.15
17	1.13	1.38	1.02	1.54	.90	1.71	.78	1.90	.67	2.10
18	1.16	1.39	1.05	1.53	.93	1.69	.82	1.87	.71	2.06
19	1.18	1.40	1.08	1.53	.97	1.68	.86	1.85	.75	2.02
20	1.20	1.41	1.10	1.54	1.00	1.68	.90	1.83	.79	1.99
21	1.22	1.42	1.13	1.54	1.03	1.67	.93	1.81	.83	1.96
22	1.24	1.43	1.15	1.54	1.05	1.66	.96	1.80	.86	1.94
23	1.26	1.44	1.17	1.54	1.08	1.66	.99	1.79	.90	1.92
24	1.27	1.45	1.19	1.55	1.10	1.66	1.01	1.78	.93	1.90
25	1.29	1.45	1.21	1.55	1.12	1.66	1.04	1.77	.95	1.89
26	1.30	1.46	1.22	1.55	1.14	1.65	1.06	1.76	.98	1.88
27	1.32	1.47	1.24	1.56	1.16	1.65	1.08	1.76	1.01	1.86
28	1.33	1.48	1.26	1.56	1.18	1.65	1.10	1.75	1.03	1.85
29	1.34	1.48	1.27	1.56	1.20	1.65	1.12	1.74	1.05	1.84
30	1.35	1.49	1.28	1.57	1.21	1.65	1.14	1.74	1.07	1.83
31	1.36	1.50	1.30	1.57	1.23	1.65	1.16	1.74	1.09	1.83
32	1.37	1.50	1.31	1.57	1.24	1.65	1.18	1.73	1.11	1.82
33	1.38	1.51	1.32	1.58	1.26	1.65	1.19	1.73	1.13	1.81
34	1.39	1.51	1.33	1.58	1.27	1.65	1.21	1.73	1.15	1.81
35	1.40	1.52	1.34	1.58	1.28	1.65	1.22	1.73	1.16	1.80
36	1.41	1.52	1.35	1.59	1.29	1.65	1.24	1.73	1.18	1.80
37	1.42	1.53	1.36	1.59	1.31	1.66	1.25	1.72	1.19	1.80
38	1.43	1.54	1.37	1.59	1.32	1.66	1.26	1.72	1.21	1.79
39	1.43	1.54	1.38	1.60	1.33	1.66	1.27	1.72	1.22	1.79
40	1.44	1.54	1.39	1.60	1.34	1.66	1.29	1.72	1.23	1.79
45	1.48	1.57	1.43	1.62	1.38	1.67	1.34	1.72	1.29	1.78
50	1.50	1.59	1.46	1.63	1.42	1.67	1.38	1.72	1.34	1.77
55	1.53	1.60	1.49	1.64	1.45	1.68	1.41	1.72	1.38	1.77
60	1.55	1.62	1.51	1.65	1.48	1.69	1.44	1.73	1.41	1.77
65	1.57	1.63	1.54	1.66	1.50	1.70	1.47	1.73	1.44	1.77
70	1.58	1.64	1.55	1.67	1.52	1.70	1.49	1.74	1.46	1.77
75	1.60	1.65	1.57	1.68	1.54	1.71	1.51	1.74	1.49	1.77
80	1.61	1.66	1.59	1.69	1.56	1.72	1.53	1.74	1.51	1.77
85	1.62	1.67	1.60	1.70	1.57	1.72	1.55	1.75	1.52	1.77
90	1.63	1.68	1.61	1.70	1.59	1.73	1.57	1.75	1.54	1.78
95	1.64	1.69	1.62	1.71	1.60	1.73	1.58	1.75	1.56	1.78
100	1.65	1.69	1.63	1.72	1.61	1.74	1.59	1.76	1.57	1.78

(continued)

n = number of observations; P = number of independent variables.

Source: This table is reproduced from *Biometrika*, 41 (1951): 173 and 175, with the permission of the *Biometrika* Trustees.

$\alpha = .01$

n	P = 1 d_L	d_U	P = 2 d_L	d_U	P = 3 d_L	d_U	P = 4 d_L	d_U	P = 5 d_L	d_U
15	.81	1.07	.70	1.25	.59	1.46	.49	1.70	.39	1.96
16	.84	1.09	.74	1.25	.63	1.44	.53	1.66	.44	1.90
17	.87	1.10	.77	1.25	.67	1.43	.57	1.63	.48	1.85
18	.90	1.12	.80	1.26	.71	1.42	.61	1.60	.52	1.80
19	.93	1.13	.83	1.26	.74	1.41	.65	1.58	.56	1.77
20	.95	1.15	.86	1.27	.77	1.41	.68	1.57	.60	1.74
21	.97	1.16	.89	1.27	.80	1.41	.72	1.55	.63	1.71
22	1.00	1.17	.91	1.28	.83	1.40	.75	1.54	.66	1.69
23	1.02	1.19	.94	1.29	.86	1.40	.77	1.53	.70	1.67
24	1.04	1.20	.96	1.30	.88	1.41	.80	1.53	.72	1.66
25	1.05	1.21	.98	1.30	.90	1.41	.83	1.52	.75	1.65
26	1.07	1.22	1.00	1.31	.93	1.41	.85	1.52	.78	1.64
27	1.09	1.23	1.02	1.32	.95	1.41	.88	1.51	.81	1.63
28	1.10	1.24	1.04	1.32	.97	1.41	.90	1.51	.83	1.62
29	1.12	1.25	1.05	1.33	.99	1.42	.92	1.51	.85	1.61
30	1.13	1.26	1.07	1.34	1.01	1.42	.94	1.51	.88	1.61
31	1.15	1.27	1.08	1.34	1.02	1.42	.96	1.51	.90	1.60
32	1.16	1.28	1.10	1.35	1.04	1.43	.98	1.51	.92	1.60
33	1.17	1.29	1.11	1.36	1.05	1.43	1.00	1.51	.94	1.59
34	1.18	1.30	1.13	1.36	1.07	1.43	1.01	1.51	.95	1.59
35	1.19	1.31	1.14	1.37	1.08	1.44	1.03	1.51	.97	1.59
36	1.21	1.32	1.15	1.38	1.10	1.44	1.04	1.51	.99	1.59
37	1.22	1.32	1.16	1.38	1.11	1.45	1.06	1.51	1.00	1.59
38	1.23	1.33	1.18	1.39	1.12	1.45	1.07	1.52	1.02	1.58
39	1.24	1.34	1.19	1.39	1.14	1.45	1.09	1.52	1.03	1.58
40	1.25	1.34	1.20	1.40	1.15	1.46	1.10	1.52	1.05	1.58
45	1.29	1.38	1.24	1.42	1.20	1.48	1.16	1.53	1.11	1.58
50	1.32	1.40	1.28	1.45	1.24	1.49	1.20	1.54	1.16	1.59
55	1.36	1.43	1.32	1.47	1.28	1.51	1.25	1.55	1.21	1.59
60	1.38	1.45	1.35	1.48	1.32	1.52	1.28	1.56	1.25	1.60
65	1.41	1.47	1.38	1.50	1.35	1.53	1.31	1.57	1.28	1.61
70	1.43	1.49	1.40	1.52	1.37	1.55	1.34	1.58	1.31	1.61
75	1.45	1.50	1.42	1.53	1.39	1.56	1.37	1.59	1.34	1.62
80	1.47	1.52	1.44	1.54	1.42	1.57	1.39	1.60	1.36	1.62
85	1.48	1.53	1.46	1.55	1.43	1.58	1.41	1.60	1.39	1.63
90	1.50	1.54	1.47	1.56	1.45	1.59	1.43	1.61	1.41	1.64
95	1.51	1.55	1.49	1.57	1.47	1.60	1.45	1.62	1.42	1.64
100	1.52	1.56	1.50	1.58	1.48	1.60	1.46	1.63	1.44	1.65

n = number of observations; P = number of independent variables.

Source: This table is reproduced from *Biometrika*, 41 (1951): 173 and 175, with the permission of the *Biometrika* Trustees.

Lower and Upper Critical Values W of Wilcoxon Signed-Ranks Test

n	One-Tailed: $\alpha = .05$ Two-Tailed: $\alpha = .10$	$\alpha = .025$ $\alpha = .05$	$\alpha = .01$ $\alpha = .02$	$\alpha = .005$ $\alpha = .01$
	(Lower, Upper)			
5	0,15	—,—	—,—	—,—
6	2,19	0,21	—,—	—,—
7	3,25	2,26	0.28	—,—
8	5,31	3,33	1,35	0,36
9	8,37	5,40	3,42	1,44
10	10,45	8,47	5,50	3,52
11	13,53	10,56	7,59	5,61
12	17,61	13,65	10,68	7,71
13	21,70	17,74	12,79	10,81
14	25,80	21,84	16,89	13,92
15	30,90	25,95	19,101	16,104
16	35,101	29,107	23,113	19,117
17	41,112	34,119	27,126	23,130
18	47,124	40,131	32,139	27,144
19	53,137	46,144	37,153	32,158
20	60,150	52,158	43,167	37,173

Source: Adapted from Table 2 of F. Wilcoxon and R. A. Wilcox, *Some Rapid Approximate Statistical Procedures* (Pearl River, NY: Lederle Laboratories, 1964), with permission of the American Cyanamid Company.

APPENDIX Q

Control Chart Factors

Number of Observations in Sample	d_2	d_3	D_3	D_4	A_2
2	1.128	0.853	0	3.267	1.880
3	1.693	0.888	0	2.575	1.023
4	2.059	0.880	0	2.282	0.729
5	2.326	0.864	0	2.114	0.577
6	2.534	0.848	0	2.004	0.483
7	2.704	0.833	0.076	1.924	0.419
8	2.847	0.820	0.136	1.864	0.373
9	2.970	0.808	0.184	1.816	0.337
10	3.078	0.797	0.223	1.777	0.308
11	3.173	0.787	0.256	1.744	0.285
12	3.258	0.778	0.283	1.717	0.266
13	3.336	0.770	0.307	1.693	0.249
14	3.407	0.763	0.328	1.672	0.235
15	3.472	0.756	0.347	1.653	0.223
16	3.532	0.750	0.363	1.637	0.212
17	3.588	0.744	0.378	1.622	0.203
18	3.640	0.739	0.391	1.609	0.194
19	3.689	0.733	0.404	1.596	0.187
20	3.735	0.729	0.415	1.585	0.180
21	3.778	0.724	0.425	1.575	0.173
22	3.819	0.720	0.435	1.565	0.167
23	3.858	0.716	0.443	1.557	0.162
24	3.895	0.712	0.452	1.548	0.157
25	3.931	0.708	0.459	1.541	0.153

Source: Reprinted from ASTM-STP 15D by kind permission of the American Society for Testing and Materials.

APPENDIX R

PART I:

Additional Content for Chapter 11, ANOVA Cases and DOE Materials

Agency for New Americans

After graduating with a degree in accounting, Diane Walker began a satisfying career with the federal government, but like many women, she decided to stay at home after she and her husband started a family. Now that their youngest was in high school she needed something more to do than manage the household. As a transition back to the workplace, Diane took a volunteer position with the Agency for New Americans near her home in Raleigh, North Carolina.

The Agency for New Americans purpose is to help new immigrants to this country become comfortable with the basic activities necessary to function in American society. Counselors like Diane provide advice and assistance in a variety of areas. One of these is shopping for food and other necessities. Supermarkets and large chain discount stores are unfamiliar entities for many newcomers to the United States. Most new families are on a limited budget and need to make wise choices in where to shop to make the most of their resources.

Reed Farnum, Diane's supervisor, has asked her to conduct a study of three national discount chains (k-Mart, Shopko, and Wal-Mart) with stores in the Raleigh area to determine whether one of them has lower average prices for products that a new family with children might be purchasing. To complete the assignment, Diane and a student intern for the Agency randomly selected 27 products that are available at all three stores. Last Tuesday, the intern went to each store to record the prices for the 27 products. These data are provided in the data file, **New Americans.**

Unfortunately, neither Diane nor the intern is sure how to use the data to most effectively compare the stores. Diane thought maybe the best thing to do was to just count how many times each store had the lowest price on an item and recommend the store with the highest number of low prices. Her intern thought maybe they could apply a statistical tool called analysis of variance but was unsure about how to proceed. Diane did know that three days from now she would need to have a complete report ready for Reed Farnum. She drafted the following outline for the report:

Statement of Purpose
Data Collection Methods
Descriptive Analysis of the Data
Inferential Analysis Comparing the Three Stores
Summary and Conclusions

She needs your help in preparing the report and any advice you might have for her to improve the study should she do a similar one again in the future.

McLaughlin Salmon Works

In 1999, John McLaughlin purchased property in the Hagerman Valley in southern Idaho and started a commercial fish farm to supply "Idaho Trout" to markets throughout the United States. It was really John's father who was responsible for John going into this line of business. A number of years ago, John's father correctly predicted that a combination of a declining population of wild, ocean-going salmon and an increase in demand for fish in general would create a growing market for salmon grown in "fish farms." Over recent years, an increasing percentage of fish such as salmon, trout and catfish have been supplied by commercial fish farming operations rather than being caught in the ocean. At first operating a fish farm consisted of finding an appropriate location, installing the pens, putting in smelt and feeding the fish until they grew to the appropriate size. However, as the number of competitors has increased, John has been required to take a more scientific approach to raising fish.

Over the past year John has been studying the relationship between food intake and weight gain. Since fish food is a major cost of his operation, the higher the weight gain for a given amount of food the more cost effective John's operation will be. The fish food consists of pellets that contain various food ingredients. Recently John has been trying to determine the relationships among four food component mixes and three size progressions for the food pellets.

In conducting the study, John started with 60 small trout that all weighed 0.300 pounds. He constructed twelve small pens. Five fish were placed in each pen. He then carefully controlled the feeding by giving fish in each pen a different combination of pellet mix and pellet size progression. After four weeks, John weighed each fish. The resulting data are provided are shown in Figure A and are located in the file titled **McLaughlin Salmon Works.**

John is interested in not only whether one component mix, or one pellet size progression, leads to higher mean weight gain, but he would also like to find one combination of mix and size progression that proved to be superior.

FIGURE A
Trout Weights

	Size Progression 1	Size Progression 2	Size Progression 3
Mix A	0.713	0.549	0.730
	0.639	0.631	0.639
	0.697	0.574	0.721
	0.680	0.516	0.508
	0.754	0.475	0.754
Mix B	0.451	0.492	0.574
	0.549	0.451	0.549
	0.492	0.393	0.672
	0.500	0.426	0.615
	0.525	0.475	0.631
Mix C	0.728	0.738	0.882
	0.803	0.713	0.902
	0.730	0.763	0.873
	0.745	0.754	0.861
	0.761	0.779	0.868
Mix D	0.549	0.443	0.639
	0.713	0.549	0.664
	0.574	0.459	0.648
	0.590	0.566	0.656
	0.533	0.492	0.631

NW Pulp & Paper

As she approached her parking spot in the company parking garage, Cassie Coughlin was busy thinking about the fact that she had less than a week to finish a presentation to the CEO of NW Pulp & Paper. Cassie had inherited a project started by her predecessor as head of the company's new product development section, and by the nature of the industry—dealing with wood products—projects tended to have long lifetimes. Her predecessor, Mark Milne, had successfully predicted the consequences of a series of events that had now taken place:

1. The western United States, where NW Pulp & Paper has its operations, was running short of water as a result of a combination of demand from population growth and increased irrigation demands. The situation has been made worse by several years of drought. As a result, many farming operations are in financial trouble.

2. The amount of timber harvesting allowed from national forests continued to be limited by Federal Government policies. Thus, NW Pulp & Paper is having to pay higher prices for the wood products it needs for paper production.

Based on these factors, eight years ago Mark convinced the company to purchase a 2,000-acre farm in the state of Washington for the purpose of raising fast-growing tree products that the company could use to augment its wood supply. This farm has a soil profile that contains sections with four different types of soil commonly found in the west. The farm also has senior water rights from the Columbia River. Water rights in the west are granted by the state. Property owners with senior rights are those that will continue to be able to get irrigation water after those with junior rights are cut off. Mark's contention at the time was it might be economically feasible for the company to purchase more farms so the company could become self-sufficient in its supply of raw material for making paper. However, while he was able to convince the company to make this first land purchase, senior managers wanted more information about the tree farm idea before they were willing to commit to more investment. In particular, they wanted a study done to determine how effectively trees could be grown in this region.

A year after the land purchase, Mark initiated an experimental study at the farm in which he marked off twelve 24-foot-by-24-foot plots. Three of the plots were in an area of the farm with one particular soil type, three other plots were on a second soil type and so forth. He then obtained saplings from three types of genetically modified poplar trees (these are generally fast-growing trees that are good for generating paper pulp) and planted four of each tree type so that each tree type was planted on each soil type plot. His plan was to measure the tree growth at the end of seven years.

When Mark retired three months ago just short of the seven-year growing period for the trees, Cassie found herself in charge of the project, and two weeks ago, she visited the experiment site to measure the trees. She measured the girth of each tree at a distance of three feet above the ground. The data are shown in Figure B and can be found in the file **NW Pulp Paper.**

The problem is that now Cassie must present the experimental data to the CEO and be prepared to show whether one type of poplar species is generally superior. She also needs to show whether a particular soil type is better than the others. Finally, she needs to determine whether there is some unique combination of soil type and tree type that should be recommended. From past experience, Cassie knows that CEO likes to have presentations be visual and statistically accurate.

FIGURE A
Tree Growth Results

	Tree Type 1	Tree Type 2	Tree Type 3
Soil Type 1	57	37	59
	48	47	47
	62	28	62
	53	41	55
Soil Type 2	25	30	40
	37	25	37
	30	28	52
	31	27	44
Soil Type 3	71	60	74
	68	57	80
	59	68	68
	63	55	76
Soil Type 4	37	24	48
	57	37	51
	40	26	49
	45	31	46

Quinn Restoration, Inc.

Last week John Quinn sat back in the chair on his deck and nodded to his wife, Kate. They had just finished a conversation that would likely influence the direction their lives took for the next several years or longer.

John retired a little less than a year ago after 25 years in the Lake Oswego Police Department. He had steadily moved up the ranks and retired as a Captain. While his career had, in his mind, gone very well, he had spending many long hours on the job with very little time left to do other things. Initially upon retiring John had reveled in the ability to spend time doing things he was never able to do while working: complete repairs around the house, do some traveling with his wife, spend time with the children still at home and visit those who had moved out. He was even able to knock 5 strokes off his golf handicap. However, he had become increasingly restless and both he and Kate agreed he needed something to do.

John had, over the years, bought, restored and sold a series of older Corvettes. While this had been only a hobby, it also had been a profitable one. The discussion John and Kate just concluded had involved expanding this hobby not into a full-time job, but into a part-time business. John would handle the actual restoration, which he enjoyed, and Kate would cover the paperwork, ordering parts, keeping track of expenses, and billing clients, which John did not like. The last part of their conversation involved ordering parts.

In the past John had ordered parts for old Corvettes from one of three possible sources: Ecklers, Mid America or Corvette Central. He would do a cost comparison among the three and go with the lowest-priced part. But Kate said she didn't want to call all three any time John needed a part. Instead she thought it best to set up an account with one of the three and be able to order parts over the Internet. However, she was also aware that they needed to be cost conscious. If they went with Kate's plan, they agreed, the company selected should be the company that provides the lowest average costs.

John agreed to develop a randomly selected list of thirty parts that all three suppliers routinely carry. He then used the Internet sites for the three suppliers to determine the current asking price for each part. Figure C shows the resulting cost data, and the data are also in the file called **Quinn Restoration.** After collecting the data, John and Kate now need some help in determining whether one particular supplier has lower average prices than the others.

FIGURE C
Corvette Part Costs

Part Name	Mid America	Ecklers	Corvette Central
Airfilter	9.95	10.95	11.95
Alternator	189.95	289.95	399.95
Battery	78.95	80.95	129.95
Carburator	299.95	249.95	269.00
Coil	28.95	26.95	23.85
Distributor	489.95	465.95	499.95
Exhaust	269.00	279.95	316.00
Front Brakes	29.90	29.95	24.95
Gas Tank	229.00	342.95	199.00
Head light	11.95	11.95	8.95
Headers	170.95	168.95	141.95
Hood Emblem	89.95	69.95	99.95
Intake Manifold	204.95	204.95	475.00
Mufflers	199.00	187.95	174.00
Oil Filter	9.95	9.95	10.95
Oil Pump	34.95	34.95	39.00
Plug Wires	26.95	26.95	49.95
Racing Tires	229.00	184.95	168.00
Radiator	259.00	259.95	279.00
Rear Brakes	48.95	52.95	46.95
Rims	479.95	419.95	280.00
Shocks (ea.)	29.95	28.95	39.95
Spark Plugs (ea.)	3.44	2.95	4.50
Starter	119.00	123.95	189.65
Tachometer Cable	13.95	20.95	15.95
Thermostat	10.95	10.50	16.45
Transmittion	1,209.95	1,460.95	890.95
Valve Covers	89.95	85.95	189.00
Water Pump	169.00	184.95	199.95
Steering Box	300.00	220.00	309.00

The Basics of Design of Experiments

This section seeks to introduce you to the basic concepts of an important statistical area known as design of experiments (DOE). You were introduced to the concept of experiments in Chapter 1 of the text as one of the means by which data are obtained in business situations. The formulation of how the experimental process is to be carried out has come to be called the **experimental design.**

An experimental design involves specific, controlled changes in inputs, called **factors,** to some activity or process, with the objective of gaining knowledge about the effect of these changes on an output variable, called the **response variable.** For example, a wood products company with its own tree plantations might control such factors as irrigation, fertilizer, and soil quality (the factors) at various specified levels and then observe the growth rate of the trees (the response) that results.

In general, in an experiment, a process is assigned inputs (factors), which might involve defined levels of material, people, equipment, policies, methods, or the environment. The process blends these inputs and produces outputs related to such things as service levels or product characteristics. Originally, experiments were conducted using "one-factor-at-a-time" tests, but this approach is very inefficient and not practical in today's business climate. The concept of design of experiments (DOE) has replaced the "trial and error" approach and is considered the best way to identify the key input factors that impact the response variable of interest. DOE is more efficient in helping managers to define the relationship between the inputs and the response variable and to be able to determine the "optimal" settings for the input factors to achieve the highest quality, lowest variability, minimum cost and so forth, depending on the application.

This text has already introduced you to several experimental designs. Table DOE-1 shows some the most basic experimental designs and where in the text these designs are discussed.

TABLE DOE-1
Experimental Design Text Materials

Experimental Design	Text Chapter
Single Factor	Chapter 9 (Two Sample Tests for Means or Proportions)
	Chapter 11 (One-Way ANOVA)
Two Factor	Chapter 11 (Multiple Sample ANOVA Tests With and Without Replications)

Single Factor Experiments

In Chapter 9, you learned about hypothesis tests for testing whether two populations have the same means. These tests (experiments) could be designed such that the random samples from the two populations are independent and a *two-sample t-test* could be used to analyze whether there is a statistical difference between the sample means for a single factor from the two populations. For instance, if a maker of ice cream is interested in determining whether the mean quality rating for its ice cream is affected by the shape of the container (box versus cylinder), the company might randomly select two samples of people and have one group taste test ice cream from a box container. The second sample would taste test ice cream from the cylinder container. Each person would assign a rating on scale of 1-100. The same ice cream is used in each container type. The samples are independent since the scores given by the people in one group would not be affected by those given by people in the other group.

Chapter 9 also introduced an experimental design in which two independent samples from two populations can be used to test whether the populations have equal proportions of items with a particular attribute. A number of years ago, the soft-drink company Pepsi-Cola conducted what it called the Pepsi Taste Challenge. A random sample of people who professed to be die-hard Coke drinkers was blindfolded and given a taste of both Coke and Pepsi. They had to pick their favorite from the two. The same thing was done for confirmed Pepsi drinkers. At issue was whether the proportion of Coke drinkers who would select Coke as their favorite was the same as the proportion of Pepsi drinkers who would identify Pepsi as their favorite. A *two sample test for proportions* is used to analyze the sample data. By the way, Pepsi was the clear winner in these taste tests but has not overtaken Coke in international sales.

Chapter 11 introduced a statistical procedure referred to as *one-way analysis of variance,* which is used to test whether three or more populations have equal means. This method is an extension of the two-sample t-test introduced in Chapter 9 and discussed earlier in the context of the ice cream example. One-way ANOVA would be the appropriate tool for an advertising agency's experimental design used to determine whether the mean television viewing time per week is the same for individuals in the following five age categories:

"under 16"   "16-19"   "20-29"   "30-49"   "50 and over"

Not only did the material in Chapter 10 provide a means for testing whether the means are different, but if the agency did conclude that differences existed, the Tukey method for multiple comparisons was introduced, which would help the agency determine which age groups are responsible for the differences in mean TV viewing time.

Two Factor Designs

In reviewing the ice cream example mentioned earlier, suppose the company is concerned that not all individuals use the same criteria for rating ice cream quality. Some people assign lower scores than others in general. To avoid the possibility that by chance a large share of easy raters is assigned to the cylinder container, thus giving that container an unfair advantage, the company might alter the experimental design. Instead of two independent samples, the company would select one random sample of people and have each person rate ice cream from both containers. The sample ratings are now considered paired samples, and a *paired sample t-test* introduced in Chapter 9 would be used to determine whether mean ratings for the two container types are equal. Thus, there are two factors: the container type (the primary factor), and the individuals doing the rating (a controlling factor). The results consistently show that even though it's the same ice cream, people rate the ice cream in the cylinder carton as superior in quality.

Chapter 11 expanded the concept of two factor experimental designs by introducing the following designs: *Randomized Complete Block Design* and *Two-factor ANOVA with Replications*. The randomized complete block design is an extension of the paired sample t-test by allowing for tests involving more than two levels of the primary factor. For instance, the ice cream maker may be interested in modifying its traditional recipe for its chocolate ripple flavor. In addition to the traditional recipe, it has narrowed the possible alternatives down to four other blends. In a randomized block design, a random sample of taste testers would be given a chance to taste ice cream made with each recipe and provide a quality ration on a scale between 0-100. This design controls for potential rating scale differences between the people selected in the study by having each person taste each recipe.

In the randomized block design, there is only one measurement at each level for each factor. That is, each person provides only one rating for each of the five ice cream recipes. However, in some instances, it may be important to determine whether the two factors involved *interact*. For instance, a plywood manufacturer is interested in determining whether the species of wood and the type of glue used in making the plywood have an influence on the strength of the plywood. However, it is also concerned that certain combinations of glue and wood species might work best together. This is called the *interactive effect* between the two factors (glues and wood). In order to assess whether interaction is present, you must have a minimum of two measurements (called *replications*) for each combination of wood and glue. The Two-Factor ANOVA Design with Replications method that was introduced in Chapter 11 is capable of providing managers with the information necessary to reach conclusions about each factor individually and about whether interaction between the two factors is present.

Full Factorial Designs

When an experiment involves two or more factors, a design that requires measurements to be obtained for all factor combinations is called a *Full Factorial Design*. If your experiment has only a few factors and only a few levels of each factor, a full factorial design may be feasible. For instance, in the plywood example, we had two factors (glue and wood species). Suppose the experiment involves 4 species of wood and 3 types of glue. In this situation, there are $3 \times 4 = 12$ experimental conditions. Thus a minimum of 12 experiments will need to be performed. If the interaction between the factors is a concern, then the total number of experimental tests will be the 12 times the number of replications (assuming an equal number of replications for each combination of wood and glue. Suppose three replications are used. The total number of experimental runs is $3 \times 12 = 36$. This is illustrated in Figure DOE-2.

FIGURE DOE-2
Full Factorial Design With Replications

	Wood 1	Wood 2	Wood 3	Wood 4
Glue 1	x111	x121	x131	x141
	x112	x122	x132	x142
	x113	x123	x133	x144
Glue 2	x211	x221	x231	x241
	x212	x222	x232	x242
	x213	x223	x233	x244
Glue 3	x311	x321	x331	x341
	x312	x322	x332	x342
	x313	x323	x333	x344

where: Xijk = ith glue, jth wood, and kth replication

However, for experiments involving more factors or more levels, the number of combinations gets very large very quickly. For instance, suppose a manufacturer of industrial cable is planning an experiment to analyze cable strength. Bonding temperature, pressure and ten other factors need to be controlled. Assuming only two levels of each factor, ignoring replications, a full factorial design will involve $2^{12} = 4,096$ experimental conditions. This may take too much time and require too many resources to be feasible.

In situations where a full factorial design is not feasible, a solution may exist that is referred to as *Fractional Factorial Designs*. While a discussion of fractional factorial designs is beyond the scope of this course, you should know that when a fractional design is used the number of experimental runs can be reduced substantially but you will be required to assume away some of the possible interaction effects between factors.

Other designs such as *Foldover Designs, Plackett-Burman Designs, Latin Squares for 3 Level Designs* and many others are more efficient than a full factorial design in certain situations. Should you have the opportunity to take a full course in DOE, you will be introduced to these designs and many more. One particular class of experimental designs, known as *Taquchi Designs,* is somewhat controversial among statisticians since these designs stress only a few of the basic designs most frequently employed in industry. Further, Taguchi provides tables for these designs and a "cookbook" form of analysis. Even with the criticism surrounding the Taguchi designs, their use seems to be expanding, probably due to their simplicity and because companies continue to provide information about successful applications.

PART II:
Additional Content for Chapters 13-14, Regression Cases

A&A Industrial Products

Alex Court, the cost accountant for A & A Industrial Products, was puzzled by the repair cost analysis report he had just reviewed. This was the third consecutive report where unscheduled plant repair costs were out of line with the repair cost budget allocated to each plant. A & A budgets for both scheduled maintenance and unscheduled repair costs for its plants' equipment, mostly large industrial machines. Budgets for scheduled maintenance activities are easy to estimate and are based on the equipment manufacturer's recommendations. The unscheduled repair costs, however, are harder to determine. Historically, A & A Industrial Products has estimated unscheduled maintenance using a formula based on the average number of hours of operation between major equipment failures at a plant. Specifically, plants were given a budget of $65.00 per hour of operation between major failures. Alex had arrived at this amount by dividing aggregate historical repair costs by the total number of hours between failures. Then plant averages would be used to estimate unscheduled repair cost. For example, if a plant averaged 450 hours of run time before a major repair occurred, the plant would be allocated a repair budget of 450 * $65 = $29,250 per repair. If the plant was expected to be in operation 3,150 hours per year the company would anticipate 7 unscheduled repairs (3,150/450) annually, and budget $204,750 for annual unscheduled repair costs.

Alex was becoming more and more convinced that this approach was not working. Not only was upper management upset about the variance between predicted and actual costs of repair, plant managers believed that the model did not account for potential differences among the company's three plants when allocating dollars for unscheduled repairs. At the weekly management meeting Alex was informed that he needed to analyze his cost projections further and produce a report that provided a more reliable method for allocating repair costs. Upon leaving the meeting, Alex had his assistant randomly pull 64 unscheduled repair reports. The data are in the file **A & A Costs.xls.** The management team is anxiously waiting for Alex's analysis.

Glaser Machine Works

Glaser Machine Works had experienced a significant change in its business operations over the past 50 years. Glaser started business as a machine shop that produced specialty tools and products for the timber and lumber industry. This was a logical fit given its location in the southern part of the United States. However, over the years Glaser looked to expand its offerings beyond the lumber and timber industry. Initially, its small size coupled with its rural location made it difficult for it to be noticed by large companies that could use its products. All of that began to change as Glaser developed the ability not only to fabricate parts and tools but to also assemble products for customers who needed special components in large quantities. Glaser's business really took off when first foreign, and then domestic, automakers began to build automobile plants in the southern United States. Glaser was able to provide quality parts quickly for firms that expected high quality and responsive delivery. Many of Glaser's customers operated with little inventory and required that suppliers be able to provide shipments with short lead times.

As part of its relationship with the automobile industry, Glaser was expected to buy into the lean manufacturing and quality improvement initiatives of its customers. Glaser had always prided itself on its quality, but as the number and variety of its products increased, along with ever higher expectations by its customers, Glaser knew that it would have to respond by ensuring that its quality and operations were continually improving. Of recent concern to Glaser was the performance of its manufacturing line 107B. This line produced a component part for a Japanese automobile company. The Japanese firm had initially been pleased with Glaser's performance, but lately it appeared that the number of defects was at an unacceptable level. Managers of the 107B line knew that the line and its workers had been asked to ramp up production to meet increased demand and that some workers were concerned with the amount of overtime that was being required. There was also concern about the second shift now being run at 107B. Glaser had initially run only one shift at the 107B line but when demand for its product became so high that there was not sufficient capacity with one shift, additional workers were hired to operate a night shift.

Management was wondering if perhaps the new shift had been stretched beyond its capabilities. Glaser plant management asked Kristi Johnson, the assistant production supervisor for line 107B, to conduct an analysis of product defects for the line. Kristi randomly selected several days of output and counted the number of defective parts produced on the 107B line. This information, along with other data collected by Kristi, is contained in the file **Glaser Machine Works.xls.** Kristi promised to have a full report to the management team by the end of the month.

Hawlins Manufacturing

Ross Hawlins had done it all at Hawlins Manufacturing, a company founded by his grandfather 63 years ago. Among his many duties, Ross oversaw all the plant's operations, a task that had grown in responsibility given the company's rapid growth over the past three decades. When Ross's grandfather founded the company there were only two manufacturing sites. Expansion and acquisition of competitors over the years had caused that number to grow to over 50 manufacturing plants in 18 states.

Hawlins had a simple process that produced only two products, but the demand for these products was strong and Hawlins had spent millions of dollars upgrading its facilities over the past decade. Consequently most of the company's equipment was less than 10 years old on average. Hawlins' two products were produced for local markets as shipping costs made it prohibitive to ship the product for long distances. Product demand was sufficiently strong to support two manufacturing shifts (day and night) at every plant, and every plant had the capability to produce both products sold by Hawlins. Recently, the management team at Hawlins noticed that there were differences in output levels across the various plants. They were uncertain what, if anything, might explain these differences. Clearly, if some plants were more productive than others there might be some meaningful insights that could be standardized across plants to boost overall productivity.

Because his duties required him to be involved in a variety of activities, Ross Hawlins has asked Lisa Chandler, an industrial engineer at the company's headquarters, to conduct a study of the plant's productivity. Lisa has randomly sampled 159 weeks of output from various plants together with the number of plant employees working that week, the plants' average age in years, the product mix produced that week (either product A or B), and whether the output was from the day or night shift. The sampled data are contained in the file **Hawlins Manufacturing.xls.** The Hawlins management team is expecting a written report and a presentation by Lisa when they meet again next Tuesday.

Sapphire Coffee

Jennie Garcia could not believe that her career had moved so far so fast. When she left graduate school with a master's degree in anthropology she intended to work at a local coffee shop until something else came along that was more related to her academic background. But after a few months she came to enjoy the business and in a little over a year she was promoted to store manager. When the company for which she worked continued to grow, Jennie was given oversight over a few stores.

Now, eight years after she started as a barista, Jennie was in charge of operations and planning for the company's southern region. As a part of her responsibilities, Jennie tracks store revenues and forecasts coffee demand. Historically, Sapphire Coffee would base its demand forecast on the number of stores, believing that each store sold approximately the same amount of coffee. This approach seemed to work well when the company had shops of similar size and layout, but as the company grew, stores became more varied. Now, some stores had drive thru windows, a feature that top management added to some stores believing that it would increase coffee sales for customers who wanted a cup of coffee on their way to work but who were too rushed to park and enter the store to place an order.

Jennie noticed that weekly sales seemed to be more variable across stores in her region and was wondering what, if anything, might explain the differences. The company's financial vice president had also noticed the increased differences in sales across stores and was wondering what might be happening. In an e-mail to Jennie he stated that weekly store sales are expected to average $5.00 per square foot. Thus, a 1,000-square-foot store would have average weekly sales of $5,000. He asked that Jennie analyze the stores in her region to see if this rule of thumb was a reliable measure of a store's performance.

Jennie had been in the business long enough to know that a store's size, while an important factor, was not the only thing that might influence sales. She had never been convinced of the efficacy of the drive thru window, believing that it detracted from the coffee house experience that so many of Sapphire Coffee customers had come to expect. The V.P. of finance was expecting the analysis to be completed by the weekend. Jennie decided to randomly select weekly sales records for 53 stores, along with each store's size, whether it was located close to a college, and if it had a drive thru window or not. The data are in the file **Sapphire Coffee.xls.** A full analysis would need to be sent to the corporate office by Friday.

Wendell Motors

Wendell Motors manufactures and ships small electric motors and drives to a variety of industrial and commercial customers in and around St. Louis. Wendell is a small operation with a single manufacturing plant. Wendell's products are different from that of other motor and drive manufacturers because Wendell only produces small motors (25 horsepower or less) and because its products are used in a variety of industries and businesses that appreciate Wendell's quality and speed of delivery. Because it has only one plant, Wendell ships motors directly from the plant to its customers. Wendell's reputation for quality and speed of delivery allows it to maintain low inventories of motors and ship make-to-order products directly to its customers. Wendell's customers are willing to wait for their orders if lead times are responsive.

As part of its on-going commitment to lean manufacturing and continuous process improvement, Wendell carefully monitors the cost associated with both production and shipping. The manager of shipping for Wendell, Tyler Jenkins, regularly reports the shipping costs to Wendell's management team. Because few finished goods inventories are maintained, competitive delivery times often require that Wendell expedite shipments. This is almost always the case for those customers who operate their business around the clock every day of the week. Such customers might maintain their own back-up safety stock of a particular motor or drive, but circumstances often result in cases where replacement products have to be rushed through production and then expedited to the customer.

Wendell's management team wondered if these special orders were too expensive to handle in this way and if it might be less expensive to produce and hold certain motors as finished goods inventory, enabling off-the-shelf delivery using less expensive modes of shipping. This might especially be true for orders that must be filled on a holiday, which incurred an additional shipping charge. At the last meeting of the management team Tyler Jenkins was asked to analyze expedited shipping costs and to develop a model that could be used to estimate the cost of expediting a customer's order.

Donna Layton, an industrial engineer in the plant, was asked to prepare an inventory cost analysis to determine how expensive it would be to hold additional finished goods inventory. To begin his analysis, Tyler randomly selected 45 expedited shipping records. The sampled data can be found in file **Wendell Motors.xls.** The management team expects a full report in 5 days. Tyler knew he would need a model for explaining shipping costs for expedited orders and that he would also need to answer their questions as to what effect, if any, shipping on a holiday had on costs.

PART III:
Capstone Projects

Business Statistics Capstone Project 1
Theme: Multiple Regression Analysis

Project Objective

The objective of this business statistics capstone project is to provide you with an opportunity to integrate the statistical tools and concepts that you have learned in your business statistics course. Like all real-world applications, it is not expected that through the completion of this project you will have utilized every statistical technique that you have been taught in this course. Rather, an objective of the assignment will be for you to determine which of the statistical tools and techniques are appropriate to employ for the situation you have selected.

Project Description

You are to identify a business or organizational issue that is appropriately addressed using multiple regression analysis. The emphasis of the project should be to develop either a predictive model or a descriptive model. You are to collect raw data using any appropriate data collection technique including observation, written or phone survey or experimentation, or through a reputable secondary source. The quality and quantity of independent variables for which data are collected should meet or exceed the minimum that are needed to fully address the central issue of the project. In most cases this will mean having both quantitative and qualitative variables in your data set.

There is no set sample size requirement, but the sample size should be large enough to provide sufficient data for the purposes of the analysis. Typically, the easier it is to acquire the data, the larger the sample size should be. You are responsible for making sure that the data are accurate. All methods (or sources) for data collection should be fully documented.

Project Deliverables

To successfully complete this capstone project, you are required to deliver, at a minimum, the following items in the context of a management report:

- A complete description of the central issue of your project and a background on the company or organization that you have selected as the basis for the project.
- A clear and concise explanation of the data collection method used. If you used a survey methodology, describe the steps used to develop the survey and provide a copy of the survey instrument in the appendix to the report
- A complete descriptive analysis of the dependent and independent variables including both numerical and graphical analysis.
- A comprehensive correlation analysis including any pertinent statistical tests of significance.
- A complete discussion of the process used in arriving at your final multiple regression model.
- An analysis of the final regression model including any appropriate statistical tests of significance, residual analysis, and a discussion of potential multicolinearity problems that might be present in the model.
- A review of the final application of the regression model for predictive or descriptive purposes tying the results back to the central issue of your project.
- All pertinent appendix materials.

The final report should be presented in a professional format using the style or format suggested by your instructor.

Business Statistics Capstone Project 2
Theme: Time-Series Analysis and Forecasting

Project Objective

The objective of this business statistics capstone project is to provide you with an opportunity to integrate the statistical tools and concepts that you have learned in your business statistics course. Like all real-world applications, it is not expected that through the completion of this project you will have utilized every statistical technique that you have been taught in this course. Rather, an objective of the assignment will be for you to determine which of the statistical tools and techniques are appropriate to employ for the situation you have selected.

Project Description

You are to identify a business or organizational issue that is appropriately addressed using time-series analysis and forecasting. The emphasis of the project should be to develop an effective forecasting model. You may choose to develop a smoothing based model or a regression based model. You are to obtain time-series data from a business or organizational process. The data may be weekly, monthly, or annual depending on the application.

There is no minimum number of data periods. You should obtain as much relevant historical data as possible given the application you have selected. You are responsible for making sure that the data are accurate. All methods (or sources) for data collection should be fully documented.

Project Deliverables

To successfully complete this capstone project, you are required to deliver, at a minimum, the following items in the context of a management report:

- A complete description of the central issue of your project and a background on the company or organization that you have selected as the basis for the project.
- A clear and concise explanation of the data collection method used.
- A complete descriptive analysis of all variables in the data set including both numerical and graphical analysis.
- A time-series analysis of the primary variable to be forecasted including the identification of relevant time-series components that are present in the data.
- A discussion of the rationale for selecting your particular forecasting approach.
- A detailed description of the steps you have taken to develop your model illustrating interim results.
- Demonstration of the forecasting capability of the model against test or hold-out data including the presentation of pertinent measures of forecasting performance. Include numeric and graphic output in your discussion.
- A discussion of the final application of the forecasting model based on the initial objectives of the project.
- All pertinent appendix materials.

The final report should be presented in a professional format using the style or format suggested by your instructor.

Business Statistics Capstone Project 3
Theme: Analysis of Variance

Project Objective

The objective of this business statistics capstone project is to provide you with an opportunity to inte grate the statistical tools and concepts that you have learned in your business statistics course. Like al real-world applications, it is not expected that through the completion of this project you will have utilize every statistical technique that you have been taught in this course. Rather, an objective of the assign ment will be for you to determine which of the statistical tools and techniques are appropriate to emplo for the situation you have selected.

Project Description:

You are to identify a business or organizational issue that is appropriately addressed using analysis o variance or experimental design. You will need to specify one or more sets of null and alternative hypothe ses to be tested in order to reach conclusions pertaining to the business or organizational issue yo have selected. You are responsible for designing and carrying out an "experiment" or otherwise col lecting appropriate data required to test the hypotheses using one or more of the analysis of varianc designs introduced in your text and statistics course.

There is no minimum number sample size. The sample size should depend on the design you choos and the cost and difficulty in obtaining the data. You are responsible for making sure that the data ar accurate. All methods (or sources) for data collection should be fully documented.

Project Deliverables

To successfully complete this capstone project, you are required to deliver, at a minimum, the follow ing items in the context of a management report:

- A complete description of the central issue of your project and a background on the compan or organization that you have selected as the basis for the project.
- A clear and concise explanation of the data collection method used. Included should be a dis cussion of your rational for selecting the analysis of variance technique(s) used in your analysis
- A complete descriptive analysis of all variables in the data set, including both numerical an graphical analysis. You should demonstrate the extent to which the basic assumptions of the analy sis of variance designs have been satisfied.
- Provide a clear and concise review of the hypotheses tests that formed the objective of you project. Show any post ANOVA multiple comparison tests.
- Offer a summary and conclusion section that relates back to the central issue(s) of your projec discussing the results of the hypothesis tests.
- All pertinent appendix materials.

The final report should be presented in a professional format using the style or format suggeste by your instructor.

Business Statistics Capstone Project 4
Theme: Financial Data Analysis

Project Objective

The objective of this business statistics capstone project is to provide you with an opportunity to integrate the statistical tools and concepts that you have learned in your business statistics course. Like all real-world applications, it is not expected that through the completion of this project you will have utilized every statistical technique that you have been taught in this course. Rather, an objective of the assignment will be for you to determine which of the statistical tools and techniques are appropriate to apply for the situation you have selected.

Project Description

Assume that you are working as an intern for a financial management company. Your employer has a large number of clients who trust the company managers to invest their funds. In your position, you have the responsibility for producing reports for clients when they request information. Your company has two large data files with financial information for a large number of U.S. Companies. The first is called US Companies 2003, which contains financial information for the companies' 2001 or 2002 fiscal year end. The second file is called US Companies 2005, which has data for the fiscal 2003 or 2004 year end. The 2003 file has data for 7,441 companies. The 2005 file has data for 6,992 companies. Thus, many companies are listed on both files but some are just on one or the other.

The two files have many of the same variables but the 2003 file has a larger range of financial variables than the 2005 file. For some companies, the data for certain variables are not available and a code of NA is used to so indicate. The 2003 file has special worksheet that contains the description of each variable. These descriptions apply to the 2005 data file as well.

You have been given access to these two data files for use in preparing your reports. Your role will be to perform certain statistical analyses that can be used to help covert these data into useful information in order to respond to the clients' questions.

This morning, one of the partners of your company received a call from a client who asked for a report that would compare companies in the financial services industry (SIC codes in the 6000's) to companies in production-oriented business (SIC codes in the 2000's and 3000's) There are no firm guidelines on what the report should entail but the partner has suggested the following:

- Start with the 2005 data file. Pull the data for all companies with the desired SIC codes into as new work sheet.
- Prepare a complete descriptive analysis of key financial variables using appropriate charts and graphs to help compare the two types of businesses.
- Determine whether there are statistical differences between the two classes of companies in terms of key financial measures.
- Using data from the 2003 file for companies that have these SIC codes and that are also in the 2005 file, develop a comparison that shows the changes over the time span both within SIC code grouping and between SIC code grouping.

Project Deliverables

To successfully complete this capstone project, you are required to deliver a management report that addresses the partner's requests (listed above) and also contains at least one other substantial type of analysis not mentioned by the partner. This latter work should be set off in a special section of the report.

The final report should be presented in a professional format using the style or format suggested by your instructor.

Business Statistics Capstone Project 5
Theme: Six-Sigma Quality

Project Objective:

The objective of this business statistics capstone project is to provide you with an opportunity to integrate the statistical tools and concepts that you have learned in your business statistics course. Like all real-world applications, it is not expected that through the completion of this project you will have utilized every statistical technique that you have been taught in this course. Rather, an objective of the assignment will be for you to determine which of the statistical tools and techniques are appropriate to apply for the situation you have selected.

Project Description

The goal of this capstone assignment is to involve you in a six-sigma quality improvement project in a public or private sector organization. After selecting the organization and obtaining management support for the project, you will identify a product or process on which a six-sigma quality initiative will focus. You will need to determine the key measurement characteristic for the product or process along with the specification limits associated with this characteristic. After statistically analyzing the current status of the product or process relative to the six-sigma goal, you will work with employees and management of the organization to improve the quality level of the product or process. It is expected that you will apply appropriate statistical tools to help in this effort.

Project Deliverables

To successfully complete this capstone project, you are required to deliver a management report that contains at a minimum the following:

- An overview of the organization on which the project is based.
- An description of the product or process that is the focus of the project.
- A complete description of any data collected on the beginning quality status for the product or process, including a statistical analysis of the quality level relative to the six-sigma objective.
- A detailed discussion of the quality improvement approach that you implemented within the organization, including at a minimum the following:
  - Summary of the organizational roles of team members who participated in the project.
  - Description of the statistical tools used in the project and the role that these tools played.
- A chronological review of the steps taken in the project and the outputs/results that were observed at each step, including examples of any statistical analyses that you employed.
- A discussion of the results achieved and the quality level of the product or process at the close of the project.
- A discussion of any future plans by the organization to carry on the work started by your project to both increase quality levels and hold the gains made by your project.

The final report should be presented in a professional format using the style or format suggested by your instructor.

PART IV: Six-Sigma Quality

Six-Sigma

Introduction

Managers at the Motorola Corporation developed the foundation for what has become known as Six-Sigma Management in the 1980's. Soon after, other companies including General Electric, Honeywell, DuPont, and Toshiba adopted the basic six-sigma concepts introduced by Motorola and expanded them into a management philosophy being implemented by organizations around the world. The six-sigma philosophy offers a framework for tying together organizational improvements and quality initiatives and making sure an organization's goals are aligned and that measures involving productivity, cost-effectiveness, and quality are utilized. A six-sigma company is focused on eliminating waste, mistakes, and rework by using statistical analyses of data collected from its business processes.

In today's business environment, numerous organizations have turned to six-sigma management as a means for maintaining their competitive edge in a global marketplace that demands high quality at low prices. Our purpose here is to briefly introduce the basics of the six-sigma concept and to illustrate the important role that statistical tools like those introduced in this text play in its implementation.

What Is Six-Sigma Quality?

The concept of six-sigma quality is centered around the idea of ***process capability.*** Process capability refers to the ability of a process to produce products or services that consistently meet ***customer specifications.*** Customer specifications are typically defined by upper and lower limit values between which the customer expects all products to fall. Sometimes the specifications are referred to as ***tolerances.*** For instance, suppose the diameter of a sparkplug needs to be within the range 0.480 inches to 0.490 inches to fit properly in a vehicle. This range constitutes the product specifications referred to as the *upper specification limit* (USL) and the *lower specification limit* (LSL). Processes that produce "high" percentages of products or services within the customers' specifications are deemed to be more capable than those that deliver "low" percentages of acceptable products or services.

The capability of a process is determined by the relationship between the specifications range (USL–LSL) and the actual variation in the output of the product. This is analogous to driving a car into a garage. Think of the width of the garage door as the range between the USL and the LSL. The objective is to drive the car through the garage a very high percentage of the time without hitting the door frame on either side. Think of the width of the car as the actual variation in the product being produced. If the car is only slightly narrower than the garage door, you can enter the garage without a problem as long as you are pointed almost exactly at the center of the door opening. But if you are off-centered even slightly you would hit the side. This is illustrated in Figure SS-1. It would be better if the garage door was much wider than the car, as shown in Figure SS-2.

In the sparkplug example, the specifications called for sparkplugs to have diameters between 0.480 and 0.490 inches. Suppose that the manufacturing process produces sparkplugs with diameters that are normally distributed with a standard deviation equal to 0.01 inches. Figure SS-3 shows that in this situation the process is incapable of producing high-quality sparkplugs on a consistent basis even if the

FIGURE SS-1
Process Capability—The Car and Garage Analogy

FIGURE SS-2
Process Capability—The Car and Garage Analogy
A Highly Capable Process

FIGURE SS-3
Initial Sparkplug Process Capability Analysis

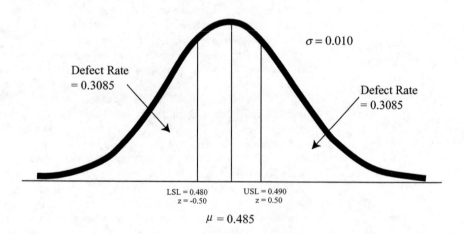

process can remain centered at a mean diameter of 0.485 inches. A large number of defects will be made. The reason for this is that the USL and LSL are only a relatively short distance from the mean, as illus trated in the computations for the z-value associated with each specification limit:

USL z-value:

$$z = \frac{USL - \mu}{\sigma} = \frac{0.490 - 0.485}{0.01} = 0.50$$

LSL z-value:

$$z = \frac{LSL - \mu}{\sigma} = \frac{0.480 - 0.485}{0.01} = 0.50$$

Thus, the specification limits are only 0.50 standard deviations either side of the process average. Using the normal distribution, and assuming that the process stays centered at a diameter equal to 0.485 inches, the projected defect rate is 0.3085 + 0.3085 = 0.6170. On a parts per million (ppm) basis, the defect rate is 617,000. Obviously this is totally unacceptable.

The problem facing the sparkplug maker is that the standard deviation for the diameters is too large. This is like having a car that is wider than the garage door. In order for the manufacturing process to be capable, either the specification limits will have to be widened or the standard deviation for the diameters will have to be reduced. Assuming there is nothing the company can do right now about the specification limits, the only answer lies in reducing the standard deviation. If the company can cut the standard deviation from 0.01 inches to 0.002 inches, the z-values for the specification limits are:

USL z-value:

$$z = \frac{USL - \mu}{\sigma} = \frac{0.490 - 0.485}{0.002} = 2.50$$

LSL z-value

$$z = \frac{LSL - \mu}{\sigma} = \frac{0.480 - 0.485}{0.002} = 2.50$$

As illustrated in Figure SS-4, the specification limits are now moved out to ± 2.50 standard deviations from the mean. If the process could remain centered at a diameter of 0.485 inches, you can use the normal distribution table to determine a projected defect rate of 0.0062 + 0.0062 = 0.0124. Thus, the defect rate is projected to be 12,400 ppm.

Table SS-1 illustrates the defect rates for processes that are assumed to stay centered at a target midway between the USL and LSL.

TABLE SS-1
Defect Rates for Centered Process

Z	ppm	Yield
2	45,600	95.44%
2.5	12,400	98.76%
3.0	2,600	99.74%
4.0	63	99.994%

If all processes remained centered between the USL and LSL, then the specification limits would need to be somewhere between 4 and 5 standard deviations either side of the center to achieve world-class quality standards. Unfortunately, experience shows that processes do not remain centered. Instead

FIGURE SS-4
Sparkplug Example Process Capability Analysis

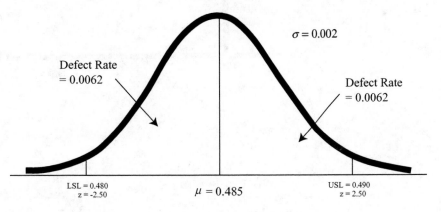

$\sigma = 0.002$

Defect Rate = 0.0062

Defect Rate = 0.0062

LSL = 0.480
z = -2.50

$\mu = 0.485$

USL = 0.490
z = 2.50

they tend to drift up or down from the target by an average of 1.5 standard deviations. Figure SS-5 illustrates a hypothetical process with a mean equal to 10 and a standard deviation equal to 2. The specification limits (LSL = 4 and USL = 16) correspond to z = 3 standard deviations from the mean (a three-sigma process) but the process center has drifted to 1.5 standard deviations above the mean (10 + 1.5*2 = 13). The revised z-value for the USL is:

USL z-value:

$$z = \frac{USL - \mu}{\sigma} = \frac{16 - 13}{2} = 1.50$$

Using the normal distribution table, the probability of a value exceeding 1.5 standard deviations is 0.0668. This translates into a defect rate of 66,800 ppm.

A six-sigma process is one which has six standard deviations between the target mean and the specification limits on both sides. To achieve this for this hypothetical example, the standard deviation must be reduced from 2 to 1. Figure SS-6 illustrates the situation for an upward drift of 1.5 standard deviations to 10 + 1.5(1) = 11.5. The revised z-value for USL limit is:

USL z-value:

$$z = \frac{USL - \mu}{\sigma} = \frac{16 - 11.5}{1} = 4.50$$

Using the normal distribution table, the probability of a value exceeding 4.5 standard deviations is 0.0000034. This translates into a defect rate of 3.4 ppm.

Thus, a process that is a true six-sigma process is capable of producing a product with a maximum defect rate of 3.4 defects per million parts produced. This has come to be known as the six-sigma defect rate.

FIGURE SS-5
A Three-Sigma Process with Drift
Mean = 10
Standard Deviation = 2

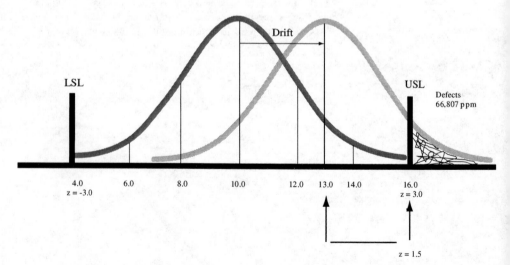

FIGURE SS-6
A Six-Sigma Process with Drift
Mean = 10
Standard Deviation = 1

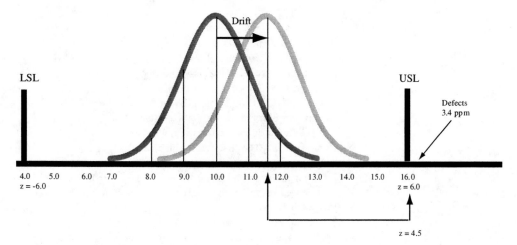

Table SS-2 shows the defect rate and yield percentage for various process performance levels for processes with drift.

TABLE SS-2
Defect Rates for Non-Centered Processes

Z	ppm	Yield
2.0	308,527	69%
3.0	66,807	93.3%
4.0	6,210	99.3%
5.0	233	99.98%
6.0	3.4	99.9997%

As you might suspect, reaching a six-sigma quality level is incredibly difficult. Doing so requires the efforts and expertise of many people within the organization working together for the common purpose. It also requires that the leaders of the effort have the necessary training and education. A major portion of six-sigma training and education is directly related to statistical analysis. Many of the topics introduced in this text are directly useful in the six-sigma effort and are included in the training that employees receive in six-sigma organizations.

The Role of Statistics in Six-Sigma

Organizations like the American Society for Quality (ASQ) provide training and education aimed at helping to prepare people to implement six-sigma programs in their organizations. Depending on the source of the training and its extent, individuals can receive certification as a six-sigma green belt, brown belt, black belt or even a gold belt holder. The training covers a variety of topics ranging from team skills to leadership skills to project management to statistical analysis. However, far and away the biggest piece of the six-sigma training is in the area of statistical analysis.

You can already see from the previous section titled "What Is Six Sigma Quality?" that statistics is a key part of six-sigma. We use basic statistics (normal distribution, standard deviation, z-values) introduced in the early chapters of the text to explain what the six-sigma concept means. But because the main way to achieve six-sigma quality is through reducing variation in processes, six-sigma practitioners apply many additional statistical tools and techniques. Many of these additional tools are introduced in this text. In addition, the background you have gained in this course will be valuable as you learn about other statistical tools used in six-sigma quality improvement efforts.

Table SS-3 lists many of the key statistical tools used to help achieve six-sigma quality and quality improvement in general. We have cross-referenced these tools with the chapters in the text where they are discussed. One major six-sigma topic not included in this text is design of experiments (DOE).

Chapter 11 on Analysis of Variance is actually an introduction to DOE but only introduces the most basic experimental designs. As a supplement, we prepared a short overview of DOE to give you a feeling for what is involved. Many universities offer an entire course or sequence of courses in DOE that address the topic in great depth. Virtually all six-sigma training programs include DOE.

Conclusion

As we indicated, achieving a six-sigma quality level is not an easy task. It means that the outputs of your processes have defect levels of approximately 3.4 defects per million items. However, organizations that have adopted the six-sigma approach are focused on quality improvement and are data driven. These organizations believe in continuous improvement aimed at achieving the world-class quality levels implied by six-sigma. The leaders of these organizations recognize the important role that statistical analysis plays in quality improvement.

Six-sigma quality efforts apply to both manufacturing and to services. We share two examples from Motorola. The first deals with electronic pagers, a product line where Motorola is the recognized world leader. A few years ago, Paul Noakes, then a senior manager in charge of quality, reported that for a particular model pager, Motorola had developed its manufacturing process to the point that a pager could be made from start to finish in 26 minutes without inspection. He noted that after selling this pager for two years, the company had not yet had a single unit returned for warranty repair.

He also told of a problem Motorola had been having within its own billing department. Motorola sends out thousands of invoices monthly. Unfortunately, many invoices contained errors. Invoice amounts that were too low caused Motorola to lose revenue. Invoices that were too high resulted in delayed payments from customers and required re-work to correct. Motorola applied the same six-sigma quality efforts to the billing process that it had applied to pager manufacturing and at the time of Paul Noakes' report, the company had gone nearly 18 months without a known billing error. In both these cases, statistical analysis played a key part in helping Motorola managers make the process changes that were necessary to achieve these high-quality results.

TABLE SS-3
Common Six-Sigma Statistical Tools
ASQ Black Belt Training Course

Statistical Topic	Chapter Coverage
Basic Probability	4 and 5
Graphical Analysis	2
Central Limit Theorem	6
Confidence Interval Estimation	7 and 9
Power and Samples Size	7 and 8
Regression Analysis	13 and 14
Hypothesis Testing	8 and 9
ANOVA	11
Statistical Process Control	17
Nonparametric Statistics	16

ANSWERS TO SELECTED ODD-NUMBERED PROBLEMS

Worked-out solutions to all the odd-numbered problems are in the Student Solutions Manual that accompanies this text. Please note solutions were done using Excel, which outputs answers to several decimal places. The precision shown may be more than required in some instances.

CHAPTER 1

1-1 A histogram is a graph showing the distribution of a quantitative variable. The horizontal axis contains the individual possible values for the variable or classes containing the possible values. The vertical bars have a height corresponding to the frequency of occurrence of each value or class. A bar chart is used to graphically describe a variable that has been broken down into distinct categories. The bars represent the value of the variable at each category level. The bars can be vertical or horizontal.

1-3 Males: average = $5,434.00; females: average = $5,545.00. For these data, females tended to have higher total charges than males.

1-5 Under 75 years: average = $3,356.50; Over 75 years: Average = $6,331.60. Based on these results it seems that older patients have higher average total charges at the hospital than do younger patients.

1-7 Estimation is a technique by which we can know about all the data in a data set whenever the data set is so large that it is impractical for us to work with all the data. By looking at a subset of the larger data set estimates are formed that give us some insight into the larger data set.

1-9 Hypothesis testing is used whenever one is interested in testing claims that concern a population. Using information taken from samples, hypothesis testing evaluates the claim and makes a conclusion about the population from which the sample was taken. Estimation is used when we are interested in knowing something about all the data, but the population is too large, or the data set is too big for us to work with all the data. In estimation, no claim is being made or tested.

1-11 a A commonly used measure of the center of the data is the mean or average. **b** To determine a value for the percentage of people in the market area that are senior citizens, the executives would rely on estimation—a set of statistical techniques that allow one to know something about a data set by using a subset of the data whenever the data set is too large to work with all the data. **c** The executives might want to test the hypothesis that the percentage of senior citizens in the market area is greater than the percentage of senior citizens nationwide. The executives could also test the hypothesis that the percentage of senior citizens is greater than or less than a specific value, say 27%.

1-13 Some representative examples might include estimates of the number of CEOs who will vote for a particular candidate, estimates of the percentage increase in wages for factory workers, estimates of the average dollar advertising expenditures for pharmaceutical companies in a specific year, and the expected increase in R&D expenditures for the coming quarter.

1-15 Both telephone surveys and mail questionnaires can use open-end questions.

1-17 Telephone surveys are most frequently used for political polls. The reason is that the survey can be conducted in a shorter time span (usually over a 24-hour period).

1-19 Nonresponse bias is the most common type of bias when mail surveys are used. Most surveys end up with between a 5 and 10 percent return rate. Those that don't respond may have different opinions or provide different results than those that do respond.

1-21 The bias that might be interjected in an experiment of this kind is measurement error. The times might be recorded incorrectly or different data collectors might use different start and end points resulting in measurement error.

1-23 Measurement error is the most likely bias because it would be very possible to make a mistake in timing a customer. Selection bias is another possibility because the data collector may target certain customers who may not be representative of the general population.

1-25 Among the advantages of using a mail questionnaire are the relatively low cost and the avoidance of any interviewer injected bias. However, mail questionnaires often suffer from low response rates (nonresponse bias) and in some cases people who feel strongly one way or the other on an issue may heavily weight responses. Written surveys may also suffer from inaccurate responses when people refuse to tell the truth about sensitive matters such as age and income.

1-27 a Student answers will vary, but most likely a personal interview would be used. **b** The advantages are that the interviewer can meet directly with the customer and get immediate feedback after the customer is in the store. The disadvantages include the high cost of conducting the personal interviews and the time required on the part of the customer who may be in a hurry to get home or to another store in the mall.

1-29 b It would be necessary to read the open-end response and code the response into one of several general categories and assign a number or letter to the response based on the judgment of the person reading the response.

1-31

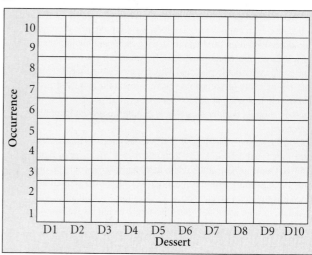

1-33 The basic requirement for a sample to be considered a statistical sample is that the items selected must be selected randomly. Some system of randomness must be in place to assure that the possible samples have an equal chance of being selected at the onset. Different statistical sampling techniques exist including simple random sampling, stratified random sampling, cluster random sampling, and systematic random sampling.

1-35 Even though the term systematic implies that some prior plan is being used to select the items, systematic (or sequential) random sampling is still considered a statistical sampling because the starting point is randomly determined. Thus, all possible samples have the same chance of being selected at the onset of the sampling.

1-37 The first three random numbers would be: 24709; 47970; 25640.

1-39 The resulting random numbers generated are:

> 344.4182
> 91.51183
> 537.2394
> 809.2961
> 796.264

Note: Students' answers will differ because Excel generates different streams of random numbers each time it is used. Also, if the application requires integer numbers, the **Decrease Decimal** option can be used.

1-41 The November value is an estimate so it is not a parameter; rather, it is a statistic. The value for October is a known value so it is a population parameter.

1-43 a Stratified random sampling **b** Simple random sampling or possibly cluster random sampling **c** Systematic random sampling **d** Stratified random sampling

1-45 There may be cases where the sample size required to obtain a certain desired level of information from a simple random sample is greater than time or money will allow. In such cases, stratified random sampling has the potential to provide the desired information with a smaller sample size.

Student responses will vary but a possible example could involve a market research study looking at consumer expenditures for a product by family income. By dividing the population into the three income strata—low, medium, and high—the desired information can be obtained using a smaller sample size than would be the case with simple random sampling.

1-47 Student answers will vary. In Excel, use either the method outlined in solution to problem 1-39 or the **RANDBETWEEN** function.

1-49 a Because there are 4,000 customer files we could give each file a unique identification number consisting of 4 digits. The first file would be given the identification number "0001." The last file would be given the identification number of "4000." By assigning each employee a number and randomly selecting the number allows each possible sample an equal chance of being selected. **b** Either use a random number table (randomly select the starting row and column), or use a computer program, such as Microsoft Excel or Minitab, which has a random number generator. **c** Because each employee is assigned a 4-digit identification number, we would need a 4-digit random number for each random number selected.

1-51 a Ease of use and timeliness **b** Assuming you want to use a nonstatistical method you could actually survey the first 100 people entering the store or you could wander around the store and just ask any 100 people that you happen to observe. **c** Student answers will vary but they should consider bias of how people are selected and bias by evaluators.

1-53 a Cross-sectional data **b** Time-series data **c** Time-series data **d** Cross-sectional data **e** Cross-sectional data **f** Time-series data

1-55 a Question 1 would be ratio data; question 2 would be ordinal data **b** Question 1 would be quantitative; question 2 is qualitative since it is divided into categories **c** Question 1 would allow you to calculate it more accurately but Question 2 would also allow you to do this if you assume that all values would be at the midpoint of the interval.

1-57 a Because the top category is greater than three this would have to be considered ordinal data. **b** No, not as the survey is currently constructed. Because the last category < 3 does not allow us to identify the exact number of children that belong to customers checking this category we cannot calculate the average number of children. We could modify the survey so that the question is open-ended, such as "How many children do you have?" _____. By allowing for a specific numeric response, rather than the > 3 category, we can calculate the average number of children.

1-59 a Ratio data **b** Ordinal data **c** Ratio data **d** Nominal data

1-61 If the data were collected and used by Anheuser–Busch they would be primary data. If the data were then used by competitors they would be considered secondary data: distributor name—nominal; brands carried—nominal

1-63 a They would probably want to sample the cartons as they come off the assembly line at the Illinois plant for a specified time period. They would want to use a random sample. One method would be to take a systematic random sample. They could then calculate the percentage of the sample that had an unacceptable texture. **b** The product is going to be ruined after testing it. You would not want to ruin the entire product that comes off the assembly line.

1-65 a Student answers will vary but one method would be personal observation at grocery stores or another method would be to simply look at their sales. Are suppliers of the beer ordering bottles or cans? **b** If using personal observation just have people at grocery stores observe people over a specified period of time and note which are selecting cans and which are selecting bottles and look at the percentages of each. **c** You would be looking at ratio data because you could have a true 0 if, for example, no one purchased bottles. **d** The data are quantitative.

CHAPTER 2

2-1 40 is the minimum width for each class. The following classes could be developed: 300 to < 340; 340 to < 380; 380 to < 420; etc.

2-3 a Classes = $1 + 3.322 (\log_{10}(160)) = 1 + 3.322 (2.204) = 8.32 = 9$ **b** Round this up to 0.68 or maybe even to 0.70 for clarity. **c** Using 0.70 as the class width we get: -2.80 to < -2.10; -2.10 to < -1.40; etc.

2-5 a 6.907 rounds to 7; 1.14, which we round up to 2.0. The relative frequency distribution is:

Class	Frequency	Relative Frequency
2–3	2	0.0333
4–5	25	0.4167
6–7	26	0.4333
8–9	6	0.1000
10–11	1	0.0167

b The cumulative frequency distribution is:

Class	Frequency	Cumulative Frequency
2–3	2	2
4–5	25	27
6–7	26	53
8–9	6	59
10–11	1	60

c

Class	Frequency	Relative Frequency	Cumulative Relative Frequency
2–3	2	0.0333	0.0333
4–5	25	0.4167	0.4500
6–7	26	0.4333	0.8833
8–9	6	0.1000	0.9833
10–11	1	0.0167	1.0000

d The ogive is a graph of the cumulative relative frequency distribution.

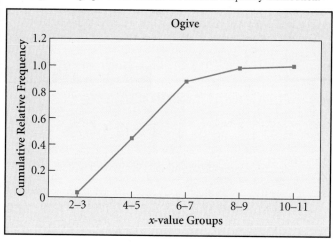

Classes	Frequency
0.95 < 1.00	4
1.00 < 1.05	11
1.05 < 1.10	12
1.10 < 1.15	9
1.15 < 1.20	5
1.20 < 1.25	5
1.25 < 1.30	2
1.30 < 1.35	2
1.35 < 1.40	0
1.40 < 1.45	0
1.45 < 1.50	0
1.50 < 1.55	0
1.55 < 1.60	0
1.60 < 1.65	0
1.65 < 1.70	1

2-7 a The proportion of those having at least five years of college that earn at least \$40,000 = 0.2120. The proportion of those having less than 5 years of college and earning at least \$40,000 = 0.1862. **b** The proportion of those having more than four years of college that earn at least \$60,000 = 0.0544. **c** Proportion that make less than \$20,000 = 0.2550. Of those that have not gone to college the proportion that makes less than \$20,000 = 16/50 = 0.32 **d** The proportion that have not gone to college that make at least \$60,000 = 3/50 = 0.06. The proportion that went to college 1–2 years that makes ≥ \$60,000 = 5/78 = 0.0641. The proportion that went to college 3–4 years that makes ≥ \$60,000 = 15/106 = 0.1415. The proportion that went to college 5–6 years that makes ≥ \$60,000 = 13/91 = 0.1429. The proportion that went to college more than 6 years that makes ≥ \$60,000 = 6/24 = 0.25.

2-9 a Data array in ascending order:

0.96	0.96	0.97	0.98	1.01	1.01	1.02	1.03	1.03	1.03
1.03	1.04	1.04	1.04	1.04	1.05	1.05	1.06	1.07	1.07
1.08	1.09	1.09	1.09	1.09	1.09	1.09	1.10	1.10	1.10
1.10	1.11	1.11	1.11	1.11	1.12	1.16	1.17	1.17	1.18
1.18	1.20	1.21	1.21	1.21	1.23	1.26	1.29	1.31	1.32
1.66									

b Frequency distribution and histogram with five classes: Class width = (1.66 − 0.96)/5 = 0.14 round to 0.15

Classes	Frequency
0.95 < 1.10	27
1.10 < 1.25	19
1.25 < 1.40	4
1.40 < 1.55	0
1.55 < 1.70	1

Frequency distribution and histogram with 15 classes:
Class width = (1.66 − 0.96)/15 = 0.0467 round to 0.05

2-11 Class width = 2,400 round to 2,500. *Note:* rounding up is not required.

Class

1,000 < 3,500
3,500 < 6,000
6,000 < 8,500
8,500 < 11,000
11,000 < 13,500
13,500 < 16,000
16,000 < 18,500
18,500 < 21,000
21,000 < 23,500
23,500 < 26,000

2-13 a

	KNOWLEDGE LEVEL			
	Savvy	Experienced	Novice	Total
Online Investors	32	220	148	400
Traditional Investors	8	58	134	200
	40	278	282	600

b

	KNOWLEDGE LEVEL		
	Savvy	Experienced	Novice
Online Investors	0.0533	0.3667	0.2467
Traditional Investors	0.0133	0.0967	0.2233

c 0.3667 **d** 0.6667

2-15 a

Classes	Frequency
0–799.99	25
800–1599.99	3
1600–2399.99	7
2400–3199.99	0
3200–3999.99	3

b

Classes	Frequency	Relative Frequency
0–199.99	23	23/38 = 0.6053
200–399.99	4	4/38 = 0.1053
400–599.99	3	3/38 = 0.0789
600–799.99	6	6/38 = 0.1579
800–999.99	0	0.0000
1000–1199.99	0	0.0000
1200–1399.99	1	1/38 = 0.0263
1400–1599.99	1	1/38 = 0.0263

c

Classes	Frequency	Relative Frequency	Cumulative Relative Frequency
30–179.99	25	0.65789	0.65789
180–329.99	9	0.23684	0.89473
330–479.99	0	0.00000	0.89473
480–629.99	3	0.07895	0.97368
630–779.99	1	0.02632	1.00000

2-17 a and **b**

Classes	Frequency	Relative Frequency
21–30	3	1.50%
31–40	5	2.50%
41–50	5	2.50%
51–60	125	62.50%
61–70	44	22.00%
71–80	5	2.50%
81–90	1	0.50%
91–100	12	6.00%

c.

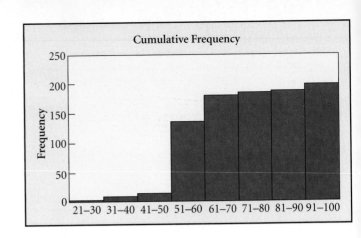

d WIM length

Classes	Frequency	Relative Frequency
21–30	4	2.01%
31–40	4	2.01%
41–50	2	1.01%
51–60	133	66.83%
61–70	38	19.10%
71–80	3	1.51%
81–90	2	1.01%
91–100	13	6.53%

e

	A	B	C	D	E	F	G	H	I	J	K
1	Sum of Month Code	WIM Tot									
2	POE Total Length	21-30	31-40	41-50	51-60	61-70	71-80	81-90	91-100	101-110	Grand Total
3	21-30	16									16
4	31-40	3	16						8		27
5	41-50		5	12	2	5					24
6	51-60				639	12			8		659
7	61-70				40	146	7		8		201
8	71-80					18	10				28
9	81-90							8			8
10	91-100							8	73	8	89
11	Grand Total	19	21	12	681	181	17	16	97	8	1052

Doc1.xls — Sheet1 / Sheet2 / Sheet3

2-19 a

Product 1 Classes	Frequency
−14.99 through −10.00	1
−9.99 through −5.00	5
−4.99 through 0.00	20
0.01 through 5.00	34
5.01 through 10.00	28
10.01 through 15.00	3

Product 2 Classes	Frequency
−9.99 through −5.00	3
−4.99 through 0.00	29
0.01 through 5.00	23
5.01 through 10.00	23
10.01 through 15.00	3
15.01 through 20.00	2

Placebo Classes	Frequency
−14.99 through −10.00	7
−9.99 through −5.00	19
−4.99 through 0.00	29
0.01 through 5.00	23
5.01 through 10.00	10
10.01 through 15.00	1

b

Product 2

Product 1

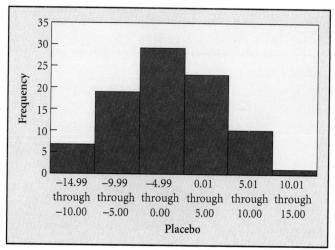

Placebo

c

Product 1 Classes	Frequency	Relative Frequency
−14.99 through −10.00	1	0.0110
−9.99 through −5.00	5	0.0549
−4.99 through 0.00	20	0.2198
0.01 through 5.00	34	0.3736
5.01 through 10.00	28	0.3077
10.01 through 15.00	3	0.0330

Product 2 Classes	Frequency	Relative Frequency
−9.99 through −5.00	3	0.0361
−4.99 through 0.00	29	0.3494
0.01 through 5.00	23	0.2771
5.01 through 10.00	23	0.2771
10.01 through 15.00	3	0.0361
15.01 through 20.00	2	0.0241

Placebo Classes	Frequency	Relative Frequency
−14.99 through −10.00	7	0.0787
−9.99 through −5.00	19	0.2135
−4.99 through 0.00	29	0.3258
0.01 through 5.00	23	0.2584
5.01 through 10.00	10	0.1124
10.01 through 15.00	1	0.0112

d

Plan	Lost Weight	Gained Weight
Product 1	28.6%	71.4%
Product 2	38.6%	61.4%
Placebo	61.8%	38.2%

2-21

2-23

2-25

STEM AND LEAF DISPLAY

Stem Unit	1
0	7 8
1	0 1 4 7 8
2	0 0 1 4 8
3	0 3 8
4	3 4
5	3 4 4
6	3 4

2-27 a

b

2-29 a

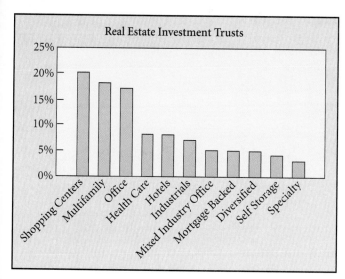

b The pie chart may be more effective because we are looking at percentages.

2-31

STEM AND LEAF DISPLAY

Stem Unit	10
1	7
2	5 6 6 7 7 7 8 8 8 9 9 9 9 9 10 10
3	0 0 1 1 1 2 2 2 2 2 2 3 3 3 3 3 3 4 4 5 5 6 6 6 6 7 7 7 7 7 9 10 10
4	1 3

2-33

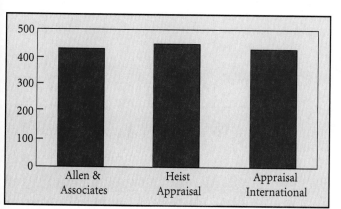

2-35

COUNT OF 1997
MEDIAN PRICE   REGION

1997 Median Price	East	North	South	West	Grand Total
70000–109999	10	15	18	4	47
110000–149999	9	6	11	9	35
150000–189999	4	2		5	11
190000–229999	2			1	3
230000–269999				2	2
270000–309999				1	1
310000–349999				1	1
Grand Total	25	23	29	23	100

2-37

2-39

2-41

2-43 a

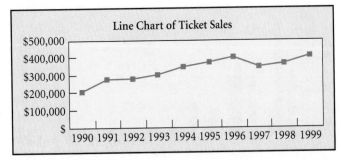

b Based on the trend before 1997 he would have reached his goal in about 1999. **c** The director should reach his goal now in about 2002.

2-45 It appears that profits increase by about $100,000–$150,000 for every $1,000,000 increase in revenue. Because the trend line is approximately at a 45% angle there does not appear to be decreasing economies of scale in the relationship.

2-47 a

b

2-49 a

b

Classes	Frequency	Relative Frequency
0 to less than 400	8	0.0234
400 to less than 800	12	0.0351
800 to less than 1,200	20	0.0585
1,200 to less than 1,600	50	0.1462
1,600 to less than 2,000	125	0.3655
2,000 to less than 2,400	103	0.3012
2,400 to less than 2,800	24	0.0702

c

Classes	Frequency	Relative Frequency	Cumulative Relative Frequency
0 to less than 400	8	0.0234	0.0234
400 to less than 800	12	0.0351	0.0585
800 to less than 1,200	20	0.0585	0.1170
1,200 to less than 1,600	50	0.1462	0.2632
1,600 to less than 2,000	125	0.3655	0.6287
2,000 to less than 2,400	103	0.3012	0.9299
2,400 to less than 2,800	24	0.0702	1.0000

b

Stem and Leaf Display

Stem Unit	1
0	3 4 5 7
1	0 0 0 0 4 5 5 9
2	0 0 0 0 0 4 5 5 5 7
3	0 0 0 0 0 2 5 5 5 5 6
4	0 0 0
5	
6	4 5
7	5
8	3
9	0 0 2
10	
11	0
12	0 0
13	
14	
15	
16	0
17	5

2-51 a

b

c

2-53 a Using Sturges's rule = 6.5851 or 7 classes. To determine the class width $(17.5 - 0.3)/7 = 2.46$ so round up to 2.5 to make it easier.

Classes	Frequency
0.1 to 2.5	21
2.6 to 5.0	15
5.1 to 7.5	3
7.6 to 10	4
10.1 to 12.5	3
12.6 to 15	0
15.1 to 17.5	2

d

2-55 a 0.1029

Classes (in seconds)	Number	Relative Frequency
<15	456	0.0899
15 < 30	718	0.1415
30 < 45	891	0.1756
45 < 60	823	0.1622
60 < 75	610	0.1202
75 < 90	449	0.0885
90 < 105	385	0.0759
105 < 120	221	0.0435
120 < 150	158	0.0311
150 < 180	124	0.0244
180 < 240	87	0.0171
≥240	153	0.0301

b $522 \times \$30 = \$15,660$ month.

2-57 a

b It appears there is a linear relationship between hours worked and weekly sales.

2-59 a

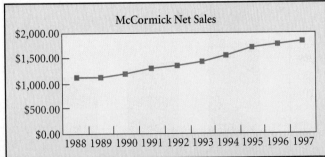

There is an upward trend in sales during the years 1988–1997. **b** It appears that capital expenditures increase as net sales increase in most instances.

c

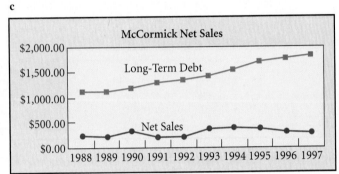

2-61 a Using Sturges's rule: = 30,004 round to 30,100.

Classes	Frequency
70,001–100,100	36
100,101–130,200	37
130,201–160,300	13
160,301–190,400	7
190,401–220,500	2
220,501–250,600	3
250,601–280,700	0
280,701–310,800	2

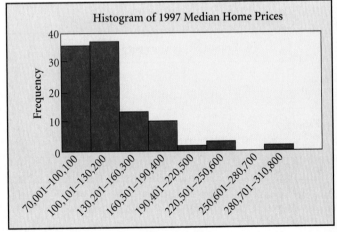

b

Classes	Frequency	Relative Frequency	Cumulative Relative Frequency
70,001–100,100	36	0.36	0.36
100,101–130,200	37	0.37	0.73
130,201–160,300	13	0.13	0.86
160,301–190,400	7	0.07	0.93
190,401–220,500	2	0.02	0.95
220,501–250,600	3	0.03	0.98
250,601–280,700	0	0	0.98
280,701–310,800	2	0.02	1.00

b

c

Classes	Frequency
70,001–120,000	65
120,001–170,000	23
170,001–220,000	8
220,001–270,000	3
270,001–320,000	2

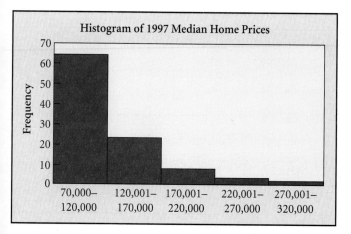

CHAPTER 3

3-1 $\mu = \dfrac{\sum x}{N} = 40/8 = 5$; median $= (5 + 6)/2 = 5.5$; mode $= 6$

3-3 a $\mu = \dfrac{\sum x}{N} = 234.19/11 = \$21.29$; median $= \$20.79$; mode $= \$25.49$;

because the mean (21.29) is greater than the median (20.79) these data are right-skewed. **b** The 1st quartile is equal to the 25th percentile,

$i = \dfrac{p}{100}(n + 1) = (25/100)(12) = 3$ or 3rd observation $= 18.95$; the 3rd

quartile is equal to the 75th percentile, $i = \dfrac{p}{100}(n + 1) = (75/100)(12) = 9$
or 9th observation $= 25.49$

3-5 $\mu = \dfrac{\sum x}{N} = 1194/12 = 99.5$; median $= (94 + 97)/2 = 95.5$; no mode;
$Q1 = 84.75$, $Q2 = 112.50$

3-7 a $\bar{x}_W = \dfrac{\sum w_i x_i}{\sum w_i} = 25{,}555/1{,}185 = 21.57$ **b** median $= 21$

2-63 a

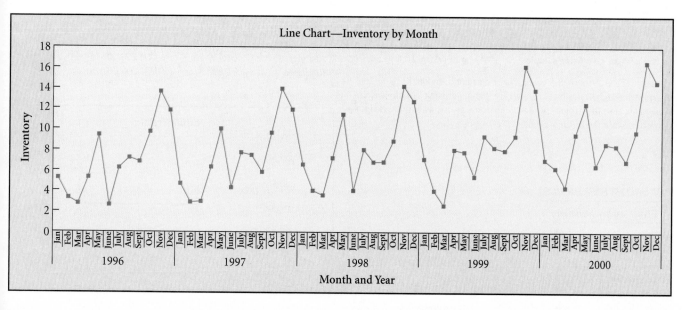

3-9 a Box and whisker plot done using PHStat.

b Based on the box and whisker plot, it appears that the data are skewed.
3-17 a Mean = 42,350; median = 42,582
b

BOX AND WHISKER PLOT

Five-Number Summary

Minimum	21124
First Quartile	31444
Median	42581.5
Third Quartile	51269
Maximum	67452

BOX AND WHISKER PLOT

Five-Number Summary

Minimum	10
First Quartile	15
Median	16
Third Quartile	19
Maximum	22

The lower limit is computed as $Q1 - 1.5(Q3 - Q1) = 15 - 1.5 \times (19 - 15) = 9$; the upper limit is $Q3 + 1.5(Q3 - Q1) = 19 + 1.5 \times (19 - 15) = 25.0$. Because no value is less than 9 nor greater than 25, there are no outliers in these data.
b Thus, the 60th percentile is somewhere between the 27th and 28th value from the top of the data sorted from low to high. This value is 17.
3-11 a Because the data are ordinal level, the median is a preferred measure of the center. The median is the center value when the data have been arranged in numerical order. The median is 8. **b** The interquartile range is: $Q3 - Q1$; $Q3 = 9$ and $Q1 = 7$; $IQR = 9 - 7 = 2$.

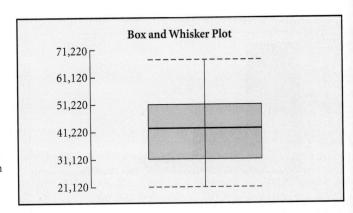

3-13 a Pre-advertising sample: $\bar{x} = \dfrac{\sum x}{n} = 378/10 = 37.8$ years; median = (34 + 36)/2 = 35 years. Because no values are repeated there is no mode. Post-advertising sample: $\bar{x} = \dfrac{\sum x}{n} = 304/10 = 30.4$ years; median = (28 + 29)/2 = 28.5 years. These data are bi-modal because 28 occurs twice and 40 occurs twice. **b** The pre-advertising sample is right-skewed because the mean > median. The post-advertising sample is right-skewed because the mean > median.

3-19 a

Category	Mean	Median
Commercial	61,780.70	65,000.00
Consumer	61,439.66	60,250.00
Real Estate	72,896.83	74,000.00

b

3-15 a

BOX AND WHISKER PLOT

Five-Number Summary

Minimum	0
First Quartile	2085
Median	2506
Third Quartile	3145.5
Maximum	8345

Consumer

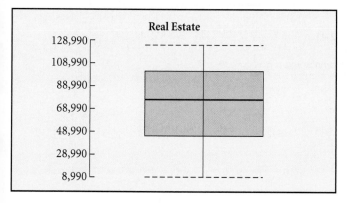

Real Estate

3-21 Range = high − low = 42 − 17 = 25; variance = $s^2 = \dfrac{\sum(x-\bar{x})^2}{n-1}$

= 48.87; standard deviation = $s = \sqrt{s^2} = \sqrt{48.87} = 6.99$

3-23 a Range = 22.95 − 9.95 = 13, $\bar{x} = \dfrac{\sum x}{n} = 168.81/10 = 16.881$;

b $s^2 = \dfrac{\sum(x-\bar{x})^2}{n-1} = 166.0125/(10-1) = 18.4458$;

$s = \sqrt{s^2} = \sqrt{18.4458} = 4.2949$ **c** $Q3 = 19.95 + 0.25(21.98 - 19.95) = 20.46$. For $Q1 = 11.22 + 0.75(14.52 - 11.22) = 13.70$. Then the interquartile range is $Q3 - Q1 = 20.46 - 13.70 = 6.76$.

3-25 a Range = 4,000 − 1,560 = 2,440 **b** $\sigma^2 = \dfrac{\sum(x-\mu)^2}{N} =$

3,847,533/6 = 641,255.5 **c** $\sigma = \sqrt{\sigma^2} = \sqrt{641,255.5} = 800.7843$

3-27 a Range = 33 − 21 = 12; $\bar{x} = \dfrac{\sum x_i}{n} = 261/10 = 26.1$;

$s^2 = \dfrac{\sum(x-\bar{x})^2}{n-1} = 148.9/(10-1) = 16.5444$; $s = \sqrt{s^2} = \sqrt{16.5444}$

= 4.0675; interquartile range = 28 − 23 = 5

3-29 a $\bar{x} = \dfrac{\sum x_i}{n} = 15,826/32 = 494.5625$; to compute the median, rank the observations and compute the average of the middle two; median = (485 + 487)/2 = 486; mode = 485; range = 595 − 413 = 182; interquartile range = 541.75 − 463 = 78.75; $s^2 = \dfrac{\sum(x-\bar{x})^2}{n-1} = 2,388.8347$;

$s = \sqrt{s^2} = \sqrt{2,388.83} = 48.88$

b

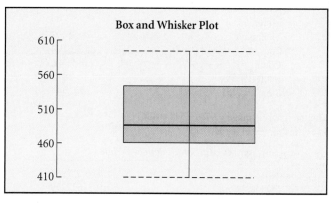

Box and Whisker Plot

3-31 a Median = $3,125; there is no mode; range = $1,660; population variance = 187,801.9; population standard deviation = 433.36.
b PHStat's box and whisker tool can be used to develop the graph:

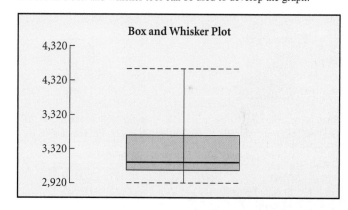

Box and Whisker Plot

c Excel's Graph tool can be used to develop a line chart:

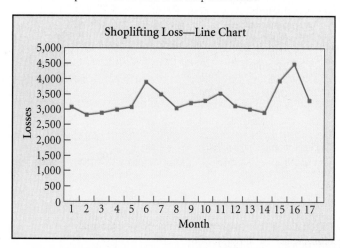

Shoplifting Loss—Line Chart

3-33 a Excel output

Credit Card Account Balance

Mean	753.68
Standard error	17.00202273
Median	737
Mode	600
Standard deviation	294.4836719
Sample variance	86720.63304
Kurtosis	−0.517456441
Skewness	0.113822027
Range	1394
Minimum	99
Maximum	1493
Sum	226104
Count	300
Largest (75)	974
Smallest (75)	544

The interquartile range = 974 − 544 = 430

b For males: Excel output

Credit Card Balances—Male

Mean	746.512931
Standard error	19.33632279
Median	738.5
Mode	1018
Standard deviation	294.5220941
Sample variance	86743.2639
Kurtosis	−0.605714694
Skewness	0.085179909
Range	1344
Minimum	99
Maximum	1443
Sum	173191
Count	232
Largest (58)	960
Smallest (58)	538

The interquartile range is the largest (58) from the table above minus the smallest (58) from the table above. 960 − 538 = 422. For females:

Credit Card Balances—Female

Mean	778.1323529
Standard error	35.80014705
Median	737
Mode	600
Standard deviation	295.2155754
Sample variance	87152.23595
Kurtosis	−0.199115911
Skewness	0.219080607
Range	1358
Minimum	135
Maximum	1493
Sum	52913
Count	68
Largest (17)	990
Smallest (17)	587

The interquartile range = 990 − 587 = 403.

3-35 For distribution A we get: $CV = \dfrac{\sigma}{\mu}(100) = \dfrac{100}{500}(100) = 20\%$.

For distribution B we get: $CV = \dfrac{\sigma}{\mu}(100) = \dfrac{4.0}{10.0}(100) = 40\%$.

Distribution B is relatively more variable because the mean of A is so much greater than the mean of B.

3-37 Distribution A: $z = \dfrac{50,000 - 45,600}{6,333} = 0.6948$;

distribution B: $z = \dfrac{40 - 33.40}{4.05} = 1.6296$. The value from distribution A is relatively closer to its mean.

3-39 a For population A: mean = 201.63, standard deviation = 37.75; for population B: mean = 1,013.63, standard deviation = 98.65 **b** For population A:

$CV = \dfrac{37.75}{201.63}(100) = 18.72\%$; for population B:

$CV = \dfrac{98.65}{1,013.63}(100) = 9.73\%$. Because population A has the higher coefficient of variation, it is relatively more variable than population B.

3-41 a $z = \dfrac{x - \mu}{\sigma} = \dfrac{455 - 400}{30} = 1.833$ **b** $z = \dfrac{x - \mu}{\sigma} =$

$\dfrac{400 - 400}{30} = 0.00$

3-43 a Type A: $\bar{x} = \dfrac{\sum x}{n} = 2963/10 = 296.3$; $s^2 = \dfrac{\sum (x - \bar{x})^2}{n - 1}$

$= 536.1/(10 - 1) = 59.567$; $s = \sqrt{s^2} = \sqrt{59.567} = 7.718$. Type B:

$\bar{x} = \dfrac{\sum x}{n} = 2984/10 = 298.4$; $s^2 = \dfrac{\sum (x - \bar{x})^2}{n - 1} = 1352.4/$

$(10 - 1) = 150.267$; $s = \sqrt{s^2} = \sqrt{150.267} = 12.258$. Using the Tchebysheff's Rule, 89% of the observations should lie within this range. Type A: 273.146 − 319.45. Type B: 261.626 − 335.174. The technician is probably correct because for Type A at three standard deviations 274 would barely be in the range. **b** To be more conservative you should probably look at two standard deviations. Type A: 280.864 − 311.736. Type B: 273.884 − 322.916. **c** Based on the calculations in a and b there is a small chance that a Type B ball could go this far.

3-45 Plant 1: (810 − 700)/200 = 0.55 standard deviations; plant 2: (2600 − 2300)/350 = 0.86 standard deviations; plant 3: (1320 − 1200)/30 = 4 standard deviations. Plant 3 performed far better than the other plants on a relative basis.

3-47 a Yes, the data support the premise that cars will get better mileage on the highway than around town. The mean for highway (24.8) is higher than the mean for city (18.4) but there is not a lot of difference between the standard deviations. **b** Highway CV = 4.1778/24.8333 = 16.8%; city CV = 2.9548/18.4 = 16.1%. City driving has slightly less variability than highway driving. **c** $z = (24.8333 - 18.4)/2.9548 = 2.17$

3-49 The median would be preferred to the mean in data sets that have extremely high or low values that affect the mean. The median is also preferred as a measure of the center if a quantitative variable is measured on an ordinal scale.

3-51 By definition a sample is a subset of a population. The most different sample selected from a population will have a different mean because it includes different values on which the mean is calculated. The sample mean will rarely equal the population mean exactly.

3-53 Some problems are that it does not look at total hours taken. One student could have taken one class on campus and got an A so would have a 4.0 grade point average. Another student could have taken many hours and got all A's except for one or two B's and would have lower than a 4.0 grade point average. People might conclude that the first student is a better student than the second based only on grade point average.

3-55 The standard deviation is an average measure of the differences from the mean. The mean is considered to be the center of the data so this measures how spread out the data are from the mean.

3-57 a $\bar{x} = \dfrac{\sum x}{n} = 127/8 = 15.875$ **b** Median = $(13 + 16)/2 = 14.5$

c The modes are 12 and 16. **d** $s^2 = \dfrac{\sum (x - \bar{x})^2}{n - 1} = 346.875/(8 - 1) =$

49.5536; $s = \sqrt{s^2} = \sqrt{49.5536} = 7.0394$ **e** The extreme value does not affect the median or the mode. **f** In this case the median might be a better measure because you have an extreme outlier. **g** $Q3 = 16 + 0.75(17 - 16) = 16.75$

3-59 a $\bar{x} = \dfrac{\sum x}{n} = 371/15 = 24.7333$; median = 20; the median < mean, which means the data are skewed right. **b** The mode is 19.
c The standard deviation is essentially an average of how the data are spread around the mean:

$s^2 = \dfrac{\sum (x - \bar{x})^2}{n - 1} = 1720.9333/(15 - 1) = 122.9238$;

$s = \sqrt{s^2} = \sqrt{122.9238} = 11.0871$ **d** Interquartile range = $34 - 19 = 15$ **e** The box plot shows that the distribution is not symmetrical because the median line is not centered in the box but instead is located very close to the $Q1$ value.

3-61 a $\mu = \dfrac{\sum x}{N} = 10,605/20 = 530.25$; median = $(400 + 450)/2 =$

425 **b** The 33rd percentile is: $i = \dfrac{p}{100}(n + 1) = (33/100)(20 + 1) = 7$ or

7th observation = 300 **c** The first 6 oil wells will be closed, which are those producing at 75, 100, 200, 230, 250, 250.

3-63 a $\bar{x} = \dfrac{\sum x}{n} = 4373/12 = 364.4167$ **b** $s^2 = \dfrac{\sum (x - \bar{x})^2}{n - 1} =$

$183,288.9167/(12 - 1) = 16,662.6288$; $s = \sqrt{s^2} = \sqrt{16,662.6288} = 129.0838$
3-65 a Spokane–St. Louis = $(299 - 364.4167)/129.0838 = -0.5068$; Miami–Kansas City = $(502 - 443)/58 = 1.0172$. The agent was relatively closest to the mean for the Spokane–St. Louis route. **b** Spokane–St. Louis = $129.0838/364.4167 = 0.3542$ or 35.42%; Miami–Kansas City = $58/443 = 0.1309$ or 13.09%. The Spokane–St. Louis route has the largest relative variation.

3-67 a

	Net Sales	Cap. Exp.	Curr. Debt	LT Debt	Equity
Average	1,413.06	67.90	112.72	279.75	415.12
Median	1,362.40	73.85	96.80	283.85	415.50
St. Dev.	262.77	15.08	85.51	65.05	69.88

b

Year	z-value Net Sales	z-value Cap. Exp.	z-value Curr. Debt	z-value LT Debt	z-value Equity
1988	−1.19	−1.16	−0.74	−0.77	−1.73
1989	−1.15	−0.96	−1.08	−1.06	−0.99
1990	−0.94	−0.63	−0.96	0.49	−0.73
1991	−0.52	0.34	−0.40	−1.11	−0.37
1992	−0.34	0.76	0.12	−1.21	0.33
1993	−0.05	0.54	−0.33	1.02	0.74
1994	0.44	1.31	1.18	1.45	1.07
1995	1.06	0.94	2.16	1.07	1.49
1996	1.22	0.45	−0.04	0.18	0.50
1997	1.48	−1.59	0.10	−0.05	−0.32

The years 1988 and 1989 are somewhat unique in that all the variables were below their means because all z-values are negative. In the same way 1994 and 1995 are unique in that all the variables were above their means.

3-69 a $\bar{x} = \dfrac{\sum x}{n} = 703/18 = 39.0556$ **b** Median = $(34 + 36)/2 = 35$

c $s^2 = \dfrac{\sum (x - \bar{x})^2}{n - 1} = 3726.944/(18 - 1) = 219.232$; $s = \sqrt{s^2} = \sqrt{219.232} = 14.81$

d

Classes	Frequency
15–24	4
25–34	5
35–44	4
45–54	2
55–64	2
65–74	1

e

f

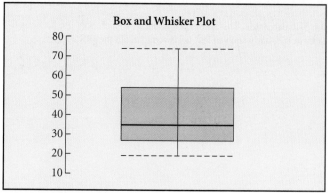

g 54 minutes

3-71 a Seed Type C produces the greatest average yield per acre.
b CV of Seed Type A = 25/88 = 0.2841 or 28.41%; CV of Seed
Type B = 15/56 = 0.2679 or 26.79%; CV of Seed Type C = 16/100 =
0.1600 or 16%; Seed Type C shows the least relative variability.
c Seed Type A: Approximately 68% will be within one standard deviation 88 ± 25 = 63 to 113; approximately 95% will be within two standard deviations 88 ± 2(25) = 38 to 138; approximately 100% will be
within three standard deviations 88 ± 3(25) = 13 to 163. Seed Type B:
Approximately 68% will be within one standard deviation 56 ± 15 = 41
to 71; approximately 95% will be within two standard deviations
56 ± 2(15) = 26 to 86; approximately 100% will be within three standard deviations 56 ± 3(15) = 11 to 101. Seed Type C: Approximately
68% will be within one standard deviation 100 ± 16 = 84 to 116;
approximately 95% will be within two standard deviations 100 ± 2(16)
= 68 to 132; approximately 100% will be within three standard deviations 100 ± 3(16) = 52 to 148. **d** Seed Type A because the 135 is
within two standard deviations. Because it has higher variability there is
a greater chance that it will produce 135. **e** Seed Type C because it has
a higher mean to begin and now the 115 would be within one standard
deviation.

3-73 b

Classes	Frequency
−6928.42 to −5077.00	1
−5076.99 to −3225.57	5
−3225.56 to −1374.14	11
−1374.13 to 477.29	7
477.30 to 2328.72	12
2328.73 to 4180.15	9
4180.16 to 6031.58	3
6031.59 to 7883.01	2

c Excel output

Difference	
Mean	**415.52**
Standard Error	436.0660531
Median	**621.5**
Mode	#N/A
Standard Deviation	**3083.452632**
Sample Variance	**9507680.132**
Kurtosis	−0.501771097
Skewness	0.177525892
Range	12960
Minimum	−5077
Maximum	7883
Sum	20776
Count	50

d $i = \dfrac{p}{100}(n+1)$ so $29 = p/100(50+1)$ $p = 56.86$ or approximately
the 57th percentile. This shows that about 57% percent of the tax consultants in this study showed less tax owed than did the IRS.

3-75 a

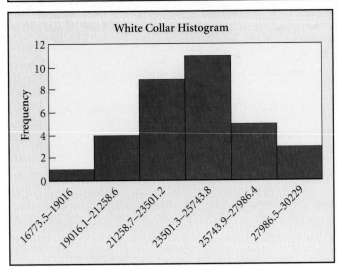

b

	Manufacturing	White Collar
Mean	26398.18	24117.06
Median	27204	24139
Mode	None	None

d City 22 is the only city that meets this criteria.
3-77 a The average 1997 median price is $122,344.
b

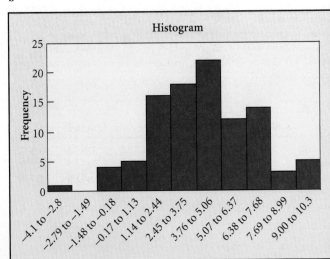

c

1993–98 Annualized Change

Mean	4.213
Median	4.15
Standard Deviation	2.545332627

d 9.76%. It appears very unlikely that you could obtain a quick profit and sell the house for $120,000.

CHAPTER 4

4-1 a $P(\text{male}) = 0.5075$ **b** $P(20\text{--}40) = 0.4716$ **c** $P(20\text{--}40 \text{ and male}) = 0.2545$ **d** $P(<20|\text{males}) = 0.2478$; $P(<20|\text{females}) = 0.3161$. Gender and age are not independent.

4-3 $P(\text{red}) = \frac{1}{4} = 0.25$.

4-5 $1 - P(\text{rain}) = 1 - 0.125 = 0.875$.

4-7 $P(\text{smoke}) = 0.30$

4-9 a $P(\text{early}) = 0.1875$ **b** $P(\text{Los Angeles}) = 0.5625$ **c** $P(\text{early given Los Angeles}) = 0.2222$. $P(\text{early}) = 0.125$

4-11 a $P(\text{female}) = 0.4643$ **b** Relative frequency **c** The events are not independent.

4-13 a Yes **b** No **c** Events cannot be both mutually exclusive and independent.

4-15 a $P(\text{Atlanta}) = 0.2182$ **b** $P(\text{wiring}) = 0.2091$ **c** $P(\text{Atlanta and wiring}) = 0.0727$ **d** $P(\text{day shift and Atlanta and cracked lens}) = 8/110 = 0.0727$

4-17 a $P(\text{dry}) = 0.50$ **b** $P(\text{rainy or cloudy and dry}) = 0.40 + 0.30 - 0.0 = 0.70$ **c** $P(\text{cloudy}|\text{dry}) = \dfrac{P(\text{cloudy and dry})}{P(\text{dry})} = \dfrac{0.30}{0.50} = 0.60$

4-19 This method will not work because the roulette wheel (if it is fair) has no memory and thus the outcomes are independent.

4-21 a $P(\text{matched}) = 2/3$ **b** $P(\text{both wrong}) = 1/9$

4-23 $P(\text{Michigan1 and Maryland2}) + P(\text{Maryland1 or Michigan2}) = 0.00072$

4-25 a 0.02060 **b** $P(G\text{-}G\text{-}G) = 0.03704$ **c** 0.00076; because this probability is so low that if it really did happen then the assignments are probably not made randomly.

4-27 This probability is $1 - [(0.2)(0.2)(0.2)(0.2)] = 0.9984$. They cannot get to 99.9% on color copies regardless of the configuration.

4-29 $P(\text{line1}|\text{defective}) = (0.05)(0.4)/0.0725 = 0.2759$; $P(\text{line2}|\text{defective}) = (0.10)(0.35)/0.0725 = 0.4828$; $P(\text{line3}|\text{defective}) = (0.07)(0.25)/0.0725 = 0.2413$; the unsealed cans probably came from Line 2.

4-31 $P(\text{clerk 1}|\text{defective}) = (0.02)(0.4)/0.02 = 0.4$; $P(\text{clerk 2}|\text{defective}) = (0.025)(0.3)/0.02 = 0.375$; $P(\text{clerk 3}|\text{defective}) = (0.015)(0.3)/0.02 = 0.225$; clerk 1 is most likely responsible for the boxes that raised the complaints.

4-33 Ten weeks can be covered by this schedule.

4-35 There is a total of 6 companies. **a** $P(\text{ace}) = 1/6 = 0.1667$ **b** $P(\text{win1 and win2}) = 0.0278$ **c** $P(\text{lose1 and lose2}) = (5/6)(5/6) = 0.6944$ **d** $P(\text{win1 and lose2}) + P(\text{lose1 and win2}) = (1/6)(5/6) + (5/6)(1/6) = 0.2778$ **e** $P(\text{win1 and lose2}) + P(\text{lose1 and win2}) + P(\text{win1 and win2}) = 0.1389 + 0.1389 + 0.0278 = 0.3056$ or $1 - P(\text{lose 1 and lose 2}) = 1 - 0.6944 = 0.3056$

4-37 $P(\text{free gas}) = 0.0003 + 0.00059 + 0.0005 = 0.00139$

4-39 a $P(\text{wiring}|\text{Atlanta}) = P(\text{wiring and Atlanta})/P(\text{Atlanta}) = 0.3333$ **b** $P(\text{Boise}|\text{return}) = 78/110 = 0.7091$; $P(\text{Atlanta}|\text{return}) = 24/110 = 0.2182$; $P(\text{Reno}|\text{return}) = 8/110 = 0.0727$

4-41 a $E(x) = 138$ **b** $\text{Var}(x) = 636$ **c** $\text{Std Dev}(x) = 25.219$

4-43 Expected value = $1.25 + -\$4.86 = -\$3.61$

4-45 For variable x: $E(x) = 225$; for variable y: $E(y) = 415$; then $E(x + y) = 225 + 415 = 640$

4-47 The covariance is 3,275. The relationship between the two variables is positive; $\sigma_x = \sqrt{9{,}875} = 99.37$; $\sigma_y = \sqrt{12{,}2751} = 110.79$; the correlation is: $\rho = \dfrac{\sigma_{xy}}{\sigma_x \sigma_y} = (3{,}275)/[(99.37)(110.79)] = 0.2975$.

4-49 a $E(x) = 2.885$ **b** 1.7725 **d** The coefficient of variation is: $CV = \dfrac{1.7725}{2.885}(100) = 61.44\%$ **e** 12 employees

4-51 The mean of the current plan is $53.40 with a standard deviation of $23.67. To determine the salary for $6 per hour you would need to assume 8 hours in a day, which would be a constant wage of $48. Because this is a constant $48 this would be the expected value of this pay plan. Employees would be better off staying with the $2 per car because it has an expected value of $53.40.

4-53 The relative frequency of occurrence approach takes the number of times the item of interest occurred and divides it by the total number of times the event or activity was done.

4-55 Classical probability assessment, sometimes referred to as *a priori* probability, is the method of determining probability based on the ratio of the number of ways the event of interest can occur to the total number of ways any event can occur when the individual elementary events are equally likely.

4-57 The probability assessment used here is the subjective probability method. Thus, each student could arrive at a different probability.

4-59 If the selection is made without replacement, the events for the two selections are dependent. **a** $P(D \text{ and } G) + P(G \text{ and } D) = 0.5333$ **b** $P(G \text{ and } G) = 0.3333$

4-61 a $e_1 = $ bid awarded; $e_2 = $ bid not awarded **b** $SS = (e_1, e_2)$ **c** $SS = (e_1, e_2, e_3, e_4, e_5, e_6, e_7, e_8)$

4-63 a $P(\text{win}) = 1/500 = 0.002$ **b** $P(\text{win}) = 3/500 = 0.006$ **c** Classical probability approach

4-65 a $P(\text{on time}) = 4900/10000 = 0.49$ **b** $P(\text{late}) = 4000/10000 = 0.40$ **c** $P(\text{early}) = (10000 - 4900 - 4000)/10000 = 0.11$

4-67 a $P(C \text{ and } C \text{ and } C) = 0.25 \times 0.25 \times 0.25 = 0.0156$ **b** $P(\text{Passing}) = 0.0156 + 0.0469 + 0.0469 + 0.0469 = 0.1563$ **c** $P(\text{Passing}) = 0.1250 + 0.1250 + 0.1250 + 0.1250 = 0.5000$.

4-69 a $E(x) = 750$; $E(y) = 100$ **b** Std Dev$(x) = 844.0972$; Std Dev$(y) = 717.635$ **c** $CV(x) = 844.0972/750 = 1.1255$; $CV(y) = 717.635/100 = 7.1764$

4-71 If two events are independent then the probability of both events occurring should be equal to the product of the two individual events, so if the two stocks are independent then $0.6(0.7) = 0.42$ which does not equal 0.15. Therefore, the two events are not independent.

4-73 $P(\text{Sales}) = 0.7 + 0.18 + 0.06 + 0.024 = 0.964$

4-75 a $P(\text{favor}) = 0.5958$ **b** $P(\text{office worker and against}) = 0.0875$ **c** They are not independent.

4-77 $P(AE|MC) = P(AE \text{ and } MC)/P(MC) = 0.2/(0.4 + 0.2) = 0.3333$

4-79 Find: $P(\text{Profit}|\text{NoGovernor}) = \dfrac{P(\text{Profit and NoGovernor})}{P(\text{NoGovernor})} = $

$\dfrac{(0.90)(0.20)}{(0.90)(0.20) + (0.10)(0.40)} = \dfrac{0.18}{0.22} = 0.82$. Thus, if the governor can't attend, the chances of a profitable conference drops from 0.90 to 0.82.

CHAPTER 5

5-1

x	$P(x)$
0	0.4096
1	0.4096
2	0.1536
3	0.0256
4	0.0016

5-3 a $P(x = 10) = 0.1171$ **b** $P(7 < x < 12) = 0.1797 + 0.1597 + 0.1171 + 0.0710 = 0.5275$ **c** $P(x \geq 12) = 0.0355 + 0.0146 + 0.0049 + 0.0013 + 0.0003 = 0.0566$

5-5 a $\dfrac{8!}{4!(8-4)!}=70$ ways **b** $C_6^{10}=\dfrac{10!}{6!(10-6)!}=210$ ways

c $C_3^{10}=\dfrac{10!}{3!(10-3)!}=120$ ways **d** $C_7^{10}=\dfrac{10!}{7!(10-7)!}=120$ ways

5-7 a $P(x=4)=0.0768$ **b** $P(x\ge4)=0.0768+0.0102=0.0870$
c $E[x]=np=5(0.40)=2$; $SD[x]=\sqrt{npq}=\sqrt{5(0.40)(0.60)}=1.0954$

5-9 a $P(x=5)=0.0746$ **b** $P(x\ge7)=0.1124+0.0609+0.0271+$
$0.0099+0.0030+0.0008+0.0002=0.2143$ **c** $E[x]=np=20(0.30)=6$
d $SD[x]=\sqrt{npq}=\sqrt{20(0.30)(0.70)}=2.0494$

5-11 a $E(x)=\Sigma xP(x)=0(0.4096)+1(0.4096)+2(0.1536)+3(0.0256)+$
$4(0.0016)=0.80$ **b** $E(x)=np=4(0.20)=0.80$

5-13 a $P(x=5\text{ males})=0.1681$ **b** $P(x=0\text{ males})=0.0024$

5-15 a $P(x\ge2)=1-P(x\le1)=1-0.7361=0.2639$ **b** $P(x\ge2)=$
$1-P(x\le1)=1-0.5443=0.4557$

5-17 a $P(x=5)=0.0971$ **b** $P(x<4)=P(x\le3)=0.6626$ **c** $P(x>2)=$
$P(x\ge3)=1-P(x\le2)=1-0.3811=0.6189$

5-19 $E[x]=np=6(0.67)=4.02$

5-21 a Expected number $=5(0.21)=1.05$ **b** Variance $=5(0.21)(0.79)=$
0.8295; standard deviation $=0.9108$

5-23 a $P(x\le2)=0.0746+0.3151+0.5987=0.9884$ **b** Suppose
$p=0.10$: $P(x\le2)=0.1937+0.3874+0.3487=0.9298$ **c** Thus the
plan is one-sided. It favors the supplier.

5-25 a It is a binomial distribution with $n=3$, $p=$ probability of defective module. **b** $p=0.05$; $P(x\ge1)=1-P(x=0)=1-0.8574=0.1426$;
yes it is larger. **c** For $n=3$ the highest the p level can be such that the
$P(x\ge1)<0.025$ is less than 0.01 (0.0084). At $p=0.01$, $P(x\ge1)=$
$1-0.9703=0.0297$ which is still slightly larger than the required 0.025
level. At $p=0.0084$, $P(x\ge1)=0.02499$.

5-27 a $P(x=5)=0.1755$ **b** $P(x\le5)=0.6160$ **c** $P(x\ge3)=1-P(x\le$
$2)=1-0.12465=0.87535$

5-29 a Mean $=E[x]=\lambda t=5(2)=10$; standard deviation $=SD[x]=$
$\sqrt{\lambda t}=3.1623$ **b** $P(x\le3)=0.0076+0.0023+0.0005+0.0000=0.0104$

5-31 Hypergeometric distribution

5-33 $P(2,2,6)=\dfrac{C_2^{10}\cdot C_2^{15}\cdot C_6^{15}}{C_{10}^{40}}=\dfrac{45\cdot105\cdot5{,}005}{847{,}660{,}528}=0.0279$

5-35 a $P(x=0)=0.000123$ **b** $P(x>14)=P(x\ge15)=1-P(x\le14)=$
$1-0.9585=0.0415$ **c** $P(x<9)=P(x\le8)=0.4557$ **d** There is only a
4.15% chance of finding 15 or more errors if the claim is actually true.
Students will probably conclude that the error rate is higher than 3 per 400.

5-37 $P(x\ge1)=1-P(x=0)$; $P(0)=\dfrac{C_{4-0}^{20-4}\cdot C_0^4}{C_4^{20}}=\dfrac{1{,}820\cdot1}{4{,}845}=0.3756$;
$1-0.3756=0.6244$

5-39 a $0.0058+0.0019+0.0278=0.0355$ **b** $P(0,3,1)=0.0218$
c $P(0,2,2)=0.0709$

5-41 a $P(x>18.7)=P(z>(18.7-15)/2.5)=P(z>1.48)=0.5-$
$0.4306=0.0694$ **b** $P(z>\text{some value})=(100-90\text{th percentile})=0.1$;
$z=1.28$; $1.28=(x-15)/2.5$; $x=18.2$ is the 90th percentile **c** $P(-2<$
$z<2)=0.4772+0.4772=0.9544$

5-43 a $P(0.00<z\le2.33)=0.4901$ **b** $P(-1.00<z\le1.00)=0.3413+$
$0.3413=0.6826$ **c** $P(1.78<z<2.34)=(0.4904)-(0.4625)=0.0279$

5-45 a $P(x\ge8.5)=0.50-0.1293=0.3707$ **b** $P(x\ge6.5)=0.50+$
$0.1293=0.6293$ **c** $P(x\ge9.5)=0.50-0.2486=0.2514$ **d** $P(3.0\le x\le$
$5.5)=0.4332-0.2486=0.1846$

5-47 a $z=3.00$; $z=\dfrac{x-\mu}{\sigma}$; $3.00=\dfrac{x-10.5}{4.087}$; $x=22.76$ **b** $-1.96=$
$\dfrac{x-10.5}{4.087}$; $x=2.49$

5-49 a $z_{.37}=-1.13$; $z=\dfrac{x-\mu}{\sigma}$; $-1.13=\dfrac{23-\mu}{9.3}$; $\mu=33.51$ **b** $P(\text{at least}$
four out of five are 1 standard deviation below the mean) $=1-P(0$ of
four >1 standard deviation below the mean); $P(z<-1.00)=0.50-$
$0.3413=0.1587$; $P(z\ge-1.00)=1-0.1587=0.8413=P(\ge1$ standard
deviation below mean); $P(0$ of four 1 standard deviation or more below
mean) $=P(\text{all 4 are at or above 1 standard deviation below the mean})=$

$0.8413\times0.8413\times0.8413\times0.8413=0.5010$; $P(\text{at least 1 out of four 1}$
standard deviation or more below the mean) $=1-0.5010=0.4990$

5-51 $z_{.25}=-0.675$; $-0.675=\dfrac{17-22}{\sigma}$; $\sigma=7.407$

5-53 a The average cost is 0.4232 million or \$423,200. **b** The average
number of firefighters is 136.29 or 137. The standard deviation is the
square root of 563.42 = 23.74. **c** The z-value for 75% is 0.675; $0.675=$
(firefighters $-137)/23.74$; 153.02 or 154 firefighters. **d** $P(x<160)=$
$P(z<(160-137)/23.74)=P(z<0.97)=0.5+0.3340=0.8340$

5-55 a $P(x>85)=P(z>(85-72)/4)=P(z>3.25)=$ essentially 0 percent
b $P(x>82)=P(z>(82-72)/4)=P(z>2.5)=0.5-0.4938=0.0062$ **c**
The number of fliers is actually a discrete variable. The normal distribution
assumes that the value can take on an infinite number of possible outcomes.

5-57 a $P(x>16.7)=0.5-0.4772=0.0228$ **b** The mean would need to
be 15.8. **c** $2.575=(16.7-16)/\text{standard deviation}$; std dev $=0.2718$
d Because you want 16-ounce drinks it would probably be better to have
your mean ounces be 16 and adjust the standard deviation.

5-59 a $15.62+2(0.35)=16.32$ **b** $P(x>16.32)=0.5-0.4772=0.0228$
c $P(x>16.32)=0.5-0.3186=0.1814$; $P(x>2|n=3,p=0.1814)=P(z>$
$[2-(3)(0.1814)]/\sqrt{(3)(0.1814)(1-0.1814)}=P(z>2.18)$ which is
$0.5000-0.4854=0.0146$.

5-61 a $z=\dfrac{x-\mu}{\sigma}=\dfrac{7.50-4.11}{1.37}=2.48$; $P(x>\$7.50)=0.50-$

$0.4934=0.0066$ **b** $-1.645=\dfrac{3.50-\mu}{1.37}$; $\mu=\$5.75$

5-63 With a probability of no more than 5%, $z=-1.645$; $-1.645=$
$(3.5-\text{mean})/0.5$; the mean would have to be 4.32 inches
5-65 a

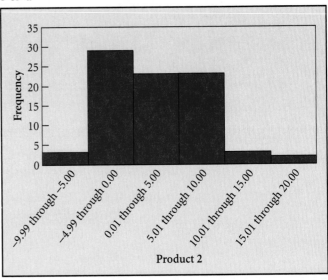

Product 2

It does not appear that Product 2 is as close to normal distribution as Plan
1 was. **b** Students can use Excel's descriptive statistics to determine the
mean and standard deviation. Excel output

Product #2	
Mean	**2.584337349**
Standard Error	0.539795898
Median	2.4
Mode	-1.9
Standard Deviation	**4.917774678**
Sample Variance	24.18450779
Kurtosis	-0.045617579
Skewness	0.480907671
Range	23.7
Minimum	-6.6
Maximum	17.1
Sum	214.5
Count	83

c $P(x < -12) = 0.5 - 0.4985 = 0.0015$ **d** No, this would not be an appropriate claim.

5-67 a

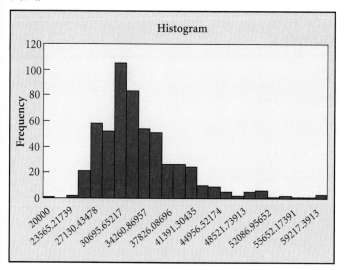

It could be considered approximately normally distributed.
b Students can use Excel's descriptive statistics feature to make these calculations. Excel output

Household Annual Income

Mean	**32801.09489**
Standard Error	266.1365661
Median	31000
Mode	30000
Standard Deviation	**6230.097282**
Sample Variance	38814112.14
Kurtosis	3.044243192
Skewness	1.481126946
Range	41000
Minimum	20000
Maximum	61000
Sum	17975000
Count	548

c $P(x > 40,000) = 0.5 - 0.3770 = 0.1230$ **d** The income cutoff would be $23,581.36.
5-69 a $P(x > 50) = (60 - 50)/(60 - 20) = 0.25$ **b** $P(x = 45) = 0$; you cannot find the probability of a specific value in a continuous distribution.
c $P(25 < x < 35) = (35 - 25)/(60 - 20) = 0.25$ **d** $P(x < 34) = (34 - 20)/(60 - 20) = 0.35$
5-71 a $P(x > 200) = 200/300 = 0.67$ **b** $P(150 < x < 300) = 150/300 = 0.50$ **c** $P(180 < x < 260) = 80/300 = 0.2667$
5-73 a

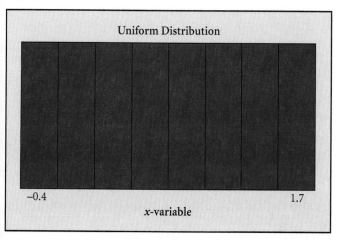

b $P(x > 0) = (1.7 - 0.0)/(1.7 - 0.40) = 1.7/2.10 = 0.8095$
5-75 a $P(0.20 \leq x \leq 0.60) = P(x \leq 0.60) - P(x < 0.20); P(x \leq 0.60) = 1 - 0.8607 = 0.1393; P(x < 0.20) = 1 - 0.9512 = 0.0488; P(0.20 \leq x \leq 0.60) = 0.1393 - 0.0488 = 0.0905$ **b** $P(x > 4) = 1 - P(x \leq 4) = 1 - (1 - 0.3679) = 0.3679$ **c** $P(x > 0.30) = 0.9277$
5-77 a $P(x < 7) = (7 - 5)/(8.5 - 5) = 2/3.5 = 0.5714$; the probability of the growth being less than 7 inches is more than 50%, so the model would probably overstate the actual pine tree growth. **b** $P(x > 6) = (8.5 - 6)/(8.5 - 5) = 0.7143$; if they use this as the constant growth rate they will probably understate the actual pine tree growth.
5-79 $\lambda = 12/hour = 0.2$ per minutes; $P(x < 4) = 1 - e^{-(.2)(4)} = 1 - 0.4493 = 0.5507$
5-81 a $\lambda = 1/4000 = .00025; P(x < 2100) = $ EXPONDIST(2100,0.00025,true) $= 0.4084$; yes, because this is a pretty high probability of a failure at less than 2100.
b $100,000(0.4084) = 40,840$
5-83 If sampling is done without replacement then the probability of an outcome changes because the total outcomes decrease by 1 each time an item is removed. However, if the total outcomes are large the change in the probability will be so small it would still be acceptable to use the binomial distribution.
5-85 As the sample size is increased for a given level of the probability of success, p, the probability distribution becomes more symmetric, or bell-shaped.
5-87 The mean and the variance of the Poisson distribution are the same so if you reduce one you will also be reducing the spread, which is the variance.
5-89 To calculate the probability of a continuous distribution you must calculate the area under the curve. A single point has no area so the probability of a specific value must be zero.
5-91 a $f(x) = 1/(0.80 - 0.40) = 2.5$

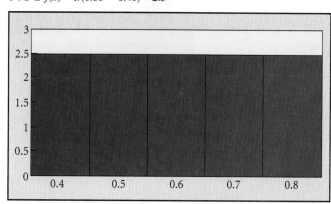

b $P(x < 0.65) = (0.65 - 0.4)/(0.8 - 0.4) = 0.625$ **c** $P(x > 0.7) = (0.8 - 0.7)/(0.8 - 0.4) = 0.25$ **d** $P(0.6 < x < 0.75) = (0.75 - 0.6)/(0.8 - 0.4) = 0.375$ **e** $(0.8 - 0.4)(0.9) = 0.36$ so $0.4 + 0.36 = 0.76$ which is the 90th percentile
5-93 a $P(x > 8) = 1 - P(x \leq 8) = 1 - 0.9319 = 0.0681$ **b** $P(3 \leq x \leq 6) = 0.1404 + 0.1755 + 0.1755 + 0.1402 = 0.6376$ **c** $P(x < 3 | mean = 2.5) = P(x \leq 2) = 0.5438$
5-95 a $P(x = 0) = 0.6065$ **b** $P(x < 3) = 0.6065 + 0.3033 + 0.0758 = 0.9856$ **c** Mean $= 0.5(3) = 1.5; P(x = 0) = 0.2231$ **d** $P(x \geq 5) = 1 - P(x \leq 4) = 1 - 0.9998 = 0.0002$. Because the probability of this occurring is so small if the mean error is actually 0.5 then you would conclude that the mean error is actually higher than 0.5.
5-97 a $P(x \geq 5) = 0.0250 + 0.0036 + 0.0002 = 0.0288$ **b** $np = 7(0.3) = 2.1$
5-99 $n = 15, p = 0.10$; **a** $P(x < 7) = P(x \leq 6) = 0.9997$ **b** $P(x = 0) = 0.2059$
5-101 a Because the mean and median are different, this cannot be a normal distribution. **b** It would be possible for the mean to be $700 and the standard deviation to be $600. However, because an account balance cannot likely be negative, a distribution with mean = $700 and standard deviation equal to $600 is most likely not a normal distribution because we would expect data within ± 3 standard deviations.

5-103 a Minimum level should be 12.96 or 13 gallons **b** $P(x < 13) = P(z < -0.17) = 0.5 - 0.0675 = 0.4325$

5-105 a $P(x > 4.90) = P(z > 0.36) = 0.5 - 0.1406 = 0.3594$ **b** $P(x < 6.25) = P(z < 1.59) = 0.5 + 0.4441 = 0.9441$ **c** $P(3.25 < x < 5.75) = P[(3.25 - 4.5)/1.1 < z < (5.75 - 4.5)/1.1] = P(-1.14 < z < 1.14) = 2(0.3729) = 0.7458$

5-107 a $E[x] = np = 10(0.10) = 1.0$ **b** $SD[x] = \sqrt{npq} = \sqrt{10(0.10)(0.90)} = \sqrt{0.9} = 0.9487$

5-109 a The trim saw length should be set to 10′ 5.4675″. **b** The standard deviation should be 0.892″

5-111 $P(x > 74) = P(z > 1.14) = 0.5 - 0.3729 = 0.1271$; $P(x > 90) = P(z > 2.29) = 0.5 - 0.489 = 0.011$

5-113 a $P(5.85 < x < 6.15) = P(-1.5 < z < 1.5) = 2(0.4332) = 0.8664$; because this is less than 99% Bryce Brothers should not purchase this machine. **b** 0.058 inch

5-115 a $P(x \geq 4) = 1 - P(x \leq 3) = 1 - 0.9130 = 0.0870$ **b** The expected number = $5(0.4) = 2.0$

5-117 a $P(x < 20) = 1 - e^{-(20)(.05)} = 1 - 0.3679 = 0.6321$
b $P(x > 30) = e^{-(30)(.05)} = 0.2231$ **c** $P(30 < x < 60) = P(x < 60) - P(x < 30) = 0.9502 - 0.7769 = 0.1733$

5-119 One way to determine if you think the problem is with the disks is to observe the results from other operators. If similar results occur you could conclude it is the disk. If other operators are not having this problem then you could probably conclude that it is the operator.

5-121 a

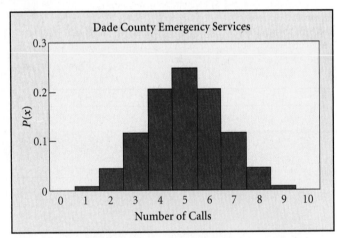

The distribution does appear to be symmetrical because the probability is equal to 0.5.

b

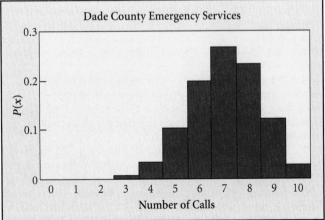

As the probability moves away from 0.5 in either direction the distribution will become skewed, which is the case in this problem.

5-123 a $P(x < 90) = P(x \leq 89) = 0.4168$ **b** $P(x > 10) = 1 - P(x \leq 10) = 1 - 0.5832 = 0.4168$ **c** $P(x = 78) = 0.0002$

5-125 a $P(x < 10) = 0.5 - 0.4279 = 0.0721$ **b** This allows you to have a log with a diameter of 9.375. $P(x < 9.375) = 0.5 - 0.4525 = 0.0475$

CHAPTER 6

6-1 a Population mean = 5.8 **b** Sample mean = 5.8333; the sampling error = $5.8333 - 5.8 = 0.0333$. **c** Highest possible sample mean for $n = 6 = 8.6667$; lowest possible sample mean for $n = 6 = 2.6667$; range of extreme sampling error = -3.1333 to 2.8667

6-3 a Sampling error = $216.67 - 177.64 = 39.03$ **b** Sampling error = $101.67 - 177.64 = -75.97$; sampling error = $310.0 - 177.64 = 132.36$; the range in potential sampling error is -75.97 to 132.36. **c** Sampling error = $110.8 - 177.64 = -66.84$; sampling error = $254.0 - 177.64 = 76.36$

6-5 a $\mu = \dfrac{864}{20} = 43.20$ days **b** $\bar{x} = 41.20$ days; sampling error = $41.20 - 43.20 = -2$ days **c** The range in sampling error is from -28.4 days to 40.4 days.

6-7 Sampling error = $17.06 - 16.9 = 0.16$ gallon.

6-9 The sample mean = 40.9.

6-11 a $z = \dfrac{970 - 1,000}{\dfrac{200}{\sqrt{5}}} = -0.34$; $P(z < -.34) = 0.50 - 0.1331 = 0.3669$ **b** $z = \dfrac{970 - 1,000}{\dfrac{200}{\sqrt{10}}} = -0.47$; $P(z < -0.47) = 0.50 - 0.1808 = 0.3192$ **c** The probability of extreme sampling error is reduced when the sample size is increased because the sampling distribution is less variable.

6-13 a $P(x > 450) = 0.1587$ **b** $P(\bar{x} > 450) = 0.0418$ **c** As the sample size increases the standard deviation of the sampling distribution is reduced. This means the spread of the sampling distribution is reduced.

6-15 a Sampling error = $24.69 - 24.90 = -0.21$ **b** $z = \dfrac{24.69 - 24.9}{\dfrac{1.30}{\sqrt{40}}} = -1.02$; $P(z \leq -1.02) = 0.50 - 0.3461 = 0.1539$

6-17 $P(\bar{x} > 200) = 0.5 - 0.4984 = 0.0016$

6-19 a $P(\bar{x} < 31) = 0.5$ **b** Standard error = 0.86 **c** To reduce the standard error the company could increase the sample size.

6-21 a $P(\bar{x} > 15) = 0.1762$ **b** We can quite safely say that the original assumptions are false.

6-23 a $P(\bar{x} > 0.392) = 0.0082$ **b** You should conclude that the sample is not representative of the population if the true population thickness is 0.375. On the other hand you might conclude that because the probability of this observed result is so low, the standards are not being satisfied.

6-25 a Mean = 468.89; standard deviation = 804.12

6-27 $z = \dfrac{450 - 0}{\dfrac{2000}{\sqrt{200}}} = 3.18$; $P(z > 3.18) = 0.50 - 0.50 \cong 0.0$

6-29 a 0.8000 **b** Sampling error = $0.4667 - 0.8000 = -0.3333$ **c** Range of sampling error = $(0.3333 - 0.8000) \longrightarrow (1.0000 - 0.8000) = -0.4667$ to 0.2000. **d** The range of extreme sampling error becomes $(0.6667 - 0.8000) \longrightarrow (1.000 - 0.8000) = -0.1333$ to 0.2000.

6-31 a $\sigma = \sqrt{\dfrac{0.65(1 - 0.65)}{100}} = 0.0477$; $z = \dfrac{0.63 - 0.65}{\sqrt{\dfrac{0.65(1 - 0.65)}{100}}} = -0.42$; $P(z < -0.42) = 0.50 - 0.1628 = 0.3372$ **b** $z = \dfrac{0.63 - 0.65}{\sqrt{\dfrac{0.65(1 - 0.65)}{200}}} = -0.59$; $P(z < -0.59) = 0.50 - 0.2224 = 0.2776$

6-33 $z = \dfrac{0.33 - 0.30}{\sqrt{\dfrac{0.30(1 - 0.30)}{60}}} = 0.51$; $P(z > 0.51) = 0.50 - 0.1950 = 0.3050$

6-35 a $z = \dfrac{0.42 - 0.40}{\sqrt{\dfrac{0.40(1 - 0.40)}{1000}}} = 1.29; P(z < 1.29) = 0.50 + 0.4015 = 0.9015$

b $z = \dfrac{0.44 - 0.40}{\sqrt{\dfrac{0.40(1 - 0.40)}{1000}}} = 2.58; P(z > 2.58) = 0.50 - 0.4951 = 0.0049$

6-37 a $p = 35/300 = 0.1167$ **b** $P(p \geq 0.1167) = 0.0096$
6-39 a $P(p < 0.68) = 0.1635$
6-41 a $P(\text{Medicare}) = 116/138 = 0.8406$ **b** $P(p > 0.8406) = 0.117$
6-43 a The $P(>55) = 47/200 = 0.235$ **b** $P(p \leq 0.235) = 0.0222$
6-45 A sampling distribution is made up of all possible values that a particular estimator can take for a population.
6-47 Sampling error is the difference between the population mean and a particular sample mean. Because the distribution of sample means centers on the population mean, the estimate of the spread of the sampling distribution also estimates the average amount by which the sample mean differs from the population.
6-49 The sampling distribution of the sample mean will have less dispersion than the population because the means cannot take on values as extreme as those in the population.
6-51 a The true population mean is 405.55. The mean of the sample means should be the same as the population mean. **b** sigma = 159.83
6-53 The population mean = 56.78; The population standard deviation: $9.6 = \text{sigma}/\sqrt{400}$; sigma = 192
6-55 If the population is normally distributed, the distribution of all possible sample means will also be normally distributed.
6-57 a The mean of the sampling distribution will be 68; it is the same as the population mean. The standard deviation for the sampling distribution of the mean is $12/\sqrt{100} = 1.2$. **b** For $n = 100$, the standard deviation is 1.2 and for $n = 500$, the standard deviation is 0.537.
6-59 a The reduction is a factor of $1 - 1/\sqrt{2}$. **b** $P(z > 2.5) = 0.5 - 0.4938 = 0.0062$
6-61 a The mean of the sampling distribution will be \$21,500 and the standard deviation will be $1700/\sqrt{200} = \$120.21$. **b** The mean would be \$21,500 and the standard deviation would be $1700/\sqrt{60} = \$219.47$.
c $P(\bar{x} > 21300) = 0.8186$
6-63 a $P(\bar{x} < 26) = 0.0367$ **b** $P(\bar{x} < 28) = 0.1867$
6-65 a $P(\bar{x} \leq 24.25) = 0.0228$ **b** $P(\bar{x} \geq 34) = 0$
6-67 a $P(19500 < x < 22000) = 0.3161$ **b** $P(19500 < \bar{x} < 22000) = 0.8413$
6-69 $P(\bar{x} \geq 31.14) = 0.0401$
6-71 a $P(\bar{x} > 120.2) = 0.0668$ **b** $P(\bar{x} < 119.73) = 0.0212$ **c** $P(\bar{x} > 120.3) = 0.0122$ **d** You need to calculate the probability that a board would be more than 1.5 different from 120. $P(z > 1.5/0.8) = P(z > 1.88) = 0.5 - 0.4699 = 0.0301$. Because you are looking for either 1.5 larger or smaller than the mean the probability would be the same. The probability that any one board would be more than 1.5 different is then $(0.0301)(2) = 0.0602$. Because they are ordering 1000 boards, the expected number of boards that would be different would be $(0.0602)(1000) = 60.2$. Therefore it is not a good proposition for the company.
6-73 a Sampling error **b** $P(p \leq 0.28) = 0.0143$
6-75 a $p = 18/49 = 0.367; (p < 0.367) = 0.121$ **b** The maximum sampling error we might expect is $0.6632 - 0.45 = 0.2132$.
6-77 a $p = 250/625 = 0.40; P(p \geq 0.4) = 0.0606$ **b** $P(p < 0.5) = 0.9964$
6-79 a $P(p \geq 0.3) = 0.0655$ **b** $P(p \geq 0.3) = 0.3121$
6-81 $P(0.25 < p < 0.29) = 0.6876$
6-83 a The sample proportion of business plan customers is 0.74.
b $P(p \geq 0.74) = 0.1093$

CHAPTER 7

7-1 a $t = 2.0595$ **b** $t = 1.6973$ **c** $t = 2.6245$ **d** $t = 2.8784$ **e** $t = 1.3253$
f $t = 1.7459$
7-3 a $102.36 \pm 1.645(1.26/\sqrt{17})$; 101.8573 ——— 102.8627 **b** $56.33 \pm 1.7247(22.4/\sqrt{21})$; 47.8995 ——— 64.7605

7-5 a $e = \pm 2.33(6.58/\sqrt{12})$; ±4.4258 **b** $e = \pm 2.0860(2.33/\sqrt{21})$; ±1.0606
c $e = \pm 1.28(15.6/\sqrt{500})$; ±0.8930

7-7 a $e = \pm 2.681(15.6/8\sqrt{13})$; ± 11.6593 **b** $e = \pm 2.575(3.47/\sqrt{25})$; ±1.7871 **c** $e = \pm 2.33(2.356)$; ±5.4895

7-9 $92.2 \pm 2.2622(15.562/\sqrt{10})$; 92.2 ± 11.1326; 81.0674 ——— 103.3326

7-11 a Point estimate = $\bar{x}$ = \$4.22 **b** $4.22 \pm 1.96(2.59/\sqrt{200})$; 4.22 ± 0.359; \$3.861 ——— \$4.579
7-13 a $54.5 \pm 1.96(14.0/\sqrt{200})$; 52.5597 ——— 56.4403 per car
b $(52.5597)(0.25)(200)$ ——— $(56.4403)(0.25)(200)$; \$2,627.99 ——— \$2,822.02 **c** The margin of error is comprised of the critical value, the standard deviation of the population or sample, and the sample size. If you decrease the confidence level (i.e., from 90% to 80%) you will decrease the margin of error. If you decrease the standard deviation you will decrease margin of error. If you increase the sample size you will decrease the margin of error.
7-15 a $1.2 \pm 1.96(0.5/\sqrt{200})$; 1.1307 ——— 1.2693 **b** $1.2 \pm 1.645(0.5/\sqrt{200})$; 1.1418 ——— 1.2582 **c** The interval in part b is more precise, and, because it is narrower it may be more useful in decision making.
7-17 a $311 \pm 1.645(72/\sqrt{144})$; 301.13 ——— 320.87 **b** If you decrease the confidence level (i.e., from 90% to 80%) you will decrease the margin of error. If you increase the sample size you will decrease the margin of error.
7-19 a $67 \pm 1.7709(14.5285/\sqrt{14})$; 67 ± 6.8762; 60.1238 ——— 73.8762 **b** No **c** (1) It does look like heart rates did increase because the interval estimate for the mean heart rate, $P(z \geq (67 - 55)(14.5285/\sqrt{14})) = P(z \geq 3.09) = 0.50 - 0.50 = 0$
7-21 a $2.505 \pm 1.645(1.5071/\sqrt{200})$; 2.3297 ——— 2.6803 **b** If you decrease the confidence level (i.e., from 90% to 80%) you will decrease the margin of error. If you increase the sample size you will decrease the margin of error.
7-23 a $268.4359 \pm 1.9913(50.8955/\sqrt{78})$; 256.9605 ——— 279.9113; corrosion: $274.1333 \pm 2.0452(54.0196/\sqrt{30})$; 253.9623 ——— 294.3043

7-25 $\dfrac{(1.96^2)(40^2)}{2.5^2} = 983.44 = 984$

7-27 $\dfrac{(1.645^2)(246.667^2)}{60^2} = 45.73 = 46$

7-29 a. $\dfrac{(1.645^2)(900^2)}{40^2} = 1,369.9 = 1,370$ **b** $\dfrac{(1.96^2)(900^2)}{40^2} = 1,944.8 = 1,945$; the percentage change is equal to a 41.97% increase.
7-31 a The margin of error can be decreased by either decreasing the confidence level, or decreasing the population standard deviation, or some combination of both. **b** If the confidence level is increased for a given size sample, the margin of error will be increased. **c** Both confidence level and margin of error can be decreased at the same time by increasing the required sample size or by reducing the population standard deviation.
7-33 $n = (1.645)^2(0.80)^2/(0.2)^2 = 43.29$ or 44
7-35 a $n = (1.96)^2(200)^2/(50)^2 = 61.4656$ or 62 so you would need to sample $62 - 40 = 22$ more **b** \$620 with pilot: savings of $\$1390 - \$620 = \$770$

7-37 $\dfrac{(2.33^2)(1.91^2)}{0.10^2} = 1,980.5 = 1,981$; the additional required sample size is $1,981 - 88 = 1,893$ items.

7-39 a $6,1780.7018 \pm 1.96(35,620.9230/\sqrt{171})$; 56,441.6617 ——— 67,119.7419; because \$67,500 is outside the confidence interval the promotion was probably not a success. **b** $n = (1.96)^2(35,620.9230)^2/(2,135.616)^2 = 1,068.75$ or $1,069 - 171$ current = 898 additional **c** He would need to change the confidence level.
7-41 $0.30 \pm 1.96(\sqrt{[(0.3)(1 - 0.3)]/400})$; 0.2551 ——— 0.3449

7-43 $0.1833 \pm 1.645(\sqrt{[(0.1833)(1 - 0.1833)] / 300})$; $0.1833 \pm .0367$; 0.1466 ——— 0.2200

7-45 $\dfrac{2.33^2(0.22)(1 - 0.22)}{0.03^2} = 1,035.1 = 1,036$; additional items needed

$= 1,036 - 50 = 986$

7-47 a $\dfrac{1.96^2(0.70)(1 - 0.70)}{0.03^2} = 896.37 = 897$ **b** $\dfrac{1.96^2(0.30)(1 - 0.30)}{0.03^2}$

$= 896.37 = 897$

7-49 $\bar{p} = 88/300 = 0.2933$; $0.2933 \pm 1.44(\sqrt{[(0.2933)(1 - 0.2933)] / 300})$;

0.2554 ——— 0.3312

7-51 $\bar{p} = 22/50 = 0.44$; $n = 1.645^2(0.44)(1 - 0.44)/(0.05)^2 = 266.71$ or

$267 - 50$ pilot sample $= 217$ more

7-53 a $0.10 \pm 1.645(\sqrt{[(0.10)(1 - 0.10)] / 130})$; $0.10 \pm .0433$; 0.0567

——— 0.1433 **b** Reduce the confidence level or take a larger sample size.

7-55 a $\dfrac{1.96^2(0.50)(1 - 0.50)}{0.03^2} = 1,067.1 = 1,068$

b $0.18 \pm 1.96(\sqrt{[(0.18)(1 - 0.18)] / 1,068})$; 0.18 ± 0.0230; 0.1570

——— 0.2030

7-57 a $0.7144 \pm 1.96(\sqrt{[(0.7144)(1 - 0.7144) / 900}) = 0.6849$ ———

0.7439 **b** If the proportion in the eastern states is 0.75, they should use a different ratio for the western states. The interval estimate for the western states does not include 0.75. **c** $1.96(\sqrt{[(0.7144)(1 - 0.7144) / 900}) = 0.0295$ **d** The options available to reduce the margin of error are to reduce the confidence level or to increase the sample size.

7-59 a $0.23 \pm 1.645(\sqrt{[(0.23)(1 - 0.23)] / 499})$; 0.1990 ——— 0.2610

b The point estimate would be 0.23 and the margin of error would be 0.031.

c $e = \sqrt{\dfrac{z^2(p)(1 - p)}{n}} = \sqrt{\dfrac{1.645^2(0.23)(1 - 0.23)}{300}} = 0.04$

7-61 The margin of error for a proportion is $z\sqrt{[(\bar{p})(1 - \bar{p})] / n}$. The only thing that is going to change is the numerator $(\bar{p})(1 - \bar{p})$. The larger the numerator, the larger margin of error.

7-63 This is not correct. The average number of miles people commute is a single value. Therefore it has no probability.

7-65 a $\bar{x} = \$178$ **b** $1.96(271 / \sqrt{48}) = 7.6383$ **c** 170.3617 ——— 185.6383

7-67 a $1,345.78 \pm 1.96(257.90 / \sqrt{300})$; $\$1,316.5959$ ——— $\$1,374.9641$ **b** Increasing the sample size and/or decreasing the confidence level. **c** We typically think of the smallest and largest values being three standard deviations from the mean. Using this assumption the smallest population mean as specified by the confidence interval we get the lowest price to be $\$1,316.60 - 3(257.90) = \$542.90$; and the largest price would be $\$1,316.60 + 3(257.90) = \$2,090.30$ However, if we assumed that the population mean was at the upper limit of the confidence interval then the smallest value might be $\$1,374.96 - 3(257.90) = \$601.26$ and the largest price would be $\$1,374.96 + 3(257.90) = \$2,148.66$. **d** approximately normally distributed

7-69 $\dfrac{1.96^2 7^2}{1^2} = 188.24 = 189$

7-71 $n = 1.88^2(0.5)(1 - 0.5)/(.04)^2 = 552.25$ or 553

7-73 $11.9991 \pm 1.96(0.2002 / \sqrt{5000})$; 11.9936 ——— 12.0046; the confidence interval does include the 12 ounces.

7-75 a $0.7 \pm 1.96\sqrt{[(0.7)(1 - 0.7] / 1024}$; 0.6719 ——— 0.7281

b $1.96\sqrt{[(0.5)(1 - 0.5)] / 1024}$; 0.0306

7-77 c The population mean is 63668.5714. At a 90% confidence interval you would expect 90% of your 10 samples, which would be 9.

7-79 a $\bar{p} = 546/758 = 0.7203$; $0.7203 \pm 1.96\sqrt{[(0.7203)(1 - 0.7203)] / 758}$;

0.6883 ——— 0.7523 **b** Number of males $= 758 - 316 = 442$; number of males who have gambled $= 546 - 187 = 359$; $\bar{p} = 359/442 = 0.8122$;

$0.8122 \pm 2.575\sqrt{[(0.8122)(1 - 0.8122)] / 442}$; 0.7644 ——— 0.8600

c $\bar{p} = 22/442 = 0.0498$; $0.0498 \pm 1.96\sqrt{[(0.0498)(1 - 0.0498)] / 442}$;

0.0295 ——— 0.0701

7-81 a $0.625 \pm 2.575\sqrt{[(0.625)(1 - 0.625)] / 64}$; 0.4692 ——— 0.7808

b Student answers will vary but one approach might be that because 50% is within the range of the confidence interval they may want to produce half mint and half plain.

CHAPTER 8

8-1 a $H_O: \mu \le 20$; $H_A: \mu > 20$ **b** $H_O: \mu = 50$; $H_A: \mu \ne 50$ **c** $H_O: \mu \ge 35$;
$H_A: \mu < 35$ **d** $H_O: \mu \le 87$; $H_A: \mu > 87$ **e** $H_O: \mu \le 6$; $H_A: \mu > 6$

8-3 a If $\bar{x} > 205.2344$, reject H_O, if $\bar{x} \le 205.2344$, do not reject H_O; if $z > 1.645$, reject H_O, if $z \le 1.645$, do not reject H_O **b** Because $z = 1.41 < 1.645$, do not reject H_O; because $204.5 < 205.2344$, do not reject H_O **c** The alternative hypothesis

8-5 a If $\bar{x} < 3966.2775$, reject H_O, if $\bar{x} \ge 3966.2775$, do not reject H_O; if p-value < 0.05, reject H_O, if p-value ≥ 0.05, do not reject H_O **b** Because $3980 > 3966.2775$, do not reject H_O, because p-value $= 0.1635 \ge 0.05$, do not reject H_O **c** The two research hypotheses that could have produced the null and alternative hypotheses are: the population mean is less than 4,000; the population mean is at least 4,000

8-7 a Type I error **b** Type II error **c** Type I error **d** Type II error

8-9 a p-value $= 0.0182$ **b** p-value $= 0.0322$ **c** p-value $= 0.2005$
d p-value $= 0.9803$

8-11 a Decision rule: If $\bar{x} < 4,158.4$, reject H_O, if $\bar{x} > 4,741.6$, reject H_O; otherwise, do not reject **b** Because $\bar{x} = 4,475.6$ is $> 4,158.4$ and $< 4,741.6$, do not reject the null hypothesis.

8-13 a $H_O: \mu \ge 30,000$; $H_A: \mu < 30,000$ **b** Because $z = -1.00 > -1.645$, do not reject the null hypothesis.

8-15 a $H_O: \mu \le 6$ days; $H_A: \mu > 6$ days **b** Because $2.7406 > 1.96$, reject H_O **c** p-value $= 0.0031$; because $0.0031 < 0.025$, reject the null hypothesis. **d** If $\bar{x} > 6.4649$, reject the null hypothesis; otherwise, do not reject.

8-17 a $H_O: \mu \le 4,000$; $H_A: \mu > 4,000$ **b** Because $t = 1.2668 < 1.7959$ there is insufficient evidence to reject the null hypothesis.

8-19 a $H_O: \mu \ge 40$, $H_A: \mu < 40$ **b** Because $z = -0.8052 > -1.28$ do not reject H_O and conclude that the average age is not less than 40. **c** Type II error

8-21 a $H_O: \mu = 0.75$ inch, $H_A: \mu \ne 0.75$ inch **b** Because $z = 0.9496 < 2.58$, do not reject H_O **c** If $\bar{x} < 0.7413$, reject the null hypothesis, if $\bar{x} > 0.7586$, reject the null hypothesis; otherwise, do not reject the null hypothesis **d** Type II error

8-23 a $z_\alpha = 1.645$; $= 0.40 + 1.645\left(\sqrt{\dfrac{0.40(1 - 0.40)}{150}}\right) = 0.4658$

b $z_\alpha = -1.28$; $= 0.70 - 1.28\left(\sqrt{\dfrac{0.70(1 - 0.70)}{200}}\right) = 0.6585$

c $z_\alpha = 1.645$; $= 0.85 \pm 1.645\left(\sqrt{\dfrac{0.85(1 - 0.85)}{100}}\right) = 0.7913$ and 0.9087

8-25 p-value $= 0.1902$; because $0.1902 > 0.07$, do not reject the null hypothesis.

8-27 a Because $0.27 < 0.3103$, do not reject the null hypothesis
b Because $0.7024 < 1.645$, do not reject.

8-29 a $H_O: p \ge 0.70$, $H_A: p < 0.70$; because $z = -1.5275 > -1.645$, do not reject. **b** A Type II error in this problem would mean that the proportion of students passing the test is actually less than 0.70 but the sample results lead the administrators to believe that it is actually 70% or better. This would mean that a test that must be too difficult would continue to be administered.

8-31 a $H_O: p \ge 0.01$, $H_A: p < 0.01$; because $z = -0.7107 > -1.645$ do not reject. **b** 0.0075 ± 0.006; 0.0015 ——— 0.0135

8-33 a $H_O: p \le 0.30$, $H_A: p > 0.30$ **b** Because $z = 0.9258 < 1.28$ do not reject the null hypothesis.

8-35 a $H_O: p \le 0.50$, $H_A: p > 0.50$ **b** Because $z = 5.889 > 1.645$, reject the null hypothesis.

8-37 a H_O: $p \le 0.80$, H_A: $p > 0.80$ **b** Because $z = 2.5 > 1.28$, reject and conclude that the proportion of calls answered within 5 minutes is greater than 80%. **c** 0.8410 ——— 0.9590; consistent

8-39 a Use Excel's Pivot Table—use percent of rows option and group handicaps as shown below. Note there are 67 golfers with handicaps of 20 or more.

Count of Club Status	Club Status		
USGA Handicap	Copy	Original	Grand Total
0–19.99	27.31%	72.69%	100.00%
20.00–39.98	25.37%	74.63%	100.00%
Grand Total	26.87%	73.13%	100.00%

H_O: $p \ge 0.40$; H_A: $p < 0.40$ **b** Because $z = -2.4444 < -1.645$, reject H_O

8-41 a Beta $= 0.4922 + 0.3078 = 0.80$ **b** Power of the test $= 1 - 0.80 = 0.20$ **c** The power increases, and beta decreases, as the sample size increases. We could also increase alpha because alpha and beta are inversely related. **d** Because $\bar{x} = 1.23$ then $1.0938 < 1.23 < 1.3062$, do not reject H_O.

8-43 a $\bar{x}_\alpha = 4,350 - 1.645(200 / \sqrt{100})$; $\bar{x}_\alpha = 4,317.10$; beta $= 0.5 + 0.4192 = 0.9192$ **b** Power $= 1 - 0.9192 = 0.0808$ **c** The power increases, and beta decreases, as the sample size increases. We could also increase alpha because alpha and beta are inversely related. **d** Because $\bar{x} = 4,337.5 > 4,317.1$, do not reject the null hypothesis.

8-45 H_O: $\mu \ge 18.0$, H_A: $\mu < 18.0$ **a** Beta $= 0.50 - 0.4985 = 0.0015$ **b** Beta $= 0.50 - 0.1480 = 0.352$ **c** The probability of a Type II error would be smaller. **d** The probabilities of Type II errors would be reduced for larger sample sizes.

8-47 a Beta $= 0.8686$ **b** No changes needed.

8-49 A Type I error occurs when the decision maker rejects a true null hypothesis. A Type II error occurs when a false null hypothesis is accepted.

8-51 The critical value is the cut-off point or demarcation determining the rejection regions in a hypothesis test. It may be expressed in terms of a value of the sample mean or as a z-value.

8-53 The probability of committing a Type I error is denoted by alpha (α) and is usually specified by the decision maker. The choice of alpha reflects the cost of making a Type I error.

8-55 You use the population proportion to calculate the standard error. If you were testing that the population proportion were 0 then the standard error would be 0. This would make it impossible to make a logical calculation.

8-57 a H_O: $\mu \le 100$, H_A: $\mu > 100$; because $z = 1.98 > 1.28$, reject H_O **b** $\bar{x} = 109.051$

8-59 a H_O: $\mu \ge 20$, H_A: $\mu < 20$; because $-6.3586 < -1.645$, reject H_O. **b** $P(z < -6.36) = 0.50 - 0.50 = 0$; this is called the p-value.

8-61 a H_O: $\mu \le 10$, H_A: $\mu > 10$; because $1.56 < 1.645$, do not reject H_O. **b** 9.9181 ——— 10.7219

8-63 a H_O: $\mu \le 3$, H_A: $\mu > 3$ research from Union perspective **b** If $z > 2.33$ reject H_O, otherwise do not reject H_O. **c** Because $z = 1.98 < 2.33$, do not reject H_O.

8-65 a H_O: $\mu \ge 40$, H_A: $\mu < 40$ **b** Because $z = -3.3334 < -1.28$, reject H_O.

8-67 a H_O: $\mu \le 417$, H_A: $\mu > 417$ **c** Because $z = 0.80 < 1.645$, do not reject H_O.

8-69 a H_O: $\mu \le 3$, H_A: $\mu > 3$; because $t = 3.35 > 1.7291$, reject and conclude that the mean exceeds 3 tries.

8-71 a H_O: $\mu \ge 10$, H_A: $\mu < 10$ **b** Decision rule: If $z < -1.28$, reject H_O; otherwise do not reject H_O. **c** Because $z = -1.3944 < -1.28$, reject H_O and conclude that the average savings is less than 10 ounces. **d** Type I error

8-73 a H_O: $\mu \le \$3$, H_A: $\mu > \$3$ **b** Because $z = 0.6108 < 1.645$, do not reject H_O. **c** The consumer group would be more concerned with a Type I error. The company would be more concerned with a Type II error.

8-75 a H_O: $p \le 0.30$, H_A: $p > 0.30$; because $2.1602 > 1.28$, reject H_O. **b** 0.3138 ——— 0.4262; $156.90 ——— $213.10

8-77 H_O: $\mu \ge 25,000$, H_A: $\mu < 25,000$; because $z = -1.8461 < -1.645$, reject H_O.

8-79 H_O: $p \le 0.35$, H_A: $p > 0.35$; because $1.0377 < 1.645$, do not reject H_O.

CHAPTER 9

9-1 a 13.541 ——— 16.459 **b** 12.933 ——— 17.067

9-3 a 329.297 ——— 358.703 **b** 331.827 ——— 356.173 **c** A lower confidence level gives a more precise, narrower interval. However, the chances of an interval not containing the true population mean are increased.

9-5 a -25.49 ——— 17.49 **b** -34.439 ——— 26.439

9-7 a -0.1043 ——— 2.7043

9-9 -20.8069 ——— 38.6011; these results do not suggest that the manager needs to focus on one location or the other.

9-11 a -48.1297 ——— 111.3687 **b** The interval includes the value 0.

9-13 $946.9545 - 854.7143 = 94.2402$; no **b** 48 ——— 136.5 **c** 63.7 ——— 120.8

9-15 a 1.6461 ——— 3.3539; yes **b** Company A: $\bar{x} = 41.0813$; Company B: $\bar{x} = 38.4184$

9-17 The hypotheses are: H_O: $\mu_1 = \mu_2$, H_A: $\mu_1 \ne \mu_2$; $t = -0.0479$, do not reject H_O.

9-19 a The hypotheses are: H_O: $\mu_1 \le \mu_2$, H_A: $\mu_1 > \mu_2$; reject H_O if $t < -2.0227$ or $t > 2.0227$. **b** $t = -0.4058$, do not reject H_O.

9-21 a The hypotheses are: H_O: $\mu_1 = \mu_2$, H_A: $\mu_1 \ne \mu_2$; the Decision Rule is: if $z > 1.96$ or $z < -1.96$, reject H_O; otherwise do not reject H_O. **b** Because $5.630 > 1.96$, reject H_O.

9-23 a If the difference is Sample 1 $-$ Sample 2, the hypotheses are: H_O: $\mu_d \ge 0$, H_A: $\mu_d < 0$ **b** $t = -3.64$; because $-3.64 < -1.3968$, reject H_O. **c** -2.1998 ——— -0.7122. This confidence interval does not contain 0.

9-25 H_O: $\mu_F - \mu_M \le 1$, H_A: $\mu_F - \mu_M > 1$; because $z = 1.6136 < 1.645$, do not reject H_O and conclude that the difference is not greater than 1.

9-27 a H_O: $\mu_N - \mu_O \le 0$, H_A: $\mu_N - \mu_O > 0$; because $z = 2.2907 > 1.28$, reject H_O and conclude that the new cartridge will result in a longer lasting product. **b** 2.537 ——— 15.463; yes

9-29 a H_O: $\mu_B - \mu_A \le 0.35$, H_A: $\mu_B - \mu_A > 0.35$; because $t = 0.8781 < 2.4286$, do not reject H_O. **b** You have to assume independent samples, and that each population has a normal distribution.

9-31 a H_O: $\mu_D - \mu_S \le 0$, H_A: $\mu_D - \mu_S > 0$; because $t = 3.0853 > 1.6909$, reject H_O and conclude that the children who have been in day care have a higher mean time in interactive situations than the stay-at-home children. **b** Type I error

9-33 a H_O: $\mu_d = 0$, H_A: $\mu_d \ne 0$; because $t = -0.1526 > -2.1448$, do not reject H_O. **b** Yes **c** -8.0302 ——— 6.9636; yes

9-35 Because $z = -2.7594 < -1.645$, reject H_O.

9-37 a Because $z = 2.4059 > 2.05$, reject H_O. **b** p-value $= 0.00800$, which is less than $\alpha = 0.02$.

9-39 a $n_1\bar{p}_1 = 0.62(745) = 462 > 5$; $n_1(1 - \bar{p}_1) = 745(1 - 0.62) = 283 > 5$; $n_2\bar{p}_2 = 0.49(455) = 223 > 5$; $n_2(1 - \bar{p}_2) = 455(1 - 0.49) = 232 > 5$. Because both are greater than 5, the normal approximation is appropriate. **b** H_O: $p_1 - p_2 = 0$, H_A: $p_1 - p_2 \ne 0$; because $z = 4.414 > 1.96$, reject H_O.

9-41 0.1832 ——— 0.3000

9-43 H_O: $\mu_W - \mu_O = 0$, H_A: $\mu_W - \mu_O \ne 0$; because p-value $= 0.3738 > 0.05$, do not reject H_O.

9-45 Because $z = -2.4237 < -1.96$, reject H_O and conclude that there is a difference in graduation rates.

9-47 Because $z = 1.8464 > 1.28$, reject H_O.

9-49 a You must assume that the populations are normally distributed. **b** H_O: $\mu_A - \mu_B \le 0$, H_A: $\mu_A - \mu_B > 0$; because $t = 0.4544 < 1.7823$, do not reject H_O.

9-51 a $n_m\bar{p}_m = (81/280)(280) = 81 > 5$; $n_m(1 - \bar{p}_m) = 280(1 - 0.2893) = 199 > 5$; $n_w\bar{p}_w = (74/280)(280) = 74 > 5$; $n_w(1 - \bar{p}_w) = 280(1 - 0.2643) = 206 > 5$ **b** H_O: $p_m - p_w = 0$, H_A: $p_m - p_w \ne 0$; because $z = 0.6611 < 1.645$, do not reject H_O.

9-53 a Because p-value $= (0.5 - 0.3051)2 = 0.3898 > 0.05$, do not reject H_O. **b** A Type I error would be if there is no difference but we concluded there was a difference. A Type II error would be if there is a difference but we concluded there was not a difference.

9-55 a H_O: $\mu_{BB} - \mu_S \leq 0$, H_A: $\mu_{BB} - \mu_S > 0$ **b** Because $z = -1.7502 < 2.33$, do not reject H_O.

9-57 H_O: $\mu_M - \mu_F = 0$, H_A: $\mu_M - \mu_F \neq 0$; if $z > 1.96$ or $z < -1.96$, reject H_O; otherwise do not reject H_O. Because $z = 0.7771 < 1.96$, do not reject H_O.

9-59 a H_O: $p_U - p_G \leq 0$, H_A: $p_U - p_G > 0$; because $z = 1.66 > 1.645$,

reject H_O. **b** $0.4333 \pm 1.96\sqrt{\dfrac{0.4333(0.5667)}{60}} = 0.4333 \pm 0.1254 = 0.3079 \text{———} 0.5587$

Graduate minimum/maximum number of seats $= 500(0.3079) = 154$ to $500(0.5587) = 279$

$0.575 \pm 1.96\sqrt{\dfrac{0.575(0.425)}{80}} = 0.575 \pm 0.1083 = 0.4667\text{———}0.6833$

Undergraduate minimum/maximum number of seats $= 2000(0.4667) = 934$ to $2000(0.6833) = 1,367$.

CHAPTER 10

10-1 a $\chi^2 = 16.919$ **b** $\chi^2 = 32.8523$ **c** $\chi^2 = 16.919$

10-3 a Because $\chi^2 = 20.25 > 18.5493$, reject the null hypothesis.
b Because $\chi^2 = 50.75 > 42.5569$, reject the null hypothesis.

10-5 a Because $\chi^2 = 25.3333 < 30.1435$, do not reject H_O and conclude that the population variance is less than 300. **b** Because $\chi^2 = 17.1267 < 21.0641$, do not reject H_O.

10-7 a H_O: $\sigma^2 \leq 2{,}025$, H_A: $\sigma^2 > 2{,}025$ **b** Because $\chi^2 = 28.1481 > 27.2036$, reject the null hypothesis.

10-9 a H_O: $\mu = 0$, H_A: $\mu \neq 0$; because $t = 1.1597 < 2.2010$, do not reject H_O. **b** H_O: $\sigma^2 \leq 4$, H_A: $\sigma^2 > 4$; because $\chi^2 = 68.1655 > 19.6752$, reject H_O. **c** From parts a and b airlines should conclude that on the average the planes arrive on time but with variance greater than 4.

10-11 H_O: $\mu \leq 14.25$, H_A: $\mu > 14.25$; because $z = 2.8553 > 1.645$, reject H_O. H_O: $\sigma^2 \geq 41.4736$, H_A: $\sigma^2 < 41.4736$; because $\chi^2 = 204.0936 > 136.2992$, reject H_O and conclude that the population variance is greater than or equal to 41.4736. Thus, the standard deviation has not been reduced.

10-13 a $F = 3.619$ **b** $F = 3.106$ **c** $F = 3.051$

10-15 a If the calculated $F > 2.865$, reject H_O; otherwise, do not reject H_O. **b** Because $F = 1.1995 < 2.865$, do not reject H_O.

10-17 a If the calculated $F > 3.858$, reject H_O; otherwise, do not reject H_O. **b** Because $F = 0.46390 < 3.858$, do not reject H_O.

10-19 H_O: $\sigma_d^2 = \sigma_w^2$, H_A: $\sigma_d^2 \neq \sigma_w^2$; because $F = 2.7778 < 3.284$, do not reject H_O.

10-21 H_O: $\sigma_A^2 = \sigma_B^2$, H_A: $\sigma_A^2 \neq \sigma_B^2$ because $F = 1.4833 < 3.0274$, do not reject H_O.

10-23 H_O: $\sigma_c^2 \leq \sigma_n^2$, H_A: $\sigma_c^2 > \sigma_n^2$; because $F = 1.445 < 2.276$, do not reject H_O.

10-25 a H_O: $\sigma_A^2 \leq \sigma_T^2$, H_A: $\sigma_A^2 > \sigma_T^2$; because $F = 2.0818 < 2.534$ do not reject H_O. **b** You would have rejected a true null hypothesis, which is a Type I error. You could decrease the alpha level to decrease the probability of a Type I error or you could increase the sample sizes.

10-27 H_O: $\sigma_A^2 = \sigma_Z^2$, H_A: $\sigma_A^2 \neq \sigma_Z^2$; because $F = 1.2129 < 2.231$, do not reject the null hypothesis.

10-29 H_O: $\sigma^2 \leq 0.90^2$, H_A: $\sigma^2 > 0.90^2$; because $\chi^2 = 42.451 > 38.885$, reject the null hypothesis.

10-31 H_O: $\sigma_1^2 \leq \sigma_2^2$, H_A: $\sigma_1^2 > \sigma_2^2$; because $F = 1.0582 < 1.599$, do not reject the null hypothesis.

10-33 H_O: $\sigma^2 \geq 29.2^2$, H_A: $\sigma^2 < 29.2^2$; because $\chi^2 = 26.826 < 29.788$, reject the null hypothesis.

10-35 H_O: $\sigma_N^2 \geq \sigma_C^2$, H_A: $\sigma_N^2 < \sigma_C^2$; because $F = 2.109 > 1.748$, reject the null hypothesis.

10-37 H_O: $\sigma^2 \leq 3{,}900^2$, H_A: $\sigma^2 > 3{,}900^2$; because $\chi^2 = 202.5424 < 224.9568$, do not reject the null hypothesis.

10-39 a H_O: $\sigma_{1998}^2 \leq \sigma_{1997}^2$, H_A: $\sigma_{1998}^2 > \sigma_{1997}^2$; because $F = 1.4263 < 9.2766$, do not reject the null hypothesis. **b** H_O: $\sigma_{Dept}^2 \leq \sigma_{Misc}^2$, H_A: $\sigma_{Dept}^2 > \sigma_{Misc}^2$; because $F = 1.132 < 4.8759$, do not reject the null hypothesis.

10-41 a H_O: $\sigma_H^2 \geq 2.5^2$, H_A: $\sigma_H^2 < 2.5^2$; H_O: $\sigma_{SD}^2 \geq 2.5^2$, H_A: $\sigma_{SD}^2 < 2.5^2$; H_O: $\sigma_B^2 \geq 2.5^2$, H_A: $\sigma_B^2 < 2.5^2$; H_O: $\sigma_R^2 \geq 2.5^2$, H_A: $\sigma_R^2 < 2.5^2$; H_O: $\sigma_{TW}^2 \geq 2.5^2$, H_A: $\sigma_{TW}^2 < 2.5^2$; $\chi_H^2 = \dfrac{(n-1)s^2}{\sigma^2} = 19.2005 > 15.6587$, do not reject; $\chi_{SD}^2 = \dfrac{(n-1)s^2}{\sigma^2} = 23.0552 > 15.6587$, do not reject; $\chi_B^2 = \dfrac{(n-1)s^2}{\sigma^2} = 11.4861 < 15.6587$, reject; $\chi_R^2 = \dfrac{(n-1)s^2}{\sigma^2} = 19.7802 > 15.6587$, do not reject; $\chi_{TW}^2 = \dfrac{(n-1)s^2}{\sigma^2} = 12.8191 < 15.6587$, reject; if $\chi^2 < 15.6587$, reject the null hypothesis. **b** H_O: $\sigma_{TW}^2 \leq \sigma_B^2$, H_A: $\sigma_{TW}^2 > \sigma_B^2$; because $F = 1.1160 < 1.7019$, do not reject the null hypothesis.

10-43 a H_O: $\sigma^2 \geq 10^2$, H_A: $\sigma^2 < 10^2$; because $\chi^2 = 29.1577 < 32.2676$, reject the null hypothesis. **b** H_O: $\sigma_{P/C}^2 = \sigma_{IS}^2$, H_A: $\sigma_{P/C}^2 \neq \sigma_{IS}^2$; because $F = 1.0801 < 1.8163$, do not reject the null hypothesis and conclude that there is no difference in the variability of sales between the two sales channels.

10-45 a H_O: $\sigma_B^2 \leq 1.5^2$, H_A: $\sigma_B^2 > 1.5^2$; because $\chi^2 = 45.0477 < 59.3035$, do not reject the null hypothesis. **b** H_O: $\sigma_{AS}^2 \leq \sigma_E^2$, H_A: $\sigma_{AS}^2 > \sigma_E^2$; because $F = 1.2027 < 1.5653$, do not reject the null hypothesis.

CHAPTER 11

11-1 a 7
b

Source	SS	df	MS	F
Between Samples	1,745	6	290.833	14.667
Within Samples	4,759	240	19.829	
Total	6,504	246		

c H_O: $\mu_1 = \mu_2 = \mu_3 = \mu_4 = \mu_5 = \mu_6 = \mu_7$, H_A: at least two population means are different **d** F-critical $= 2.8778$ (Minitab), $F = 14.667 > 2.8778$ reject H_O

11-3 a H_O: $\mu_1 = \mu_2 = \mu_3$, H_A: at least two population means are different **b** $SSB = 53.444$ **c** $SSW = 33.592$
d
ANOVA

Source of Variation	SS	df	MS	F	p-value
Between Groups	53.44444	2	26.72222	11.93252	0.000792
Within Groups	33.59167	15	2.239444		
Total	87.03611	17			

11-5 a
ANOVA

Source of Variation	SS	df	MS	F
Between Groups	55.6	2	27.8	7.419635
Within Groups	101.164	27	3.746815	
Total	156.764	29		

F-critical $= 3.3541$; reject H_0.
b No change.

11-7
ANOVA

Source of Variation	SS	df	MS	F
Between Groups	7620	3	2540	16.08667
Within Groups	12000	76	157.8947	
Total	19620	79		

$F = 16.08667 > 2.7249$ reject H_0.

11-9 a Because $0.00001 < 0.05$ reject H_0. **b** Recommend Car 2.
c $\$461.76$ —— $\$786.84$
11-11 a Because $5.5342 > 2.8661$ reject H_0. **b** Recommendation:
Display Type A or Display Type C.
11-13 a

ANALYSIS OF VARIANCE

Source	DF	SS	MS	F	p-value
Blocks	9	8346.3	927.4	10.56	0.000
Groups	2	248.3	124.1	1.41	0.269
Error	18	1580.4	87.8		
Total	29	10175.0			

b H_0: $\mu_{b1} = \mu_{b2} = \mu_{b3} = \mu_{b4} = \mu_{b5} = \mu_{b6} = \mu_{b7} = \mu_{b8} = \mu_{b9} = \mu_{b10}$, H_A: not all block means are equal; because $10.56 > 2.456$ reject H_0. **c** p-value $0.269 > 0.05$ do not reject H_0. **d** Multiple comparisons are not necessary.
11-15 a 7 **b** 15 **c** 3.638 **d** Blocking was effective.
e 10.2601 **f** $10.2601 > 2.2086$ reject H_0.
11-17 a Because $7.656659 > 3.098393$ reject H_0. **c** Because $26.6951 > 3.2874$ reject H_0.
f
LEAST SIGNIFICANT DIFFERENCE (LSD)   293.112167

	Mean Difference	Absolute Mean Difference	Significant?
D1–D2	263.33	263.33	No
D1–D3	−555	555	Yes
D1–D4	−835	835	Yes
D2–D3	−818.33	818.33	Yes
D2–D4	−1098.33	1098.33	Yes
D3–D4	−280	280	No

11-19 b Because $952.6155 > 1.8673$ reject H_0. **c** Because the p-value = 2.68E-10 reject H_0. **d** Store 2 has the highest average prices.
11-21 a Because $0.4617 < 3.8853$ conclude no interaction. **b** Because $2.3766 < 3.8853$ do not reject H_0. **c** Because $5.7532 > 4.7472$ reject H_0.
d

	Absolute Differences	Critical Range	Significant?
Level 1–Level 2	5.777777778	5.2462	yes

11-23 a
ANOVA

Source of Variation	SS	df	MS	F-ratio
Factor A	279.94	2	139.97	17.6309
Factor B	409.46	3	136.49	17.1902
AB Interaction	33.2	6	5.53	0.6965
Error	952.7	120	7.94	
Total	1675.3	131		

b $0.6965 < 2.175$ do not reject H_0. **c** $17.6309 > 3.0718$ so reject H_0.
d $17.1902 > 2.6802$ so reject H_0.
11-25 b Because $0.7085 < 3.40282$ do not reject H_0. **c** Because $41.1856 > 4.2597$ reject H_0 and conclude that not all means are equal.
d Because p-value $= 0.1407 > 0.05$ conclude there is no difference among the manufacturers. **e** Not appropriate.
11-27 a Because p-value $= 0.0570 > 0.01$ conclude no interaction between water temperature and vat hours. **b** Because $2.9945 < 6.0129$ do not reject H_0. **c** Because p-value $= 0.4829 > 0.1$ do not reject H_0.
11-37 a Because $6.1212 > 4.8672$ conclude interaction between layout and product. **b** Because interaction is present must test with a feasible one-way ANOVA: because $52.2622 > 7.63566$ conclude a difference due to the type of product being assembled with the flex-flow layout. **c** Because interaction is present must test with a feasible one-way ANOVA: Product 1 seems to be the most likely level to find differences in Factor A.

11-39 a Because $0.59153 < 2.16795$ conclude there is no interaction.
b Because $0.74628 < 3.0648$ conclude there is no significant effect due to the type of driver used.
11-41 a Because the p-value $= 8.74$E-30 < 0.05 reject H_0.
b

	Absolute Difference	Critical Range	Significant?
Wichita–Little Rock	5773.64	1504.719	yes
Little Rock–Tulsa	1157.57	1504.719	no
Tulsa–Memphis	1774.17	1504.719	yes

c 98
11-43 b Because $1.542 > 1.4829$ conclude that blocking was effective.
c Because $28.38721 > 3.0892$ reject H_0 and conclude that at least two populations means are different. **d** Center 3 takes the greatest amount of time to handle calls.
11-45 a H_0: $\mu_1 = \mu_2 = \mu_3$, H_A: not all means are equal **b** Because $0.3858 < 4.7476$ conclude there is no difference. **c** 0.680554
d $P(t > 0.6059) = 0.2727$

CHAPTER 12

12-1 The calculated chi-square value $= 122.015 > 14.0671$, reject H_0. Because the null hypothesis was rejected, a Type I error could have been committed.
12-3 The calculated chi-square statistic is $0.3636 < 6.6349$, do not reject H_0.
12-5 a The calculated chi-square statistic is $117.76 > 15.5073$, conclude the distribution is not uniformly distributed. **b** The chi-square goodness-of-fit test was significant in problem 12-3. Apparently the data come from a normal distribution.
12-7 a H_0: ATM usage distribution is Poisson distributed with $\mu = 5$ per hour; H_A: ATM usage distribution is not Poisson distributed with $\mu = 5$ per hour. **b** Calculated chi-square $= 132.8171 > 10.6446$, reject H_0.
12-9 a H_0: airline usage pattern has not changed from a previous study, H_A: airline usage pattern has changed from a previous study **b** Calculated chi-square $= 66.4083 > 15.08632$, reject H_0.
12-11 Chi-square $= 0.365652$ is less than any reasonable value, reject H_0.
12-13 Calculated chi-square test statistic $= 1.0377 > 3.8415$, do not reject H_0 and conclude that response to question 1 is independent of question 2.
12-15 a $z = 1.82$. The critical value for a two-sided hypothesis test is 1.96. There is not enough evidence to indicate a difference.
b Calculated chi-square test statistic $= 3.339 > 3.8415$; conclude that the data indicate the proportion of bad calls is the same for each official.
c $\chi^2 = 3.339 \approx (1.82)^2 = z^2$
12-17 a H_0: type of car owned is independent of union membership, H_A: type of car owned is not independent of union membership; calculated chi-square test statistic $= 27.9092 > 3.8415$, reject H_0. **b** Use Excel's CHITEST function to find 0.0000001271442.
12-19 a Calculated chi-square $= 2.3536 < 9.4877$; conclude gender and citations issued are independent. **b** 0.39241
12-21 a Because calculated chi-square $= 61.5267 > 15.5073$, reject H_0 and conclude that strike length tolerance is not independent of time with company. **b** $z = -3.53$, do not conclude the proportion is larger for the first group.
12-23 Calculated chi-square $= 11.1167 > 9.21035$, reject H_0 and conclude type of accident and shift are not independent.
12-25 Calculated chi-square $= 30.2753$. The p-value $= 0.00003484$.
12-27 You need to combine swing and graveyard and combine wiring and sound. Because calculated chi-square $0.307967 < 5.9915$, conclude the type of problem and shift are independent.
12-31 a Because calculated chi-square $= 120.148 > 7.81472$, conclude check stand use is not uniformly distributed. **b** A series of two sample tests would compound the α value.
12-33 Because calculated chi-square $= 25.2975 > 16.8118$, conclude length is not normally distributed with a mean of 3.05 and a standard deviation of 0.015.

12-35 a Because calculated chi-square = 1.1495 < 9.4877, conclude that price and return treatment are independent. **b** The type of injury or problem, travel distance, individual's income.

12-37 a Because calculated chi-square = 172.50 > 16.9190, conclude "taxable income" and "taxes paid" are not independent. **b** As income increases the amount of taxes paid increases.

12-39 a Because calculated chi-square = 7.8991 > 5.9915, conclude the distribution is normally distributed. Because H_O is not rejected, don't worry about the expected value less than 5. Answers will vary with class limits. **b** 23.3715 ——— 31.1286

12-41 a

1998 Unemployment	LABOR STRESS INDEX		
	80–99	100–120	Total
3.2–less than 4.5	2	9	11
4.5–less than 5.8	6	12	18
5.8–7.1	3	1	4
Total	11	22	33

b Because the calculated value = 4.2614 < 7.8241, conclude unemployment and labor stress index are independent. Because we do not reject H_O, don't worry about expected values less than 5.

12-43 a Class sizes will vary. Because calculated chi-square = 75.6451 > 5.9915, conclude PE ratios are not normally distributed.
b H_O: $\mu \le 25$, H_A: $\mu > 25$, $z = 1.2758$; because 1.2758 < 1.645, conclude the claim is not correct.

12-45 Values may vary depending on class sizes used. Because calculated chi-square = 179 > 16.9190, conclude that growth rates are not uniformly distributed.

CHAPTER 13

13-1 A very weak curvilinear relationship.

13-3 Because the two variables have a negative linear relationship as x increases y will decrease.

13-7 a A fairly strong positive relationship. **b** 0.847065. **c** Because 3.5638 > 2.5706, reject H_O and conclude the correlation coefficient is not 0. **d** Type I error.

13-9 a A fairly strong positive linear relationship. **b** Because p-value is essentially = 0 < 0.1, reject H_O.

13-11 a No **b** Probably

13-13 a Almost no linear relationship. **b** −0.1087. **c** Because p-value = 0.3825 > 0.025, do not reject the null hypothesis.

13-15 a $R^2 = 0.568498$ **b** (1) $\hat{y} = 58.7246 + 12.9410(0) = 58.7246$; (2) the y-intercept

13-17 a $\hat{y} = 19.75 − 0.08346(10) = 18.9154$ **b** (1) $\hat{y} = 19.75 − 0.08346 (117.22) = 9.9668$

13-19 a A weak positive linear relationship. **b** $r = 0.6239$; because $t = 2.2580 < 3.3554$, do not reject H_O. **c** (1) $\hat{y} = 0.9772 + 0.0034(x)$

13-21 $r = 0.9963$; because $t = 34.7774 > 2.2622$, reject H_O.

13-23 a $\hat{y} = 1,096.7502 + 4.6585(x)$ **b** Because $−2.3060 < 0.7846 < 2.3060$, do not reject H_O. **c** Type II

13-25 a A positive linear relationship. **b** $r = 0.7658$ **c** $\hat{y} = -7203.81 +185.3649(x)$ **d** $\hat{y} = \$17,449.7217$; residual = $20278 − 17,449.7217 = 2,828.2783$ **e** Because $F = 39.6979 > 7.6357$, reject H_O.

13-27 a A positive linear relationship. **b** $r = 0.2283$ **c** $\hat{y} = 4.5225 +0.0000001239(x)$; because p-value = 0.20135 > .05, do not reject H_O.

13-29 a The p-value = 0.0000 < 0.10, therefore reject H_O. **b** 0.7925 ——— 1.0573; it does contain 1.

13-31 a −17858.6143 ——— −17853.3857

b $1.7341(6.6677)\sqrt{\dfrac{1}{20} + \dfrac{(80 - 67.2)^2}{145,789}} = 2.614339$

13-33 b 400.48 ——— 1623.52 **c** 249.38 ——— 762.71

13-35 a $\hat{y} = −4.7933 + 1.0488x$ **b** $\hat{y} = 100.09$ **c** 82.2671 ——— 117.9129 **d** 95.0939 ——— 105.0861

13-37 a $\hat{y} = 18.8378$ **b** Confidence interval lower limit = 16.25832354; confidence interval upper limit = 21.10019247 **c** Prediction interval lower limit = 12.33289554; prediction interval upper limit = 25.02562048 **f** The confidence interval is found by finding the confidence interval of the slope coefficient and multiplying it by the difference in weight. The lower 90% = $13.3 \times 135.318 = 1799.73$, the upper 90% = $13.3 \times 235.412 = 3130.98$

13-41 The student is correct.

13-45 a A positive linear relationship **b** 0.9389 **c** Because $t = 11.57 > 2.1009$, reject H_O.

13-47 Because 1.9082 < 2.3376, do not reject H_O.

13-49 a 0.0148 ——— 0.0152 **b** No **c** Because 122.95 > 1.98, reject H_O.

13-51 b $\hat{y} = 1219.8035 + (−9.1196)(x)$ **c** Lower 90%: $25 \times −22.7314 = −568.285$; upper 90%: $25 \times 4.4922 = 112.305$ **d** Because $F = 1.5 < 5.117$, do not reject H_O.

13-53 a A possible positive linear relationship **b** $\hat{y} = 66.7111 + 10.6167(x)$

13-55 a 0.7059 **b** Because $t = 3.8598 > 1.3406$, reject H_O.

13-57 Multiplying 0.0002385 ——— 0.0008175 by 10,000 gives: 2.385 ——— 8.175

13-59 a Lower 95%: $50 \times 7.5673 = 378.365$; upper 95%: $50 \times 11.8416 = 592.08$ **b** No **c** Confidence interval lower limit = 2115.458156; confidence interval upper limit = 2687.465486

13-61 a 105.7397 ——— 116.2603 **b** 87.2979 ——— 134.7021

13-63 3.4358 ——— 3.4922

CHAPTER 14

14-1 a Holding x_2 constant and increasing x_1 by one unit, the average y is estimated to increase by 4.14 units. $b_2 = 8.72$. This implies that, holding x_1 constant and increasing x_2 by one unit, the average y is estimated to increase by 4.14 units. **b** 107.71

14-3 a $\hat{y} = 10.437 + 1.3108x_1$ **b** $\hat{y} = −29.83 + 3.500x_2$ **c** $\hat{y} = −21.82 + 0.7513x_1 + 2.4357x_2$

14-5 No

14-7 a Excel Output

	Calls Received	Ads Placed Previous Week	Calls Received the Previous Week	Airline Bookings
Calls Received	1			
Ads Placed Previous Week	0.5843589	1		
Calls Received the Previous Week	0.654483	0.709017466	1	
Airline Bookings	0.5339732	0.360694798	0.219988054	1

b Calls Received − Ads Placed Previous Week—indicates a weak positive linear relationship; Calls Received − Calls Received Previous Week—indicates a weak positive linear relationship; Calls Received − Airline Bookings—indicates a weak positive linear relationship. A multiple regression model is possible, but the relations are not strong.
c $\hat{y} = −93.0196 + 36.0196$ (Ads); $\hat{y} = −18.3280 + 1.0679$ (Calls); $\hat{y} = 27.4730 + 0.1206$ (Bookings) **d** The second model has the largest F-value, the highest R^2, and the smallest s^2.

14-9 a A positive linear relationship between team win/loss percentage and attendance; a positive linear relationship between opponent win/loss percentage and attendance; a positive linear relationship between games played and attendance; no relationship between temperature and game attendance. **b** A significant relationship between game attendance and team win/loss percentage and games played. Therefore, a multiple regression model could be effective.

c Excel output

	Coefficients	Standard Error	t-Stat	p-value
Intercept	14122.24086	4335.791765	3.25713079	0.007637823
Team Win/Loss %	63.15325348	14.93880137	4.227464568	0.001418453
Opponent Win/Loss %	10.09582009	14.31396102	0.705312811	0.49528028
Games Played	31.50621796	177.129782	0.177870811	0.862057676
Temperature	−55.4609057	62.09372861	−0.89318047	0.390882768

d 77.53% **e** p-value = 0.00143, conclude the overall model is significant. **f** For team win/loss percentage the p-value = 0.0014 < 0.08 significant; for opponent win/loss percentage the p-value = 0.4953 > 0.08 not significant; for games played the p-value = 0.8621 > 0.08 not significant; for temperature the p-value = 0.3909 > 0.08 not significant **g** 1184.1274

h

	VIF
Team win/loss percentage and all other x	1.57
Temperature and all other x	1.96
Games played and all other x	1.31428258
Opponent win/loss percentage and all other x	1.50934547

The low VIF values indicate multicollinearity is not a problem.

i Excel output

	Lower 95%	Upper 95%
Intercept	4579.222699	23665.25902
Team Winn/Loss %	30.27315672	96.03335024
Opponent Win/Loss %	−21.40901163	41.6006518
Games Played	−358.3540008	421.3664367
Temperature	−192.12835	81.20653863

14-11 a 3 **b** $y = \beta_0 + \beta_1 x_1 + \beta_2 x_2 + \beta_3 x_3 + \beta_4 x_4 + \varepsilon$; $x_1 = \{1$ for level 1, 0 otherwise$\}$; $x_2 = \{1$ for level 2, 0 otherwise$\}$, $x_3 = \{1$ for level 3, 0 otherwise$\}$
14-13 $x_4 = 1$ if gas water heater, 0 otherwise; $x_5 = 1$ if constructed before 1974, 0 otherwise; $y = \beta_0 + \beta_1 x_1 + \beta_2 x_2 + \beta_3 x_3 + \beta_4 x_4 + \beta_5 x_5 + \varepsilon$
14-17 a $x_2 = 1$ if manufacturing, 0 otherwise; $x_3 = 1$ if service, 0 otherwise; $\hat{y} = -586.2556 + 22.8611(x_1) + 2302.2670(x_2) + 1869.8130(x_3)$
b $F = 5.3934 > 4.3468$ the model is significant **c** p-value for hours = 0.4613 **d** $\hat{y} = 71 + 2689(x_2) + 2127(x_3)$ **e** 495.8326 ——— 4,882.16
14-19 b $\hat{y} = 9.398 + 0.5181x$. Not significant. **c** $\hat{y} = -5.445 + 3.8509x - 0.14793x^2$ not significant; better R^2.
14-21 b $\hat{y} = 4.937 + 1.2643x$ significant **c** $\hat{y} = -25.155 + 18.983 \ln x$ significant; better fit
14-23 a $\hat{y} = 2902.965 + 12.263x$; $\hat{y} = -1070.398 + 293.483x - 4.536x^2$ **b** The simple linear model is not a significant model; the 2nd order model is a significant model. **c** No. **d** The 2nd order model
14-25 a $\hat{y} = 5.9023 + 2.8426x - 0.8049x^2$ **b** $r = 0.9477$ significant
c $\hat{y} = -4.9533 + 3.8123x$ **d** The nonlinear model was shown in part a and has a higher R-square.
14-27 a Price = 207311.77 − 2192.3367 (age) + 6.8385 (age sq)
c Price = 205722.97 − 1856.76 (age)
14-29 a

	y	x_1	x_2
x_1	−0.088		
	0.765		
x_2	0.062	−0.366	
	0.834	0.198	
x_3	0.383	−0.128	0.129
	0.176	0.664	0.660

Cell Contents: Pearson correlation, p-value
b $\hat{y} = 26.19 + 0.42x_3$ with a high alpha to enter. **c** $\hat{y} = 27.9 - 0.035x_1 - 0.002x_2 + 0.412x_3$

14-31 a $\hat{y} = -18.33 + 1.07x_2$ **b** There is one independent variable (x_2) and one dependent variable (y).
14-33 a Team win/loss percentage **b** Only one step occurred in this model. **c** No other variables are significant. **d** The model is significant with a p-value of 3.2237E-05. The team win/loss percentage is significant with a p-value of 3.2237E-05.
14-35 a $\hat{y} = 5.494 + 1.2213x$ **b** Yes. p-value = 0.002
c

RESI1	SRES1
−7.82146	−2.07346
3.51475	0.85039
5.40844	1.20642
2.52340	0.55140
0.63835	0.14135
−3.46796	−0.82305
−0.79552	−0.23246

No significant evidence.
14-37 a $\hat{y} = 16.928 + 0.286x$ **b** No
c
RESIDUAL OUTPUT

Observation	Predicted y	Residuals	Standard Residuals
1	21.49957134	−6.499571341	−0.594099288
2	22.35676669	−2.356766687	−0.215422424
3	23.7854256	4.214574403	0.385237044
4	24.92835273	−9.928352725	−0.907510199
5	26.07127985	8.928720147	0.816137866
6	27.49993876	−7.499938763	−0.685538791
7	29.21432945	25.78567055	2.356962899
8	34.07176975	−9.071769749	−0.829213446
9	37.21481935	−5.214819351	−0.476665352
10	38.35774648	1.642253521	0.150111691

Perhaps increasing variance.

14-41 a Excel output

	Coefficients	Standard Error	t Stat	p-value
Intercept	14122.24086	4335.791765	3.25713079	0.0076378
Team Win/Loss Percentage	63.15325348	14.93880137	4.227464568	0.0014185
Opponent Win/Loss Percentage	10.09582009	14.31396102	0.705312811	0.4952803
Games Played	31.50621796	177.129782	0.177870811	0.8620577
Temperature	−55.4609057	62.09372861	−0.89318047	0.3908828

c The plot of residuals does not appear to have a pattern, therefore the constant variance assumption has apparently not been violated. **d** The plot of the residuals against time shows a systematic variation about zero, indicating that the residuals are dependent. **e** Based on the normal probability plot, which is almost a straight line, we can assume the model error terms are approximately normally distributed.
14-43 a The residuals do not exhibit a constant variance. When $Days^2$ is small the variance of the residuals is large and decreases as $Days^2$ increases. **b** The residuals seem to possess a normal distribution. **c** Within 1 standard deviation = 9/16 = 56.25%; within 2 standard deviations = 16/16 = 100%; within 3 standard deviations = 16/16 = 100%; because there are 68.75% within one standard deviation and 100% within two standard deviations, the residuals appear to be normally distributed.
14-51 Excel output

	Coefficients	Standard Error	t Stat	p-value
Intercept	21.48048774	10.53116151	2.039707	0.066137
Case Analysis Score	2.363993584	1.183937188	1.996722	0.071203
Written Presentation Score	1.531347982	1.773536135	0.863443	0.406327
Oral Presentation Score	3.807380091	2.493027189	1.527212	0.154937

14-53 a The calculated F is 16.6931 > 3.5874, so conclude that the overall regression model is significant. **b** Improve oral presentation skills because this is the most highly correlated of the three independent variables.
14-55 a The R^2 is 0.8199. This factor is measured by SSR/TSS. **b** Job rating = 21.4805 + 2.3640(9.1) + 1.5313(9.4) + 3.8074(9.3) = 92.7959
c −2.3722 ——— 5.4349; effect could be 0 because this interval contains 0.
14-57 a $R^2 = 0.8448$; because $F = 13.6076 > 3.4780$, conclude that the overall model is significant.

b

	Coefficients	Lower 95%	Upper 95%
Intercept	−125307.8062	−194563.0421	−56052.6
Pages x_1	175.8963214	87.28373715	264.5089
Competing Books x_2	−1573.777885	−6020.812614	2873.257
Advertising Budget x_3	1.591706487	0.601381026	2.582032
Age of Author x_4	1613.747496	221.1082826	3006.387

c The critical t-value would be ±2.2281.

	Coefficients	Standard Error	t Stat	p-value
Intercept	−125307.8062	31082.09519	−4.031510921	0.002393684
Pages x_1	175.8963214	39.76976966	4.422864977	0.001288354
Competing Books x_2	−1573.777885	1995.851361	−0.788524595	0.448679286
Advertising Budget x_3	1.591706487	0.444463005	3.581190042	0.005001797
Age of Author x_4	1613.747496	625.0234231	2.581899232	0.027327123

Competing books not significant.

d The interval is: 175.8963 ± 2.2281(39.7698); 87.2852 ——— 264.5074
14-59 There appears to be a negative linear relationship between age and purchases; there appears to be a slight positive linear relationship between purchases and family income; based on the scatter plot it is difficult to detect any pattern of relationship between family size and purchases; there does not appear to be any relationship between age and family income; there appears to be a slightly positive linear relationship between age and family size; there seems to be little correlation between income and family size.
14-61 It had the highest correlation with average monthly purchases.

14-63 The interval is: 0.000329 − 0.003653.

14-65 Issues to address: (1) Did the adjusted R^2 increase?; (2) Did the standard error decrease?; (3) For a model that will be used for forecasting purposes, is the added variable significant?; (4) Does the introduction of the new variable into the model introduce a high level of multicollinearity?

14-73 $x_7 = 1$ if NYSE, 0 otherwise, $x_8 = 1$ if NASDAQ, 0 otherwise; if both are 0, the designation is OTC. Excel output

	Growth %	Sales	EPS	Profits	Last Yr Price	P/E Ratio	x_7	x_8	Stk-Price
Growth %	1								
Sales	−0.09866	1							
EPS	0.358471	−0.15644	1						
Profits	−0.1172	0.744225	−0.01751	1					
Last Yr Price	−0.16851	0.505016	0.214602	0.668754	1				
P/E ratio	0.00722	0.27566	0.150827	0.1032	0.0857454	1			
x_7	0.006398	0.209664	−0.03129	0.143019	0.2176906	−0.10315	1		
x_8	−0.09525	−0.09168	−0.22298	−0.07548	0.00200916	0.09867	−0.16479	1	
Stk-Price	−0.07107	0.201503	0.447163	0.507966	0.65544737	0.306452	0.024908	−0.07927	1

The best predictors would be the ones most highly correlated with the stock price.

CHAPTER 15

15-9 a

Year	Radio Advertising	Index	Newspaper Ads	Index
1	300	100.00	400	100
2	310	103.33	420	105
3	330	110.00	460	115
4	346	115.33	520	130
5	362	120.67	580	145
6	380	126.67	640	160
7	496	165.33	660	165

b

Year	Radio Advertising	Newspaper Ads	Sum	Index
1	300	400	700	100.0
2	310	420	730	104.29
3	330	460	790	112.86
4	346	520	866	123.71
5	362	580	942	134.57
6	380	640	1020	145.71
7	496	660	1156	165.14

c

Year	Radio Advertising	Percent Radio	Newspaper Ads	Laspeyres
1	300	30	400	100.00
2	310	35	420	104.59
3	330	35	460	113.78
4	346	38	520	126.43
5	362	40	580	139.08
6	380	42	640	151.89
7	496	45	660	165.08

d

Year	Radio Advertising	Percent Ratio	Newspaper Ads	Paasche
1	300	30	400	100.00
2	310	35	420	104.52
3	330	35	460	113.56
4	346	38	520	124.42
5	362	40	580	135.75
6	380	42	640	147.32
7	496	45	660	165.13

15-11 From the time-series plot we see that there is a positive, linear trend. We can also see that there are movements that are not attributed to the trend. In other words random components. No seasonal or cyclical components are present.

15-13 Both graphs show an upward trend with random components and perhaps a cyclical component.

15-15 See Student Solutions Manual.

Year	Hourly Wages	Index	Labor Cost	Average Material Cost	Index	Laspeyres Index
1992	30.10	1.00	44333	66500	1.00	1.00
1993	30.50	1.01	44922	68900	1.04	1.03
1994	31.70	1.05	46690	70600	1.06	1.06
1995	32.50	1.08	47868	70900	1.07	1.07
1996	34.00	1.13	50077	71200	1.07	1.09
1997	34.50	1.15	50814	71700	1.08	1.10
1998	35.10	1.17	51697	72500	1.09	1.11
1999	35.05	1.16	51624	73700	1.11	1.13
2000	34.90	1.16	51403	73400	1.10	1.12
2001	33.80	1.12	49783	74100	1.11	1.12
2002	34.20	1.14	50372	74000	1.11	1.12

15-17 Follow the procedure outlined in Figures 15-19 and 15-20.

15-19

	Ratio-to-MA Values			Total	Seasonal Index	Normalized Index
January	0.792	0.903	0.860	2.556	0.852	0.849
February	0.781	0.878	0.938	2.598	0.866	0.863
March	0.708	0.851	0.816	2.375	0.792	0.789
April	0.796	0.915	0.898	2.608	0.869	0.866
May	0.880	0.962	0.944	2.785	0.928	0.925
June	0.969	0.935	0.905	2.809	0.936	0.933
July	0.963	1.006	0.940	2.909	0.970	0.966
August	1.031	1.027	1.001	3.060	1.020	1.016
September	1.091	1.072	1.075	3.238	1.079	1.075
October	1.188	1.086	1.143	3.417	1.139	1.135
November	1.360	1.252	1.170	3.782	1.261	1.256
December	1.478	1.252	1.266	3.996	1.332	1.327
				Sum = 12.045		

The normalized index for January, 0.849, compared to July, 0.966, indicates that both months have sales below the average trend value for the year, but January's are lower than July's.

15-21 The sales data show a slight upward trend with a likely seasonal component with lower sales during July and November of each year. The Durbin-Watson Statistic is less than 1.21, the value of d_L for an $\alpha = 0.01$, indicating autocorrelation is present.

15-23 The seasonally adjusted model provides a better fit—it is more significant, has a higher multiple R value, and a lower standard error; unadjusted model: tickets sold = 1271.02 + 16.38 (month); seasonally adjusted model: tickets sold = 1224.63 + 19.05 (month)

15-25 a There appears to be an upward linear trend but you also see a seasonal component as a slight drop in the 3rd quarter.

b

Quarter	Seasonal Index
1	1.035
2	1.021
3	0.960
4	0.984

c $MSE = 36.955$, $MAD = 4.831$

d and **e**

Quarter	Period	Seasonally Unadjusted Forecast	Seasonal Index	Seasonally Adjusted Forecast
Quarter 1 2001	17	250.1526	1.0350	258.9113
Quarter 2 2001	18	256.1667	1.0209	261.5201
Quarter 3 2001	19	262.1808	0.9599	251.6764
Quarter 4 2001	20	268.1950	0.9842	263.9452

15-27 b

Month	Seasonal Index
January	0.9590
February	0.8831
March	0.8880
April	0.9929
May	1.0273
June	0.9244
July	0.9776
August	1.0172
September	1.0489
October	1.0040
November	1.1116
December	1.1661

c $MSE = 52.360$, $MAD = 5.146$, because $114.12 > 4.0069$, reject H_O and conclude that the overall model is significant. **d** Prediction interval lower limit = 108.6077603, prediction interval upper limit = 144.2316447; this should be multiplied by 10,000 but it shows his goal is not realistic.

e

Year 2002	Adjusted Forecast
January	94.8188
February	87.8334
March	88.8379
April	99.9134
May	103.9839
June	94.1102
July	100.0930
August	104.7470
September	108.6245
October	104.5635
November	116.4182
December	122.8128

15-29 b

MSE	MAD
976.339	29.887

c

Quarter	Index
1	1.0290
2	0.9207
3	1.0789
4	0.9714

d

Quarter 2001	Period	Forecast
1st quarter	13	256.562
2nd quarter	14	260.088
3rd quarter	15	263.615
4th quarter	16	267.141

e

Period	Forecast	Seasonal Index	Adjusted Forecast	Actual	Differences	Difference Squared	Absolute Differences
13	256.562	1.0290	264.0107	229	−35.0107	1225.7504	35.0107
14	260.0884	0.9207	239.4574	221	−18.4574	340.6745	18.4574
15	263.6149	1.0789	284.4074	248	−36.4074	1325.4997	36.4074
16	267.1413	0.9714	259.5053	231	−28.5053	812.5503	28.5053
						MSE	MAD
						926.1187	29.5952

f The adjusted model has a lower MSE and MAD.

15-31 a Without transformation = 210.0376; with transformation = 244.1914, **b** Without transformation: Lower limit = 161.76, upper limit = 258.316; with transformation: Lower limit = 55.52, upper limit = 97.433

15-33 Equation 15-16 is used for this exercise. **a** 259.67 **b** 268.92 **c** *MAD* for part a was 14.091. *MAD* for part b was 11.459 so $\alpha = 0.25$ produced the smaller *MAD*.

15-35 a For $\alpha = 0.2$, *MAD* = 352.6123; $\alpha = 0.5$, *MAD* = 341.5508; $\alpha = 0.8$, *MAD* = 333.7059. **b** $\alpha = 0.8$ provides the smallest *MAD*. The forecast would be 2011.552. **c** Equations 15-18, 15-19, and 15-20 are used. Using linear regression $C_O = 1711.33$ and $T_O = 9.21$. Minimum *MAD* when both α and β are 0.2.

15-37 *MAD* = 138.13, October forecast = 23,703.7

15-39 b Forecast = 15,912.50 *MAD* = 1,286 **c** Forecast = 15790.30, *MAD* = 1366.48 **d** *MAD* is smaller for an alpha of 0.25.

15-41 a There is a random component to the series. Also, it appears that sales are trending upward over time with sales in the later months higher than the earlier months. **b** Forecast = 64626.48, *MAD* = 7583.51 **c** Use $\alpha = 0.55$, forecast = 69338.82, *MAD* = 7084.16. Using alpha = 0.30, the forecast for week 17 is 64,626.48 with a *MAD* of 7,583.51.

15-43 Lower limit = 49781.28; upper limit = 92539.224

15-49 b Sales = $-680183698.5 + 342385.2941$(year), $R^2 = 0.899$, *p*-value = 2.431E-8, highly significant. **c** *MAD* = 461216.73
d

Year	Forecast
2001	4,929,275.00
2002	5,271,660.29
2003	5,614,045.59
2004	5,956,430.88
2005	6,298,816.18

e Lower limit = 5066720.85; upper limit = 7530911.50

15-51 a The starting values are $-891,275,11$ and 342,385.29. *MAD* = 526262.47
c

	BETA VALUES			
	0.5	0.4	0.3	0.2
ALPHA VALUES 0.1	$568,793.54	$547,728.21	$523,915.68	$498,375.36
0.2	$538,592.87	$526,262.47	$515,577.21	$497,639.06
0.3	$481,539.18	$466,164.76	$459,595.63	$452,681.23
0.4	$454,803.56	$449,962.38	$436,850.70	$421,877.56

The combination of alpha = 0.4 and beta = 0.2 produced the smallest *MAD*.

15-53 Use the procedure developed for the Taft Ice Cream example of Section 15-2. **a** Sales = $-570875.32 + 177644.89$ (year) **c** *MAD* = 257898.24 **d** Lower limit = 2781607; upper limit = 4248307.29

15-55 b Sales = $-3044.57 + 1.531$(year), $R^2 = 0.939$, *p*-value = 2.104E-7. **c** 17.031 **d** H_O: $\beta_1 = 0$, H_A: $\beta_1 \neq 0$; because 12.43 > 2.228, reject H_O. **e** This plot suggests a curvilinear model: Sales = $472031.72 - 474.86$ (years) + 0.12 (years^2).

15-57 Use Equations 15-18, 15-19, 15-20 and follow Example 15-7. **a** The starting values are found using regression, -1.4 and 1.53. *MAD* = 1.34.
c

	BETA			
	1.3447	0.5	0.4	0.3	0.2
ALPHA VALUES 0.1	1.46	1.41	1.37	1.32
0.2	1.48	1.45	1.41	1.36
0.3	1.43	1.40	1.34	1.29
0.4	1.33	1.31	1.29	1.25

The combination of alpha = 0.4 and beta = 0.2 produced the smallest *MAD*.

15-59 a Using a linear regression model 290.60 to 389.34 **b** 102.2184 or month number 103

15-61 a *MAD* = 5181.12 **c** The *MAD* for the double exponential model is 5181.12. The *MAD* for the linear trend model based on deseasonalized data is 1,419.13. Recommend the linear trend model.
d

	BETA			
	0.3	0.25	0.2	0.1
ALPHA VALUES 0.1	5190.35	5101.89	5013.90	4823.45
0.15	5397.24	5258.43	5130.99	4892.37
0.2	5538.02	5354.95	5181.12	4872.93
0.3	5374.41	5192.38	5019.96	4709.27

Alpha = 0.30 and beta = 0.10 provides the lowest *MAD*.

15-63 Use Equation 15-16 or Equation 15-17 and follow Example 15-6. **a** Initial forecast = 1375. Forecast for period 37 = 1722.89. **b** *MAD* = 144.83
d

Alpha	MAD
0.1	172.57
0.2	144.83
0.3	138.26
0.4	134.30
0.5	131.35

The lowest *MAD* value of 131.35 corresponds to the alpha value of 0.5.

15-65 a

Month	Index
January	0.7860
February	0.5190
March	0.4137
April	0.9487
May	1.2799
June	0.6073
July	1.0082
August	0.9605
September	0.8764
October	1.2023
November	1.8250
December	1.5729

b and c

Month	Period	Unadjusted Forecast	Seasonal Index	Adjusted Forecast
January	61	9.4703	0.7860	7.4434
February	62	9.5226	0.5190	4.9425
March	63	9.5748	0.4137	3.9614
April	64	9.6271	0.9487	9.1333
May	65	9.6793	1.2799	12.3889
June	66	9.7315	0.6073	5.9098
July	67	9.7838	1.0082	9.8644
August	68	9.8360	0.9605	9.4474
September	69	9.8883	0.8764	8.6661
October	70	9.9405	1.2023	11.9512
November	71	9.9927	1.8250	18.2369
December	72	10.0450	1.5729	15.8000

CHAPTER 16

16-1 Calculated W = 39 < 45, do not reject H_O.

16-3 Because calculated W = 36 > 13, do not reject H_O.

16-5 a H_O: $\tilde{\mu} \leq 4000$, H_A: $\tilde{\mu} > 4000$ **b** Calculated W = 59 < 61, do not reject H_O.

16-7 H_O: $\tilde{\mu} \geq 11$, H_A: $\tilde{\mu} < 11$; rank 19 values, calculated W = 92 > 53, do not reject H_O.

16-9 H_O: $\tilde{\mu} = 30$, H_A: $\tilde{\mu} \ne 30$; calculated $W = 71.5$, 81.5, Wilcoxon test values are 34 and 119 ($\alpha = 0.05$) and 23 and 130 ($\alpha = 0.01$)

16-11 a Because the calculated $\chi^2 = 3.50 < 5.9915$ data are normally distributed. **b** H_O: $\mu \ge 7.4$, H_A: $\mu < 7.4$; $z = 10.13 > -1.645$, do not reject H_O.

16-13 a Use U_2, reject if $U \le 11$. **b** Use U_1, reject if $U \le 55$. **c** Use smallest of U_1 or U_2, reject if $U \le 64$. **d** Use z-value from Equation 16-6. Reject if $z < -1.645$. **e** Use z-value from Equation 16-6. Reject if $z < -1.645$ or $z > 1.645$.

16-15 a H_O: $\tilde{\mu}_1 - \tilde{\mu}_2 \ge 0$; H_A: $\tilde{\mu}_1 - \tilde{\mu}_2 < 0$ **b** Use U_2 as the test statistic; because $U = 8 < 21$, reject H_O.

16-17 H_O: $\tilde{\mu}_1 - \tilde{\mu}_2 = 0$, H_A: $\tilde{\mu}_1 - \tilde{\mu}_2 \ne 0$; solve using Minitab; $W = 1384.0$; test of $ETA_1 = ETA_2$ vs. ETA_1 not $= ETA_2$ is significant at 0.1502; cannot reject at alpha $= 0.05$.

16-19 H_O: $\tilde{\mu}_1 - \tilde{\mu}_2 = 0$, H_A: $\tilde{\mu}_1 - \tilde{\mu}_2 \ne 0$; because $T = 23.5 > 8$, do not reject H_O.

16-21 H_O: $\tilde{\mu}_1 - \tilde{\mu}_2 = 0$, H_A: $\tilde{\mu}_1 - \tilde{\mu}_2 \ne 0$; because $T = 13 > 2$, do not reject H_O.

16-23 H_O: $\tilde{\mu}_2 = \tilde{\mu}_1$, H_A: $\tilde{\mu}_2 \ne \tilde{\mu}_1$; because $T = 8 > 0$, do not reject H_O.

16-25 H_O: $\tilde{\mu}_P = \tilde{\mu}_H$, H_A: $\tilde{\mu}_P \ne \tilde{\mu}_H$, $U_1 = 43$, $U_2 = 37$; because $37 > 13$, do not reject H_O.

16-27 H_O: $\tilde{\mu}_S - \tilde{\mu}_J = 0$, H_A: $\tilde{\mu}_S - \tilde{\mu}_J \ne 0$, U test $= 22$; the p-value $= 0.426$, do not reject H_O.

16-29 H_O: $\tilde{\mu}_1 = \tilde{\mu}_2$, H_A: $\tilde{\mu}_1 \ne \tilde{\mu}_2$, $z = 0.94$; p-value $= 0.3472$, do not reject H_O.

16-31 a H_O: $\tilde{\mu}_S \ge \tilde{\mu}_D$, H_A: $\tilde{\mu}_S < \tilde{\mu}_D$, $z = -2.936$; because $-2.936 < -1.645$ reject H_O. **b** Type I

16-33 a H_O: $\tilde{\mu}_S = \tilde{\mu}_P$ H_A: $\tilde{\mu}_S \ne \tilde{\mu}_P$; calculated $T = 50 > 21$, do not reject H_O. **b** $t = 0.1526$; because $0.15261 < 2.1448$, do not reject H_O. **c** Because you cannot assume a normal distribution with the Wilcoxon Matched-Pairs Signed-Ranks Test.

16-35 a You will want to use a paired t test, $t = -1.785$; because $-1.785 > -2.2622$, do not reject H_O. **b** H_O: $\tilde{\mu}_O \ge \tilde{\mu}_N$, H_A: $\tilde{\mu}_O < \tilde{\mu}_N$; because calculated $T = 5.5 < 6$, reject H_O. **c** Because you cannot assume the underlying populations are normal, use the technique from part b.

16-37 a H_O: $\tilde{\mu}_1 = \tilde{\mu}_2 = \tilde{\mu}_3$; H_A: not all population medians are equal
b

H test statistic	5.4163
Critical value	5.9915
p-value	0.0667

Do not reject the null hypothesis
c Excel output
ANOVA

Source of Variation	SS	df	MS	F	p-value	F crit
Between groups	336.0833	2	168.0417	3.447	0.05075	3.467
Within groups	1023.75	21	48.75			
Total	1359.833	23				

Because calculated $F = 3.447 < 3.467$, do not reject H_O.
d The Kruskal–Wallis test.

16-39 a H_O: $\tilde{\mu}_1 = \tilde{\mu}_2 = \tilde{\mu}_3 = \tilde{\mu}_4$; H_A: not all population medians are equal **b** At $\alpha = 0.05$, $H = 41.11 > \chi^2_\alpha > = 7.8147$, reject H_O.

16-41 a No **b** Adjustment is only necessary when the null hypothesis is not rejected.

16-43 H_O: $\tilde{\mu}_1 = \tilde{\mu}_2 = \tilde{\mu}_3$, H_A: Not all population medians are equal; Using PHStat:

H test statistic	14.854
Critical value	5.9914
p-value	0.00059

Reject the null hypothesis

16-45 H_O: $\tilde{\mu}_1 = \tilde{\mu}_2 = \tilde{\mu}_3$, H_A: Not all population medians are equal, $H = 13.9818$; testing at $\alpha = 0.05$, $\chi^2_\alpha = 5.9915$; because $13.9818 > 5.9915$, reject H_O.

16-53 a H_O: $\tilde{\mu}_1 - \tilde{\mu}_2 = 0$, H_A: $\tilde{\mu}_1 - \tilde{\mu}_2 \ne 0$, U test $= 42$; because $42 > 27$, do not reject H_O. **b** H_O: $\mu_1 - \mu_2 = 0$, H_A: $\mu_1 - \mu_2 \ne 0$; use the t-test for unequal variances; find 10 degrees of freedom; $t = 0.0661$, do not reject H_O; assume normal populations and independence in sampling.

16-55 a H_O: $\tilde{\mu}_1 - \tilde{\mu}_2 = 0$, H_A: $\tilde{\mu}_1 - \tilde{\mu}_2 \ne 0$, U test $= 58$; because $58 > 24$, do not reject H_O. **b** H_O: $\mu_1 - \mu_2 = 0$, H_A: $\mu_1 - \mu_2 \ne 0$; variances are equal; $t = -0.2518$; because $-0.2518 > -2.5280$, do not reject H_O; assume independence when sampling from normal populations with equal variances.

16-57 H_O: $\tilde{\mu}_1 = \tilde{\mu}_2 = \tilde{\mu}_3$, H_A: not all population medians are equal, $H = 12.252$, Chi square $= 5.9915$; because $12.252 > 5.9915$, reject H_O.

16-59 a H_O: $\tilde{\mu} = 8.03$, H_A: $\tilde{\mu} \ne 8.03$ **b** If $\alpha = 0.05$, using Appendix P, reject if $W \le 25$ or $W > 95$. Calculated values are 57.5 and 62.5.

16-61 a H_O: $\tilde{\mu}_1 = \tilde{\mu}_2$, H_A: $\tilde{\mu}_1 \ne \tilde{\mu}_2$, $\alpha = 0.05$, reject if $T \le 21$ or if $T \ge 84$; because calculated $T = 44.5 > 21$, do not reject H_O. **b** Conclude the medians are the same when they are not.

16-63 a The Wilcoxon Matched-Pairs Signed Rank **b** H_O: $\tilde{\mu}_{w/oA} \ge \tilde{\mu}_A$, H_A: $\tilde{\mu}_{w/oA} < \tilde{\mu}_A$; using $\alpha = 0.025$, $T_\alpha = 4$; because $6 > 4$, do not reject H_O.

CHAPTER 17

17-11 $\bar{p} = 0.090$ UCL $= 0.176$, LCL $= 0.004$

17-15 a

	x-bar	Range
Hour 41	0.7386	0.048
Hour 42	0.7834	0.033
Hour 43	0.7946	0.054

There is no evidence that a special cause of variation is present.
b Yes. You need the charts to determine when special cause variation is present.

17-17 a Several observations are below the LCL.

17-19 a p-chart. UCL $= 0.1603$, LCL (3×0.0270) $= -0.0017$, which is then set equal to 0.0000. **b** The process is in control. **c** The process is still in statistical control.

17-21 a Because time is measured, both the x-bar and R-charts are required. **b** 82.46 **c** 12.33 **d** UCL $= 82.46 + (0.58 \times 12.33) = 89.61$. LCL $= 82.46 - (0.58 \times 12.33) = 75.31$ **e** UCL $= 2.11 \times 12.33 = 26.02$, LCL $= 0 \times 12.33 = 0$ **f** Range chart has a run of nine values above the centerline. The x-bar chart has means above the upper control limit and below the lower control limit.

17-23 a UCL $= 288.855$, LCL $= 0$ **b** UCL $= 488.574$, LCL $= 342.026$ **c** Week 15 is above the upper control limit on the R-chart.

17-25 a p-chart **b** UCL $= 0.0294 + 3(0.0239) = 0.1011$; LCL $= 0.0294 - 3(0.0239) = -0.0423$ so set to 0 **c** All points are above the UCL. **d** The sample proportion is again above the UCL.

17-27 a c-chart, UCL $= 45.5814$, LCL $= 13.0852$ **b** The process is out of control. **c** You need to convert the data to bags per passenger by dividing bags by 40 and then developing a u-chart.

17-29 a $A_2 = 1.02$, $D_4 = 2.57$. **b** UCL $= 2.056$, LCL $= 0$ **c** UCL $= 3.146$, LCL $= 1,514$

17-31 UCL $= 0.345$, LCL $= 0.135$

17-33 not c-chart, UCL $= .9989$, LCL $= .8315$

17-35 UCL $= 0.1193$, LCL $= 0$

GLOSSARY

Adjusted *R*-squared—A measure of the percentage of explained variation in the dependent variable that takes into account the relationship between the sample size and the number of independent variables in the regression model.

Aggregate Price Index—An index that is used to measure the rate of change from a base period for a group of two or more items.

All-inclusive classes—A set of classes that contains all the possible data values.

Alternative hypothesis—The hypothesis that includes all population values not covered by the null hypothesis. The alternative hypothesis is deemed to be true if the null hypothesis is rejected.

Aptness—The degree to which a regression model satisfies the basic assumptions of multiple regression, including the following.
1. The relationship between the dependent and independent variables is linear.
2. The variance of the model errors is constant over the range of the values of the independent variables.
3. The model errors are independent from observation to observation.
4. The model errors are normally distributed.

Arithmetic mean, or average—The sum of all the values divided by the number of values.

Autocorrelation—Correlation of the error terms (residuals) occurs when the residuals at successive points in time are related.

Average—The sum of all the values divided by the number of values.

Balanced design—An experiment has a balanced design if the factor levels have equal sample sizes.

Bar chart—A graphical representation of a categorical data set in which a rectangle or bar is drawn over each category or class. The length of each bar represents the frequency or percentage of observations, or some other measure associated with the category. The bars may be vertical or horizontal. The bars may all be the same color or they may be different colors depicting different categories. Additionally, multiple variables can be graphed on the same bar chart.

Base period index—The time-series value to which all other values in the time series are compared. The index number for the base period is defined as 100.

Between-sample variation—Dispersion among the factor sample means is called the *between-sample variation*.

Binomial probability distribution characteristics—A distribution that gives the probability of *x* successes in *n* trials in a process that meets the following conditions.
1. A trial has only two possible outcomes: a success or a failure.
2. There is a fixed number, *n*, of identical trials.
3. The trials of the experiment are independent of each other. This means that if one outcome is a success, this does not influence the chance of another outcome being a success.

4. The process must be consistent in generating successes and failures. That is, the probability, *p*, associated with a success remains constant from trial to trial.
5. If *p* represents the probability of a success, then $(1 - p) = q$ is the probability of a failure.

Box and whisker plot—A graph that is composed of two parts: a box and the whiskers. The box has a width that ranges from the first quartile to the third quartile. The whiskers extend to the right and to the left of the box a distance of 1.5 times the distance between the first and third quartiles. A vertical line through the box is placed at the median.

Business statistics—A collection of tools and techniques that are used to convert data into meaningful information in a business environment.

Census—An enumeration of the entire set of measurements taken from the whole population.

Central limit theorem—For simple random samples of *n* observations taken from a population with mean μ and standard deviation σ, regardless of the population's distribution, provided the sample size is sufficiently large, the distribution of the sample means, $\bar{x}$, will be approximately normal with a mean equal to the population mean ($\mu_{\bar{x}} = \mu$) and a standard deviation equal to the population standard deviation divided by the square root of the sample size $\left(\sigma_{\bar{x}} = \dfrac{\sigma}{\sqrt{n}} \right)$. The larger the sample size, the better the approximation to the normal distribution.

Certainty—A decision environment in which the results of selecting each alternative are known before the decision is made.

Class boundaries—The upper and lower values of each class.

Class width—The distance between the lowest possible value and the highest possible value for a frequency class.

Classical probability assessment—The method of determining probability based on the ratio of the number of ways the event of interest can occur to the number of ways *any* event can occur when the individual elementary events are equally likely.

Closed-end questions—Questions that require the respondent to select from a short list of defined choices.

Cluster sampling—A method by which the population is divided into groups, or clusters, that are each intended to be mini-populations. A simple random sample of *m* clusters is selected. The items selected from a cluster can be selected using any probability sampling technique.

Coefficient of determination—The portion of the total variation in the dependent variable that is explained by its relationship with the independent variable. The coefficient of determination is also called *R*-squared and is denoted as R^2.

Coefficient of partial determination—The measure of the marginal contribution of each independent variable, given that other independent variables are in the model.

Coefficient of variation—The ratio of the standard deviation to the mean expressed as a percentage. The coefficient of variation is used to measure the relative variation in data.

Completely randomized design—An experiment is completely randomized if it consists of the independent random selection of observations representing each level of one factor.

Composite model—The model that contains both the basic terms and the interaction terms.

Conditional probability—The probability that an event will occur *given* that some other event has already happened.

Confidence coefficient—The confidence level divided by 100%—that is, the decimal equivalent of a confidence level.

Confidence interval—An interval developed from sample values such that if all possible intervals of a given width were constructed, a percentage of these intervals, known as the confidence level, would include the true population parameter.

Confidence level—A percentage less than 100 that corresponds to the percentage of all possible confidence intervals, based on a given sample size, that will contain the true population parameter.

Contingency table—A table used to classify sample observations according to two or more identifiable characteristics. It is also called a *cross-tabulation table*.

Continuous data—Data whose possible values are uncountable and which may assume any value in an interval.

Continuous random variables—Random variables that can assume any value in an interval.

Convenience sampling—A sampling technique that selects the items from the population based on accessibility and ease of selection.

Correlation coefficient—A quantitative measure of the strength of the linear relationship between two variables. The correlation ranges from -1.0 to $+1.0$. A correlation of ± 1.0 indicates a perfect linear relationship, whereas a correlation of 0 indicates no linear relationship.

Correlation matrix—A table showing the pairwise correlations between all variables (dependent and independent).

Critical value—The value of a statistic corresponding to a given significance level. This cutoff value determines the boundary between those samples resulting in a test statistic that leads to rejecting the null hypothesis and those that lead to a decision not to reject the null hypothesis.

Cross-sectional data—A set of data values observed at a fixed point in time.

Cumulative frequency distribution—A summary of a set of data that displays the number of observations with values less than or equal to the upper limit of each of its classes.

Cumulative relative frequency distribution—A summary of a set of data that displays the proportion of observations with values less than or equal to the upper limit of each of its classes.

Cyclical component—A wave-like pattern within the time series that repeats itself throughout the time series and has a recurrence period of more than one year.

Data array—Data that have been sorted in ascending or descending order.

Decision tree—A diagram that illustrates the correct ordering of actions and events in a decision-analysis problem. Each act or event is represented by a branch on the decision tree.

Degrees of freedom—The number of independent data values available to estimate the population's standard deviation. If k parameters must be estimated before the population's standard deviation can be calculated from a sample of size n, the degrees of freedom are equal to $n - k$.

Demographic questions—Questions relating to the respondents' own characteristics, backgrounds, and attributes.

Dependent events—Two events are dependent if the occurrence of one event impacts the probability of the other event occurring.

Dependent variable—A variable whose values are thought to be a function of, or dependent on, the values of another variable called the *independent variable*. On a scatter plot, the dependent variable is placed on the y axis and is often called the response variable.

Discrete data—Data whose possible values are countable.

Discrete random variable—A random variable that can assume only a countable number of possible values.

Dummy variables—A variable that is assigned a value equal to either zero or one, depending on whether the observation possesses a given characteristic.

Elementary events—The most rudimentary outcomes resulting from a simple experiment.

Equal-width classes—The distance between the lowest possible value and the highest possible value in each class is equal for all classes.

Event—A collection of elementary events.

Expected value—The mean of a discrete probability distribution. The average value when the experiment that generates values for the random variable is repeated over the long run.

Expected-value criterion—A decision criterion that employs probability to select the alternative that will produce the greatest average payoff or minimum average loss.

Experiment—A process that produces a single outcome whose result cannot be predicted with certainty.

Experimental design—A plan for performing an experiment in which the variable of interest is defined. One or more factors are identified to be manipulated or changed so that the impact (or influence) on the variable of interest can be measured or observed.

Experiment-wide error rate—The proportion of experiments in which at least one of the set of confidence intervals constructed does not contain the true value of the population parameter being estimated.

Exponential smoothing—A time-series and forecasting technique that produces an exponentially weighted moving average in which each smoothing calculation or forecast is dependent on all previous observed values.

Factor—A quantity under examination in an experiment as a possible cause of variation in the response variable.

Forecasting horizon—The number of future periods covered by a forecast. It is sometimes referred to as *forecast lead time*.

Forecasting interval—The frequency with which new forecasts are prepared.

Forecasting period—The unit of time for which forecasts are to be made.

Frequency distribution—A summary of a set of data that displays the number of observations in each of the distribution's distinct categories or classes.

Frequency histogram—A graph of a frequency distribution with the horizontal axis showing the classes, the vertical axis showing the frequency count, and (for equal class widths) the rectangles having a height equal to the frequency in each class.

Independent events—Two events are independent if the occurrence of one event in no way influences the probability of the occurrence of the other event.

Independent samples—Samples selected from two or more populations in such a way that the occurrence of values in one sample has no influence on the probability of the occurrence of values in the other sample(s).

Independent variable—A variable whose values are thought to impact the values of the *dependent variable*. The independent variable, or explanatory variable, is often within the direct control of the decision maker. On a scatter plot, the independent variable, or explanatory variable, is graphed on the x axis.

Interaction—The case in which one independent variable (such as x_2) affects the relationship between another independent variable (x_1) and a dependent variable (y).

Interquartile range—The interquartile range is a measure of variation that is determined by computing the difference between the third and first quartiles.

Least squares criterion—The criterion for determining a regression line that minimizes the sum of squared residuals.

Left-skewed data—A data distribution is left skewed if the mean for the data is smaller than the median.

Levels—The categories, measurements, or strata of a factor of interest in the current experiment.

Line chart—A two-dimensional chart showing time on the horizontal axis and the variable of interest on the vertical axis.

Linear trend—A long-term increase or decrease in a time series in which the rate of change is relatively constant.

Margin of error—The amount that is added and subtracted to the point estimate to determine the endpoints of the confidence interval.

Maximax criterion—An optimistic decision criterion for dealing with uncertainty without using probability. For each option, the decision maker finds the maximum possible payoff and then selects the option with the greatest maximum payoff.

Maximin criterion—A pessimistic (conservative) decision criterion for dealing with uncertainty without using probability. For each option, the decision maker finds the minimum possible payoff and selects the option with the greatest minimum payoff.

Mean—A numerical measure of the center of a set of quantitative measures computed by dividing the sum of the values by the number of values in the data.

Median—The median is a center value that divides a data array into two halves. We use $\tilde{\mu}$ to denote the population median and M_d to denote the sample median.

Minimax regret criterion—A decision criterion that considers the results of selecting the "wrong" alternative. For each state of nature, the decision maker finds the difference between the best payoff and each other alternative and uses these values to construct an opportunity-loss table. The decision maker then selects the alternative with the minimum opportunity loss (or regret).

Mode—The mode is the value in a data set that occurs most frequently.

Model—A representation of an actual system using either a physical or a mathematical portrayal.

Model diagnosis—The process of determining how well a model fits past data and how well the model's assumptions appear to be satisfied.

Model fitting—The process of determining how well a specified model fits past data.

Model specification—The process of selecting the forecasting technique to be used in a particular situation.

Moving averages—The successive averages of n consecutive values in a time series.

Multicollinearity—A high correlation between two independent variables such that the two variables contribute redundant information to the model. When highly correlated independent variables are included in the regression model, they can adversely affect the regression results.

Mutually exclusive classes—Classes that do not overlap so that a data value can be placed in only one class.

Mutually exclusive events—Two events are mutually exclusive if the occurrence of one event precludes the occurrence of the other event.

Nonstatistical sampling techniques—Those methods of selecting samples using convenience, judgment, or other nonchance processes.

Normal distribution—The normal distribution is a bell-shaped distribution with the following properties:

1. It is *unimodal*; that is, the normal distribution peaks at a single value.
2. It is *symmetrical*; this means that the two areas under the curve between the mean and any two points equidistant on either side of the mean are identical. One side of the distribution is the mirror image of the other side.
3. The mean, median, and mode are equal.
4. The normal approaches the horizontal axis on either side of the mean toward plus and minus infinity ($\pm\infty$). In more formal terms, the normal distribution is *asymptotic* to the x-axis.
5. The amount of variation in the random variable determines the width of the normal distribution.

Null hypothesis—The statement about the population value that will be tested. The null hypothesis will be rejected only if the sample data provide substantial contradictory evidence.

One-tailed test—A hypothesis test in which the entire rejection region is located in one tail of the sampling distribution. In a one-tailed test, the entire alpha level is located in one tail of the distribution.

One-way analysis of variance—An analysis of variance design in which independent samples are obtained from k levels of a single factor for the purpose of testing whether the k levels have equal means.

Open-end questions—Questions that allow respondents the freedom to respond with any value, words, or statements of their own choosing.

Opportunity loss—The difference between the actual payoff that occurs for a decision and the optimal payoff for the same state of nature.

Paired samples—Samples that are selected in such a way that values in one sample are matched with the values in the second sample for the purpose of controlling for extraneous factors. Another term for paired samples is dependent samples.

Parameter—A measure computed from the entire population. As long as the population does not change, the value of the parameter will not change.

Pareto principle—80% of the trouble comes from 20% of the causes.

Payoff—The outcome (profit or loss) for any combination of alternative and state of nature. The payoffs associated with all possible combinations of alternatives and states of nature constitute a *payoff table*.

Percentiles—The pth percentile in a data array is a value that divides the data set into two parts. The lower segment contains at least $p\%$, and the upper segment contains at least $(100 - p)\%$, of the data. The 50th percentile is the median.

Pie chart—A graph in the shape of a circle. The circle is divided into "slices" corresponding to the categories or classes to be displayed. The size of each slice is proportional to the magnitude of the displayed variable associated with each category or class.

Pilot sample—A sample taken from the population of interest of a size smaller than the anticipated sample size that is used to provide an estimate for the population standard deviation or population proportion.

Point estimate—A single number, determined from a sample, that is used to estimate the corresponding population parameter.

Population—The set of all objects or individuals of interest or the measurements obtained from all objects or individuals of interest.

Population proportion—The fraction of values in a population that have a specific attribute.

Power—The probability that the hypothesis test will reject the null hypothesis when the null hypothesis is false.

Probability—The chance that a particular event will occur. The probability of an event will be a value in the range 0 to 1. A value of 0 means the event will not occur. A probability of 1 means the event will occur. Anything between 0 and 1 reflects the uncertainty of the event occurring. The definition given is for a countable number of events.

p-**Value**—The probability (assuming the null hypothesis is true) of obtaining a test statistic at least as extreme as the test statistic we calculated from the sample. The p-value is also known as the *observed significance level*.

Qualitative data—Data whose measurement scale is inherently categorical.

Quantitative data—Measurements whose values are inherently numerical.

Quartiles—Quartiles in a data array are those values that divide the data set into four equal-sized groups. The median corresponds to the second quartile.

Random component—Changes in time-series data that are unpredictable and cannot be associated with a trend, seasonal, or cyclical component.

Random variable—A variable that assigns a numerical value to each outcome of a random experiment or trial.

Range—The range is a measure of variation that is computed by finding the difference between the maximum and minimum values in a data set.

Ratio data—Data that have all the characteristics of interval data but also have a true zero point (at which zero means "none").

Regression hyperplane—The multiple regression equivalent of the simple regression line. The plane has a different slope for each independent variable.

Regression slope coefficient—The average change in the dependent variable for a unit increase in the independent variable. The slope coefficient may be positive or negative, depending on the relationship between the two variables.

Relative frequency—The proportion of total observations that are in a given category. Relative frequency is computed by dividing the frequency in a category by the total number of observations. The relative frequencies can be converted to percentages by multiplying by 100.

Relative frequency of occurrence—The method that defines probability as the number of times an event occurs divided by the total number of times an experiment is performed in a large number of trials.

Research hypothesis—The hypothesis the decision maker attempts to demonstrate to be true. Because this is the hypothesis deemed to be the most important to the decision maker, it will not be declared true unless the sample data strongly indicate that it is true.

Residual (prediction error)—The distance between the y-coordinate of an (x,y) point and the estimate of that y-coordinate produced by the regression line.

Right-skewed data—A data distribution is right skewed if the mean for the data is larger than the median.

Sample—A subset of the population.

Sample space—The collection of all elementary outcomes that can result from a selection, decision, or experiment.

Sampling distribution—A distribution of the possible values of a statistic for a given-size random sample selected from a population.

Sampling error—The difference between a value (a statistic) computed from a sample and the corresponding value (a parameter) computed from the population.

Scatter diagram—A two-dimensional graph of plotted points in which the vertical axis represents values of one variable and the horizontal axis represents values of the other. Each plotted point has coordinates whose values are obtained from the respective variables.

Scatter plot—A two-dimensional plot showing the values for the joint occurrence of two variables. The scatter plot may be used to graphically represent the relationship between two variables. It is also known as a scatter diagram.

Seasonal component—A wave-like pattern that is repeated throughout a time series and has a recurrence period of at most one year.

Seasonal index—A number used to quantify the effect of seasonality in time-series data.

Seasonally unadjusted forecast—A forecast made for seasonal data that does not include an adjustment for the seasonal component in the time series.

Significance level—The maximum allowable probability of committing a Type I statistical error. The probability is denoted by the symbol α.

Simple random sample—A sample selected in such a manner that each possible sample of a given size has an equal chance of being selected.

Skewed data—Data sets that are not symmetric. For skewed data, the mean will be larger or smaller than the median.

Spurious correlation—When a correlation exists between two seemingly unrelated variables, the correlation is said to be a spurious correlation.

Standard deviation—The standard deviation is the positive square root of the variance.

Standard normal distribution—A normal distribution that has a mean = 0 and a standard deviation =1. The horizontal axis is scaled in z-values that measure the number of standard deviations a point is from the mean. Values above the mean have positive z-values. Values below the mean have negative z-values.

Standardized data values—The number of standard deviations a value is from the mean. Standardized data values are sometimes referred to as z-scores.

States of nature—The possible outcomes in a decision situation over which the decision maker has no control.

Statistic—A measure computed from a sample that has been selected from a population. The value of the statistic will depend on which sample is selected.

Statistical inference tools—Tools that allow a decision maker to reach a conclusion about a population of data based on a subset of data from the population.

Statistical sampling techniques—Those sampling methods that use selection techniques based on chance selection.

Stratified random sampling—A statistical sampling method in which the population is divided into subgroups called *strata* so that each population item belongs to only one stratum. The objective is to form strata such that the population values of interest within each stratum are as much alike as possible. Sample items are selected from each stratum using the simple random sampling method.

Structured interview—Interviews in which the questions are scripted.

Student's *t*-distribution—A family of distributions that is bell-shaped and symmetric like the standard normal distribution but with greater area in the tails. Each distribution in the t-family is defined by its degrees of freedom. As the degrees of freedom increase, the t-distribution approaches the normal distribution.

Subjective probability assessment—The method that defines probability of an event as reflecting a decision maker's state of mind regarding the chances that the particular event will occur.

Symmetric data—Data sets whose values are evenly spread around the center. For symmetric data, the mean and median are equal.

Systematic random sampling—A statistical sampling technique that involves selecting every kth item in the population after a randomly selected starting point between 1 and k. The value of k is determined as the ratio of the population size over the desired sample size.

Tchebysheff's theorem—Regardless of how data are distributed, *at least* $(1 - 1/k^2)$ of the values will fall within k standard deviations of the mean.

Test statistic—A function of the sampled observations that provides a basis for testing a statistical hypothesis.

Time-series data—A set of ordered data values observed at successive points in time.

Total quality management—A journey to excellence in which everyone in the organization is focused on continuous process improvement directed toward increased customer satisfaction.

Total variation—The aggregate dispersion of the individual data values across the various factor levels is called the *total variation* in the data.

Two-tailed test—A hypothesis test in which the entire rejection region is split into the two tails of the sampling distribution. In a two-tailed test, the alpha level is typically split evenly between the two tails.

Type I error—*Rejecting* the null hypothesis when it is, in fact, true.

Type II error—*Failing to reject* the null hypothesis when it is, in fact, false.

Unbiased estimator—A characteristic of certain statistics in which the average of all possible values of the sample statistic equals a parameter.

Uncertainty—A decision environment in which the decision maker does not know what outcome will occur when an alternative is selected.

Unstructured interview—Interviews that begin with one or more broadly stated questions, with further questions being based on the responses.

Variance—The population variance is the average of the squared distances of the data values from the mean.

Variance inflation factor—A measure of how much the variance of an estimated regression coefficient increases if the independent variables are correlated. A VIF equal to 1.0 for a given independent variable indicates that this independent variable is not correlated with the remaining independent variables in the model. The greater the multicollinearity, the larger the VIF.

Variation—A set of data exhibits variation if all the data are not the same value.

Weighted mean—The mean value of data values that have been weighted according to their relative importance.

Within-sample variation—The dispersion that exists among the data values within a particular factor level is called the *within-sample variation*.

INDEX

two-way = Chiinv (a, df)

chi-test = chi dist (chi square stat, df)
Fcritical = finv (a, dfi, df2)